Selected Orbit and C

Requirements Definition

Orbit Properties

Orbit Design

Specialized Orbits

Station Passes & Coverage

Station Passes & Coverage (cont.)

Constellation Design

Constellation Maintenance

Boxed Examples

MISSION GEOMETRY; ORBIT AND CONSTELLATION DESIGN AND MANAGEMENT

THE SPACE TECHNOLOGY LIBRARY

Published jointly by Microcosm Press and Kluwer Academic Publishers

An Introduction to Mission Design for Geostationary Satellites, J. J. Pocha
Space Mission Analysis and Design, 1st edition, James R. Wertz and Wiley J. Larson
Space Mission Analysis and Design, 2nd edition, Wiley J. Larson and James R. Wertz
Space Mission Analysis and Design, 3rd edition, James R. Wertz and Wiley J. Larson
Space Mission Analysis and Design Workbook, Wiley J. Larson and James R. Wertz
Handbook of Geostationary Orbits, E. M. Soop
Spacecraft Structures and Mechanisms, From Concept to Launch, Thomas P. Sarafin
Spaceflight Life Support and Biospherics, Peter Eckart
Reducing Space Mission Cost, James R. Wertz and Wiley J. Larson
The Logic of Microspace, Rick Fleeter
Space Marketing: A European Perspective, Walter A. R. Peeters
Fundamentals of Astrodynamics and Applications, David A. Vallado

Spacecraft Orbit and Attitude Systems

Mission Geometry; Orbit and Constellation Design and Management

James R. Wertz
Microcosm, Inc.

with contributions by:
***Hans F. Meissinger**, Microcosm, Inc.*
***Lauri Kraft Newman**, Goddard Space Flight Center*
***Geoffrey N. Smit**, The Aerospace Corporation*

Preparation of this volume has been sponsored by the Naval Center for Space Technology at the Naval Research Lab under the direction of Marvin Levenson, Attitude Control Section.

Space Technology Library

Published Jointly by

Microcosm Press
El Segundo, California

Kluwer Academic Publishers
Dordrecht / Boston / London

Library of Congress Cataloging-in-Publication Data

A C.I.P. Catalogue record for this book is available from
the Library of Congress

ISBN 1-881883-07-8 (pb) (acid-free paper)
ISBN 0-7923-6903-3 (hb) (acid-free paper)

Cover photo of Earth from Space: View of Africa and Saudi Arabia taken in Dec. 1972 by Apollo 17, the last of the Apollo missions to explore the Moon. Photo courtesy of NASA.

Cover design by Elizabeth Estavillo.

Published jointly by
Microcosm Press
401 Coral Circle, El Segundo, CA 90245 USA
and
Kluwer Academic Publishers,
P.O. Box 17, 3300 AA Dordrecht, The Netherlands.

Kluwer Academic Publishers incorporates
the publishing programmes of
D. Reidel, Martinus Nijhoff, Dr. W. Junk and MTP Press.

Sold and distributed in the USA and Canada
by Microcosm, Inc.
401 Coral Circle, El Segundo, CA 90245 USA
and Kluwer Academic Publishers,
101 Philip Drive, Norwell, MA 02061 USA

In all other countries, sold and distributed
by Kluwer Academic Publishers Group,
P.O. Box 322, 3300 AA Dordrecht, The Netherlands.

Printed on acid-free paper

Printed in the United States of America

Table of Contents

PART I. Overview

PART II. Space Mission Geometry

PART III. Orbit and Constellation Design

Appendices

Inside Front Cover

Inside Rear Cover

Authors

Portions of the text not ascribed to others have been written by:

James R. Wertz. President, Microcosm, Inc., El Segundo, California. Ph.D. (Relativity and Cosmology), University of Texas at Austin; M.S. (Administration of Science and Technology), George Washington University; S.B. (Physics), Massachusetts Institute of Technology.

The following individuals have contributed specific sections as listed:

Hans F. Meissinger. Chief Engineer. Space Systems Division, Microcosm, Inc., El Segundo, CA. M.S., B.S., (Engineering), Berlin Technical University; M.S. (Math), New York University. Section 12.7—*Design of Interplanetary Orbits.*

Lauri Kraft Newman. Aerospace Engineer, NASA Goddard Space Flight Center, Greenbelt, MD. M.S., B.S., (Aerospace Engineering), University of Maryland. Chapter 14—*Operations Considerations in Orbit Design—Launch, Orbit Acquisitions, and Disposal.*

Geoffrey N. Smit. Senior Engineering Specialist, The Aerospace Corporation, El Segundo, CA. Ph.D. (Mechanical Engineering/Astronautical Sciences), University of Illinois; MBA (Business Administration), University of Chicago; B.S. (Mechanical Engineering). Section 5.4—*Introduction to Error Analysis*, Appendix C—*Statistical Error Analysis.*

The following individuals in the Microcosm Space Systems Division have made major technical contributions to the work via analysis contained in many equations, plots, and tables throughout the book:

Robert L. Bell. M.S./B.S. (Aerospace Engineering), University of Southern California.

John T. Collins. B.S. (Aerospace Engineering), University of Illinois; B.S. (Astronomy), University of Illinois.

Simon D. Dawson. MSc (Spacecraft Technology and Satellite Communications), University College London, University of London; BSc (Hons) (Physics and European Studies), University of Sussex.

David M. Diaz. B.S., (Aerospace Engineering), California State Polytechnic University; M.S. (Aeronautics/Astronautics), Stanford University.

Kevin S. Polk. A.B. (Astrophysics), Princeton University; M.S. (Astronomy), University of Washington.

Curtis W. Potterveld. B.A./M.S. (Physics), Rensselaer Polytechnic University; M.S. (Aerospace Engineering), Arizona State University.

Herb Reynolds. B.S., (Math), University of California; M.S. (Math), California State University.

Preface

Mission Geometry; Orbit and Constellation Design and Management (OCDM) is intended to take the Mission Engineering process first introduced in SMAD* to a new level of detail. By space mission engineering, I mean the refinement of requirements and definition of mission parameters to meet the objectives of the space mission at minimum cost and risk. Thus, in a sense, this volume is a major expansion of what was started in SMAD Chapters 4, 5, 6, 7, and portions of 11, 14, and 18.† If you need additional detail than SMAD provides on requirements definition, mission geometry, orbit and constellation design, relative motion of satellites, and similar topics, then this book addresses that need.

However, it is intended to do much more as well. In terms of practical space systems, orbit, attitude, and some components of timing and mission geometry should be treated together as elements of an overall Orbit and Attitude System. These subsystems are, of course, not identical. Nonetheless, our goal in mission engineering is to minimize the cost and risk of the system as whole. Orbit and attitude requirements most commonly derive from the same source (the need for pointing and mapping), use many of the same analytic techniques, can often use the same hardware for sensing and actuation, and should typically be done in the same on-board processor. We can often trade back and forth between orbit and attitude accuracy to best achieve our system objectives. Particularly with the widespread use of GPS, timing systems are also often coupled to orbit and attitude. And the basic concepts of mission geometry—i.e., the geometrical relationships inherent in a CCD array looking at stars or the Earth below, or the relative motion of the spacecraft with respect to a target, ground station, the Sun, or another spacecraft—tie together orbit, attitude, and the mission payload.

OCDM is divided into 4 parts:

Part I. Orbit, Attitude, and Timing Systems

This provides a broad introduction to the topic appropriate to someone with no prior background. Nonetheless, it goes into substantially more detail than the corresponding SMAD material, contains all of the practical first-order equations needed by the experienced mission designer, and includes material simply not available elsewhere. These discussions include, for example, drag coefficients for common shapes, attitudes, and surface conditions; causes and basic equations for all fundamental specialized orbit types (including numerical expressions for Earth orbit and analytic expressions to be used with data in the appendices to extend these to other solar system bodies), spacecraft attitude motion in the absence of control and the on-orbit performance history of most types of attitude sensors; a detailed discussion of time systems and time discontinuities on-board spacecraft; GPS, GLONASS, and autonomous navigation and orbit control; and the most

* SMAD = *Space Mission Analysis and Design*, 3rd ed., edited by James R. Wertz and Wiley J. Larson. Dordrecht, the Netherlands, and El Segundo, CA; Kluwer Academic Publishers and Microcosm Press, 1999.

† These are: Chap. 4 "Requirements Definition," Chap. 5 "Space Mission Geometry," Chap. 6 "Introduction to Astrodynamics," Chap. 7 "Orbit and Constellation Design," Sec. 11.1 "Attitude Determination and Control," Sec. 11.7 "Guidance and Navigation," Sec. 18.2 "Launch System Selection Process," and portions of Chap. 14 "Missions Operations" on orbit and attitude.

extensive tables available on error sources and the creation of mapping and pointing budgets. Each chapter ends with an annotated bibliography of all of the major reference sources in the field.

Part II. Space Mission Geometry
This part provides by far the most extensive discussion available of space mission geometry, position and attitude measurements, Earth coverage, relative motion of satellites, and viewing and lighting conditions. It introduces entirely new mathematical approaches (full-sky geometry and the dual-axis spiral) which provide both added insight and simple, closed-form expressions for the relative motion of distant satellites, the satellite ground trace, ground station passes, or the full-sky coverage of a rotating sensor on a spinning spacecraft. It examines large scale and small scale motion in formations and constellations. The results lead to interesting new insights, such as the role of the Euler axis (usually associated with attitude motion) in ground station coverage. This part provides simple expressions for items such as the position, shape, and projected angular area of any pixel in an array sensor, the direction of shadows on the Earth's surface as seen from space, or the location (and fuzziness) of the terminator between light and dark as seen from space.

Part III. Orbit and Constellation Design
This is the most complete and quantitative discussion available of this key element of the mission design process. Orbit selection and design is covered in detail, from equations for estimating the launch cost and available on-orbit mass to the design of general and specialized orbits (near Earth, interplanetary, and around other planets) to the relativistic equations for interstellar flight. Similarly, constellation design and management is discussed in terms of constellation patterns, coverage, stationkeeping, collision avoidance, and the constellation design process. The final chapter deals with operational issues in orbit design including launch windows and end-of-life disposal.

Appendices
Finally, for those who have used the SMAD appendices, there is much more of the same—over 120 pages of formulas and data. The familiar Earth Satellite Parameter tables inside the rear cover of SMAD have been substantially expanded and also extended in the appendices to include satellites of the Moon, Mars, and the Sun. There are orbit, physical, optical, and gravitational parameters for the planets and natural satellites. There is a detailed discussion of statistical error analysis and complete solutions to all possible spherical triangles in which all of the angles and sides can range from 0 to 360 deg to make automated processing of measurement data very straightforward. This include a complete treatment of singularities (and practical approaches for dealing with them), differential spherical trig, and the angular area for a wide range of spherical figures. And, of course, we include all standard units and conversion factors to their full available accuracy and the most recently updated values of the fundamental physical and astronautical constants.

Much like SMAD, OCDM is intended for a wide variety of audiences. The background material on orbit, attitude, and timing systems is strongly physically motivated without providing the detailed mathematical proofs found in Battin or Vallado. Consequently, it is appropriate to either advanced undergraduate or graduate courses in Space Mission Analysis and Design or Orbit and Attitude Systems. Because of the very practical orientation of the material, we believe it will prove to be an invaluable reference for those doing mission design, orbit and constellation design, satellite operations, or analysis and evaluation of mission data. Many of the most practical and useful equations do not appear elsewhere in the literature. For this reason, anyone interested in a more detailed version of the SMAD mission engineering process will find this work to be exceptionally useful. Finally, for those interested in mathematical methods of mission analysis, this book contains many equations and approaches which do not exist elsewhere, including the first complete coverage of "full-sky spherical trig" in which any of the sides or angles can take on any values ranging 0 to 360 deg.

This volume uses the metric system throughout, except that degrees are used rather than the standard SI unit of radians. A complete set of conversion factors is given for all common astronautical units. Whenever units in common practice differ significantly from SI units (i.e., antenna gain in db or stellar magnitudes), the units are both defined and motivated.

It is impossible to thank sufficiently the great many people who worked to bring this volume about. The project was started by Col. Gene Dionne at the Air Force Research Laboratory who was convincing in the need to update and expand older reference works. As always in such projects, a key ingredient is funding which was provided entirely by the Naval Center for Space Technology at the Naval Research Laboratory. At the NCST, excellent leadership for the project was provided by Marvin Levenson with exceptional support from Ed Senasack and the NCST Director, Peter Wilhelm. Their support for a project that was much longer than any of us envisioned is greatly appreciated. Without NRL, this book would not have been possible.

Many people contributed to the writing of the volume as shown in the author list. It is always much harder than anyone anticipates. I would particularly like to thank Lauri Kraft Newman of the Goddard Space Flight Center, who wrote Chap. 14 on Operational Considerations, Hans Meissinger of Microcosm who wrote Sec. 12.7 on Interplanetary Mission Design, and Geoffrey Smit of The Aerospace Corporation who wrote both Sec. 5.4 and App. C on Error Analysis. Ben Chang of Intelsat contributed information for Sec. 1.1.2. In addition, many individuals within the Microcosm Space Systems Division contributed greatly via analysis, explanations, equations, plots, tables, and recommendations that appear in and influence every section (except for the material on spherical trig, for which they would like to ensure that I take all the blame). Major analytical contributions were provided by Robert Bell, John Collins, Simon Dawson, David Diaz, Hans Koenigsmann, Kevin Polk, Curtis Potterveld, and Herb Reynolds, all under the direction and guidance of Gwynne Gurevich, the head of the Microcosm Space Systems Division. At various times, Simon, David, Kevin, and Curtis all had the thankless task of managing the innumerable analytic inputs and did exceptionally well at it. I believe David and Rob now have Excel or MatLab models for essentially every table, graph, or analytic process in the book.

Quite a few students had the misfortune to pass through Microcosm while the project was ongoing. The contributions of Karen Burnham, Allen Chen, Nathan Cobb, Moriba Jah, Paul Murata, Stefan Winkler, Don Shimohara, Ales Tomaier, and Julie Wertz are very much appreciated.

Of course in the end, a book is a combination of the process of writing about the subject and coordinating, preparing, creating, drawing, editing, and doing all of the other major tasks required to actually produce a finished volume. The task was undertaken with enormous care, skill, and patience by the Microcosm Publications Department. The book significantly increases the amount of orbit and attitude systems artwork in the literature base thanks to the excellent work of Joy Sakaguchi and Elizabeth Estavillo. They did a remarkable job of both creating graphics from very bad sketches and taking computer generated graphs and plots, all of which look nearly identical at first glance, and turning them into meaningful graphics that make the underlying story clear and unambiguous. Joy, Wendi Huntzinger, and Regina Jenkins created most of the original text and corrected it more times than was reasonable to ask. Judith Neiger proofed most of the chapters. All of this was done under the able and patient leadership of Donna Klungle, who managed the project, coordinated inputs, gave out assignments, typed manuscripts, and in her spare time did corrections, page layout, and indexing. In many respects the book belongs more to Donna than to any of us. I hope that the content lives up to the quality of her manuscript preparation.

Finally, I want to thank Microcosm itself for letting me take on this task and complete much of it on internal funding. (There is absolutely no truth to the rumor that the Microcosm managers took up a collection to keep the project going in order to keep me otherwise occupied and out of their hair for extended periods.) Of course, for any project of this sort, the writing and editing always occurs at night, on weekends, on travel, and, unfortunately, on vacations. Consequently, Alice is the one who suffered most through the project (both at Microcosm and at home). Thank you.

As always with any such project, there will be errors and omissions of all sorts. We would very much appreciate these being brought to the attention of either Donna or me at *bookproject@smad.com*. Errata, which are an inevitable necessity, will be posted on the Microcosm website at *www.smad.com*. Mostly, I hope that you find the material useful, helpful, and at times interesting. I would appreciate hearing from you at any time.

James R. Wertz
Microcosm, Inc.
401 Coral Circle
El Segundo, CA 90245

August, 2001

Phone: 310-726-4100
FAX: 310-726-4110
E-mail: jwertz@smad.com

PART I

OVERVIEW

Part I provides a broad overview of spacecraft orbit, attitude, and timing systems with sufficient equations to allow first-order calculations of all elements that would have a principal effect on system design. There are annotated bibliographies at the end of each chapter.

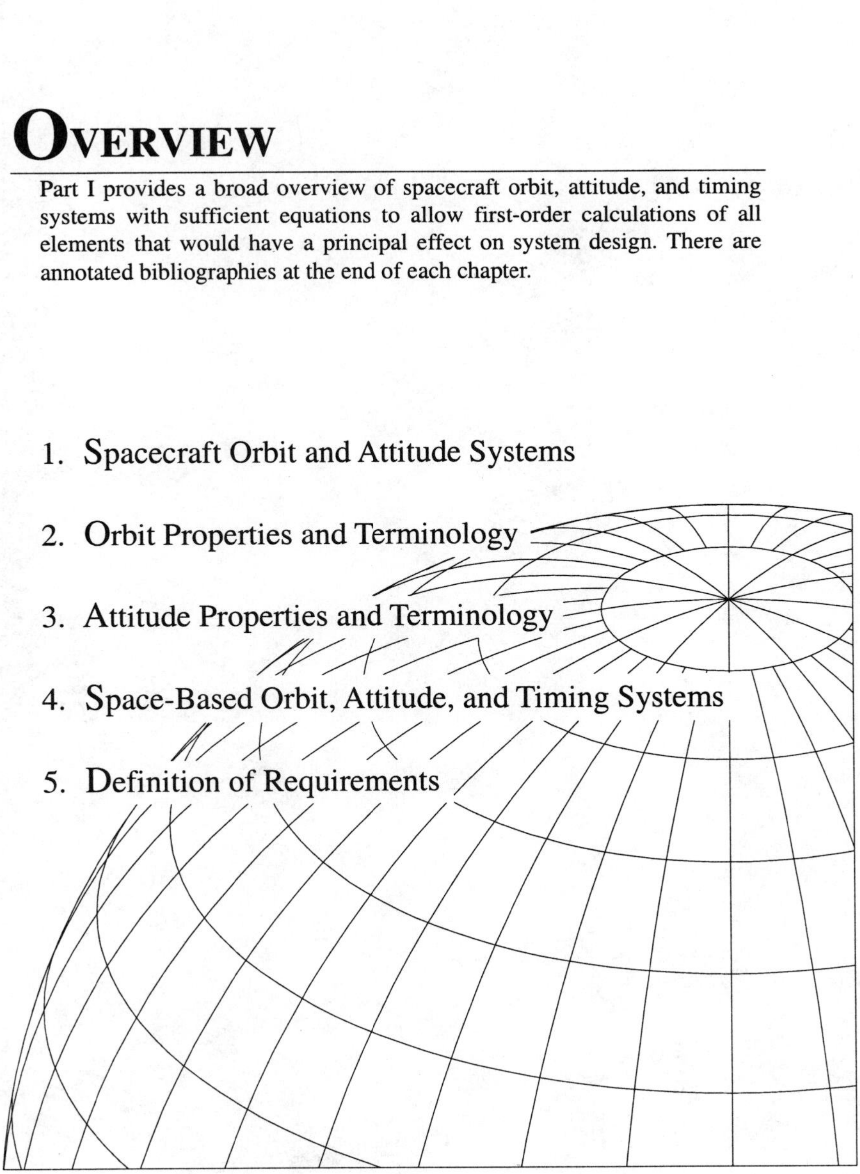

Chapter 1

Spacecraft Orbit and Attitude Systems

The *orbit* of a spacecraft is its path through space. The *attitude* is its orientation in space. *Orbit and attitude systems* are the hardware, software and processes used to analyze, design, measure, and control these mission elements. This set of books is concerned with all aspects of spacecraft orbit and attitude: how they are determined; how they are controlled; and how the future motion is predicted and adjusted. We describe simple procedures for estimating values and sophisticated methods used to obtain the maximum accuracy from a given data set. In addition, we will describe time measurement systems which are an integral part of the orbit and attitude process. In the first five chapters, we will introduce the basic terminology and provide an overview of orbit, attitude, and timing systems, their place in the overall space mission, and the process by which requirements for these systems are defined and specified. Each of these initial chapters ends with an annotated bibliography of the principal sources of additional information.

The motion of a spacecraft is specified by its position, velocity, attitude, and attitude rate. The first two quantities describe the translational motion of the center of mass of the spacecraft and are the subject of what is variously called *orbit analysis*, *celestial mechanics*, or *space navigation,* depending upon the aspect of the problem that is emphasized. The latter two quantities describe the rotational motion of the body of the spacecraft about the center of mass and are the subject of *attitude analysis* or *spacecraft dynamics*.

Orbit and attitude are interdependent. For example, in low-Earth orbit the attitude affects atmospheric drag which affects the orbit. The orbit determines the spacecraft position, which determines both the atmospheric density and the magnetic field which, in turn, affects the attitude. Traditionally, this coupling has been largely ignored and analysis, design, and engineering has been separated into the discrete topics of orbit or attitude. One of the purposes of this book series is to bring these topics together once again. The purpose of doing so is not to emphasize the typically weak interaction between the two, but to demonstrate clearly how orbit and attitude are both elements of spacecraft dynamics responding to internal and external forces and torques and operating under similar control laws and frequently implemented with the same hardware components. In space systems engineering, our goal is not to make orbit and attitude systems identical, but to design them together so that the space system as a whole meets its mission objectives at minimum cost and risk. Realistically, this will only be done if we work with them together.

In spite of a strong interrelationship, orbit and attitude problems have very different backgrounds, both in terms of historical development and how they have been traditionally implemented in space systems. Predicting the orbital motion of celestial objects is one of the oldest sciences and was the initial motivation of much of Newton's work. Although the space age and computer analysis have brought vast new subjects and tools for orbit analysis, a large body of theory directly related to celestial mechanics has existed for several centuries. In contrast, while some of the techniques are old, most attitude determination and control work has occurred since the opening of the space age with the launch of Sputnik on October 4, 1957. Rotational dynamics has, of course, been studied for a long time. However, there has been relatively little prior work on the analysis or control of the orientation of space systems. Consequently, relatively little information is recorded in traditional texts or other comprehensive reference sources. In addition, the language of attitude analysis has evolved largely in modern times and many of the technical terms do not have universally accepted meanings or are only now becoming accepted. One of the purposes of this book is to provide a reference of orbit and attitude terminology and to clarify how various terms are used in practice.

The second major difference between spacecraft orbit and attitude systems is the way they have been implemented in traditional space missions. With remarkably few exceptions, attitude is controlled onboard the spacecraft with an autonomous *attitude control system,* which may change modes or initiate maneuvers by ground command, but fundamentally operates independently of human interaction. One of the reasons for this is that attitude systems operate in a frequency range of a few Hertz which makes it difficult, risky, and expensive to operate from the ground. The spacecraft is largely allowed to control its own attitude because it is too expensive and hard to do otherwise.

In contrast, the orbit has traditionally been analyzed, determined, measured, and controlled by analysts and software operating on the ground. Orbit determination has been done by tracking from ground stations with the data from multiple stations around the world being brought together and analyzed such that orbit determination occurs after the fact. To determine where the spacecraft is now, we do orbit determination from past data and predict or *propagate* where the spacecraft is at any future time. Orbit maneuvers or orbit maintenance commands have traditionally been computed on the ground and sent to the spacecraft for later implementation.

In the past, these distinctions have served to enforce the separation between attitude as a spacecraft subsystem and orbit as a ground activity. However, several recent events will have a major impact on this separation between orbit and attitude. First, the deployment of the GPS* constellation provides the potential for low cost, precise, onboard, real-time orbit determination for spacecraft in low-Earth orbit. Second, the introduction of highly capable, general-purpose, onboard computers means that autonomous navigation and orbit control can be done reliably and economically onboard the spacecraft using sensors and actuators already on most spacecraft, but which have not been a part of the navigation process in the past. Third, there is a continuing world-wide demand for reducing the cost and increasing the efficiency of space systems. Because orbit and attitude systems use much the same hardware and software, there is potentially a major cost savings by regarding these as two aspects of a single system rather than as discrete space-based and ground-based systems which are to be handled independently of each other. We may not wish to solve for the orbit and attitude in one giant Kalman filter. Nonetheless, it is clear that we will do a better job of space mission engineering if we look at the problem of orbit and attitude systems together and find the solution for both which maximizes the performance and minimizes the cost and risk for the space mission as a whole.

Orbit and attitude analysis are typically divided into determination, prediction, and control. *Orbit and attitude determination* are the processes of computing the trajectory and the orientation of the spacecraft relative to either an inertial reference frame or some object of interest, such as the Earth or a planet. Attitude determination typically involves multiple sensors on the spacecraft and frequently uses sophisticated data processing procedures unique to each spacecraft. The attitude is usually determined by a combination of processing procedures and sensing hardware. Orbit determination, also called *navigation*, traditionally involves data from multiple ground stations around the world processed in a single ground location to determine the spacecraft trajectory with high accuracy. The same process is used for most spacecraft. Consequently, the orbit accuracy is typically comparable for most space missions and depends primarily on the particular spacecraft orbit. However, orbit determination is changing rapidly with the advent of both GPS receivers for spacecraft and autonomous orbit determination, which can use many of the same sensors used for attitude determination.

Orbit and attitude prediction is the process of forecasting the future trajectory and orientation, typically by extrapolating from the satellite history. *Propagation* is the process of using the dynamic equations of motion and models of environmental forces and torques to model either the orbit or attitude for an extended time period. The limiting features of our ability to predict the orbit and attitude are the knowledge of the applied and environmental forces and torques and the accuracy of the mathematical model of the spacecraft dynamics and hardware. For the attitude, the level of spacecraft flexibility which results in both complex motion and *damping* or removing rotational energy are the principal components which limit the capacity for attitude prediction. For orbits, the gravitational forces, particularly when not close to the surface of any planet, are extremely well known and prediction can be very precise. In the vicinity of planets, irregular mass distributions and the presence of an atmosphere which provides forces that are extremely difficult to model make orbit prediction very difficult and limit the capacity to predict the future position of the spacecraft.

Orbit and attitude control are the processes of maintaining the spacecraft in specific predetermined orientations and trajectories. Again, this may be with respect

---

* GPS is fundamentally a position determining system. However, in order to do this accurately, GPS receivers use signals from 4 satellites to solve simultaneously for the position and the time. In addition, GPS receivers with multiple antennas can be used as a space interferometer to solve for the attitude as well, although the resulting attitude measurement is typically less precise than can be achieved by more traditional means.

to inertial space (of interest to many scientific satellites) or with respect to the Earth or a target planet (of interest for Earth observations, communications, or exploration). *Attitude stabilization* and *orbit maintenance* are the processes of maintaining existing parameters. *Maneuver control* is the process of controlling the reorientation or trajectory change from one orbit or attitude to another. The boundary between stabilization and maneuver control is not totally distinct. For example, stabilizing spacecraft with one axis toward the Earth implies a continuous change in its inertial orientation. Similarly, maintaining the orbit frequently consists of a sequence of small orbit maneuvers to readjust the trajectory. For attitude control the limiting factor is typically the performance of the hardware and the control logic, although with the introduction of more sophisticated spacecraft computers, the control logic can become significantly more complex and the accuracy of orbit and attitude information will become a more limiting feature. For orbit control the accuracy limitation has traditionally been the desire to minimize the number of maneuvers, since maneuvers had to be computed on the ground, uploaded to the spacecraft, and implemented onboard, and, therefore, are time consuming and expensive. With the introduction of autonomous systems, the principal limitation to orbit control accuracy will be the sensing and accuracy of the dynamic modeling.

Orbit and attitude determination are required for essentially all spacecraft. Knowledge of the position is usually necessary for payload operation, but, in any case, is critical to maintaining ground contact with the satellite. Similarly, some type of attitude determination is usually required for the payload to function. The housekeeping functions of the spacecraft can typically be done with attitude determination and control to an accuracy of approximately 1 deg. Payload functions require accuracies that vary widely depending upon the nature of the mission. They may be as coarse as several degrees for relatively low data rate communications systems to thousandths of a degree for high accuracy observations. Quite frequently, spacecraft will need to point different components in different directions at the same time, such as pointing solar arrays at the Sun, communication antennas at a ground station, and payload equipment at a target that is being observed. This implies the use of gimbals on board the spacecraft, which adds significantly to the cost and complexity as well as the difficulty of maintaining a specific orientation. Because the orbit is concerned only with the motion of the center of mass of the spacecraft, internal motion between components does not impact the orbit and, therefore, has minimal impact on orbit determination and control. On the other hand, any internal motion will move one component with respect to another and, therefore, will result in attitude motion of the spacecraft as a whole. If we move an antenna, turn on a tape recorder, rotate a filter wheel, or slosh propellant in a tank, the body of an otherwise rigid spacecraft will respond to that internal torque. This is part of what makes attitude prediction and control complex and requires the use of a control system which can maintain the orientation of the spacecraft in spite of these small, but cumulative disturbances.

Finally, spacecraft tend to be categorized by both their orbit and attitude. *Low-Earth orbit* or LEO spacecraft are those below the Van Allen belts at roughly 1,000 km altitude. *Geosynchronous orbit* (GEO) is at an altitude of 35,786 km above the equator, where the orbital rate of the spacecraft equals the rotation rate of the Earth on its axis, such that the spacecraft remains approximately fixed over a point on the equator. Orbits between LEO and GEO are frequently referred to as *medium-Earth orbits* or MEO. Earth orbiting spacecraft above GEO are called *super synchronous* and spacecraft which entirely leave the vicinity of the Earth are referred to as *interplanetary*. Those which leave the solar system entirely are called *interstellar probes*.

The spacecraft themselves are often categorized by the process by which they are stabilized. The simplest procedure is to spin the spacecraft. The angular momentum of *spin-stabilized* spacecraft remains approximately fixed in inertial space because external torques which affect it are typically very small. If a platform is added to a spinning spacecraft which maintains its orientation toward some target such as the Earth, then it is called a *dual-spin* spacecraft. If the orientation of 3 mutually perpendicular spacecraft axes are controlled, then the spacecraft is *three-axis stabilized*. In this case, some form of active control is usually required because environmental torques, although small, will normally cause the spacecraft orientation to drift. Another type is *gravity-gradient stabilization* in which the spacecraft naturally maintains a long axis pointed toward the Earth or whatever planet we are orbiting. Many missions consist of phases with the spacecraft spin-stabilized at times and three-axis stabilized at other times, depending on the activities of each particular mission phase. The use of multiple orbit regimes and multiple stabilization techniques adds significantly to the complexity of any space mission and ordinarily is a major driver of both cost and complexity.

1.1 Space Mission Profiles

The simplest spacecraft do not have orbit, attitude, or timing systems because they do not need them. For very simple missions, the orbit is whatever is provided by the launch vehicle; the attitude is either unstabilized or passively stabilized by any of several means; and timing is provided by the ground system which collects and distributes the data. While this approach is certainly economical, it is insufficiently precise for most applications. Consequently, most spacecraft have orbit, attitude, and timing systems onboard the spacecraft for reasons that are introduced in Sec. 1.2.

In order to understand the role of orbit, attitude, and timing systems, we will look at 4 typical but very different mission profiles and see what is involved in each. We would like to give at least some idea of the range of orbit, attitude, and timing systems and the functions they fulfill.

A key issue in studying spacecraft and space systems is the wide variety of space mission types and, consequently, the sources of orbit and attitude requirements. We tend to think of space activity as monolithic, i.e., in terms of some particular mission type with which we are most familiar, such as communications, interplanetary exploration, or manned flight. In fact, as shown in Table 1-1, the range of space missions is dramatically wide. We should not expect the orbit and attitude requirements to have much in common between a commercial communications satellite, a microgravity science experiment, or an interplanetary probe of the Jupiter magnetic fields. Even within specific mission types, there can be a wide range of requirements such as the varying needs of an amateur communications satellite versus a high bandwidth commercial communications constellation. Consequently, while the four missions below are intended to be representative of the broad spectrum of system requirements and implementations, they by no means span the full range of spacecraft orbit, attitude, and timing systems.

1.1.1 Ørsted, A Low-Cost, Low-Earth Orbit Science Mission

Ørsted is a small, 60 kg, Danish scientific satellite, shown in Fig. 1-1, intended to provide high accuracy geomagnetic field measurements and provide global monitoring of high-energy particles in the Earth's environment. The total system cost (satellite, launch, ground segment, and operations) was approximately $20 million. The program began in 1993. Ørsted was to have been launched "piggyback" with the U.S. Air Force Argos mission on a Delta II in March, 1997. As is often the case for small and large missions, the launch was delayed for several years. Ørsted was finally launched on Feb. 23, 1999.

TABLE 1-1. Representative Types of Space Missions. The range of space missions is dramatically broad which, in turn, leads to widely varying requirements on orbit and attitude systems. Even within mission types, requirements will vary strongly due to differing methods and needs, such as using laser vs. RF communications crosslinks.

Mission Type	Field*	Typical Orbit Requirement	Typical Attitude Requirement
Communications, Broadcasting	Com/Mil	Geosynchronous, low-Earth constellation	Antenna pointing for Earth coverage
Space manufacturing	Com	Any available at low cost	Very small disturbances
Space burial	Com	Any low cost	Any
Earth observations	Com/Sci/Mil	Orbit control not critical, but precise position knowledge required	High precision
Data store and forward	Com/Sci	Low-Earth orbit with minimal requirements	Little or no requirements
Space interferometer	Sci	Very high precision formation flying	Mid-precision
Space telescope	Sci	Minimal requirements	Highest available precision
Interplanetary exploration	Sci	Precision targeting	Camera and antenna pointing
Global Positioning System	Mil/Civ	Very high precision knowledge	Moderate
Space-based laser	Mil	High precision knowledge needed	Very high precision

* Com = Commercial, Sci = Scientific, Mil = Military, Civ = Civilian

A broad timeline for the mission is shown in Table 1-2. As with most missions, Ørsted started with a period of deployment, check-out, and calibration. This serves to verify that all of the equipment has survived the launch and to identify and, hopefully, fix any problems that may have arisen. Often the orbit and attitude requirements are significantly less stringent during this phase than for the operational portion of the mission. For Ørsted, the satellite is initially tumbling. During the early check-out, an 8 m gravity-gradient boom is extended which serves to stabilize the satellite with its long axis pointed towards the Earth as illustrated in Fig. 1-1.

TABLE 1-2. Ørsted Mission Timeline. Ørsted is a relatively simple mission in terms of both orbit and attitude requirements. It has no propulsion system and is passively stabilized by gravity-gradient forces.

Phase	Duration	Orbit	Attitude
Deployment, check-out, and calibration	2 months	450 km × 850 km; 96.1 deg inclination	Tumbling
Operations	12 months; possible 3 year extension	Initially 450 km × 850 km; decays to ~ 400 km circular, then spirals in	Earth-oriented with low accuracy control
End-of-life	N/A	Reentry at time of next solar maximum	No requirement; will tumble and burn on reentry

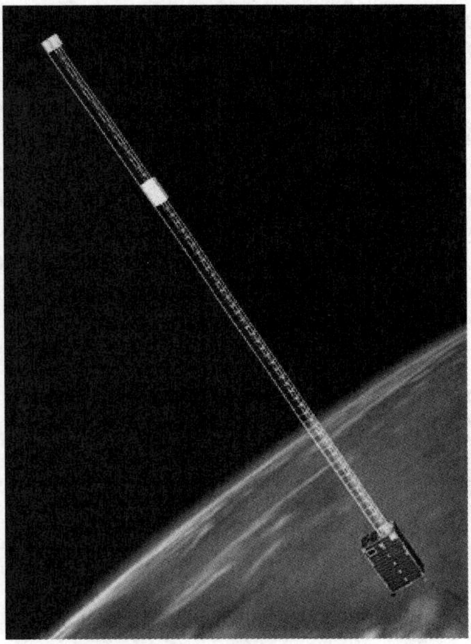

Fig. 1-1. The Ørsted Spacecraft. Ørsted is a small scientific spacecraft intended primarily to update geomagnetic field models. The long deployable boom is characteristic of many magnetic field spacecraft. It serves to get the scientific magnetometers away from stray magnet fields on the spacecraft and also provides gravity-gradient attitude stabilization with the boom pointing away from the Earth.

The orbit control process is particularly straightforward for Ørsted—it doesn't have any and there is no propulsion system on the spacecraft. Therefore, the lifetime and orbit evolution are determined entirely by how the launch vehicle puts the satellite in orbit and on variations in atmospheric density (and, therefore, the amount of drag). In an elliptical orbit, such as Ørsted, most of the drag will occur at *perigee*, the lowest point in the orbit where the atmospheric density is greatest. This has the interesting effect of keeping perigee nearly constant and lowering *apogee*, or the highest point in the orbit 180 deg away. Thus, drag will initially circularize the orbit. After it has become circular, it will spiral slowly downward and eventually reenter and burn up in the atmosphere. At satellite altitudes, atmospheric density varies dramatically with the phase in the 11-year solar cycle, with the density being as much as 100 times greater at solar maximum than at solar minimum. Consequently, as a practical matter, almost all of the orbit decay occurs during solar maximum. Thus, the Ørsted orbit will decay very little during solar minimum and then decay rapidly and ultimately reenter at the next solar maximum.

Table 1-3 summarizes the orbit and attitude control systems for Ørsted. The functional block diagram for the spacecraft is shown in Fig. 1-2. Nearly all space craft are divided into two basic parts. The *payload* is the equipment that does what the spacecraft mission is about, i.e., the imagers for an Earth resources satellite or the telephone equipment for a communications satellite such as Iridium or Global-Star. In contrast, the *spacecraft bus*, often called just the *bus*, provides all of the support services such as power, thermal control, or orbit and attitude determination and control. Typically, the bus and payload functions are totally separate and often built by different organizations. In the case of Ørsted, the star camera and the TorboRogue GPS receiver were experiments and, therefore, part of the payload rather than the bus. This means that they would be available for supporting the spacecraft bus functions only on a back-up or emergency basis. Thus, like most small satellites, Ørsted is primarily *single-string* with only one set of equipment to handle most of the orbit and attitude functions. Often the builder will find clever ways to use on-board equipment or very low cost alternatives to provide some back-up in case of failure. In contrast, the higher cost systems in the following examples will often have multiply redundant equipment to protect against the very high cost of losing the mission if a single element fails.

TABLE 1-3. Ørsted Orbit and Attitude System. Ørsted was intended from the outset to be a low-cost mission and, therefore, uses low-cost equipment and processes wherever possible.

Function	Equipment	Approximate Accuracy	Comments
Orbit determination	• Trimble GPS receiver	• 50 m (3 σ)	• Main system
	• Turborogue GPS receiver	• 50 m (3 σ)	• Experiment (Back-up)
Orbit control	None	Uses orbit that the launch vehicle supplies	Secondary payload onboard Delta
Attitude determination	• 8 hemispherical Sun sensors	• 1–2 deg	• Primary attitude source
	• Vector magnetometer	• 0.5 nT	• Payload instrument
	• Star camera	• 5 arc sec	• Experiment; wide field-of-view
Attitude control	Gravity gradient stabilized with 8 m deployable boom	5 deg	Boom holds payload experiment

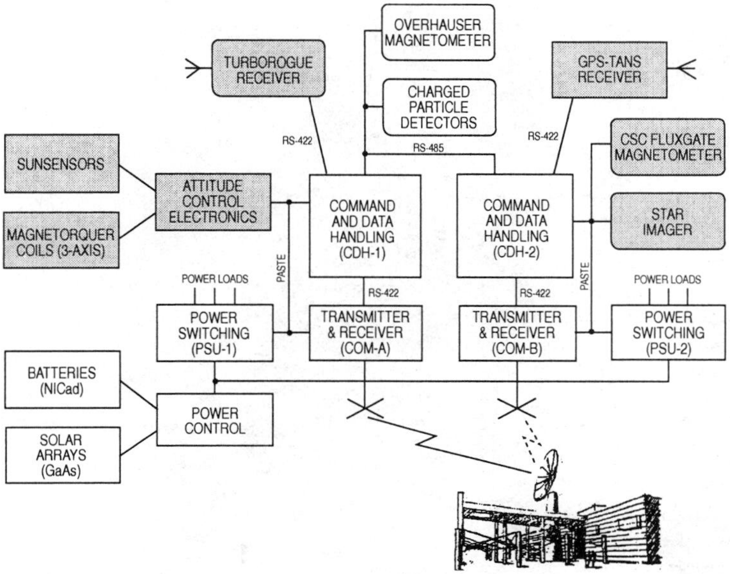

Fig. 1-2. Ørsted Functional Block Diagram. Orbit and attitude equipment is shaded.

1.1.2 Intelsat 901, A Geosynchronous Communications Satellite*

Intelsat 901 is the first in a new series of geostationary communications satellites initially launched in 2001. The spacecraft is built by Space Systems Loral and owned and operated by Intelsat LLC,† an international consortium of 144 member countries and regions. Since 1965, INTELSAT has launched and operated 53 satellites in *geostationary or geosynchronous orbit*, usually called just *GEO*, where a satellite remains nearly fixed relative to the ground, at an altitude of 35,786 km over a location on the Earth's equator approved by the International Telecommunication Union. Intelsat LLC's satellites provide global telecommunications including voice, data, video, and internet services. It was largely the introduction of the GEO communications satellites in the 1960's and 70's that was responsible for the dramatic increase in availability and reduction in cost of international telephone calls, expanding to TV and internet services in the 1980's and 90's.

As shown in Fig. 1-3, the satellite is very large, nearly 10 m wide and over 30 m long from one end of the solar arrays to the other. At the beginning of life, the spacecraft mass is 2872 kg and generates 9.2 kW of electric power. (The power output drops over time due to degradation of the solar array performance by radiation.)

The launch to geosynchronous orbit is a relatively standard process, but is, nonetheless, operationally complex. The spacecraft is launched from French Guiana on an

* Information for this section was provided by Ben Chang of Intelsat Global Services Corp.

† In 2001, the International Telecommunications Satellite Organization (INTELSAT) was privatized via a transfer of substantially all of its assets and liabilities to Intelsat, Ltd. and its subsidiaries. The Intelsat 901 was transferred to Intelsat LLC, an indirect subsidiary of Intelsat, Ltd.

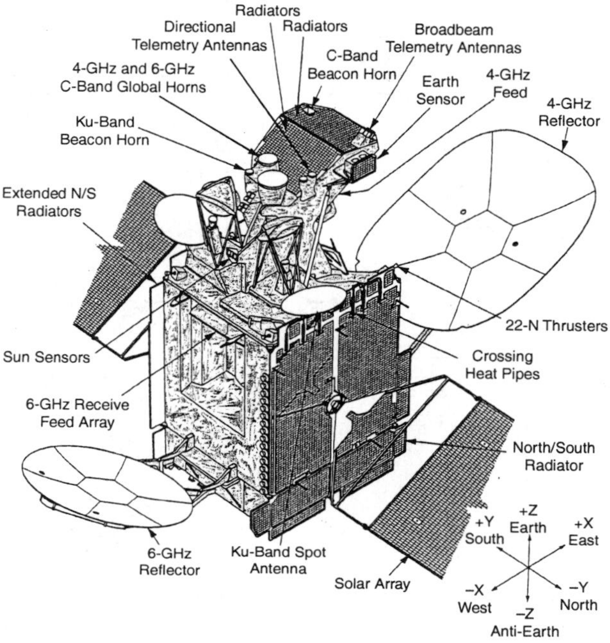

Fig. 1-3. Intelsat 901 On-Orbit Configuration. The spacecraft was built by Space Systems Loral and launched on an Ariane 44L from French Guiana.

Ariane 44L launch vehicle into a *geosynchronous transfer orbit*, *GTO*. A typical mission sequence is shown in Fig. 1-4. Approximately 20 minutes after lift-off, the satellite is separated from the third stage of the launch vehicle, which also starts the satellite rotating at 1.5 deg/sec about the x-axis of the satellite. Twenty minutes later, the ground station at Perth acquires the telemetry signal. The mission team at the Intelsat facilities in Washington D. C. takes over the control of the satellite at this point and initiates the transfer orbit mission sequence. A large number of commands are required to configure the satellite prior to the apogee maneuvers. These maneuvers are usually performed within visibility of 2 ground stations, one serving as primary and the other as back-up. The ground stations in the Intelsat network are Perth in Australia, Beijing in the People's Republic of China, Raisting in Germany, Fucino in Italy, Clarksburg, Maryland and Paumalu, Hawaii. Sometimes, due to the specific maneuver plans, additional station coverage may be required.

Prior to launch, the longitude for on-orbit payload tests is determined. This longitude, 292.0 deg East for Intelsat 901, is usually near the operational longitude to minimize the time and propellant required for relocation at the end of testing. During payload on-orbit tests, all communication links on-board the satellite are verified and the antenna performance is measured. To map the performance of the antennas, multiple ground stations within the satellite's field of view are used to collect the radio signals while the satellite is commanded to a sequence of different attitudes. (In effect, the antenna pattern is mapped by keeping the ground station antennas fixed and changing the attitude of the satellite.) Today, due to the large number of communication satellites distributed around the geostationary ring, it is difficult to find a longitude where

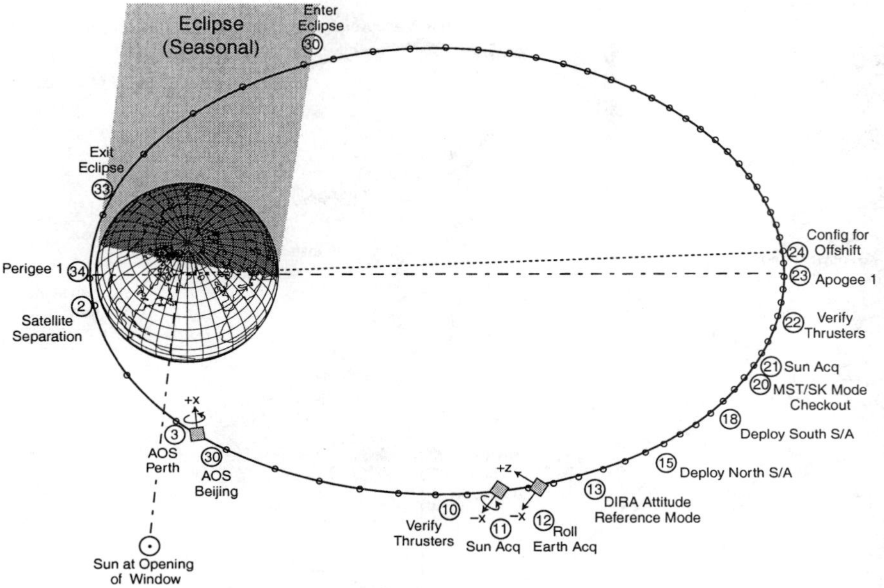

Fig. 1-4. Mission Sequence During Geosynchronous Transfer Orbit. The figure shows the first 34 steps in the 217 step sequence to fully deploy the spacecraft.

payload testing can be performed without causing interference with other operational satellite. A satellite with both C-Band and Ku-Band transponders may be forced to test at two different longitudes, at the expense of extra propellant to relocate the satellite. While commanding the satellite, it is desirable not to cause any radio interference with other satellites. Therefore, maneuvers are planned to take place when the satellite is between two adjacent satellites.

Once the longitude for on-orbit tests is determined, the primary and back up plans for apogee engine firing are established. Each plan requires several iterations on the mission software, due to the constraints imposed on mission maneuvers. The constraints for the Intelsat 901 mission are:

- Maximum duration of any maneuver is 120 minutes due to the design of the apogee engine
- 2 ground stations have to be visible to the satellite during maneuvers to provide redundancy in commanding
- Maneuvers are not usually planned in the U.S. domestic arc, due to the long process required to coordinate with other satellite operators

As shown in Fig. 1-5, a nominal maneuver plan consists of 4 apogee burns that are properly phased to place the satellite at the desired longitude and drift rate at the end of the last maneuver. Due to the thrust uncertainty, the last maneuver is planned at a location several degrees to the west of the longitude selected for on-orbit testing, with a residual eastward drift. The satellite arrives at the desired longitude over a period of several days, during which the engineers perform on-orbit tests on the spacecraft bus. Back-up plans are prepared for each maneuver in case they are missed.

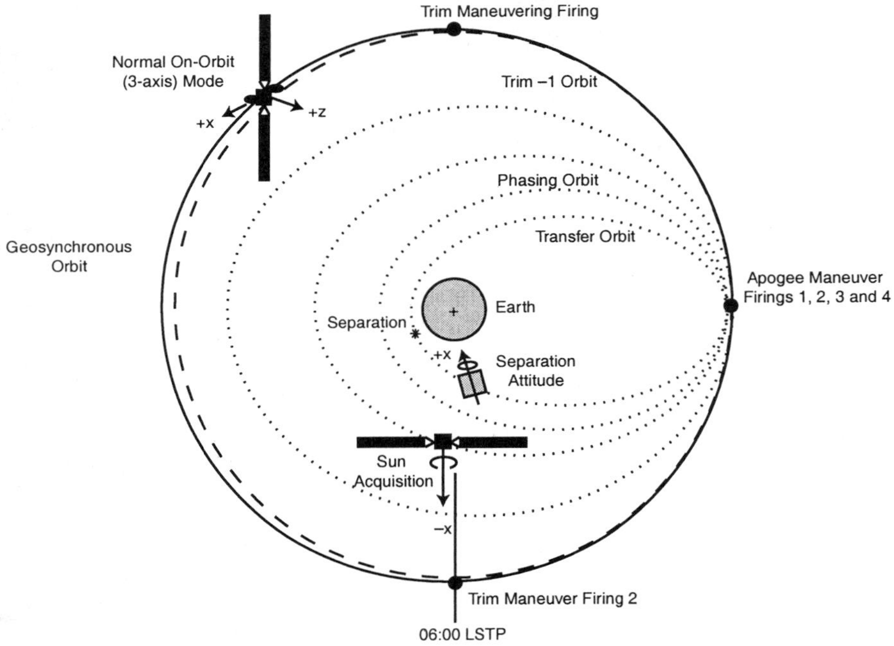

Fig. 1-5. A sequence of 4 Apogee Motor Firings are Used to Go From Transfer Orbit to Geosynchronous Orbit. In GEO, the spacecraft starts out in a drift orbit, goes to a test and check-out location, and finally to its operational slot for its 10 to15 year mission life.

Both orbit and attitude maneuvers require substantial preparation. For example, a sequence of maneuvers is used to prepare for deployment of the solar arrays that includes warming the solar array hinges by exposing them to sunlight. Orbit maneuvers are often timed for operational reasons as well as astrodynamics. Thus, the first apogee burn maneuver is done on the third apogee to allow the mission team approximately 20 hours of rest. Subsequent burns are planned for every other apogee.

The entire sequence of launch and on-orbit check-out takes 5 to 6 weeks. The satellite is then relocated to the final operational longitude where it will remain for 10 to 15 years. (However, geosynchronous satellites are a marketable commodity. From time to time, they are sold, moved to other orbital slots, and replaced with newer or more powerful systems.) Finally, at the end of its useful life, the spacecraft will be raised to approximately 500 km above the geostationary ring. Satellites in GEO are far too high to be deorbited with any reasonable amount of propellant. The *graveyard orbit* above GEO is convenient for satellite disposal because orbit perturbations will not affect it sufficiently to bring the spacecraft back into the geostationary orbit for over 100,000 years.

The orbit and attitude systems for Intelsat 901 are shown in Table 1-4. Their relationship to the rest of the spacecraft is shown in the block diagram in Fig. 1-6. Because of the high launch cost to GEO, expensive systems, the need for high operational reliability and long lifetimes, geosynchronous spacecraft use very high reliability parts and systems, typically with substantial redundancy for any components for which failure is at all likely. Redundancy can be achieved either by having multiple components or internal redundancy within components. For example, thrusters typically have redundant wiring for maximum reliability.

TABLE 1-4. Intelsat 901 Orbit and Attitude Systems. GEO communications satellites are expensive and intended for 10 to 15 years of on-orbit life. Consequently, they use high reliability parts and extensive redundancy.

Function	Equipment	Approximate Accuracy	Comments
Orbit Determination	• Done by ground tracking	100 m	Continuously in view of ground station
Orbit Control	• 12 22-N bipropellant thrusters • 490-N apogee motor	±0.05 deg E/W ±0.05 deg N/S	Done by ground command to stay in assigned slot
Attitude Determination	• Earth sensors • Sun sensors • Gyros	0.015 deg 0.125 deg 0.0001deg/s	Gyros used for control when firing thrusters
Attitude Control	• 2 momentum wheels • Magnetic torquers	Roll 0.015 deg Pitch 0.006 deg Yaw 0.305 deg	Has non-zero angular momentum for stiffness Normal mode pointing performance shown

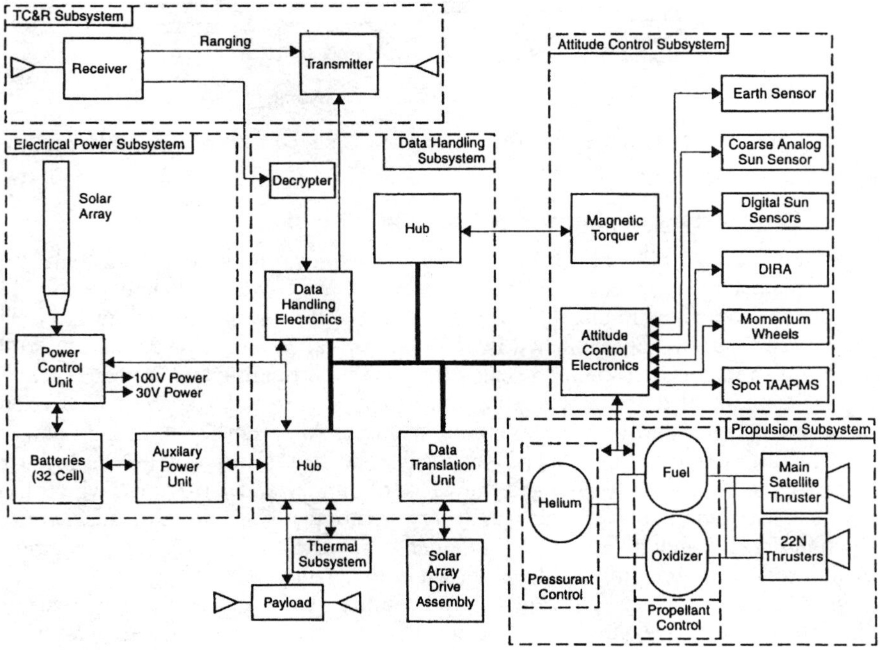

Fig. 1-6A. Intelsat 901 Functional Block Diagram.

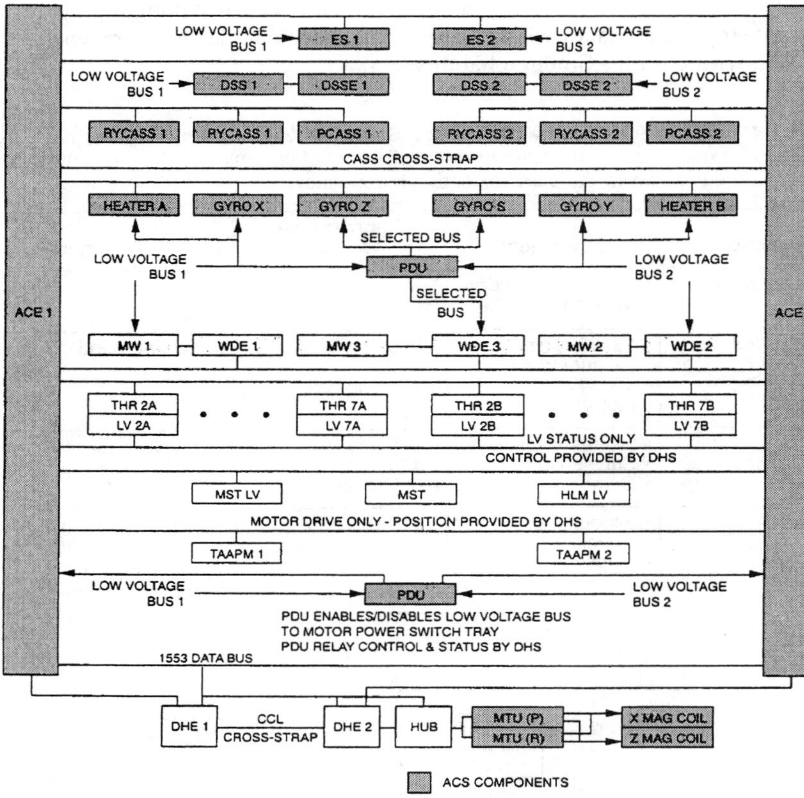

Fig. 1-6B. Intelsat 901 ACS Simplified Block Diagram. Orbit and attitude equipment is shaded.

1.1.3 Interplanetary Exploration—The Galileo Mission

Galileo is a 2,200 kg, $1.2 billion mission to explore Jupiter and its moons. Like many of the large science missions, it covered a very extended time period. The mission was conceived in the mid-1960's and received its initial funding in 1977. The spacecraft was ultimately launched in 1989, arrived at Jupiter in 1995, and will ultimately finish its mission some 25 years after the initial funding and 35 years after the original conceptual designs. The spacecraft includes 10 major science instruments plus a probe that went into the Jovian atmosphere. Although the high gain antenna failed to fully deploy after launch, the images and data returned with the low gain antenna have dramatically changed our view of Jupiter and its moons, which have proven to be remarkably complex and very geologically active. The spacecraft is shown in Fig. 1-7 and the principal components are identified in Fig. 1-8. A sample of the high resolution imaging results is shown in Fig. 1-9.

The Galileo trajectory is exceptionally complex. It was originally intended to be launched on the Space Shuttle with a powerful Centaur upper stage to provide the energy needed to get a large spacecraft to Jupiter. Following the Challenger disaster in 1986, safety issues on the Shuttle were re-evaluated and the Centaur was declared too

Fig. 1-7. The Galileo Spacecraft. The high-gain antenna on the left did not fully deploy after launch. Communications with Earth was done via the low-gain antenna, which can be seen in the center of the high-gain antenna. (Photo courtesy of NASA/JPL/Caltech.)

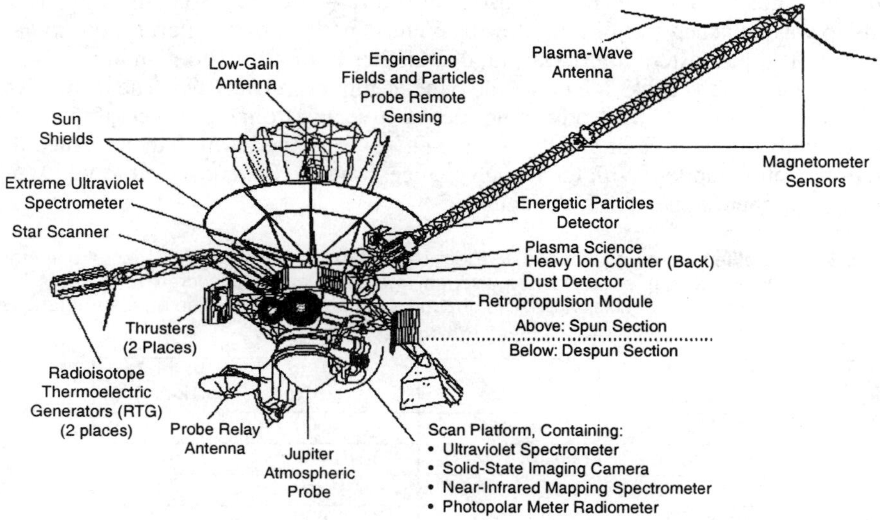

Fig. 1-8. Major Components of the Galileo Spacecraft. Galileo is a dual-spin spacecraft with a 3-axis stabilized platform "despun section" and a spinning segment. Because of the extremely long and expensive interplanetary mission, all of the components were designed for the highest reliability and long life. (Drawing courtesy of NASA/JPL/Caltech.)

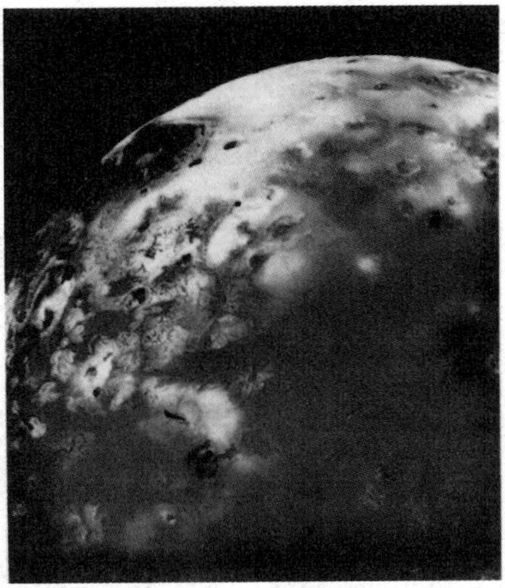

Fig. 1-9. The Jovian Moon Io as Seen by Galileo. Io is one of the most geologically active bodies in the solar system and undergoes nearly continuous volcanic activity. (Photo courtesy of NASA).

hazardous for use on manned flights. Consequently, the Inertial Upper Stage, or IUS, is used with the Shuttle to launch Galileo in 1989. Unfortunately, the IUS was substantially less powerful than the Centaur with its cryogenic propellants. As a result, Galileo used a series of planetary fly-bys to gain sufficient energy to get to Jupiter as summarized in Table 1-5 and Fig. 1-10. It also visited a few asteroids along the way. Thus, Galileo was launched from Earth, flew by Venus and then by the Earth (both to gain energy), flew past asteroid 951 Gaspra, did another Earth fly-by to gain more energy and flew past asteroid 243 Ida before arriving at Jupiter in late 1995. The design was complex, not only from a astrodynamics perspective, but from the spacecraft perspective as well. Galileo was originally designed to go from the Earth to the much colder environment of Jupiter. With the launch change, it had to be redesigned to withstand the much higher temperatures at Venus.

TABLE 1-5. Galileo Mission Timeline. Galileo used an extremely complex series of planetary flybys to get enough energy to get the very large spacecraft to Jupiter. This increased the mission timeline, the mission complexity, and the number of requirements on the orbit and attitude systems.

Event	Date	Altitude (km)	Velocity (km/s)
Earth Launch	Oct 18, 1989	300	3.6
Venus Flyby	Feb 10, 1990	16,000	4.9
Earth Flyby #1	Dec 8, 1990	960	8.5
Asteroid 951 Gaspra	Oct 29, 1991	1,600	N/A
Earth Flyby #2	Dec 8, 1992	305	8.9
Asteroid 243 Ida	Aug 28, 1993	2,400	N/A
Jupiter Arrival	Dec 7, 1995	200,000	5.6

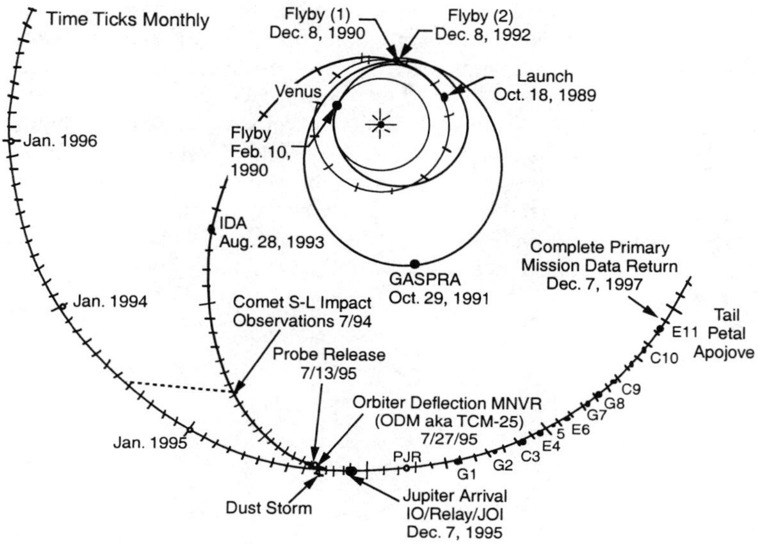

Fig. 1-10. The Galileo Orbit. Because of the swing-by trajectory, the satellite had to survive being as close to the Sun as Venus, as well as being as far away as Jupiter. (Drawing courtesy of NASA/JPL/Caltech.)

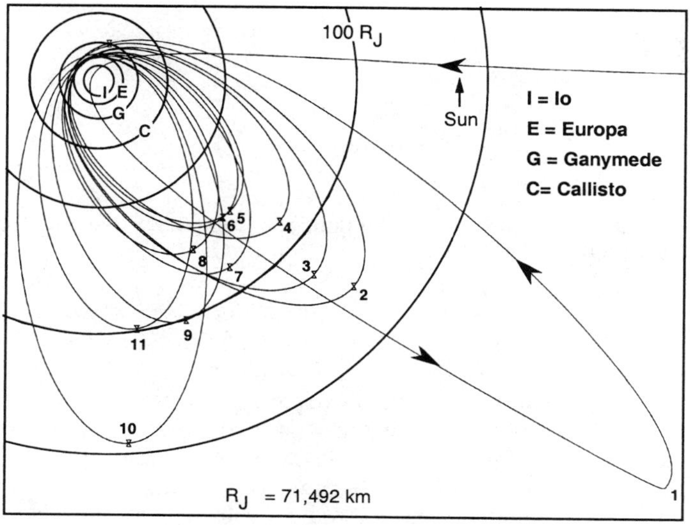

Fig. 1-11. Galileo Orbit at Jupiter. The swing-bys of the moons serve to both collect science data and adjust the orbit to achieve the next phase. (Photo courtesy of NASA/JPL/Caltech.)

After reaching Jupiter, the spacecraft went through an equally complex series of fly-bys of both Jupiter and various Jovian moons. (See Fig. 1-11.) These serve the dual purpose of adjusting the spacecraft orbit (much like the planetary fly-bys) and providing opportunities to explore Jupiter's moons from close range. The orbit control problem is made even more complex by the large distances involved. Tracking and orbit determination is provided by the Deep Space Network, or DSN, from ground stations near Goldstone, CA, Madrid, Spain, and Canberra, Australia. The travel time for radio signals to Jupiter is about 45 minutes, depending on the relative positions of the Earth and Jupiter in their orbits. This means that all orbit commands must be fully predetermined, uploaded to the spacecraft, and executed on board with no potential for ground override or correction. By the time the ground station knows what happened, the orbit maneuvers will have been over for more than a half hour.

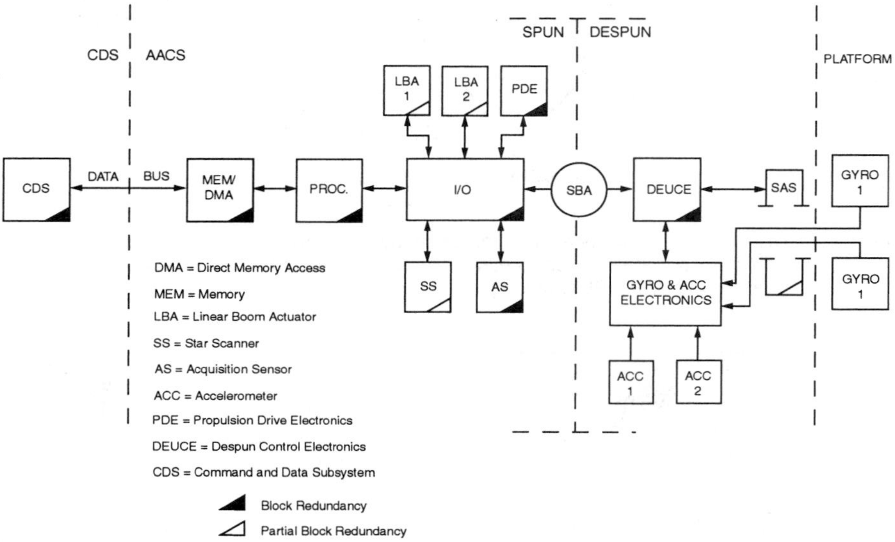

Fig. 1-12. Galileo Attitude and Articulation Control System Block Diagram. (Drawing courtesy of NASA/JPL/Caltech.)

In contrast, the Galileo Attitude and Articulation Control System (AACS) is precise, but not significantly more complex than that flown on many Earth-orbiting spacecraft. A block diagram of the AACS is shown in Fig. 1-12. Galileo is called a *dual-spin spacecraft* because it consists of two parts—an inertially fixed platform containing most of the payload instruments plus a rotating component that includes the high gain antenna pointing back to Earth. (Hughes used a similar, and very successful, dual-spin design for all of their early communications satellites in geosynchronous orbit.) The angular momentum associated with the rotating platform makes the spacecraft *stiff*, i.e., keeps it from drifting in attitude due to the inevitable small internal and external torques. The inertial platform can be rotated about the spin axis by simply torquing against the rotating portion. Small thrusters are used to move the spin axis to track the very slow angular motion of the Earth. Because of the large distances, the Galileo computer includes failure detection logic with the ability to switch in redundant components in order to continue operation if anomalies occur. The orbit and attitude system properties are summarized in Table 1-6.

TABLE 1-6. Galileo Orbit and Attitude System. Galileo is a major high-precision science instrument. The attitude and orbit requirements are extremely complex, due to the multiple mission phases and the various types of encounters.

Function	Equipment	Approximate Accuracy	Comments
Orbit Determination	Deep Space Network Tracking		
Orbit Control	• 1 400-Newton main engine • 12 10-Newton thrusters		Monomethyl Hydrazine Nitrogen Tetroxide
Attitude Determination	• 2 sets of gyroscopes and accelerometers • 2 V-slit star scanners • 2 Sun sensors	• 0.02 deg (platform) • 0.03 deg (spin)	
Attitude Control	• Dual-spin (3.15 rpm) • Thrusters	• 0.01 deg (platform) • 0.15 deg (spin)	• Same thrusters as above • 8 sec settling time
Processing	2 4-MHz processors		• 7700 lines of code • 8 mission modes

1.1.4 The International Space Station

The International Space Station, ISS, is the largest, most expensive, and probably most complex spacecraft ever built. The completed station will have a mass of nearly 500,000 kg and cost approximately $95 billion. It is built and run by a partnership of 16 nations with the principal habitable modules coming from the United States, Russia, ESA, and Japan. As shown in Table 1-7, it is assembled by a sequence of 45 flights of the U.S. Space Shuttle and the Russian Proton and Soyuz launch vehicles. The completed ISS is shown in Fig. 1-13, although various structural changes are likely as the program proceeds. The Station will be used for a variety of experiments, particularly in microgravity. There will also be biological and medical studies, Earth observations, and a significant portion of the area and services set aside for possible commercial ventures. In 2001, the Russians, over the strong objections of NASA, launched the first space tourist. California businessman Dennis Tito paid Russia $20 million for a 6-day trip to the ISS.

Fig. 1-13. The International Space Station. This will be the largest "spacecraft" launched to date. (Photo courtesy of NASA.)

TABLE 1-7. International Space Station Assembly Sequence. The Space Station is extremely complex in terms of both mission phases and objectives. From the first module put on orbit through completion, there are more than 40 distinct on-orbit configurations—each with unique attitude requirements and different moments of inertia.

Flight	Launch Vehicle	Element
1A/R	Russian Proton	• Zarya Control Module (Functional Cargo Block — FGB)
2A	US Orbiter STS-88	• Unity Node (1 stowage rack) • 2 Pressurized Mating Adapters attached to Unity
2A.1	US Orbiter STS-96	• Spacehab Double Cargo Module
1R	Russian Proton	• Service Module
2A.2	US Orbiter STS-101	• Spacehab Double Cargo Module
3A	US Orbiter STS-92	• Integrated Truss Structure (ITS) Z1 • PMA-3 • Ku-band Communications System • Control Moment Gyros (CMGs)
4A	US Orbiter STS-97	• Integrated Truss Structure P6 • Photovoltaic Module • Radiators
2R	Russian Soyuz	• Soyuz • Expedition 1 Crew
5A	US Orbiter STS-98	• US Laboratory Module
5A.1	US Orbiter STS-102	• Logistics and Resupply; Lab Outfitting • Multi-Purpose Logistics Module (MPLM) carries equipment racks
6A	US Orbiter STS-100	• Leonardo MPLM (US Lab Outfitting) • Ultra High Frequency (UHF) antenna • Space Station Remote Manipulating System (SSRMS)
7A	US Orbiter STS-104	• Joint Airlock • High Pressure Gas Assembly
7A.1	US Orbiter	• MPLM
4R	Russian Soyuz	• Docking Compartment Module-1 (DCM-1)
UF-1	US Orbiter	• MPLM • PV Module batteries • Spares Pallet (spares warehouse)
8A	US Orbiter	• Central Truss Segment (ITS S0) • Mobile Transporter (MT)
UF-2	US Orbiter	• MPLM with payload racks • Mobile Base System (MBS)
9A	US Orbiter	• First Starboard Truss Segment (ITS S1) with radiators • Crew and Equipment Translation Aid (CETA) Cart A
9A.1	US Orbiter	• Russian provided Science Power Platform (SPP) w/ 4 solar arrays
11A	US Orbiter	• First Port Truss Segment (ITS P1) • Crew and Equipment Translation Aid (CETA) Cart B
3R	Russian Proton	• Universal Docking Module
12A	US Orbiter	• Second Port Truss Segment (ITS P3/P4) • Solar array and batteries
5R	Russian Soyuz	• Docking Compartment 2 (DC2)

TABLE 1-7. International Space Station Assembly Sequence. (Continued)

Flight	Launch Vehicle	Element
12A.1	US Orbiter	• Third Port Truss Segment (ITS P5) • Multi-Purpose Logistics Module (MPLM)
13A	US Orbiter	• Second Starboard Truss Segment (ITS S3/S4) • Solar array set and batteries (Photovoltaic Module)
10A	US Orbiter	• Node 2
1J/A	US Orbiter	• Japanese Experiment Module Experiment Logistics Module (JEM ELM PS) • Science Power Platform (SSP) solar arrays
1J	US Orbiter	• Japanese Experiment Module (JEM) • Japanese Remote Manipulator System (JEM RMS)
9R	Russian Proton	• Docking and Stowage Module (DSM)
UF-3	US Orbiter	• Multi-Purpose Logistics Module (MPLM) • Express Pallet
UF-4	US Orbiter	• Express Pallet • Spacelab Pallet carrying "Canada Hand" (Special Purpose Dexterous Manipulator) • Alpha Magnetic Spectrometer
2J/A	US Orbiter	• Japanese Experiment Module Exposed Facility (JEM EF) • Solar array batteries
14A	US Orbiter	• Cupola • Science Power Platform (SPP) solar arrays • Service Module Micrometeroid and Orbital Debris Shields (SMMOD)
8R	Russian Soyuz	• Research Module 1
UF-5	US Orbiter	• Multi-Purpose Logistics Module (MPLM) • Express Pallet
20A	US Orbiter	• Node 3
10R	Russian Soyuz	• Research Module 2
17A	US Orbiter	• Multi-Purpose Logistics Module (MPLM) • US Lab racks for Node 3
1E	US Orbiter	• European Laboratory — Columbus Orbital Facility (COF)
18A	US Orbiter	• US Crew Return Vehicle (CRV)
19A	US Orbiter	• Multi-Purpose Logistics Module (MPLM)
15A	US Orbiter	• Solar arrays and batteries (Photovoltaic Module S6)
UF-6	US Orbiter	• Multi-Purpose Logistics Module (MPLM) • Batteries
UF-7	US Orbiter	• Centrifuge Accommodation Module (CAM)
16A	US Orbiter	• US Habitation Module

Several features of the ISS make the orbit and attitude systems exceptionally complex. First, the on-orbit assembly sequence covering a period of years gives the Station over 40 distinct and very different configurations, each of which has unique moments of inertia, center of mass, total mass, and attitude and orbit requirements. Every time a new module is added, the basic mass properties of the system change and must, of course, be accommodated by the Station's control system. In addition, the Station is exceptionally large and heavy such that normal spacecraft attitude control components—such as momentum wheels, magnetic torquers, and small thrusters

—simply don't provide enough torque to move or control the massive ISS. Consequently, the ISS typically flies in a Torque Equilibrium Attitude in which the major disturbance torques (primarily aerodynamic and gravity gradient) average out over the course of an orbit. This minimizes the amount of control torque that must be applied and, therefore, the mass and propellant utilization of the control system.

As with any spacecraft, much of the ISS orbit and attitude complexity comes from inherently conflicting requirements from the various activities. In several of the early configurations, a key attitude requirement is to maintain an orientation that provides sufficient power on the solar arrays. This forces the Station away from the simple Torque Equilibrium Attitude. During later phases, the multiple on-board experiments generate internal conflicts. Microgravity experiments are best done in a completely stable, motionless environment with minimal disturbances. However, both medical experiments and the health of the astronauts requires them to undertake strenuous activity. It's much like trying to use a powerful telescope in a rowboat while the rest of the passengers trade seats.

TABLE 1-8. Space Station Orbit and Attitude System. Space Station orbit and attitude is also made more complex by the need to provide safety for manned flight and accommodate the vagaries of human activity within a "stable" space platform—similar to taking long exposure photos using a camera tripod on a small boat with other people in the boat jumping up and down.

Function	Equipment	Comments
Position Determination	• GPS antennas (4) • GLONASS antennas (4) • Navigation software	GPS and GLONASS permit the Station to independently determine its position and velocity without ground support.
Orbit Control	• Russian orbital segment • Motion control system • Reboost control software • 4,100 N main engines (2)	The Station maintains its altitude by performing reboosts every 3 months to offset orbital decay from aerodynamic drag. The primary method for conducting a reboost is using the main engine of a docked transport cargo vehicle, typically a Progress M1.
Attitude Determination	• Attitude determination software • Rate gyros (2) • Star sensors (3) • Sun sensors (4) • Horizon sensors (3) • GLONASS receivers (2) • GPS receivers (2) • Magnetometers (2)	
Attitude Control	• Attitude control software • Control moment gyros (4) • 390 N thrusters (24) • 13 N Vernier thrusters • 130 N kg thrusters (32) • 3,100 N gimbaled engines (2) • Gyrodynes (6)	300 kg CMGs with 260 Nm, each of torque. By repositioning the axes of the 4 gyroscopes, the control software directs the CMGs to generate torques that counter some of the Station's attitude disturbances.

Table 1-8 shows the basic orbit and attitude equipment flown on the ISS, perhaps best summarized as 2 or more of every type of space sensor and actuator known to man. For example, attitude determination is done by using data from gyros, star sensors, Sun sensors, Earth sensors, magnetometers, and GPS receivers. This situation is made more complex by introducing international politics. As shown in Fig. 1-14 and Fig. 1-15, the orbit and attitude control functions are duplicated in both the Russian and American segments of the Station. Each runs independently with its own hardware. For example, the U.S. portion relies on GPS for orbit determination and the Russian portion relies on the equivalent Russian navigation constellation, GLONASS. The two systems continuously exchange attitude, attitude rate, and orbit data and occasionally operate interactively, such as when the U.S. system asks the Russian system for thruster firings to dump excess angular momentum. However, each system uses its own distinct coordinate system for computations such that the potential for error is significantly increased.

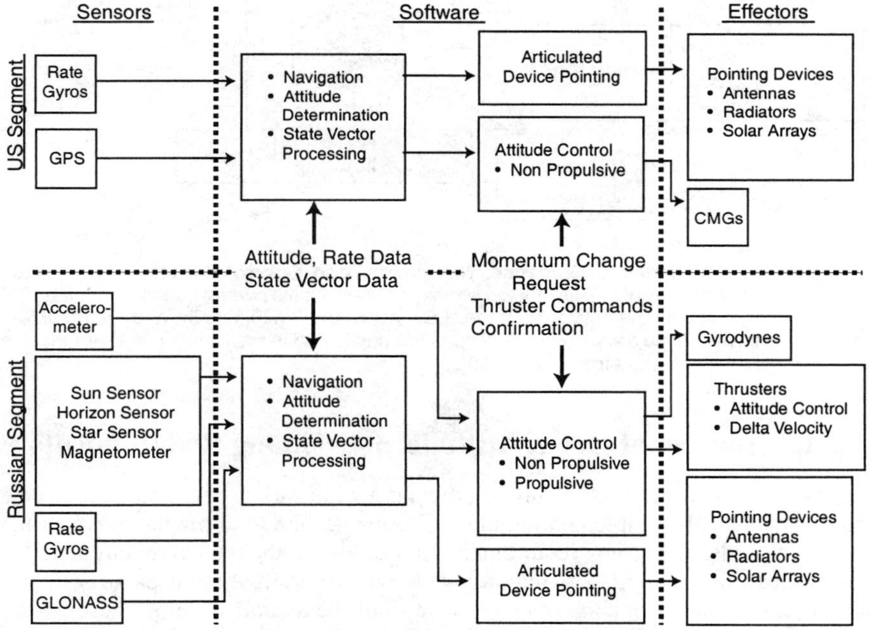

Fig. 1-14. Space Station Orbit and Attitude Functional Block Diagram. The U.S. and Russian segments exchange data continuously, but each uses its own unique coordinate system.

Finally, the Station equipment is made more complex and expensive by the requirement to be man-rated, i.e., sufficiently safe and reliable to be used in an environment where people are nearby and human lives may depend on its successful operation. In many respects, the ISS has an inherently simple orbit and attitude control problem. It is in a benign low Earth orbit, has very few orbit control requirements, and has the altitude maintained by occasional orbit raising maneuvers by visiting vehicles. Similarly, there are no major attitude maneuvers, rapidly moving platforms, or a need to track high speed external targets while continuously pointing an antenna at the distant Earth as does Galileo. Nonetheless, the size, complexity, international aspects, and human factors all combine to create a very complex and challenging orbit and attitude determination and control problem for the Station.

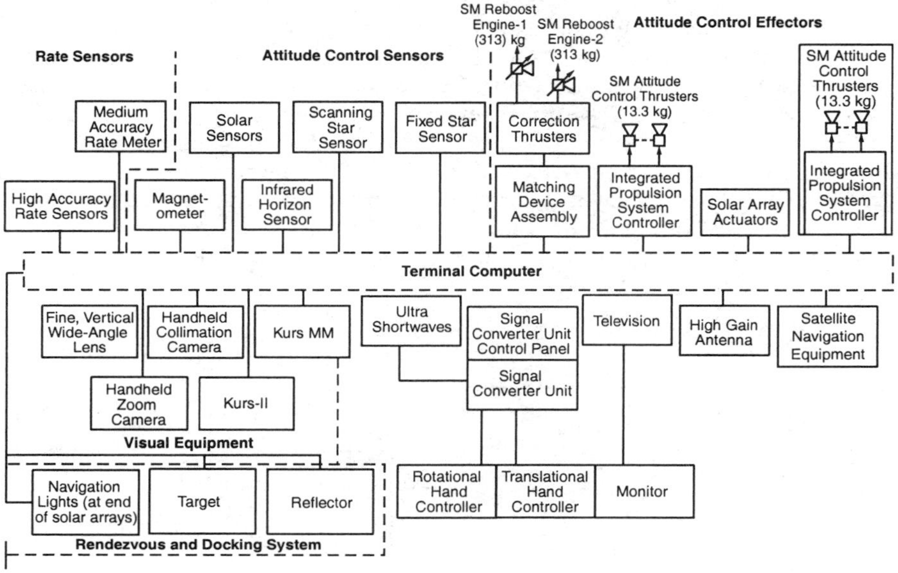

Fig. 1-15. Summary of the Guidance, Navigation, and Control System on the Russian Service Module. This module provides the exclusive control capability for the ISS prior to arrival and activation of the U.S. Laboratory (on Flights 5A and 8A in Table 1-7), at which time most control functions are duplicated in the Russian and American segments. Adapted from Lee [2000].

1.2 Sources of Orbit, Attitude, and Timing Requirements

As shown in the previous examples, there is a wide variety of mission requirements and mechanisms for implementing them. We would like to know the overall sources of orbit, attitude, and timing requirements and an idea of the typical requirement levels that result from them. Also of importance are the trades that are capable of reducing these requirements and, consequently, the cost of the overall system. These questions are introduced here and are discussed in more detail in Chap. 5.

A spacecraft is typically divided into two distinct pieces. The *payload* is that portion of the equipment which does the central mission function, i.e., the transmitters and receivers for a commercial communications satellite, or the spectroscope and camera for an interplanetary mission. The remainder of the spacecraft is called the *bus* and provides the so-called *housekeeping functions* of orbit, attitude, power, communications, thermal control, and structural rigidity needed for the payload to carry out its mission. Thus, the orbit, attitude, and timing systems are normally a part of the spacecraft bus. However, the functional requirements for these systems may come from either the housekeeping needs of the spacecraft or the specialized needs of the payload.

Housekeeping requirements are derived from the mission itself, such as the need for power or communications. Typical sources and levels for these requirements are summarized in Table 1-9. Frequently, the orbit requirements flow directly from the definition of the mission, i.e., the need to get somewhere, put the spacecraft in a specific orbit, maintain it there, and dispose of it at end-of-life. For these functions, the attitude and timing requirements are simply to provide sufficient accuracy to support the orbit maneuvers. Although stringent requirements are possible, these maneuvers can typically be supported with attitude accuracies of the order of 0.5 to 1 deg and timing accurate to approximately 1 sec. Additional housekeeping requirements tend to fall more on the attitude system than on the orbit and may be the source of substantial additional requirements and constraints. Typical requirements include pointing the solar array within a few degrees of the Sun; avoiding having the Sun shine on a sensitive instrument or cryogenic dewar; and pointing communications antennas either at a ground station or relay satellite. As with orbit maneuver support, accuracy requirements on the order of 0.25 deg to several degrees are the most common.

TABLE 1-9. The Principal "Housekeeping" Sources of Orbit, Attitude, and Timing Requirements. Of course, not all requirements are applicable to all missions and some missions may have much more stringent requirements than others. See Chap. 5 for further discussion.

Function	Orbit Requirement	Attitude Requirement	Timing Requirement
Power	Eclipse timing or duration	Point solar arrays at Sun (~5 deg)	None
Communications	Knowledge of spacecraft & ground station location (1–100 km)	Antenna pointing (0.5–5 deg)	Need to track relative motion (~5 sec for acquisition, ~0.5 sec for tracking)
Thermal	Eclipse timing or duration (req. is minimal)	Keep heat sensitive surfaces shaded (~5 deg)	Typically none
Sensitive Equipment	Typically none	Keep pointed away from Sun (~ 5 deg)	Typically none
Orbit Maneuvers	Accurate velocity correction (0.01–1.0 m/s)	Thruster pointing (0.5–1 deg)	Maneuver timing (~1 sec)
Station Acquisition	Accurate velocity correction (~1 m/s)	Sufficient for orbit maneuvers (~1 deg)	Sufficient for orbit maneuvers (~1 sec)
Constellation Maintenance	Maintain spacing, collision avoidance (~5 km)	Sufficient for orbit maneuvers (~1 deg)	Sufficient for orbit maneuvers (~1sec)
End-of-life	De-orbit or move to benign orbit	Sufficient for orbit maneuvers (~5 deg)	Sufficient for orbit maneuvers (~5 min)

Because they are derived from much the same sources, housekeeping requirements tend to be similar between varying missions. In contrast, requirements derived from the payload are both mission dependent and strongly varying. These requirements ordinarily represent the principal cost drivers for the orbit, attitude, and timing systems. Typical sources of these requirements are shown in Table 1-10.

Perhaps the most important issue in payload derived requirements is that the end user is almost never really interested in the spacecraft orbit or attitude. For nearly all end users it is the orbit and attitude related functions of pointing and mapping that are ultimately of interest. *Mapping* is of interest to observation missions and consists of determining the geographic coordinates or direction in inertial space of specific fea-

TABLE 1-10. Typical Payload-Derived Requirements for Various Mission Types. Payload-derived requirements are both more stringent and more varied than mission or housekeeping requirements.

Mission Type	Typical Requirements
Communications	• Antenna pointing
Observations or Surveillance	• Instrument pointing • Mapping of identified features or targets • Observation timing (critical only for some missions)
Navigation	• Similar to communications, but satellite position may be part of transmitted message
Space Manufacturing	• Maintain stable microgravity environment • Material recovery
Exploration	• Getting somewhere • Pointing and mapping requirements only if observations are required
Manned Missions	• Requirements driven by mission function (e.g., observations or manufacturing); main impact of people is to add reliability requirements and large unmodelled disturbance torques due to crew motion

tures or objects seen by the payload. *Pointing* consists of orienting the payload instrument in a specific direction and is of interest to both observation and communications missions. Timing is often of interest to the end user. However, since an Earth-orbiting spacecraft is moving at about 7 km/sec, the timing of a specific observation rarely needs to be known as accurately as needed to fulfill the pointing and mapping functions. **The importance of this issue is that by specifying our needs in terms of pointing and mapping we can trade back and forth between orbit, attitude, and timing in order to meet the mission objectives at the lowest possible cost**. We will return to this issue on many occasions. The major message is as follows:

> **Payload related requirements should be expressed in terms of what is desired (i.e., pointing and mapping) rather than how to achieve it (i.e., orbit, attitude, and timing accuracy).**

So long as our goals are expressed in terms of pointing and mapping, we can trade between orbit and attitude to achieve these with the least cost and risk. As soon as we have transferred these requirements into specifications on the orbit and attitude, this trade space is no longer available to us and we have eliminated one of the major mechanisms for reducing cost and risk.

Much of the cost of the mission is determined at the time the requirements are specified. Once the requirements have been fully defined, there is very little that can be done that will significantly influence the cost, risk, or schedule associated with building the spacecraft or completing the mission. Consequently, the requirements definition process should be thought of as a trade between what you want and what you can afford, much as it is in almost any other aspect of human activity. If we set out to buy a car or a house, we begin by looking at what we can afford, surveying the market to see what is available, and trying to decide which features are most important to us. Most of us cannot afford to buy a car or a house which satisfies all of our desires. Instead, we settle for a purchase that is some balance between what we would like to have and what is reasonable within realistic budget constraints. The same logic should apply to systems bought for the government or business. We need to find systems that can meet our needs at an affordable price. Trading on mission requirements is the single most important mechanism for doing this. (For a more extended discussion, see Wertz [1996]). Unfortunately, system requirements rarely flow down this way to the engineer in charge of orbit, attitude, and timing systems. Typically, they flow as specific requirements on these components. However, it is important for everyone involved in the process to keep in mind that this traditional approach is needlessly expensive and should be revised in systems where it is important to constrain mission cost.

Making requirements more stringent or adding additional requirements to the mission ordinarily drives cost and can do so dramatically. Table 1-11 summarizes the principal requirements trades associated with orbit, attitude, and timing systems that typically have a large impact on mission cost. If any of these requirements are made more stringent than typical mission equipment can support, costs can rise rapidly. For example, the TOPEX mission used an on-orbit radar system to measure wave heights and sea states. To do this effectively requires measuring the height of the ocean surface to a resolution of a few meters or better. This, in turn, implies that we must know the orbit of the spacecraft with a precision better than the altitude measurement requirements. Because these were more stringent requirements than any previous orbit, an entirely new geopotential model for the Earth had to be developed. Prior to the TOPEX mission, most spacecraft orbits had been analyzed using a 21×21 geopotential model (i.e., a 21×21 matrix representing terms in the spherical harmonic expansion of the Earth's gravitational potential function). Because of TOPEX, 70×70 and 100×100 geopotential models of the Earth were developed. Thus, a part of the cost of studying the surface of the ocean from space was the need to develop a far more accurate model of the Earth's mass distribution.

TABLE 1-11. Typical Requirements Trades that have a Large Impact on Mission Cost. Making any requirement more stringent typically increases cost, usually in a non-linear fashion.

- Multiple payload instruments or mission functions (frequently leads to competing requirements)
- Multiple mission modes or phases
- Onboard, long-term precision timing
- Need for attitude maneuvers (if maneuvers are needed, fast maneuvers with short settling times are expensive)
- Position accuracy beyond that available from ground tracking or GPS
- Precision pointing (precision pointing knowledge is lower cost; good stability for short periods is lower still)
- Precision arrival or landing constraints

1.3 The Need for an Orbit-Attitude Systems Approach

Orbit and attitude are the two fundamental aspects of spacecraft dynamics and satellite motion. Nonetheless, as discussed in the Introduction, orbit and attitude systems have developed almost entirely independently of each other and are implemented on spacecraft in remarkably different ways. It is possible to regard these as two elements of a single system which is to be optimized to meet our mission objectives at minimum cost and risk. The question is whether combining these traditionally separate disciplines into a single systems approach is worthwhile or whether they are better kept as separate elements of the space mission engineering task.

The essence of space mission engineering is to begin with the basic system objectives and constraints. For most missions, objectives are expressed in terms of pointing and mapping requirements which, in turn, are flowed down into requirements on orbit, attitude, and timing systems. To arrive at an efficient low-cost solution, we need to be able to trade back and forth between orbit and attitude. As illustrated in Fig. 1-16, a given geopositioning accuracy for determining the location of an object seen from space can be achieved by various combinations of orbit and attitude accuracies. We have no a priori way of knowing which combination will result in the lowest cost. Indeed, as technology evolves, it is likely that the mix of orbit and attitude will shift as one element of technology becomes more economical or more precise than another. This is perhaps the most important reason for treating orbit and attitude as a single system. They both need to be worked together to ensure that we achieve the best possible solution at the lowest cost and risk.

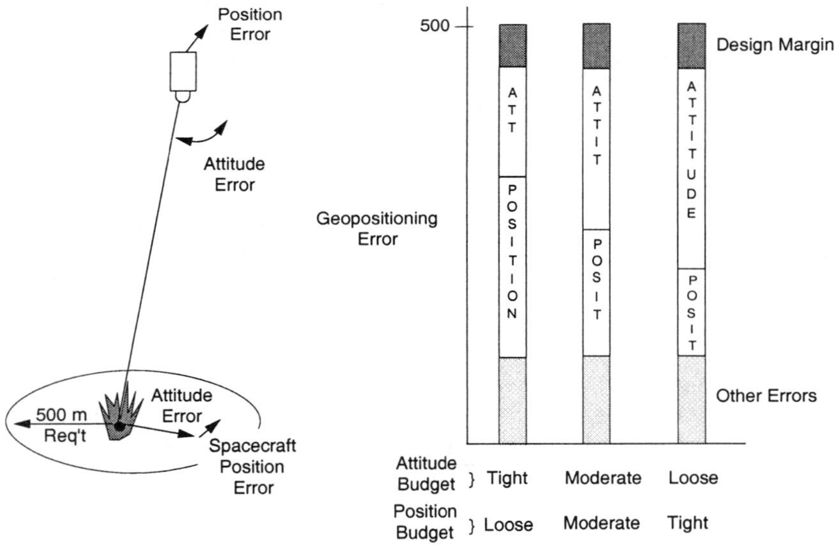

Fig. 1-16. Geopositioning Accuracy is an Example of Being Able to Trade Between Orbit and Attitude to Achieve a Given End Result. [Wertz and Larson, 1999].

In addition to trading requirements between orbit and attitude, the two systems often use many of the same sensors and actuators. Many of the algorithms use common elements. Although the processing for orbit and attitude is not identical, using the same processor for both provides a substantial cost savings and allows for efficient coding, analysis, and data transfer.

Any sensor used for attitude determination can also be used as one component of an orbit sensing system. For example, star sensors are used to provide high accuracy attitude with respect to inertial space. They do not contain any direct information about the orbit because the relative position of the stars will look the same from anywhere in the solar system. Similarly, Earth sensors provide an attitude measurement with respect to the direction of the center of the Earth. Again, these provide no orbit information because they do not tell us where the spacecraft is with respect to the Earth. Nonetheless, star sensors and Earth sensors together can provide both orbit and attitude. If I simultaneously observe the direction to known stars and the direction and distance to the Earth, then I can determine where the Earth is with respect to the background stars. This, in turn, tells me where I am looking from—i.e., where the spacecraft is with respect to the Earth and the background of the fixed stars. The Earth sensor and star sensor working together provide an excellent basis for autonomous navigation and orbit determination as well as attitude determination with respect to the Earth and inertial space. In addition, algorithms have been developed for autonomous navigation based on observations of the Sun, Moon, and Earth and on magnetometer data over a large fraction of an orbit. The principal sensors used for both orbit and attitude determination are listed in Table 1-12.

TABLE 1-12. Principal Sensors Used for Both Orbit and Attitude. Directional antennas and laser crosslinks are candidates for future missions.

Sensor	Orbit Application	Attitude Application
GPS Receiver	High accuracy orbit determination	Low accuracy (~0.5 deg), intermittent attitude sensing
Star Sensor, Sun Sensor	Moderate to high accuracy orbit determination when used with an Earth sensor	High accuracy inertial attitude sensing
Earth Sensor	Moderate to high accuracy orbit determination when used with any inertial sensor (Sun/Moon/stars)	Moderate accuracy attitude sensing with respect to the Earth
Magnetometer	Low accuracy orbit determination (10–100 km)	Low accuracy attitude determination (2–5 deg)

Much of the onboard sensor data processing is associated with target identification, data checking, bias determination, and calibration procedures. Consequently, if we are using the same sensors for orbit and attitude much of the processing will be common to both activities. In addition, many of the same algorithms and mathematical techniques are used in both fields. Data averaging approaches and Kalman filtering are widely used for both orbit and attitude. Since they are using much of the same data and many of the same algorithms and intermediate steps, processing both attitude and orbit in the same computer is a logical approach. Further, much of the payload sensor processing depends on both orbit and attitude. To point the communications antenna at a ground station requires knowing both the orbit and attitude of the spacecraft. Similarly, both elements are needed to determine the geographic location of a target identified in a sensor image. The basic complement of spacecraft bus sensors provide both orbit and attitude data, and the results of both the orbit and attitude are critical to the processing of most payload data.

In terms of actuators, there is a broad class which provides only torque and, therefore, is relevant only for attitude control. Magnetic torquers and wheels of all types are exclusively attitude devices. They do not provide any net force with respect to on the center of mass of the spacecraft. However, any actuators capable of exchanging linear momentum with the environment can be used for both orbit and attitude. The principal orbit actuator is the thruster or rocket motor, which is also used for attitude control and for desaturation of momentum wheels as they accumulate excess angular momentum. Solar radiation pressure is a significant perturbation for both orbit and attitude for some spacecraft and has been used for attitude actuation and proposed for spacecraft propulsion via solar sailing. Although they are not identical, there is significant commonality between the sources of forces and torques on many spacecraft.

There are certainly substantial differences between orbit and attitude systems. Attitude systems are classified primarily by how the attitude is controlled and secondarily, by how it is sensed. Attitude control tends to be unique to each spacecraft and varies strongly from mission to mission, depending on the environment, the needed accuracy, and the sensor complement. In contrast, orbits are first characterized by what orbit the spacecraft is in. Essentially all orbit control uses thrusters, although other forces such as aerodynamics and solar radiation pressure have been used occasionally. Traditionally, orbit sensing has been done exclusively by ground tracking, although it is now available using onboard equipment, as well as the ground. Because the same data was used, the same orbit determination software is used for many spacecraft. For example, the space tracking network at Cheyenne Mountain processes orbit data for all low-Earth orbit objects which it can track. This represents both spacecraft and debris larger than approximately 10 cm in diameter. In contrast, there is remarkably little commonality in attitude data processing and that is unlikely to change significantly.

Finally, the time scales for orbit and attitude processing are very different. Attitude disturbances work over relatively short periods of time such that attitude control systems most often work in the frequency regime of 1–10 Hz. For most spacecraft, if the attitude control system stops working for even a few minutes, the spacecraft will tumble with potentially disastrous consequences due to pointing communications antennas away from the Earth, solar arrays away from the Sun, or sensitive instruments toward the Sun. In contrast, orbit changes occur over periods of hours or, for interplanetary spacecraft, days or weeks. Orbit control systems function at frequencies of 10^{-4} to 10^{-6} Hz and the orbit control computer will be remarkably unbusy most of the time. (This is another good reason for implementing orbit control in the attitude computer. Orbit control adds almost nothing to the computer throughput requirements.) Although large rocket maneuvers are critically important, low thrust orbit control failures could typically go unnoticed for several days as the spacecraft drifts slowly from its assigned position.

In spite of these differences, we can make use of combined orbit and attitude sensing to provide a high level of functional redundancy as shown in Table 1-13. The principal advantage of this approach is that we can improve system reliability at a small increase in cost and can also significantly reduce operations costs by transferring functions onboard the spacecraft.

Nonetheless, there are significant drawbacks to a combined orbit and attitude system, and both autonomous navigation and onboard orbit control have been extremely slow to come about. The principal drawback is that orbit and attitude have traditionally been done by two distinct groups of people within the astronautics community. Mission designers and orbit analysts are simply not comfortable with thinking of orbit determination and orbit control as onboard functions. These have been tradi-

TABLE 1-13. Representative Combined Orbit and Attitude Systems. Combined orbit and attitude sensing can provide a high level of functional redundancy which improves system reliability at a small increase in cost. Typically thrusters are the only mechanism for providing a positive ΔV to the spacecraft, and therefore, serving as orbit actuators.

Function	Primary	Back-Up
Navigation (Orbit Determination)	GPS	1. Onboard propagation 2. Optical navigation
Attitude Determination	Optical (Earth sensor, star sensor)	GPS
Orbit Control	Thrusters	
Attitude Control	Wheels; Magnetic torquing for desaturation	Thrusters for attitude maneuvers, recovery, or desaturation
Control Logic	Integrated orbit/attitude software	1. Hardware for fail-safe 2. Separate de-orbit function

tional ground functions and have been done under the watchful eye of mission planners and astrodynamists. On the other hand, onboard attitude control is typically required for both cost and safety. The attitude system has been onboard the spacecraft since the beginning of the space program. The control system has a relatively short response time and it would be unrealistic to do most attitude control activities from the ground. Orbit control, on the other hand, requires navigation information that was, in the past, typically available only on the ground. Thus, commands needed to be generated on the ground based on the available information and the only realistic option for orbit adjustments was to send stored commands to the spacecraft for later execution. The principal reasons for reattaining ground control over orbit functions are listed in Table 1-14, along with the principal counter reasons as spacecraft technology continues to evolve.

TABLE 1-14. Principal Reasons for Retaining or Giving Up Ground Control Over Orbit Maneuvers.

Reason for Ground Control	Reason to Give Up Ground Control
Navigation Information is on the Ground	Both GPS and autonomous navigation provide onboard solutions
Firing Large Motors or Engines is "Mission Life-Threatening"	For most on-orbit applications, low thrust maneuvers are equally or more efficient and far less dangerous to the mission and the spacecraft
Propellant is a Limited, Mission-Critical Resource	Ground commanding can introduce errors as well as catch them; limiter on burn duration can provide fail-safe autonomous on-orbit operation
Tradition	Onboard control reduces operations cost and allows more efficient systems

There is a continuing demand to reduce the cost and complexity of space missions and, consequently, to begin to think of the spacecraft as a complete system rather than as a set of separate divisible parts. The creation of a combined orbit and attitude control system is a natural beginning to this process.

A combined orbit and attitude system does not have to be implemented entirely onboard the spacecraft. It can include portions of either system done on the ground. A good example is the TDRS system used to provide data and communications for the Space Shuttle, Space Telescope, and other high data rate low Earth orbit spacecraft. Each TDRS spacecraft has two large, single access antennas which track low Earth orbit spacecraft as they move. The autotracking for the TDRS single access antennas is done at the ground station at White Sands. It is the ground station which determines the relative signal strength and sends back up the necessary commands to step the gimbals on the large antennas. In this case, the critical pointing function was achieved directly by ground activity. Similarly, treating the orbit and attitude together does not imply solving simultaneously for orbit and attitude in a single, large Kalman filter or doing orbit and attitude maneuvers simultaneously. It simply means looking at the larger system issues and attempting to reduce the cost, increase the performance, and improve the reliability for both functions taken together.

The strongest argument for retaining orbit and attitude systems as inherently separate functions is tradition. Most prime contractors and government agencies are organized with orbit and attitude in separate divisions. Thus, most organizations do not have the systems perspective to adequately address orbit and attitude problems as a single combined system. This is a key reason for the creation of this set of books—to clearly establish the interrelationship between orbit and attitude, to help define both the similarities and differences, and to create a systems perspective in which both can be dealt with in a way that produces the most efficient and effective space mission.

1.4 Space Systems Engineering Bibliography

Each of the five chapters in Part 1 provides an annotated bibliography listing the principal books in print which provide additional information on orbit and attitude systems. Together this set of books provides the basic foundation for modern orbit, attitude, and timing system analysis and design.

Agrawal, B. N. 1986. *Design of Geosynchronous Spacecraft.* Englewood Cliffs, NJ: Prentice-Hall. 459 p.

Emphasis on the analysis, theory, and design of geostationary communications spacecraft, bus subsystems, and communications payloads; discussion of geosynchronous orbits and stationkeeping.

Brown, C. D. 1998. *Spacecraft Mission Design* (2nd ed). Washington, DC: AIAA. 210 p. + software diskette.

The title of this volume is misleading—the book is about orbit design with an emphasis on interplanetary missions and some discussion of both general and specialized Earth orbits. Includes a copy of ORB, a PC program for computing orbits for Earth and planetary missions.

Burger, J. J. [updated annually]. *Space 2000.* Colorado Springs, CO: Space Analysis and Research, Inc.

A complete data base of all space launches, including most launch failures, and many planned launches. Includes Space Command and international designations;

launch date, time, vehicle, and origin; spacecraft name, owner, weight, frequencies, and mission; orbital elements; and current spacecraft status. Can be sorted on nearly all fields.

Chetty, P. R. K. 1991. *Satellite Technology and Its Applications* (2nd ed). Blue Ridge Summit, PA: TAB Books. 554 p.

Practical discussion of the design and characteristics of spacecraft subsystems; includes substantial hardware discussion and data; discusses satellite applications with an emphasis on geostationary communications satellites.

Churchill, Suzanne E. 1997. *Fundamentals of Space Life Sciences.* 2 vols. Malabar, FL: Krieger Publishing Co. 364 p.

A detailed presentation of practical aspects of human spaceflight. Covers nearly all aspects of physiological response to spaceflight, including areas such as food and nutrition, health care delivery, and countermeasures to 0 g. Also includes related topics such as design for habitability, extended duration missions, EVA, and many similar topics. Applicable to both mission design and requirements definition. 2 volume set, but each volume is only 170 pages.

Davidoff, M. 1998. *The Radio Amateur's Satellite Handbook.* Newington, CT: ARRL. 370 p.

This AMSAT book provides a detailed recipe for the design and operation of very low-cost communications satellites; practical, relevant data and methods applicable to many missions; lots of references. This replaces the older version [Davidoff, 1990], which was also an excellent summary.

Eckart, P. 1994. *Spaceflight Life Support and Biospherics.* Dordrecht, the Netherlands and Torrance, CA: Kluwer Academic and Microcosm Press. 444 p.

A detailed summary of the principal aspects and requirements for life support in space or on other planets. Looks at the Earth's biosphere and examines the requirements for other man-made biospheres.

Elbert, Bruce R. 1999. *Introduction to Satellite Communication* (2nd ed). Boston, MA: Artech House Publishers. 557 p.

An excellent and very broad discussion of satellite communication systems. Discusses the normal satellite communications technologies, but also many topics less frequently addressed, such as operations, economics, launch vehicles and services, spacecraft bus subsystems, and LEO vs. GEO. Includes both historical perspective and projections for the future. Other good, related books by Elbert are *International Telecommunications Management*, *The Satellite Communications Applications Handbook*, and *Networking Strategies for Information Technology.*

Fleeter, R. 2000. *The Logic of Microspace.* Dordrecht, The Netherlands and Torrance, CA: Kluwer Academic Publishers and Microcosm Press. 447 p.

Presents the fundamentals of microspacecraft design and applications in a very readable format. Intended for both technical and non-technical audiences, the book presents key design issues by one of the leading authorities in this area.

Fortescue, P., and J. Stark. 1995. *Spacecraft Systems Engineering* (2nd ed). NY: John Wiley and Sons. 424 p.

Broad overall discussion of space technology and spacecraft systems engineering. Discusses specific techniques employed by most of the major subsystems. Good textbook for an introductory technical space systems course.

Griffin, M., and J. R. French. 1991. *Space Vehicle Design.* Washington, DC: AIAA. 465 p.

An excellent summary of the spacecraft design process. Well-written, practical orientation. Also has discussions of mission design, launch, orbits, the space environment, and re-entry.

Helvajian, Henry (ed). 1999. *Microengineering Aerospace Systems.* El Segundo Press, CA: The Aerospace Press. 707 p.

Provides a very thorough discussion of microengineering, micropropulsion, microelectronics, and microelectromechanical systems (MEMS). Includes a more high-level discussion of applications of microsatellites and microsatellite clusters. A key volume for anyone interested in this technology.

Maral, G. and M. Bousquet. 1998. *Satellite Communications Systems—Systems, Techniques and Technology* (3rd ed). NY: John Wiley and Sons. 688 p.

General text on essentially all aspects of communications satellite systems, including both spacecraft and ground stations. Extensive discussion of link analysis, transmission techniques, satellite networks, and communications payloads. Some discussion of support subsystems, the space environment, orbits, and reliability.

Meyer, Rudolf X. 1999. *Elements of Space Technology.* San Diego, CA: Academic Press. 329 p.

This book is intended as an introductory space technology text for aerospace engineering students. Good explanations, but contents covers only a selected subset of topics — i.e., orbits, rocket propulsion, orbit maneuvers, attitude control, and spacecraft thermal design.

Morgan, W. L., and G. D. Gordon 1989. *Communications Satellite Handbook.* NY: John Wiley and Sons. 900 p.

Principally discusses communications satellite systems and multiple-access techniques. Has one of the best available discussions of satellite technology and spacecraft subsystems. (Covers all subsystems well, not just communications.) Extensive, practical discussion of orbits and viewing geometry appropriate for satellite communications.

Nicogossian, A. E., S. R. Mohler, O. G. Gazenkio, and A. I. Grigoryev (series eds) 1994. *Space Biology and Medicine.* Washington, DC and Moscow: AIAA and Nauka Press.

This is an exceptional three volume series resulting from a collaborative project between NASA and the Russian Academy of Sciences to document the foundations of space biology and medicine and the lessons learned through the mid 1990s. Most topics are covered in excellent depth by well-respected Russian and American authors. Vol. I, *Space and Its Exploration* (1993, 337 p.), covers the history of space exploration, the space environment, life in the universe, and spacecraft technology. Vol. II, *Life Support and Habitability* (1994, 423 p.), discusses the requirements for human safety when working outside of the Earth's atmosphere. Vol. III, *Humans in Space Flight* (1996, 600 p. in 2 books), provides a very detailed discussion of physiological adaptation to the space environment.

Pisacane, V. L., and R. C. Moore. 1994. *Fundamentals of Space Systems*. NY: Oxford University Press. 772 p.

Defines the spacecraft design process as done at APL, a long-standing member of the low-cost spacecraft community. The emphasis of the book is on the analytical and physical basis of spacecraft system and subsystem design with some treatment of related issues such as operations, systems engineering, and the space environment.

Pocha, J. J. 1987. *An Introduction to Mission Design for Geostationary Satellites*. Dordrecht, the Netherlands: Kluwer Academic. 222 p.

Extensive and complete discussion of orbits and orbit operations for geostationary missions; includes launch window, orbit transfer, stationkeeping, orbit propagation, tracking, and orbit determination.

Sarsfield, Liam. 1998. *The Cosmos on a Shoestring: Small Spacecraft for Space and Earth Science*. Santa Monica, CA: RAND Corp. 185 p.

Discussion of small spacecraft and their role in meeting national space objectives. Based on the results of a RAND study for the Office of Science and Technology Policy and the Office of Management and Budget. Focuses principally on NASA science missions and how to achieve more with constrained resources.

Wertz, J. R. and W. J. Larson (eds). 1996. *Reducing Space Mission Cost*. Dordrecht, the Netherlands and Torrance, CA: Kluwer Academic and Microcosm Press. 617 p.

Presents both processes and technology for reducing cost in spacecraft manufacturing, launch, and operations. Includes discussion of cost modeling, reliability, and implementation strategies. Has detailed case studies of 10 missions (with actual dollar costs) which have reduced cost by factors of 2 to 10 relative to tradition expectations.

Wertz, J. R., and W. J. Larson (eds). 1999. *Space Mission Analysis and Design* (3rd ed.) Dordrecht, The Netherlands and Torrance, CA: Kluwer Academic Publishers and Microcosm Press. 920 p.

Often referred to as SMAD. Has become a standard reference for space mission engineering and the mission analysis and design process. Process-oriented with many data tables. Broad coverage of all mission aspects—including topics not covered in other volumes, such as mission engineering, mission geometry, orbit selection and design, cost modeling, and low-cost spacecraft.

Williamson, M. 1990. *The Communications Satellite.* New York: I.O.P. Publishing. 420 p.

A largely non-mathematical, yet technical introduction to satellites with an emphasis on communications satellites. Aimed primarily at undergraduates and young engineers. Discusses all of the spacecraft subsystems plus Earth stations and launch vehicles. Discussion of space insurance not found in most books. Includes an extensive case study on the design of a geosynchronous direct broadcast satellite.

Woodcock, G. 1986. *Space Stations and Platforms.* Melbourne, FL: Krieger. 220 p.

Most detailed discussion available of the system engineering and design principles for space stations and manned space platforms.

References

Lee, Roscoe. 2000. "Evolution of International Space Station GN&C System Across ISS Assembly Stages." AAS Paper No. 00-021, presented at the 23rd Annual AAS Guidance and Control Conference, Breckenridge, CO, Feb. 2–6.

Wertz, J. R. and W. J. Larson (eds). 1996. *Reducing Space Mission Cost.* Dordrecht, the Netherlands and Torrance, CA: Kluwer Academic and Microcosm Press.

Wertz, J. R., and W. J. Larson (eds). 1999. *Space Mission Analysis and Design* (3rd ed.*)*. Dordrecht, The Netherlands and Torrance, CA: Kluwer Academic Publishers and Microcosm Press.

Chapter 2
Orbit Properties and Terminology

This chapter is a general introduction to orbits and defines the terminology used in orbit analysis and mission planning. It provides physical motivation for the principal effects important to orbit and mission design, formulas or approximations for all of the basic astronautical computations, and formulas needed for orbit and constellation design and the computation of ΔV budgets. As listed in the annotated bibliography in Sec. 2.8, many books in celestial mechanics and orbit analysis are widely available. Those which provide the most comprehensive mathematical background are Battin [1999] and Seidelmann [1992]. Particularly good modern volumes dealing with spacecraft orbits are Chobotov [1996] and Vallado [2001].

The *orbit* or *trajectory* is the path of a spacecraft or natural body through space. We will use orbit and trajectory interchangeably, although some authors prefer to use *orbit* to mean only a closed circular or elliptical path and *trajectory* to refer to other shapes such as hyperbola or paths which intersect the surface of the Earth. *Astrodynamics* is the mathematical analysis of orbits and their properties. An orbit is ordinarily specified by a *state vector* which can be the position and velocity of the spacecraft at some specified time or *epoch,* or a number of other equivalent forms described in Sec. 2.2. In principle, the state vector at any one time allows us to predict the position and velocity of the spacecraft at all future times. The list of successive positions of a satellite or planet is known as its *ephemeris* (plural *ephemerides*). Planetary ephemerides are published annually by the Government Printing Office. They are either in tabular form, such as *The Astronomical Almanac*, or more typically in machine readable form.

A *Keplerian orbit* is one in which gravity is the only force; the central body is spherically symmetric; the central body's mass is much greater than that of the satellite; and the central body and satellite are the only two objects in the system. Although this appears to be a large number of constraints, Keplerian orbits provide a remarkably good approximation for most spacecraft motion. A *perturbation* is a deviation from Keplerian motion of which there are two types. *Secular perturbations* are those for which the effects build up over time. *Cyclic perturbations* are periodic such that the effects cancel after one cycle or orbit.

Generally, this chapter addresses astrodynamics from a mission analysis and design perspective such that we can understand the underlying physics and make use of approximations and top-level formulas to evaluate most orbit effects. The detailed mathematical basis of astrodynamics is available from most volumes listed in the bibliography.

2.1 Keplerian Orbits

Predicting the motion of the Sun, Moon, and planets was a major part of the scientific revolution of the 16th and 17th centuries. Galileo's discovery of the satellites of Jupiter in 1610 provided a break with Aristotelian science and a strong argument for Copernicus' heliocentric theory. Danish astronomer Tycho Brahe determined the positions of the planets to about 1 minute of arc (1/60 deg) and the length of the year to about 1 sec with the unaided eye. Brahe's German assistant, Johannes Kepler, used these precise observations to derive empirically the rules of planetary motion which would later be justified by Newton.

It was the search for the underlying cause of the motion of celestial objects that motivated much of Newton's development of mechanics. In 1665, he determined that if gravity were an inverse square force it could account both for objects falling at the Earth's surface and for the motion of the Moon. However, he did not publish the detailed theory until 1687 in *Philosophiae Naturalis Principia Mathematica.* A major cause of this 22-year delay was Newton's inability to show that spherically symmetric objects (e.g., the Earth) behave gravitationally as though all the mass were concentrated at the center, the proof of which required development of the calculus. Having achieved this, Newton was able to combine his second law of motion, $\mathbf{F} = m\mathbf{a} \equiv m\ddot{\mathbf{r}}$, with his law of gravitation, $\mathbf{F} = -(\mathrm{G}Mm/r^3)\,\mathbf{r}$, to obtain the two-body equation of motion which closely approximates the motion of spacecraft and planets:

$$\ddot{\mathbf{r}} = -(\mathrm{G}M/r^3)\mathbf{r} \equiv -(\mu/r^3)\mathbf{r} \tag{2-1}$$

where $\mathbf{F}$ is the force between two objects of mass m and M, $\mathbf{r}$ is the vector between them, $\mathbf{a}$ is the acceleration of the small body, G is Newton's constant of gravitation, and $\mu \equiv \mathrm{G}M$ is the measure of the gravitational effect of the large body. Accurate orbit work includes the effect of the non-spherical symmetry of the Earth, perturbations due to other bodies, and non-gravitational forces—but nearly all of the basic foundations of orbit theory are direct extrapolations of Newton's work as foreseen by Newton himself.

Although this is a relatively simple set of equations, they provide very interesting consequences for satellite motion. First, notice that the right-hand side of Eq. (2-1) does not contain any properties of the spacecraft (m canceled in the two preceding equations). This implies that the acceleration and subsequent motion of objects in space does not depend on any physical properties of the objects themselves, so long as we ignore non-gravitational forces. A feather follows the same orbit as a bowling ball or a large spacecraft. Consequently, when the astronaut lets go of their pen, it follows the same trajectory that the spacecraft is following and appears to float next to the astronaut because they are both falling together with the same acceleration. This is the phenomenon often called *weightlessness* or *zero g*. However, gravity has not gone away and objects are certainly not weightless. An object sitting on a tall platform attached to the Earth, but at the altitude of the Space Shuttle, would weigh about 95% of what it does on the surface of the Earth. Gravity is very strong and objects are falling very rapidly. It's just that they are falling together, such that the motion relative to each other is very slow. The result is the astronaut and their pen floating gently at 7 km/s relative to the Earth's surface.

There is a second more subtle implication of these equations. In Newton's second law, m is the *inertial mass* which is the property of an object which resists acceleration or gives it momentum. A feather or ping pong ball has relatively little inertial mass whereas a freight train has a great deal. On the other hand, the m in the law of gravitation is the *gravitational mass*, which is a measure of the gravitational charge or how strong gravity acts. This is equivalent to the electrical charge on an object which determines how strong the electrical forces are. Objects with a similar mass can have very different electrical charges and, consequently, behave very differently in the presence of electrical fields. For some reason, this simply isn't true of gravity. Objects with the same inertial mass all have the same gravitational charge and all of them behave the same in the presence of a gravitational field. It is this very strange equivalence of gravitational and inertial mass that led Einstein, in the early 20th century, to develop the theory of relativity which implies, in part, that gravity is more a property of space than a property of objects, as electrical forces are. The theory of relativity plays a very minor role in the orbits of planets (particularly Mercury) and spacecraft designed specifically to test gravitational theories. For all but remarkably demanding applications, relativistic effects may be totally ignored in spacecraft calculations. Nonetheless, it is interesting that the seeds of relativity lie in the very foundations of Newtonian mechanics.

Using gravitational theory and his laws of mechanics, Newton was able to derive Kepler's three laws of planetary motion. These laws apply to any two point masses (or spherically symmetric objects) moving under their mutual gravitational attraction. Kepler's laws in the form derived by Newton are:

- **Kepler's First Law:** *If two objects in space interact gravitationally, each will describe an orbit that is a conic section with the center of mass at one focus. If the bodies are permanently associated, their orbits will be ellipses; if not, their orbits will be hyperbolas.*

- **Kepler's Second Law:** *If two objects in space interact gravitationally (whether or not they move in closed elliptical orbits), a line joining them sweeps out equal areas in equal intervals of time.*

- **Kepler's Third Law:** *If two objects in space revolve around each other due to their mutual gravitational attraction, the sum of their masses multiplied by the* *square of their period of mutual revolution is proportional to the cube of the mean distance between them; that is,*

$$(m + M)P^2 = \frac{4\pi^2}{\mathrm{G}} a^3 \tag{2-2}$$

where P is their mutual period of revolution, a is the mean distance between them, m and M are the two masses, and G *is Newton's gravitational constant.*

The more massive of the two objects, *M,* is called the *primary* and the other, *m*, is called the *secondary*, or *satellite*. The *barycenter* is the location of the center of mass between the two objects. Kepler's empirical relations presented in two works in 1609 and 1619 were essentially the same as those derived by Newton, except that the constant of proportionality in the third law was obtained empirically and the shape of the orbits specified in the first law was an ellipse (one of 4 possible conic sections) because his experience was limited to planets.

In 1673, Christian Huygens introduced the quantity $\frac{1}{2}mV^2$ which he called the *vis viva* or "living force," to explain the motion of the compound pendulum. This concept was further developed by Gottfried Leibnitz in terms of "living" and "dead" forces which later came to be known as kinetic and potential energy. The application of this theory to celestial mechanics led to the fourth fundamental relationship for two objects rotating under their mutual gravitational attraction, the *vis viva equation*:

$$\varepsilon = \frac{V^2}{2} - \frac{\mu}{r} = -\frac{\mu}{2a} \tag{2-3}$$

where ε is the total *specific energy* (i.e., energy per unit mass), and $V^2/2$ and $-\mu/r$ are the kinetic energy and potential energy respectively of the satellite, r is the instantaneous separation of the objects, and V is the magnitude of the relative velocity.

For some time there was bitter controversy between the followers of Huygens and Leibnitz, who believed that $\mathbf{F}\Delta x = (\frac{1}{2}mV^2)$ was the correct measure of the effect of a force, $\mathbf{F}$, and the followers of Galileo and Newton, who believed that $\mathbf{F}\Delta t = \Delta(mV)$ was the proper measure. The controversy was resolved in 1743 when Jean D'Alembert published his *Traité de Dynamique*, which showed that both measures were correct and that they were not equivalent. (For a discussion of this controversy see, for example, Girvin [1948] or Dugas [1955].)

2.1.1 Kepler's First Law

Kepler's first law states that the orbits of celestial objects are *conic sections*, i.e., figures produced by the intersection of a plane and a cone (Fig. 2-1 and Table 2-1) or any quadratic function in a plane. If the objects are permanently associated, this figure will be an *ellipse*, as shown in Fig. 2-2. Geometrically, an ellipse is defined by two points known as *foci*; the ellipse is then the locus of all points such that the sum of the distances from each point on the ellipse to the two foci is $2a$, where a is called the *semimajor axis* and is half the long axis or *major axis* of the ellipse. The semimajor axis is also the mean distance between either focus and points on the ellipse and is often listed this way in tables of orbit parameters. In Fig. 2-2, the quantity c is half the distance between the foci, and the *semiminor axis*, b, is half the short axis or *minor axis* of the ellipse. One of the foci is the center of mass or *barycenter* of the two objects; the other focus is of only geometric interest and is an empty point in space. Finally for some computations it is convenient to define the *semiparameter*, *p*, which is the distance from the focus to the orbit measured perpendicular to the major axis.

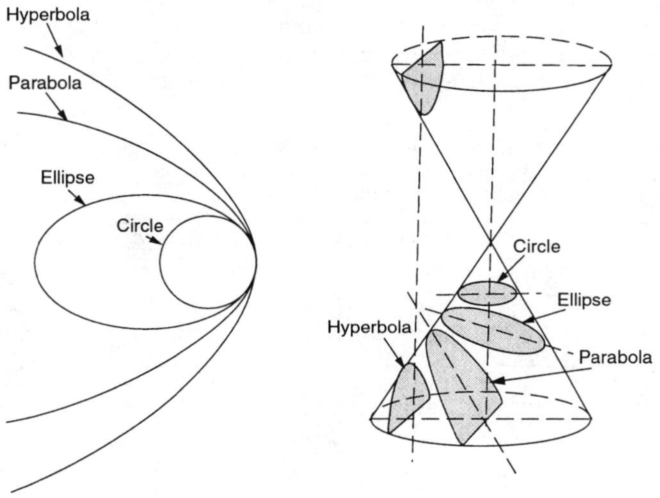

Fig. 2-1. The 4 Conic Sections Result from the Intersection of a Plane and a Right Circular Cone. Two special cases occur when the angle between the plane and axis of the cone is either 90 deg (resulting in a circle) or equal to the angular radius of the cone (resulting in a parabola).

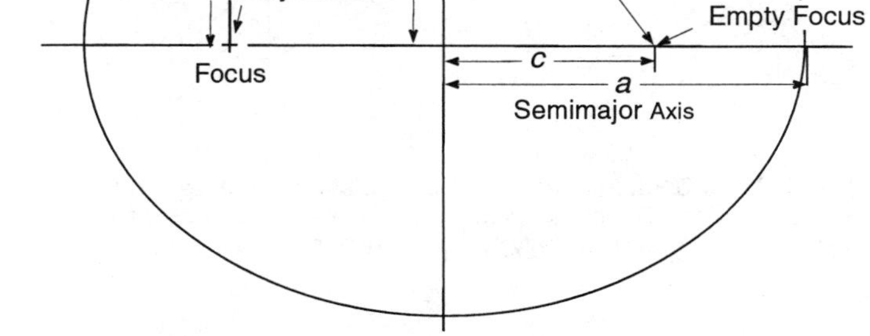

Fig. 2-2. Geometry of an Elliptical Orbit with Eccentricity $e \equiv c/a = 0.6$. Both the satellite and the primary go around their mutual center of mass. However, for most practical problems (except double stars), this center of mass is nearly the same as the center of mass of the primary.

The shape of an ellipse is uniquely specified by a single parameter, such as the ratio of the semimajor and semiminor axes. The parameter normally used to specify this shape is the *eccentricity, e*, defined as the ratio $c/a = (a^2 - b^2)^{1/2} / a$. The eccentricity also serves as a convenient ratio to parameterize all the conic sections as listed in Table 2-1. Specifically, $e = 0$ for a circle; $0 < e < 1$ for an ellipse; $e = 1$ for a *parabola*; and $e > 1$ for a *hyperbola*. In the last case, the nearest point on the curve to the focus is between the focus and the center of the two branches of the hyperbola. These 4 classes of curves are illustrated in Fig. 2-3 and their properties are summarized at the end of the section.*

TABLE 2-1. Orbit Properties for the 4 Conic Sections. In practice only elliptical and hyperbolic orbits occur. Circular and parabolic orbits are special cases, but are convenient approximations for many orbits.

Conic	Total Energy, ε	Semimajor Axis, a	Eccentricity, e
Circle	< 0	= radius (> 0)	= 0
Ellipse	< 0	> 0	$0 < e < 1$
Parabola	= 0	∞	= 1
Hyperbola	> 0	< 0	> 1

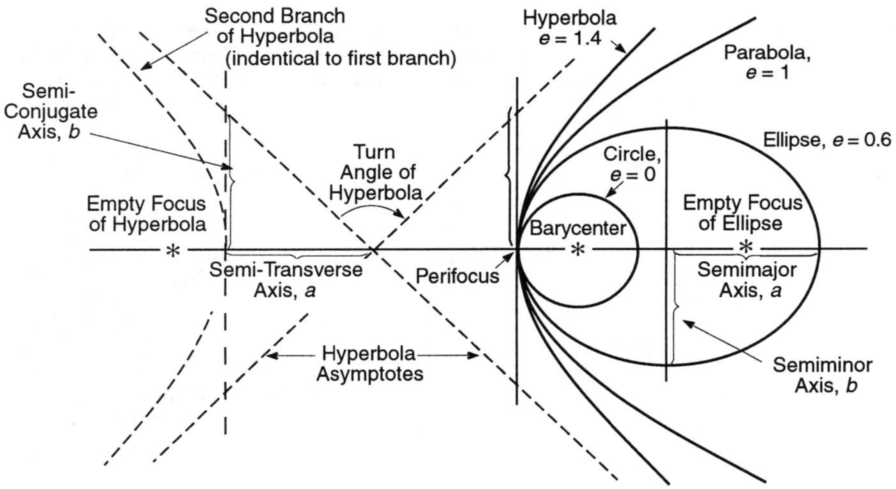

Fig. 2-3. The 4 Conic Sections. The circle and ellipse are closed "bound" orbits which continuously repeat. The parabola and hyperbola are open "unbound" orbits such that the satellite passes perifocus only once and then recedes to infinity.

---

* Alternatively, we may define a conic section as the locus of all points which maintains a fixed ratio between the distance to the focus and the perpendicular distance to a fixed line called the *directrix*. The directrix is perpendicular to the major axis of any conic section. The ratio of the distance to the focus and to the directrix is the *eccentricity, e*.

Both the circle and parabola represent special cases of the infinite range of possible eccentricities and therefore will never occur in nature. Orbits of objects which are gravitationally bound will be elliptical and orbits of objects which are not bound will be hyperbolic. Thus, an object approaching a planet from "infinity," such as a spacecraft approaching Mars, travels on a hyperbolic trajectory relative to the planet and will swing past the planet and recede to infinity, unless some non-gravitational force (a rocket firing or a collision with the planet) intervenes. Similarly, a rocket with insufficient energy to escape a planet must travel in an elliptical orbit in the absence of non-gravitational forces. Because the ellipse is a closed curve, the rocket will eventually return to the point in space at which the engine last fired.

2.1.2 Kepler's Second Law

As shown in Fig. 2-4, Kepler's second law is a restatement of the conservation of angular momentum. The angular momentum is proportional to the magnitude of the radius vector, r, multiplied by the perpendicular component of the velocity, $V_\perp$. In any infinitesimal time interval δt, the area swept out by a line joining the barycenter and the satellite will be $\frac{1}{2} V_\perp r \delta t$. Hence, the area swept out per unit time is proportional to the angular momentum per unit mass which is a constant.

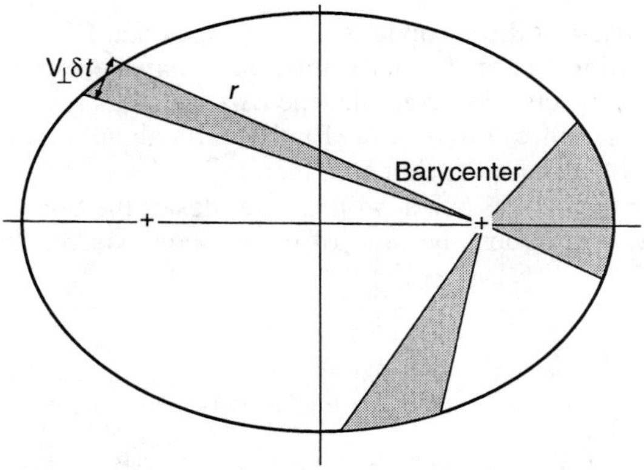

Fig. 2-4. Kepler's Second Law. Because the shaded areas are equal the time required for the satellite to sweep out each area is equal. The area swept out is directly proportional to both the time interval and the satellite's angular momentum.

2.1.3 Kepler's Third Law

Kepler's third law applies only to elliptical orbits and relates the orbital period to the semimajor axis. In the case of Earth satellites, and very nearly in the case of the planets orbiting the Sun, we may ignore the mass of the secondary and write:

$$a^3 = \left[G(M+m)/4\pi^2\right]P^2 \approx \left(GM/4\pi^2\right)P^2$$
$$\equiv \left(\mu/4\pi^2\right)P^2 \qquad \text{or} \tag{2-4a}$$

$$P = 2\pi\sqrt{a^3/\mu} \tag{2-4b}$$

The values of $\mu \equiv GM$ for the Earth, Moon, Sun, and Mars are given in Table 2-2 and for the major objects in the solar system in App. A. Note that μ can be measured with considerable precision by astronomical observations. However, the values of M are limited by the accuracy of G to about 0.06%. (This is the most poorly known of the fundamental physical constants.) Therefore, the use of G is normally avoided and calculations are best done in terms of μ and the ratio of the masses of solar system objects.

TABLE 2-2. Values of $\mu \equiv GM$ for the Earth, Sun, Moon, and Mars. (See App. E for other values).

Central Body	μ (m^3/s^2)	$\mu / 4\pi^2$ (m^3/s^2)
Earth	$3.986\,004\,41 \times 10^{14}$	$1.009\,666\,71 \times 10^{13}$
Moon	$4.902\,798\,882 \times 10^{12}$	$1.241\,893\,465 \times 10^{11}$
Earth and Moon	$4.035\,031\,135 \times 10^{14}$	$1.022\,085\,327 \times 10^{13}$
Mars	$4.287\,1 \times 10^{13}$	$1.085\,9 \times 10^{12}$
Sun	$1.327\,124 \times 10^{20}$	$3.361\,644 \times 10^{18}$

As long as the mass of the secondary is small, such that Eq. (2-4a) holds, then the constant of proportionality in Kepler's third law may be evaluated directly from observing orbiting objects. For example, the *astronomical unit*, or *AU*, is a unit of length equal to the semimajor axis of the Earth's orbit about the Sun; thus, in units of years and AU, $\mu / 4\pi^2 = 1$ for the Sun and, therefore, $a^3 = P^2$ in units of astronomical units and years for the planets and any other satellites of the Sun. Similarly, for Earth satellites at different altitudes, the ratio of the periods may be determined from the expression

$$P = P_0 \left(\frac{a}{a_0} \right)^{3/2} \tag{2-5}$$

where P_0 and a_0 are any known period and semimajor axis.

2.1.4 Vis Viva Equation

If we again assume that the mass of the secondary is small, the *vis viva* equation may be rewritten as

$$V^2 = GM \left(\frac{2}{r} - \frac{1}{a} \right) \tag{2-6a}$$

$$\frac{1}{2} V^2 - \frac{GM}{r} = -\frac{\mu}{2a} \equiv \mathcal{E} \tag{2-6b}$$

where the *total specific energy,* $\mathcal{E}$, is the total energy per unit mass (kinetic plus potential) of the orbiting object. Thus, the semimajor axis is a function **only** of the total energy. Because the potential energy is a function only of position, the semimajor axis for a satellite launched at any point in space will be a function only of the launch velocity and not the direction of launch. (The shape and orientation of the orbit will, of course, depend on the launch direction). The orbit is hyperbolic if $\varepsilon > 0$ and elliptical if $\varepsilon < 0$. The special case between these, zero total energy, is an orbit with infinite semimajor axis. The velocity in this case is called the *parabolic velocity*, or *velocity of escape*, V_e. At any distance, R, from the center of a spherically symmetric object we have:

$$V_e \equiv \sqrt{2\mu / R} \equiv \sqrt{2GM / R} \tag{2-7}$$

A satellite launched with this velocity in any direction will not return, assuming that there are no other forces.

The vis viva equation may be used to obtain two other velocities of particular interest. If $R = a$, then

$$V_c \equiv \sqrt{\mu/R} \tag{2-8}$$

is the *circular velocity,* or the velocity needed for circular orbit of radius R. Finally,

$$V_h \equiv \sqrt{2\varepsilon} = \sqrt{V^2 - 2\mu / R} \tag{2-9}$$

is the *hyperbolic velocity*, or the velocity of an object infinitely far away from the primary. Here V is the instantaneous velocity in the hyperbolic orbit at an arbitrary distance R from the center of the massive object. Values of the circular velocity and escape velocity for the Earth, Moon, Mars, and the Sun are shown in Table 2-3.

TABLE 2-3. Values of the Circular Velocity and Escape Velocity for the Earth, Sun, Moon, and Mars. Constants are evaluated at the surface, except for the last row. (See App. D.1 for other values.)

Central Body	Equatorial Radius (km)	Circular Velocity (km/s)	Circular Period (min)	Escape Velocity (km/s)
Earth	6,378.14	7.905	84.49	11.180
Moon	1,738	1.680	108.36	2.375
Mars	3,390	3.551	100.19	5.021
Sun (at surface)	695.990	436.7	166.91	617.5
Sun (at Earth's orbit)	1.496×10^8	29.78	5.260×10^5	42.12

2.1.5 Keplerian Orbit Elements and Terminology

For a purely Keplerian orbit, if we know the position and velocity at any given instant, we can integrate the equations of motion to determine the position and velocity at all future times. Consequently, a Keplerian orbit can be fully specified by giving the three components of the position and three components of the velocity at any instant. This numerical specification of an orbit is called the *orbit elements*. The position and velocity at any instant is convenient for computer applications but provide relatively little insight into the fundamental characteristics of the orbit. A convenient set for conceptualization are the classical or *Keplerian elements* described below. (Unfortunately, in many cases, these are inconvenient for numerical computation). The information needed to fully specify an orbit is:

- the orbit size and shape (2 parameters)
- the orientation of the orbit plane in space (2 parameters)
- the rotational orientation of the semimajor axis within that plane (1 parameter)
- where the satellite is on the orbit (1 parameter)

Orbit Size and Shape. For either hyperbolic or elliptical orbits, *perifocus* is the point on the orbit where the secondary is closest to the center of mass (Fig. 2-5). The *periapsis* or *perifocal distance* is the distance between the center of mass and the perifocus. This is equal to $a + c = a(1 - e)$ for an elliptical orbit of semimajor axis, a, and eccentricity, e. Unfortunately, the terminology here is both well established and awkward because different words are used for the point of closest approach to different primaries. Thus, we have *perihelion* (closest approach to the Sun), *perigee* (closest approach to the Earth), *pericynthiane* or *perilune* (closest approach to the Moon), *perijove* (closest approach to Jupiter) and even *periastron* (closest approach of two stars in a binary pair).

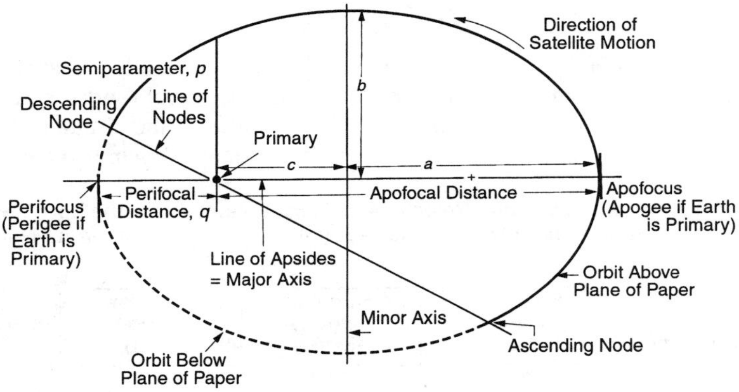

Fig. 2-5. Orbit Terminology for an Elliptical Orbit. The orbit is tilted, or inclined, with respect to the plane of the paper such that the dashed segment is below the paper which is assumed to be the reference plane.

Perihelion and perifocal distance are measured from the center of mass, but *perigee height*, frequently shortened to "perigee" in common usage, is measured from the surface of the Earth. (See Fig. 2-6.) This terminology arises because we are interested primarily in the height above the surface for low-altitude spacecraft. The most unambiguous procedure is to use perigee height or perigee altitude whenever the distance is being measured from the surface;* however, this is frequently not done.

In elliptical orbits, the most distant point from the primary is called *apofocus*; the *apoapsis* or *apofocus distance* is $a + c = a\,(1 + e)$. Again, the words *aphelion*, *apolune*, and *apogee* or *apogee height* are used, the latter being measured from the Earth's surface. The straight line connecting apogee, perigee, and the two foci is called the *line*

* Throughout this book when discussing distances relative to the Earth, we use height exclusively for distances measured from the Earth's surface; e.g., apogee height, perigee height, or height of the atmosphere.

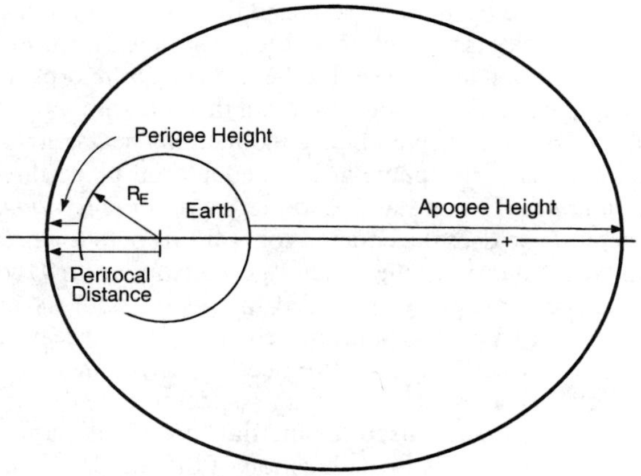

Fig. 2-6. Definition of Perigee Height and Apogee Height.

of apsides, which is the same as the major axis of the ellipse. If, h_p, h_A, and R_E are the perigee height, apogee height, and radius of the Earth, respectively, then for an Earth satellite, the semimajor axis is:

$$a = R_E + (h_p + h_A)/2 \tag{2-10}$$

The size and shape of any Keplerian orbit can be defined equivalently by either the semimajor axis and eccentricity or the apogee height and perigee height. Both methods are in common use depending on the application.

Orientation of the Orbit Plane. As shown in Fig. 2-7, the *inclination, i,* is the angle between the orbit plane and a reference plane which also contains the center of mass. The most commonly used reference planes are the *equatorial plane* (the plane of the Earth's equator) for Earth's satellites and the *ecliptic* (the plane to the Earth's orbit about the Sun) for interplanetary orbits.

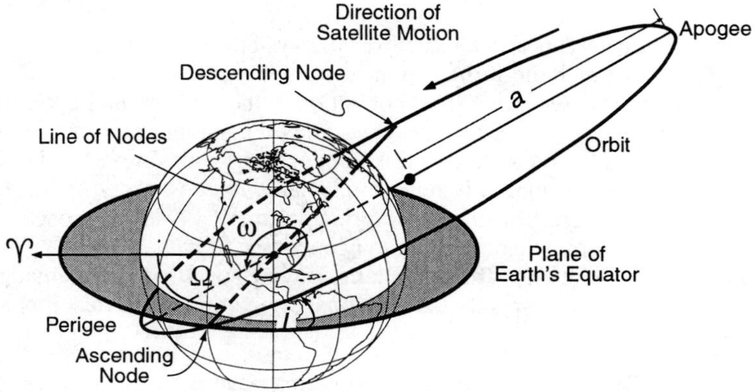

Fig. 2-7. Keplerian Orbit Elements. ♈ marks the direction of the vernal equinox. The line of nodes is the intersection between the equatorial plane and the orbit plane. Ω is measured in the equatorial plane, and ω is measured in the orbit plane.

Both the rotation of the Earth on its axis and the revolution of the Earth around the Sun are in a counterclockwise direction as seen from the North Pole. Most satellites travel in this same direction and are said to be in a *prograde* orbit which has an inclination between 0 and 90 deg. Satellites traveling in a direction opposite the rotation of the Earth are in a *retrograde* orbit and have inclinations between 90 deg and 180 deg.

The intersection of the orbit plane and the equatorial plane through the center of mass is the *line of nodes*. For an Earth satellite the *ascending node* is the point in its orbit where the satellite crosses the equator going from south to north. The *descending node* is the point where it crosses the equator going from north to south.

To fully define the orbit plane, we need to specify both its inclination and the orientation of the line of nodes around the equator. Because the Keplerian orbit is approximately fixed in inertial space,* we need to define this rotational orientation with respect to inertial space rather than with respect to the surface of the Earth. The reference point that is ordinarily used for inertial space is the ascending node of the Earth's orbit about the Sun. This is the location of the Sun in the sky on the first day of spring. It is called the *vernal equinox* or *first point of Aries*. This is the zero point for *right ascension* in the sky which is the equivalent of longitude measured on the surface of the Earth. (See Sec. 6.1.2.) Consequently, the orientation of the ascending node on the sky is defined by the *right ascension of the ascending node*, Ω, (often called RAAN in computer code), which is the angle in the equatorial plane measured eastward from the vernal equinox to the ascending node of the orbit. At times, it is also convenient to specify the *longitude of the ascending node* measured on the surface of the Earth from the Greenwhich meridian to the ascending node. However, this parameter is changing continuously as the Earth rotates underneath the orbit.

The vernal equinox is universally used as the zero point for coordinates in inertial space, i.e., relative to the "fixed" stars. Unfortunately, this is an exceptionally inconvenient reference because it is moving very slowly through the sky due to the precession of the Earth's axis as described in Sec. 2.2. The motion is remarkably slow with a period of approximately 26,000 years. Nonetheless, it implies that all inertial coordinate systems have a date or *epoch* attached to them. Modern almanacs list the locations of stars in *2000 coordinates*, which means that they are expressed in a coordinate system in which the vernal equinox has been precessed to January of the year 2000.

Equally unfortunately, nearly all satellite orbit systems use what are called *true-of-date coordinates* in which the vernal equinox is precessed to the time of specification of the orbit called the *orbit epoch*. This correction to the fundamental coordinate system is extremely small and is easily done by standard computer routines. However, it means that it is very difficult to verify orbit computations with simple hand calculators because there are always small differences in the answer due simply to differences in the coordinate system specification. The principal merit of this approach is that it provides continued employment for astrodynamicists.

Orientation of the Orbit within the Plane. Having specified the orientation of the orbit plane, we now need to specify the rotational orientation of the major axis (line of

---

* Friction with the Earth's surface drags the atmosphere around as the Earth rotates on its axis. This friction is negligible in orbit. Thus, a satellite orbit remains approximately fixed in inertial space (except for orbit perturbations described in Sec. 2.4) as the Earth rotates once per day underneath the orbit. This causes the satellite to view almost all of the Earth's surface twice daily—once on the upward portion of the orbit and once on the downward portion.

apsides) within that plane. This is normally done by defining the *argument of perigee*, ω, which is the angle at the center of mass of the Earth measured in the orbital plane in the direction of the satellite's motion from the ascending node to perigee.

Position of the Satellite within the Orbit. Finally, we need some mechanism to specify where the satellite is in its orbit. The *true anomaly*, ν, is the angle measured at the center of mass between perigee and the satellite. This gives us a series of three angular measurements. The right ascension of the ascending node is measured eastward from the vernal equinox to the ascending node of the orbit. The argument of perigee is then measured from the ascending node in the direction of the motion of the satellite to perigee, and, finally, the true anomaly is measured in the direction of motion from perigee to the location of the satellite.

Unfortunately, the true anomaly is difficult to calculate. Consequently, those who were first studying the mathematics of orbital motion introduced the *mean anomaly, M,* as 360 $(\Delta t / P)$ degrees where P is the orbital period and Δt is the time since perigee passage. Thus, $M = \nu$ for a satellite in a perfectly circular orbit. The mean anomaly at any time is a trivial calculation and of no physical interest. The quantity of real interest is the true anomaly which is difficult to calculate. The *eccentric anomaly, E,* was introduced as an intermediate variable relating the two.* The mean and eccentric anomalies are related by *Kepler's equation* (not related to Kepler's laws):

$$M = E - e \sin E \tag{2-11}$$

where e is the eccentricity. E is then related to ν by *Gauss' equation*:

$$\tan\left(\frac{\nu}{2}\right) = \left(\frac{1+e}{1-e}\right)^{1/2} \tan\left(\frac{E}{2}\right) \tag{2-12a}$$

or

$$\tan\left(\frac{E}{2}\right) = \left(\frac{1-e}{1+e}\right)^{1/2} \tan\left(\frac{\nu}{2}\right) \tag{2-12b}$$

$E/2$ and $\nu/2$ are used because these quantities are always in the same quadrant.

The above approach was used for historical computations. In modern computer programs, the true anomaly is determined by simply integrating the equations of motion and taking into account other forces, as well as the purely central body forces which produce Keplerian motion. Alternatively, for a Keplerian orbit the mean anomaly and true anomaly can be determined by the following recursive formula:†

$$E_{i+1} = E_i + \frac{M - E_i + e \sin E_i}{1 - e \cos E_i} \tag{2-13}$$

For small eccentricities, ν may be expressed directly as a function of M by expanding in a power series in e to yield:

---

* E is defined as the angle measured at the center of the orbit between perigee and the projection of the satellite perpendicular to the major axis onto a circular orbit with the same semimajor axis as shown in Fig. 2-8.

† This convenient formula is from David Diaz, Microcosm, Inc.

$$\nu = M + 2e\sin M + \frac{5}{4}e^2 \sin 2M - \frac{1}{4}e^3 \sin M$$

$$+\frac{13}{12}e^3 \sin 3M + \mathcal{O}(e^4)^* \quad (2\text{-}14)$$

Finally, it is often convenient to discuss variations in the orbital elements in terms of the *mean angular rate,* often called the *mean motion, n,* which is simply the rate of change of the mean anomaly. If n is in rad/s, then

$$n \equiv dM/dt = 2\pi/P \quad (2\text{-}15)$$

$$M = M_0 + n(t-t_0) \quad (2\text{-}16)$$

where P is the period, and M_0 is the mean anomaly at epoch t_0. From Eq. (2-4a), we have

$$n = \sqrt{\mu / a^3} \quad (2\text{-}17)$$

where $\mu \equiv GM$ and a is the semimajor axis. Thus, n and M are easily determined form fundamental orbit parameters and can then be used as the basis for computing the true anomaly and the variations in the elements due to orbit perturbations as discussed in Sec. 2.4.

Summary. The elements of an orbit are the parameters needed to fully specify the motion of a satellite. Table 2-4 and Figs. 2-7 and 2-8 show the classical elements or Keplerian elements for an Earth satellite (planetary elements are slightly different and are defined in Sec. 2.2). The semimajor axis and eccentricity define the size and shape of the orbit; the inclination and right ascension of the ascending node define the orbit plane. The argument of perigee defines the rotation of the orbit within the plane, and finally, the true anomaly or mean anomaly specifies the position of the satellite in its orbit at the epoch time at which the orbit is specified.

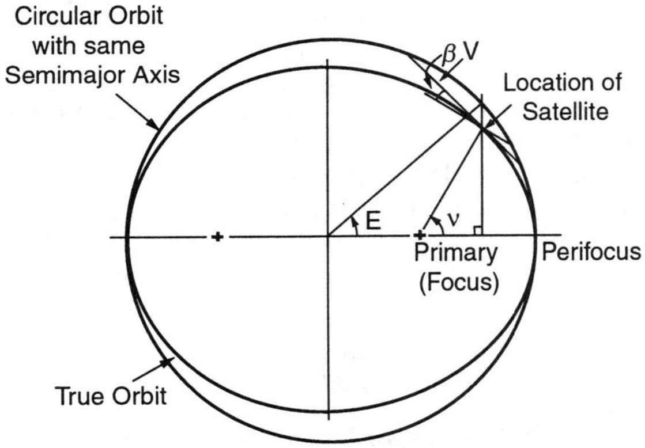

Fig. 2-8. Definition of the True Anomaly, ν, and Eccentric Anomaly, E. The *flight path angle,* β, is the angle between the velocity vector and the perpendicular to the radius vector.

* $\mathcal{O}$ in Eq. (2-14) and subsequent equations stands for "of order" and refers to subsequent terms in the expansion. Thus, Eq. (2-14) includes all terms of order e^3 or lower and excludes terms of order e^4 and higher.

TABLE 2-4. Properties of Keplerian Orbits. See Fig. 2-2, 2-3, 2-5, 2-6, and 2-8 for illustration of the variables.

Quantity	Circle	Ellipse	Parabola	Hyperbola
Defining Parameters	a = semimajor axis = radius	a = semimajor axis b = semiminor axis	p = semi-latus rectum q = perifocal distance	a = semi-transverse axis ($a < 0$) b = semi-conjugate axis
Parametric Equation	$x^2 + y^2 = a^2$	$x^2/a^2 + y^2/b^2 = 1$	$x^2 = 4qy$	$x^2/a^2 - y^2/b^2 = 1$
Eccentricity, e	$e = 0$	$e = \sqrt{a^2 - b^2}/a \quad 0 < e < 1$	$e = 1$	$e = \sqrt{a^2 + b^2}/a^2 \quad e > 1$
Perifocal Distance, q	$q = a$	$q = a(1 - e)$	$q = p/2$	$q = a(1 - e)$
Velocity, V, at Distance, r, from Focus	$V^2 = \mu/r$	$V^2 = \mu(2/r - 1/a)$	$V^2 = 2\mu/r$	$V^2 = \mu(2/r - 1/a)$
Total Energy Per Unit Mass, ε	$\varepsilon = -\mu/2a < 0$	$\varepsilon = -\mu/2a < 0$	$\varepsilon = 0$	$\varepsilon = \mu/2a > 0$
Mean Angular Motion, n	$n = \sqrt{\mu/a^3}$	$n = \sqrt{\mu/a^3}$	$n = \sqrt{\mu}$	$n = \sqrt{\mu/(-a)^3}$
Period, P	$P = 2\pi/n$	$P = 2\pi/n$	$P = \infty$	$P = \infty$
Anomaly	$\nu = M = E$	Eccentric anomaly, E $\tan\frac{\nu}{2} = \left(\frac{1+e}{1-e}\right)^{1/2} \tan\left(\frac{E}{2}\right)$	Parabolic anomaly, D $\tan\frac{\nu}{2} = D/\sqrt{2q}$	Hyperbolic anomaly, F $\tan\frac{\nu}{2} = \left(\frac{e+1}{e-1}\right)^{1/2} \tanh\left(\frac{F}{2}\right)$
Mean Anomaly, M	$M = M_0 + nt$	$M = E - e \sin E$	$M = qD + (D^3/6)$	$M = (e \sinh F) - F$
Distance from Focus, $r = q(1+e)/(1 + e\cos\nu)$	$r = a$	$r = a(1 - e\cos E)$	$r = q + (D^2/2)$	$r = a(1 - e\cosh F)$
$r\, dr/dt \equiv r\dot{r}$	0	$r\dot{r} = e\sqrt{a\mu}\,\sin E$	$r\dot{r} = \sqrt{\mu}\,D$	$r\dot{r} = e\sqrt{(-a)\mu}\,\sinh F$
Areal Velocity, $\frac{dA}{dt} = \frac{1}{2}r^2\frac{d\nu}{dt}$	$\frac{dA}{dt} = \frac{1}{2}\sqrt{a\mu}$	$\frac{dA}{dt} = \frac{1}{2}\sqrt{a\mu(1-e^2)}$	$\frac{dA}{dt} = \frac{1}{2}\sqrt{\frac{\mu q}{2}}$	$\frac{dA}{dt} = \frac{1}{2}\sqrt{a\mu(1-e^2)}$

Note: μ = GM is the gravitational constant of the central body; ν is the true anomaly, and $M \equiv n(t - T)$ is the mean anomaly, where t is the time of observation, T is the time of perifocal passage, and n is the mean angular motion. See App. C for additional formulas and a discussion and listing of terminology and notation.

Unfortunately, the Keplerian elements are poorly defined under conditions that commonly occur for Earth satellites. For near circular orbits, perigee will be very poorly defined and consequently, both the argument of perigee and true anomaly will not be well-defined. In this case, the *longitude of the satellite* measured from the ascending node is often used. If the orbit plane is near the equatorial plane, then the ascending node will also be poorly defined and, in this case, the basic angle will be measured from the vernal equinox. For a hyperbolic orbit, the period is undefined and is replaced by the *aerial velocity* or area per unit time swept out by a line joining the satellite and the planet (i.e., the angular momentum per unit mass). The equations for this are in Table 2-4.

In practice, a variety of orbit perturbations described in Sec. 2.4 cause continuing changes and oscillations in the orbit elements. The *mean orbit elements* given in most general purpose tables define the average motion over some span of time. For more precise calculations, it is preferable to use *osculating elements* which are the elements of a true Keplerian orbit instantaneously tangent to the real orbit. Thus, the *osculating elements* fluctuate continuously as various forces (e.g., atmospheric drag and perturbations from other planets) alter the simple shape defined by Kepler's laws.

Keplerian orbits are not sufficiently accurate for spacecraft ephemerides or for calculations which require a precise knowledge of the spacecraft's position or velocity; however, they are accurate enough to estimate overall mission characteristics in most regions of space. Table 2-4 summarizes the numerical properties of Keplerian orbits. The normal procedure for adding additional detail to orbit analysis is to treat orbits as Keplerian with additional perturbations produced by any of the various interactions which may be important. Approximations for the most important perturbations are discussed in Sec. 2.4.

2.2 Orbits of the Moon and Planets

Orbits of the planets and other natural objects in the solar system exhibit considerable regularity. With the exception of cometary orbits, they are all nearly circular, coplanar, and regularly spaced.

Although perturbations due to third bodies (mostly Jupiter) must be taken into account for computing accurate planetary ephemerides, the description of planetary orbits in terms of Keplerian elements describes most orbital characteristics quite well. The position of the center of mass of the solar system relative to the Sun depends on the position of all the planets but is typically somewhat below the surface of the Sun in the general direction of Jupiter. For most practical purposes we can regard the Sun as the center of mass of the Solar System and, therefore, as at one focus for all planetary orbits.

To define the Keplerian elements for the orbits of either planets or interplanetary spacecraft we must establish a reference plane for the solar system. The standard plane chosen for this is the *ecliptic* or the plane of the Earth's orbit about the Sun. This plane is inclined to the Earth's equatorial plane by 23.44 deg, an angle known as the *obliquity of the ecliptic*. The intersection of the plane of the ecliptic and the plane of the Earth's equator define two opposite directions in space known as the *vernal* and *autumnal equinoxes* represented by the symbols, ♈ and ♎, respectively. The vernal equinox is the direction of the Sun (viewed from the center of the Earth) as it crosses the equatorial plane from south to north on the first day of spring. It serves as the reference direction for coordinate systems using either the equatorial or ecliptic plane. Perturbative forces on the Earth cause the rotational axis of the Earth to move in a cone of 23.44 deg radius about a vector perpendicular to the ecliptic plane. This *precession of the equinoxes* has a period of 25,700 years. This implies that all celestial or "inertial" coordinate systems will have a date attached to them. (As discussed further in Sec. 6.1.2.)

Because the Earth's orbit is not perfectly Keplerian, and because of the drift of the vernal equinox, the orbital period of the Earth about the Sun (and similarly the periods of the other planets) depends on how it is measured. The *sidereal year*, about 365.26 days, is the period of revolution of the Earth relative to the fixed stars. The *tropical year* is the Earth's period relative to the vernal equinox, and is about 20 minutes shorter than the sidereal year. This is the basis of the civil calendar, since for calendar purposes we are interested in the seasons, which are determined by the position of the Sun relative to the Earth's equatorial plane. Finally, the *anomalistic year*, 5 minutes longer than the sidereal year, is the period of the Earth relative to perihelion. Recall that *perihelion* is the perifocal point when the Earth is closest to the Sun. The drift in the inertial position of perihelion is due to perturbations from the other planets.

The orbital elements of the planets and other Solar System objects are analogous to the Earth satellite elements defined in Table 2-4 with the Earth's equatorial plane replaced by the ecliptic plane.* Thus the semimajor axis and eccentricity retain the same definitions. The inclination of planetary orbits is measured relative to the ecliptic so the inclination of the Earth's orbit is zero. The *longitude of the ascending node,* Ω, is the angle from the vernal equinox to the ascending node of the planet's orbit measured eastward (i.e., in the direction of motion of the Earth in its orbit) along the ecliptic plane. The *argument of perihelion*, ω, is the angle from the ascending node to perihelion measured along the planet's orbit in the direction of its motion. In some tables, ω is replaced by the *longitude of perihelion*, $\tilde{\omega}$, defined as $\Omega + \omega$. Note that this is not a true angular measure because Ω and ω are measured in different planes. Finally, the mean anomaly of satellite orbits is replaced by the *time of perihelion passage*, which is one of the times, usually the most recent, when the planet was at perihelion. Numerical values for the planetary orbital elements are given in App. D.

Planetary orbits within the Solar System are fairly uniform in both shape and orientation; with the exception of Pluto and Mercury, the orbital inclinations are all less than 3.5 deg and the eccentricities are less than 0.1. The semimajor axes of the planetary orbits are also nearly regular and are approximately given by an empirical relationship known as *Bode's Law* in which the semimajor axes of the planets and asteroid belt in AU are approximately 0.4, 0.7, 1.0, 1.6, 2.8, 5.2, and so on.

For both interplanetary spacecraft and for determining the brightness of the planets as seen by Earth-orbiting spacecraft, we are interested in the orientation of the planets relative to the Earth and Sun, as well as the orientation relative to the fixed stars. The various geometrical orientations of the planets relative to the observer and the Sun are called *planetary configurations*, or *aspects*, and are defined in Fig. 2-9. An *inferior planet* is one with an orbit closer to the Sun than the observer, and a *superior planet* is one farther from the Sun. *Conjunction* and *opposition* occur when the planet and the

---

* Note that longitude in the Solar System is measured in the ecliptic plane from the vernal equinox and is not the same as longitude on the surface of the Earth or right ascension in the sky which is measured along the celestial equator.

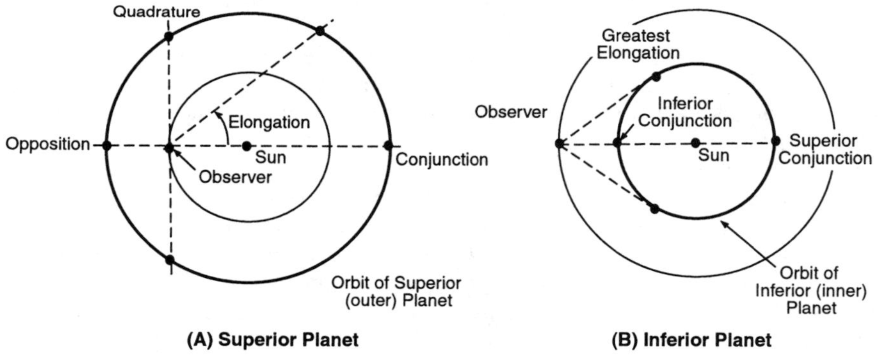

Fig. 2-9. Planetary Configurations Refer to the Position of other Planets with Respect to the Earth. They could also be applied to observers on other planets.

Sun are in the same and opposite directions, respectively.* "The same direction" throughout this discussion is in terms of the relative planet-observer orientation around the ecliptic regardless of the distance above or below the ecliptic plane. Thus, a full Moon occurs when the Moon is at opposition.

Conjunction and opposition may also be applied to two planets. For example, Mars and Jupiter are in conjunction for a particular observer if both planets are in the same direction from the observer. (If only one planet is mentioned, the implied second object is the Sun. "Mars is at opposition" means that Mars and the Sun are in opposition.) For an inferior planet, *inferior conjunction* occurs when the planet is between the Earth and the Sun and *superior conjunction* occurs when the Sun is between the Earth and the planet. *Elongation* is the angular separation between a planet and the Sun measured in the plane of the ecliptic. A superior planet will be brightest near opposition, and an inferior planet will be brightest near greatest elongation when it is at the farthest angular separation from the Sun. *Quadrature* occurs when the Sun-observer-planet angle is 90 deg. In astronomical tables the standard symbols defined in Fig. 2-10 are frequently used for various aspects of the planets. For example, ☌ ♀ ♄ is read "Venus and Saturn in conjunction." A discussion of visual magnitude and other optical aspects of the planets is presented in Sec. 11.6.

A critical characteristic for interplanetary flight is the length of time it takes for planets to return to the same relative orientation known as the *synodic period, S*, which is more formally defined as the interval between successive oppositions of a superior planet or successive inferior conjunctions of an inferior planet. The relation between the synodic period and the sidereal period, *P*, relative to the fixed stars is shown in Fig. 2-11. In this example, the innermost planet has made one and one-third revolutions in the period of time that the outer planet has made one-third of a revolution.

If P_{inner} and P_{outer} are the periods of the inner and outer planets, respectively, then in general:

---

* *Syzygy*, an astronomical contribution to crossword puzzles, refers to either conjunction or opposition, i.e., when the planet, the Sun and the observer lie on a straight line. The term is derived from the Greek expression for putting two oxen together ("syn") on one yoke ("zygnymai"). A bit strange, but then most constellations are named after animals.

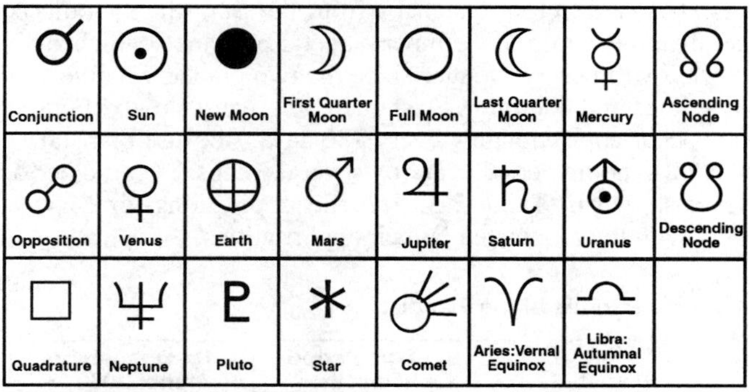

Fig. 2-10. Standard Astronomical Symbols.

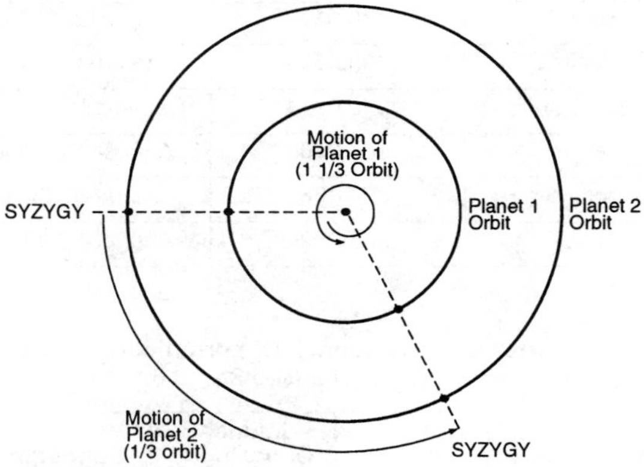

Fig. 2-11. Determining the Synodic Period or Period with Respect to the Earth.

$$S^{-1} = P_{inner}^{-1} - P_{outer}^{-1} \quad \text{or} \tag{2-18a}$$

$$S = \frac{P_{outer} P_{inner}}{P_{outer} - P_{inner}} \tag{2-18b}$$

For an observer on the Earth, if S and P are both expressed in years, then for superior planets the synodic period is given by:

$$S_{superior}^{-1} = 1 - P_{outer}^{-1} \quad \text{or} \tag{2-19a}$$

$$S_{superior} = P_{outer} \,/\, (P_{outer} - 1) \tag{2-19b}$$

and for an inferior planet by:

$$S_{inferior}^{-1} = P_{inner}^{-1} - 1 \quad \text{or} \tag{2-20a}$$

$$S_{inferior} = P_{inner} \,/\, (1 - P_{inner}) \tag{2-20b}$$

For planets at very different distances from the Sun, the synodic period will be slightly longer than the period of the inner planet. For planets which are close together the synodic period will become longer since the two planets revolve about the Sun at nearly the same rates and, therefore, pass each other very slowly. For example, oppositions of Mars occur approximately every 780 days. Because planetary orbits are not circular, the actual synodic periods vary by several weeks. Synodic periods of the various planets are shown in Table 2-5. Specific oppositions for Mars are shown in Table 2-6 along with the associated launch opportunities.

TABLE 2-5. Synodic Periods of the Planets.

Planet	Synodic Period (Days)	1st Opposition after 2000
Mercury	115.9132	February 12, 2001
Venus	583.9178	March 29, 2001
Mars	779.9317	June 13, 2001
Jupiter	398.8854	January 1, 2002
Saturn	378.0914	December 3, 2001
Uranus	369.6563	August 15, 2001
Neptune	367.4861	June 30, 2001
Pluto	366.7326	June 2, 2001

TABLE 2-6. Earth-Mars Oppositions and Launch Opportunities, 1990–2050. Launch opportunities assume a Hohmann Transfer (see Sec. 2.6.1.)

Launch Opportunity	Opposition	Arrival Date	Launch Opportunity	Opposition	Arrival Date
8/22/90	11/27/90	5/8/91	9/1/22	12/7/22	5/18/23
10/2/92	1/7/93	6/18/93	10/10/24	1/15/25	6/26/25
11/7/94	2/12/95	7/24/95	11/14/26	2/19/27	7/31/27
12/9/96	3/16/97	8/25/97	12/18/28	3/25/29	9/3/29
1/16/99	4/23/99	10/2/99	1/25/31	5/2/31	10/11/31
3/8/01	6/13/01	11/22/01	3/22/33	6/27/33	12/6/33
5/23/03	8/28/03	2/6/04	6/10/35	9/15/35	4/24/36
8/2/05	11/7/05	4/18/06	8/14/37	11/19/37	4/30/38
9/17/07	12/23/07	6/2/08	9/27/39	1/2/40	6/12/40
10/24/09	1/29/10	7/10/10	11/1/41	2/6/42	7/18/42
11/27/11	3/3/12	8/12/12	11/5/43	2/10/44	7/21/44
12/31/13	4/7/14	9/16/14	1/10/46	4/17/46	9/26/46
2/15/16	5/22/16	10/31/16	2/28/48	6/4/48	11/13/48
4/20/18	7/26/18	1/4/19	5/8/50	8/13/50	1/22/51
7/8/20	10/13/20	3/24/21			

Planetary configurations are important for interplanetary flight as well as for observations because they define the opportunities for planetary travel. For example, as discussed in Sec. 2.6.1, trips to Mars along a minimum energy trajectory will leave the Earth about 97 days before opposition, and will arrive at Mars about 162 days after opposition (see Table 2-6), although various factors may cause the actual flight times, (particularly the arrival), to vary by several weeks. Because an opposition of Mars occurred on March 17, 1997, we would expect flights that left Earth on about December 10, 1996, to arrive at Mars about August 26, 1997. The two spacecraft flown during this launch opportunity, Mars Pathfinder and Mars Global Surveyor, were launched on December 4, 1996, and November 7, 1996, and arrived at Mars on July 4, 1997, and September 11, 1997, respectively. Similarly, because of the Mars opposition on December 24, 2007, we can expect flights to Mars at that time to leave Earth about September 18, 2007, and arrive at Mars about June 3, 2008.

The orbits of the natural satellites in the Solar System are generally less uniform than the orbits of the planets primarily because perturbations cause substantial variations in satellite orbits. For example, the perigee location for the Moon makes one complete revolution about the Moon's orbit in only 8.85 years, and the line of nodes rotates fully around the orbit in 18.6 years. Thus, in analogy with the various types of years, the month is defined in several ways, depending on the measurement reference. For most purposes the fundamental intervals are the *sidereal month*, relative to the fixed stars, about 27.32 days, the *synodic month* from new moon to new moon, about 29.53 days and the *nodical* or *draconic month* between successive ascending nodes, about 27.21 days. Other periods are listed in App. D.

2.3 Spacecraft Orbit Terminology

Objects launched into space are categorized by their orbit. *Ballistic missiles, sounding rockets* and *suborbital vehicles* travel in elliptical orbits which intersect the surface of the Earth. This is frequently called a *ballistic trajectory* because it is also the path of a baseball, bullet, or cannonball. The ballistic missile and sounding rocket are distinguished by their functions. The missile is used to strike some specific target, whereas the sounding rocket or suborbital vehicle is used to make measurements in or above the Earth's atmosphere. The sounding rocket may either impact the surface, burn up in the atmosphere, or be recovered by parachute.

The semimajor axis of a satellite orbit must be at least as large as the radius of the planet, whereas the semimajor axis for a sounding rocket or suborbital vehicle may be as small as approximately half the radius of the planet.* Because the total energy of a spacecraft depends only on the semimajor axis, the energy of a sounding rocket is normally, though not necessarily, much less than that of an Earth satellite. However, sounding rockets and ballistic missiles frequently reach altitudes well above those of low-Earth satellites because they travel in very elongated elliptical orbits.

---

* Assume all the mass of the Earth is concentrated at its center and a high platform is built to the former location of New York City. An object dropped from the platform will *not* go all the way to the former location of Australia, but will swing very rapidly around the central mass (with perigee essentially at the former center of the Earth) and return to apogee at the platform tip. [Use Eq. (2-5) with $V = 0$.] Therefore, the semimajor axis will be about half the radius of the Earth and the total energy will be a factor of two less than that for a circular orbit at the Earth's surface.

Any object which travels in an elliptical orbit around a planet is called a *satellite* of that planet. As shown in Table 2-7, Earth satellites are typically classified by their distance. The principal differences between the orbit altitudes is the energy or velocity required to achieve them and the radiation level in that environment, as shown in Fig. 2-12. Most Earth satellites are in *low-Earth orbit*, or *LEO*, below the Van Allen radiation belts, which start somewhat above 1,000 km. This orbit is both easy to get to and has a much lower radiation density than higher orbits and, therefore, has the potential for more economical satellites. The next most common is *geosynchronous orbit* or *GEO*, at an altitude of 35,786 km at which the satellite's orbit period is just equal to the Earth's rotation period so the satellite remains approximately fixed over a location on the Earth's equator. This is the single most used satellite orbit. Between LEO and GEO is a broad regime known as *medium-Earth orbit* or *MEO*, which typically contains relatively few satellites because of high levels of radiation in the Earth's Van Allen belt. A few satellites are in *super-synchronous orbits* above GEO, but below the Moon. Finally, a few Earth satellites are at approximately the distance of the Moon, in what are called *Lagrange point orbits*. As discussed further in Sec. 2.5, the *Lagrange points* are five points relative to the Earth and Moon at which the satellite will maintain the same orientation relative to the Earth-Moon system.

TABLE 2-7. Orbit Classification by Distance from the Earth. This classification is convenient since it represents approximately the difficulty of getting there and, therefore, the cost and time. See text for additional discussion of each.

Name	Location	Uses	Examples
LEO (Low-Earth Orbit)	< 3,000 km (most < 900 km)	All applications (cheapest to get to)	Space Telescope, Space Station, LandSat, Iridium
MEO (Medium-Earth Orbit)	3,000 km to GEO	Communications, navigation, some observation	GPS
GEO (Geosynchronous)	35,856 km	Communications, weather	TDRS, Intelsat, DBS, BrazilSat
Super-Synchronous	Above GEO, below the Moon	Limited	Vela
Lunar and Lagrange Point	At or near Moon distance (350,000 km)	Science, potentially manufacturing	Apollo, Lunar Orbiter, Lunar Prospector
Interplanetary, Deep Space	Beyond the Moon, within the solar system	Exploration	Viking, Mars Pathfinder, Galileo
Interstellar	Outside the solar system	Exploration	Pioneer 10,11

If the velocity of an object is greater than the escape velocity of a planet it will be an *interplanetary probe*, or deep space spacecraft traveling in a hyperbolic trajectory relative to the planet and, after it has left the vicinity of the planet, traveling in an elliptical orbit about the Sun. Finally, if an object attains a velocity greater than the Sun's escape velocity, it will be an *interstellar probe*. Pioneer 10, swinging past Jupiter in December 1973, gained sufficient energy in the encounter, as described in Sec. 2.5, to become the first man-made interstellar probe.

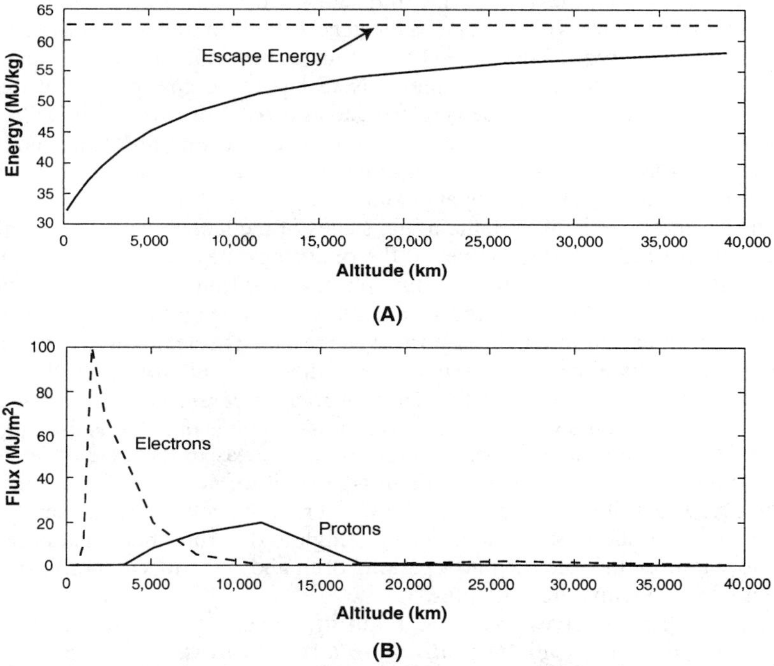

Fig. 2-12. The Principal Differences Between Orbit Altitudes is (A) the Energy Required to Get There and (B) the Radiation Level.

All known satellites or probes are assigned an international designation by the World Warning Agency on behalf of the Committee on Space Research, COSPAR, of the United Nations. These designations are of the form 2005-27c, where the first number is the year of launch, the second number is a sequential numbering of launches in that year, and the letter identifies each of the separate objects launched by a single vehicle. Thus, 1997–069c was the third of five Iridium satellites orbited on the 69th launch of 1997 (a Delta II launched from Vandenberg Air Force Base on Nov. 9, 1997).

In addition to the international designation, most satellites are assigned a name by the launching agency. For NASA, spacecraft in a series are given a letter designation prior to launch, which is changed to a number after a successful launch. Thus, the second Synchronous Meteorological Satellite was SMS-B prior to launch, and SMS-2 after being successfully orbited. Because of launch failures or out of sequence launches, the lettering and numbering schemes do not always follow the pattern A=1, B=2, etc. For example, in the Interplanetary Monitoring Platform series, IMP-B failed on launch, IMP-E was put into a lunar orbit and given another name and IMP-H and -I were launched in reverse order. Thus IMP-I became IMP-6 and IMP-H became IMP-7. The satellites may also be assigned names in different series; IMP-6 was also Explorer-43 and IMP-7 was Explorer-47.

The *trajectory* of a spacecraft is its path through space; if this path is closed (i.e., elliptical), then the trajectory is formally an *orbit*. Thus, correct usage would refer to a satellite in elliptical orbit or a probe on a hyperbolic trajectory. Although this distinction is maintained at times, orbit and trajectory are often used interchangeably. Throughout this book we will use orbit as the generic term for the path of a spacecraft.

For satellites it is frequently convenient to number the orbits so that we can refer to "a maneuver on the 17th orbit." In standard NASA practice, that portion of the orbit preceding the first descending node is referred to as *orbit 0*, or *revolution 0. Orbit 1* or *revolution 1* goes from the first ascending node to the second ascending node, etc. Note that *revolution* refers to one object moving about another in an orbit, whereas *rotation* refers to an object spinning about an axis.

When spacecraft are launched, the initial stages of the launch vehicle are typically jettisoned or returned to Earth. However, the final stage may remain inactive and attached to the spacecraft during the coasting phase or parking orbit. The final stage is then ignited or reignited to *inject* the spacecraft, or place it into its proper orbit. The orbit in which the satellite conducts normal operations is referred to as the *mission orbit*, and is typically either *Earth-referenced*, if the principal purpose of the satellite is to observe or communicate with the Earth, or *space-referenced* if its principal purpose is to be or look somewhere in space. A *transfer orbit* is one that is used to transport a spacecraft from one orbit or location to another, as in the case of an Apollo transfer orbit to the Moon or the Mars Pathfinder orbit to Mars. Finally, at the end of its useful life, a satellite is typically *deorbited* or brought back to Earth, usually burning up in the atmosphere. If the satellite is too high to de-orbit, then an alternative at end of life is to raise the satellite into a parking orbit above the mission orbit such that it will not interfere with other satellites.

A satellite which revolves above the Earth in the same direction that the planet rotates on its axis is in a *prograde* or *direct orbit*. If it revolves in a direction opposite to the rotation, the orbit is *retrograde*. As shown in Fig. 2-13, the inclination of an Earth satellite orbit is measured from east toward north. Therefore the inclination of a prograde satellite is less than 90 deg, and the inclination of a retrograde satellite is greater than 90 deg. In a *polar orbit* i = 90 deg. Most satellites are launched in a prograde direction, because the rotational velocity of the Earth provides a part of the orbital velocity. Although this effect is not large (0.46 km/s for the Earth's rotational velocity at the equator compared with a circular velocity of 7.91 km/s), the available energy is typically the limiting feature of a space mission. Thus, all factors that change the energy which must be supplied by the launch vehicle are important.

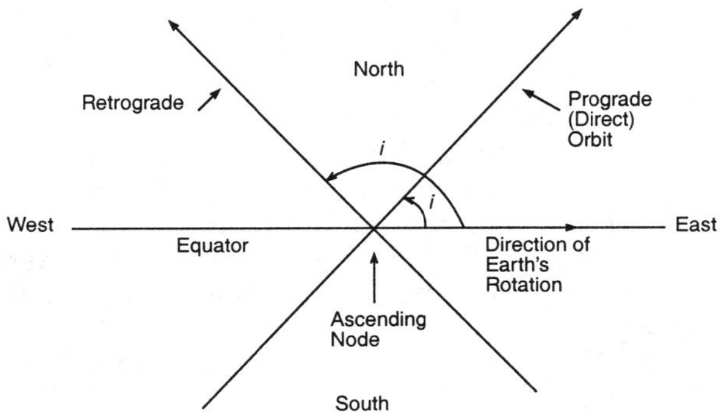

Fig. 2-13. Inclination, *i*, for Prograde and Retrograde Orbits. Satellite is moving from south to north.

2.4 Orbit Perturbations, Geopotential Models, and Satellite Decay

Recall that Kepler's laws are based on a spherically symmetric mass distribution and do not take into account non-gravitational forces or the gravity of other bodies. Consequently, real orbits never follow Kepler's laws precisely, although at times they come very close. Keplerian orbits provide a convenient analytic approximation to a true orbit. In contrast, a *definitive orbit* is the best estimate that can be obtained with all available data of the actual path of a satellite. Because formal analytic solutions are almost never available for real orbit problems with multiple forces, observed orbits are generated numerically based on both orbit theory and observations of the spacecraft. Thus, definitive orbits are only generated for times that are past, although the information from the definitive orbit is frequently extrapolated to the future to produce a predicted or *propagated* orbit.

A *reference orbit* is a relatively simple, precisely defined orbit (usually, though not necessarily, Keplerian) which is used as an initial approximation to the spacecraft's motion. *Orbit perturbations* are the deviations of the true orbit from the reference orbit and are typically classified according to the cause, e.g., perturbations due to the Earth's oblateness, atmospheric drag, or the gravitational force of the Moon. In this section we describe the causes of orbit perturbations, the principal effects caused by them, and, where possible, formulas to determine the approximate magnitude of specific effects. More detailed methods for the numerical treatment of perturbations may be found in any of the references in the annotated bibliography at the end of the chapter.

TABLE 2-8. Summary of Forces Acting on a Spacecraft in Earth Orbit.

Source	Regime	Effect in LEO
Earth (point mass)	Dominant force for orbits between Earth and Moon*	Results in Keplerian orbit of satellite about the Earth's center of mass
Earth (higher-order geopotential)	Significant perturbing force at GEO and below; declines rapidly with increasing altitude	Depends on specific orbit; orbit rotation of up to 14 deg/day is possible
Sun/Moon (point mass)	Dominant force for interplanetary flight; minor perturbing force in Earth orbit	Low level perturbations; orbit rotation of up to 0.007 deg/day
Atmosphere	LEO only, decays exponentially with altitude	Reentry occurs rapidly below 150 km Atmosphere negligible above 1,000 km
Solar Radiation Pressure	Minor perturbing force for normal spacecraft	Small eccentricity growth
Relativistic Effects	Near massive objects	Negligible
Incidental Forces (leaks, RF, explosive bolts)	Very minor perturbing force for normal spacecraft	Negligible in most circumstances

* The solar perturbing force is less than 0.01 times the central force below 370,000 km; the Earth perturbing force is less than 0.01 times the central solar force above 2.5×10^6 km.

Effects which modify simple Keplerian orbits are shown in Table 2-8. These may be divided into four classes: non-gravitational forces (principally atmospheric drag and solar radiation pressure), third body interactions, non-spherical mass distributions, and relativistic mechanics. For some orbits the first two effects dominate the motion of the spacecraft, as in satellite re-entry into the atmosphere or motion about both the Earth and the Moon. Although the effects of non-spherical mass distributions never dominate spacecraft motion, they do provide the major perturbation relative to Keplerian orbits for most intermediate altitude satellites, i.e., those above the atmosphere and below where effects due to the Moon and Sun become important. Additionally, the nonspherical mass distribution becomes much more important for orbits about small bodies such as comets or asteroids where the basic object itself may be fundamentally nonspherical. Finally, relativistic mechanics may be completely neglected in essentially all applications except those specifically intended to test elements of relativity. The largest orbit perturbation in the solar system due to general relativity is the rotation of the perihelion of Mercury's orbit by about 0.012 deg/century or 3×10^{-5} deg/orbit. Although a shift of this amount is measurable, it is well below the magnitude of other effects which we will consider.

The relative importance of the various orbit perturbations will depend upon the construction of the spacecraft, the specific orbit it's in, and even the level of solar activity. Nonetheless, the Keplerian orbit is an excellent approximation for most astrodynamic problems, with a few important exceptions. For Earth orbits these are:

- Atmospheric drag in low-Earth orbit (less than 1,000 km)
- Rotation of the ascending node and perigee due to Earth's oblateness
- Resonance and Lunar-Solar effects at geosynchronous altitudes

Each of these effects is discussed below. For interplanetary orbits, places where perturbations are important or may dominate include:

- Atmospheric drag in low orbits about planets with an atmosphere or in the vicinity of comets where the gravitational forces are very weak
- Oblateness effects near rapidly rotating planets, such as Jupiter
- Higher order nonspherical effects near small bodies such as natural satellites or asteroids
- Multiple body effects in regions where gravitational forces approximately balance, e.g., between the Earth and the Moon or the Earth and the Sun (often called Lagrange point orbits, see Sec. 2.5)

The impact of each of the major perturbation is discussed in the following subsections.

As a practical matter, most current orbit computations are done by simply integrating the equations of motion to obtain a numerical approximation of the motion of the spacecraft. This process works extremely well for computer calculations but provides little physical insight into the effects which are occurring. We began the discussion at the front of the chapter by applying $\mathbf{F} = m\mathbf{a}$ and letting $\mathbf{F}$ be the gravitational force due to a spherically symmetric central body. We can generalize this approach to take additional forces into account by writing:

$$
\begin{aligned}
m\mathbf{a} &= \mathbf{F}_{\text{central body}} + \mathbf{F}_{\text{spherical harmonics}} + \mathbf{F}_{\text{drag}} + \mathbf{F}_{\text{Sun}} + \mathbf{F}_{\text{Moon}} + \mathbf{F}_{\text{solar pressure}} + \cdots \\
&= -m\nabla U = -m\nabla\big(\text{central body} + \text{perturbations}\big) \qquad \text{(2-21a)} \\
&= -m\nabla(\mu / r) - m\nabla R
\end{aligned}
$$

Therefore:

$$\mathbf{a} = -(\mu r^{-3})\mathbf{r} - \nabla R \qquad \text{(2-21b)}$$

where as usual, m is the mass of the spacecraft, $\mathbf{a}$ is the vector acceleration, U is the potential energy of the orbit, $\mu \equiv GM$ for the central body and R is the potential function of the perturbation, i.e., representing all of the forces other than the symmetric central body force. R is called the *disturbing potential* and provides a convenient mechanism for evaluating the impact of various forces acting on a spacecraft minus the central body effects.

We can use the above decomposition of the forces to derive *Lagrange's planetary equations* for the variation of the Keplerian orbital elements with time. (The derivation is given in most of the astrodynamics books listed in Sec. 2.7). The results are:

$$\frac{da}{dt} = \frac{2}{na}\left(\frac{\partial R}{\partial M}\right) \qquad \text{(2-22a)}$$

$$\frac{de}{dt} = \frac{(1-e^2)^{1/2}}{na^2 e}\left\{(1-e^2)^{1/2}\left(\frac{\partial R}{\partial M}\right) - \left(\frac{\partial R}{\partial \omega}\right)\right\} \qquad \text{(2-22b)}$$

$$\frac{di}{dt} = \frac{1}{na^2(1-e^2)^{1/2}\sin i}\left\{\cos i\left(\frac{\partial R}{\partial \omega}\right) - \left(\frac{\partial R}{\partial \Omega}\right)\right\} \qquad \text{(2-22c)}$$

$$\frac{d\omega}{dt} = \frac{1}{na^2}\left\{-\frac{\cos i}{(1-e^2)^{1/2}\sin i}\left(\frac{\partial R}{\partial i}\right) + \frac{(1-e^2)^{1/2}}{e}\left(\frac{\partial R}{\partial e}\right)\right\} \qquad \text{(2-22d)}$$

$$\frac{d\Omega}{dt} = \frac{1}{na^2(1-e^2)^{1/2}\sin i}\left(\frac{\partial R}{\partial i}\right) \qquad \text{(2-22e)}$$

$$\frac{dM}{dt} = n - \frac{1-e^2}{na^2 e}\left(\frac{\partial R}{\partial e}\right) - \frac{2}{na}\left(\frac{\partial R}{\partial a}\right) \qquad \text{(2-22f)}$$

where $R(a, e, i, \omega, \Omega\, M)$ is the disturbing potential and n is the mean motion. Note that here a is the semimajor axis and not the acceleration, and M is the mean anomaly (measured relative to the moving perigee) and not the mass of the central body. In the absence of any orbit perturbations all of the partial derivatives are zero, so that only M changes with time as is appropriate for a Keplerian orbit. The advantage of Lagrange's planetary equations is that they allow us to analytically assess the effects of any disturbance on a Keplerian orbit.

2.4.1 Nonspherical Mass Distribution

The Earth is very nearly spherically symmetric. However, the rotation of the Earth causes it to assume approximately an equilibrium configuration of an oblate spheroid with an equatorial bulge and flattening at the poles. The difference between the equatorial radius, a, and the polar radius, c, is 21.4 km which produces a *flattening factor* or *ellipticity* ≡ $(a - c)/a$ of 1/298.257. As illustrated in Fig. 2-14 this is imperceptible as seen in almost any photograph or illustration.

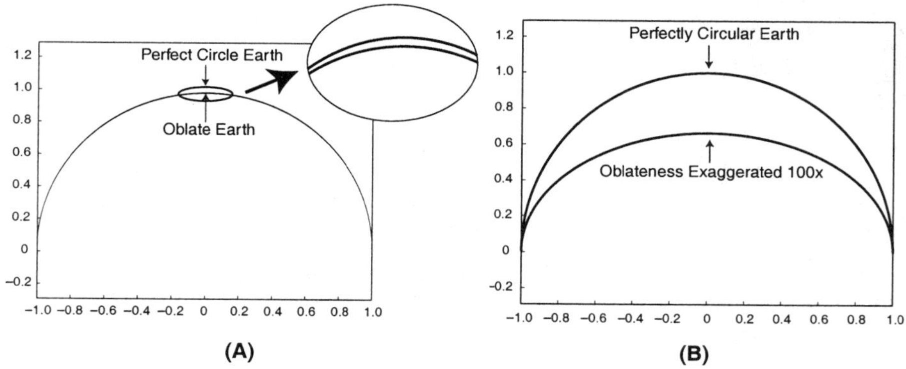

Fig. 2-14. The Difference Between a Spherical Earth and an Oblate Earth is Very Small.

In addition, the Earth has a slight pear shape at the equator (approximately 100 m out of round) and a variety of minor mass anomalies such as continents, mountain ranges, and San Francisco. Mathematically, this is dealt with by expanding the geopotential function at the point (r, θ, ϕ) in a series of spherical harmonics:

$$U(r,\theta,\phi) = \sum_{n=0}^{\infty}\left(r/R_e \right)^{n+1} J_n P_{n0}(\cos\theta)$$

$$+ \sum_{n=1}^{\infty}\sum_{m=1}^{n}\left(r/R_e \right)^{n+1}\left[C_{nm}\cos m\phi + S_{nm}\sin m\phi\right]P_{nm}(\cos\theta) \qquad (2\text{-}23)$$

where J_n is defined to be C_{n0}, μ=*GM* is the Earth's gravitational constant, R_e is the Earth's equatorial radius, P_{nm} are Legendre polynomials, *r* is the geocentric distance, θ is the latitude, and ϕ is the longitude. Terms with $m=0$ are called *zonal harmonics* and J_n are the zonal harmonic coefficients. The zonal harmonics are independent of the longitude and have *n* sign changes over the full range of latitude on the Earth. As shown in Fig. 2-15A, they divide the Earth into a series of longitude independent zones analogous to the temperate and tropic zones. Terms with $n = m$ are called *sectoral harmonics* since they divide the Earth into sectors which are independent of latitude as shown in Fig. 2-15B. Finally, terms with $m \neq 0$ and $m \neq n$ are called *tesseral harmonics* from the Latin *tessera* for tiles, since these divide the world into a tiled pattern as shown in Fig. 2-15C.

A *geopotential model* of the Earth is a set of coefficients in the spherical harmonic expansion. For example, one of the more widely used is the *Goddard Earth Model 10b* or *GEM10b* which is a 21 × 21 geopotential model, meaning that it is a 21 × 21 spherical harmonic expansion. These geopotential models are determined by analyzing tracking data for a large number of satellites. The need for higher accuracy orbit determination has led to more complex geopotential models. Models that are 50 × 50, 70 ×70, and 100 × 100 are in use, although of course most of the terms in higher order models will be extremely small.

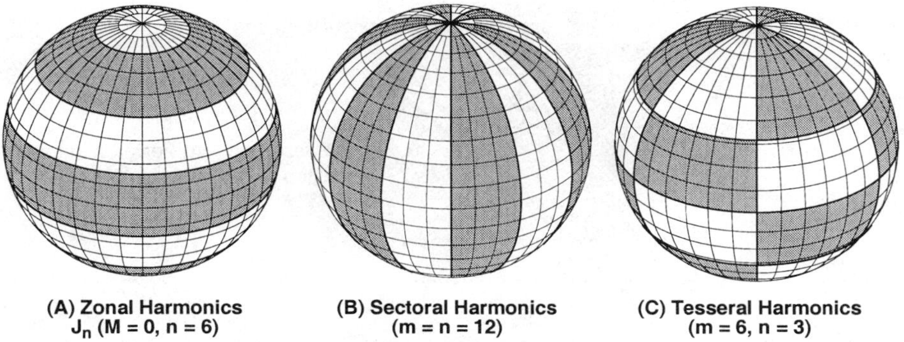

Fig. 2-15. Basis of Spherical Harmonic Expansions. Boundaries between shaded regions are where the expansion changes sign. Thus, J_2 represents a change of sign on either side of the equator and, therefore, is the principal term representing the equatorial bulge.

The J_0 term in the spherical harmonic expansion represents the spherically symmetric or point mass distribution for which the potential falls off as $1/r$. The J_1 term changes sign at the equator and therefore represents the difference in mass between the northern and southern hemispheres. The J_2 term has two changes in sign between the north and south poles and thus represents the mass distribution of the equatorial bulge and is, by far, the largest of the geopotential terms. (The words "J_2" and "Earth oblateness" are frequently used interchangeably.) Beyond J_2, coefficients become small quickly as can be seen by looking at the first several terms:

$$
\begin{aligned}
J_0 &= 1 \\
J_1 &= 0 \\
J_2 &= 0.001\,082\,63 \\
J_3 &= -0.000\,002\,54 \\
J_4 &= -0.000\,001\,61
\end{aligned}
\tag{2-24}
$$

$J_0 = 1$ by definition. In addition, because the coordinate frame is defined as going through the center of mass, $J_1 \equiv 0$. The oblateness term, J_2, is much larger than any of the other perturbations and has important effects for the orbit in that it causes both the right ascension of the ascending node and the argument of perigee to rotate at rates of several degrees per day. Because of the importance of these effects for orbit design they will be described in more detail in Sec. 2.5.2 and 2.5.3.

In addition to rotating the orbit, the principal effect of the non-spherical mass distribution is to cause small changes in the shape of the orbit. Rather than a perfect ellipse in a well-defined inertial plane, actual spacecraft move in a shape more like that of a potato chip, with maximum deviations from a Keplerian orbit on the order of 3 km, as shown in Figs. 2-16 and 2-17. Again this difference in shape is dominated by the equatorial bulge and, consequently, has a pattern in the various components that is nearly sinusoidal.

Typically the effects of the higher order harmonics are extremely small, except for special circumstances. For example, in geosynchronous orbit, a satellite remains largely over one location on the Earth; therefore, the sectoral harmonics are applied continuously and pull the satellite in an east-west direction. Similarly, in a repeating ground-track orbit, the satellite flies over the same locations on the ground, day after

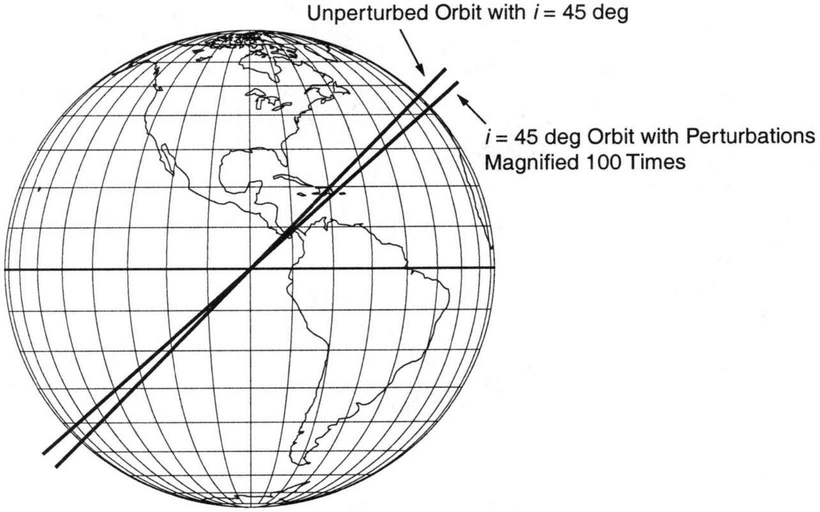

Fig. 2-16. Greatly Exaggerated Shape of a "Circular" Low-Earth Orbit.

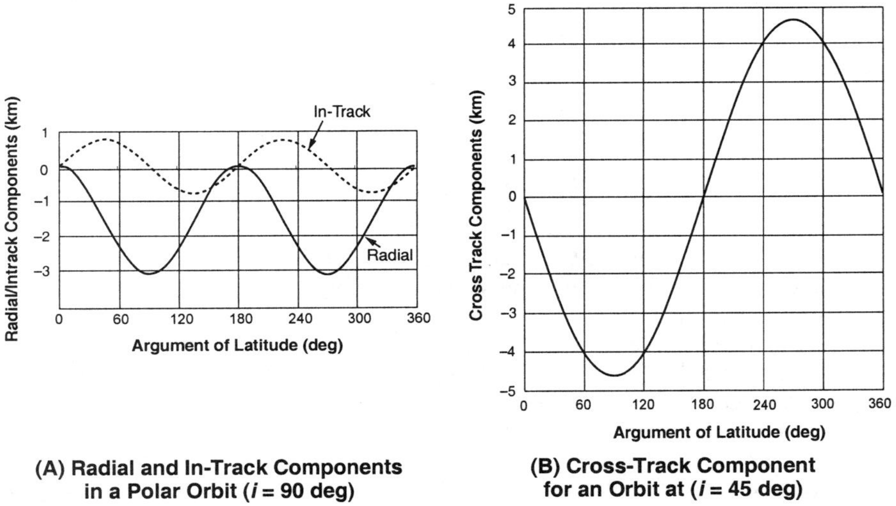

Fig. 2-17. Effect of Nonspherical Earth on the Satellite Orbit. The three curves are the difference between the position of a real satellite and a satellite in a perfectly circular orbit about a point-mass Earth. *In-track* is the direction of the velocity vector; *cross-track* is toward the normal to the orbit.

day, and it is possible for resonances to build up when the satellite continuously passes, for example, to the right of the Himalayas, such that the effects of tesseral terms can be substantially magnified. As central bodies become less spherically symmetric the impact of the higher order harmonics becomes more important. For example, the Moon has a variety of mass concentrations or *mascons* which cause large variations in the orbits of lunar spacecraft and make it difficult to predict the orbits even though atmospheric drag plays no role. Orbits around asteroids or other very small objects will also be dominated by higher order harmonics both because of the distinctly nonspherical shape and the smallness of the point mass gravitational forces.

2.4.2 Third Body Interactions

The gravitational forces of the Sun and the Moon cause periodic variations in all of the orbit elements. The effect is generally similar to that of the Earth's equatorial bulge as described in Sec. 2.5.3, i.e., the Sun and the Moon apply an external torque to the orbits and cause the angular momentum vector to rotate. This effect is extremely small and in LEO is dominated by the orbit rotations caused by the Earth's oblateness. However, as described in Sec. 2.5.1 the effect becomes important in geosynchronous orbit and is the dominant source of the need for stationkeeping in GEO.

For nearly circular orbits, the Lagrange planetary equations can be used to determine the approximate rotation rates for the ascending node, Ω, and the argument of perigee, ω, due to the Sun and the Moon. These are:

$$\dot{\Omega}_{MOON} = -0.003\,38(\cos i)\,/\,n \tag{2-25}$$

$$\dot{\Omega}_{SUN} = -0.001\,54(\cos i)\,/\,n \tag{2-26}$$

$$\dot{\omega}_{MOON} = 0.001\,69\left(4 - 5\sin^2 i\right)/\,n \tag{2-27}$$

$$\dot{\omega}_{SUN} = 0.000\,77\left(4 - 5\ \sin^2 i\right)/\,n \tag{2-28}$$

where i is the orbit inclination, n is the number of orbit revolutions per day, and $\dot{\Omega}$ and $\dot{\omega}$ are in deg/day. The equations neglect the variations caused by the changing orientation of the orbital plane with respect to the Moon's orbit and the ecliptic plane and, therefore, are only average values.

2.4.3 Solar Radiation Pressure

Solar radiation pressure causes periodic variations in all of the orbit elements. The effect is strongest for satellites which have low mass and large cross-sectional areas, such as balloons or spacecraft with a large solar sail. The magnitude of the acceleration a_r in m/s^2 due to solar radiation pressure is:

$$a_r \approx -4.5 \times 10^{-8}\,\frac{A}{m} \tag{2-29}$$

where A is the cross-sectional area of the satellite normal to the Sun in m^2 and m is the mass of the satellite in kg. This formula applies to an absorbing surface. A mirror normal to the Sun would have twice the acceleration. For satellites below approximately 800 km altitude the acceleration from atmospheric drag is typically much greater than from solar radiation pressure. Above 800 km however, the acceleration from solar radiation pressure can become an important perturbing force. It is frequently the dominant perturbing force for interplanetary spacecraft simply because the other perturbations become dramatically small.

2.4.4 Atmospheric Drag and Satellite Decay

Atmospheric drag is the principal nongravitational force acting on most satellites in low-Earth orbit. Drag acts opposite the direction of the velocity vector, thus slowing the satellite and removing energy from the orbit. This reduction of energy causes the orbit to get smaller, leading to increases in the drag until eventually the altitude becomes so small that the satellite reenters the atmosphere. Below approximately 120 km, the satellite lifetime is extremely short and it will reenter quickly. Above 600 km the lifetimes due to drag will typically exceed spacecraft operational lifetime of approximately 10 years, although drag may still be important for orbit maintenance or maintaining the structure of a constellation.

Although the physics of atmospheric drag is very well understood, drag is nearly impossible to predict with even moderate precision and, therefore, is a major source of the unpredictability of satellite positions at future times and of when and where they will reenter the atmosphere. There are two reasons for this difficulty in predicting drag:

- Drag can vary by as much as an order of magnitude due to the attitude of the spacecraft and, particularly, the orientation of the solar arrays, with respect to the velocity vector.
- The atmospheric density at satellite altitudes varies by as much as two orders of magnitude depending upon the solar activity level which itself varies dramatically.

The net result is that the lifetime and impact point of satellites are extremely difficult to predict and satellite lifetimes themselves vary dramatically depending on a variety of circumstances and conditions. In this section, we provide a brief summary of the physical basis for drag and its effect on satellite orbits, a discussion of the atmosphere and the causes of the variability, and simple mechanisms for bounding the drag level to be expected for satellites in various low-Earth orbits.

The equation for acceleration due to drag, a_D, is:

$$a_D = -(1/2)\, \rho\, (C_D A/m) V^2 \tag{2-30}$$

where ρ is the atmospheric density, C_D is the dimensionless *drag coefficient* of the satellite (typically $c_D \approx 2.2$ as discussed below), A is the cross-sectional area, m is the satellite mass, and V is its velocity. The quantity $m/C_D A$ is called the *ballistic coefficient* and is typically in the range of 25 to 100 kg/m^2 for satellites.

The atmospheric density, ρ, decreases approximately exponentially as altitude increases:

$$\rho \approx \rho_0 e^{-\Delta h / h_0} \tag{2-31}$$

where ρ and ρ_0 are the density at any two altitudes, Δh is the altitude difference, and h_0 is the atmosphere *scale height*, area which the atmosphere density drops by 1/e. The scale height is typically between 50 and 100 km at satellite altitude. The scale height and density at various altitudes are given just inside the rear cover. For circular orbits, drag will act approximately continuously, and the orbit will spiral downward. Because of the exponential character of the atmosphere, drag for elliptical orbits will act predominantly at perigee and, therefore, will lower apogee while having relatively little effect on the perigee height. As shown in Fig. 2-18, this divides the drag effect on elliptical orbits into two distinct phases. In the first phase, the elliptical orbit is circularized by reducing apogee and having only a small effect on perigee. As the orbit becomes more circular, drag operates over the entire orbit and the orbit spirals inward more quickly. For elliptical orbits the approximate changes in semimajor axis, a, and eccentricity, e, per orbit are:

$$\Delta a_{rev} = -2\pi(C_D A/m)\, a^2 \rho_p \exp(-c)\, [I_0 + 2eI_1] \tag{2-32}$$

$$\Delta e_{rev} = -2\pi(C_D A/m)\, a \rho_p \exp(-c)\, [I_1 + e/2(I_0 + I_1)] \tag{2-33}$$

where ρ_p is the atmospheric density at perigee, $c \equiv ae/h$, h is the atmospheric scale height, and I_j are the modified Bessel functions of order j and argument c.

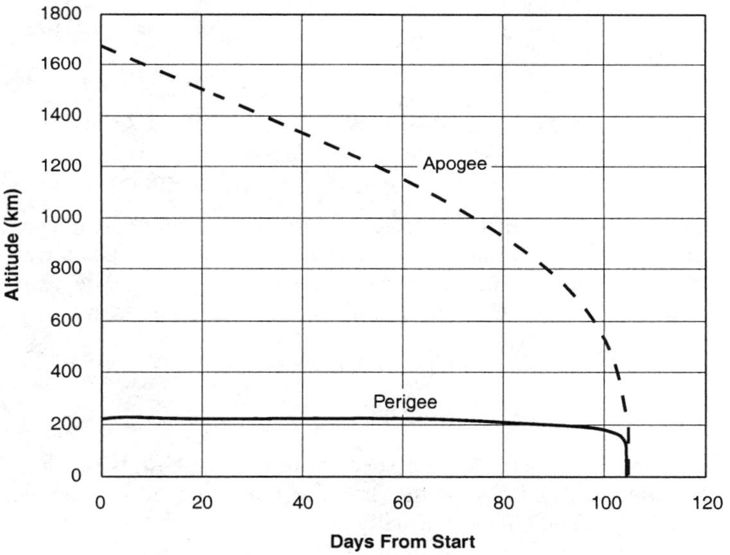

Fig. 2-18. Evolution of an Elliptical Orbit Due to Drag. Orbit began with a perigee height of 215 km and apogee height of 1,680 km.

For circular orbits, Eqs. (2-32) and (2-33) can be substantially simplified, to yield:

$$\Delta a_{rev} = -2\pi(C_D A/m)\rho a^2 \tag{2-34}$$

$$\Delta P_{rev} = -6\pi(C_D A/m)\rho a^2/V \tag{2-35}$$

$$\Delta V_{rev} = \pi(C_D A/m)\rho a V \tag{2-36}$$

$$\Delta e_{rev} = 0 \tag{2-37}$$

where P is the orbit period, and V is the satellite velocity. Thus, the computation of effective drag is straightforward with the minor complication that the key parameters (atmospheric density and ballistic coefficient) are largely unknown.

The spacecraft drag coefficient, C_D, depends largely on four factors*:

- Shape
- Attitude
- Surface condition: smooth (*specular reflection*), rough (*diffuse reflection*), or sticky (*absorption* or *skin friction*)
- Multi-collision effects (*form drag*)

Form drag is very important at low speeds and low altitudes but is negligible for satellites. This is fortunate, because form drag is very difficult to compute.

Ignoring multi-collision effects, the coefficient of drag C_D can be computed using the following expressions:

$$C_D = \frac{4}{A}\int_S \cos^3\psi\, dS \qquad \text{Specular Reflection} \qquad (2\text{-}38)$$

$$C_D = 2 + \frac{1}{A}\int_S \cos^2\psi\, dS \qquad \text{Diffuse Reflection} \qquad (2\text{-}39)$$

$$C_D = 2 \qquad \text{Absorption} \qquad (2\text{-}40)$$

where A is the cross-sectional area, S is the surface area, and ψ is the angle between the velocity vector and normal to the surface. The integral is taken over the entire forward-facing surface, so that ψ is always between 0 deg and 90 deg. Note that $dA = \cos\psi\, dS$. For any satellite, C_D can be divided into three components:

$$C_D = \alpha\, C_{DS} + \beta\, C_{DD} + \gamma\, C_{DA} \qquad (2\text{-}41)$$

$$\alpha + \beta + \gamma = 1 \qquad (2\text{-}42)$$

where C_{DS} is the drag coefficient for specular reflection, C_{DD} is the drag coefficient for diffuse reflection, and C_{DA} is the drag coefficient for absorption. The drag coefficients C_{DS}, C_{DD}, and C_{DA}, can usually be computed from the shape and attitude of the spacecraft. The component fractions, α, β, γ, however, must be determined by experiment. For most satellites, C_D is dominated by specular reflection. Table 2-9 gives values of C_D for various common shapes and attitudes.

The mass of the satellite is ordinarily very well known. However, the ballistic coefficient depends on both C_D and the cross-sectional area, A, perpendicular to the velocity vector. The fundamental difficulty is that most spacecraft have large deployable solar arrays which are very thin and thus have a high cross-sectional area perpendicular to their face and very low cross-sectional area when flying edge-on. Typically the solar arrays rotate to track the Sun and antennas, instruments, and other appendages rotate to track ground targets, geosynchronous relay satellites, or targets in space. Consequently, the cross-sectional area into the wind can vary by approximately a factor of ten, as shown in Table 2-10 for a number of representative low-Earth orbit satellites.

---

* The discussion of drag coefficients is due to Leo Early.

TABLE 2-9. Drag Coefficients for Common Shapes, Attitudes, and Surface Conditions. See text for discussion. (Formulas due to Leo Early.)

Shape	Surface	Drag Coefficient
Flat Plate, Face First	Specular Diffuse	4 3
Flat Plate, Angle of Incidence α	Specular Diffuse	$4\cos^2\alpha$ $2 + \cos\alpha$
Sphere	Specular Diffuse	2 8/3 = 2.667
Circular Cylinder, Side First	Specular Diffuse	8/3 = 2.667 $2 + \pi/4 = 2.785$
Octagonal Cylinder, Side Face First	Specular	$2\sqrt{2} = 2.828$
Octagonal Cylinder, Side Edge First $\alpha = \cos 22.5°$ $\beta = \cos 67.5°$	Specular	$4\frac{\alpha^3+\beta^3}{\alpha+\beta} = 2.586$
Octagonal Cylinder, Side First, Average Over All Side-first Orientations	Specular	$C_D A = 2.812\ A_{\text{face first}}$
Circular Cone, Half-angle α, Point First	Specular, Diffuse	$4\sin^2\alpha$ $2 + \sin\alpha$

TABLE 2-10. Typical Ballistic Coefficients for Low-Earth Orbit Satellites. Values for cross-sectional area and drag coefficients are estimated from the approximate shape, size, and orientation of the satellite and solar arrays. [XA = cross-sectional area].

Satellite	Mass (kg)	Shape	Max. XA (m^2)	Min. XA (m^2)	Max. Drag Coef.	Min. Drag Coef.	Max. Ballistic Coef. (kg/m^2)	Min. Ballistic Coef. (kg/m^2)	Type of Mission
Oscar-1	5	box	0.075	0.0584	4	2	42.8	16.7	Comm.
Intercos.-16	550	cylind.	2.7	3.16	2.67	2.1	82.9	76.3	Scientific
Viking	277	octag.	2.25	0.833	4	2.6	128	30.8	Scientific
Explorer-11	37	octag.	0.18	0.07	2.83	2.6	203	72.6	Astronomy
Explorer-17	188.2	sphere	0.621	0.621	2	2	152	152	Scientific
Sp. Teles.	11,000	cylind.*	112	14.3	3.33	4	192	29.5	Astronomy
OSO-7	634	9-sided	1.05	0.5	3.67	2.9	437	165	Solar Physics
OSO-8	1,063	cylind.*	5.99	1.81	3.76	4	147	47.2	Solar Physics
Pegasus-3	10,500	cylind.*	264	14.5	3.3	4	181	12.1	Scientific
Landsat-1	891	cylind.*	10.4	1.81	3.4	4	123	25.2	Rem. Sens.
ERS-1	2,160	box*	45.1	4	4	4	135	12.0	Rem. Sens.
LDEF-1	9,695	12-face	39	14.3	2.67	4	169	93.1	Environment
HEAO-2	3,150	hexag.	13.9	4.52	2.83	4	174	80.1	Astronomy
Vanguard-2	9.39	sphere	0.2	0.2	2	2	23.5	23.5	Scientific
SkyLab	76,136	cylind.*	462	46.4	3.5	4	410	47.1	Scientific
Echo-1	75.3	sphere	731	731	2	2	0.515	0.515	Comm.
Extrema							437	0.515	

*With solar arrays

The next fundamental problem in calculating atmospheric drag is the extreme variation in atmospheric density. Variations in solar activity, particularly over the course of a solar cycle, cause both a variety of geomagnetic effects and heating of the upper atmosphere due primarily to extreme ultraviolet radiation which is not monitored from the Earth. When the atmosphere is heated, it expands and becomes denser at any given altitude. This seems counter-intuitive because heating a gas causes it to expand and to become less dense. The explanation here is that heating the atmosphere causes it to expand and rise, such that portion of the atmosphere which was previously at 200 km is now at 250 km and represents a much denser atmosphere for a satellite at that altitude.

Figures 2-19 through 2-22 provide a means of estimating satellite lifetimes based on a general evaluation of atmospheric densities. Fig. 2-19 shows the historical record of solar activity. What is plotted is the mean daily f10.7 index of radio flux from the Sun. The *f10.7 index* is simply a measure of the radio flux at a wavelength of 10.7 cm measured in units of 10^{-22} watts/m^2/Hz. This is a convenient measure largely because data for the f10.7 index is available for historical periods beginning in 1945. The peaks in the f10.7 index correspond approximately to solar maxima, to levels of high solar activity, and, therefore, to levels of high atmospheric density. Several things are immediately clear from the plot. First there is an 11-year RF solar cycle corresponding essentially to the sun spot cycles which have been observed for centuries. In addition, it is clear that there are very large month-to-month variations and that while the overall solar cycle can be predicted, the level at any specific time cannot be predicted with any reasonable accuracy. In addition, some solar cycles have levels which are much higher than other solar cycles. Consequently, while the average f10.7 index over an extended period of time is well known, predicting the level at any specific future time is highly uncertain.

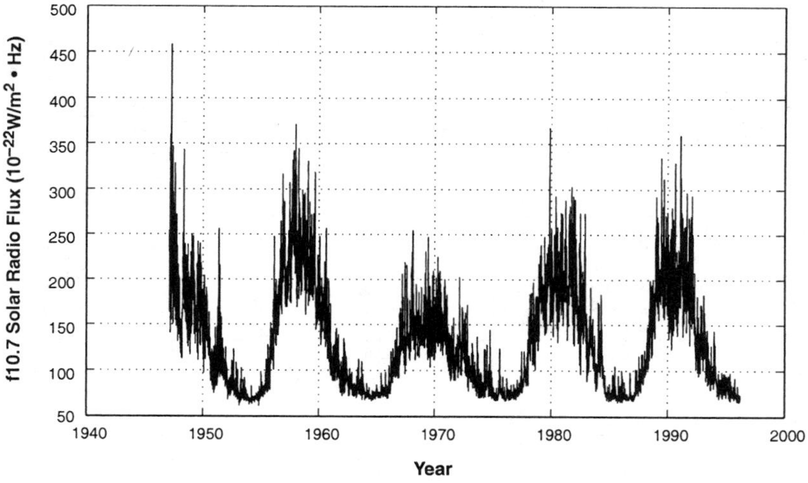

Fig. 2-19. Observed Daily Mean Radio Flux at 10.7 cm. This flux is called the f10.7 index.

Figure 2-20 shows atmospheric density versus altitude corresponding to various values of the f10.7 index. These densities were obtained from the MSIS atmospheric model. Below approximately 150 km, the density is not strongly affected by solar activity. However, at satellite altitudes in the range of 400–800 km, the density variations between solar maximum and solar minimum are approximately two orders of magnitude. Because of these large density variations, satellites will decay far more rapidly during periods of solar maximum and more slowly during solar minimum.

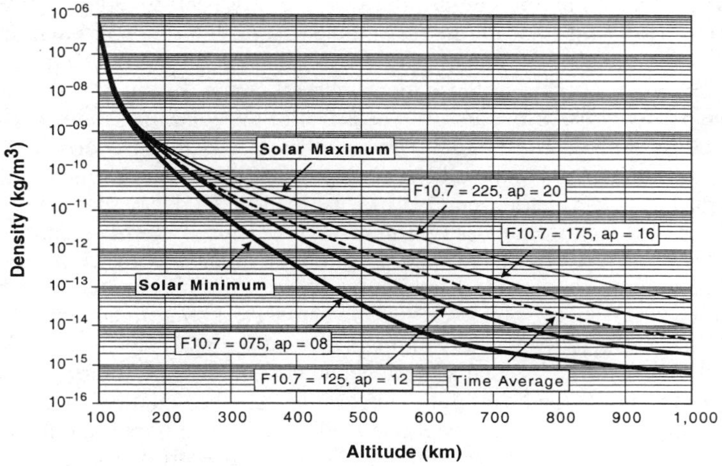

Fig. 2-20. Density vs. Altitude for Various f10.7 Values.

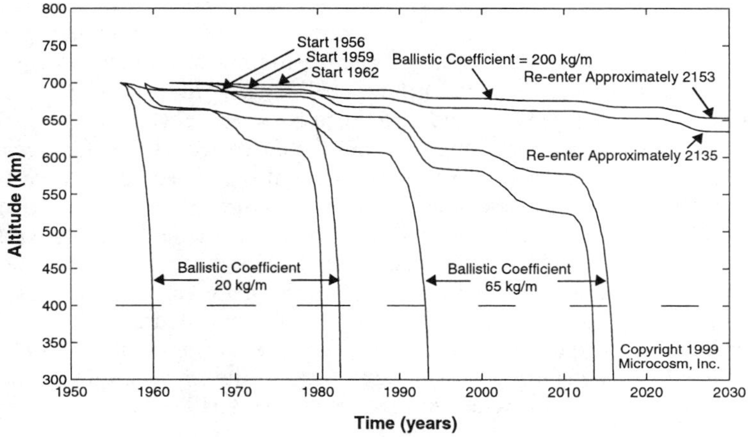

Fig. 2-21. Altitude as a Function of Date for 9 Hypothetical Satellites Launched Over a 6-year Period.

To demonstrate the wide fluctuations in spacecraft lifetimes, we "launched" nine satellites in a computer model, with the results shown in Fig. 2-21. All of the satellites were started at an initial altitude of 700 km in circular orbits. Three were launched in 1956 at the beginning of solar maximum, three were launched in 1959 near the peak of solar activity, and three were launched in 1962 at the beginning of the subsequent solar minimum. Within each set, one satellite had a ballistic coefficient of 20 kg/m^2, one was at 65 kg/m^2, and one at 200 kg/m^2, corresponding roughly to light, moderate and dense satellites respectively. The histories of the nine satellites are shown on the graph. The bars at approximately 400 km altitude mark the periods of solar maxima where the f10.7 index was above 150.

Several characteristics of satellite decay are easily seen in Fig. 2-21. Satellites decay very little during solar minimum and then rapidly during solar maximum. For any one satellite, each solar maximum period will generally produce greater decay than the previous maximum because the satellite is lower. It will also depend on the level of the particular solar maximum. The effect of the solar maximum also depends on the satellite ballistic coefficient. Those with a low ballistic coefficient respond quickly to the atmosphere and tend to decay promptly. Those with high ballistic coefficients push through a larger number of solar cycles and decay much more slowly. In the end the time for satellite decay is generally measured better in solar cycles than in years. All 9 satellites reentered during periods of solar maxima. For the range of ballistic coefficients shown, the lifetimes varied from approximately one-half of a solar cycle (5 years) to 17 solar cycles (190 years). Predicting in advance where any of the satellites come down would be remarkably difficult.

For a specific satellite whose parameters and current or expected orbit are known, the best way to predict the orbit lifetime is to integrate the equations of motion in an orbit propagator with realistic atmospheric models and assumptions about the satellite cross section. Alternatively, if the altitude is high such that orbit propagation over the satellite lifetime will take excessive computer time, we can simply integrate the equations for the change in altitude to provide approximate lifetime predictions, as was done for Fig. 2-21.

A third alternative, shown in Fig. 2-22, is to estimate a range of lifetimes based on the satellite ballistic coefficient and the approximate time of launch with respect to the solar cycle. The three sets of curves show satellite lifetime as a function of initial circular altitude for satellites with three different ballistic coefficients. The spread of the curves near the center represents the difference between solar maximum and solar minimum. At high altitudes and long lifetimes the curves come together because the satellite will see a large number of solar cycles and it will make very little difference when the satellite starts. Satellites in the midrange go through only a few solar maxima, so the lifetimes will depend strongly on when in the solar cycle the satellite is launched. Notice the steep bends in the curves at multiples of the 11-year solar cycle. As the satellite starts out lower and lower, the atmospheric variations are less, so the curves tend to come together again. Thus, a satellite launched at 100–200 km will decay very quickly irrespective of solar maximum or solar minimum. This chart provides a convenient mechanism for estimating the satellite lifetime range. The actual lifetime will depend on detailed design parameters, the details of the actual orbit, and the launch date relative to the solar cycle.

2.5 Specialized Orbits

Spacecraft orbits fall into two broad groups. First, there is a continuum of orbits with varying eccentricities and altitudes ranging from low-Earth to higher orbits, to eventually interplanetary and interstellar orbits. Typically, most such orbits are nearly Keplerian and are conveniently described and analyzed by the techniques in Sec. 2.2.

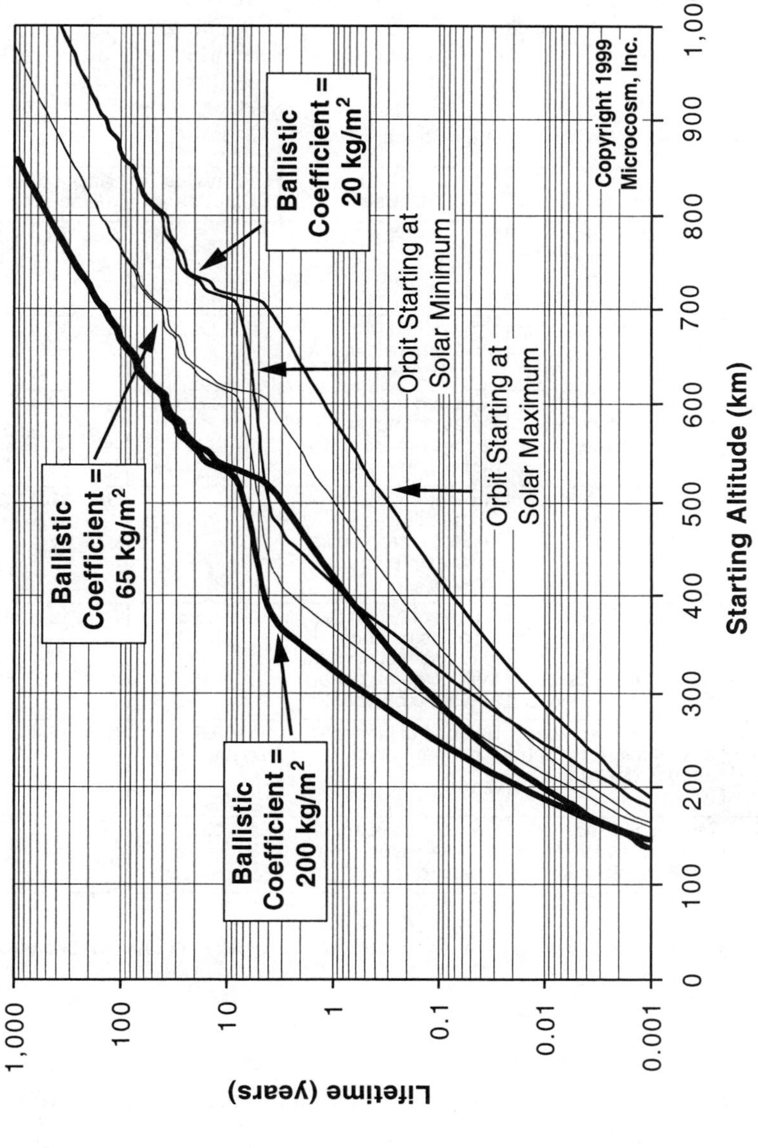

Fig. 2-22. Satellite Lifetime as a Function of Altitude, Relationship to the Solar Cycle, and Representative Ballistic Coefficients. For each ballistic coefficient, the upper curve represents launch during solar minimum and the lower curve represents launch during solar maximum.

In addition, superimposed on this orbit continuum is a set of specialized orbits summarized in Table 2-11. Within this group, geosynchronous orbits and the repeating ground track come about simply because of the relationship between the orbit period and the rotation period of the Earth. All the rest of the specialized orbits are the result of special effects arising from one of the major orbit perturbations described in Sec. 2.4. This section describes each of these specialized orbits. For each we discuss the physical effect which produces it, the basic equations which govern it, and why these orbits are important. Specific applications of these orbits are discussed in Chap. 12.

TABLE 2-11. Specialized Orbits and Their Cause.

Specialized Orbit	Characteristic	Cause	Physics Discussed	Applications Discussed
Geostationary	Maintains nearly fixed position with respect to the surface of the Earth	Orbit period = 1 day	Sec. 2.5.1	Sec. 12.4.2.1
Repeating Ground Track	Ground trace repeats after k orbits in n days	Orbit period = n / k days, where n and k are integers	Sec. 2.5.2	Sec. 12.4.2.4
Sun Synchronous	Orbit plane maintains approximately fixed orientation relative to the Sun	Torque due to equatorial bulge causes orbit to rotate 360 deg in 1 year	Sec. 2.5.3	Sec. 12.4.2.2
Molniya	Apogee and perigee don't rotate at i = 63.4 deg	Greater equatorial force balanced by lesser polar force so that net in-plane rotation is 0	Sec. 2.5.4	Sec. 12.4.2.3
Lagrange Point	Maintains fixed position with respect to 2 bodies (e.g., Earth-Moon, Earth-Sun)	Forces between the 2 bodies balance to cause motion with their common period about the barycenter	Sec. 2.5.5	Sec. 12.5
Frozen Orbit	Orbit with fixed, low eccentricity for which apogee doesn't rotate	Balance of higher order harmonics	Sec. 2.5.6 Vallado [2001]	Sec. 12.4.2.5
Statite	Maintains fixed position relative to the Earth and Sun	Gravity balanced by solar radiation pressure	Sec. 12.5	Sec. 12.5

Whenever possible, expressions for the characteristics of specialized orbits are given in three forms:

- Analytic expressions applicable to any central body
- First order approximations applicable to any central body
- Expressions where constants have been evaluated for satellites in Earth orbit

The purpose is to allow the equations to be used for any planet or other central body and to allow them to be evaluated quickly for Earth orbits. In addition, a complete numerical evaluation for circular Earth orbits at various altitudes for most of these expressions is contained in App. D and the inside rear end papers.

2.5.1 Geosynchronous Orbit

Geosynchronous orbit or *GEO* is both the simplest and most used of the specialized orbits. Approximately half of the spacecraft launched are geosynchronous spacecraft intended principally for Earth observation and communications. The period of satellites in low-Earth orbit is approximately 90 min. As the altitude increases, the orbit period also increases, according to Kepler's third law. At an altitude of 35,786 km, the period becomes 1,436 min, which is just the rotation period of the Earth relative to the fixed stars, called the *sidereal day*. Consequently, a satellite in a circular orbit at 0 inclination at this altitude will remain indefinitely fixed over a point on the Earth's equator.* In practice, of course, the orbit is never exactly circular nor at zero inclination and, consequently, will move relative to the surface of the Earth. For a perfectly circular orbit of inclination, i, the path of the satellite as seen from the center of the Earth will be a narrow analemma or figure 8 with the following dimensions:

$$\text{height}_{inc} = \pm i \tag{2-43}$$

$$\text{width}_{inc} = \pm\left(\frac{i}{4}\right)\sin i \tag{2-44}$$

This is illustrated in Fig. 2-23A. A small eccentricity, e, in geosynchronous orbit with $i = 0$ will produce a back and forth motion with 1 cycle per orbit. The amplitude of this, in radians, will be:

$$\text{width}_{ecc} = \pm 2e \tag{2-45}$$

In most cases the sidewise component of the eccentricity effect will be larger than that of the inclination effect such that the resulting figure will be an approximately oval shape of height $\pm i$ and width $\pm 2e$ (Fig. 2-23B).

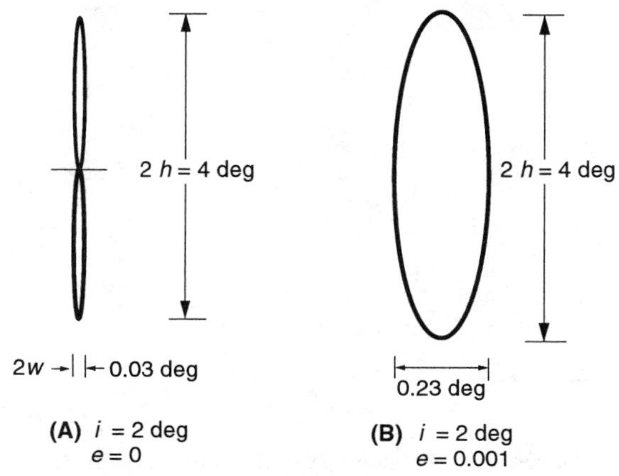

Fig. 2-23. Apparent Daily Motion of a Satellite in Geosynchronous Orbit. Horizontal scale is exaggerated to show the shape.

* Geosynchronous orbit was first described by the popular science and science fiction writer, Arthur C. Clarke in the October 1945 issue of *Wireless World* [Clarke, 1945]. Clarke often commented on the potential impact had he chosen to patent GEO.

In addition to the daily oscillations due to small variations in the orbit elements, perturbations continuously act to change the orbit. The largest perturbation in GEO is a north-south drift or inclination change caused by the gravitational interaction with the Sun and the Moon. If not corrected, this perturbation will cause the inclination to vary between 0 and 15 deg over a period of approximately 55 years. As shown in Fig. 2-24, the general motion of the orbit pole under the effect of solar lunar perturbations will be a circle of approximately 7.5 deg radius centered at a point between the ecliptic pole and the equatorial pole. Because the Sun and the Moon are effectively point gravitational masses and are moving continuously with respect to the Earth and the geostationary satellite, the motion is a complex spiral. The approximate worst case changes in velocity per year are given by:

$$\Delta V_{Moon} = 102.67 \cos\alpha \ \sin\alpha \ \text{(m/s per year)}$$
$$\approx 36.93 \text{ m/s per year, for } i = 0 \tag{2-46}$$

$$\Delta V_{Sun} = 40.17 \cos\gamma \ \sin\gamma \ \text{(m/s per year)}$$
$$\approx 14.45 \text{ m/s per year, for } i = 0 \tag{2-47}$$

where α is the angle between the orbit plane and the Moon's orbit, and γ is the angle between the orbit plane and the ecliptic. The net effect of these forces is an inclination drift for satellites in GEO of approximately 0.9 deg/year.

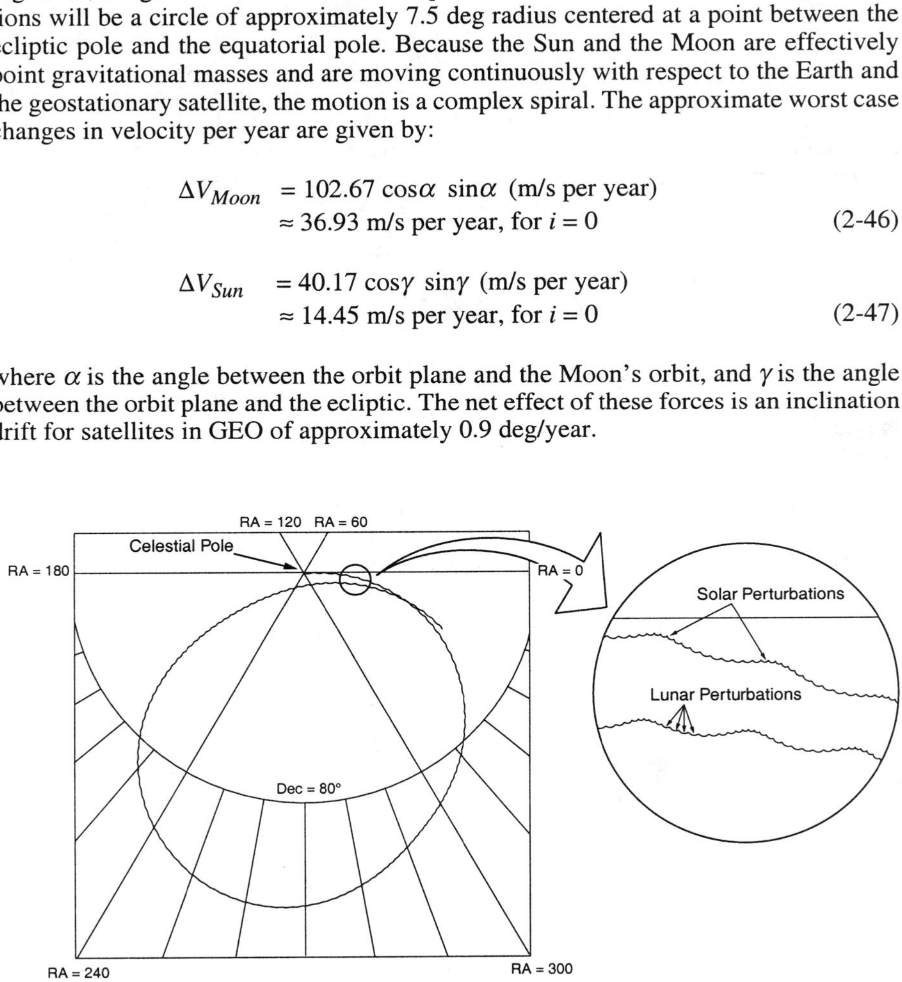

Fig. 2-24. Motion of the Orbit Pole over 60 Years for a Satellite in Geosynchronous Orbit. The celestial pole is at the coordinate intersection near the top of the plot in the center. The long term motion is roughly a circle of 15 deg radius centered on a right ascension of 270 deg and a declination of 82.5 deg. As can be seen in the figure, the real motion is substantially more complex because of the motion of the Sun and Moon relative to the spacecraft. The large "waves" are due to the Sun and have a 6 month periodicity. The smaller ones (best seen in the enlarged view) are semimonthly "waves" due to the Moon. In general, geosynchronous satellites drift about 0.9 deg per year in inclination. RA = right ascension, Dec = declination.

In addition, there is an east-west drift caused by the out of roundness of the Earth's equator (i.e., the J_{22} sectoral term in the spherical harmonic expansion of the geopotential). If uncorrected, this transverse acceleration would result in a sinusoidal motion about either of 2 stable longitudes located at approximately 75 deg and 255 deg East longitude. The ΔV in m/s/year required to compensate for the East-West drift is given by:

$$\Delta V = 1.715 \sin (2 | l_D - l_s |) \tag{2-48}$$

where l_D is the desired longitude and l_s is the closest stable longitude. Typically, the ΔV required for East-West stationkeeping is approximately 10% of that required for North-South stationkeeping.

None of the above perturbations serve to change the radius of the geostationary orbit. Whereas atmospheric drag provides a housekeeping function in low-Earth orbit, there is no natural perturbation which provides a similar process for removing satellites from the geostationary ring. Consequently, a satellite in GEO which dies will drift in inclination and drift back-and-forth in longitude among the other geosynchronous satellites. Similarly, if one of the spacecraft in GEO explodes or collides with another satellite, the resulting debris cloud will also remain in geosynchronous orbit. Thus, geosynchronous orbit is both a unique resource and a fragile environment because of the potential for debris to accumulate. The key to this problem is to raise spacecraft 500 km above geosynchronous orbit when they have finished their useful life. At this altitude, they will remain essentially indefinitely with no perturbations to bring them back into the geostationary arc. Such a maneuver takes an extremely small amount of propellant. The largest difficulty with spacecraft disposal is that it must be done while the spacecraft itself is still operating so that thrusters can be commanded to make the appropriate maneuver.

The synchronous altitude for any central body can be obtained immediately from Kepler's Third Law by setting the orbit period, P_{sync}, equal to the rotation period of the central body relative to the fixed stars, D^*, typically called the sidereal day. Thus:

$$P_{sync} = D^* \tag{2-49}$$

$$a_{sync} = (\mu/4\pi^2)^{1/3} (D^*)^{2/3} \tag{2-50}$$

$$H_{sync} = a_{sync} - R_{planet} \tag{2-51}$$

where as usual $\mu \equiv GM$ for the planet, a_{sync} is the semimajor axis of the synchronous orbit, R_{planet} is the equatorial radius of the planet, and H_{sync} is the synchronous altitude. Values of the synchronous altitude for principal bodies in the solar system are listed in Table 2-12.

2.5.2 Repeating Ground Track Orbits

In a *repeating ground track orbit*, the spacecraft returns after one or more days to the same location with respect to the surface of the Earth such that the path of the spacecraft then repeats itself. For this to occur, an integral number of orbit periods, j, must equal an integral number of days, k. For example, if a spacecraft makes exactly 15.25 orbits per day, then it will make $j = 61$ orbits in $k = 4$ days and will have a 4 day repeating ground track. Every 4th day, the satellite will follow the same path and,

TABLE 2-12. Synchronous Orbits for Major Solar System Objects.

Central Object	Sidereal Period (days)	Equatorial Radius (km)	Synchronous Altitude (km)
Earth	0.99726	6,378.14	35,786
Moon	27.322	1,738	86,715
Sun	25.38	695,990	24,588,000
Mercury	58.6462	2,439.7	240,453
Venus	243.01	6,051.9	1,530,500
Mars	1.02596	3,397	17,031
Jupiter	0.41354	71,492	88,565
Saturn	0.44401	60,268	51,981

therefore, will see the same geometry relative to features on the ground and will move across the sky in the same apparent path as seen by a ground observer. An example of a 2-day repeating ground track orbit is shown in Fig. 2-25.

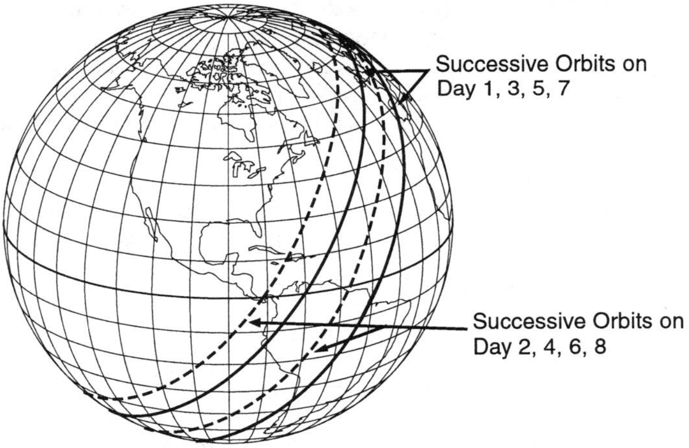

Fig. 2-25. **A 2-day Repeating Ground Track Orbit** will cross the Equator on the second day midway between where it crossed on the first day and then repeat the day/crossings on day 3. The pattern repeats at 2-day intervals.

The actual period for a repeating ground track is made more complex by the presence of orbit perturbations which cause the orbit itself to rotate. We want the orbit period to be a harmonic of the rotation of the Earth relative to the orbit plane, rather than the fixed stars. Consequently, we need to take into account the rotation of the orbit (in node, perigee, and mean anomaly) due to the oblateness of the Earth. Because the oblateness effects are function of the altitude, solving for the altitude for a given ground track repeat pattern is an iterative process. Our initial, but inaccurate, estimate, H_0, is the repeating ground track altitude ignoring the effects of oblateness:

$$H_0 = \mu^{1/3}\left(\frac{2\pi j}{D^* k}\right)^{-2/3} - P_E \tag{2-52a}$$

$$\equiv k_1 (j/k)^{-2/3} - R_E \tag{2-52b}$$

$$k_1 \equiv \mu^{1/3} (2\pi / D^*)^{-2/3} \tag{2-52c}$$

$$\approx 42{,}164.173 \text{ km} \tag{2-52d}$$

where $D^* \approx 86164.10035$ is the sidereal rotation period of the Earth (i.e., relative to the fixed stars), R_E is equatorial radius of the Earth, and $\mu = GM$ is the Earth's gravitational constant. We then determine the rotation rate of the Earth, $\dot{L}$, and the rotation rate of the three orbit parameters due to oblateness as follows:

$$\dot{L} = 360 \text{ deg/ day}^* \tag{2-53}$$

$$\dot{\Omega} = -2k_2 a^{-7/2} \cos i \left(1 - e^2\right)^{-2} \tag{2-54}$$

$$\dot{\omega} = k_2 a^{-7/2}\left(5\cos^2 i - 1\right)\left(1 - e^2\right)^{-2} \tag{2-55}$$

$$\dot{M} = k_2 a^{-7/2}\left(3\cos^2 i - 1\right)\left(1 - e^2\right)^{-3/2} \tag{2-56}$$

where

$$k_2 \equiv 0.75\, J_2 \mu^{1/2} R_E^2 \tag{2-57a}$$

$$\approx 1.029\,549\,648 \times 10^{14} \text{ km}^{3.5}/\text{day}^* \tag{2-57b}$$

where $\dot{\Omega}$ is the rate of change of the ascending node, $\dot{\omega}$ is the rate of change of perigee, $\dot{M}$ is rate of change of the mean anomaly, J_2 is the Earth's oblateness, e is the orbit eccentricity, i is the inclination, and a is the estimate of the semimajor axis. For the first iteration, we take $a \approx H_0 + R_E$. All of the angular rates are expressed in deg/sidereal day ≡ deg/day*. We next estimate the mean angular motion, n, for the repeating ground track as:

$$n = (j/k)\left(\dot{L} - \dot{\Omega}\right) - \left(\dot{\omega} + \dot{M}\right) \tag{2-58}$$

Finally, the revised estimate for the repeating ground track altitude, H, is:

$$H = \mu^{1/3} (n\pi / 180)^{-2/3} - R_E \tag{2-59}$$

If necessary, we can then recompute a and iterate again from Eq. (2-54) on. Note that for prograde orbits, cos i is positive, for retrograde orbits, cos i is negative, and that a must be in km if the value of k_2 in Eq. (2-57b) is used. Values for the above constants for different objects in the solar system are given in Sec. 12.4.3.4.

The principal advantage of this type of orbit is that the ground track and, therefore, the geometry relative to the surface of the Earth repeats. This, in turn, means that we can view the surface of the Earth from the same viewpoint on a recurring basis and, therefore, compare one image or data set with another taken at a later time from the same orientation. This makes the interpretation of changes and variations far easier. In addition, the geometry of the satellite's path as seen by the ground also remains the same such that a ground station can follow the path of the satellite more easily since it will follow the same path on a recurring basis. The principal demerit of the repeating ground track is that it has the potential for resonance effects with the Earth's higher order harmonics. If we pass just to the left of a major mass concentration such as the Himalayas today, then we will do so again tomorrow, and the day after, and so on. Thus, perturbations have the potential to accumulate over time, and resonance effects can build up which will significantly distort the orbit. Consequently, repeating ground tracks are useful for observations, but should generally be avoided unless there is a specific reason for using them.

There are a very large number of potential repeating ground track orbits. For the Earth, there are 15 orbits per day at an altitude of 482.25 and 14 per day at an altitude of 817.14. However, in between these we have 14.33 orbits per day, 14.5 per day, 14.75 per day, 14.8 per day, and so on. This set of representative repeating ground track orbits is shown in Table 2-13.

TABLE 2-13. Representative Repeating Ground Track Orbits. A large number of such orbits are possible.

Altitude (km)	Inclination (deg)	Period (min)	Orbits per Day	Repeat Pattern
817.14	28	101.24	14.0	14 orbits/day
701.34	28	98.80	14.33	43 orbits/3 days
645.06	28	97.63	14.50	29 orbits/2 days
562.55	28	95.91	14.75	59 orbits/4 days
546.31	28	95.57	14.8	74 orbits/5 days
482.25	28	94.25	15.0	15 orbits/day

An interesting subgroup of the repeating ground track orbits are those for which the inclination and, therefore, node rotation rate is adjusted such that the repeat occurs on precise multiples of the civil day of 24 hours. For these orbits, the ground track not only repeats, but does so at the same time each day, every other day, or on a weekly basis depending upon the orbit perimeters. These *civil orbits* are discussed further in Sec. 12.4.2.4.

2.5.3 Sun-Synchronous Orbits

Because the gravitational force is conservative, the total energy and mean values of the semimajor axis, apogee and perigee heights, and eccentricity do not change due to oblateness or other higher order terms in the Earth's geopotential. Nonetheless, secular variations in some of the orbit elements can occur. Perhaps the easiest of these to visualize is the rotation of the orbit due to the torque produced by the Earth's oblateness. In this context, it is easiest to visualize the Earth as a point mass plus a ring of additional mass along the equator representing the equatorial bulge (the J_2 term). The gravitational effect of the equatorial bulge is to continuously try to pull the orbit plane downward toward the equatorial plane. However, the result of this force is not a change in the inclination, but a rotation of the right ascension of the ascending node.

The reason for this effect is the angular momentum of the orbit. In this regard, we can think of the orbit as a rotating wheel with its axis along the normal to the orbit plane. Recall from freshman physics that when a bicycle wheel is rotated rapidly and one end is allowed to drop, it does not fall, but rather precesses, i.e., the axis rotates in a horizontal direction. A similar result applies to the spacecraft orbit. As shown in Fig. 2-26, when the spacecraft is north of the equator, the oblate Earth is pulling it down thus producing a torque into the paper. Similarly, when the spacecraft is south of the equator, the equatorial bulge is pulling it up and, again, there is a torque into the paper. This continuous torque causes the angular momentum vector to move in the direction of the torque, i.e., to rotate about the Earth's pole. For a satellite in a prograde orbit, this rotation is in the westward direction opposite the direction of the Earth on its axis. Consequently, this motion is called the *regression of the nodes*. So long as the other orbit elements do not change, the orbit will rotate indefinitely in inertial space and the node will continue to change while the inclination remains constant.

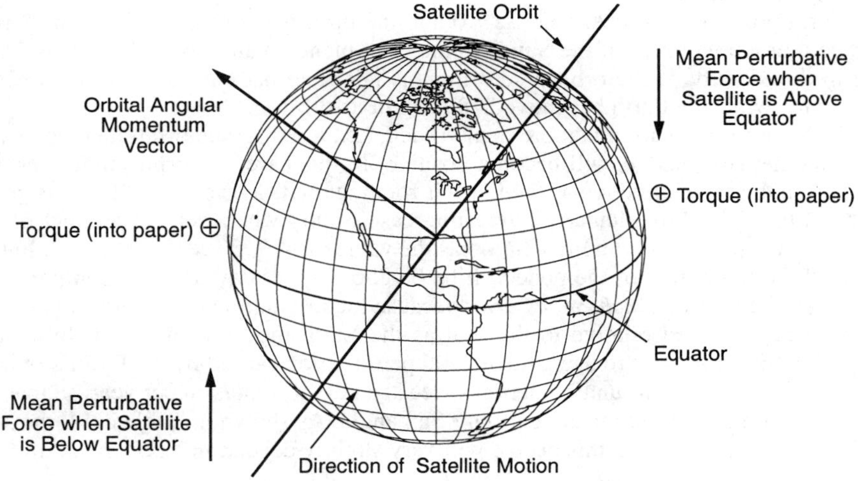

Fig. 2-26. Regression of the Nodes Due to Oblateness. The equatorial bulge of the Earth produces a torque on the orbit, causing prograde orbits to rotate from east to west (i.e. regress). Retrograde orbits rotate from west to east due to oblateness.

To evaluate the rate of node rotation, we will return to the Lagrange planetary equations (Eq. 2-22e) and evaluate the impact of the J_2 term. When only the secular variations due to J_2 are considered, the right ascension of the ascending node, Ω, at time t is given by:

$$\Omega = \Omega_0 + \frac{d\Omega}{dt}(t - t_0) \tag{2-60a}$$

$$= \Omega_0 - \frac{3}{2} J_2 n \left(\frac{R_E}{a}\right)^2 \left(1 - e^2\right)^{-2} (\cos i)(t - t_0) \tag{2-60b}$$

$$\approx \Omega_0 - \frac{3}{2} J_2 \sqrt{\mu} R_E^2 a^{-7/2} (1-e^2)^{-2} (\cos i)(t-t_0) + \mathcal{O}(J_2^2) \tag{2-60c}$$

$$= \Omega_0 - 2.064\,74 \times 10^{14} a^{-7/2} (1-e^2)^{-2} (\cos i)(t-t_0) + \mathcal{O}(J_2^2) \tag{2-60d}$$

where in the last form, $t\text{–}t_0$ is in days, Ω is in degrees, a is the semimajor axis in km, e is the eccentricity, i is the inclination, and Ω_0 is Ω at the epoch time t_0. In the final two forms, n is approximated by n_0 which may produce an error as large as 0.1% in the $d\Omega/dt$ term.

For example, in a circular low-Earth orbit at 500 km, we may further evaluate Eq. (2-60d) to yield $\dot{\Omega} = -7.652 \cos i$. Consequently, for low inclination orbits, the node can rotate up to 7.7 deg per day. This represents a significant motion of the orbit plane over the lifetime of most satellites, since the orbit could rotate through 360 deg in only about 45 days.

For a polar orbit, i = 90 deg, $\dot{\Omega} = 0$ and the orbit plane remains fixed in inertial space. For a polar orbit, if the Sun is in the orbit plane on any given date, then it will be in the vicinity of the orbit pole 3 months later and back in the orbit plane after 6 months when the Earth has moved 180 deg in its orbit.

If the orbit inclination is more than 90 deg, i.e., a retrograde orbit, then cos i will become negative and $\dot{\Omega}$ will become positive. In this case, the orbit progresses and rotates in the same direction as the Earth is rotating on its axis or as the Earth is going around the Sun. A particularly interesting case occurs whenever the product of the three terms in a, e, and i in Eq. (2-45) has the value of -4.7737×10^{-15} km$^{-3.5}$. In this case, the rotation rate of the node will be 0.9856 deg per day or 1 rotation per year. This is called a *Sun-synchronous orbit* because the orientation of the orbit plane will remain nearly fixed relative to the Sun as the Earth moves in its orbit. In a Sun-synchronous orbit, we are using the natural perturbation caused by the Earth's oblateness to pull the orbit around in inertial space at a rate of 1 rotation per year, so that we can maintain an approximately constant Sun angle. As shown in Table 2-14, the specific inclination in which this occurs will vary slightly depending upon the altitude of the satellite.

The effect of oblateness on the rotation of the orbit remains essentially constant throughout the year. Consequently, the orbit pole will move at a uniform rate at a fixed angle relative to the celestial pole. On the other hand, because of the eccentricity of the Earth's orbit, the Sun moves at a nonuniform rate going faster at perihelion and more slowly at aphelion. In addition, the Sun moves along the ecliptic inclined at 23.5 deg to the Earth's equator. This means that relative to the celestial pole, the Sun moves north and south through a total angle of 47 deg and additionally moves more rapidly along the equator at some times of the year than at other times. (The general character of this motion including the reasons for different speeds along the equator are explained in detail in Chap. 10.) The net result is that throughout the year, the Sun moves in an analemma or figure 8 relative to the position of the orbit as shown in Fig. 2-27. The general path of the Sun relative to the orbit plane will be an analemma with a half height equal to 23.5 deg. The width of the analemma will be 2.5 deg due simply to the obliquitity of the ecliptic. When the eccentricity of the Earth's orbit is taken into account, the analemma will be 3.8 deg across in the northern hemisphere and only 1.3 deg in the southern hemisphere.

TABLE 2-14. Inclination for Sun-Synchronous Orbits at Varying Altitudes.

Mean Altitude (km)	*e* = 0	*e* = 0.1		
	i (deg)	i (deg)	h_P (km)	h_A (km)
0	95.68	—	—	—
200	96.33	—	—	—
400	97.03	—	—	—
600	97.79	—	—	—
800	98.60	98.43	82	1,518
1,000	99.48	99.29	262	1,738
2,000	104.89	104.59	1,162	2,838
3,000	112.41	111.94	2,062	3,938
4,000	122.93	122.19	2,962	5,038
5,000	138.60	137.32	3,862	6,138
5,974	180.00	168.55	4,738	7,209

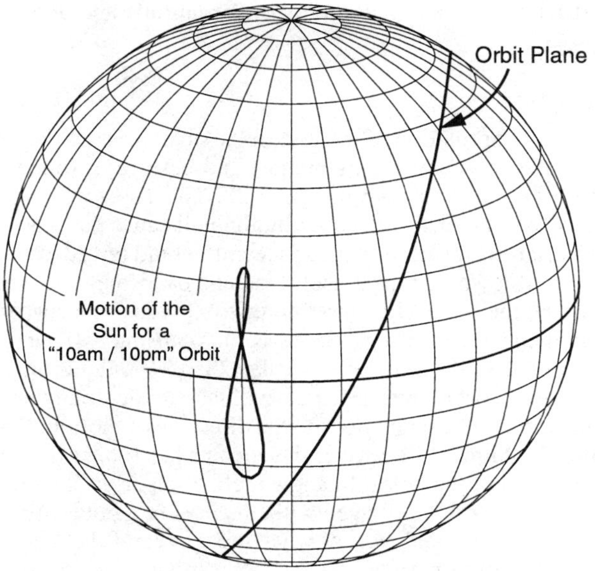

Fig. 2-27. Changing Position of the Sun Relative to the Orbit Plane in a Sun-Synchronous Orbit. The position of the Sun remains approximately fixed. However, since the J_2 perturbation is being used to balance the non-uniform revolution of the Earth about the Sun, and because the Sun isn't in the equatorial plane, the relative position will change somewhat throughout the year.

Sun-synchronous orbits are typically labeled by the approximate orientation of the Sun relative to the Earth. If the Sun is approximately in the orbit plane, it is called a *noon-midnight orbit* since it will be either noon or midnight at the subsatellite point. If the Sun is near the orbit pole, it is called a *twilight orbit* or *6 am—6 pm orbit*, since the Sun will be nearly at right angles to the direction to the Earth. In twilight orbits, the Sun is always in the vicinity of the orbit pole and, therefore, there are no eclipses and the available power is at a maximum. In addition, the lighting on the ground below has very long shadows and, therefore, good contrast. The applications of the Sun-synchronous orbits are discussed in Sec. 12.4.2.2.

Finally, it is convenient to compute the local mean time* at the subsatellite point of the spacecraft. For any satellite in a circular orbit, the local mean time, T, at which the satellite is over latitude λ is given by:

$$T = \frac{1}{15}\left[-\alpha_s + \Omega + \arcsin\left(\frac{\tan\lambda}{\tan i}\right)\right] + 12 \tag{2-61a}$$

$$\approx \frac{1}{15}\left[-\frac{360}{365.24}\Delta D + \Omega + \arcsin\left(\frac{\tan\lambda}{\tan i}\right)\right] + 12 \tag{2-61b}$$

where α_s is the right ascension of the mean Sun, Ω is the right ascension of the ascending node of the orbit, i is the orbit inclination, ΔD is the number of days from the vernal equinox to the time Ω is evaluated, the angular quantities in square brackets are in degrees, and T is in hours. For Sun-synchronous orbits, $\alpha_s - \Omega$ is constant and, therefore, the local mean time is a function only of the latitude and does not change from orbit to orbit.

2.5.4 Molniya Orbits

In addition to causing rotation of the nodes, the oblateness of the Earth also causes the major axis of the orbit connecting apogee and perigee to rotate within the orbit plane. The reason for this is shown in Fig. 2-28. The $1/r^2$ force corresponding to a perfectly spherically symmetric mass distribution will cause the spacecraft to move in an elliptical Keplerian orbit such that the spacecraft would return exactly to its starting conditions and the orbit would repeat itself over and over in inertial space. If the force is stronger than $1/r^2$, the orbit will curve more strongly and the spacecraft will return to perigee sooner than it otherwise would have, thus causing perigee to rotate in a positive direction. Similarly, if the force is weaker than $1/r^2$, the orbit will rotate more slowly than a Keplerian orbit, the spacecraft will take longer than one period to return to perigee and the orbit will rotate opposite the direction of motion. For the case of the oblate Earth, the gravitational force over the equator is stronger than $1/r^2$ and weaker than $1/r^2$ in the vicinity of the poles. In a low inclination orbit, the spacecraft will feel a stronger force at all times and perigee will advance. In a polar orbit, the forces will be stronger over the equator and weaker when the spacecraft is over the pole. The net effect is that in a polar orbit perigee rotates backwards but not as rapidly as it rotates forward for an equatorial orbit.

---

* The *local mean time* is the solar time that would be the case if the Sun moved at a uniform rate along the equator rather than at a varying rate along the ecliptic. Thus local mean time does not take into account either time zones or the eccentricity and obliquity of the ecliptic.

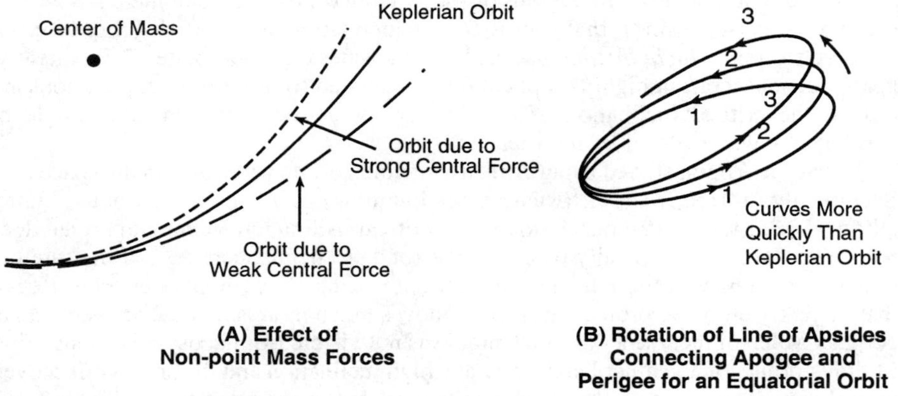

Fig. 2-28. Physical Basis for Rotation of Eccentric Orbits. Near the equator the force will be greater than the $1/r^2$ force from the Earth point mass and the orbit will rotate faster than the closed Keplerian orbit. Near the pole it will be less and the orbit will be more open.

Once again, we can use the Lagrange planetary Eqs. (2-22d) to evaluate the rate at which the argument of perigee, ω, rotates:

$$\omega = \omega_0 + \frac{d\omega}{dt}(t - t_0) \tag{2-62a}$$

$$= \omega_0 + \frac{3}{2} J_2 n \left(\frac{R_E}{a}\right)^2 \left(1 - e^2\right)^{-2} \left(2 - \frac{5}{2}\sin^2 i\right)(t - t_0) \tag{2-62b}$$

$$\approx \omega_0 + \frac{3}{2} J_2 \sqrt{\mu} R_E^2 a^{-7/2} (1 - e^2)^{-2} \left(2 - \frac{5}{2}\sin^2 i\right)(t - t_0) + \mathcal{O}\left(J_2^2\right) \tag{2-62c}$$

$$\approx \omega_0 + 2.064\,74 \times 10^{14} a^{-7/2} \left(1 - e^2\right)^{-2} \left(2 - \frac{5}{2}\sin^2 i\right)(t - t_0) + \mathcal{O}\left(J_2^2\right) \tag{2-62d}$$

where in the last term $t - t_0$ is in days, ω is in degrees, a is the semimajor axis in kilometers, e is the eccentricity, i is the inclination, and ω_0 is the value of ω at the epoch t_0. For example, we can evaluate the expression for a circular orbit at 500 km to obtain $\dot{\omega} = 3.826\,(4 - 5\sin^2 i)$. This implies that for an equatorial orbit, the line of apsides or major axis will rotate in the direction of motion by up to 15.3 deg per day and for polar orbits it will rotate opposite the direction of motion by as much as –3.8 deg per day.

The rotation of perigee can be even more rapid than the rotation of the line of nodes. For example, in a low eccentricity, low inclination orbit that begins with apogee over the northern most latitude, apogee will have rotated to the equator after only a week, and in 2 weeks will be at the southern most latitude. At this high rate of rotation, it would be difficult to find strong utility for highly elliptical orbits except perhaps to successively sample different regions of space. Notice, however, that there is a term in the expansion $(4 - 5 \sin^2 i)$ that goes to 0 at an inclination of 63.435 deg. For an elliptical orbit at this *critical inclination*, the line of apsides does not rotate. Consequently, nearly all spacecraft in highly elliptical orbits intended for long-term applications are also at the critical inclination of 63.435 deg, or at the complementary angle of 116.565 deg which also does not rotate.

The Soviet Union started using critically inclined orbits very early in the space age. Specifically, a *Molniya* orbit (Russian for lightning) is a semisynchronous, highly elliptical orbit with a 12-hour period at the critical inclination such that perigee does not rotate. Perigee is typically placed in the southern hemisphere so that the satellite remains above the northern hemisphere for approximately 11 hours per orbit. Recall that in highly elliptical orbits, the satellite moves much more slowly at apogee than at perigee. Much of the former Soviet Union was not visible from geosynchronous orbit. Molniya orbits, on the other hand, were at a high inclination and the spacecraft moved very slowly at apogee and, therefore, was in view for an extended period. Thus, 2 or 3 spacecraft in a Molniya orbit could provide communications for northern latitude regions well beyond the reach of geosynchronous satellites. Consequently, most of the Soviet communications satellites were placed in Molniya orbits. The basic parameters of representative Molniya orbits are shown in Table 2-15.

TABLE 2-15. Characteristics of Representative Molniya Orbits.

Rev. Per Day	Period (sec)	Semimajor Axis (km)	Inclination (deg)	Altitude at Apogee (km)	Altitude at Perigee (km)	Eccentricity
1	86,164	42,164	63.4	53,622	17,951	0.423
2	43,082	26,562	63.4	39,863	504	0.740
3	28,721	20,270	63.4	33,659	504	0.660

The rate of perigee rotation depends on the value of J_2 and, therefore, will be different for different central bodies. Note, however, that the critical inclination of 63.4 deg is a function only of the fact that the expansion is in terms of spherical harmonics and thus will be the same for all planets. Consequently, Molniya-like orbits about any of the planets will be inclined at 63.4 deg to the planet's equator.

2.5.5 Lagrange Point Orbits

Most specialized orbits are defined with respect to a single central body such as the Earth or the Moon. *Lagrange point orbits**, however, are defined with respect to 2 large co-orbiting bodies such as the Earth and the Moon or the Sun and the Earth. This is often called the *circular restricted three-body problem*, which refers to the two large bodies being in circular orbits about each other and the mass of the spacecraft or small body being much less than the mass of the other two objects. For convenience, we will define the Lagrange points for the Earth-Moon system. However, they can be applied to any pair of co-orbiting large bodies.

---

* Named after the 18th century French mathematician and astronomer Joseph Lagrange.

As shown in Fig. 2-29 the *Lagrange points** or *libration points* for the Earth and the Moon are the five points such that an object placed at one of them will remain there indefinitely relative to the Earth-Moon system. All five of the Lagrange points are in the plane of the Moon's orbit. The 3 Lagrange points on the Earth-Moon line are positions of unstable equilibrium, i.e., any small change causes the object to drift away. However, L_4 and L_5 which form equilateral triangles with the Earth and the Moon in the plane of the Moon's orbit are positions of stable equilibrium. A satellite placed in the vicinity of L_4 or L_5 with an appropriate velocity will continue to orbit in that vicinity indefinitely.

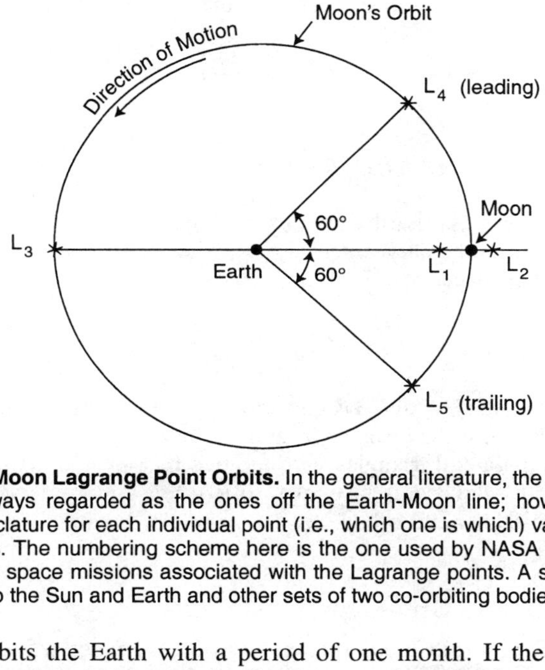

Fig. 2-29. Earth-Moon Lagrange Point Orbits. In the general literature, the L_4 and L_5 locations are always regarded as the ones off the Earth-Moon line; however, the specific nomenclature for each individual point (i.e., which one is which) varies widely among authors. The numbering scheme here is the one used by NASA and, therefore, applied to space missions associated with the Lagrange points. A similar set of points apply to the Sun and Earth and other sets of two co-orbiting bodies.*

The Moon orbits the Earth with a period of one month. If the Moon were not present, a satellite placed closer to the Earth, say at L_1, would rotate with a period shorter than a month and one placed at L_2 would rotate with a period longer than a month. For the satellite at L_1, "putting the Moon back" decreases the central force and, therefore, increases the period. Similarly, the satellite at L_2, the Moon increases the central force and decreases the period. L_1 and L_2 are simply the points at which the change is just sufficient to make the period exactly equal to the Moon's orbital period. Similarly, at L_3 the sum of the forces due to the Earth and the Moon are just enough to cause the satellite to rotate in a period of one month. The source of the stable equilibria at L_4 and L_5 is a bit more difficult to conceptualize. Although we usually think

---

* The naming convention for the Lagrange points is particularly bad. First, the numbering scheme varies widely between authors. Fig. 2-29 shows the scheme adopted by NASA. Second, the two central bodies are often left unstated. L_1 and L_2 missions most often refer to the Sun-Earth Lagrange points, while L_4 and L_5 most often refer to the Earth-Moon ones. The best approach is to be unambiguous, i.e, "the L_1 Lagrange point between the Earth and the Sun."

in terms of the Moon revolving around the Earth, in fact, both the Earth and the Moon revolve around their *barycenter*, or mutual center of mass. (For the Earth-Moon system the center of mass is displaced from the center of the Earth approximately 4,700 km toward the Moon, i.e., still below the Earth's surface.) The effect of the Moon's gravitational force on the L_4 and L_5 Lagrange points is to displace the net gravitational force away from being directed toward the center of the Earth, changing the direction just enough so that the total force on the small satellite is directed toward the barycenter of the Earth-Moon system and, again, produce a period of revolution equal to that of the Moon.

Ehricke [1960] provides the following approximations for the locations of the Lagrange points for a spacecraft of negligible mass. For L_1 and L_2:

$$L_1: \quad \rho_1 = R_B\left[1-\left(\frac{m}{3M}\right)^{1/3}\right] \tag{2-63}$$

$$L_2: \quad \rho_2 = R_B\left[1+\left(\frac{m}{3M}\right)^{1/3}\right] \tag{2-64}$$

where M is the larger mass (Earth in our example), m is the smaller mass (the Moon), R_B is the distance from the barycenter to the smaller mass, and ρ is the distance from the barycenter to the spacecraft. For L_3:

$$L_3: \quad \rho_3 = R_M\left[1-\left(\frac{7m}{12M}\right)^{1/3}\right] \tag{2-65}$$

Here M and m are as above, but R_M is now the distance from larger mass to the smaller mass and, similarly, ρ_3 is the distance from the larger mass to the spacecraft. Because L_4 and L_5 form equilateral triangles with the two masses, the distance of these two locations from both M and m is just equal to R_M. For a more detailed discussion of Lagrange point missions and orbits, see for example, Farquhar, et al. [1977, 1993, 1994, 1998.]

2.5.6 Other Specialized Orbits

Circular low-Earth orbits are not inherently stable. Higher order harmonics cause the eccentricity to oscillate about a small nonzero value as shown in Fig. 2-30. To avoid this, we can put a spacecraft in an orbit with a low eccentricity and an argument of perigee of 90 deg or 270 deg and the orbit will be stable. This is called a *frozen orbit*. Frozen orbits can be used with any low-Earth orbit. They are not so much a specialized orbit as a mechanism for maintaining a more stable orbit and avoiding a low level oscillation. The argument of perigee, ω_f, and eccentricity, e_f, for frozen orbits are as follows:

$$\omega_f = 90 \text{ deg or } 270 \text{ deg} \tag{2-66}$$

and

$$e_f \approx -\frac{J_3}{2J_2}\left(\frac{R_E}{a}\right)\sin i \ \sin\omega_f \tag{2-67a}$$

$$\approx +7.459\,335\left(\frac{\sin i \ \sin\omega_f}{a}\right) \tag{2-67b}$$

where, as usual, i is the inclination, R_E is the equatorial radius of the Earth, J_2 and J_3 are the second and third terms in the spherical harmonic expansion of the geopotential, and a is the semimajor axis, expressed in km in Eq. (2-67b). For a polar orbit of 500 km, $e_f \approx 0.00108$. (Including higher order terms will add about 0.00010 to this value.) In addition, both the eccentricity and argument of perigee will be frozen at the critical inclination of 63.4 deg or 116.6 deg and any values of e or ω.

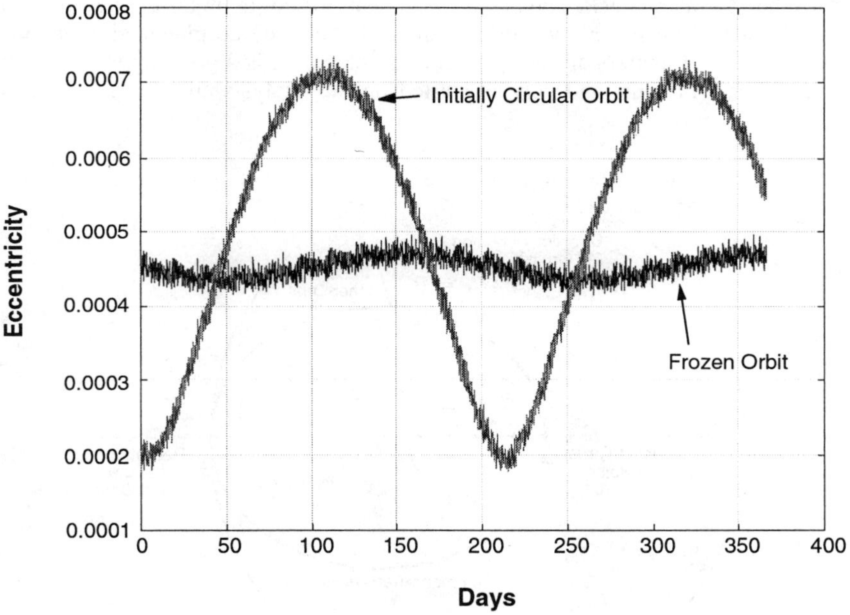

Fig. 2-30. Eccentricity Oscillation in an Initially Circular LEO Orbit. Central line shows the eccentricity in a comparable frozen orbit. Orbit shown is at 650 km at an inclination of 57 deg.

In 1989, Bob Forward invented and patented the *statite* [Forward, 1989]. It is not called a satellite because it is not in an orbit but is an object fixed with respect to the Earth and Sun using solar radiation pressure to balance gravity. Because solar radiation pressure tends to be remarkably small, the statite is required to be very light weight, have an extremely large cross-sectional area, and be at a substantial distance from the Earth or other gravitating bodies. Thus far, no spacecraft have been placed in statite "orbits."

2.6 Orbit Maneuvers

Thus far we have discussed primarily orbits which are either constant or slowly varying with time. In this section we discuss the physics and provide basic equations for orbit maneuvers intended to transport the spacecraft from one orbit to another, typically for the purpose of getting somewhere, such as transfer orbits to a geosynchronous orbit or to the Moon or Mars. This section discusses the basic physics of such orbits. Chapter 12 discusses the principal advantages and disadvantages of the various alternatives and reasons for selecting them.

2.6.1 Transfer Orbits

One of the fundamental goals of space missions is to get from one place to another—from the Earth to Mars, from low-Earth orbit to a higher orbit, or from the Earth to the Moon and back. The basic mechanism for doing this is the *transfer orbit.* The simplest and most common orbit transfer is between co-planar circular orbits. While most orbit transfers are not precisely co-planar, it is a good approximation to many transfer problems, and gets us started on the analysis and design of transfer orbits.

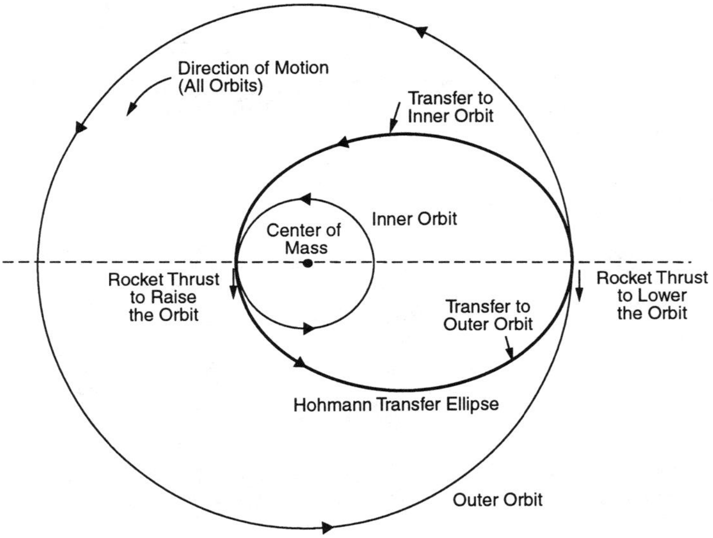

Fig. 2-31. The Hohmann Transfer Trajectory. This is the lowest energy approach for going between two co-planar circular orbits.

Putting mass and, therefore, propellant into space is remarkably expensive. Consequently, nearly all transfer orbits are intended to minimize the propellant required to achieve the desired end orbit. The most fundamental and most often used is the *Hohmann transfer trajectory*, which is the lowest energy transfer between two co-planar circular orbits. This approach is based on the analytical results published in 1925 by Walter Hohmann, who was at the time the city architect of Essen, Germany. As shown in Fig. 2-31, the Hohmann transfer is an elliptical orbit with perigee tangent to the inner orbit and apogee tangent to the outer orbit, 180 deg away. If we're starting in a low orbit and wish to transfer to a higher one, we need to add energy. The most efficient way to do this is to increase the velocity of the spacecraft without changing its direction. Consequently, we point our rocket in the direction of motion (i.e., with the rocket exhaust going out the back, opposite the direction of motion). We then fire the rocket engine 180 deg from where we wish to end up and simply add ΔV to the current circular velocity. This creates an elliptical orbit with perigee where the engine fired. At this first firing, we provide just enough ΔV to raise apogee to the radius of our higher circular target orbit. When the spacecraft arrives at apogee, 180 deg later, we again fire the rocket engine in the direction of motion in order to raise perigee to the value of the apogee altitude, circularizing the orbit at the target altitude. The fundamental equations for the Hohmann transfer are as follows:

$$a_T = \frac{1}{2}(a_L + a_H) \tag{2-68}$$

$$\Delta V_L = \sqrt{\mu}\left[\left(\frac{2}{a_L} - \frac{1}{a_T}\right)^{1/2} - \left(\frac{1}{a_L}\right)^{1/2}\right] \tag{2-69}$$

$$\Delta V_H = \sqrt{\mu}\left[\left(\frac{1}{a_H}\right)^{1/2} - \left(\frac{2}{a_H} - \frac{1}{a_T}\right)^{1/2}\right] \tag{2-70}$$

$$T = \frac{1}{2} P_T = \pi a_T^{3/2} \mu^{-1/2} \tag{2-71}$$

where a is the semimajor axis, ΔV is the change in velocity, T is the transfer time, P is the orbit period, the values of μ for principal solar system objects are given in Table 2-2 and the subscripts L, H, and T refer to the lower circular orbit, higher circular orbit, and Hohmann transfer orbit, respectively. For transfers between orbits at nearly the same altitude, the equations for the ΔV and transfer time may be further simplified to:

$$\Delta V_L \approx \Delta V_H \approx \frac{1}{2}(V_L - V_H) \tag{2-72}$$

$$T \approx \frac{1}{4}(P_L + P_H) \tag{2-73}$$

where the subscripts have the same meaning as above. Finally, if the initial orbit is circular and the magnitude of a single ΔV burn is known, then:

$$\Delta a = 2a\frac{\Delta V}{V} = 2\Delta V a^{3/2} \mu^{-1/2} \tag{2-74}$$

$$\Delta H = 2\,\Delta a \tag{2-75}$$

where Δa is the change in semimajor axis due to the single burn and ΔH is the corresponding change in altitude which will occur 180 deg away from where the burn was made.

A Hohmann transfer orbit from a higher orbit to a lower orbit is simply the reverse of the above process. The first burn is opposite the direction of motion and lowers perigee to the altitude of the inner orbit. When perigee is reached, 180 deg later, a second ΔV is applied, also opposite the direction of motion, to lower apogee and to circularize the orbit. Thus it takes the same total ΔV to go from a high orbit to a low one as from a low orbit to a high one. Although we may at times use mechanisms such as atmospheric drag to slow the spacecraft, the fundamental problem of going to a lower energy orbit is just as difficult as going to a higher energy orbit.

Another interesting characteristic can be seen from Eqs. 2-68 to 2-73. If we start in a circular orbit with a velocity of 7 km/s and **add** 1 km/s in a two-burn Hohmann transfer then we will end up in a higher orbit with a velocity of 6 km/s. By adding energy to the orbit, more of the energy has been transferred into potential energy, and the total kinetic energy has been reduced. Similarly, if we go from a high orbit to a lower one, we will reduce the velocity and the total energy, but will end up in a lower orbit at a higher velocity and higher kinetic energy.

Most practical orbit transfers are relatively close to a Hohmann transfer because of the need to maximize efficiency. Nonetheless, as shown in Fig. 2-32 and listed in Table 2-16, alternative direct transfer orbits are used from time to time. Fig. 2-32A shows the classical Hohmann transfer. Fig. 2-32B shows a high-energy transfer which takes less time, but requires a higher ΔV. In the first burn, the ΔV will be higher because apogee will be above the higher orbit. In the second burn, the ΔV will also be higher because we will need to change both the magnitude and the direction of the velocity. There are two practical applications for the high-energy transfer, one is for simply hitting a target in the higher orbit rather than matching velocities with it, since the second ΔV is not necessary in this case. The other application is when transfer time is critical and more rapid transfers are necessary.

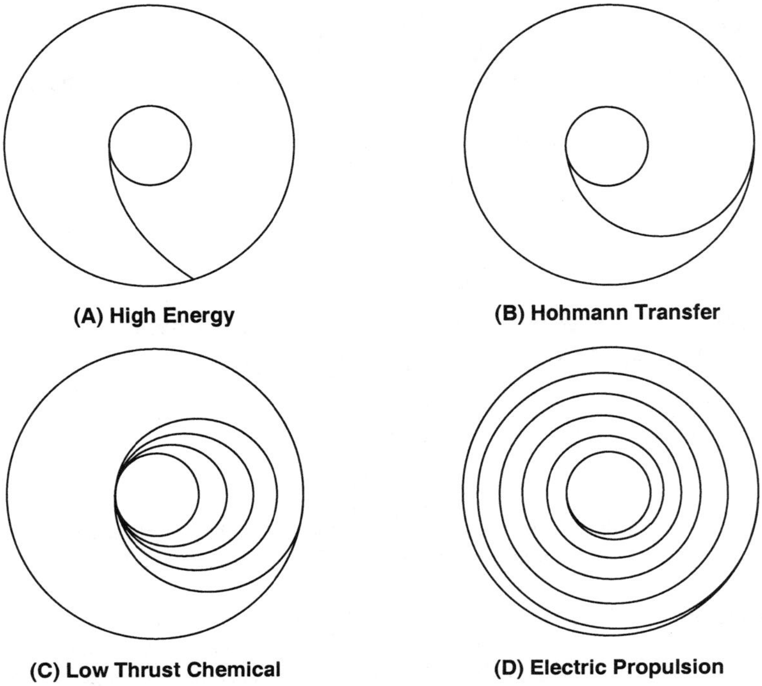

Fig. 2-32. Alternative Direct Transfer Orbits. See Table 2-16 for characteristics and Table 12-20 for advantages and disadvantages.

TABLE 2-16. Physical Characteristics of the Alternative Transfer Trajectories Shown in Fig. 2-32. (See Table 12-20 in Sec. 12.6 for advantages and disadvantages.)

Transfer Type	Orbit Type	Typical Acceleration	ΔV	Typical Transfer Time
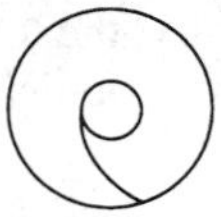 High Energy	Elliptical or hyperbolic	10 g	> Hohmann	< T
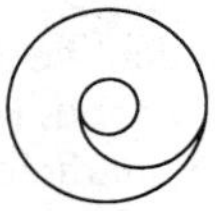 Hohmann (minimum energy, high thrust)	Hohmann transfer	1 to 5 g	Eqs. (2-69), (2-70), (2-72)	T= 1/2 orbit period, P is given by Eq. (2-71) and (2-73)
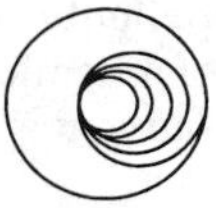 Low thrust chemical	Hohmann transfer segments	0.02 to 0.5 g	Same as Hohmann	3 to 4 times P = 6 to 8 times T
 Electric propulsion	Spiral transfer	0.0001 to 0.001g	Eq. (2-76)	60 to 120 times P

Both the Hohmann transfer and high-energy transfer assume impulsive burns, i.e., rocket engines which are large enough that the ΔV is applied over a short period of time. Alternatively, as described in Sec. 12.6, there can be significant advantages to using smaller rocket engines and applying the ΔV over a longer period such that the burn time is no longer short relative to the orbit period. Two specific cases are of practical interest. Fig. 2-32C shows the orbit path for a low-thrust chemical transfer in which rocket engines from the size of a few pounds to a few hundred pounds of thrust are used. In this case, the ΔV for a large orbit transfer cannot be applied in a single orbit, but must instead be applied over several orbits. First, a series of burns is made at successive perigees, such that the perigee height remains essentially unchanged, but the apogee height is raised by each maneuver until it ultimately reaches the desired final apogee. Then one or two burns are used at apogee to raise perigee to the circular orbit height. (Fewer burns are needed at apogee than at perigee because the spacecraft is moving at a lower velocity there.) For the low-thrust chemical transfer, the time for the transfer covers several orbits, and can be determined by adding up the orbit periods using Eq. (2-52). The total ΔV that is required is identical to the ΔV used in the Hohmann transfer. Consequently the low-thrust chemical approach has the same optimal transfer efficiency as the Hohmann transfer, but a significantly lower thrust and, therefore, lower acceleration using a smaller engine and providing smaller disturbance forces on the spacecraft.

Finally, Fig. 2-32D shows the characteristics for electric propulsion transfer. Electric propulsion thrusters are much smaller than chemical ones, with thrust levels that are only a small fraction of a pound. Consequently, it is not practical for any large transfer to be done with burns only at perigee because the transfer time would be excessively long. In this case, the ΔV is applied continuously for the entire period of the orbit transfer. Because the thrust is very low, transfer from low-Earth orbit to geosynchronous orbit still takes many months rather than the few hours required for a Hohmann transfer. In addition, because apogee and perigee are being raised simultaneously, the electric propulsion transfer is significantly less efficient than the Hohmann transfer for large maneuvers, such as transfer to GEO. Specifically, the total ΔV required to transfer between coplanar circular orbits via spiral electric propulsion is given by:

$$\Delta V_T = V_L - V_H \tag{2-76}$$

where the parameters have the same definitions as above. Note once again that we are adding velocity to the orbit to get to a lower final velocity but higher energy orbit. For the ultra low-thrust transfer, transfer time is longer and the ΔV is greater. Nonetheless electric propulsion is inherently much more efficient than chemical propulsion and, therefore, can use a much lower propellant mass. *(I_{sp},* a measure of propellant efficiency, is 5 to 10 times higher for electric propulsion systems than for chemical propulsion.) See Sec. 12.6 for further discussion of the advantages and disadvantages of the different methods of orbit transfer.

2.6.2 Plane Change and Phase Shifts

The previous section described transfer orbits which changed the total energy of the orbit itself. However, we may wish to change the orbit without changing the semimajor axis or the total energy. The two most common transfers in which this is done are changing the orbit plane (i.e., the inclination or the right ascension of the ascending node) or leaving the orbit the same and simply changing where we are in the orbit (i.e., moving forward or backward relative to an imaginary satellite which remains in the original orbit position).

Changing the orbit plane is required when the desired orbit plane is different from where we are initially. For example, in going from the Earth to Mars, we need to change the plane of the spacecraft from the Earth's orbital plane, i.e., the ecliptic, to the orbit plane of Mars. Similarly, for a spacecraft launched from anywhere not on the equator and, therefore, at a nonzero inclination, we need to make a plane change in order to put the spacecraft into geosynchronous orbit. In both of these examples, as in many plane change maneuvers, the need for the plane change occurs at the same time that the semimajor axis is to be changed. Consequently, combined plane-change and orbit-raising maneuvers are common.

As shown in Fig. 2-33, plane change maneuvers are simply a matter of vector addition. We have a velocity vector, V_i, which defines the initial orbit plane, and need to obtain a different velocity, V_f, to define a different orbit plane and potentially a different semimajor axis. Combining a plane change with an altitude change is more efficient in terms of the total ΔV than doing the two maneuvers separately. (See Fig. 2-34.) Also, the ΔV required to undertake a plane change will be proportional to the velocity itself. Consequently, because spacecraft velocities are very large, plane change maneuvers typically require a very large ΔV, sometimes as much or more than the original orbital velocity. This implies that plane change maneuvers are highly energy intensive and will usually be undertaken only when absolutely necessary. Normally plane changes are done only once in the course of a mission and everything possible is done to reduce the ΔV required for the plane change.

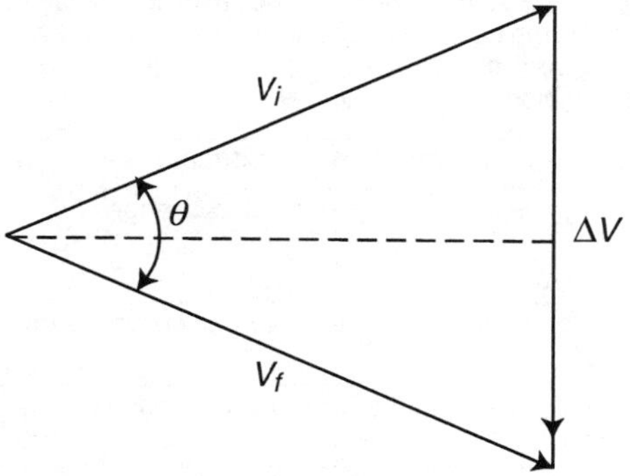

Fig. 2-33. Plane Change ΔV. Plane change maneuvers are simply problems in vector addition.

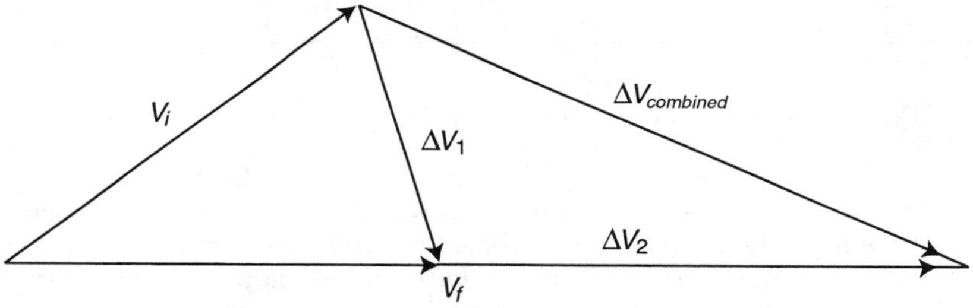

Fig. 2-34. Combining Plane Change and Orbit Raising Reduces the Total ΔV Required. The savings will be $|\Delta V_1| + |\Delta V_2| - |\Delta V_{combined}|$.

Because the plane change is simply a vector sum, we can determine the total ΔV required as a function of the initial and final velocities as:

$$\Delta V = \left(V_i^2 + V_f^2 - 2V_i V_f \cos\theta\right)^{1/2} \tag{2-77}$$

where V_i is the initial velocity, V_f is the final velocity, and θ is the required angular change. If V_i equals V_f, then the magnitude of the required ΔV reduces to:

$$\Delta V = 2V_i \sin\left(\theta/2\right) \tag{2-78}$$

As shown in Table 2-17, there are a number of mechanisms that are used to reduce the total ΔV needed for orbit plane changes. In addition to combining the ΔV with orbit raising, it is clear from the above equations that we should also do plane change maneuvers at the lowest velocity and, therefore, at the highest altitude in the orbit. Consequently, plane change maneuvers are typically done predominately at apogee.*

---

* Part of the plane change will be done at perigee because a small amount of plane change takes very little ΔV. The correct ratio is determined by trial and error with Eq. (2-77) evaluated at apogee and perigee.

TABLE 2-17. Methods for Reducing the ΔV Required for Orbit Plane Change. It may be possible to combine techniques to increase the amount of plane change. See Table 12-20 for a discussion of the advantages and disadvantages of each. See text for discussion.

Method	Mechanism for reducing ΔV	Computations
Do ΔV at Lowest Velocity (Highest Altitude)	Smallest velocity is easiest to change.	Eqs. (2-77), (2-78)
Combine ΔV with Orbit Raising	Vector sum is less than sum of components	Eqs. (2-77), (2-78)
3-Burn Transfer	Go to high altitude where plane change ΔV is low and then lower orbit	Eqs. (2-77), (2-78)
Use Differential Node Rotation	Allow natural perturbations to change plane	Eq. (2-61a)
Aero-Assist Trajectory	Use aerodynamic forces to change direction	[Albee, et al., 1998]
Planetary Fly-By	Elastic "collision" with a planet changes direction	Sec. 2.6.3

If the plane change is very large, then it may be more efficient to use a *bielliptic* or *three burn transfer* rather than a two burn Hohmann transfer with plane change. In this case, we use the first burn to take the spacecraft to a very high altitude above the desired final orbit where the apogee velocity is very low. Here the plane change ΔV is small. At the high altitude we do a combined maneuver to raise perigee to the end altitude and change the plane. We then do a third and final burn to circularize the orbit at the final altitude. In this process we have used more than the minimum required energy to change altitude, but have still saved propellant by substantially reducing the ΔV required for the plane change.

Another technique for changing the ascending node of the orbit is to make use of the node rotation caused by the Earth's oblateness. If satellites are at different altitudes the node rotation rate will be different; the orbits will slide relative to each other in an East-West sense. Consequently, we can change that ascending node by changing the altitude, allowing differential node rotation to work, and then returning the altitude to its original value after the node has shifted as far as needed. Depending on the speed of the desired node rotation, we can use this mechanism to change the node with very small amounts of propellant.

We can also use the atmospheres of the Earth or other planets as a means of changing the orbit plane, using *aero-assist trajectories* in which aerodynamic forces on the spacecraft are used to provide a turn maneuver. Such maneuvers can be efficient, but also place additional stress on the spacecraft by applying significant aerodynamic forces. For example, Mars Global Surveyor used an aero-assist trajectory to adjust its orbit around Mars, but larger than anticipated initial forces caused the mission to be delayed to reduce further stress on the solar arrays [Albee, et al., 1998].

If we are going to change the altitude of the spacecraft then a small amount of plane change can be obtained at very low cost. This implies that when combining orbit raising and plane change it is most efficient to do some plane change at both apogee and perigee with most done at apogee. The process is optimized by iterating on the amount of plane change done at apogee and perigee to determine the total ΔV. An example of the potential savings is shown in Table 2-18.

TABLE 2-18. Alternative Approaches For Going from a 250 km Circular Orbit at 28.5 Deg Inclination to an Equatorial Geosynchronous Orbit. Because the last alternative uses the least propellant, it is essentially always used in practice.

Approach	Total ΔV (m/s)
Plane change at 300 km followed by Hohmann transfer to GEO	7.696
Hohmann transfer to GEO altitude followed by separate plane change	5.425
Combined maneuver, all plane change at perigee	6.483
Combined maneuver, all plane change at apogee	4.273
Combined maneuver, 4.0 deg plane change at perigee, 24.5 deg plane change at apogee	4.265

In addition to plane changes, spacecraft are frequently required to adjust their relative phasing in the orbit. Unlike plane changes, this requires very little ΔV and can be accomplished easily. To make the spacecraft drift relative to its nominal position we simply raise or lower the orbit to a slightly different altitude and, therefore, change the orbit period and in-track velocity. When we are done shifting it as far as we would like, we return the spacecraft to its original altitude. The transfer into a *drift orbit* can be done either using a two burn Hohmann transfer, or a single burn so that the drift orbit is elliptical, with apogee or perigee remaining at the initial altitude. In either case, the drift rate, ω_{drift}, in deg/orbit, is given by:

$$\omega_{drift} = 1{,}080 \frac{\Delta V}{V} \tag{2-79}$$

where ΔV is the applied velocity change (in either one burn or both burns) and V is the nominal orbit velocity. The total ΔV required to shift phase depends only on the drift velocity and, therefore, the time for making the phase change. Thus in total:

$$\Delta V_{total} = \Delta V_{start} + \Delta V_{stop} \tag{2-80a}$$

$$= (\omega_{drift} V) \,/\, 540 \tag{2-80b}$$

where ω_{drift} is in deg/orbit. For a satellite in geosynchronous orbit, $V = 3.0747$ km/s and consequently:

$$\Delta V_{total} = 5.6939\ \omega_{drift} \tag{2-81}$$

where ΔV is in m/s and ω_{drift} is in deg/day. Sample calculations of the ΔV required as a function of the time are given in Table 2-19.

2.6.3 Planetary Assist Trajectories

For interplanetary spacecraft, we can perform both plane change and velocity change maneuvers by one or more interactions with other planets or with the Earth. The general process of a planetary fly-by is shown in Fig. 2-35. (See Minovitch [1963].) We assume the spacecraft is initially in an orbit about the Sun a long way from any planet. With respect to the planet, the spacecraft approaches on a hyperbolic trajectory. It swings by the planet at "periplanet" and leaves on the other leg of the hyperbolic trajectory at the same velocity **with respect to the planet** at which it came

TABLE 2-19. Drift Rate and Total ΔV Required to Shift a Geosynchronous Satellite 60 deg in Longitude. In general, rapid maneuver requirements correspond to high propellant usage.

ω_{drift} (deg/day)	ΔV (m/s)	Time to Shift 60 deg (days)
1	5.7	60
2	11.4	30
6	34.2	10
10	56.9	6
30	170.8	2
60	341.6	1

in. The total angle through which the spacecraft orbit velocity has changed is known as the *turn angle*, ψ, and is the angle between the two asymptotes of the hyperbola. Because the orbit has undergone an angular change, this can be used to either change the orbit plane or increase or decrease the energy. Because Jupiter has a very large mass and, consequently, can produce a large turn angle, it is the planet most commonly used for fly-bys. Depending upon our objective, we can use a fly-by of Jupiter to increase the spacecraft velocity and therefore increase the mass or reduce the transfer time to the outer planets, to decrease the velocity and allow the spacecraft to go to the vicinity of the Sun, or to change the plane of the spacecraft's orbit to allow us to explore space in the direction of the ecliptic poles.

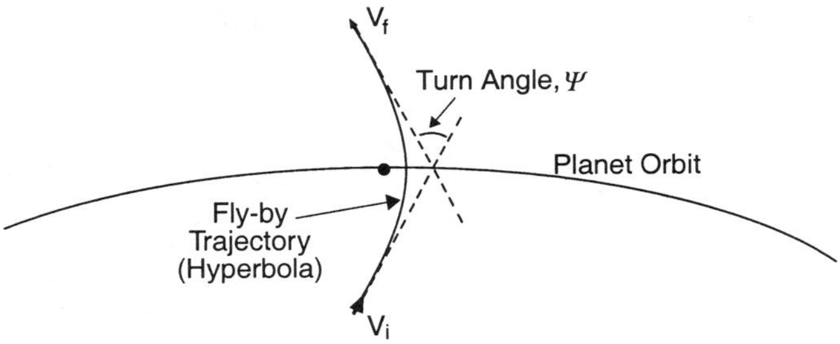

Fig. 2-35. Geometry of a Planetary Fly-By. The spacecraft velocity with respect to the planet remains the same incoming as outgoing. However, the vector sum of the planet and spacecraft velocities can be used to increase energy, decrease energy, or change direction.

A planetary fly-by is equivalent to an elastic collision between a baseball and a bat. The velocity of the baseball with respect to the bat is the same coming from the pitcher as leaving toward the outfield. The difference is that the baseball has picked up the velocity of the bat in the interaction, or in the case of a pop up, has principally changed direction.* Conceptually, we can think of the spacecraft as bouncing off the planet

* Hans Meissinger [1970] was the first to point out that the Earth could be used for a planetary fly-by. (See also Hollenbeck, [1975].) Continuing our baseball analogy, this is similar (though not mathematically equivalent) to throwing the baseball up in the air and then hitting it with the bat when it comes down.

without having to undergo the excessive acceleration associated with actually hitting the surface. Sec. 1.1.3 provides an example of several planetary fly-bys used by the Galileo mission to increase the velocity sufficiently to allow the spacecraft to explore Jupiter.

The turn angle, ψ, obtained in a planetary fly-by is:

$$\sin(\psi/2) = 1/e \tag{2-82}$$

where e is the eccentricity of the hyperbolic trajectory. This may also be expressed in a form more convenient for analysis as:

$$\sin(\psi/2) = \left(1 + \frac{V_\infty^2 q}{\mu}\right)^{-1} \tag{2-83}$$

where q is the perifocal distance or distance of closest approach to the planet, V_∞ is the hyperbolic velocity or the velocity of the spacecraft with respect to the planet when it is infinitely far away, and as usual $\mu \equiv GM$ for the planet. The magnitude of the velocity change, ΔV, resulting from the fly-by is a function of the turn angle between the two asymptotes and is given by:

$$|\Delta V| = 2V_\infty \sin(\psi/2) \tag{2-84}$$

Table 2-20 lists the values of the turn angle and velocity change for fly-bys of the principal objects of interest in the Solar System.

TABLE 2-20. Representative Turn Angle, ψ, and Velocity Change, ΔV, for Fly-by Missions to the Planets. The assumed hyperbolic verocity, V_∞, is the velocity of approach for a Hohmann transfer orbit. R_p is the radius of the planet and q is the perifocal distance or distance of closest approach.

Planet	Assumed V_∞ (km/s)	$q = R_p$ (Grazing) Ψ (deg)	$q = R_p$ (Grazing) $\|\Delta V\|$ (km/s)	$q = 2R_p$ Ψ (deg)	$q = 2R_p$ $\|\Delta V\|$ (km/s)	$q = 10\ R_p$ Ψ (deg)	$q = 10\ R_p$ $\|\Delta V\|$ (km/s)
Mercury	9.6	10.2	1.7	5.4	0.9	1.1	0.2
Venus	2.7	123	4.8	104	4.2	50	2.3
Earth	3.5	114	5.8	92	5.0	40	2.4
Moon	0.8	109	1.3	87	1.1	36	0.5
Mars	2.6	81	3.4	58	2.5	18	0.8
Jupiter	5.6	159	11.0	150	10.8	116	9.5
Saturn	5.4	146	10.3	133	9.9	86	7.4
Uranus	4.7	132	8.6	114	7.9	61	4.8
Neptune	4.1	141	7.7	127	7.3	78	5.1
Pluto	3.7	65	4.0	48	3.0	12	0.8

2.6.4 Spacecraft Disposal

Orbital debris is potentially a major problem for space missions, particularly in regions of high spacecraft density such as low-Earth orbit or geosynchronous orbit.

Consequently, spacecraft disposal is becoming a key element of mission design. NASA guidelines require that spacecraft in low-Earth orbit be removed from orbit within 25 years of the end of their useful life. Of course it is desirable to remove them from orbit much more rapidly, but it may require more propellant to do so.

There are two basic ways to deorbit a satellite in low-Earth orbit. The first approach is to lower perigee to a low enough value, approximately 75 km, that the orbit will decay and the spacecraft will reenter essentially immediately. The second approach is to reduce perigee to the point where atmospheric drag will cause the satellite to decay within an appropriate period of time, though not immediately. With this approach we will have an approximate idea of how long reentry will take, but have no way of knowing or controlling when or where it will occur. Rough estimates of the re-entry time required for representative orbits and spacecraft parameters are given in Table 2-21.

TABLE 2-21. Spacecraft Disposal Options. For perigee below approximately 75 km the spacecraft will re-enter very rapidly.

Perigee	From 600 km circular		From 1,200 km circular	
	ΔV (m/s)	Approx. Lifetime* (yr.)	ΔV (m/s)	Approx. Lifetime* (yr.)
50	157	0.033	304	0.038
75	149	0.035	297	0.039
100	142	0.038	290	0.042
125	134	0.168	282	0.629
150	127	1.686	276	6.150
200	112	14.86	261	58.02
250	97.8	46.02	247	180.9
300	83.5	143.0	233	624

*Assumes a ballistic coefficient of 100 kg/m^2

The ΔV required for a satellite to drop from an initial circular altitude H_i to a reentry perigee altitude H_e is given by

$$\Delta V_{deorbit} \approx V\left[1-\sqrt{\frac{2(\mathrm{R_E}-H_e)}{2\mathrm{R_E}+H_e+H_i}}\right] \tag{2-85a}$$

$$\approx V\left[\frac{0.5(\mathrm{H}_i-H_e)}{2\mathrm{R_E}+H_i+H_e}\right] \tag{2-85b}$$

where V is the initial satellite velocity and $\mathrm{R_E}$ is the radius of the Earth.

For high altitude orbits deorbiting the spacecraft is impractical because of the large ΔV required. Nonetheless, there is still a strong desire to remove spent spacecraft from their operational orbit, particularly if they are part of a constellation with many satellites at that altitude or part of an orbit region, such as GEO, where there are a large number of different satellites. In this case the preferred option is to raise the orbit by several hundred kilometers above the nominal value. In the regime where atmospheric drag is no longer relevant, the spacecraft will be left in an orbit where the orbit elements oscillate, but where the spacecraft will remain for thousands or hundreds of thousands of years, effectively eliminating it as a threat to other spacecraft. The disposal orbit is placed above the operational orbit so that spent spacecraft do not interfere with new operational spacecraft being brought up from the Earth. Spacecraft in disposal orbits still represent a theoretical threat to other spacecraft passing through that regime. However, this threat is dramatically reduced relative to the threat that is present if they remain in the operational orbit. In the future it may be possible to retrieve or destroy old spacecraft, but this is not a practical option at the present time.

The ΔV needed to raise a spacecraft to a higher altitude is typically very low. For example, in geosynchronous orbit the ΔV requirement is given by:

$$\Delta V_{disposal} = 0.0365 \text{ (m/s)/km} \tag{2-86}$$

Thus, an increase of 500 km above geosynchronous altitude requires a ΔV of only 18 m/s, as opposed to a deorbit ΔV of 4,000 m/s. The principal problem with any of the spacecraft disposal options is that they must be done at a time when both commanding and thruster firings can still be achieved by the spacecraft, and, therefore, at least critical spacecraft subsystems are still operating and propellant remains available.

2.7 Orbit Determination and Control

This section deals primarily with traditional, ground-based orbit determination and control techniques. Onboard and autonomous systems, such as GPS, are discussed in Chap. 4.

Unfortunately the language of orbit determination and control is still evolving as is the technology. It is important to keep in mind that different books will use the same terminology to mean very different things depending upon the context and the background in which the work is done. Throughout this volume we use *navigation** and *orbit determination* interchangeably to mean determining the satellite's position and velocity or, equivalently, its orbital elements as a function of time. We use *guidance* to mean adjusting the orbit to meet some pre-determined conditions. *Orbit maintenance* refers to maintaining the orbit elements, but not the timing of when a satellite is in a particular location in its orbit. *Stationkeeping* and *orbit control* both refer to main-

* The evolution of the terminology causes some confusion, particularly when reading older sources or references not associated with satellites. *Navigation* traditionally referred to determining how to get a craft where we wanted it to go. The term *guidance* was introduced with rockets and missiles to mean computing the steering commands needed to make the rocket go where we wanted it to (thus, a *guided* missile); *control* meant carrying out these steering commands to adjust the vehicle's direction of flight. Thus, an intercept missile would have a *guidance and control (G&C)* system, and a space plane or interplanetary spacecraft would have a *guidance, navigation, and control (GN&C)* system. However, for spacecraft we now use *navigation* to mean orbit determination, *guidance* to mean orbit control, and *control system* as a shortened form of attitude control system.

taining the satellite within a predefined moving box, which includes maintaining both the in-track position and the orbital elements. *Altitude maintenance* is an example of orbit maintenance in which occasional thruster firings are used to overcome drag and keep the orbit from spiraling downward; however, the in-track position is not controlled. *Geosynchronous stationkeeping* maintains the satellite in a box over a fixed location on the Earth. Stationkeeping in low-Earth orbit includes *constellation maintenance* in which each satellite is maintained in a moving box defined relative to the rest of the satellites in the constellation. From a satellite control perspective, stationkeeping in low-Earth orbit is conceptually equivalent to geosynchronous stationkeeping, since the relative motion of the Earth underneath has limited consequences for the astrodynamics.

2.7.1 Orbit Determination

Orbit analysis is most often done using the orbital elements discussed in previous sections. On the other hand, the results of orbit determination on real satellites are most often expressed in terms of the satellite *ephemeris*, which, as discussed earlier, is a tabular listing of the position and possibly the velocity as a function of time, usually in electronic form. It is important to distinguish the satellite ephemeris from the *solar ephemeris* which lists the representative positions of the Earth and Sun as the Earth travels in its orbit and *lunar* and *planetary ephemerides* which provide similar data for other solar system bodies. The ephermeris is used as an output format because the user can simply interpolate on the tabular values to find the position and velocity at any time and doesn't need the sophisticated orbit models used to create it. In addition, if we were to express the results of orbit determination as a set of elements, then our ability to reconstruct the actual orbit would depend on our using the same mathematical model used for the orbit determination process. For example, the orbit elements do not tell us how much drag is acting on the satellite or how the level of drag varies with time. Thus, the ephemeris is the least ambiguous method of accurately defining the motion of a real satellite.

There are two types of orbit determination, differentiated by timing. *Real-time orbit determination* provides the best estimate of where a satellite is at the present time, and may be important for operations such as thruster firing or accurate pointing at a target. *Definitive orbit determination* is the best estimate of the satellite's position and orbital elements at some earlier time. It is done after gathering and processing all relevant observations. Because interpolation is inherently more accurate than extrapolation, definitive orbit determination is more accurate when it is based on data both before and after the time at which accurate positions are needed.

Orbit propagation refers to integrating the equations of motion to determine where a satellite will be at some other time. Usually orbit propagation refers to looking ahead in time from when the data was taken. It is used either for planning or for operations. Occasionally orbits will be propagated backward in time, either to determine where a satellite was in the past or examine historical astronomical observations in the case of comets or planets.

Traditionally, ground stations around the world provide tracking data to a mission-operations center. When all the data is available, definitive orbit determination provides a best estimate of the orbit. This is used to process the payload data for science or observation missions. The best estimate of the orbit is then propagated forward for real-time operations (such as star catalog selection, payload pointing, or maneuver timing) and farther forward for mission planning. As discussed in Chap. 4, the use of GPS in low-Earth orbit and autonomous navigation in various orbits is changing this traditional process in ways that will significantly reduce the cost of satellite operations.

The specific algorithms for orbit determination are beyond the scope of this section, and are discussed at length in the astrodynamics texts listed in Sec. 2.8. Battin [1999], Escobal [1965], and Vallado [2001] provide particularly complete treatments. In practice, most modern orbit determination is done by large software systems, using some type of filtering to smooth large amounts of observation data. Traditionally, navigation or orbit determination have been ground processes. However with modern onboard processors, it is possible to undertake these same activities on board the spacecraft. One of the major advantages of doing the work on board is that the need for orbit propagation into the future is greatly reduced because the current position of the spacecraft is available on a continuing basis onboard. In principle, this should significantly reduce the orbit determination accuracy requirements. However with the continually growing demand for more precise position determination, this has typically not occurred.

In general, defining the orbit requires us to determine the six orbital elements or equivalently, the position and velocity at any instant in time. The most common methods for doing this are listed in Table 2-22, and illustrated in Fig. 2-36. Although these are the usual approaches, other alternatives are possible. For example, the New Millennium Program determines the orbit of interplanetary spacecraft by tracking the apparent positions of asteroids. We could also track the apparent positions of natural satellites of the planets when we are in the vicinity of a planetary system. Alternatively, we could do beacon tracking of other spacecraft or track beacons on the ground specifically established for this purpose. Here we will describe the process of determining the orbit elements given measurements of the position and velocity and determining the position and velocity at any time when the orbital elements are known.

TABLE 2-22. The Most Common Measurement Sets Used for Orbit Determination.

	Measurement Set	Typical Application	Where Discussed
1	Position and velocity at one time	Injection from the launch vehicle; results of a maneuver	Sec. 2.7.1
2	3 or more distinct observations of direction with respect to the background stars	Traditionally used for comets and asteroids	Escobal [1965] or Roy [1991]
3	Sequence of range and range rate measurements	Used in ground tracking systems	Bate, et al. [1971], Sec. 2.7
4	Sequence of position observations	GPS-based orbit determination	Sec. 4.2
5	Sequence of observations of the inertial direction and distance to a nearby central body	Basis of most optical autonomous navigation	Sec. 4.3

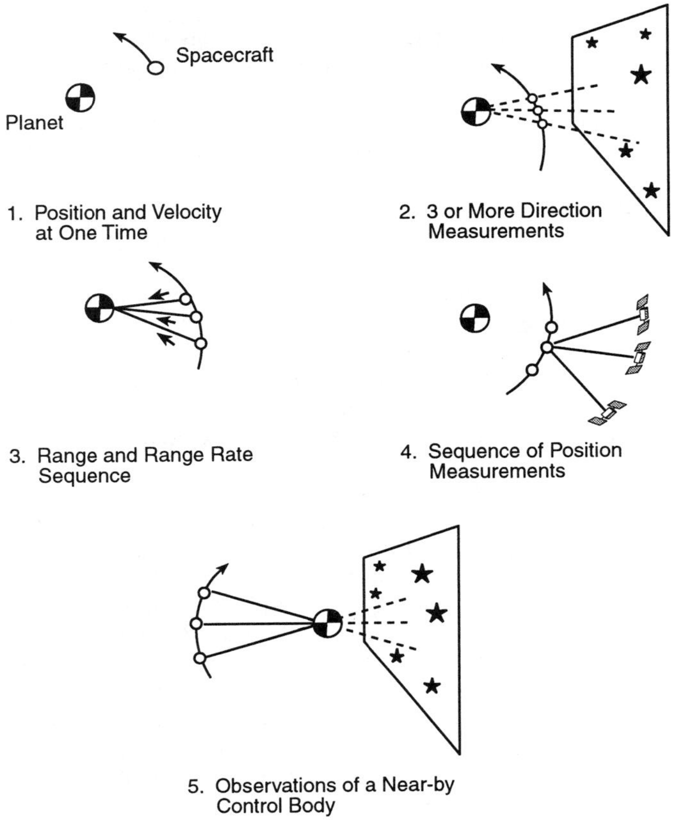

Fig. 2-36. Basic Techniques of Orbit Determination. See Table 2-22 for discussion.

2.7.1.1 Determining the Orbit Elements from the Position and Velocity

Given the position and velocity at any time, we can determine in principle the orbital elements, and from that, the position and velocity at all future times. In practice we are limited by both the accuracy of the orbit determination process, and by the accuracy with which the forces on the spacecraft are known. Generally the problem is much easier for interplanetary travel, since the forces are predominantly point-mass gravitational forces and the positions of the Sun and planets are extremely well known.

For precise computations, sophisticated orbit determination routines are needed because of the difference between osculating and mean orbit elements as described in Sec. 2.1. The biggest problem with determining the elements is that the errors grow with time, and therefore, very precise orbit propagation is required in order to determine where a real spacecraft will be at some future time. However, for many orbits and for most aspects of orbit analysis, simple computations can provide good approximations of the final results, and can correctly indicate the magnitude and approximate character of the orbit and the results of orbit maneuvers.

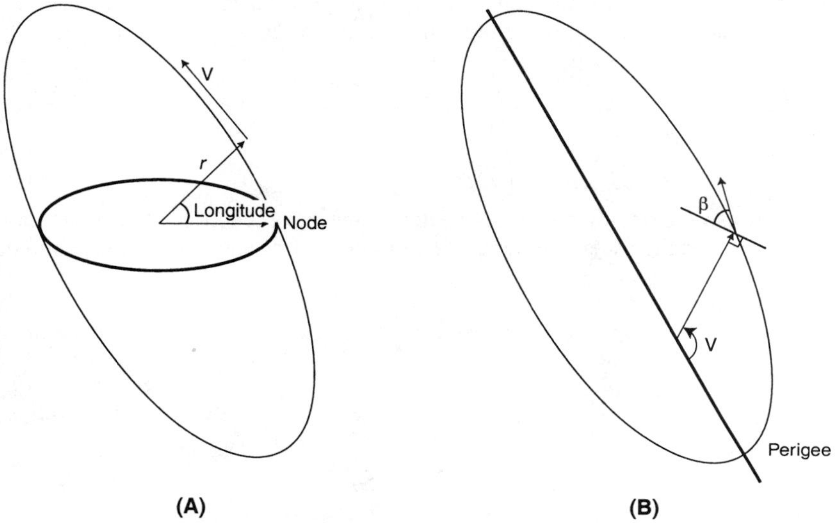

Fig. 2-37. Determining Orbit Elements from Position and Velocity. The Total Energy Determines the Semimajor Axis. (A) The position and velocity vectors determine the plane of the orbit and the right ascension of the ascending node. (B) The flight path angle, β, then determines the eccentricity, true anomaly, and argument of perigee.

The basic geometry of determining the orbit elements from the position, $\mathbf{r}$, and velocity, $\mathbf{V}$, is shown in Fig. 2-37. First we find the magnitude of the position and the velocity vectors as:

$$r = |\mathbf{r}|$$
$$V = |\mathbf{V}| \tag{2-87}$$

we next determine the orbit angular momentum, $\mathbf{h}$, and the vector to the ascending node, $\mathbf{N}$:

$$\mathbf{h} = \mathbf{r} \times \mathbf{V}$$
$$\mathbf{N} = \hat{\mathbf{z}} \times \hat{\mathbf{h}} = \hat{\mathbf{z}} \times \mathbf{h} / |\mathbf{h}| \tag{2-88}$$
$$\hat{\mathbf{N}} = \mathbf{N} / |\mathbf{N}|$$

where $\hat{\mathbf{z}}$ is the unit vector normal to the equatorial plane. The *eccentricity vector*, $\mathbf{e}$, which lies in the direction of perigee and has a magnitude equal to the eccentricity is given by:

$$\mathbf{e} = \frac{\mathbf{V} \times \mathbf{h}}{\mu} - \frac{\mathbf{r}}{r} \tag{2-89}$$

The above expressions determine the fundamental directions in space. To find the semimajor axis we first find the total energy as:

$$E = \frac{V^2}{2} - \frac{\mu}{r} \tag{2-90}$$

where as usual $\mu \equiv GM$ for the central body. From Eq. (2-90), we can determine the semimajor axis, a, for an ellipse or the semi-parameter, p, for a hyperbola, as:

$$a = -\frac{\mu}{2E} = \left(\frac{2}{r} - \frac{V^2}{\mu}\right)^{-1} \tag{2-91}$$

$$p = |\mathbf{h}|^2 / \mu \tag{2-92}$$

We then use the vector quantities to determine the eccentricity, e, inclination, i, right ascension of the ascending node, Ω, argument of perigee, ω, and true anomaly, ν, by:

$$e = |\mathbf{e}| \tag{2-93}$$

$$\cos i = h_z / |\mathbf{h}| \tag{2-94}$$

$$\tan \Omega = N_y / N_x \tag{2-95}$$

$$\cos\omega = \hat{\mathbf{e}} \cdot \hat{\mathbf{N}} = \mathbf{e} \cdot \hat{\mathbf{N}} / e \tag{2-96}$$

$$\cos\nu = \hat{\mathbf{r}} \cdot \hat{\mathbf{e}} = \mathbf{r} \cdot \mathbf{e} / (er) \tag{2-97}$$

In this set i is defined over the range –90 deg to +90 deg, Ω is defined over the range 0 to 360 deg and can be determined using the atan2 function. The argument of perigee ω will be between 0 and 180 deg when $(\hat{\mathbf{N}} \times \mathbf{e})\ \mathbf{h} > 0$ and between 180 and 360 deg when this quantity is less than zero. Similarly, the true anomaly, ν, will be between 0 and 180 deg when $(\mathbf{e} \times \mathbf{r})\ \mathbf{h} > 0$ and between 180 and 360 deg when this quantity is less than zero. From these values, all of the other orbit parameters can be determined using the equations in Table 2-4.

2.7.1.2 Determining Position and Velocity from the Orbital Elements

We now wish to solve the reverse problem of the previous section. Given the orbital elements at any one time, we want to determine the elements at all future times, and from them, the position and velocity at future times.* In the absence of perturbations, the only element which changes with time is the true anomaly, ν, or, equivalently, the mean anomaly, M. Unfortunately, as described in Sec. 2.8.1, given the true anomaly it is easy to transform orbital elements into position and velocity, but not easy to propagate over time. Conversely, the mean anomaly is easy to propagate, but difficult to transform into useful quantities. This is the classical problem for which Newton, Gauss, and Kepler worked unsuccessfully at finding closed-form solutions. The normal answer in modern computer-based systems is to integrate the equations of motion, taking into account all of the perturbing forces and handling the problem with good numerical precision. Nonetheless, simple expressions are available that give good approximations for most orbits. [See Eqs. (2-12a) to (2-14) in Sec. 2.1.5 and the corresponding equations for parabolic and hyperbolic orbits in App. D.]

Once we have found the true anomaly, ν, at the time in question, it is straightforward to find the position and velocity in inertial space. We begin in the *perifocal coordinate system* in which the orbit plane is the x/y plane with the x axis in the

---

* For simplicity, we describe here only the case of elliptical or circular orbits. The relevant equations for parabolic and hyperbolic orbits are given in App. D.

direction of perigee. As defined in Sec. 2.1.1, the *semiparameter*, p, is the perpendicular distance from the center of mass to the orbit, measured perpendicular to the major axis, i.e., along the y axis in the perifocal system. In terms of other elements, the semiparameter is given by:

$$p = b^2 / a = a(1 - e^2) \tag{2-98}$$

where, as usual, a is the semimajor axis, b is the semiminor axis, and e is the eccentricity.

Using the subscript *pf* for the perifocal coordinate system, the position coordinates, $r_{x\text{-}pf}$ and $r_{y\text{-}pf}$, are given by:

$$r_{x\text{-}pf} = p \cos \nu / (1 + e \cos \nu) \tag{2-99a}$$

$$r_{y\text{-}pf} = p \sin \nu / (1 + e \cos \nu) \tag{2-99b}$$

and the velocity components, $V_{x\text{-}pf}$ and $V_{y\text{-}pf}$, are given by:

$$V_{x\text{-}pf} = -\sqrt{\mu / p}\, \sin \nu \tag{2-100a}$$

$$V_{y\text{-}pf} = \sqrt{\mu / p}\, (e + \cos \nu) \tag{2-100b}$$

where $\mu \equiv GM$ is the gravitational constant of the central body. Note that here p is the semiparameter and not the orbit period, P.

Given the coordinates in the perifocal coordinate system, it remains to transform them into inertial coordinates (using the subscript int), by:

$$\mathbf{r}_{\text{int}} = \mathrm{C}_{\text{pf-int}}\, \mathbf{r}_{\text{pf}} \tag{2-101a}$$

and

$$\mathbf{r}_{\text{int}} = \mathrm{C}_{\text{pf-int}}\, \mathbf{r}_{\text{pf}} \tag{2-102a}$$

where the coordinate transformation, $\mathrm{C}_{\text{pf-int}}$, is given by:

$$\mathrm{C}_{\text{pf-int}} = \begin{bmatrix} \cos\Omega \sin\omega & -\cos\Omega\sin\omega & \sin\Omega \sin i \\ -\sin\Omega\sin\omega\cos i & -\sin\Omega\cos\omega\cos i & \\ \sin\Omega\cos\omega & -\sin\Omega\sin\omega & -\cos\Omega\sin i \\ +\cos\Omega\sin\omega\cos i & +\cos\Omega\cos\omega\cos i & \\ \sin\omega\sin i & \cos\omega\sin i & \cos i \end{bmatrix} \tag{2-103}$$

where i is the inclination, ω is the argument of perigee, and Ω is the right ascension of the ascending note. See App. D for the relevant formulas for parabolic and hyperbolic orbits.

2.7.2 Orbit Maintenance and Control

Previous sections have presented the relevant ΔV equations for orbit maintenance and control. This section discusses when orbit control is necessary, and what options are available to achieve it. Chap. 4 discusses the process of autonomous orbit maintenance and control as part of autonomous spacecraft systems.

Most small spacecraft do not require orbit maintenance or control and have no onboard propulsion. This has the advantage of eliminating one spacecraft subsystem and therefore reducing the overall cost, weight, and complexity. However, once the spacecraft is separated from the launch vehicle or upper stage, no further control of the satellite orbit is possible, and it will be subject to drag and orbit decay in low-Earth orbit, and cumulative secular perturbations in all orbits. Usually this is acceptable only for satellites that will last a few years or less, but may be acceptable for longer periods in some cases. For example, the Voyager spacecraft, having left the solar system, will be uncontrolled indefinitely. However, at this time the only real objective is to maintain communications, and to some degree sample the interstellar medium.

It is not necessary to have a propulsion system in order to do orbit maintenance. Space Telescope for example, does orbit maintenance by occasional repositioning with the Space Shuttle Orbiter at the same time that instrument exchanges are made. This was done to eliminate the potential for contamination and also the small disturbance due to propellant slosh. Some small spacecraft use the attitude of the solar arrays to provide drag control. In addition, however, for most spacecraft orbit maintenance or control requires the use of onboard propulsion.

Orbit maintenance will be required whenever there is a need to adjust or maintain the orbit elements over the life of a mission, i.e., if the long term secular drift resulting from orbit perturbations and initialization errors is unacceptable. In general, orbit control is needed when any of the following is required:

- *Targeting to achieve an end orbit or position*—as in a satellite rendezvous or interplanetary missions
- *To maintain absolute or relative orientations*—such as geosynchronous stationkeeping or constellation maintenance in low-Earth orbit

Targeting to achieve a particular orbit or location in space is the most common reason for orbit control. Typically, we achieve the orbit objectives with one or two large maneuvers using several small maneuvers in between or near the end for fine adjustments. For example, in transfer to geosynchronous orbit, the initial large maneuver occurs at perigee in low-Earth orbit. A second large maneuver follows at apogee near geosynchronous altitude. Finally, several small orbit maneuvers over an extended period place the satellite in its final position. This has traditionally been done using large high-thrust engines for the major maneuvers, and smaller engines for fine orbit adjustments. However, as described in Sec. 2.6, low-thrust engines can often be used efficiently for large ΔVs. This typically means small, lighter, less expensive engines and much smaller, simpler control systems. Propulsive maneuvers usually are the largest attitude disturbance on the spacecraft and, therefore, affect the required size and speed of the attitude control system. Small thrusters can reduce the weight, complexity, and cost of other components as well as the propulsion system itself.

Typically, major orbit changes occur during the early phases of a mission, but they can occur throughout the spacecraft life. For example, many geosynchronous spacecraft are shifted at various times during their lifetime, such that the longitude is adjusted to meet changing needs, or if the spacecraft is sold. Spacecraft can also be retargeted to achieve new objectives, such as the retargeting of ISEE-C spacecraft to rendezvous with Comet Giacobini-Zinner in 1985. The need for maneuvers of this type may arise after the spacecraft has been launched. They are not planned in advance, but simply take advantage of existing resources. Finally, as described in Sec. 2.6.4, it is becoming more critical to use an end-of-life maneuver for spacecraft disposal either by deorbiting from low-Earth orbit or raising to a higher orbit in medium altitude or geosynchronous orbit.

Nearly all constellations require some type of orbit maintenance or control to prevent collisions between satellites and to maintain the constellation pattern over time. In principle, we could use *relative stationkeeping*, in which we maintain the relative positions between satellites but not their absolute position. In practice, however, this makes orbit maintenance more complex and does not save propellant or reduce the number of computations or burns. In a low-Earth orbit constellation with relative stationkeeping we would, in principle, maintain all satellites in the constellation to decay at the same rate as the slowest decaying satellite at any time. But the entire constellation would still decay in the process. Therefore, it would slowly change its altitude, and would need to be reboosted at some later time.

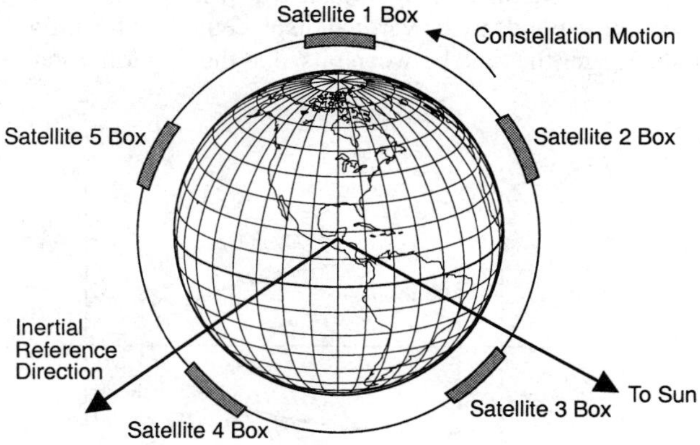

Fig. 2-38. Stationkeeping Maintains a Satellite Within a "Box" which is Moving in a Predefined Pattern in Inertial Space.

The alternative is *absolute stationkeeping*, shown in Fig. 2-38. Here we maintain each spacecraft within a mathematically defined box moving with the constellation pattern. As long as we maintain the constellation altitude, absolute stationkeeping is more efficient than relative stationkeeping, because the satellite is always at its highest altitude where atmospheric drag is least. All in-track stationkeeping maneuvers are done firing in the direction of motion to put back energy taken out by atmospheric drag. We put in more or less energy at any given time, depending on the atmospheric density and the amount of drag. The amount of drag makeup for any satellite in the constellation depends on the satellite's observed drift relative to its assigned box. At the forward edge of the box, the applied ΔV is increased, thus increasing the orbit altitude and period and sliding the satellite rearward in phase relative to the box. Similarly, at the trailing edge, the applied ΔV is decreased, thus decreasing the altitude and period and sliding the satellite forward in phase. Because of the high spacecraft velocities in low-Earth orbit, timekeeping is critical to maintaining the satellites' relative positions. A 1 sec difference in time corresponds to a 7 km difference in in-track position. Maintaining the time on board the satellite to the required accuracies is important, but not difficult.

Although the perturbative forces are different, constellation maintenance in low-Earth orbit is analogous to stationkeeping in geosynchronous orbit. *In-track* and *cross-track orbit maintenance* in low-Earth orbit, correspond respectively to east-west and north-south stationkeeping in geosynchronous orbit. When this activity is done from the ground, the fundamental goal is to minimize the number of stationkeeping maneuvers and maximize the time between them. The logic of doing this is shown in Fig. 2-39 which is applicable to either in-track stationkeeping in low-Earth orbit or north-south and east-west stationkeeping in geosynchronous orbit. In these cases the secular perturbative force is always in the same direction. Consequently, we allow the spacecraft to slide toward one end of the stationkeeping box, and then apply a ΔV such that it begins to drift in the opposite direction. The perturbative force slows the drift, brings the satellite back toward the original end where the ΔV is applied again and the process is repeated. Physically this is equivalent to keeping a ping-pong ball in the air by continuously hitting it with a paddle. We bat it upward with the paddle, gravity slows it, stops it, and eventually brings it back down, where we hit it again. The stationkeeping box corresponds to the vertical displacement of the ping-pong ball. The harder we hit it, the longer the time between hits, and the larger the stationkeeping box will need to be.

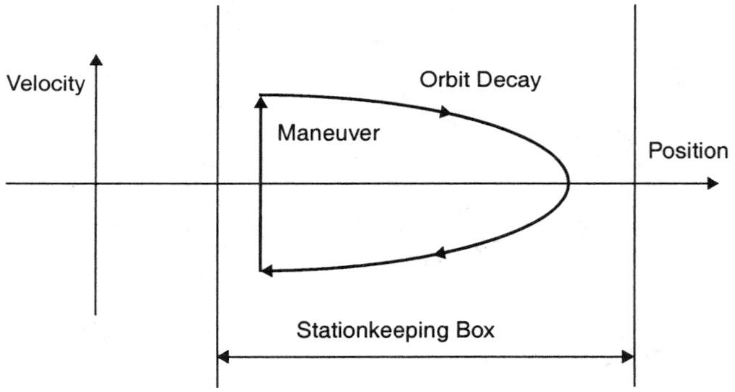

Fig. 2-39. Representative Stationkeeping Maneuver Timeline. In stationkeeping from the ground, the goal is to minimize the number of stationkeeping maneuvers and maximize the time between them. As discussed in Chap. 4, a different logic prevails for autonomous stationkeeping.

As described in Chap. 4, this process of maximizing the time between stationkeeping maneuvers is no longer a key factor when orbit control is done onboard the spacecraft. In this case, we are much more interested in minimizing the size of the stationkeeping box, minimizing propellant utilization, or maintaining other orbit characteristics, such as zero eccentricity. In the onboard orbit control process, this is done simply by adjusting the timing and magnitude of the stationkeeping thruster firings.

2.8 Spacecraft Orbit Bibliography

Astrodynamics, General

There are many good books available in this area. New volumes are forthcoming regularly.

Bate, Roger R., Donald D. Mueller, and Jerry E. White. 1971. *Fundamentals of Astrodynamics.* NY: Dover Publications. 455 p.

An older treatment, but a bargain price (~$10); well worth the money.

Battin, Richard H. 1999. *Introduction to the Mathematics and Methods of Astrodynamics.* Washington, DC: AIAA. 250 p.

The complete standard reference; very mathematical.

Bond, Victor R. and Mark C. Allman. 1996. *Modern Astrodynamics: Fundamentals and Perturbation Methods.* Princeton, NJ: Princeton University Press. 250 p.

A careful mathematical development of the two-body equations of motion with an emphasis on perturbation theory.

Chobotov, Vladimir A. 1996. *Orbital Mechanics* (2nd ed). Washington, DC: AIAA. 365 p.

One of the best overall modern treatments of practical spacecraft astrodynamics; Revised and somewhat expanded from the first edition. Includes new material on space debris, orbit coverage, and a PC educational software disk.

Danby, J.M.A. 1992. *Fundamentals of Celestial Mechanics.* Richard, VA: Willman-Bell. 483 p.

An introductory text in celestial mechanics, oriented toward numerical astronomy rather than spaceflight. Provides good mathematical background material and discussions of many numerical procedures. An extensive set of appendices with both mathematical methods and data, including series expansions for the orbital elements of the planets.

Logsdon, Tom. 1998. *Orbital Mechanics: Theory and Applications.* NY: John Wiley and Sons. 268 p.

A general introduction to orbital mechanics using very limited mathematics. Provides good physical insight for the non-engineering reader. Discusses astrodynamics, rockets and boosters, selecting orbit and constellation architecture, and advanced technology transportation systems.

Madonna, Richard G. 1997. *Orbital Mechanics.* Malabar, FL: Krieger Publishing Co. 126 p.

Introductory textbook on orbital mechanics. Emphasizes applications rather than derivations. Somewhat expensive for the length.

Prussing John E. and Bruce A. Conway. 1993. *Orbital Mechanics*. NY: Oxford University Press. 194 p.

Introductory text on orbital mechanics for seniors or first year graduate students.

Roy, A. E. 1991. *Orbital Motion* (3rd ed). Bristol: Institute of Physics Publishing. 532 p.

An excellent, modern general treatment; high quality paperback version.

Seidelmann, P. Kenneth (ed.) 1992. *Explanatory Supplement to the Astronomical Almanac*. Mill Valley, CA: University Science Books. 600 p.

An excellent, detailed, complete reference for time systems, coordinate systems, and methods for Earth, Moon, and planet ephemerides; very economical for what it contains.

Szebehely, Victor G. and Hans Mark. 1998. *Adventures in Celestial Mechanics,* 2nd ed. NY: John Wiley and Sons. 310 p.

An excellent introductory text for orbital mechanics of both natural systems and spacecraft. Provides both a mathematical introduction and good physical insight into why various effects occur. Also conveys a good sense of the history of celestial mechanics and its development over time.

Vallado, David A. 2001. *Fundamentals of Astrodynamics and Applications* (2nd ed). El Segundo, CA and Dordrecht the Netherlands; Microcosm Press and Kluwer Academic. 958 p.

An excellent modern reference oriented specifically toward spacecraft orbits. Well-written, complete, with many practical methods and algorithms. Free software.

Vinti, John P. 1998. *Orbital and Celestial Mechanics*. Reston, VA: AIAA. 409 p.

Vinti presents a highly mathematical and unique approach to orbital mechanics using the Hamilton-Jacobi equation as a starting point for the "Vinti spheroidal method' for orbits and ballistic trajectories. Makes use of Lagrange and Poisson brackets and canonical transformations for the theory of general perturbations. Includes software. However, the licensing agreement which states that the software can not be sold, rented, or lent to another person is strictly enforced—i.e., the code can not be used in operational software without paying a substantial additional fee.

Wiesel, William E. 1997. *Spaceflight Dynamics* (2nd ed). Boston, MA: Irwin/McGraw-Hill. 332 p.

This book is an introductory mathematical text on both orbit and attitude dynamics. Orbit and attitude determination are discussed very briefly. Control is discussed at greater length, but not in detail. There is an extended discussion of gyros and inertial navigation, rocket performance, and reentry dynamics.

Astrodynamics, Specialized Topics

Beletsky,Vladimir V. and Evgenii M. Levin. 1993. *Dynamics of Space Tether Systems*. Vol. 83, Advances in the Astronautical Sciences. San Diego, CA: American Astronautical Society. 499 p.

An excellent and thorough discussion of space tethers. Covers both general physics and tethers and detailed discussion of particular applications—i.e., atmospheric probe, electrodynamic tether, oscillation damping, and anchored tethers.

Boulet. Dan L. 1991. *Methods of Orbit Determination for the Micro Computer*. Richmond, VA: Willman-Bell. 565 p.

Practical guide to simple orbit determination computations. Programs in BASIC intended principally for amateur astronomers, but also applicable to satellite orbits.

Brumberg, Victor A. and Eugene V. Brumberg. 1999. *Celestial Dynamics at High Eccentricities*. Amsterdam, The Netherlands: Gordon and Breach Publishers. 210 p.

This book extends the domain of analytic and semi-analytic techniques in classical celestial mechanics to the case of motion in highly eccentric orbits. This is done by replacing the traditional mean, true, and eccentric anomalies with the elliptic anomaly which allows the motion to be expressed using Fourier expansions of Jacobi elliptic functions. Provides detailed analysis for both spacecraft and asteroids in highly elliptic orbits.

Escobal, Pedro Ramon. 1965. *Methods of Orbit Determination*. Malabar, FL: Robert E. Krieger Publishing Company. 479 p.

Old, but remains excellent and appropriate; widely used. Perhaps the best available book on orbit determination.

Gurzadyan, G.A. 1996. *Theory of Interplanetary Flights*. Amsterdam, The Netherlands: Gordon and Breach Publishers. 383 p.

An excellent and very thorough text on the orbital mechanics of interplanetary spaceflight. This is an English revision of a work originally done in Russian; however, the English is excellent and the explanations very clear and easy to read. Covers multiple topics well, both in terms of mathematics and physical explanations. An excellent volume for anyone working interplanetary missions.

Hankey, Wilbur L. 1988. *Re-entry Aerodynamics*. Washington, DC: AIAA. 144 p.

Specialized reference on the reentry process.

Labunsky, A.V., O. V. Papkov, and K. G. Sukhanov. 1998. *Mutiple Gravity Assist Interplanetary Trajectories*. Williston, VT: Gordon and Breach Science Publishers. 285 p.

Most detailed discussion available of a very specialized topic area. Discusses both analytical techniques (such as optimal multi-body trajectories and navigation during near-planet segments) and specific applications (such as missions to multiple planets, multiple satellites within a planetary system, and asteroid and comet missions).

Milani, Andrea, Anna Maria Nobili, and Paolo Farinella. 1987. *Non-gravitational Perturbations and Satellite Geodesy*. Bristol, UK: Adam Hilger. 125 p.

A good discussion of using satellites for geodesy; expensive for its length.

Noton, Maxwell. 1998. *Spacecraft Navigation and Guidance*. London: Springer-Verlag. 181 p.

A condensed but thorough discussion of guidance and navigation for space vehicles. Includes discussion of the launch phase, perturbations and maneuvers for Earth satellites, mid-course maneuvers and gravity assist for interplanetary missions, low thrust missions, orbit determination, and atmospheric reentry.

Regan, Frank J. and Satya M. Anandakrishnan. 1993. *Dynamics of Atmospheric Re-entry*. Washington, DC: AIAA. 588 p.

A specialized reference, but very thorough and complete; good references and appendices.

Soop, E. M. 1994. *Handbook of Geostationary Objects*. Dordrecht, The Netherlands: Kluwer Academic Publishers. 309 p.

Detailed and complete discussion of both theory and practice of geostationary orbits.

Zarchan, Paul. 1998. *Tactical and Strategic Missile Guidance,* 3rd ed. Reston, VA: AIAA. 611 p.

Basics of missile guidance, homing, and proportional navigation.

Zee, Chong-Hung. 1989. *Theory of Geostationary Satellites*. Dordrecht, The Netherlands: Kluwer Academic Publishers. 267 p.

Very complete analytical treatment of geostationary orbits; relatively expensive.

Orbit Design

There is no complete treatment of this subject, although some specialized topics are well covered.

Brown, Charles D. 1998. *Spacecraft Mission Design,* (2nd ed). Washington, DC: AIAA. 210 p. + software disk.

The title is misleading. This is a book on interplanetary trajectories and provides an excellent treatment of that topic.

Logsdon, Tom. 1995. *Mobile Communications Satellites: Theory and Applications*. NY: McGraw Hill. 277 p.

Chap. 6 provides a good semi-technical discussion of constellation design.

Pocha, J.J. 1987. *Introduction to Mission Design for Geostationary Satellites*. Dordrecht, The Netherlands: Kluwer Academic Publishers. 222 p.

Very good, practical discussion of geostationary orbit design.

Teles, Jerome (ed). 1989. *Orbital Mechanics and Mission Design*. San Diego, CA: AAS. 848 p.

A good collection of individual conference papers on this topic.

Wertz, James R., and Wiley J. Larson (eds). 1999. *Space Mission Analysis and Design*, (3rd ed). Torrance, CA, and Dordrecht, The Netherlands: Microcosm, Inc., and Kluwer Academic Publishers. 920 p.

Chap. 7 provides a complete top-level summary of the orbit design process.

References

Albee, A. L., F. D. Palluconi, and R. E. Arvidson. 1998. "Mars Global Surveyor Mission: Overview and Status," *Science*, vol. 279: pp. 1671–2, March 13.

Battin, Richard H. 1999. *Introduction to the Mathematics and Methods of Astrodynamics*. Washington, DC: AIAA.

Chobotov, Vladimir A. 1996. *Orbital Mechanics* (2nd ed). Washington, DC: AIAA.

Clarke, Arthur C. 1945. "Extra-Terrestial Relays—Can Rocket Stations Give Worldwide Coverage." *Wireless World*, October, pp. 305–307.

Dugas, René. 1955. *A History of Mechanics*. Translated into English by J.R. Maddox. Neuchatel, Switzerland: Éditions du Griffon.

Ehricke, Krafft A. 1960. *Space Flight: Environment and Celestial Mechanics*. New York: Van Nostrand Company.

Escobal, Pedro Ramon. 1965. *Methods of Orbit Determination*. Malabar, FL: Robert E. Krieger Publishing Company.

Farquhar, Robert W. 1994. "Utilization of Libration-Point Orbits, Lunar Gravity-Assist, and Earth-Return Trajectories." Proceedings of 34th Israel Annual Conference on Aerospace Sciences, Feb. 16–17, Haifa, Israel. pp. 238–245.

———. 1998. "The Flight of ISEE-3/ICE—Origins, Mission History, and a Legacy." AIAA Paper 98-994. AIAA/AAS Astrodynamics Specialist Conference and Exhibit, Aug. 10–12, Boston, MA.

Farquhar, Robert W. and David W. Dunham. 1990. "Use of Libration-Point Orbits for Space Observation." In *Observations in Earth Orbit and Beyond*. Dordrecht, The Netherlands: Kluwer Academic Publishers.

Farquhar, Robert W., Daniel P. Muhonen, and David L. Richardson. 1977. "Mission Design for a Halo Orbiter of the Earth." *Journal of Spacecraft and Rockets*, Vol. 14, No. 3, pp. 170–177. March.

Forward, R. L. 1989. "Statite: Spacecraft that Utilizes Light Pressure and Method of Use." U.S. Patent No. 5,183,225. Issued February 2, 1993.

Girvin, Harvey F. 1948. *A Historical Appraisal of Mechanics*. Scranton, PA: International Textbook Co.

Hollenbeck, G. R. 1975. "New Flight Techniques for Outer Planet Missions." AAS Paper 75-087 presented at the AAS/AIAA Astrodynamics Specialist Conference, Nassau, Bahamas, July 28–30.

Meissinger, Hans F. 1970. "Earth Swingby—A Novel Approach to Interplanetary Missions Using Electric Propulsion." AIAA Paper No. 70-1117, presented at the AIAA 8th Electric Propulsion Conference, Stanford, CA, August 31–September 2.

Minovitch, M. A. 1963. "Determination and Characteristics of Ballistic Interplanetary Trajectories under the Influence of Multiple Planetary Attractions," Technical Report No. 32-464, Jet Propulsion Laboratory.

Seidelmann, P. Kenneth (ed.) 1992. *Explanatory Supplement to the Astronomical Almanac.* Mill Valley, CA: University Science Books.Sergeyevski, Audrey B., Gerald C. Snyder, Rose A. Cunniff [1983], *Interplanetary Mission Design Handbook, Volume I, Part 2: Forth to Mars Ballistic Mission Opportunities 1990–2005*, JPL Publication 82-42.

U.S. Naval Observatory and Royal Greenwich Observatory. February 1999. *Astronomical Almanac for the Year 2000.* Washington DC: Government Printing Office.

Vallado, David A. 2001. *Fundamentals of Astrodynamics and Applications* (2nd ed). El Segundo, CA and Dordrecht the Netherlands; Microcosm Press and Kluwer Academic.

Chapter 3

Attitude Properties and Terminology

The purpose of this chapter is to provide an overview of the language, methods, and technology associated with attitude determination and control. As defined in Chap. 1, the *attitude* is the orientation of the spacecraft. *Attitude determination* is the process of using sensor data to estimate the orientation. *Attitude control* is the process of using either natural forces (*passive control*) or actuators (*active control*) to maintain or change the orientation. *Attitude propagation* is the process of using the dynamic equations of motion to determine the history of the spacecraft orientation.

The spacecraft attitude and orbit have a great deal in common. They frequently use the same sensors and actuators. If done on board, they would typically use the same processor. Nonetheless, as shown in Table 3-1, there are fundamental differences. The major one is the time scale on which they occur. Orbit control operates in the frequency regime of 10^{-4} to 10^{-5} Hz or slower. Attitude control systems operate in the 1 to 10 Hz range. This frequency difference brings about another major difference, the importance of continuous action. The timing of some orbit burns is critical, but orbit burns tend to be a long time apart. At any given time, the next orbit burn may be hours, days, or months away. Attitude adjustments, on the other hand, are essentially continuous and if, they don't occur, the results can be disastrous for the spacecraft. If the attitude system stops functioning for even a few minutes, the solar arrays will typically point away from the Sun, antennas will point away from the Earth, sensitive instruments may be pointed toward the Sun, and the entire spacecraft and mission may be lost.

Largely because of the slowness of the time scale over which action occurs, orbit control has historically been done from the ground. Although this may be changing, it is certainly the traditional pattern. Attitude control, on the other hand, is virtually always done on the spacecraft as a real-time activity. Consequently, the orbit control system typically consists of the onboard propulsion system and the ground logic

TABLE 3-1. Comparison of Orbit and Attitude Characteristics and Systems. See text for discussion.

Characteristic	Orbit	Attitude
Definition	Motion of the center of mass	Motion about the center of mass
Responds To	Forces	Torques
Typical Period	Hours to years	0.1 sec to 1 min
Control Frequency	10^{-4} to 10^{-5} Hz or slower	1 to 10 Hz
Typical Sensors	Ground tracking[1], GPS[2], autonomous optical navigation[3]	Earth, Sun, stars, magnetic field, payload targets[4]
Estimation Techniques	Deterministic, long-term filtering	Deterministic, long-term filtering
Typical Active Actuators	Rocket engines (wide range of sizes)	Magnetic torquing, thrusters
Passive Actuators	Planetary fly-by, solar radiation pressure, aerodynamics	Gravity gradient, spin stabilization, aerodynamics, solar radiation pressure
Operations	Ground controlled[5]	Autonomous, on board

[1]Typically either range and range rate from active tracking systems or passive optical or radar tracking; [2]Low-Earth orbit only; [3]Planned for future missions, not yet common. Will frequently use same sensors as attitude system; [4]Also some GPS in low-Earth orbit only; [5]Autonomous orbit control still in infancy.

needed to compute the next orbit maneuver. It is basically a ground operations activity. The attitude system, on the other hand, is a much more traditional control process with controllers operating on board the spacecraft, similar in many respects to an auto-pilot process on an airplane. One of the purposes of this book is to show how orbit and attitude are related and, if done on board, how many of the same components and systems could be used for both. We introduced this approach in Chap. 1 and will return to it again in Chap. 4.

3.1 Introduction to Attitude Systems

Spacecraft attitude systems go by a variety of names—*Attitude Control System (ACS), Attitude Determination and Control System (ADCS), Guidance Navigation and Control (GN&C),* and sometimes, just the *Control System.* We will use these terms interchangeably. In any case, whatever we call it, the purpose of the attitude system is to both measure and control the orientation of the spacecraft.

Attitude systems vary dramatically in accuracy, complexity, and cost. Nonetheless, all have the same basic components as shown in the block diagram in Fig. 3-1. This section provides an overview of each of these parts. Additional detail is provided in subsequent sections and quantitative development of the mathematical models is contained in the remaining volumes of this series.

The attitude process begins with attitude sensors used to measure the orientation of the spacecraft. These sensors fall into three broad categories.

- *Inertial sensors*, such as gyroscopes or inertial measuring units, measure the orientation or change in orientation of the spacecraft with respect to inertial space itself.

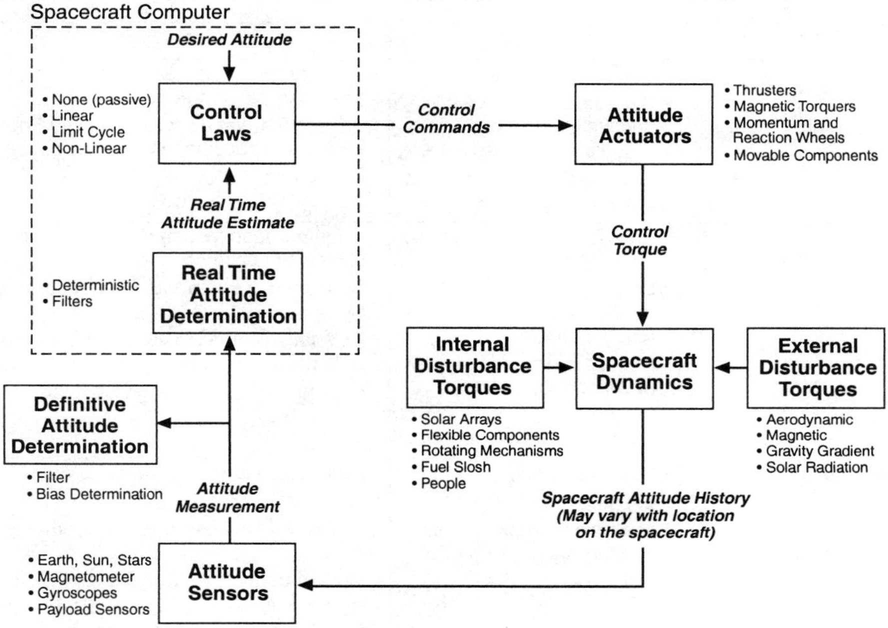

Fig. 3-1. Spacecraft Attitude System Block Diagram. See text for discussion.

- *Reference direction sensors* measure the orientation with respect to some external reference direction, such as the direction to the Sun, Earth, stars, or the orientation of the Earth's magnetic field.
- *Payload instruments*, such as directional antennas or Earth imaging payloads, carry out the fundamental space mission and can be used as a source of attitude information from the mission data.

The advantages and disadvantages of various attitude determination reference sources are summarized in Table 3-2. Typically, no one sensor can do the entire job, and a combination of sensors is normally used. For example, gyros provide rapid rate measurements and are extremely good for attitude maneuvers. However, they cannot determine the absolute attitude and must always be used in conjunction with some other sensor, such as star or Earth sensors. Payload sensors are extremely accurate and provide measurements with respect to the ultimate target of interest. However, they are not always available and do not provide the continuous attitude needed for maintaining spacecraft control. Sun and Earth sensors are excellent for acquisition, or if the spacecraft is lost, but are less accurate than needed for many applications. Among the most commonly used combinations are:

- Magnetometer and coarse Sun sensors (low accuracy, low cost)
- Earth and Sun sensors (moderate accuracy, moderate cost)
- Star sensors and gyros (high accuracy, high cost)

TABLE 3-2. Advantages and Disadvantages of Attitude Determination Reference Sources.

Reference	Advantages	Disadvantages
Sun	• Bright, unambiguous • Sensors are low power and weight • Usually must be known for solar power generation and equipment protection	• May not be visible during parts of orbit around large central body • 0.5 deg angular diameter (viewed from Earth) limits accuracy to ~1 arc min
Earth, or Other Central Body	• Always available for nearby spacecraft • Bright, largely unambiguous (may be Moon interference) • Necessary for many types of sensor and antenna coverage • Analysis relatively easy	• Requires scan motion or multiple fields of view to sense horizon • Sensors must be protected from the Sun • Resolution limited to ~0.1 deg because of horizon definition • Orbit and attitude strongly coupled
Magnetic Field	• Low-cost sensor • Light weight • Low-power requirements • Always available for low-altitude spacecraft	• Poor resolution (> 0.5 deg) • Good only near Earth • Limited by field strength and modeling accuracy • Orbit and attitude strongly coupled • Spacecraft must be magnetically clean (or inflight calibration required) • Sensitive to biases
Stars (Including Distant Planets)	• High accuracy (~10^{-3} deg) • Available anywhere in sky • Essentially orbit independent, except for velocity aberration	• Sensors heavy, complex, and expensive • Identification of stars for multiple target sensors is complex, time consuming, and may cause large errors • Sensors need protection from Sun • Double and triple stars cause problems • Usually require second attitude system for initial attitude estimates
Inertial Space (Gyroscopes; Accelerometers)	• Requires no external sensors • Orbit independent • High accuracy for limited time intervals • Easily done on board	• Senses change in orientation only — no absolute measurement • Subject to drift • Some sensors have rapidly moving parts subject to wear and friction • Relatively high power and large mass
Other Spacecraft	• Data may be available from crosslink • Moderate to high accuracy	• Requires ephemeris of both spacecraft • Narrow range • Acquisition can be difficult • Failure of one spacecraft may cause others to fail
Payload Targets	• Target is the object attitude is needed with respect to • Data available from payload sensor	• Typically narrow range • Acquisition may be difficult • Data often not continuously available • May impose added bus constraints on payload

Typically, very high accuracy systems have a narrow operating range. Consequently, they are often used in conjunction with lower accuracy systems such as Earth sensors and coarse Sun sensors which are used for both acquisition and fail-safe operations.

The next step is to process the attitude sensor measurements to do *attitude determination*, i.e., provide a numerical estimate of the spacecraft orientation. There are two broad categories of attitude determination:

- *Real-time attitude determination* is necessary for attitude control and is done immediately (i.e., in real-time) on board the spacecraft.
- *Definitive attitude determination* is frequently done after the fact and provides the most accurate available estimate of the attitude for processing payload data. This is usually done on the ground and often involves data filtering, sensor calibration, and bias determination.

Definitive attitude determination is almost always done by data *filtering* (typically using a Kalman filter) in order to provide the best possible estimates using a long span of data. Real-time attitude determination can be done either by filtering or by *deterministic* methods in which closed-form solutions are obtained based on specific sets of measurements. Filtering has the advantage of being more accurate by obtaining weighted averages over a large amount of data. However, filters can diverge in the presence of biases, data dropout, or unmodeled errors such as a thruster firing or a bright object in the sensor field of view. Deterministic solutions are generally less accurate but more stable. Nonetheless, singularities can also occur in deterministic solutions. For example, spacecraft frequently use an Earth sensor to measure the two components of where the spacecraft is pointed with respect to the Earth and a Sun sensor to measure the rotation about the vector to the center of the Earth. This fixes the 3 axes of the spacecraft, except when the Sun is at the zenith, i.e., directly opposite the direction of the center of the Earth. This occurs when the center of the Earth, the spacecraft, and the Sun all lie on a straight line. When this happens, the Sun is no longer able to provide a measure of the rotation around the line to the center of the Earth and a measurement singularity occurs. Similar singularities occur in most measurement sets and are a principal source of large attitude errors and divergence in attitude filters. Dealing with these singularities is a major part of the attitude determination process.

The result of the real-time attitude determination process is the best current estimate of the attitude. This is then compared with the desired attitude and a *control law* or correction algorithm is used to determine control commands. In older spacecraft, this was typically done in analog electronics. Today, it is done digitally in the spacecraft computer. However, many spacecraft still use simple analog control systems as a fail-safe controller in case anything goes wrong, such as a single-event upset, a power outage in the computer, or a software reset. A major advantage of attitude control in software is that it allows us to use significantly more complex control laws such that we can use simple sensors and actuators and still obtain a higher level of performance. The principal disadvantage is that it introduces all of the complexity of software design and the potential for a wide variety of new and exciting failure modes.

The simplest control law is not to have one, i.e., to design the spacecraft in such a way that it is inherently stable. This is called *passive stabilization*. As summarized in Table 3-3, there are a number of ways to achieve this. There are several advantages to passive stabilization. It doesn't break, it is typically low cost, and it may be able to last for a very long time. The principal disadvantages are that there is no control over where the spacecraft is pointed other than its original design, and the pointing accuracy is usually poor. Passive systems normally have an attitude accuracy in the range of 0.5 to 5 deg.

TABLE 3-3. Passive Stabilization Methods. These are methods in which the spacecraft is inherently stable and, therefore, require no commands and no spacecraft power or propellant for short-term stability.

Method	Advantages	Disadvantages
Spin Stabilization	• Simple • Effective nearly anywhere in any orientation • Maintains orientation in inertial space • Allows sensors to scan the sky	• Centrifugal force requires structural stability and some rigidity • Sensors and antennas cannot generally remain pointed at a specific target • Wobble (nutation) occurs if not properly balanced • Drift due to environmental torques • Sensors must scan the sky
Gravity-Gradient Stabilization	• Maintains fixed position relative to central body • Has long-term stability	• Limited to 1 or 2 possible orientations • Effective only near massive central body (e.g., Earth, Moon, etc.) • Requires long booms or elongated mass distribution • Subject to wobble (*libration*) • Control limited to ~1 deg • Problem of thermal gradients across boom • No yaw control
Solar Radiation Stabilization	• Convenient for power generation by solar cells or solar studies	• Limited to high-altitude or interplanetary orbits • Limited orientations allowed
Aerodynamic Stabilization	Special-purpose methods—Highly mission and structure dependent in all of their characteristics	
Magnetic Stabilization with Permanent Magnet		

The most common passive stabilization technique is *spin stabilization*. If the spacecraft is spinning, the conservation of angular momentum causes the direction of the spin axis to remain fixed in inertial space. This is an excellent low-cost technique, and has a number of advantages such as allowing a sensor fixed on the spacecraft to scan out the entire sky as the spacecraft rotates. Unfortunately, a spinning environment doesn't work well for many payloads and the spin axis both wobbles and drifts with time, due to external environmental torques and internal energy dissipation. Spacecraft shaped like a disk or tuna fish can are inherently stable when spinning about their axis of symmetry. On the other hand, long, slender spacecraft shaped more like a rod or pencil are unstable when spinning about their axis of symmetry and will eventually decay into a *flat spin* in which they are spinning about an axis at right angles to the longitudinal axis.

Another common passive technique is *gravity-gradient stabilization*. The spacecraft moves in its orbit in response to the net force acting on the center or mass.

However, the portions of the spacecraft closer to the Earth feel a somewhat stronger force than at the center of mass, and the portions of the spacecraft further from the Earth feel a lesser force. This results in a *gravity-gradient* or *tidal* force* which tends to pull the spacecraft apart very slightly and makes it stable in a vertical orientation, i.e., with the long axis of the spacecraft pointed toward the Earth. In many respects, gravity-gradient stabilization is similar to a bobber floating on the water, except that, unlike a bobber, gravity-gradient control is bi-stable. That is, the spacecraft is stable with either end pointing up. This means that it is possible for the spacecraft to get caught upside down, so most gravity-gradient spacecraft must have a way to turn themselves over. This, of course, increases the cost and complexity of this passive system. Another problem is that the gravity-gradient system does only a poor job of controlling the orientation about the direction to the center of the Earth. Nonetheless, gravity-gradient can be extremely economical, particularly for very large spacecraft. Consequently, this is the preferred stabilization technique for the largest space structures, such as the International Space Station.

Most spacecraft, and certainly any which require high-accuracy pointing, must have *active attitude control*, i.e., use an *attitude actuator* which is a device to provide controlled torque on the spacecraft. The *control law* is the algorithm which specifies the commands to be sent to the actuators, based on the difference between the measured and desired attitudes. Older systems frequently used linear control laws because of the cost and complexity of implementing more complex ones in analog electronics. Another simple type of control law is the *limit cycle* or *bang-bang control* in which no control is applied when the attitude is within an allowed deadband. When the attitude reaches the limit or edge of the deadband, a control torque is applied to send the system back toward the center. Thus, the spacecraft oscillates within the deadband region.

With the introduction of large spacecraft computers, much more complex control laws are now feasible.† More sophisticated approaches can substantially improve the accuracy without making the mechanical implementation more complex. For example, by using control software, it is relatively simple to apply *pre-emphasis*, which is a method of mechanically anticipating a spacecraft command. If we are going to move an antenna to the left (which will cause the spacecraft to react and move to the right), we begin by commanding the spacecraft itself to move left, such that when the antenna begins to move left, the reaction force will just balance the previous control command and the spacecraft will be more stable. It is the analysis and definition of these control laws and determination of how the spacecraft will respond that is the principal responsibility of the spacecraft control engineer.

---

* Gravity-gradient forces are frequently called tidal forces because they are responsible for tides on the Earth. The differential attraction of the Moon (1) on the surface of the Earth nearest the Moon, (2) the center of mass of the Earth, and (3) the surface of the Earth furthest from the Moon, serves to produce a bulge in the oceans toward the Moon and in the direction opposite the Moon. The rotation of the Earth under this tidal bulge produces the twice daily tide cycle. Because it is the Earth's rotation relative to the Moon that matters and the Moon moves about 15 deg/day, the average time between successive high tides will be about 12.5 hours.

† This situation is not too different from modern word processing. You can do a great deal more with a word processor than a simple typewriter, and there are many more things that can go remarkably wrong.

In an active control system, the control laws are used to command the attitude actuators which then apply the control torque to the spacecraft. The principal types of attitude actuators, and their relative advantages and disadvantages, are given in Table 3-4. Overall, these actuators fall into two major types:

- Those which provide an external torque which changes the angular momentum of the spacecraft.
- Those which provide an internal torque which changes the angular momentum of the spacecraft's body by rotating or moving an internal component but leaves the total angular momentum of the spacecraft and its internal parts unchanged.

TABLE 3-4. Advantages and Disadvantages of Alternative Attitude Actuators.

<table>
<tr><th>Method</th><th>Advantages</th><th>Disadvantages</th></tr>
<tr><td>Gas Jets (Thrusters)</td><td>• Flexible and fast
• Used in any environment
• Powerful</td><td>• Uses a consumable (fuel) with limited supply available due to fuel weight
• Too powerful for many applications (i.e., relatively coarse control)
• Complex and expensive plumbing subject to failure</td></tr>
<tr><td>Electromagnets</td><td>• Usually low power
• May be done without using consumables by use of solar power
• Simple devices—no moving parts and almost no electronics</td><td>• Slow
• Frequently heavy
• Near Earth only
• Applicability limited by direction of the external magnetic field
• Coarse control only (because of magnetic field model uncertainties and long time constants)</td></tr>
<tr><td>Reaction Wheels†</td><td>• Particularly good for variable spin rate control
• Fast, flexible, precise attitude control and/or stabilization</td><td>• Requires rapidly moving parts which implies problems of support and friction
• May need second control system to control overall angular momentum ("momentum dumping") in response to cumulative changes by environmental torques
• Expensive</td></tr>
<tr><td>Alternative Thrusters (Ion or Electric)</td><td colspan="2" rowspan="2">Primarily special purpose—less experience with these than with those listed above; characteristics are highly mission dependent; some systems may see more use in the future as further experience is gained</td></tr>
<tr><td>Active Solar Aerodynamic or Gravity-Gradient</td></tr>
</table>

†Refers to any device that may be used to exchange angular momentum with the spacecraft body.

Unfortunately, the spacecraft doesn't sit on a firm platform that we can push against.* Consequently, there are relatively few ways to actively change the spacecraft's angular momentum. One of these is to fire a thruster that is offset from the center of gravity

* This represents a major advantage of putting a future version of the Space Telescope on the Moon instead of in space. The Moon provides an inherently stable platform that we can use to control both the spacing and orientation of various parts of a telescope. In space, all of the parts react against each other. Very high accuracy pointing is achievable, but very expensive.

of the spacecraft. Unfortunately, this uses up propellant, which limits the life of the spacecraft to the amount of propellant on board.

In low-Earth orbit, we can use electromagnets (usually called *magnetic torquer*) or permanent magnets to torque against the Earth's magnetic field. Electromagnets require power but no non-renewable consumables. Unfortunately, magnetic torquing only works near the vicinity of the Earth or another planet with a non-negligible magnetic field. Geosynchronous orbit represents the limit at which magnetic torquing can be effectively used. It is used by a few geosynchronous spacecraft, although most use thrusters.

Nearly all of the internal torquing devices are wheels of some sort. As the wheel spins up, the spacecraft spins in the opposite direction. Wheels are particularly useful for absorbing cyclic torques in the environment. In one portion of the orbit the cyclic torque acts so as to spin up the wheel and in another portion of the orbit the cyclic torque spins the wheel in the opposite direction so that it returns approximately to its original spin rate. Unfortunately, in addition to the cyclic component, most environmental torques also include a secular component which builds up over time such that the wheel needs to spin faster and faster to continue to absorb the angular momentum from the disturbance environment. Sooner or later, the process must be reversed or the wheel will fly apart. This is done by *momentum unloading* or *momentum dumping*, which is the process of using an external torquing device to remove the built-up excess angular momentum and maintain the wheel speed within its operating range.

Three types of wheels are used on spacecraft:

- *Momentum wheels* operate about a nominal non-zero spin rate such that they always have a significant angular momentum, called the *momentum bias*.
- *Reaction wheels* operate about a nominally zero spin rate and spin in both directions in response to environmental disturbance torques and spacecraft commands.
- *Control moment gyros* are rapidly spinning wheels which generate torque by pushing against the rotation axis rather than by changing the wheel speed.

Momentum wheels are the most economical. In addition, they provide the spacecraft with an inherent angular momentum so that it is stable over reasonable periods of time. Reaction wheels have no net angular momentum. Therefore, they allow the spacecraft to maneuver easily between various directions and provide the highest accuracy in terms of pointing control. However, the reaction wheel momentarily stops and starts again every time the wheel's speed goes through zero. This starting and stopping is both difficult to control and subject to failure, because the starting friction is always much larger than the friction while the wheel is rotating. Thus, reaction wheels tend to be less reliable and more expensive. The control moment gyros, or CMGs, also have a large momentum bias that can provide even larger torques than momentum wheels by providing a stiff axis to push against. Control moment gyros are typically used on the largest spacecraft that need some form of active control, such as SkyLab.

Spacecraft can also incorporate a variety of moveable components to either counteract the environment or internally generated disturbances. For example, an antenna moving in one direction will cause the spacecraft to move in the opposite direction. This can be balanced either by the spacecraft control system or alternatively, by another mass which moves in a direction opposite that of the antenna. Thus, any wheel that needs to rotate quickly will frequently incorporate a wheel rotating in the opposite direction so as to eliminate the net torque on the spacecraft.

The purpose of the attitude actuator is to either change the orientation of the spacecraft (i.e., do an attitude maneuver) or, more often, simply maintain the attitude by counterbalancing the disturbance torques which are perturbing it. Like the attitude actuators, disturbance torques are both internal and external as summarized in Tables 3-5 and 3-6.

TABLE 3-5. External Disturbance Torques Acting on a Spacecraft. Disturbance torques can also be used for control as discussed in Table 3-3.

Source	Dependence on Distance from Earth	Region of Space Where Dominant
Aerodynamic	$e^{-\alpha r}$	Altitudes below ~500 km
Magnetic	$1/r^3$	~500 km to ~35,000 km (i.e., to about synchronous altitude)
Gravity-gradient	$1/r^3$	
Solar Radiation	Independent	Interplanetary space above synchronous altitude
Micrometeorites	Largely independent; high concentration in some regions of the Solar System	Normally negligible; may be important in some small regions (interior of Saturn's rings)

TABLE 3-6. Common Internal Disturbance Torques on Spacecraft.

Disturbance	Examples
Intentional mass expulsion	Equipment jettison, dumping propellants
Unintentional mass expulsion	Leaks, thrust vector misalignment, unintentional thruster firings
Thruster plume impingement	Plume fringe impinging on solar arrays
Moving hardware	Solar array, tape recorders, rotating sensors, antennas
Unintentional moving or shrinkage of hardware	Eclipses, internal heating
Propellant slosh	Propellant motion due to tank motion from internal or external torques
Crew motion	Exercise periods

Internal disturbance torques depend strongly on the details of the spacecraft itself. For manned missions, the dominant disturbance torque is typically the people, as seen in Fig. 3-2. Having astronauts exercise by running inside a spacecraft may be good for their overall fitness but is certainly not good for those experiments which demand an absolutely stable environment. For unmanned missions, internal disturbance torques come primarily from moving components. If you rotate a solar panel to follow the Sun, the spacecraft responds by rotating the other way. The impact on the spacecraft depends on both the mass and position of the moving component. Consequently, solar array motion typically has a large impact because the solar array is often responsible for a large part of the spacecraft's moments of inertia.

For many spacecraft, one of the largest internal disturbance torques is fuel sloshing in a partially full propellant tank. To the extent that the fuel is free to move, it can slosh back and forth, causing disturbances which are both large and nearly impossible to

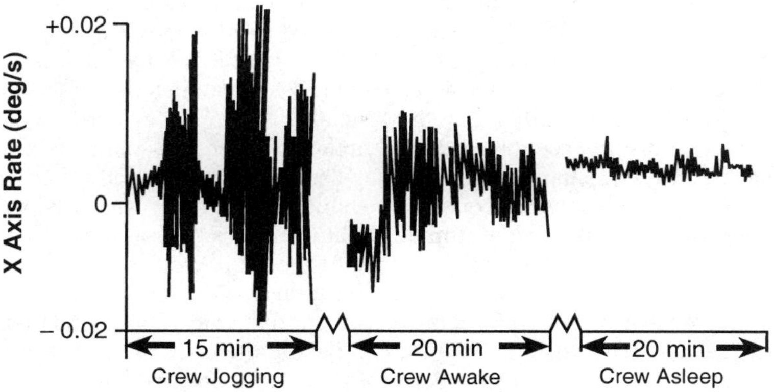

Fig. 3-2. Response of SkyLab to Astronaut Motion. Manned missions are very difficult for experiments which require minimum disturbances.

model or predict. Consequently, many spacecraft add a bladder or some other constraint to keep the fuel from moving when the thruster is not firing.

The Hubble Space Telescope (HST) has some of the most exacting requirements ever imposed on a spacecraft control system. The HST performance requires stabilizing the telescope to a fine-pointing of 0.007 arcsec (= 0.0000025 deg) to allow near-diffraction limited images to be obtained [Beals, et al., 1988]. On this spacecraft the propulsion system was entirely eliminated so there would be no fuel slosh, no torque from thrusters, and no contamination. (Because of orbit decay, Hubble was reboosted from time to time by manned Orbiter missions which also replaced the instruments and made repairs.) One of the largest disturbance torques on Space Telescope was the snap or twang that occurs when the solar arrays shrink or expand very quickly as the telescope goes in and out of an eclipse. While very small by most standards, this disturbance torque was large enough to nearly destroy the high accuracy science mission.

External torques depend strongly on both the design of the spacecraft and the region of space it is in. Spacecraft with long booms or very large antennas will have large gravity-gradient torques. However, in very low orbits, such as that of the Space Shuttle, aerodynamic torque will almost always dominate. As can be seen in Table 3-5, 3 of the 4 principal external torque sources depend on being near the Earth or another large planet. Consequently, in interplanetary space, the dominant torque source is solar radiation pressure.

Disturbance torques can be remarkably small. For example, the TDRS spacecraft used to provide communication between low-Earth orbiting spacecraft and a ground station at White Sands is largely symmetric with large solar arrays on both the north and south sides of the spacecraft. However, there is an additional antenna located on one end to provide communications with the ground station. In order to balance this antenna, a solar sail is put on the other side of the spacecraft to balance the solar radiation pressure. To give an idea of the magnitude of the forces involved, a 20 m^2 surface has a maximum force due to solar radiation pressure approximately equal to the weight of an ant on the Earth's surface. The solar sail of TDRS is far smaller than 20 m^2. Nonetheless, a number of small Earth orbiting spacecraft have used solar radiation pressure to spin up the spacecraft by using small vanes, typically of a few square inches each, that are black on one side and white on the other. Sunlight transfers approximately twice the momentum to the reflective side as it does to the side on which light is absorbed. (This phenomenon is used in a toy that is a small evacuated bulb with vanes that spin when exposed to sunlight.) We leave it as an exercise for the reader to determine the force being applied to the spacecraft in terms of the equivalent weight of something on Earth. (Hint: think small.)

The external disturbance torque can be broken down into 2 components: a cyclic component that returns the accumulated angular momentum to zero after each orbit and a secular component which continues to build up over time. The division between these components depends on the attitude and attitude variations as the spacecraft goes around in its orbit, as well as the properties of the orbit itself, such as whether it's elliptical and when eclipses occur. Magnetic, gravity-gradient, and solar radiation torques tend to have a large cyclic component. Aerodynamic torques tend to be largely secular. The important issue is how we can handle them. As described earlier, the angular momentum resulting from cyclic torques can be absorbed in wheels, or other rotating devices on the spacecraft which will then return to their original speed after one orbit. On the other hand, secular torques will continue to build up, giving the spacecraft as a whole more and more angular momentum. Ultimately, the secular torques must be mitigated by *momentum unloading*, i.e., applying an external control torque that reduces the total spacecraft angular momentum. If this does not occur, the momentum wheels will either fly apart, which is not good for the spacecraft, or reach an upper limit, such that the spacecraft itself will begin to spin as further momentum builds up.

Just as the orbit dynamics determine the motion of the center of mass of the spacecraft in response to external forces, the attitude dynamics determine the motion about the center of mass in response to the total torque, i.e., the applied control torque and both external and internal disturbance torques. Spacecraft attitude dynamics is most conveniently broken down into two broad classes of spacecraft: *momentum-bias* systems, in which the spacecraft has a significant net angular momentum and *zero momentum* systems, in which there is a very low net angular momentum.

Momentum bias systems are sometimes referred to as "stiff" because they are inherently stable in the short term. The angular momentum vector will remain approximately fixed in inertial space, typically moving slowly in response to the cumulative secular external torques. The simplest way to create a momentum bias system is to spin the spacecraft itself. The stability of this arrangement depends on the shape of the spacecraft or, more precisely, on its moments of inertia:

- An *oblate* (disc-shaped) spacecraft is inherently stable
- A *prolate* (rod-shaped) spacecraft is unstable when rotated about its long axis

A frisbee is an inherently stable oblate shape. On the other hand, a football is an inherently unstable prolate shape. Energy dissipation due to structural flexing or internal motion will result in the prolate object going into a flat spin about one of the short axes, as shown in Fig. 3-3. As discussed in Sec. 3.2.2, any object in space will be stable spinning about its maximum moment of inertia and unstable about other axes.

A second option for a momentum bias system is a *dual-spin* spacecraft in which a portion of the spacecraft is spinning and a *despun platform* remains pointed at the Earth or toward an inertial object. Hughes Space and Communications has used dual-spin spacecraft for geosynchronous communications satellites for many years. Although the design they have used is prolate and therefore inherently unstable, it has been extremely successful and never experienced a failure which caused a flat spin.

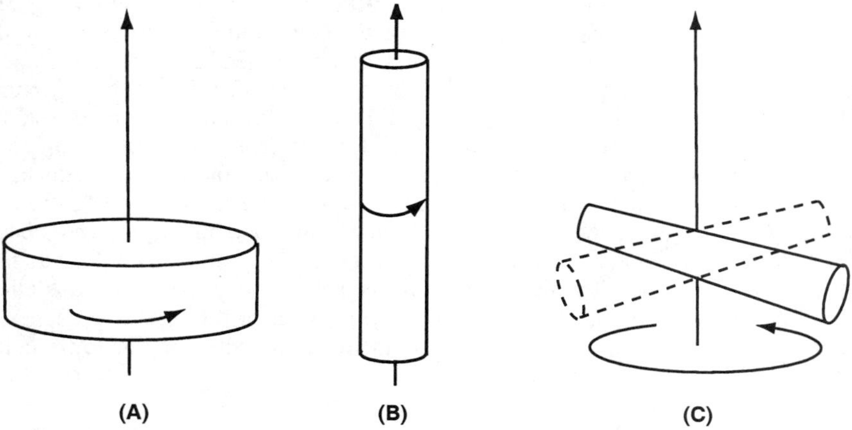

Fig. 3-3. Prolate and Oblate Spinning Objects. (A) Oblate object with stable spin. The unstable prolate spinner (B) will eventually drop into a stable "flat spin" (C).

A third option is to use one or more momentum wheels inside the spacecraft such that the spacecraft itself remains pointed toward the Earth or some other target while the wheel maintains the stiffness of the system. For Earth or planetary orbiters, the most practical configuration is to have the angular momentum vector, i.e., the spin axis of the wheel, aligned with the orbit normal. This allows the spacecraft to rotate once per orbit about the angular momentum vector so as to keep one face pointed toward the Earth.

The alternative to a momentum bias system is one with very little or no net angular momentum. Zero momentum systems can be pointed with high accuracy and easily moved from target to target since they don't have a large angular momentum vector to push around. On the other hand, there must be continuous sensing and control in all 3 axes to keep them from tumbling because they have no angular momentum to keep them stable.

Small spacecraft behave largely like rigid bodies. However, larger spacecraft or ones with large antennas, thin booms, or similar structures can be flexible. Flexible spacecraft dynamics typically make the control process far more complex and expensive. Ultimately, it is the payload that wants to be pointed or its attitude known. However, attitude sensors may be located some distance from the payload and may even be distributed across the spacecraft. Both mechanical flexibility and thermal bending add complexity and limit the level of accuracy that can be achieved in both determination and control.

One mechanism for handling flexible structures is an *attitude transfer system*. This is simply a method for determining the attitude of one part of the spacecraft with respect to other parts. For example, consider a spacecraft which uses a star sensor mounted on the body of the spacecraft and a magnetometer payload at the end of a long boom to avoid the spacecraft's magnetic fields. Here, we could use either a light on the boom tip that can be seen by the star sensor or a mirror on the boom tip and a light next to the star sensor. The position of the light can be determined with respect to the background stars which allows the attitude of the boom to be determined with respect to inertial space.

In the end, the attitude motion of the spacecraft (or of different parts of the spacecraft) is determined by the attitude sensors and the control loop begins again. In the simplest systems, such as gravity-gradient or fully unstabilized spacecraft, the entire determination and control process is passive, with no sensing hardware and no control hardware. In more complex systems, there will be not only multiple components for each function, but also multiple control modes for different aspects of the mission. Thus the spacecraft might use Sun sensors, Earth sensors, and thrusters for acquisition and stabilization, and then switch to star sensors, gyros, and reaction wheels for fine pointing while using magnetic torquing for momentum unloading, gyros and wheels for new target acquisition, and an entirely different hardware complement for fail-safe or positive de-orbit mode. The net result of this is that very few spacecraft look alike, in terms of attitude systems. A remarkably large number of different approaches to attitude determination and control have flown in space and will continue to fly in the future.

3.2 Spacecraft Attitude Motion in the Absence of Control

What is the attitude motion of an uncontrolled spacecraft? What is the natural attitude motion of objects in space? Natural bodies in the solar system fall into three basic categories of attitude motion:

- Some objects which are subject to strong perturbations have become gravity-gradient stabilized. The Moon, for example, maintains a constant face towards the Earth (see Sec. 3.2.1)
- Most large objects in the solar system (i.e., the Sun and planets) are spin stabilized, retaining essentially the same angular momentum they had when they were first formed (see Sec. 3.2.2)
- Smaller objects (asteroids, meteoroids, and other debris) are typically asymmetric and tumbling (also Sec. 3.2.2)

In the absence of controlling perturbations, such as gravity-gradient torque, the motion of a spacecraft like that of natural objects will be determined by the angular momentum. Free body (i.e., satellite) attitude motion differs in several important respects from the motion of rigid objects such as a spinning top, supported in a gravitational field. Thus, you should be careful to avoid relying on either intuition or previous analytic experience with common rotating objects which are supported in some way near the surface of the Earth*.

Basically, the uncontrolled spacecraft can be either stable, such as a gravity-gradient stabilized spacecraft (Sec. 3.2.1) or tumbling, such as most small objects or dead spacecraft (Sec. 3.2.2). Typically, we use *spinning* for a spacecraft which is in a controlled spin about an axis of symmetry and *tumbling* for one which is rotating about

---

* Fortunately, modern telephoto lenses and high-speed CCDs have provided us with the opportunity to study the attitude motion of rotating longitudinally symmetric spheroids while in the air. Given the proper initial spin, they will be spin stabilized about the long axis. When slightly misthrown, they wobble or nutate. When kicked, they will typically go into a flat spin. We leave it as an exercise to the reader to apply the formulas later in this section to determine the ratio of the moments of inertia of an elongated, inflated, leather balloon, and from that, the ratio of the nutation frequency to the spin rate. Experimental verification is typically available on Sunday afternoons or Monday evenings in the fall.

an arbitrary axis without control. In both cases, angular momentum is conserved, and the angular momentum vector remains approximately fixed in inertial space.

3.2.1 Gravity-Gradient Stabilization

In a uniform gravitational field, all of the components of an object will feel the same acceleration and, therefore, move together through space. However, in a non-uniform gravitational field, such as that resulting from a point mass or a spherically symmetric object, different parts of an extended object will feel a different gravitational force. If they are not physically attached, they will each travel in slightly different orbits. If it is a single extended object, the difference in gravitational forces will tend to pull the object apart and internal forces will be required to hold it together.

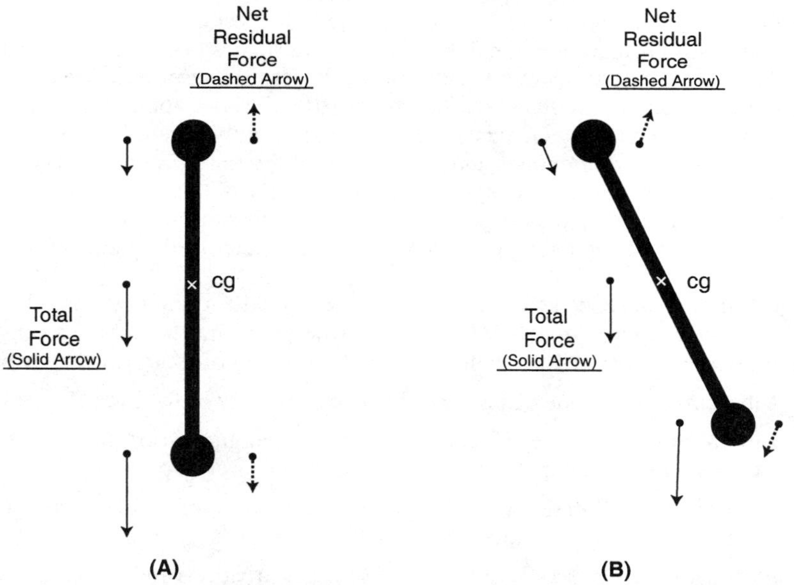

Fig. 3-4. Gravity-Gradient Stabilization is the Result of Very Small Tidal Forces Acting on the Spacecraft. See text for explanation.

For simplicity, consider the case of a dumbbell in orbit above the Earth, as shown in Fig. 3-4. The center of mass of the dumbbell moves about the center of the Earth in a Keplerian orbit, in response to the gravitational acceleration at the center of mass. Although the differences will be quite small, there will be a slightly lower gravitational force on the upper portion of the dumbbell since it is further from the center of the Earth, and a slightly larger gravitational force on the lower portion. If the dumbbell is not vertically aligned, as shown in Fig. 3-4B, then there will be a very small horizontal component as well because all of the forces are directed toward the center of the Earth which is in slightly different directions as seen from the ends of the dumbbell. Because the dumbbell as a whole is moving in response to the force on the center of mass, there remains a net residual force on both the upper and lower portions of the dumbbell, pulling them away from the center of mass. As discussed earlier, this is the force that is responsible for tides on the surface of the Earth. For a spacecraft, this gravity-gradient force is far smaller than the forces holding the spacecraft together. Nonetheless, as shown in Fig. 3-4B, it does provide a small stabilizing force which tends to hold the spacecraft so that the dumbbell is flying with its long axis oriented toward the Earth.

In a gravity-gradient stabilized system, there are 4 neutral orientations 90 deg apart. The 2 horizontal orientations are unstable. If the dumbbell is flying with its long axis along the velocity vector, any small perturbation will cause it to drift away from this orientation and reorient the long axis vertically. Unlike a bobber, which will reorient itself vertically in only one direction, both vertical orientations of a spacecraft are stable. In the presence of small disturbances, the gravity-gradient force pulls the spacecraft back to its vertical orientation. Consequently, we would expect a dumbbell, I-beam, or even a long rope in space to fly in the vertical orientation with the long axis pointed approximately toward the center of the Earth.

In its stable configuration, the dumbbell in space rotates once per orbit, and therefore, has an angular momentum vector pointed toward the orbit pole. Because of the conservation of angular momentum, the spacecraft will rotate about the orbit pole at a nearly uniform angular rate. On the other hand, in a slightly eccentric orbit, the spacecraft will move at different rates about the center of the Earth, traveling more rapidly at perigee and more slowly at apogee. As a consequence of this and small disturbance torques, the spacecraft typically wobbles about the direction of the gravity-gradient vector. This general wobble of a gravity-gradient stabilized spacecraft is called *libration*.

The Moon is an excellent example of gravity-gradient stabilization. While the Moon maintains approximately the same face toward the Earth, there is a substantial apparent libration of the Moon, which is actually the sum of four principal effects:

- Libration in longitude (± 6.3 deg) due to eccentricity of the Moon's orbit
- Libration in latitude (± 6.7 deg) due to the misalignment of the lunar rotation axis, i.e., geographic pole, with respect to the lunar orbit pole
- Diurnal (daily) libration (± 1.0 deg) due to the observer on the Earth changing position with respect to the Moon as the Earth rotates
- Physical libration (± 0.04 deg) due to other perturbations and the Moon's asymmetric shape

The result of these libration motions is that we see slightly different faces of the Moon at different times. The net effect is that 59% of the surface of the Moon can be seen from the Earth.*

3.2.2 Torque-Free Motion

In the absence of a stabilizing natural perturbation as described above, the motion of a rotating or tumbling spacecraft can appear very complex, because of the combination of rotation and nutation. In order to understand this motion, we will consider

---

* Including in 1996, the south polar region of the Moon, where the presence of ice in deep craters has been tentatively identified. The Arecibo radar antenna in Puerto Rico has been used to map this region, which can be seen at times, but is nonetheless at a very shallow angle relative to an observer on the Earth.

first the simplest case of the attitude motion of a completely rigid rotating object in space, free of all external forces or torques.

In describing this motion, 4 fundamental sets of axes are important. *Geometrical axes* are arbitrarily defined relative to the structure of the spacecraft itself. Thus, the geometrical Z axis is defined by some mark on the spacecraft or by an engineering drawing giving its position relative to the structure. This is the reference system which defines the orientation of both the payload and attitude determination and control hardware.

The 3 remaining axes are defined by the physics of satellite motion. The *angular momentum axis* is the axis through the center of mass parallel to the angular momentum vector. The *instantaneous rotation axis* is the axis about which the spacecraft is rotating at any instant. The existence of this axis is established by Euler's Theorem:

> ***The most general displacement of a rigid body with one point fixed, (i.e., the center of mass) is a rotation about some axis.*** In other words, any attitude can be expressed in terms of any other attitude by a single rotation about an axis instantaneously at rest in both frames. This axis is called the *Euler axis*, **E**, and the angle of rotation is called the *Euler angle,* Φ.

This general statement of attitude motion was developed by the Swiss mathematician Leonhard Euler in the eighteenth century. Euler created much of the mathematical foundation of modern rotational dynamics. He served as professor of mathematics and physics at St. Petersburg by direction of Catherine I and as mathematics director of the Academy of Sciences in Berlin at the direction of Frederick the Great.*

The angular momentum axis and the instantaneous rotation axis are not necessarily the same. To see this, consider the rotation of a symmetric dumbbell, as shown in Fig. 3-5. In elementary mechanics we define the angular momentum vector, **L**, of a point mass, m, at position **r** relative to an arbitrary origin as

$$\mathbf{L} = \mathbf{r} \times \mathbf{p} = \mathbf{r} \times m\mathbf{v} \tag{3-1}$$

where **p** is the momentum and **v** is the velocity of the particle in question. For a collection of n points:

$$\mathbf{L} = \sum_{i=1}^{n} \mathbf{L}_i = \sum_{i=1}^{n} \mathbf{r}_i \times \mathbf{p}_i \tag{3-2}$$

First, assume that the dumbbell is rotating with angular velocity $\boldsymbol{\omega}$ about an axis through the center of mass and perpendicular to the rod joining the masses (Fig. 3-5A). Then **L** is parallel to $\boldsymbol{\omega}$ and the motion is particularly simple because **L** and $\boldsymbol{\omega}$ remain parallel as the dumbbell rotates.

However, if the dumbbell is initially rotating about an axis through the center of mass but inclined to the normal to the central rod (Fig. 3-5B), **L** will be in the plane defined by $\boldsymbol{\omega}$ and the two end masses and perpendicular to their instantaneous velocities, $\mathbf{V}_1$ and $\mathbf{V}_2$. Thus, **L** will be perpendicular to the central rod and not parallel to $\boldsymbol{\omega}$. [Use Eq. (3-2) to calculate the angular momentum about the center of mass.] Now the free space motion is more complex. Because the conservation of angular momentum

* The great mathematicians of this period—Euler, Lagrange, Clairaut, Legendre, and d'Alembert—were colleagues and friends in both Berlin and at the Academie des Sciences in Paris.

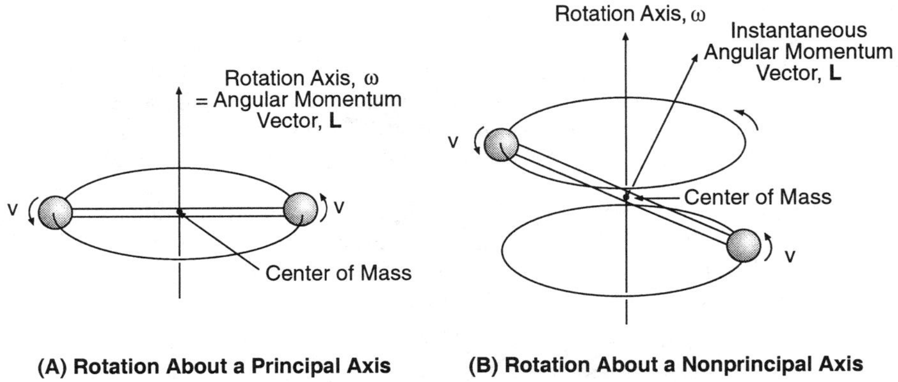

Fig. 3-5. Rotation of a Symmetric Dumbbell. The reality of the forces during asymmetric rotation (A) can be easily verified by experimentation with a simple dumbbell.

requires that **L** remain fixed in inertial space if there are no external torques, the instantaneous rotation axis, $\boldsymbol{\omega}$, must rotate as the dumbbell rotates. Conversely, if $\boldsymbol{\omega}$ is fixed in space by some external support, a torque must be supplied via the supports to change **L** as the object rotates.* Clearly the motion about the axis in Fig. 3-5A is simpler than that in Fig. 3-5B. Thus, the motion of real objects leads us to define a third physical axis system which is the preferred axes about which the motion is particularly simple. Specifically, a *principal axis,* **P**, is any axis such that the resulting angular momentum vector, **L**, is parallel to **P** when the spacecraft rotates about it. Therefore, for rotation about a principal axis, **L** is parallel to $\boldsymbol{\omega}$ and

$$\mathbf{L} = I_p \boldsymbol{\omega} = I_p \omega \mathbf{P} \tag{3-3}$$

where I_p is a constant of proportionality called the *principal moment of inertia.* Because the magnitude of the angular velocity is defined by $\omega = v / r$ where r is the rotation radius, Eqs. (3-1) through (3-3) imply that **for a principal axis** and a collection of point masses,

$$I_p = \sum_{i=1}^{n} m_i r_i^2 \tag{3-4}$$

where r is the perpendicular distance of m from the principal axis. **For rotation about nonprincipal axes, the motion is more complex, and Eq. (3-3) does <u>not</u> hold.**

The form of Eq. (3-2) shows that whenever the mass of an object is symmetrically distributed about an axis (i.e., if the mass distribution remains identical after rotating the object 360 / N degrees about the specified axis, where N is any integer greater than

---

* I highly recommend verifying the reality of this difference in motion by constructing models of the 2 dumbbells in Fig. 3-5. This can be conveniently done with Tinkertoys™ or any collection of small rods and weights. The experiment is done by simply rotating the dumbbell about the 2 different axes as shown in Fig. 3-5A and Fig. 3-5B. The differences in the forces and motion will become apparent.

1)* the angular momentum generated by rotation about the symmetry axis will be parallel to that axis. Thus, any axis of symmetry is a principal axis. In addition, it can be shown that any object, no matter how asymmetric, has 3 mutually perpendicular principal axes defined by Eq. (3-3).

The 4 sets of axes above may be used to define three types of attitude motion called pure rotation, coning, and nutation. *Pure rotation* is the limiting case in which the rotation axis, a principal axis, and a geometrical axis are all parallel or antiparallel, as shown in Fig. 3-6A. Clearly, the *angular momentum vector* will lie along the same axis, and these 4 axes will remain parallel as the object rotates.

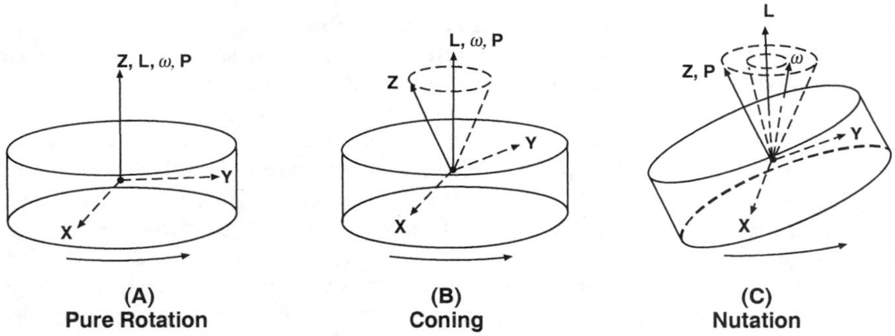

Fig. 3-6. Types of Rotational Motion. L = angular momentum vector; **P**= principal axis; ω = instantaneous rotation axis; **Z** = geometrical axis.

Coning is rotation for which a geometrical axis is not parallel to a principal axis, but the principal and rotation axes are still parallel. The physical motion of the object is precisely the same as pure rotation. However, the "misalignment" of the geometrical axis (which may be intentional) causes this axis to rotate in inertial space about the angular momentum vector, as shown in Fig. 3-6B. Coning is associated with a coordinate system misalignment rather than a physical misalignment and can be eliminated by a coordinate transformation if the orientation of the principal axes in the body of the spacecraft is known.

Finally, *nutation*† is rotational motion for which the instantaneous rotation axis is not aligned with a principal axis, as illustrated in Fig. 3-6C. In this case, the angular momentum vector, which remains fixed in space, will not be aligned with either of the physical axes. Both **P** and **ω** rotate about **L**. **P** is fixed in the spacecraft because it is defined by the spacecraft's mass distribution, irrespective of the spacecraft orientation.

* In this case, the mass distribution consists of N symmetrically distributed groups of mass points. If **L** does not lie on the axis of symmetry, then for $N > 2$ it must lie closer to, or farther away from, one group; however, this is impossible because all of the mass points contribute equally to **L**. For $N = 2$, the mass distribution has the form $m(x, y, z) = m(-x, -y, -z)$, where z is the symmetry axis. Therefore, any x or y components of **L** cancel when summed and **L** must lie along the Z axis.

† This definition of nutation is in keeping with common spacecraft usage and differs from that used in classical mechanics for describing say, the motion of a spinning top. In the latter case, nutation refers to the vertical wobble of the spin axis as it moves slowly around the gravitational field vector.

Neither **L** nor **ω** is fixed in the spacecraft. **ω** rotates both in the spacecraft and in inertial space while **L** rotates in the spacecraft but is fixed in inertial space by the conservation of angular momentum. The angle between **P** and **L** is a measure of the magnitude of the nutation called the *nutation angle*, θ. Nutation and coning can occur together, in which case none of the 4 axis systems is parallel or anti-parallel.

In practice, all spacecraft with angular momentum will have some level of nutation. Thus, it represents a basic disturbance or wobble in the motion of spacecraft that interferes with observations and measurements. More important, unless nutation is suppressed or *damped*, it can build up in an elongated (prolate) spacecraft and cause the spacecraft to flop over on its side in a flat spin.

Nutation is most easily understood for a cylindrically symmetric spacecraft in which two of the moments of inertia are equal, as show in Fig. 3-6C. In this case, the angular momentum vector, **L**, remains fixed in inertial space as a result of the conservation of angular momentum. The principal axis, **P**, which is fixed in the spacecraft, rotates about the angular momentum vector and the spacecraft rotates about the principal axis. This general motion is illustrated in Fig. 3-7. The spacecraft itself is assumed to be a rigid body. At any instant, the only motion of this rigid body is a rotation in space about some axis which itself is instantaneously at rest in inertial space (recall Euler's Theorem). As can be seen from Fig. 3-7, if **P** is rotating about **L**, and the spacecraft is rotating about **P**, then there will be some point along the line joining **P** and **L** in which the two rotations just cancel each other. In inertial space, the spacecraft will be rotating about this *instantaneous rotation axis*, (*or Euler axis*), **ω**. However, the vector **ω** is not fixed in either the spacecraft or in inertial space. It remains on the line joining **P** and **L** and therefore rotates about **L** in the inertial frame and about **P** in the spacecraft frame.

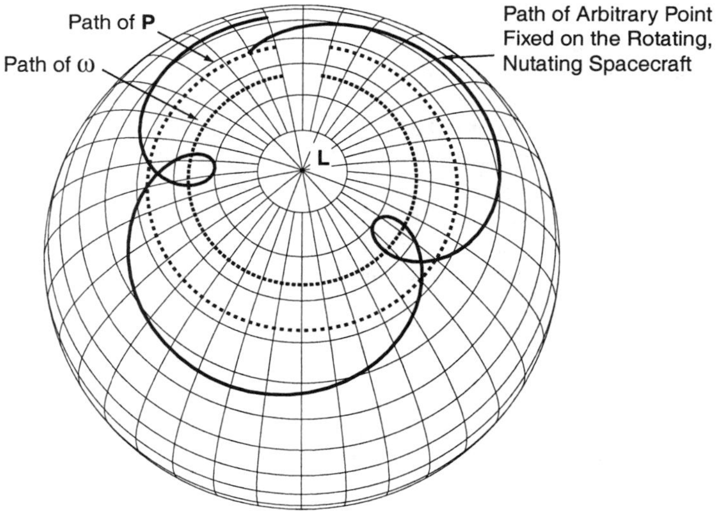

Fig. 3-7. Nutation Occurs When the Principal Axis, P, is not Aligned with the Angular Momentum Vector, L. In this case, **L** is fixed in inertial space, **P** rotates about **L**, and the spacecraft rotates about **P**. The spiral shows the motion in inertial space of a point fixed on the spacecraft. The sphere represents the projection of the various axes onto the sky. For a more detailed introduction to this type of plot, see Sec. 6.1.

Another way to describe this motion is illustrated in Fig. 3-8, which shows two cones rolling on each other. One cone, called the *space cone*, is centered on the angular momentum vector, **L**, and the other, called the *body cone*, is centered on the principal axis, **P**. The rotation of **P** about **L** is described by saying that the body cone rolls without slipping on the space cone. The instantaneous rotation axis $\boldsymbol{\omega}$ is the point of contact between the two cones. The rest of the spacecraft is attached to the body cone and carries an arbitrary point in the spacecraft around with it as it rolls as illustrated in Fig. 3-7.

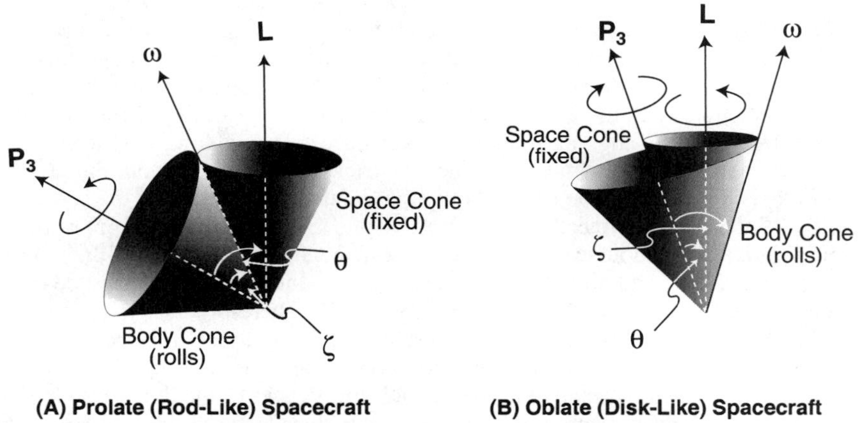

Fig. 3-8. Motion of a Nutating Spacecraft. The body cone, centered on **P**, rolls without slipping on the space cone centered on **L**.

Because the instantaneous rotation axis $\boldsymbol{\omega}$ lies along the line joining **L** and **P**, it can be broken down into components which lie along **L** and **P** as follows:

$$\boldsymbol{\omega} = \boldsymbol{\omega}_p + \boldsymbol{\omega}_l = \omega_p \mathbf{P_3} + \omega_l \mathbf{L} \tag{3-5}$$

Here $\mathbf{P_3}$ is the principal axis about which the spacecraft is symmetric and $\mathbf{P_1}$ and $\mathbf{P_2}$ will be used for the principal axes perpendicular to $\mathbf{P_3}$. The amplitude of $\boldsymbol{\omega}$ is given by:

$$\omega^2 = \omega_p{}^2 + \omega_l{}^2 + 2\omega_p\omega_l\cos\theta \tag{3-6}$$

where the nutation angle, θ, is the angle between $\mathbf{P_3}$ and **L**. The *inertial nutation rate*, ω_l, is the rotation rate of $\mathbf{P_3}$ about **L** relative to an inertial frame of reference and the *body nutation rate*, ω_p, is the rotation rate of any point **R** fixed in the body (such as a geometrical axis or a sensor field of view) about $\mathbf{P_3}$ relative to the orientation of **L**. It can be shown from the dynamic equations of motion discussed in Vol. III that ω_p and ω_l are related to each other by:

$$\omega_p = \frac{I_1 - I_3}{I_3} \omega_l \cos\theta \tag{3-7}$$

where I_3 is the moment of inertia about the axis of symmetry (the Z axis in Fig. 3-6) and $I_1 = I_2$ is the moment of inertia about the remaining 2 perpendicular axes.

By resolving $\boldsymbol{\omega}$ in Eq. (3-5) into components along $\mathbf{P_3}$ and orthogonal to $\mathbf{P_3}$ and then using Eq. (3-7), we obtain an expression for the angle ζ between $\mathbf{P_3}$ and $\boldsymbol{\omega}$ as follows:

$$\tan\zeta = \frac{\omega_l \sin\theta}{\omega_p + \omega_l \cos\theta} = \frac{I_3}{I_1}\tan\theta \tag{3-8}$$

In the terminology of Fig. (3-8), ζ is the radius of the body cone, $(\theta - \zeta)$ is the radius of the space cone, and θ is the angle between the axes of the cones.

Figure 3-8A is correct only for prolate objects such as a tall cylinder or rod for which I_1 is greater than I_3. In this case, Eq. (3-7) implies that ω_p and ω_l have the same sign. If I_3 is greater than I_1, as is the case for a thin disc or the conceptual spacecraft illustrated in Fig. (3-6), then the spacecraft is said to be oblate and ω_p and ω_l have opposite signs. In this case, the space cone lies inside the body cone and the instantaneous point of contact between the 2 cones, $\boldsymbol{\omega}$, will be along the arc joining $\mathbf{P_3}$ and $\mathbf{L}$ but on the opposite side of the angular momentum vector from $\mathbf{P_3}$ rather than between them.

The relative angular velocities are somewhat tricky to sort out. In both Fig. 3-7 and Fig. 3-8, ω_l is the rotation rate of $\mathbf{P_3}$ about $\mathbf{L}$. ω_p is the rotation rate of the spacecraft about $\mathbf{P_3}$ **relative to the direction to L**. Finally, the spacecraft inertial spin rate, ω is the rotation rate of $\mathbf{P_3}$ about $\boldsymbol{\omega}$ relative to inertial space. In Fig. 3-8A, all of the motions are counterclockwise and all have the same sign. The dot on the lip of the body cone is being carried towards the line joining $\mathbf{P_3}$ and $\mathbf{L}$. Therefore, ω_p is positive. In Fig. 3-8B, $\mathbf{P_3}$ is moving about $\mathbf{L}$ in a counterclockwise rotation, which carries the dot on the body cone in the direction of $\boldsymbol{\omega}$. However, ω itself is rotating about $\mathbf{L}$ more rapidly and consequently, relative to the line joining $\mathbf{P_3}$ and $\mathbf{L}$, the dot is moving in a backwards or clockwise direction. The differences between these 2 types of motion for prolate and oblate spacecraft are summarized in Table 3-7. In the limiting case of $I_1 = I_2 = I_3$, the space cone reduces to a line, $\omega_p = 0$ [from Eq. (3-7)], and the spacecraft rotates uniformly about $\mathbf{L}$. In this case, any axis is a principal axis.

TABLE 3-7. Differences in Nutation for Oblate and Prolate Spacecraft.

Prolate Spacecraft (Rod-Like)	Oblate Spacecraft (Disk-Like)
$I_1 = I_2 > I_3$	$I_1 = I_2 < I_3$
Rotation about $\mathbf{P_3}$ is unstable; will decay into a flat spin	Rotation about $\mathbf{P_3}$ is stable
Energy ellipsoid is oblate	Energy ellipsoid is prolate
ω is between **L** and $\mathbf{P_3}$	**L** is between ω and $\mathbf{P_3}$
ω_p and ω_l have the same sign (i.e., spin and nutation are in the same direction)	ω_p and ω_l have opposite signs (i.e., spin and nutation are in opposite directions)

The differences in nutation for oblate and prolate spacecraft can be seen most easily by looking at Figs. 3-9 and 3-10, which show the motion of a slit fixed in spacecraft coordinates similar to the field of view of a linear array or a slit sensor. In both cases, the nutation amplitude is greatly exaggerated over normal motion in order to make the effects clearly visible.

Fig. 3-9 shows the motion of a slit that is 12 deg long starting 5 deg from the principal axis, $\mathbf{P_3}$, and extending radially away from $\mathbf{P_3}$. The spacecraft is a prolate (rod-like) spheroid, such that $I_1 = I_2 > I_3$. The bottom of the slit is the same as the "arbitrary point" shown in Fig. 3-7. $\mathbf{P_3}$, **E**, and **L** remain aligned along a great circle as we have seen before. The slit, which is fixed in the body is always pointed toward $\mathbf{P_3}$, but points toward **E** and **L** only twice during each rotation period. Note that at the top of the small loop, the slit has "turned over" such that the end that is furthest from $\mathbf{P_3}$ is now closest to **L**. At this step the slit is again aligned with $\mathbf{P_3}$, **E**, and **L**, but the Euler axis, **E**, is now in the slit. By definition, the orientation of all of the points on the body return to their original orientation after one body nutation period $= 2\pi/\omega_p$. The cycle then repeats itself.

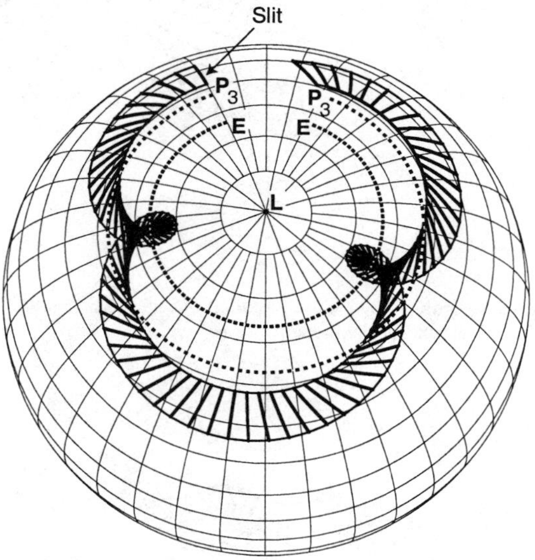

Fig. 3-9. Nutation for a Cylindrical Rod ($I_1 = I_2 > I_3$). Nutation amplitude is greatly exaggerated over normal motion. See text for discussion.

In Fig. 3-10, we see the same motion for an oblate (disk-like) spheroid. Again the slit rotates in inertial space, but always continues to point toward the principal axis, $\mathbf{P_3}$. Now the spin and nutation are in opposite directions, such that the motion takes on a more complex appearance and the slit appears to rotate "backward."

In Fig. 3-11 we have returned to the prolate spheroid of Figs. 3-7 and 3-9 and have reduced the nutation amplitude to about 5 deg. Here we are following the motion of a point near the "equator" of the spacecraft rather than near the pole. Note that the motion of the point is confined to a band about the nominal orientation and with a width equal to twice the nutation amplitude. Finally, Fig. 3-12 reverses the process and shows the motion of a point in inertial space as seen in spacecraft coordinates. Here the spacecraft is a prolate spheroid with the same parameters as the Figs. 3-7 and 3-9. Now **L** appears to rotate about $\mathbf{P_3}$ and **E** remains on the great circle arc joining **L** and $\mathbf{P_3}$. An arbitrary point fixed in inertial space remains a fixed distance from **L** and, from the point of the view of the spacecraft, follows a similar looping motion as we have seen in Fig. 3-7.

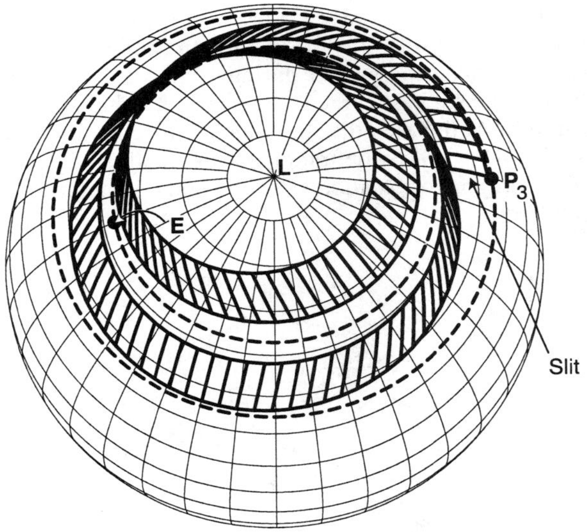

Fig. 3-10. Nutation for a Disk ($I_1 = I_2 < I_3$). Nutation amplitude is greatly exaggerated over normal motion. See text for discussion.

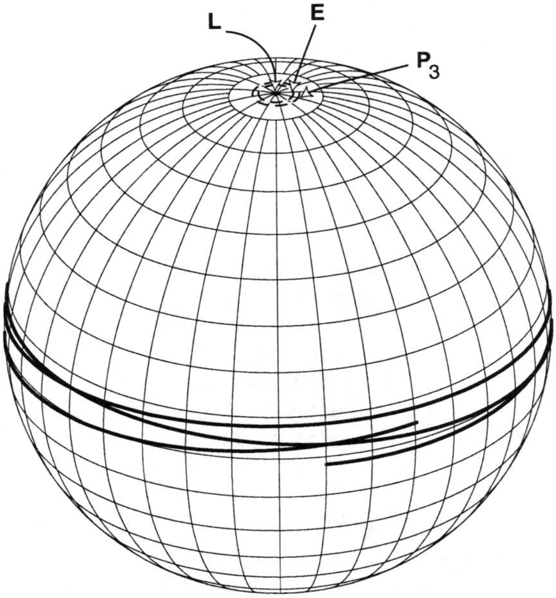

Fig. 3-11. Nutation for a Point Near the Equator for a Cylindrical Rod. Moments of inertia are the same as for Figs. 3-7 and 3-9. Nutation amplitude has been reduced to 5 deg.

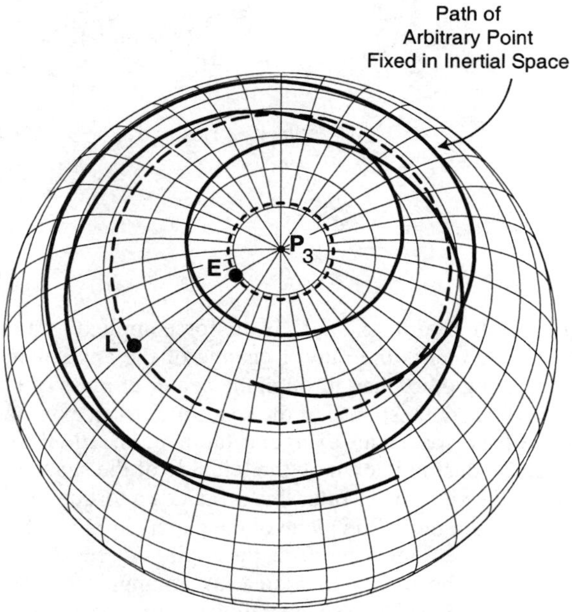

Fig. 3-12. Apparent Motion of a Point in Inertial Space Seen From a Spacecraft with the Nutation Motion Shown in Figs. 3-7 and 3-9. For an observer on the nutating spacecraft, objects in space appear to wobble in a manner opposite that of the nutational motion.

In practice, the moments of inertia I_1 and I_2 may be similar in value but will not be equal. What does this do to the spacecraft motion? The answer is that it shifts the space cone and the body cone from a perfectly circular cross-section into approximately elliptical shapes such that the nutation amplitude will no longer be constant. This is conceptually simple, but makes the mathematics of rotation substantially more complex. It also makes the appearance of the motion more complex such that either photos or computer animations of, for example, a tumbling asymmetric asteroid appear as though the asteroid is undergoing an irregular motion. However, like any spacecraft, the asteroid is simply undergoing rotation plus nutation.

3.2.3 Response to Torques*

We have seen that in the absence of torque, the general motion of the spacecraft will be rotation plus nutation about the angular momentum vector, which remains fixed in inertial space. The response of the spacecraft to either externally or internally generated torques can be obtained from the basic equation of attitude motion, Eq. (3-2), which expresses the angular momentum, **L**, of the spacecraft as a sum over the masses m_i located at positions $\mathbf{r}_i$ and moving with velocities $\mathbf{v}_i$ that make up the spacecraft. Differentiating with respect to time gives:

---

* The discussion in this section follows closely that of Markley in Sec. 15.2 of *Spacecraft Attitude Determination and Control* [Wertz, 1978].

$$\frac{\mathrm{d}}{\mathrm{d}t}\mathbf{L}=\sum_{i=1}^{n}\frac{\mathrm{d}}{\mathrm{d}t}\mathbf{L}_i=\sum_{i=1}^{n}\frac{\mathrm{d}}{\mathrm{d}t}(\mathbf{r}_i\times m_i\mathbf{v}_i)$$
$$=\sum_{i=1}^{n}(\mathbf{v}_i\times m_i\mathbf{v}_i+\mathbf{r}_i\times m_i\mathbf{a}_i)=\sum_{i=1}^{n}\mathbf{r}_i\times\mathbf{F}_i \qquad (3\text{-}9)$$
$$\equiv\sum_{i=1}^{n}\mathbf{N}_i\equiv\mathbf{N}$$

where $\mathbf{a}_i$ is the acceleration of mass m_i, $\mathbf{F}_i$ is the force applied to it, and $\mathbf{N}_i$ is defined to be the torque. The *torque* is the rate of change of the angular momentum and is produced by forces acting other than through the center of mass of the spacecraft.

As shown in Fig. 3-13, the response of the spacecraft to an external torque depends on the initial value of the spacecraft's angular momentum. In all three cases shown, the torque is applied by pushing down on the left side of the spacecraft and up on the right side. Following the right-hand rule, this produces a torque or change in angular momentum in the direction out of the plane of the paper. In Fig. 3-13A, the spacecraft has no initial angular momentum. Therefore, the applied forces cause the spacecraft to rotate in the direction of the forces, thus creating an angular momentum out of the plane of the paper. In Fig. 3-13B, the spacecraft is rotating counterclockwise such that it has an initial angular momentum directed out of the plane of the paper. In this case, the applied torque increases the angular momentum and causes the spacecraft to spin faster. In Fig. 3-13C, the spacecraft is spinning about an axis in the plane of the paper, with the left side of the spacecraft coming out and the right side moving in such that the angular momentum vector is in the plane of the paper, pointed up. In this case, the applied torque does not change the magnitude of the angular momentum, but instead causes the angular momentum vector to change direction and rotate out of the plane of the paper.

The torques $\mathbf{N}_i$ on the individual points in a rigid body are due to both forces between the points and externally applied forces. Under very general conditions, the internal torques sum to zero, and the resultant torque, $\mathbf{N}$, is simply the torque due to external forces. As discussed in Sec. 3.1, the external torques are of two kinds: (1) *disturbance torques*, caused by environmental effects such as aerodynamic drag or solar radiation pressure and (2) deliberately applied *control torques* from actuators such as gas jets or magnetic coils. (Control torques due to reaction wheels do not change the total angular momentum of the spacecraft because they are not external torques. A spacecraft with reaction wheels is not a rigid body; the control torques in this case cause a redistribution of the angular momentum between the wheels and the spacecraft body.)

A torque applied perpendicular to the existing angular momentum vector, $\mathbf{L}$, will cause the direction of $\mathbf{L}$ to change without altering its magnitude. The change in direction of the angular momentum vector due to an applied torque is called *precession.** The special case of slow precession due to a small applied torque (such that the mag-

* Note that this definition of precession, which has been adopted in spacecraft dynamics, is somewhat different from the meaning usually assumed in physics.

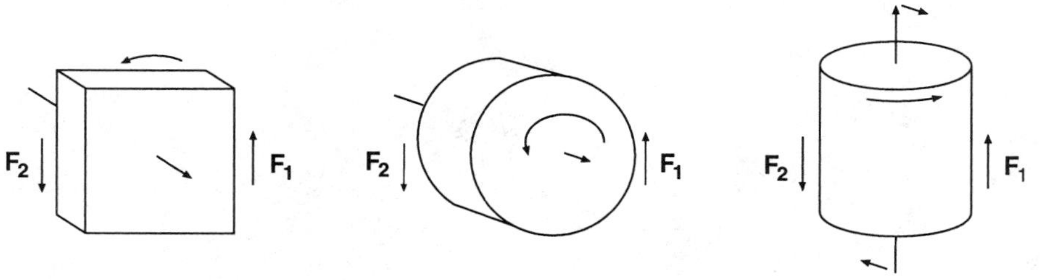

Fig. 3-13. Results of the Application of an External Torque. In all three cases the torque is applied by applying a force upward on the right and downward on the left, producing a torque out of the plane of the paper. (A) Torque on a spacecraft with no existing angular momentum rotates the spacecraft in the direction of the applied forces. (B) Torque parallel to the angular momentum vector increases or decreases the spin rate. (C) Torque perpendicular to an existing angular momentum moves the rotation axis in the direction of the applied torque, perpendicular to the existing angular momentum.

nitude of the integral of the torque over a spin period is much less than $|\mathbf{L}|$) is known as *drift*. Environmental torques are a common source of attitude drift.

Although internal torques do not change the value of the angular momentum in inertial space, they can affect the behavior of **L** in spacecraft-fixed coordinates. Additionally, if the internal forces between the components of a spacecraft lead to energy dissipation (through solid or viscous friction or magnetic eddy currents, for example) the rotational kinetic energy of the spacecraft will decrease. These effects can be understood with the aid of two concepts—the angular momentum sphere and the energy ellipsoid shown in Figs. 3-14 and 3-15. The rotational kinetic energy of a rigid spacecraft, E_k, is given by:

$$E_k = \frac{1}{2}\left(I_1\omega_1^2 + I_2\omega_2^2 + I_3\omega_3^2\right) = \frac{1}{2}\left(L_1^2 / I_1 + L_2^2 / I_2 + L_3^2 / I_3\right) \qquad (3\text{-}10)$$

where I_1, I_2, and I_3 are the spacecraft principal moments of inertia; ω_1, ω_2, and ω_3 are the angular velocity components about the body-fixed principal axes; and L_1, L_2, and L_3 are the components of the spacecraft angular momentum vector along the principal axes [the equivalence of the two forms of Eq. (3-10) follows from Eq. (3-3)].

Consider a representation of the spacecraft angular momentum as a point in a 3-dimensional *angular momentum space* with 3 coordinate axes corresponding to L_1, L_2, and L_3 respectively. The locus of points in this space consistent with the fixed rotational kinetic energy is the set of points satisfying Eq. (3-10) which can be rewritten as:

$$\frac{L_1^2}{2I_1E_k} + \frac{L_2^2}{2I_2E_k} + \frac{L_3^2}{2I_3E_k} = 1 \qquad (3\text{-}11)$$

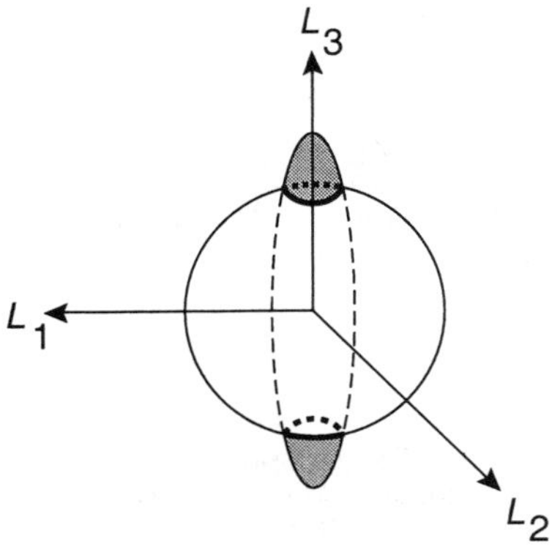

Fig. 3-14. Angular Momentum Sphere (|L| = constant) and Energy Ellipsoid (|E_k| = constant) for a Nutating Spacecraft with $I_1 = I_2 < I_3$. The coordinate frame is the angular momentum sphere in spacecraft principal coordinates. **L** is constrained to move on the intersection of the 2 surfaces. Dissipating energy leads to reducing the size of the energy ellipsoid and stable rotation about the L_3 axis. (Note that the prolate energy ellipsoid corresponds to an oblate spacecraft.)

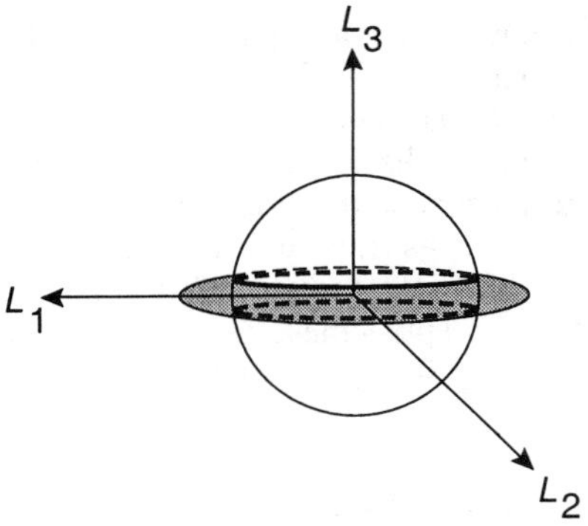

Fig. 3-15. Angular Momentum Sphere and Energy Ellipsoid for a Nutating Spacecraft with $I_1 = I_2 > I_3$. Dissipating energy leads to reducing the size of the energy ellipsoid and stable rotation about an axis in the L_1/L_2 plane, called a flat spin. (Note that the oblate energy ellipsoid corresponds to a prolate spacecraft.)

From the form of the equation, it is clear that these points lie on an ellipsoid with semi-axis lengths of $\sqrt{2I_1E_k}$, $\sqrt{2I_2E_k}$, and $\sqrt{2I_3E_k}$. This is the *energy ellipsoid* corresponding to rotational kinetic energy, E_k.

In the absence of torques, the components of **L** in inertial space are constant but time-dependent in spacecraft-fixed coordinates. The magnitude of the angular momentum, $\mathbf{L} \equiv |\mathbf{L}|$, is constant in either frame. The locus of points in angular momentum space corresponding to a fixed value of L is just a sphere of radius L, called the *angular momentum sphere*. The locus of possible values of **L** in the **spacecraft frame** is the intersection of the angular momentum sphere and the energy ellipsoid.

Figure 3-14 shows this intersection for the case $I_1 = I_2 < I_3$ and Fig. 3-15 shows it for $I_1 = I_2 > I_3$. In both cases of axial symmetry, the locus of possible values of the angular momentum consists of 2 circles about the symmetry axis. The angular momentum vector in the spacecraft frame moves at a constant rate along one of the circles. This motion is nutation as described in Sec. 3.2.2. Fig. 3-14 corresponds to Fig. 3-8B with $\mathbf{P_3}$ held fixed and Fig. 3-15 corresponds to Fig. 3-8A.

This alternative representation of nutation can be used to analyze the effects of energy dissipation. In the presence of dissipative forces, the energy ellipsoid shrinks in size while maintaining its shape and the angular momentum sphere is unchanged. The angular momentum vector continues to rotate along the intersection of the shrinking energy ellipsoid and the angular momentum sphere. This path has an approximately spiral shape. The shrinking of the energy ellipsoid continues until it lies wholly within and is tangent to the angular momentum sphere. For $I_1 = I_2 < I_3$ (Fig. 3-14), this results in $\mathbf{L}$ being aligned along the positive or negative 3-axis. For $I_1 = I_2 > I_3$ (Fig. 3-15), the limit occurs when $\mathbf{L}$ lies on the circle defined by $L_3 = 0$ and $L_1^2 + L_2^2 = L^2$. It can be shown that $\mathbf{L}$ remains fixed at a point on this circle. In both examples, nutation stops, and the motion of the body is simple rotation about a fixed axis. Clearly, at this time energy dissipation must also stop.

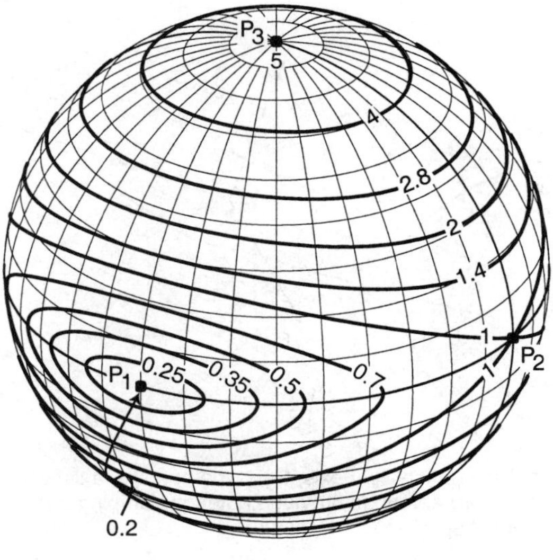

Fig. 3-16. Intersections of Angular Momentum Sphere and Energy Ellipsoid with Various Energies for Moments of Inertia (I_1:I_2:I_3) in the ratio 25:5:1. P_1, P_2, and P_3 are the principal axes.

If there is no axis of symmetry, the intersections of the energy ellipsoid and the angular momentum sphere are not circles. A family of intersections for different values of E_k with $I_1 > I_2 > I_3$ is shown in Fig. 3-16. When energy dissipation ceases, the angular momentum vector becomes aligned with the major principal axis, i.e., the axis corresponding to the largest principal moment of inertia. It is clear from Eq. (3-10) that when $\mathbf{L}$ is constant, the kinetic energy is minimized when rotation is about the major principal axis. If the nominal spacecraft spin axis is the major principal axis, nutation represents excess kinetic energy above that required by the magnitude of the angular momentum. The reduction of this excess kinetic energy and the corresponding alignment of the rotation axis with the principal axis of the largest moment of inertia is known as *nutation damping*. Several mechanisms for nutation damping are available. Passive nutation damping occurs when the flexibility of the spacecraft's structure removes excess energy. Active nutation damping occurs by specific devices intended to dissipate excess energy.

If the nominal spacecraft spin axis is a principal axis other than the major principal axis, energy dissipation results in an increase in nutation. The motion when energy dissipation stops is pure rotation about an axis perpendicular to the nominal spin axis. This is the condition known as a flat spin which we have previously described. Probably the best example of this is Explorer I (Fig. 3-17), the first American satellite, which was launched Feb. 1, 1958. It was designed to spin about its longitudinal symmetry axis, which was an axis of minimum moment of inertia, but the motion rapidly changed into a flat spin mode. This was the result of energy dissipation due to vibrational motion of the antennas. This is an example of the case illustrated in Fig. 3-15. Energy dissipation mechanisms will not reduce nutation and active nutation damping by some means of external control torque must be used.

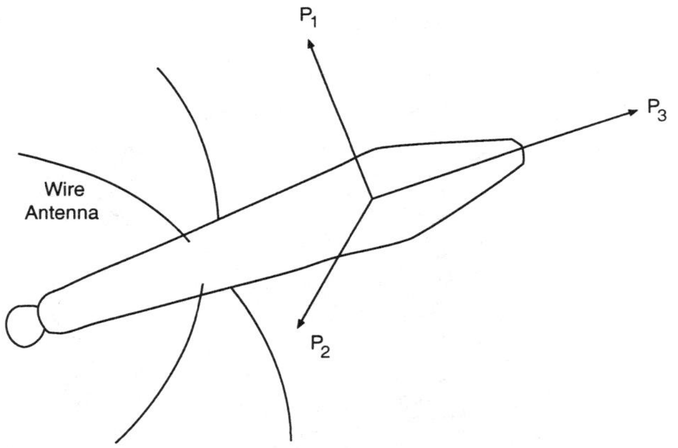

Fig. 3-17. Explorer I. The nominal spin axis, $\mathbf{P_3}$, is the principal axis with the minimum moment of inertia. The wire antennas provided nutation damping and the spacecraft dropped quickly into a flat spin.

3.3 Attitude Determination

From the point of view of the control system, attitude determination is relatively unimportant. It simply provides the difference signal used by the control algorithm. Thus, most of the reference works at the end of this chapter are on attitude control and either ignore the measurement problem altogether or treat it lightly. However, from the perspective of the end user, attitude measurements and attitude determination are critical since they provide the answer to the fundamental questions of where am I looking or where am I pointing? For the spacecraft engineer, this problem is typically equally or more complex than the control problem.

We begin by looking at how the attitude is specified, then discuss the sensors used for attitude measurements, and finally the attitude determination process itself.

3.3.1 Specifying the Attitude

There are 2 basic types of attitude specification–giving the orientation of a single axis or vector (such as the spin axis or the boresight direction that an instrument is pointing) or giving the orientation of the entire spacecraft, which means specifying both an axis and an orientation about that axis. The latter is frequently called *3-axis attitude* since specifying the complete orientation of the spacecraft is equivalent to specifying the orientation of all 3 axes.

Specifying the direction of a single axis or vector corresponds to specifying a direction in space, which requires 2 independent numbers. The most common ways of doing this are listed in Table 3-8. Specifying the 3-axis attitude requires 3 independent numbers. The easiest way to visualize this is specifying the direction of any single spacecraft axis and then the rotational orientation of the spacecraft about that axis.

TABLE 3-8. Specifying a Direction in Space (i.e., an Axis) Requires 2 Independent Numbers.

Number Pair	Use
Azimuth, Elevation	General coordinate definition
Two Components of a Unit Vector	General coordinate definition
Longitude, Latitude	Direction to a point on the Earth's surface as seen from the center of the Earth
Right Ascension, Declination (Celestial Coordinates)	Directions in inertial space
Ecliptic Longitude, Ecliptic Latitude	Directions to the planets as seen from the Sun
Azimuth, Nadir Angle (= Angle from Apparent Center of the Earth)	Coordinates with respect to the Earth as seen from the spacecraft

As we have discussed several times, the attitude is the rotational equivalent of the orbit. The orbit can be fully specified at any instant by specifying the position and velocity. From this information, all future values of the position and the velocity can be determined if the forces are accurately known. Similarly, the attitude state is fully specified by giving the attitude and attitude rate at any instant. As with the orbit, this requires 6 independent parameters. Given these 6 parameters, the full future attitude motion of the spacecraft can be determined if all of the torques and mass properties are known.

In orbit analysis, most computations are done in orthogonal inertial coordinates. This represents a "natural" frame for both computation and interpretation. Unfortunately, there is no obvious, easy-to-use, easy-to-compute comparable coordinate system for the attitude. Consequently, a number of alternatives have developed over time, some of which provide better physical insight, and others which are better for computation.

One of the most useful concepts for both analysis and interpretation is to think of the attitude as a coordinate transformation. For example, consider a camera held by an astronaut pointed at some location on the Earth's horizon, and tilted down 10 deg with respect to that horizon. I can think of the attitude of the camera as the direction it is pointed and how it is tilted. Alternatively, I can also think of the attitude as the coordinate transformation that takes objects viewed in the camera frame and transforms them into coordinates relative to my surroundings such as azimuth and elevation. Both approaches are equivalent. Given the pointing direction and orientation of the camera, I can determine the coordinate transformation that goes from the camera frame to an Earth frame or vice versa. Similarly, given the coordinate transformation, I can determine the direction of the center of the camera, and the tilt relative to the horizon. The advantage of the coordinate transformation approach is that I can now change the problem of dealing with the attitude into a problem of successive coordinate transformations. Depending on how my measurements are made, I could, for example, transform the camera coordinates into astronaut-fixed coordinates, into Orbiter coordinates, and then into elevation and azimuth relative to the center of the Earth.

Coordinate transformations are most commonly represented by an orthogonal matrix. This gives rise to the concept of an *attitude matrix*, i.e., the matrix that transforms one orientation into another. For example, we might measure the (x, y) position of a star on the focal plane of a star camera. Multiplying by the mounting matrix of the camera gives the star location in spacecraft coordinates. Multiplying again by the spacecraft attitude matrix gives the star's direction in inertial space (or with respect to the Earth, depending on what the attitude is measured with respect to). Note that the attitude matrix is a 3×3 real orthogonal matrix and, therefore, has only 3 independent components.

As shown in Table 3-9, there are a variety of alternative methods for specifying 3-axis attitude. The attitude matrix, also called the *direction-cosine matrix*, is only one option. There is no single best approach and the choice for any particular application depends on the application and the need for either computational speed or physical interpretation. For example, quaternions were first used as a means of spacecraft attitude representation at Goddard Space Flight Center for support of the MagSat mission in the 1970s which needed attitude results several times per second, 24 hours per day. While this could easily be accomplished on any personal computer today, at the time it represented a dramatic throughput requirement. Consequently, in spite of their very inconvenient physical interpretation,* quaternions were chosen because they provided the fastest processing. This is not a particularly serious issue today, although quaternions are still often selected as the attitude representation of choice. With computer speeds now available, it is likely that an alternative representation that provides better physical interpretation would often be superior to minimize the time and errors associated with data interpretation, system analysis, and debugging.

Unfortunately, the single most common method of expressing 3-axis attitude is also one of the most inconvenient. These are called *roll*, *pitch*, and *yaw* or *RPY* coordinates, and are illustrated in Fig. 3-18. The interpretation shown in the figure is the most common, but by no means the only definition of these coordinates. The definitions of the specific axes vary from mission to mission and often change even within a single mission. In this "standard" definition, roll, pitch, and yaw are positive (right-handed)

* The *quaternion* is a 4-component attitude representation. The first 3 components are $q_i = e_i \sin(\Phi/2)$. The fourth is $q_4 = \cos(\Phi/2)$. Here e_i is the ith component of the Euler axis, $\hat{\mathbf{e}}$, and Φ is the Euler rotation angle. The sum of the squares of the 4 components is 1. Quaternions have convenient arithmetic properties but not a particularly convenient physical interpretation.

TABLE 3-9. Alternative Representations of 3-Axis Attitude.

Parameter-ization	Notation	Advantages	Disadvantages	Common Applications
Attitude Matrix = Direction cosine matrix	$A = [A_{ij}]$	No singularities No trig functions Convenient product rule for successive rotations	Six redundant parameters	In analysis, to transform vectors from one reference frame to another
Euler axis/angle	$\mathbf{E}, \Phi$	Clear physical interpretation	One redundant parameter Axis undefined when $\sin \Phi = 0$ Uses trig functions	Commanding slew maneuvers
Quaternion = Euler symmetric parameters	$(q) = q_1, q_2, q_3, q_4$	No singularities No trig functions Convenient product rule for successive rotations	One redundant parameter No obvious physical interpretation	Onboard inertial navigation
Gibbs vector	$\mathbf{G}$	No redundant parameters No trig functions Convenient product rule for successive rotations	Infinite for 180-deg rotation	Analytic studies
Euler angles	ϕ, θ, ψ	No redundant parameters Physical interpretations clear in some cases	Uses trig functions Singular at some θ No convenient product rule for successive rotations	Analytic studies Input/output Onboard attitude control of 3-axis stabilized spacecraft
Roll, Pitch, Yaw	R, P, Y	Easily understood In common use Related to aviation coordinates	Easily misunderstood Do not commute Specification often incomplete in practice	Spacecraft control

rotations about the roll, pitch, and yaw axes respectively. The *yaw axis* is defined as being the direction toward the center of the Earth, the *pitch axis* is defined as toward negative orbit normal, and the *roll axis* is perpendicular to these two such that $\mathbf{R} = \mathbf{P} \times \mathbf{Y}$. In a circular orbit, the roll axis will be in the direction of the velocity vector. Roll, pitch, and yaw coordinates are then taken as right-handed rotations about their respective axes. This definition corresponds to the coordinates you would use if you were flying the spacecraft as though it were an airplane, facing in the direction of motion, with the Earth beneath you. Pitch would be an up and down motion of the nose. Roll would be a side to side rotation about the longitudinal axis. Yaw would be a change in the direction you were looking side to side, i.e., rotation about a vertical axis. Unfortunately, the axes take on different meanings for different missions and, quite frequently, are not well defined. For example, it is common to see discussions of "roll about the Sun line" which provides a definition for the roll axis (i.e., the direction toward the Sun in this case) but leaves both yaw and pitch undefined except to imply that they are in the plane orthogonal to the direction of the Sun.

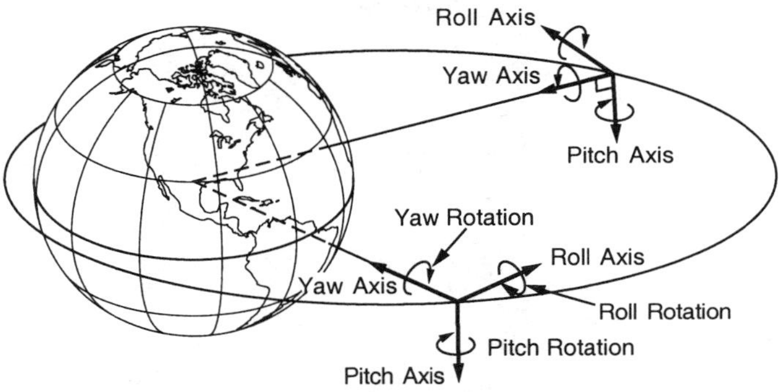

Fig. 3-18. The Roll, Pitch, Yaw (RPY) Coordinate System. See text for explanation and discussion.

A far more serious complication with RPY coordinates is that roll, pitch, and yaw do not commute. That is to say, a roll of 3 deg followed by a pitch of 2 deg is not the same as a pitch of 2 deg followed by a roll of 3 deg. You can demonstrate this for yourself by the method shown in the boxed example. Consequently, to be fully defined, RPY coordinates must specify the order of the rotations as well as the values and this is rarely done. Consequently, even if the coordinate axes are known, the end attitude is usually unknown. Roll, pitch, and yaw are frequently used for control systems and in this application, they at least work moderately well. While the rotations do not commute, they come close to commuting for small angles. Consequently, for control systems problems for small angles only, RPY coordinates typically work acceptably well, but are remarkably bad when used for large angles. Unfortunately, they are still in widespread use both in spacecraft systems and the general literature base.

3.3.2 Attitude Sensing

The process of measuring the attitude is typically one of the major cost-drivers for the spacecraft bus. Most spacecraft make use of multiple sensors because of the requirements of different mission phases, the need to maintain 3-axis attitude (usually requiring more than one sensor), and the need for backups in case of sensor failure. The relative advantages of the alternative measurement sources were given in Table 3-2. Here we discuss the performance of various sensors, how they work, and how they are evolving. The basic performance parameters for typical attitude sensors are summarized in Table 3-10, applications of these sensors are described in Table 3-12, and on-orbit performance history is summarized in Table 3-13. It is important to keep in mind that very rapid evolution of these sensors is occurring, largely because of the availability of on-orbit processing, which can make the sensors smaller, lighter-weight, and, at the same time, more accurate. Consequently, sensors on future missions can be expected to be significantly better than those listed in the tables.

TABLE 3-10. Typical Attitude Sensor Hardware Parameters. Attitude sensor evolution is proceeding very rapidly. More modern sensors should be smaller, lighter weight, and inherently more accurate.

Sensor	Accuracy (deg)	Weight (kg)	Power (W)	Representative Suppliers
Magnetometer	0.5 to 3	0.3 to 1.2	< 1	Schonstedt, Delco, Billingsly
Sun Sensor	0.005 to 3	0.1 to 2	0 to 3	Adcole, Goodrich
Earth Sensor:				
Scanning	0.03 to 0.25	1 to 4	5 to 10	Goodrich, Ithaco
Static	0.02 to 1.0	0.5 to 3	0.3 to 5	Goodrich
Star Sensor	0.0003 to 0.01	2 to 5	5 to 20	Ball, Honeywell, Hughes, Goodrich
Gyroscope	0.001 to 1 deg/hr	1 to 25	10 to 200	Northrop Grumman, Bendix, Honeywell, Litton
Directional Antennas	0.01 to 5	various	N/A	Various
GPS Receiver	0.3 to 1.0	1 to 3	5 to 10	Motorola, Honeywell, Allen Osborne Associates

Costs between alternative sensing mechanisms vary dramatically. In some cases, sensing may not be necessary at all (definitely the cheapest approach). Of the sensors listed, magnetometers typically have the lowest cost. Sun sensors can also be extremely economical, depending on the accuracy that is required. Earth sensors are in the moderate price range while star sensors and gyroscopes tend to be both highly accurate and extremely expensive. As sensors continue to evolve, the relative cost may change with time, and with it, the preferred approach may also shift. In general, the trade is between accuracy and cost, going from magnetometers at the low-cost, low-accuracy end to star sensor/gyroscope combinations with high cost and high accuracy. Robustness is also an issue, with the simpler and usually cheaper systems being more robust and the high accuracy systems having a larger number of failure modes. Consequently, a spacecraft using star sensors and gyros will frequently use Earth sensors and Sun sensors for a fail-safe mode and for attitude acquisition.

Magnetometers

Magnetometers are relatively inexpensive with very low weight and power requirements. These are traditionally used as a means to identify when to turn on magnetic torquers. Like the torquers, magnetometers are used principally in low-Earth orbit because the magnetic field strength, and therefore the accuracy of the measurement, falls off as $1/r^3$ with distance from the Earth.

Magnetometers are traditionally thought of as low accuracy devices for two reasons: (1) ambient fields generated by the spacecraft itself, and (2) inaccuracy in the magnetic field model of the Earth. With modern onboard computers, carrying a high

3 deg up, 2 deg over vs. 2 deg over, 3 deg up

Roll, pitch, and yaw are more widely used than any other attitude coordinate system. Unfortunately, a major problem is that they don't commute, i.e., the result depends on the order in which they are done. To see this, hold a book parallel to the floor so that you can read the front cover as you look down, as shown in Fig. 3-19A. The spine of the book is to the left and someone in front of you is seeing the top ends of the pages. Now rotate the book 90 deg about a "front to back" horizontal axis by bringing the left edge of the book up such that you are now reading the spine. People in front of you are still seeing the top ends of the pages, and someone to your right can now see the front cover, although sideways. Now rotate the book 90 deg about a vertical axis, by moving the top of the book to the left. You can now read the spine and someone in front of you is seeing the front cover sideways.

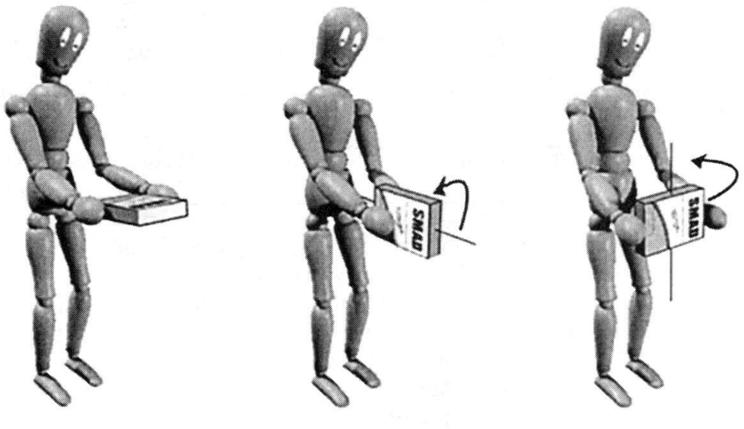

Fig. 3-19. 90 Deg Rotation About Horizontal (Front-Back) Axis Followed by 90 Deg Rotation About Vertical Axis.

Now do the **same rotations** in reverse order, as shown in Fig. 3-20. First, return the book to its original orientation, so that you are reading the front cover as you look down at it. Rotate it 90 deg about a vertical axis by moving the top of the book to the left, so a person in front of you now sees the edge of the pages opposite the spin. Now rotate it 90 deg about the front to back horizontal axis by bringing the left edge (i.e., the top of the book) up. You are now seeing the tops of the pages and the person in front of you is seeing the sides of the pages. **Two identical successive rotations of 90 deg about the same axes, but in different order, give very different results.**

The implication of this failure to commute is that in RPY coordinates, we must specify not only the coordinates but the order in which they are done. Unfortunately, this rarely occurs. One of the reasons RPY coordinates work in many cases is that the results of doing the rotations in a different order gives nearly the same results for small rotations. How nearly? Table 3-21 shows the difference between X deg over and Y deg up versus Y deg up followed by X deg over for a few representative measurements. Does this difference matter? For almost any space mission, 90 deg makes a big difference. For smaller angles, it depends upon the precision that is required for your particular application.

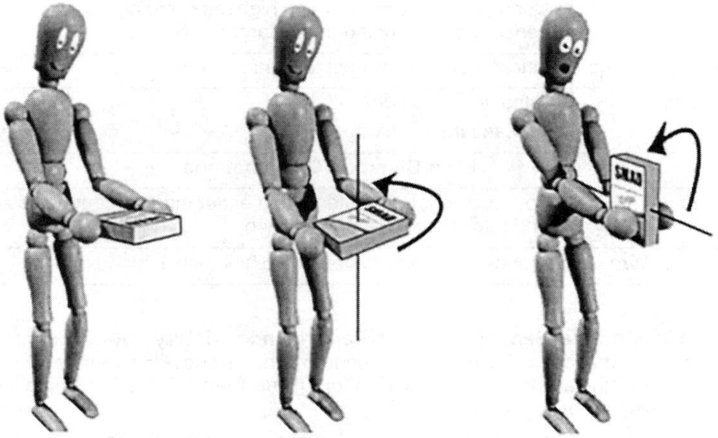

Fig. 3-20. 90 Deg Rotation About Vertical Axis Followed by 90 Deg Rotation About Horizontal (Front-Back) Axis.

TABLE 3-11. Difference in Y Up, X Over Versus X Over, Y Up. Error is the angular separation between going Y up, then X over and going X over, then Y up.)

X (alpha)	Y (delta)	Error
1	1	0.0002
1	90	1.00
90	1	1.00
5	20	0.31
10	10	0.21
20	20	1.67
30	30	5.43
60	60	35.66
90	90	90.00

TABLE 3-12. Attitude Sensor Typical Applications.

Sensor	Applications
Magnetometer	• Control momentum unloading using magnetic torquers • Low accuracy attitude
Sun Sensor	• Equipment protection • Attitude acquisition • Yaw sensing
Earth Sensor	• Roll and pitch sensing for Earth-oriented applications • Attitude acquisition
Star Sensor	• Highest accuracy sensing for all applications
Gyroscope	• Interpolation between star sensor measurements • During maneuvers (provides high data rate and coverage when other sensors are off their nominal target)
Directional Antenna	• Orientation with respect to signal source
GPS Receiver	• Attitude acquisition • Low accuracy attitude
Most Common Combinations	
Earth/Sun	• Low cost, low risk system used either independently or as acquisition and back up for star sensor/gyro
Star Sensor/Gyro	• Highest accuracy system (also high risk, high cost)

TABLE 3-13. Attitude Sensor On-Orbit Performance History. By definition, on-orbit performance is historical. More modern sensors should be more accurate. Errors are 1 sigma, after on-orbit calibration. [Data from GSFC; GPS data from RADCAL mission]

Sensor	Systematic Error (deg)	Random Error (deg)	Total Error (deg)
3-Axis Stabilized Missions			
*CCD Star Tracker**			~0.00083 (3 arc sec)
Fixed Head Star Tracker	0.003 to 0.014	0.003 to 0.004	0.004 to 0.014
Fine Sun Sensor	0.005 to 0.26	0.003 to 0.15	0.006 to 0.26
Digital Sun Sensor	0.04 to 0.2	0.09 to 0.23	0.09 to 0.3
Horizon Sensor	0.03 to 0.2	0.05 to 0.5	0.1 to 0.5
3-Axis Magnetometer	–0.4	0.35 to 1.1	0.5 to 1.2
Spin-Stabilized Missions			
Multi-Slit Star Sensor			0.017
1-Axis Fine Sun Sensor	0.05	0.004	0.05
1-Axis Digital Sun Sensor	0.12 to 0.5	0.08 to 0.5	0.1 to 0.7
V-Slit Sun Sensor	0.1 to 0.15	0.003 to 0.2	0.1 to 0.25
Horizon Sensor	0.04 to 0.5	0.02 to 0.8	0.1 to 1.0
Magnetometer	0.5	0.4	0.7
GPS Receiver	—	—	0.3 to 0.5

*Estimated value. Insufficient data for on-orbit assessment.

accuracy magnetic field model is no longer a significant problem. However, making a magnetically clean spacecraft to use a magnetometer as a high accuracy device is still difficult and expensive because of both magnetic materials and magnetic fields generated by current loops throughout the spacecraft.

Sun Sensors

Sun sensors are the single most commonly used sensors on spacecraft. The Sun is the most easily identified object in the spacecraft sky, and in some respects, the most important, because of its criticality for power generation and potential damage to many instruments. Consequently, Sun sensors are frequently used not only as an attitude reference, but also as a mechanism for pointing solar arrays or as a warning device to provide keep-out with respect to other devices (e.g., optical sensors or cryogenic dewars) which may be damaged by looking directly at the Sun or even being in sunlight.

As listed in Table 3-14, there are a wide variety of Sun sensor types ranging from very simple cosine detectors to ultra high accuracy device sensors for scientific work. The cosine detector is simply a solar cell that measures the intensity of sunlight falling on it. The energy on the surface will be simply the energy density of solar radiation (1,367 W/m^2 at the distance of the Earth) times the cosine of the angle of incidence. Thus, the solar cell measures the cosine of the angle between the direction of the Sun and the vector normal to the surface of the cell. This implies that the device will be insensitive when the Sun is normal to the cell and gain sensitivity at shallower angles. However, at all angles, the accuracy of the cosine detector is limited.

TABLE 3-14. Most Common Types of Sun Sensors.

Type	Design
Cosine detector	A solar cell used to measure the amount of sunlight falling on it (proportional to the cosine of the incidence angle); more complex units use several such cells
Digital	Uses a slit in front of a digitally coded detector
Slit sensor for 3-axis Spacecraft	Uses 1 or more slits in front of a detector pattern. Output from detectors used to determine 2 components of Sun orientation with respect to the sensor
Slit sensor for Spinners	Vertical slit used only for timing and rotation angle measurements. Vertical slit plus angled slit for elevation angle measurements

Most moderate accuracy Sun sensors make use of some type of slit design with one or more detectors behind the slit to determine the angle of the Sun relative to the sensor normal. These sensors typically have accuracies that are a moderate fraction of the Sun's angular diameter of 0.5 deg. The most accurate Sun sensors provide some means of measuring intensity across the solar disk in order to determine the direction to the centroid of the disk to better than 0.005 deg. Sun sensors come in a wide variety of designs, several of which are shown in Fig. 3-21.

Earth Sensors

Traditionally, Earth sensors have been used on most Earth-oriented spacecraft to measure pitch and roll. The Earth represents a large, easily identified target, and is the object with respect to which we usually want to know the attitude. As listed in Table 3-15, there are more different types of Earth sensors than any other sensor.

Digital Sun Sensors **Fine Sun Sensors**

Fig. 3-21. Typical Sun Sensors. (Photos courtesy of Adcole Corp.)

Most Earth sensors work in the infrared region of the spectrum from 14 to 16 microns. In the visible portion of the spectrum, the Earth shines by reflected sunlight and, therefore, is very bright in daylight and dark over the nighttime hemisphere. This makes determining the centroid of the Earth's disk extremely challenging. In addition, the boundary between the light and dark hemispheres, known as the *terminator*, is exceptionally fuzzy and frequently represents more of a fading away than a real boundary. However, like all objects, the Earth emits thermal radiation corresponding to its temperature. At an absolute temperature of about 300 K, the Earth emits an approximately uniform glow in the near infrared. This thermal radiation seen from space comes predominately from the Earth's upper atmosphere. Although the thermal spectrum is relatively broad, there are a number of absorption lines due to water that cause significant variations depending upon both the temperature and humidity of the atmosphere over any given region. Limiting sensors to the 14 to 16 micron band reduces these atmospheric variations and provides a moderately uniform target for which the centroid can be easily determined. Typically, the edge of the Earth's disk can be determined to ±0.1 to ±0.2 deg. This may be significantly improved by either algorithmic approaches or long term averaging.

An Earth sensor is also called a *horizon sensor* because it detects the transition between space and Earth, which occurs at the horizon. The preferred method of detection depends largely on the application and on the orbit, particularly the altitude. For spinning spacecraft, the simplest Earth sensor is an infrared telescope, or *pipper*,* looking out into space, which detects an *incrossing* and *outcrossing* as it goes from space to Earth and Earth to space. For more sophisticated applications, it is possible to use a stepper motor to vary the angle of the telescope with respect to the spin axis of the spacecraft, or to use a scanning sensor which sweeps out a more complex pattern on the sky. (See Sec. 8.3.1)

* The name comes from the operation of the sensor which provides a short pulse or "pip" when the field enters or leaves the disk of the Earth.

TABLE 3-15. Most Common Types of Earth Sensors. All but the last two work in the IR portion of the spectrum.

Type	Design
Spinning Spacecraft	
Pipper	Detector mounted at a fixed angle relative to the spin axis
Stepping Sensor	Detector that can be moved in steps relative to the spin axis
Scanner	Rotates continuously about an axis approximately normal to the spin axis (can provide full sky coverage)
3-Axis Stabilized Spacecraft	
Conical Scanner	Rotates to provide 2 horizon crossings with a single sensor
Dual Scanner	Field of view split to provide 4 horizon crossings per scan
Dithering	More limited scan range used primarily in geosynchronous orbit
Mini-static	Provides a single edge intersection at a fixed location
Static	Provides 6–8 edge intersection around the perimeter of the Earth
Array	Covers most or all of the Earth (typically low-cost visible sensors that work only on the daylight Earth)
UV Array	Provides an image of the Earth disk in the ultraviolet

Most spacecraft today are 3-axis stabilized. One option for such spacecraft is to use a sensor comparable to the piper with a motor providing the scan motion. The center of the in and out crossings provides the azimuthal orientation to the direction of the center of the Earth. The spacing between the in and out crossings combined with the angular size of the Earth determines the angular distance from the center of the sensor scan to the center of the Earth. Consequently, if we know the altitude of the spacecraft and if the Sun doesn't interfere with the horizon crossings, a single scan can provide both roll and pitch for the spacecraft. In addition, if we use either 2 scanners or a single scanner with 2 fields of view mounted at different angles, we can obtain 4 crossings. Because 3 points define a small circle, such as the apparent disk of the Earth, we can use these 4 crossings to provide altitude independent attitude, even when the Sun is in one of the fields of view. This same process can be used from LEO to GEO. In low-Earth orbit, the scans typically need to be very wide, whereas in geosynchronous orbit it is sufficient for them to be wide enough to cover the disk of the Earth, which is only 8.7 deg in radius. Consequently, a typical geosynchronous scanning sensor uses 2 fields of view which dither back and forth, providing a total of 4 crossings, 2 above the equator and 2 below. These can determine the position of the Earth's centroid to within approximately ±0.03 deg.

Another option for both low-Earth orbit and geosynchronous is the *static sensor* which has one or more fixed fields of view which determine where the horizon lies along one sensitive axis. The static sensors can use either a single detector in a separate package that can be mounted at various locations on the spacecraft or can combine 6 to 10 detectors into a single package. In a sense, the static sensor has very limited applications, because it is only useful for nearly circular orbits at a fixed altitude. However, this represents by far most of the spacecraft launched in both low-Earth and geosynchronous orbits.

Another option is to provide a large array so that centroiding can be done by statistically processing the edge of the Earth's disk. For the reasons described above, visible light CCD arrays do not work well. Unfortunately, IR arrays are not yet a well developed technology, although work in this area is ongoing. Honeywell has been working for some time on an array that works in the UV and can detect both the Earth's horizon and stars. This has the advantage of providing the attitude both with respect to the Earth and, at the same time, with respect to inertial space.

Another hybrid device is the Scanwheel™ produced by Ithaco, which is a scanning Earth sensor that uses the rotating motion of a momentum wheel to provide the scan. This reduces the amount of hardware and, therefore, saves cost and weight.

Earth sensors can also be modified to become planet sensors for use in the vicinity of the Moon, Mars, or other planets. For planets with atmospheres, the principal requirement is to change the bandwidth and aperture to accommodate the planet's temperature. For bodies without atmospheres, such as the Moon, the problem is much more difficult because of the very wide temperature extremes between the lit and dark portions of the planet. In this case, planet sensors will typically be much less accurate. A few of the many types of Earth and planet sensors are shown in Fig. 3-22.

Mini ESA, Radiation Hardened (Triad)

Pair of Coarse Horizon Sensors

LEO ESA

MEO (Mid-Earth Orbit) ESA

Fig. 3-22. Typical Earth Sensors. (Photos courtesy of Goodrich.)

Star Sensors

Because they are point sources of light with remarkably well-known angular positions, stars provide the most accurate attitude reference for spacecraft, and therefore are used in nearly all systems requiring high accuracy. Traditionally, star sensors have been extremely complex and expensive and there were major problems with single event upsets and star identification. However, much of this has changed, and will be changing in the future with the introduction of low-cost CCD arrays and modern processors capable of providing much more sophisticated software. The memory for large star catalogs and the throughput required to process the star data is no longer a major stumbling block.

The basic concept of the CCD star tracker is extremely simple. We use the array much like a television camera to take a picture of the star field. We then identify the stars in software and determine the transformation matrix (i.e., the attitude) which transforms this image into the known angular position of the stars from a star catalog. However, the implementation can be complex in several respects. First, stars are essentially point sources of light. If the star images are smaller than the size of a pixel in the CCD array, accuracy will be limited to the pixel size. Therefore, star images are typically defocused to spread them over a number of pixels so that the centroid of the star image can be determined more accurately than a single pixel. Typically, this process can achieve an accuracy of approximately 1/10 the size of the pixel.

In addition, substantial processing is required to do attitude determination with a star sensor. First, we must create the image and do star image centroiding. A key problem is then the identification of the star pattern which may involve complex star identification or pattern recognition algorithms. Once this has been done, it is straightforward to calculate the transformation matrix that takes this image into the known star directions in inertial space.

Due to the rapid evolution of both sensing arrays and processors, star sensor technology is evolving very rapidly, and will continue to evolve over the next several years. Star sensors are becoming both more economical and more capable of dealing with problems such as single event upsets, planets, or paint flakes which look like stars. It is not yet clear how far this evolution will proceed and whether star sensors will ultimately replace the less accurate approaches of Earth and Sun sensing. A number of the typical modern star sensors are shown in Fig. 3-23.

Unit CT-602

Unit CT-633

Fig. 3-23. Typical Modern Star Tracker Units. (Photos courtesy of Ball Corp.)

Gyroscopes

Gyroscopes use the conservation of angular momentum to sense changes in their orientation with respect to inertial space. Traditional "*iron*" or *mechanical gyroscopes* use the torque required to maintain the orientation of a rotating wheel to sense any change in the orientation of the gyroscope. The fundamental problem is that gyroscopes can sense only changes in the attitude and have no way of sensing the absolute attitude. Because gyroscopes drift with time, they ultimately lose accuracy and become unacceptable as long-term sensors. Consequently, gyroscopes are always used in conjunction with some other sensor type. A typical combination is gyroscopes and star sensors. The star sensor provides accurate absolute inertial attitude and the gyroscope provides an estimate of the attitude when stars are not being tracked. In addition, gyroscopes are extremely useful for thruster burns due to their very high update rate and their ability to sense rapid attitude motion.

As shown in Table 3-16, more modern gyroscopes use a variety of new principles rather than the physical rotating wheel. These include the *ring laser gyro* and the *interferometric fiber-optic gyro* and *hemispherical resonator gyro*. Each of these has the potential to dramatically improve performance and extend the lifetime relative to traditional mechanical gyros. At the present time, not enough history has been accumulated to say how well they will work in space applications. The gyros themselves have the potential for extremely long life. However, the support electronics are often complex and expensive. Nonetheless, as system electronics continue to evolve, this may make the newer gyro types much more promising for future space application.

TABLE 3-16. Characteristics of Different Types of Gyroscopes.

System	Manufacturer	Drift (deg/hr)	Expected Life (yrs)	Reliability	Weight (kg)
Traditional Mechanical Gyro	Many	~0.075	3	0.99 @ 10 yrs (with very limited use)	~0.15
Dynamically Tuned Gyro (DTG)	Honeywell, Kearfott, Litton	0.03 to 0.2	7 to 12	0.96 @ 3 yr	3.6 to 36
Interferometric Fiber Optic Gyro (IFOG)	Honeywell	0.0007 to 0.1	10 to 20		14
Hemispherical Resonator Gyro (HRG)	Delco	0.001 to 0.002	>15	0.998 @ 15 yrs	
Ring Laser Gyro (RLG)	Honeywell, Kearfott, Litton	0.01	18		14

Directional Antennas

The basic approach in using directional antennas is to determine the direction of maximum signal strength in the field of view of the antenna. This is done, for example, by TDRS while tracking the Space Shuttle or other spacecraft in low-Earth orbit. Directional antennas have typically been used for open or closed loop pointing of the antenna itself rather than for general purpose attitude determination. Nonetheless, this has the potential for providing attitude information with payload instruments that are already on board the spacecraft.

GPS Receivers

The most modern technique for attitude determination is the use of a GPS receiver as an interferometer. The interferometer determines the angle between a specific GPS spacecraft and the line connecting 2 GPS antennas which are simultaneously receiving the signal from a single GPS satellite. The attitude accuracy that can be achieved by the GPS receiver depends on the *baseline*, or distance between the antennas. Unfortunately, spacecraft are rarely built like an optical bench so that the larger the spacing between the antennas, the more likely there will be flexure between them due to thermal bending as the spacecraft goes from eclipse into sunlight. Because the baseline is relatively short compared to the GPS wavelength, the accuracy of GPS sensors for attitude determination is typically limited to about 0.5 deg, although somewhat higher accuracies may be obtained as GPS processors become better adapted to space applications.

As shown in Fig. 3-24, to provide full 3-axis attitude for spacecraft, we need at least 3 GPS antennas sensing at least 2 GPS spacecraft. This still leaves an ambiguity in that the GPS spacecraft could be on either side of the plane formed by the 3 antennas. This can be fully resolved by adding a fourth non-coplanar antenna, although as a practical matter, the resolution of the ambiguity can also come from the fact that GPS antennas typically have only a hemispherical field of view.

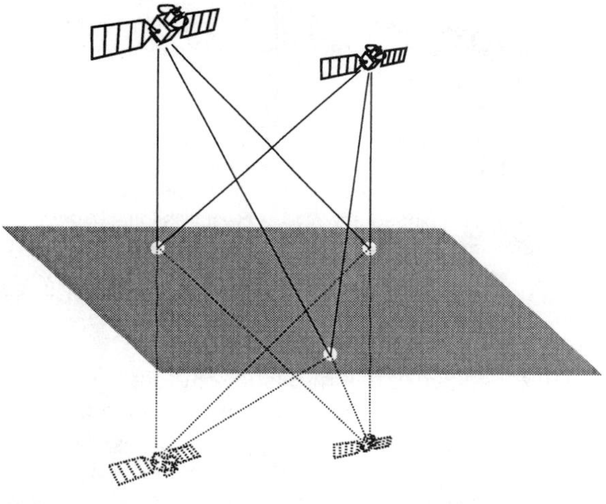

Fig. 3-24. GPS Attitude Sensing. Three GPS antennas sensing 2 GPS spacecraft provide unambiguous attitude, up to a symmetric solution based on being on the other side of the plane containing the 3 antennas.

3.3.3 Attitude Determination

Given the attitude sensor data, the remaining task is to process and combine the data in some manner to provide an estimate of the spacecraft attitude. Two basic techniques are available for doing this:

- *Deterministic attitude* uses the same number of observations as variables to obtain one or more discrete attitude solutions. These can then be improved by long term averaging and by using multiple measurement sets.

- *State estimation* or *filtering* corrects successive estimates of the attitude variables by moving an observation vector in phase space to more nearly match the latest observations. The most common method is called *Kalman Filtering** or *Extended Kalman Filtering* and provides a continuous moving estimate as new data is provided.

As listed in Table 3-17, there are advantages and disadvantages to both types of attitude solutions. The principal issue is one of accuracy versus divergence.† The filtering process can typically provide highly accurate, nearly optimal solutions. Deterministic solutions, while less accurate, are ordinarily more robust and not subject to divergence that can occur with filters in the presence of systematic errors and biases. Typically, some combination of both approaches is useful. For example, we may use a deterministic solution for initialization, as a watchdog, and to understand the information content of each of the measurements. We then use a filter to extract the most accurate statistical information from the data.

TABLE 3-17. Advantages and Disadvantages of Alternative Attitude Determination Methods.

Method	Advantages	Disadvantages
Deterministic	• Simple • Robust • Good physical insight • No initialization needed • Provides data checks • Immediate solution	• Possible multiple solutions • Singularities • Accuracy limited by noise • Hard to account for dynamics
State Estimation (Filtering)	• Highest accuracy • Statistically correct • Can account for dynamics • Can include biases directly in state vector	• Complex • Typically requires dynamic model • Potential divergence • Requires initialization • Requires time to converge • Poor physical insight • Responds badly to modeling errors

Another significant advantage of deterministic solutions is their capacity to provide data checks that can help determine whether the attitude data itself is correct or false. For example, each observation in a star sensor provides 2 coordinates for the observed star position. To determine 3-axis attitude, we need 3 independent numbers and need to observe the positions of 2 stars. The second star effectively measures the rotational

* The basic idea of Kalman filtering was developed in 1960–61 by Rudolph Kalman at the Research Institute for Advanced Studies in Baltimore and Richard Bucy of the Johns Hopkins Applied Physics Laboratory. (Kalman had just received his doctorate in 1957.) Kalman's approach was largely ignored for several years, but was then picked up by NASA as a way of dealing with satellite orbit determination. In particular, a Kalman filter was used in the Apollo 11 guidance computer on the first descent to the surface of the Moon. The Kalman filter design was started 9 months before the planned launch when Earth-based estimates proved insufficient and final check-out of the filter was completed on the day before the Apollo 11 launch.

† *Divergence* in a data filter occurs when the error becomes arbitrarily large very quickly, the filter rejects most or all of the data, and the solution becomes unrelated to the real answer. Overall, this is not a good circumstance for operational data analysis or spacecraft control.

orientation about the first star. However, observing the positions of 2 stars (or, equivalently, both coordinates for the centroids of the Sun and the Earth or the Earth and the Moon) provides 4 pieces of information and we have only 3 independent variables to determine. One way to think of the 4th piece of information is as the angular separation between the 2 stars. This angle, which is determined from the 2 observations, is not a function of the spacecraft's attitude because the angular separation between the stars is independent of the orientation of the observer. This value provides a check on both the star identification and on the accuracy of the angular measurements. If the observed angle between the 2 stars does not agree with the angle determined from the star catalog to within the estimated observation accuracy, then at least one of the stars has probably been incorrectly identified and we should not use this information for attitude determination.

Another problem in attitude determination is that of sensing in the right coordinate frame. In general, star sensors are far more accurate than Earth sensors. However, for an Earth-oriented mission, they may or may not provide more accurate results. Suppose, for example, that we wish to point our spacecraft straight down, i.e., toward the center of the Earth. If we use an Earth sensor as the attitude reference, we determine the centroid of the Earth as seen by the sensor and point the spacecraft in this direction in a traditional attitude control loop. However, if we use a more accurate star sensor for attitude determination, we can only determine the orientation of the spacecraft with respect to inertial space and not with respect to the center of the Earth. We need to know where the spacecraft is in inertial space in order to determine the direction to the Earth's center. This introduces an additional error, the spacecraft ephemeris, which may be significantly larger than the star sensor error. Consequently, although the attitude measurement itself may be more accurate with star sensors, the determination of the direction to the center of the Earth may or may not be more accurate than using an Earth sensor based system.

3.3.4 Attitude Determination Sample Problem

It is illustrative to go through a sample problem to see both how it is done and the sources of error which accumulate in the attitude determination process. To make the example simple, we choose a system that has only a single payload and a single sensor. We will assume that the mission is Earth observation, that there is a camera rigidly mounted on the spacecraft's structure, and that a star sensor is used for attitude determination. While processing an image, we identify an unknown rock formation and want to determine the latitude and longitude of the center of the formation. Simultaneously with the observation, we have seen two stars in our star sensor which we can identify.

What are the steps in determining the latitude and longitude of the center of the rock formation? Table 3-18 summarizes these steps and also lists the error sources that come into play during each step. Every step in the process introduces additional error. Some of the errors may be quite small, such as round-off error in the computer. Others, however, may be substantial and may be extremely difficult to determine, such as the difference in the mounting alignment between the star sensor and the payload. In principle, this was determined by very careful measurements at the time the spacecraft was assembled. However, the spacecraft has undergone very large accelerations and rapid vibration during launch, is now in a zero gravity environment rather than the 1 g of the integration facility, and is subject to strong thermal bending as it goes between sunlight and eclipse. All of these potentially change the relative orientation between the

TABLE 3-18. Steps in a Typical Attitude Determination and Pointing Problem. See text for discussion.

Step	Result	Error Source
Measure Star Positions Using Star Sensor	Coordinates of stars in sensor field of view	Star sensor measurement error
Multiply by Star Sensor Mounting Matrix	Orientation of stars in spacecraft coordinate frame	Star sensor mounting error
Do Attitude Determination (Find attitude matrix that transforms star positions in spacecraft frame into star positions in inertial space)	Spacecraft attitude in inertial space	Round-off and arithmetic errors (typically small) and star catalog accuracy limit (how well the star positions are known)
Measure Rock Formation Image on Payload Sensor	Rock formation coordinates in payload sensor frame	Payload sensor measurement errors
Find Rock Formation Centroid	Center coordinates in payload sensor frame	Centroiding error
Multiply by Payload Sensor Mounting Matrix	Orientation of rock formation center in spacecraft coordinate frame	Payload sensor mounting error
Multiply by Spacecraft Attitude Matrix	Direction to rock formation center in inertial space	Only small arithmetic error (attitude errors accounted for above)
Use Orbit Information to Determine Direction to Earth in Inertial Space	Direction to center of the Earth	Orbit error and timing error (LEO spacecraft moving at 7 km/s)
Determine Direction of Rock Formation Relative to Nadir	Direction to rock formation center relative to line from center of the Earth to the spacecraft	Only small arithmetic error
Project Rock Formation Position onto the Earth Frame	Position of the rock formation on the Earth relative to the subsatellite point	Projection error plus altitude error (if rock formation not at sea level, projection will put it at the wrong location)
Determine Latitude and Longitude of Rock Formation	Position of the rock formation on the Earth's surface	Error in coordinate frame transformation (i.e., knowledge of subsatellite point and direction to "north")

star sensor and the payload instrument in ways which are extremely difficult to measure once the spacecraft is on orbit.

Another key issue is the large number of error sources that come into play and that are typically cumulative in their effect on the final answer. There are errors in both the payload measurement and the attitude measurement, errors in the mounting of both instruments, errors in the orbit and the timing of the measurement, and errors in projecting the rock formation onto the surface of the Earth. For example, if the spacecraft is 45 deg from the vertical as seen from the rock formation and if we assume that the rock formation is at sea level when it is in fact at an elevation of 1 km, then we will make a 1 km error in projecting the rock formation onto a specific latitude and longitude. Finding our spacecraft position to within a few meters is of relatively little utility when errors this large can be introduced.

In addition, we have overlooked a number of further errors that normally occur in a realistic system. Typically, the payload sensor is on the nadir face, the star sensor is on the zenith (upward) face, and the structure in between is as light as possible. This implies that the thermal distortion as the spacecraft goes in and out of eclipse can be very large. In addition, we are likely to use multiple sensors to determine the attitude, each of which will have both internal errors and mounting errors with respect to the other sensors and the spacecraft reference frame. Finally, we have assumed that the observation of the rock formation and the observation of the stars were simultaneous. This is rarely the case. Typically we need to interpolate between observations and also determine the time of the observation with sufficient accuracy that we know where the spacecraft is. Recall that a spacecraft in low-Earth orbit is moving at 7 km/s. Providing an accurate location for the rock formation is far more complex and, therefore, expensive than simply obtaining the image from space.

3.4 Attitude Control

As introduced in Sec. 3.1, there are a wide variety of attitude stabilization and control techniques available. The capabilities of various approaches are summarized in Table 3-19 and discussed below. Note that the distinction between types of systems is sometimes fuzzy. For example, a pure spinner can be thought of as either passive control or active control, depending on the application and on whether the direction of spin axis is controlled or uncontrolled.

Gravity-gradient stabilization was discussed in Sec. 3.2.1. While this approach is typically economical, it provides local vertical pointing only and has a typical accuracy of only about ±5 deg. Another problem with gravity-gradient stabilization is that there is no mechanism for controlling yaw. Consequently, a gravity-gradient system may include a momentum wheel oriented along the pitch axis. The purpose of the momentum wheel is to provide both some "stiffness" to the system and a means of providing control torque so that the yaw angle can be maintained.

There is an additional "hidden" cost with gravity-gradient systems which is concerned with the design of the spacecraft itself. In order to provide gravity-gradient stabilization, typically a long boom is deployed in the vertical direction to provide increased torque. This means that a realistic assessment of the cost of gravity-gradient stabilization must include the cost of the boom and the deployment mechanism for the boom, even though these elements will not be part of an active control system. In addition, since there is the potential for capturing the spacecraft upside down, most gravity-gradient systems have some means of providing an external torque for retracting the boom or turning the spacecraft over if the instruments are initially pointed up instead of down.

The motion of a pure spinner or spin-stabilized spacecraft was described in Sec. 3.2. However, relatively few modern spacecraft are pure spinners since most prefer to be pointed at some particular location which is moving in inertial space. In some cases, this can be done by pointing a telescope along the spin axis and aiming that axis at an appropriate inertial target, such as the Sun. However, most spacecraft tend to be Earth-oriented or want to look at a variety of inertial targets. One mechanism for doing this is the *dual spin spacecraft* in which a portion of the spacecraft is spinning and a second portion called the *despun platform* is counterrotated, so as to

TABLE 3-19. Attitude Control Techniques and Their Capabilities.

Technique	Pointing Options	Attitude Maneuverability	Typical Accuracy	Lifetime Limits
Gravity-Gradient	Earth local vertical only	None to very limited	±5 deg (2 axes)	None
Gravity-Gradient & Momentum Bias Wheel	Earth local vertical only	Very limited	±5 deg (3 axes)	Life of wheel bearings
Passive Magnetic	North/south only	Very limited	±5 deg (2 axes)	None
Pure Spin Stabilization	Inertially fixed any direction; repoint with precession maneuvers	High propellant usage to move angular momentum vector	±0.1 deg to ±1 deg in 2 axes (proportional to spin rate)	Thruster propellant (if applies)*
Dual Spin Stabilization	Limited only by articulation on despun platform	Momentum vector same as above. Despun platform constrained by its own geometry	Same as above for spinning section; Despun platform dictated by payload reference and pointing	Thruster propellant (if applies)* Platform bearings
Bias Momentum (1 Wheel)	Best suited for local vertical pointing	Momentum vector of the bias wheel usually pointed to orbit normal, constraining yaw maneuvers	±0.1 deg to ±1 deg	Propellant (if applies)*; Life of sensor and wheel bearings
Bias Momentum (2 wheels)	Local vertical with off pointing	Moderate range about nadir	±0.1 deg to ±1 deg	Propellant (if applies)*; Life of sensor and wheel bearings
Zero Momentum (Thruster Only)	No constraints	No constraints; High rates possible	±0.001 deg to ±5 deg	Usually propellant; could be sensor life
Zero Momentum (3 or more Wheels)	No constraints	No constraints	±0.001 deg to ±1 deg	Propellant (if applies)*; Life of sensor and wheel bearings
Zero Momentum (CMGs)	No constraints	No constraints; High rates possible	±0.001 deg to ±1 deg	Propellant (if applies)*; Life of sensor and wheel bearings

*Thrusters may be used for slewing and momentum dumping at all altitudes. Magnetic torquers may be used from LEO to GEO.

maintain a fixed pointing orientation. A particularly convenient approach to dual spin stabilization is to have the spin axis oriented toward orbit normal and the despun platform looking continuously at the Earth as the spacecraft goes around in the orbit. This approach was used for many years by Hughes Space and Communications for communications spacecraft in geosynchronous orbit. In this case, the spinning portion of the spacecraft has solar cells which provide the power for the spacecraft and the communications payload. In this approach, only half the cells would see the Sun at any one time. However, they have better efficiency because the solar cells are cooler and this adds to the cell efficiency. The dual spin communications satellite has was an extremely successful design and was used for many years. The principal disadvantage was the relatively limited solar array area on the spinning portion of the spacecraft. Consequently, newer, higher powered communications satellites are predominately 3-axis stabilized.

Three-axis stabilized spacecraft are those which maintain an approximately fixed orientation relative either to the Earth or inertial space. Within 3-axis spacecraft, there are both *momentum-biased spacecraft* which maintain a net positive angular momentum, and *zero momentum spacecraft,* which have a very low level of angular momentum.

Momentum biased 3-axis spacecraft are inherently stiff and therefore are stable for short periods of time. Depending on the needs of the spacecraft and the level of redundancy required, momentum-biased spacecraft have anywhere from 1 to 4 momentum wheels, as shown in Fig. 3-25.

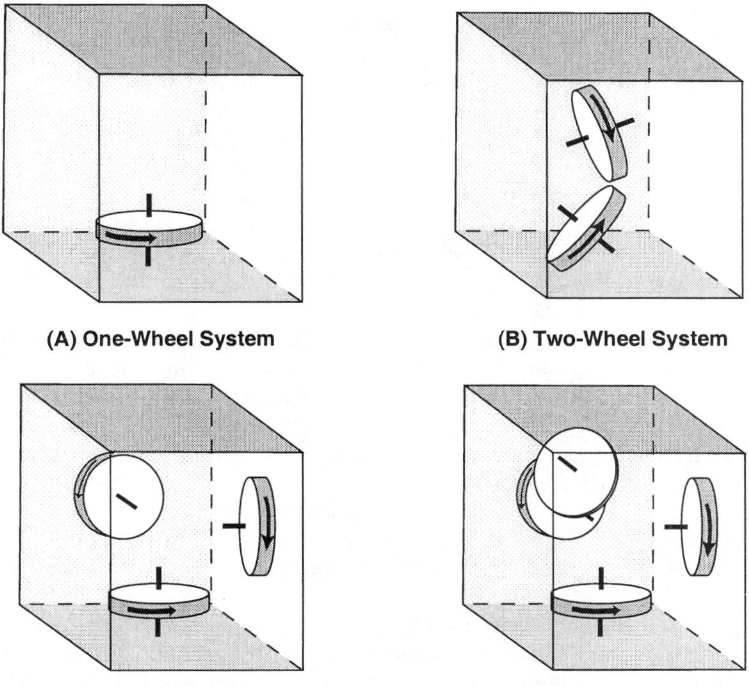

(A) One-Wheel System (B) Two-Wheel System

(C) Three-Wheel System (D) Four-Wheel System

Fig. 3-25. Alternative Momentum Wheel Configurations.

The simplest momentum-biased spacecraft has a single momentum wheel that is typically oriented along the pitch axis, i.e., with the spin axis toward orbit normal. This provides both stiffness and also a maneuver capability in the pitch direction by simply adjusting the wheel speed. Roll and yaw maneuvers, however, are difficult in such a system because they imply moving the angular momentum vector. If 2 momentum wheels are used, they can be aligned either with their axes parallel (for redundancy), or frequently, with the axes somewhat in a V configuration. Here, the wheels provide a level of redundancy but also can be used to provide attitude maneuvers about the roll axis. As one wheel is spun faster than the other, the total angular momentum remains fixed in inertial space and pointed toward orbit normal. However, the spacecraft itself tips because more of the angular momentum is contained in one wheel than the other. Thus the 2 wheel configuration provides maneuverability about 2 orthogonal axes.

Momentum wheels in all 3 axes provide both spacecraft stiffness and additional maneuverability over a limited range. In addition, we can provide redundancy for all 3 wheels by including a fourth wheel midway between the 3 perpendicular axes. This provides a highly redundant, very stable momentum bias configuration.

Recall that in contrast to momentum wheels, *reaction wheels* have a zero nominal spin speed and therefore no net angular momentum. Such a system can be easily and quickly maneuvered to point anywhere in space. This provides the highest level of accuracy and also provides flexibility by being able to point to a variety of targets on the Earth or in space. However, it requires continuous sensing in all 3 axes since the spacecraft is inherently unstable. If sensing is lost in any of the 3 axes at any time, the spacecraft can tumble. Reaction wheel systems are typically the most expensive and most complex of the spacecraft control systems.

Another type of zero momentum system is one which uses gas jets for control and does not have wheels or other internal momentum devices. The biggest problem with thruster stabilized systems is that they use a consumable for attitude control and, therefore, are limited in their lifetime by the amount of propellant on board. Thruster systems are frequently used for short duration experimental missions or for missions where rapid maneuvering is required. Thrusters are a principal control mechanism for the Orbiter and cold gas thrusters are used in the Manned Maneuvering Unit used by astronauts for extra vehicular activity. One of the advantages of thrusters is that they can be used for both orbit and attitude control.

In addition to their use as a primary control mechanism, thrusters are often used for *momentum dumping* or *momentum unloading* in order to eliminate the cumulative angular momentum that builds up in onboard momentum wheels. Momentum wheels can only absorb the disturbance torques from the environment and, because they are purely internal torquing devices, cannot exchange momentum with the environment. Magnetic torquing is also frequently used for the momentum unloading function. This has the advantages of relatively low disturbance and not using consumables. However, magnetic torquing is rarely used as the primary means of attitude control, since it provides control only about 2 spacecraft axes and cannot provide torque about the magnetic field vector.

Irrespective of the type of control system, the basic purpose of the control is to overcome both internal and external disturbance torques and to maintain the spacecraft pointed appropriately for the mission. As previously summarized in Table 3-5, there are four basic external disturbance torques. Approximate equations for sizing these torques are given in Table 3-20. In general, aerodynamic torque, which falls off exponentially with altitude, will tend to be the dominant disturbance torque for very low altitude spacecraft, such as the Orbiter. At moderate altitudes of 1,000 to several thousand km, the environmental disturbance torques will typically be dominated by gravity-gradient torque or magnetic torque, both of which fall off as $1/r^3$ with distance from the center of the Earth. Finally, at high altitudes, the disturbance will be dominated by solar radiation pressure, which is extremely small but does not vary with distance from the Earth.

TABLE 3-20. Approximate Equations for Estimating Worst Case Disturbance Torques.

Disturbance	Effect	Influenced Primarily by	Formula
Gravity-Gradient	Constant torque for Earth-oriented vehicle, cyclic for inertially oriented vehicle	• Spacecraft moments of inertia • Orbit altitude	$T_g = \frac{3\mu}{2R^3}\lvert I_z - I_y \rvert \sin(2\theta)$ where T_g is the max gravity torque; μ is the Earth's gravity constant (3.986×10^{14} m^3/s^2); R is orbit radius (m), θ is the maximum deviation of the Z-axis from local vertical in radians, and I_z and I_y are moments of inertia about z and y (or x, if smaller) axes in kg·m^2.
Solar Radiation	Cyclic torque on Earth-oriented vehicle, constant for inertially-oriented vehicle	• Spacecraft cross-sectional area and *cg* location • Spacecraft geometry • Spacecraft surface reflectivity	Solar radiation pressure, T_{sp}, is highly dependent on the type of surface being illuminated. A surface is either transparent, absorbent, or reflective, but most surfaces are a combination of the three. Reflectors are classified as diffuse or specular. In general, solar arrays are absorbers and the spacecraft body is a reflector. The worst case solar radiation torque is: $T_{sp} = F(c_{ps} - cg)$ where $F = \frac{F_s}{c} A_s (1+q)\cos i$ and F_s is the solar constant, 1,367 W/m^2, c is the speed of light, 3×10^8 m/s, A_s is the surface area, c_{ps} is the location of the center of solar pressure, cg is the center of gravity, q is the reflectance factor (ranging from 0 to 1; 0.6 is typical.), and i is the angle of incidence of the Sun.
Magnetic Field	Cyclic	• Residual spacecraft magnetic dipole • Orbit altitude • Orbit inclination	$T_m = DB$ where T_m is the magnetic torque on the spacecraft; D is the residual dipole of the vehicle in amp·turn·m^2 (A·m^2), and B is the Earth's magnetic field in tesla. B can be approximated as $2M/R^3$ for a polar orbit to half that at the equator. M is the magnetic moment of the Earth, 7.96×10^{15} tesla·m^3 and R is the radius from the dipole (Earth) center to spacecraft in m.
Aero-dynamic	Constant for Earth-oriented vehicles, variable for inertially oriented vehicle	• Spacecraft cross-sectional area and *cg* location • Orbit altitude • Spacecraft geometry and *cg* location	Atmospheric density for low orbits varies significantly with solar activity. $T_a = F(c_{pa} - cg) = FL$ where $F = 0.5\,[\rho C_d A V^2]$. F, being the force; C_d the drag coefficient (usually between 2 and 2.5); ρ the atmospheric density; A, the surface area; V, the spacecraft velocity; c_{pa} the center of aerodynamic pressure; and cg the center of gravity.

TABLE 3-21. Properties of Principal Types of Attitude Control Actuators. Also see Table 3-4.

Actuator	Typical Performance Range	Weight (kg)	Power (W)	Suppliers
Thrusters;				
Hot Gas (Typically Hydrazine)	0.5 to 10,000 N (1)	Variable	N/A	Primex Astrium TRW Kaiser Marquardt
Cold Gas (Typically Nitrogen)	< 5 N (1)	Variable	N/A	
Reaction & Momentum Wheels	0.4 to 400 N•m•s for momentum wheels at 1,200 to 5,000 rpm: max torques from 0.01 to 1 N•m	2 to 20	10 to 110	Allied Signal, Ithaco Honeywell, Teledix, Ball Aerospace
Control Moment Gyros	25 to 500 N·m of torque	> 40	90 to 150	Ball Aerospace Honeywell
Magnetic Torquers	10 to 4000 $A \cdot m^2$ [1 $A \cdot m^2$ = 1,000 pole cm] (2)	0.4 to 50	0.6 to 16	Ithaco Fokker ZARM/Microcosm

(1) Multiply by moment arm (typically 1m to 2m) to get torque.

(2) For an 800-km orbit and maximum Earth field of 0.4 gauss, the maximum torques would be 0.4×10^{-3} N·m to 0.16 N·m

As shown in Table 3-21, there are relatively few types of attitude actuators. Internal actuators are nearly always some type of wheel (Fig. 3-26A), although any moving mass could in principle be used. External actuators that exchange momentum with the environment are quite limited. In low-Earth orbit, these are either magnetic torquers (Fig. 3-26B) or thrusters and thrusters are the only available control source for interplanetary spacecraft. The sizing of either the momentum or reaction wheels is determined primarily by the need to absorb the cyclic disturbance torque over the course of an orbit. The remaining secular torque is then handled by the actuators that interact with the outside world.

(A) Control Moment Gyro

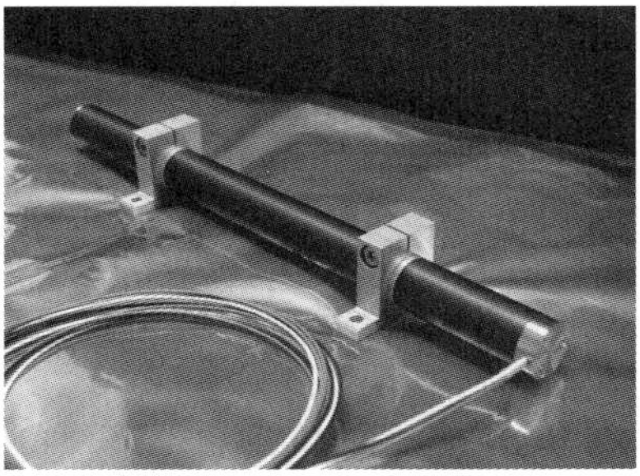

(B) Magnetic Torquers

Fig. 3-26. Representative Attitude Actuators. (Photos courtesy of Honeywell and Microcosm.)

Table 3-22 summarizes the overall effect of the required control accuracy on the design choices for the attitude control system. Generally speaking, less stringent control requirements mean both less hardware and much lower cost. The lowest cost systems are those which do not maneuver and have relatively lax control requirements, i.e., 5 deg or higher. Moderately accurate systems will have requirements in the range of 0.5 to 5 deg and can be achieved with Earth and Sun sensing and momentum bias for attitude control. Precision systems with accuracies of 0.01 deg or better will require star sensors and gyroscopes for sensing and, frequently, reaction wheels and thrusters for attitude control. In any case, the high accuracy systems will be extremely expensive and will tend to drive many of the spacecraft bus requirements to more expensive variations. Another key cost driver is the requirement to maneuver the spacecraft. Highly maneuverable spacecraft will add substantially to both cost and complexity, particularly if the maneuvers are required to be done in a short period of time. This implies the need for both large actuators and a mechanism for damping out the residual motion quickly in order to return to operational activity.

TABLE 3-22. Effect of Required Control Accuracy on Attitude System Design Options.

Required Accuracy	Effect on Spacecraft	Effect on Attitude System Design
> 5 deg	• Permits major cost savings • Permits gravity-gradient (GG) stabilization	**Without Attitude Determination:** • No sensors required for GG stabilization • Boom motor, GG damper, and a bias momentum wheel are only required actuators **With Attitude Determination:** • Sun sensors and magnetometer adequate for attitude determination at ≥2 deg • Higher accuracies may require horizon sensors or star sensors
1 deg to 5 deg	• GG not feasible • Spin stabilization feasible if stiff, inertially fixed attitude is acceptable • Payload needs may require despun platform on spinner • 3-axis stabilization will work	• Sun sensors and horizon sensors may be adequate for sensors, especially for a spinner • Accuracy for 3-axis stabilization can be met with thruster control but reaction wheels will save propellant for long missions • Thrusters and damper adequate for spinner actuators • Magnetic torquers (and magnetometer) useful
0.1 deg to 1 deg	• 3-axis and momentum-bias stabilization feasible	• Need for accurate attitude reference leads to horizon sensors or star sensors and possibly gyros • Reaction wheels typical with thrusters for momentum unloading and coarse control • Magnetic torquers feasible on light vehicles (magnetometer also required)
< 0.1 deg	• 3-axis stabilization is necessary • May require articulated and vibration-isolated payload platform with separate sensors	• Same as for 0.1 deg to 1 deg but needs star sensor and better class of gyros • Control laws and computational needs are more complex • Flexible body performance very important

Thus far, we have considered primarily spacecraft that are inherently rigid. This is a good approximation for most small spacecraft but becomes less true for large space structures or ones with long booms, large antennas, or other flexible components. The control of these flexible structures dramatically increases both the cost and complexity of attitude control.

In some ways, flexibility is much more common in space structures than on comparable Earth structures. First, mass is extremely expensive, such that space structures are ordinarily made as light as possible. Second, the absence of most gravitational effects and the elimination of the major environmental problems of winds, storms, and other weather phenomenon allow dramatically different structures than are possible here on Earth. For example, RAE-B, had four 230 m long wire booms and two other 96 m booms. Firing thrusters in the body of such a spacecraft can cause the spacecraft and the booms to oscillate with very little mechanism for damping, such that the attitude motion becomes extremely complex.

One of the most common, non-rigid spacecraft is one which is intentionally built with 2 components: an outer spacecraft structure providing approximate pointing and other spacecraft bus functions, and an inner system supporting a payload or communications antenna which provides fine guidance and pointing. For example, an outer spacecraft control system might provide spacecraft pointing to 0.1 deg while an inner control loop on a telescope or cross-link antenna provides fine pointing to 0.001 deg. This keeps the entire spacecraft from having to be pointed with a high level of precision, but nonetheless adds considerably to the cost by having 2 separate sensing and control systems.

The solution to the flexible spacecraft control problem depends strongly on the design of the particular system. It can include attitude transfer systems as described in Sec. 3.1 or additional sensors and actuators located throughout the spacecraft. These may work within the spacecraft itself or interact with the outside world. Any way it is implemented, adding an entirely new set of attitude control sensors and actuators will significantly increase the cost and complexity of the overall control system.

3.5 The Evolution of Attitude Systems

Fundamental changes are ongoing within the spacecraft attitude determination and control arena in three principal areas:

- Increased automation
- Major evolution in sensor technology
- Attitude and orbit being combined

Each of these alone can have a significant impact on how future spacecraft are designed and built. Collectively, they will ensure that, in so far as attitude determination and control are concerned, future spacecraft will bear relatively little resemblance to those that have been built in the past.

The process of automating the attitude determination and control activity will allow systems which are more complex and more responsive. In general, attitude control systems will go from being complex analog electronics to being mechanically simpler, but logically far more complex, digital systems, driven principally by software. This change to more automated systems will have 3 important impacts on attitude determination and control. First, we can expect the mechanical systems to become significantly simpler. Previously, much of the complexity of attitude sensing and actuation was contained in mechanical devices in order to make the control process and control implementation as straightforward as possible. With automated systems, this is no longer necessary. It is relatively easy to implement nonlinear control and to create complex models of simple hardware. Consequently, the tendency will be to make the hardware itself simpler, more economical, and more robust and to incorporate the complexity into the mathematical modeling done in the attitude computer.

Second, the attitude system can become significantly more complex in its implementation and more accurate in its performance. Extensive and complex filtering of attitude data is now feasible. Complex nonlinear control algorithms or control which is dependent on the environmental circumstances are both feasible. The control laws and their implementation can now be adapted to specific environments or mission phases as appropriate so that the space system can operate in far more modes and regimes.

Finally, perhaps the most important single change that comes with automation is a change to the fundamental nature of space systems. In the past, the single most important characteristic of space systems was that once they were launched, they were inaccessible. Whatever was built into the attitude control system was what would be there for the life of the mission. There was no going back, correcting errors, revising the system, expanding its capabilities, or changing how it did things in response to changing needs. Software control systems, on the other hand, are accessible from the ground. We can upgrade the software, change what it does or how it operates, add new control modes as they are needed, or make other software changes to respond to component failures, changes in the mission environment, or changes in what we want the spacecraft to do. What was originally a process that had to work for the entire mission is now one which can be adjusted and changed as conditions dictate. Indicative of this changing environment, one of the recent commercial communications constellations launched most of the satellites with the control software not yet fully complete. There was time in the schedule to complete and fully test the software after launch so that the schedule could be advanced and the costs reduced. This is a process that would have been impossible only a few years ago.

Paralleling the introduction of control system automation is a major evolution in sensor technology. This comes about both because of changes in the sensors themselves and because the sensors can also include a higher level of automation and, therefore, can become significantly more sophisticated. A wide variety of new inertial sensors are becoming available that have the potential for offering dramatically increased life and improved performance with far lower drift rates and biases. Earth sensor technology is undergoing a major evolution with the advent of a variety of new styles and types of Earth sensors responding principally to the need for smaller, lower cost systems. Similarly, star sensors are being almost entirely reinvented with the introduction of both high sensitivity, high resolution CCDs and newer types of sensor technology such as the active pixel array which has both improved performance characteristics and reduced radiation susceptibility. Because of the availability of far greater processing, the use of onboard star catalogs, sophisticated detection and attitude determination algorithms, and software mechanisms for high accuracy calibration has the promise of changing entirely both the nature of star sensors and the way they are used. In addition, GPS receivers are now a new element of attitude determination technology. They can provide both orbit and attitude from a single sensor.

Orbit and attitude are becoming both more intertwined and more a part of a common guidance, navigation, and control system. GPS receivers provide both orbit and attitude information. Similarly, optical autonomous navigation can provide orbit determination on board the spacecraft using the same sensors ordinarily used for attitude determination. We will return to this process of combined orbit and attitude in Chap. 4.

3.6 Annotated Bibliography

There are now a number of volumes which treat various aspects of spacecraft attitude determination and control. Books are listed by category and alphabetically within each category.

Attitude Dynamics and Control

There are a number of excellent books dealing with a controlled systems approached are listed below.

Bryson, Arthur E. Jr. 1994. *Control of Spacecraft and Aircraft.* Princeton: NJ: Princeton University Press.

Extended discussion of the linear-quadratic-regulator (LQR) method of feedback control and its application to both spacecraft attitude and aircraft control. Includes discussion of sensors and attitude determination, multiple control methods, and satellite flexibility and fuel slosh. Strong emphasis on mathematical modeling. Six mathematical appendices.

Chobotov, Vladimir A. 1991. *Spacecraft Attitude Dynamics and Control.* Malabar, FL: Krieger Publishing Company. 140 p.

A good, modern treatment with useful mathematical models. Does not cover attitude determination. Does not discuss attitude control hardware characteristics, but does provide useful (and sometimes hard to find) mathematical models of this hardware. Somewhat expensive for the length.

Franklin, Gene F., J.D. Powell, and M. Workman. 1998. *Digital Control of Dynamic Systems* (3rd ed). Menlo Park, CA: Addison-Wesley. 742 p.

Good introductory text on general digital control theory with problems. Includes key topics such as quantization, non-linear control, sampling, estimation, and filtering. Makes extensive use of MatLab.

Hughes, Peter C. 1986. *Spacecraft Attitude Dynamics.* NY: John Wiley & Sons. 564 p.

A standard and thorough text in attitude dynamics. Does not cover hardware characteristics or attitude determination, but provides excellent models of environmental effects, stability, and energy dissipation. Introduces the concept of a "vectrix," or column vector in which the elements are row vectors. This provides a convenient mechanism for doing attitude computations.

Junkins, John L. and Youdan Kim. 1993. *Introduction to Dynamics and Control of Flexible Structures.* Washington, D.C.: AIAA. 452 p.

A thorough treatment of this somewhat specialized topic. Includes software.

Junkins, John L. (ed). 1990. *Mechanics and Control of Large Flexible Structures.* Washington, D.C.: AIAA. 705 p.

A good collection of papers on flexible body dynamics and control. Includes topics such as precision control of large antennas, tether motion and control, and feedback control of space structures.

Kaplan, Marshall H. 1976. *Modern Spacecraft Dynamics and Control.* NY: John Wiley & Sons. 415 p.

Somewhat dated, but still widely used as a textbook. Covers both orbit and attitude dynamics. Brief discussion of attitude determination hardware and methods. More extensive discussion of control hardware and approaches, including yo-yo despin. Special topics include attitude acquisition of a momentum bias satellite and automatic detumbling.

Kane, Likins, and Levinson. 1983. *Spacecraft Dynamics.* NY: McGraw-Hill. 436 p.

A unique approach to attitude dynamics.

Sidi, Marcel J. 1997. *Spacecraft Dynamics and Control.* Cambridge: Cambridge University Press. 409 p.

Discusses both orbit and attitude dynamics and control with emphasis on attitude dynamics and control. Excellent discussion of several topics not normally discussed, including nutation control, attitude maneuvers, and propellant slosh. Includes very detailed, though dated, discussion of both attitude determination and attitude control hardware, but does not include a discussion of attitude determination.

Wie, Bong. 1998. *Space Vehicle Dynamics and Control.* Washington D.C.: AIAA. 661 p.

Covers orbit and attitude dynamics and control, with the greater emphasis on attitude and structural issues. Includes structural dynamics and control and robust optimal maneuvers. Intended as a companion volume to Battin's book on astrodynamics. Provides as an example the analysis and redesign of the pointing control system for the Hubble Space Telescope.

Wiesel, William E. 1997. *Spaceflight Dynamics* (2nd ed). NY: Irwin/McGraw-Hill. 332 p.

This book is an introductory mathematical text on both orbit and attitude dynamics. Orbit and attitude determination are discussed very briefly. Control is discussed at greater length, but not in detail. There is an extended discussion of gyros and inertial navigation, rocket performance, and reentry dynamics.

Attitude Determination

Unfortunately, this topic is not covered at all in most books on attitude dynamics and control. There is some material in the book by Sidi.

Wertz, James R. 1978. *Spacecraft Attitude Determination and Control.* Dordrecht, The Netherlands: Kluwer Academic Publishers. 858 p.

Sensor material is dated; still in use as the only reference for attitude determination techniques and models prior to this book service.

Attitude and Mission Geometry

There are no complete references on this topic. *Spacecraft Attitude Determination and Control* (above) covers attitude geometry but not orbits or mission geometry. *Space Mission Analysis and Design* (listed in Chap. 1) provides a chapter on Mission Geometry, but is too short to be a complete reference.

Canters, Frank and Hugo Decleir. 1989. *The World in Perspective: A Directory of World Map Projections*. NY: John Wiley and Sons. 181 p.

This book is about world map projections and not about space missions in any way. However, the problem of projections of the celestial sphere is identical to that of world map projections, so this is an excellent reference on the more general problem of representing a curved surface (i.e., the surface of the Earth or planets or the celestial sphere) on a flat sheet of paper. Provides general background, basis for selecting alternatives, and a detailed directory of mapping options with all needed transformation equations.

Green, Robin. 1985. *Spherical Astronomy.* Cambridge: Cambridge University Press. 520 p.

Astronomically oriented, but the only modern reference in this area; does not explicitly cover space missions.

Taff, Laurence G. 1991. *Computational Spherical Astronomy.* Malabar, FL: Krieger Publishing Co. 233 p.

The title of this book is somewhat misleading. It is not a text on spherical astronomy, but rather a mathematical treatment on positional astronomy and the reduction of stellar and planetary observations. Topics include precession and proper motion, stellar parallax, time, photographic astrometry, and astronomical catalogs. Good treatment of the detailed mathematical issues.

Reference

Beals, G. A., R. C. Crum, H. J. Dougherty, D. K. Hegel, J. L. Kelley, and J. J. Rodden. 1988. "Hubble Space Telescope Precision Pointing Control System." *Journal of Guidance, Control, and Dynamics*. Vol. 11, No. 2, March–April.

Wertz, James R. 1978. *Spacecraft Attitude Determination and Control.* Dordrecht, The Netherlands: Kluwer Academic Publishers.

Chapter 4

Space-Based Orbit, Attitude, and Timing Systems

Major changes have taken place and are still taking place in spacecraft orbit, attitude, and timing systems. Among the most substantial are:

- The introduction of GPS for timing, orbit, and possibly attitude determination in low-Earth orbit.
- The automation of spacecraft, allowing substantially more complex systems in terms of sensor processing, control implementation, autonomous navigation and the use of robust, nonlinear algorithms for many system components.
- The introduction of autonomous navigation systems.
- The introduction of autonomous orbit maintenance and control.
- The emergence of low-thrust propulsion systems for both stationkeeping and orbit raising.
- Dramatic improvements in the performance (and often weight and size) of onboard sensing systems.
- The potential for combining orbit and attitude into a single onboard system.
- The shift from largely single spacecraft to a large number of constellations, such that orbit, attitude, and timing relative to other spacecraft is often critical.

The most visible technical change is the introduction of the GPS constellation. While intended primarily for Earth-based navigation, its inherently global characteristic and high level of precision provide an excellent option for satellite navigation in low-Earth orbit. However, for commercial and international systems, a question is often raised concerning the extent to which these systems should be dependent for critical navigation data on a system maintained entirely by the American military.

The most profound and far-reaching change in spacecraft systems over the past several decades has been the introduction of large-scale onboard processing. The automation of space has substantially lagged behind the development of these systems for office and industrial use for a number of reasons. Because of the extremely high cost of space systems and their inaccessibility for physical repair, spacecraft manufacturers have been extremely conservative in introducing new technology in space. Computers, in particular, are susceptible to radiation damage and single-event upsets in the space environment, which implies the potential for space computer failures and the need for computers to be specially built for space application. Consequently, traditional spacecraft have had very low levels of automation, with processing power that would be unacceptable for even mundane home or office applications. However, most of these issues have now been resolved and modern spacecraft are typically highly automated with multiple general purpose computers on board. This implies dramatically more sophisticated processing available to the spacecraft designer and also significantly impacts cost, reliability, and flexibility of space missions.

Software-dominated space systems will have a relatively high nonrecurring cost and a much lower recurring cost. They will be more flexible in what they can achieve and in the range of solutions which are possible. They allow a single spacecraft to change its mission during flight in response to changing needs, conditions, or hardware failures. Perhaps most important, the extensive use of software changes the nature of spacecraft. Traditionally, spacecraft have been inaccessible after launch. Once they are placed in orbit, whatever equipment is there is all that is available. There is no potential for upgrades, repairs, or changes except by dramatically expensive repair missions. In contrast, software systems are fully accessible from the ground. Uploads can be made with new parameters, or entirely new programs or systems intended to update what the spacecraft does as its environment and needs evolve, or our understanding changes.

In this chapter, we describe modern space-based orbit, attitude, and timing systems that take advantage of the new hardware, new processing power, and new capabilities available to the spacecraft designer. We begin with a background discussion of time and time measurement systems. We describe the GPS satellite system and its application to low-Earth orbit spacecraft. We then introduce autonomous navigation systems and autonomous orbit maintenance and control, made possible by both GPS and the availability of extensive onboard processing. Finally, we will look at the potential architecture for combined orbit, attitude, and timing systems which will meet the need for low-cost, robust, and high-reliability systems for future space missions.

4.1 Time

Time is something we intuitively understand extremely well and, consequently, understand poorly in detail. For example, any phenomenon which repeats on a regular basis, such as a pendulum or the motion of electrons in an atom, can be used as the basis for timekeeping. However, "regularly repeating" implies that we have some standard to compare with. The only way to determine a clock's accuracy is to compare it with another clock, which of course leads to the question of which clock we should assume to be correct. Historically, the fundamental "clocks" chosen for maintaining absolute time have been the rotation of the Earth on its axis and the revolution of the Earth about the Sun. However, modern time measurements have shown these systems to be both nonuniform and extremely difficult to model with precision. For example, Fig. 4-1 shows the variations in the length of the day over the past several centuries. On average, the Earth is slowing down by 1.5 ms/century but local variations are very substantial.†

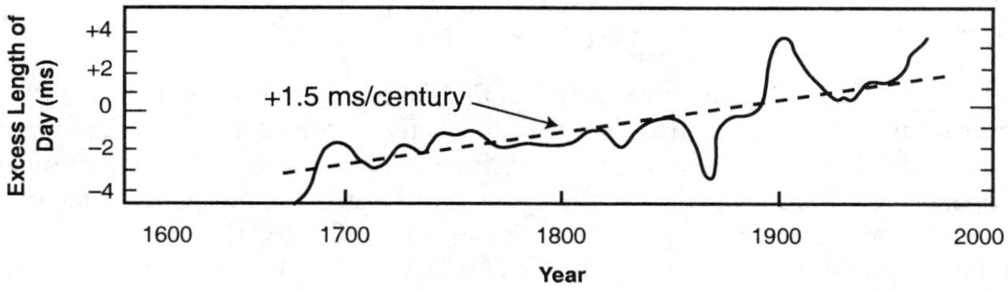

Fig. 4-1. Variations in the Length of Day. On average, the Earth is slowing down by 1.5 ms/century, but local variations are large and very difficult to model.

Unfortunately, clock errors are cumulative, and therefore, high accuracy can prove important. For example, assume a spacecraft in low-Earth orbit has a clock that is slowing down by 1 ms/day, which is small enough to be difficult to measure by many processes. This would result in a cumulative error of 0.365 sec over a year which corresponds to an error in position of the satellite of 3 km. Thus, if we wish to know the positions of satellites to tens of meters, we will need reasonably good clocks to do so.

Two basic types of time measurement are used in spacecraft systems: (1) *time intervals* between 2 events such as the spacecraft's spin period, orbital period, or the length of time a sensor sees the Earth; and (2) *absolute times* or *calendar times* of specific events, such as the time associated with some particular spacecraft observation. Of course, calendar time is simply a time interval for which the beginning event is an agreed standard.

4.1.1 Calendar Time and Long Duration Intervals

Calendar time in the usual form of date and time is used only for input and output because arithmetic is cumbersome in months, days, hours, minutes, and seconds. Nonetheless, this is used for most human interaction with space systems because it's the system with which we are most familiar. Even with date and time systems, problems can arise, because time zones are different throughout the world and spacecraft operations typically involve a worldwide network. The uniformly adopted solution to this problem is to use the local standard time corresponding to 0 deg longitude (i.e., the Greenwich meridian) as the assigned time for events anywhere in

† The overall slowing of the Earth's rotation and lengthening of the day are caused primarily by tidal friction with the Moon. Local variations are caused principally by the growth and decline in the polar ice caps which shifts large quantities of water from the pole (smaller moment of inertia and higher spin rate) to the equator (larger moment of inertia and lower spin rate).

the world or in space. This is referred to as *Universal Time* (UT), *Greenwich Mean Time* (GMT), or *Zulu* (Z), all of which are equivalent for most practical spacecraft operations. The name Greenwich Mean Time is used because 0 deg longitude is defined by the site of the former Royal Greenwich Observatory southeast of central London.

Civil time, T_{civil}, as measured by a standard wall clock or time signals, differs from Universal Time by an integral number of hours, corresponding approximately to the longitude of the observer. The approximate relation is:

$$T_{civil} \approx UT \pm (L + 7.5) / 15 \tag{4-1}$$

where T_{civil} and UT are in hours, and L is the longitude in degrees with the plus sign corresponding to East longitude and the minus sign corresponding to West longitude. The conversion between civil time and Universal Time for most North American and European time zones is given in Table 4-1. Substantial variations in time zones are created for political convenience. In addition, most of the United States and Canada observe Daylight Savings Time from the first Sunday in April until the last Sunday in October. Most European countries observe Daylight Savings Time (called "Summer Time") from the last Sunday in March to the first Sunday in October. Many countries in the southern hemisphere also maintain Daylight Savings Time, typically from October to March. Countries near the equator typically do not deviate from standard time.

TABLE 4-1. Time Zones in North America, Europe, and Japan. In most of the United States, Daylight Savings Time is used from the first Sunday in April until the last Sunday in October. In Europe, the equivalent "Summer Time" is used from the last Sunday in March to the first Sunday in October.

Time Zone	Standard Meridian (Deg, East Long.)	UT Minus Standard Time (Hours)	UT Minus Daylight Time (Hours)
Atlantic	300	4	3
Eastern	285	5	4
Central	270	6	5
Mountain	255	7	6
Pacific	240	8	7
Alaska	225	9	8
Hawaii	210	10	NA
Japan	135	–9	NA
Central Europe	15	–1	–2
United Kingdom	0	0	–1

Calendar time is remarkably inconvenient for computation, particularly over long time intervals of months or years. We need an absolute time that is a continuous count of time units from some arbitrary reference. The time interval between any two events is then found by simply subtracting the absolute time of the second event from that of the first. The universally adopted solution for astronomical problems is the *Julian Date*, JD, a continuous count of the number of days since Greenwich noon (12:00 UT) on January 1, 4713 BC,† or, as astronomers now say, –4712. Because Julian Days start at noon UT, they will be a half day off with respect to civil dates. While this is inconvenient for transforming from civil dates to Julian Dates, it was useful for astronomers because the date didn't change in the middle of the night (for European observers).

As described below, there are four general approaches for converting between calendar dates and Julian Dates.

Table Look-Up

Tabulations of the current Julian Date are in most astronomical ephemerides and almanacs. Table 4-2 lists the Julian Dates at the beginning of each year from 1990 through 2031. To find the Julian Date for any given calendar date, simply add the *day number* within the year (and fractional day number, if appropriate) to the Julian Date for Jan 0.0 of that year from Table 4-2. Day numbers for each day of the year are on many calendars or can be found by adding the date to the day number for day 0 of the month from Table 4-3. Thus 18:00 UT on April 15, 2002 = day number 15.75 + 90 = 105.75 in 2002 = JD 105.75 + 2,452,274.5 = JD 2,452,380.25.

TABLE 4-2. Julian Date at the Beginning of Each Year from 1990 to 2031. See text for explanation of use. The day number for the beginning of the year is called "Jan. 0.0" (actually Dec. 31st of the preceding year) so that day numbers can be found by simply using dates. Thus, Jan. 1 is day number 1 and has a JD 1 greater than that for Jan. 0. * = leap year.

Year	*JD* 2,400,000+ for Jan 0.0 *UT*	Year	*JD* 2,400,000+ for Jan 0.0 *UT*	Year	*JD* 2,400,000+ for Jan 0.0 *UT*
1990	47,891.5	2004*	53,004.5	2018	58,118.5
1991	48,256.5	2005	53,370.5	2019	58,483.5
1992*	48,621.5	2006	53,735.5	2020*	58,848.5
1993	48,987.5	2007	54,100.5	2021	59,214.5
1994	49,352.5	2008*	54,465.5	2022	59,579.5
1995	49,717.5	2009	54,831.5	2023	59,944.5
1996*	50,082.5	2010	55,196.5	2024*	60,309.5
1997	50,448.5	2011	55,561.5	2025	60,675.5
1998	50,813.5	2012*	55,926.5	2026	61,040.5
1999	51,178.5	2013	56,292.5	2027	61,405.5
2000*	51,543.5	2014	56,657.5	2028*	61,770.5
2001	51,909.5	2015	57,022.5	2029	62,136.5
2002	52,274.5	2016*	57,387.5	2030	62,501.5
2003	52,639.5	2017	57,753.5	2031	62,866.5

† This strange starting point was suggested by an Italian scholar of Greek and Hebrew, Joseph Scaliger, in 1582 as the beginning of the current *Julian period* of 7,980 years. This period is the product of three numbers: the *solar cycle*, or the interval at which all dates recur on the same days of the week (28 years); the *lunar cycle*, containing an integral number of lunar months (19 years); and the *indiction* or the tax period introduced by the Emperor Constantine in 313 AD (15 years). The last time that these started together was 4713 BC and the next time will be 3267 AD. Scaliger was interested in reducing the astronomical dating problems associated with calendar reforms of his time and his proposal had the convenient selling point that it pre-dated the ecclesiastically approved date of creation, October 4, 4004 BC.

To convert from Julian Days to dates, determine the year in which the Julian Date falls from Table 4-2. Subtract the Julian Date from the JD for January 0.0 of that year to determine the day number within the year. This can be converted to a date (and time, if appropriate) by using day numbers on a calendar or subtracting from the day number for the beginning of the appropriate month from Table 4-3. Thus, from Table 4-2, JD 2,451,608.25 is in the year 2000. The day number is 2,451,608.25 – 2,451,543.5 = 64.75. From Table 4-3, this is 18:00 UT, March 4, 2000.

TABLE 4-3. Day Numbers for Day 0.0 of Each Month. Leap years (in which February has 29 days) are those evenly divisible by 4. However, years evenly divisible by 100 are not leap years, except that those evenly divisible by 400 are. Leap years are indicated by * in Table 4-2.

Month	Non-Leap Years	Leap Years
January	0	0
February	31	31
March	59	60
April	90	91
May	120	121
June	151	152
July	181	182
August	212	213
September	243	244
October	273	274
November	304	305
December	334	335

Software Routines Using Integer Arithmetic

A particularly clever procedure for finding the Julian Date, JD, associated with any current year, Y, month, M, and day of the month, D, is given by Fliegel and Van Flandern [1968] as a computer statement using integer arithmetic. Note that all of the variables must be defined as integers (i.e., any remainder after a division must be truncated) and that both the order of the computations and the parentheses are critical. This procedure works in FORTRAN, C, C++, and Ada for any date on the Gregorian calendar that yields JD > 0. (Add 10 days to the JD for dates on the Julian calendar prior to 1582.) The formula is:

$$\begin{aligned} JD_0 = {} & D - 32{,}075 + 1461 \times (Y + 4800 + (M - 14) / 12) / 4 \\ & + 367 \times (M - 2 - (M - 14) / 12 \times 12) / 12 \\ & - 3 \times ((Y + 4900 + (M - 14) / 12) / 100) / 4 \end{aligned} \tag{4-2a}$$

Here JD_0 is the Julian Day beginning at noon UT on the given date and must be an integer. For a fractional day, F, in UT (i.e., day number "D.F"), the floating point Julian Day is given by:

$$JD = JD_0 + F - 0.5 \tag{4-2b}$$

For example, the Julian Day beginning at 12:00 UT on December 25, 2007 (Y = 2007, M = 12, D = 25) is JD 2,454,460 and 6:00 UT on that date (F = 0.25) is JD 2,454,459.75.

The inverse routine for computing the date from the Julian Day is given by:

$$L = JD_0 + 68{,}569 \tag{4-3a}$$

$$N = (4 \times L) / 146{,}097 \tag{4-3b}$$

$$L = L - (146097 \times N + 3) / 4 \tag{4-3c}$$

$$I = (4000 \times (L + 1)) / 1{,}461{,}001 \tag{4-3d}$$

$$L = L - (1461 \times I) / 4 + 31 \tag{4-3e}$$

$$J = (80 \times L) / 2{,}447 \tag{4-3f}$$

$$D = L - (2447 \times J) / 80 \tag{4-3g}$$

$$L = J / 11 \tag{4-3h}$$

$$M = J + 2 - 12 \times L \tag{4-3i}$$

$$Y = 100 \times (N - 49) + I + L \tag{4-3j}$$

where integer arithmetic is used throughout. Y, M, and D are the year, month, and day, and I, J, L, and N are intermediate variables. Finally, again using integer arithmetic, the day of the week, W, corresponding to the Julian Date beginning at 12:00 on that day is given by:

$$W = JD_0 - 7 \times ((JD + 1) / 7) + 2 \tag{4-4}$$

where W = 1 corresponds to Sunday. Thus, December 25, 2007 falls on Tuesday.

Software Routines Without Integer Arithmetic

While most computer languages provide integer arithmetic, common software tools such as Excel or MatLab typically do not. (See below for use of Excel and MatLab DATE functions.) Similar capabilities are available using integer (INT) or truncation (TRUNC in Excel, FIX in MatLab) functions. INT and TRUNC are identical for positive numbers, but differ for negative numbers: INT (–3.1) = –4, whereas TRUNC (–3.1) = –3. It is the TRUNC or FIX function which is equivalent to integer arithmetic. Thus, using the same variables as above, we can rewrite Eqs. (4-2a and b) for computation of JD from the date as:

$$C = \text{TRUNC}\,((M - 14) / 12) \tag{4-5a}$$

$$\begin{aligned} JD_0 = {} & D - 32{,}075 + \text{TRUNC}\,(1{,}461 \times (Y + 4{,}800 + C) / 4) \\ & + \text{TRUNC}\,(367 \times (M - 2 - C \times 12) / 12) \\ & - \text{TRUNC}\,(3 \times (\text{TRUNC}(Y + 4{,}900 + C) / 100) / 4) \end{aligned} \tag{4-5b}$$

$$JD = JD_0 + F - 0.5 \tag{4-5c}$$

where again JD_0, Y, M, D, and C are integers and F and JD are real numbers. Applying the same rules to Eqs. (4-3a–j) gives the inverse formula for the date in terms of JD as:

$$L = JD + 68{,}569 \tag{4-6a}$$

$$N = \text{TRUNC}\,((4 \times L) / 146{,}097) \tag{4-6b}$$

$$L = L - \text{TRUNC}\,((146097 \times N + 3) / 4) \tag{4-6c}$$

$$I = \text{TRUNC}\,((4000 \times (L + 1)) / 1{,}461{,}001) \quad (4\text{-}6d)$$

$$L = L - \text{TRUNC}\,((1{,}461 \times I) / 4) + 31 \quad (4\text{-}6e)$$

$$J = \text{TRUNC}\,((80 \times L) / 2{,}447) \quad (4\text{-}6f)$$

$$D = L - \text{TRUNC}\,((2{,}447 \times J) / 80) \quad (4\text{-}6g)$$

$$L = \text{TRUNC}\,(J / 11) \quad (4\text{-}6h)$$

$$M = J + 2 - 12 \times L \quad (4\text{-}6i)$$

$$Y = 100 \times (N - 49) + I + L \quad (4\text{-}6j)$$

where the variables are the same as Eq. (4-3a-j), except that D is now a real number corresponding to the date and fraction of a day. Finally, Eq. (4-4) for the day of the week becomes:

$$\begin{aligned} W &= JD - 7 \times \text{TRUNC}\,((JD + 1.5) / 7) + 2.5 \\ &= JD - 7 \times \text{INT}((JD + 1.5) / 7) + 2.5 \end{aligned} \quad (4\text{-}7)$$

where $1 \leq W < 2$ corresponds to Sunday. The examples given above can also serve as test cases for Eqs. (4-5a–c), (4-6a–j), and (4-7).

Modified Julian Date

The Julian Date presents minor problems for space applications. Because it was introduced principally for astronomical use, Julian Dates begin at 12:00 UT rather than 0 hours UT, as the civil calendar does (thus the 0.5 day differences in Table 4-2). In addition, the 7 digits required for the Julian Date did not permit the use of single precision arithmetic in older computer programs. This is no longer a problem with modern computer storage and number formats. Nonetheless, various forms of truncated Julian dates have gained at least some use.

The most common of the truncated Julian Dates for astronomy and astronautics use is the *Modified Julian Date*, MJD, given by:

$$MJD = JD - 2{,}400{,}000.5 \quad (4\text{-}8)$$

MJD begins at midnight, to correspond with the civil calendar. Thus, in using Table 4-2, MJD is given by adding the day of the year (plus fractions of a day, if appropriate) to the number in the table, with the ".5" at the end of the table-listing dropped. For example, MJD for 18:00 UT on Jan. 3, 2002 = MJD 52,277.75. The definition of MJD given here is that adopted by the International Astronomical Union in 1997. Note, however, that other definitions of MJD have been used. Thus, the most unambiguous approach remains the use of the full Julian Date.

Spreadsheets such as Excel or MatLab

Spreadsheets, such as Excel or MatLab, typically store dates internally as some form of day count and allow arithmetic operations, such as subtraction. Thus, we can either subtract two dates directly to determine a time interval or convert them to Julian Dates by simply finding the additive constant, K, given by:

$$K = JD - I \quad (4\text{-}9)$$

where I is the internal number representing a known date, JD. Once this is determined, then the JD for any date is:

$$JD = K + I \quad (4\text{-}10)$$

Many versions of Excel use Jan. 1, 1904, as "day 0," such that $K_{Excel} = 2,416,480.5$. However, this should be checked for individual programs because other starting points are sometimes used and the starting point is a variable parameter in some versions of Excel. While this can be a very convenient function, Excel date routines run only from 1904 to 2078.

MatLab typically uses Jan. 1, 0000, 0:0:0 as "day 0." Thus, in the formula above, $K_{MatLab} = 1,721,058.5$.

Any of the day counting approaches will work successfully over its allowed range. However, systems intended for general mathematics or business use may not account correctly for leap years and calendar changes when historical times or times far in the future are being evaluated. Thus, the use of the full Julian Date remains the most unambiguous solution, particularly if a program or result is to be used by more than one person or activity. For a more extended discussion of time systems, see Seidelmann [1992].

4.1.2 Modern Time Measurement—Short Duration

As one would expect, modern technology has lead to ever increasing precision in the measurement of time. However, in addition, new processes for measuring time have been introduced, as well as new and fundamentally different definitions of the meaning of time in both science and engineering. In the 1950s, *Ephemeris Time, ET*, was introduced, based on the dynamic equations of motion of the Earth. For many years, this was used as the basis of astronomical and astrophysical ephemerides, i.e., the most precise orbit calculations. In 1967, the second was redefined as having an atomic standard but ephemeris time remained in use for the motion of planets and satellites. In 1984, ephemeris time was unceremoniously abandoned in favor of *Terrestrial Dynamic Time, TDT*, in which the unit of measure was the atomic second and the scale was chosen to agree with ephemeris time in 1984. In 1991, the general theory of relativity was explicitly adopted as the theoretical background for defining both space and time reference frames, *TDT* was renamed *Terrestrial Time, TT*, and the definition of the second was "adjusted" to correspond to atomic measurements at a specific location (i.e., at mean sea level on the surface of the Earth).†

Currently, there are four basic types of time systems in use:

- *Atomic Time, TAI*, for which the unit of duration corresponds to a defined number of wavelengths for a specific atomic transition of a specific isotope.
- *Universal Time, UT*, for which the unit of duration is the rotation of the Earth with respect to the Sun, defined to be as uniform as possible despite variations in the physical rotation rate of the Earth.
- *Sidereal Time, ST*, for which the unit of duration is the rotation of the Earth with respect to the vernal equinox which, in turn, is nearly fixed with respect to the mean positions of the stars.
- *Dynamical Time, DT*, for which the unit of duration is based on the orbital motion of the Earth, Moon, and planets.

Each of these is described in more detail below. In addition, rapidly rotating pulsars may provide an even more accurate standard for future time systems. While the dif-

† An excellent discussion of the history of time systems is provided by Seidelmann [1992].

ferences between the various time systems are subtle, they can have important implications for spacecraft systems and applications. The most commonly used modern time systems are defined in Table 4-4.

TABLE 4-4. Common Time Systems.

Kind of Time	Defined By	Fundamental Unit	Regularity	Application
Sidereal (ST)	Earth's rotation relative to stars	Sidereal day, 1 rotation of Earth with respect to stars	Irregular	Astronomical observations; determining *UT* and rotational orientation of Earth
Solar				
Apparent	Earth's rotation relative to true Sun	Successive transits of Sun	Irregular and annual variations	Sundials
Mean	Earth's rotation relative to fictitious mean Sun	Mean solar day	Irregular	Confuse students and engineers
Universal				
UT0	Observed *UT*	Mean solar day	Irregular	Study of Earth's wandering pole
UT1	Corrected *UT0*	Mean solar day	Irregular	Shows seasonal variation of Earth's rotation
UT2	Corrected *UT1*	Mean solar day	Irregular	Basic rotation of Earth
UTC= GMT=Z	Atomic sec and leap sec to approximate *UT1*	Mean solar day	Uniform except for leap sec	Civil timekeeping; terrestrial navigation and surveying; broadcast time signals
Ephemeris (ET)	Fraction of tropical year 1900	Ephemeris sec	Uniform	Ephemerides prior to 1994; no longer in use
Atomic (TAI)	Frequency of Ce-133 radiation	Atomic sec = Ephemeris sec	Uniform	Basis of *ET* and *UTC*
GPS	Atomic sec without leap sec	Atomic sec	Uniform	Time component of GPS signals
Relativistic				
Terrestrial (TT)	Atomic sec at mean sea level on Earth	Atomic sec at Earth's surface	Uniform	Ephemerides
Barycentric Dynamic (TDB)	Orbital equations of motion with respect to barycenter of the Solar System	Atomic sec adjusted for relativistic effects	Uniform	Transforms Earth-based time to time kept by the motions of the planets

Fortunately, the basis for all of the modern time systems is the Système International, SI, *second*. This is defined as the duration of 9,192,631,770 periods of the radiation corresponding to the transition between 2 hyperfine levels of the ground state of the Cesium-133 atom measured at mean sea level on the Earth. This definition of the second corresponds more-or-less to 1 / 86,400 (= 1 / [60 × 60 × 24]) of the rotation period of the Earth, relative to the mean Sun. It is, of course, the "more-or-less" part which ultimately causes most of the problems in time measurement systems.

Atomic Time (TAI)

International Atomic Time, TAI (*Temps Atomique International*), is a practical implementation of a time standard based on the SI second. An excellent approximation to *TAI* can be maintained by laboratory Cesium clocks. A large number of such clocks are compared from time to time and a weighted average is prepared which provides a fine adjustment for each of the individual clocks. The use of these Cesium-based clocks provides a readily available basis for timekeeping for all types of physical, astronomical, and space-related observation.

Universal Time (UT)

Universal Time, UT, follows the irregular rotation of the Earth, and is often referred to as a type of solar time because the objective in universal time is to remain synchronized with the orientation of the Earth relative to the Sun. The most important subcategory of universal time is *Coordinated Universal Time (UTC),* which is the basis for civil timekeeping and broadcast time signals worldwide. *UTC* uses the SI second as the basic unit of time and then adds (or, in principle, subtracts) a leap second at the end of the last day of June and the last day of December as needed to maintain close agreement with the rotational orientation of the Earth. Thus, *UTC* lags behind TAI by an integral number of seconds. For example, for January 1, 1996, TAI minus UTC equaled 30 sec exactly. Because UTC depends on irregularities in the motion of the Earth, it cannot be predicted in advance, which causes a long-term continuous drift between *UTC* and *TAI.*

In applications where precision is not critical, *UTC* frequently goes by the name Greenwich Mean Time (*GMT*), Zulu (*Z*), or simply Universal Time (*UT*). The latter definition is ambiguous since *UT* is also used for *UT1*, another subcategory of universal time which more closely follows the real motion of the Earth. Fig. 4-2 shows historical differences between TAI, UTC, and UT1.

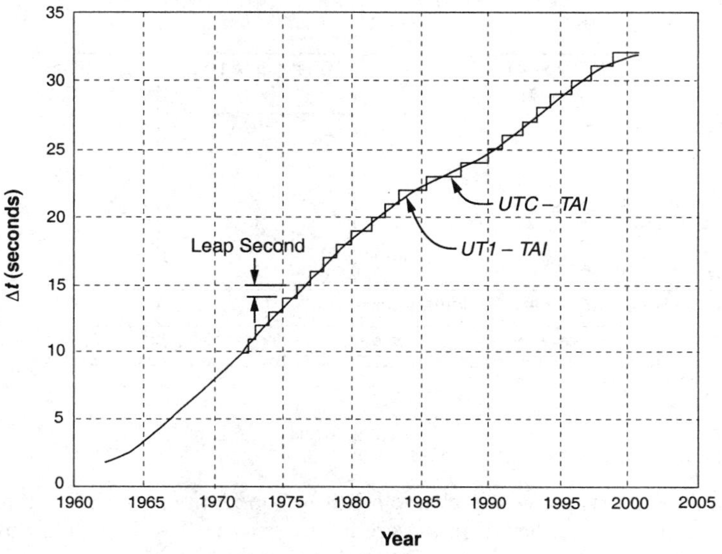

Fig. 4-2. Historical Differences Between Solar Time and Atomic Time.

Terrestrial Time (TT)

Terrestrial Time, TT, is the current substitute for what was previously identified as terrestrial dynamic time, TDT, which in turn replaced the earlier ephemeris time, *ET*. Terrestrial time also uses the SI second as the unit of measure but is more precisely defined in terms of the dynamic equations of motion for the Earth. For most practical purposes, *TT* can be defined in terms of *TAI* by a simple offset, i.e., $TT - TAI =$ 32.184 sec. (This offset is due to the historical origins of the time system. *TT* matched *ET* in 1984, when the use of *ET* was discontinued.) Consequently, in January 1966, $TT - UTC = 32.184 + 30$ sec $= 62.184$ sec. Because atomic clocks have a small drift rate, changes between *TT* and *TAI* on the order of microseconds can accumulate over a period of years. (A more precise definition of terrestrial time based on the theory of relativity is given at the end of this section.)

GPS Time

The GPS satellite system uses its own unique time called *GPS time*. Although presumably it could be accommodated with modern computer systems, the addition of a leap second is certainly inconvenient for GPS processing algorithms. Consequently, the GPS clock uses the SI second but does not introduce leap seconds. Like *TT* and *TAI*, GPS time maintains a fixed offset from *UTC* that changes by 1 sec whenever a leap second is introduced in *UTC*. In order to allow *UTC* to be recovered from the time signals broadcast by GPS, the integral number of seconds by which the two differ is included in subframe 4 of the GPS navigation message. (See Fig. 4-10 in Sec. 4.2.) Consequently, a GPS receiver may provide time output which is either GPS time or *UTC*. The GPS system is becoming a common mechanism for time transfer between two locations on the Earth or satellites in low-Earth orbit. An error budget for GPS time transfer when both locations have a common GPS satellite in view is given in Table 4-5.

TABLE 4-5. Error Budgets for GPS Time Transfer (with Two Satellites in View). [Seidelmann, 1992].

Type of Delay	Best Case RMS (ns)	Worst Case RMS (ns)
Satellite Ephemeris	3	10
Ionospheric	2	100
Tropospheric	1	20
User-Position	1	1
Multipath	1	2
Receiver	1	1
Signal-to-Noise	7	1
Total RMS (for single 13-minute track)	4.2	103

NOTE: Some of the errors depend on the distance (for example, the satellite ephemeris). The best case applies to distances of 2,000–3,000 km; the worst case is for distances of 6,000–8,000 km.

4.1.3 Discontinuous Time

One of the most interesting characteristics of modern spacecraft is that updating the spacecraft clock, either from the ground or from GPS, means that time will appear to be discontinuous on board. Because the updates are typically very small, this makes little difference to time-tagging of on-board observations and similar activities.

Spacecraft and "Discontinuous Time"

For working problems in mechanics, time and the flow of time is one of our most basic and ingrained concepts. One of our most fundamental perceptions of time is that it is continuous and in some sense "smoothly flowing." This philosophical view of time may or may not be true in the extremes of general relativity or quantum electrodynamics, but it is certainly untrue for nearly all spacecraft clocks, due simply to the problem of synchronization.

Time is kept on board a spacecraft by a clock that drifts relative to the outside world. If we let the clock drift indefinitely it becomes increasingly difficult to make or interpret observations of the world. Accurate timing of observations is critical both for many scientific observations and also to correctly locate observations on the surface of the Earth or another planet. This implies a need to update spacecraft clocks from time to time by synchronizing them with the outside world using GPS, radio time signals, or a ground station clock synchronized with the worldwide time network.

Unfortunately, this implies a discontinuity or jump in time tagging of things like the spacecraft position as a function of time. For example, we may find ourselves in a position where the spacecraft is over the equator at exactly 12:00:00 and 100 km north of the equator at 12:00:01, such that the spacecraft appears to have made a jump in the space-time continuum. Even worse, we may find that the spacecraft is in two different places at the same time. Suppose that we cross the equator at 12:00:00. We reset the spacecraft clock backwards to 11:59:59 and then proceed along in the orbit such that we are now a few km north of the equator, once again, exactly at noon. While this is a perfectly reasonable sequence of events, remarkably few spacecraft data filters are prepared to handle discontinuous time.

Figure 4-2 shows the large-scale drift of the clock on the BREM-SAT spacecraft over a year. Figure 4-3 shows the fine drift on a day-to-day basis. With this particular clock one would need to introduce a correction averaging ~3 sec per day and ranging from +12 sec to –5 sec depending on the date. This corresponds to the spacecraft being ahead or behind by up to 90 km, even if the orbit propagation is perfect. Errors of this magnitude are certainly non-trivial in the interpretation of spacecraft data, including orbit and attitude information.

Both the lack of synchronization and the need to resynchronize clocks from time to time represent significant practical problems for spacecraft operations, and should be taken into account in both system and software design.

For simple time-tagging of data, this is not typically a problem. The synchronization error is simply one more component of the time-tagging error. The problem occurs whenever we need precise time differences or make use of the dynamic equations of motion for orbit, attitude, or payload data processing. In these processes, we must verify that the software will accommodate both "time jumps" and "time reversal."

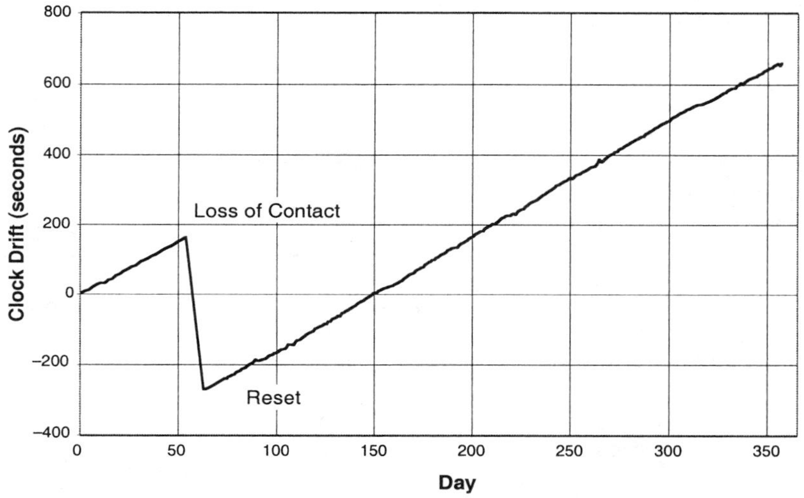

Fig. 4-3. Difference Between GPS Clock and BREM-SAT Computer Clock. This figure shows the cumulative large-scale drift of the BREM-SAT computer clock vs. a GPS clock over a year. The sharp drop shortly after day 50 reflects the loss of contact with BREM-SAT and subsequent reset after reacquisition

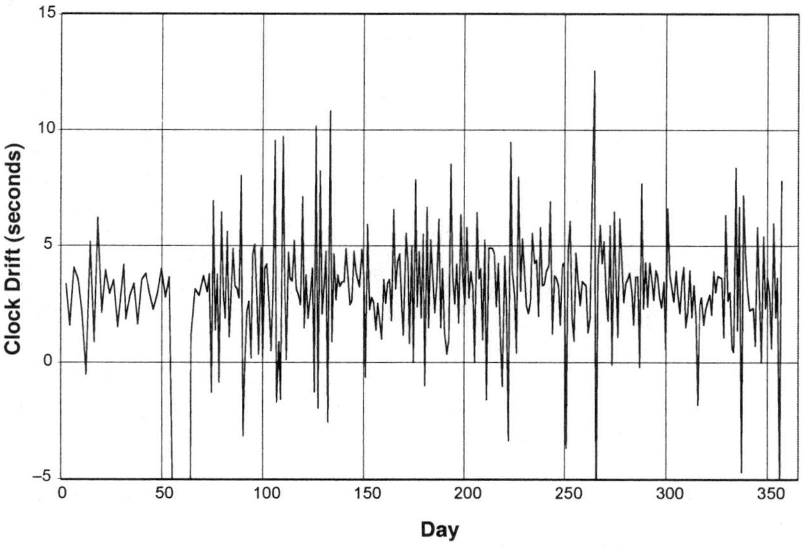

Fig. 4-4. Day-to-Day Difference Between GPS Clock and BREM-SAT Computer Clock. The figure shows fine drift of the BREM-SAT computer clock vs. a GPS clock on the ground. The results are for each day, not cumulative.

However, spacecraft are also becoming more sophisticated and dynamic equations of motion are often used in data filtering and system modeling, such as the propagation of orbit and attitude states. Unfortunately, very few analytic systems take into account the cause or effect of time discontinuities. This has the potential of causing substantial problems for on-board software and was a key (and painful) issue in one of the spacecraft I was involved with. The issue of "discontinuous time" is addressed in the adjacent boxed example. Anyone involved with time systems or high accuracy analysis of spacecraft data should be aware of this potential problem. So long as you are aware that "time" on the spacecraft can move forward, backward, or stand still over very brief intervals, finding solutions is typically not difficult—when they are planned in advance.

4.1.4 Solar Time, Sidereal Time, and Longitude on the Earth

Once we have launched a spacecraft into orbit and turned off the rockets, that orbit remains approximately fixed in inertial space, while the Earth continues to rotate beneath it. As described in Chap. 2, this means that the Earth underneath the spacecraft will change continuously, even though the spacecraft will repeat its path very nearly in inertial coordinates. To keep track of where the spacecraft is with respect to the surface of the Earth, we need to keep track of the rotational orientation of the Earth itself. This is done by knowing the *sidereal time*, which measures the rotation of the Earth relative to inertial space or the fixed stars. In contrast, civil time, such as that kept by a clock or radio signals, is a close approximation to *solar time*, which measures the rotation of the Earth with respect to the Sun. As shown in Fig. 4-5, solar time differs from

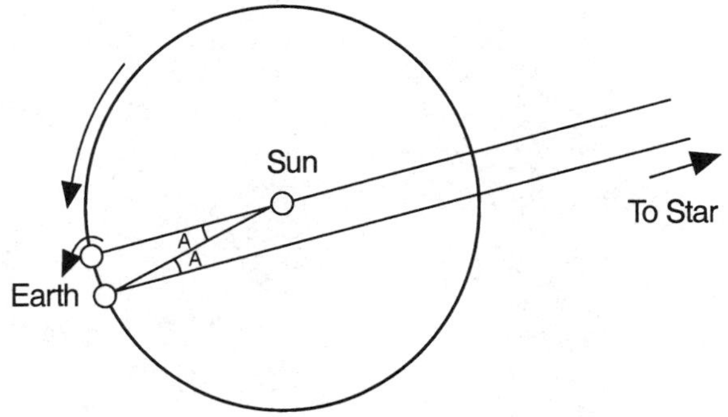

Fig. 4-5. Sidereal vs. Solar Day. The solar day (relative to the Sun) is 4 min longer than the sidereal day (relative to the stars) because the Earth has moved in its orbit during the day and must rotate further to bring the Sun overhead again. View shown is from the north ecliptic pole.

sidereal time because of the motion of the Earth in its orbit around the Sun. When the Earth has made one rotation on its axis relative to the stars, it has also moved approximately 1/365th of the way around its orbit. Consequently, it takes about 4 min longer for the Earth to return to the same orientation relative to the Sun. Therefore, a solar day, or civil day of 24 hours, will be about 4 min longer than a sidereal day of 23 hr 56 min. In order to quantify the relationship between sidereal time and civil time, we need a better understanding of solar time and the measurement of azimuth angles, both on the Earth and in the sky.†

The *celestial meridian* is the great circle in the sky passing through the celestial poles and the observer's *zenith*, i.e., the point straight overhead. As shown in Fig. 4-6, the *hour angle, HA*, is the azimuthal orientation of an object measured westward from the celestial meridian. As the Earth rotates eastward, an object on the celestial sphere (i.e., a star, planet, or the Sun) appears to move westward and its hour angle increases with time. It takes 24 hours for an object to move completely around the celestial sphere, or 1 hour to move 15 deg in *HA*; thus, 1 deg of *HA* corresponds to 4 min of time. Therefore, the rotation of the Earth allows us to measure azimuth angles either in degrees or hours, minutes, and seconds, or equivalently to measure time as either hours, minutes, and seconds, or degrees. Because of the small difference between the solar and sidereal days, 1 deg differs slightly from 4 min. The correct transformation is:

$$1 \text{ sidereal day} = 86{,}164.098\,903\,697\,32 \text{ sec} = 360 \text{ deg} \tag{4-11a}$$

Therefore,

$$\begin{aligned} 1 \text{ deg} &= 239.344\,719\,176\,937 \text{ sec} \\ &= 3 \text{ min } 59.344\,719\,176\,937 \text{ sec} \end{aligned} \tag{4-11b}$$

$$\begin{aligned} 1 \text{ sec} &= 0.004\,178\,074\,216\,297 \text{ deg} \\ &= 0.000\,072\,921\,151\,467 \text{ rad} \end{aligned} \tag{4-11c}$$

$$\begin{aligned} 1 \text{ min} &= 0.250\,684\,452\,977\,818 \text{ deg} \\ &= 0.004\,375\,269\,088\,024 \text{ rad.} \end{aligned} \tag{4-11d}$$

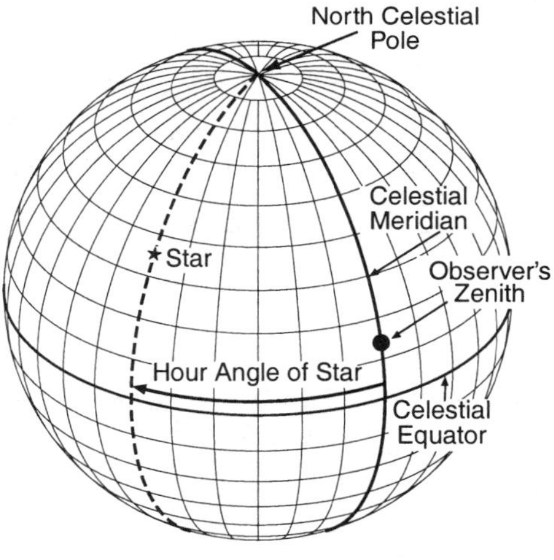

Fig. 4-6. Definition of Hour Angle. As the Earth rotates eastward, an object fixed in the sky appears to rotate westward and the hour angle increases.

† For definitions of rotation angles, the celestial sphere, and the globe plots in this section see Chap. 6.

The *apparent solar time* is the local *HA* of the Sun expressed in hours, plus 12 hours. Thus, the Sun crosses the observer's celestial meridian at an apparent solar time of 12:00 noon. Apparent solar time is measured by a sundial. We could, for example, construct a simple sundial by driving a long nail perpendicularly through a flat piece of wood. For an observer in the northern hemisphere, if the nail is then pointed to the north celestial pole, the plane of the wood is parallel to the equatorial plane, and the angle relative to south of the nail's shadow on the wood is a measure of the *HA*, or the apparent solar time

Due to the Earth's orbital motion, the Sun appears to move eastward along the ecliptic throughout the year. Because the Earth travels in an elliptical orbit it moves faster when near the Sun and slower when it is more distant. Therefore, the length of the solar day varies throughout the year.

However, even if the Earth were in a circular orbit with constant speed, the azimuthal component of the Earth's motion (parallel to the celestial equator) would vary, due to the inclination of the ecliptic relative to the equator. To illustrate this, consider a satellite in a nearly polar orbit as shown in Fig. 4-7. The satellite changes azimuth slowly while near the equator and very rapidly while near the poles. Because the inclination of the ecliptic to the Earth's equator is only 23.5 deg rather than the large inclination illustrated in the figure, the variation in the length of the day due to the inclination of the ecliptic is small. The cumulative variation due to both eccentricity and inclination reaches a maximum of 16 min in November.

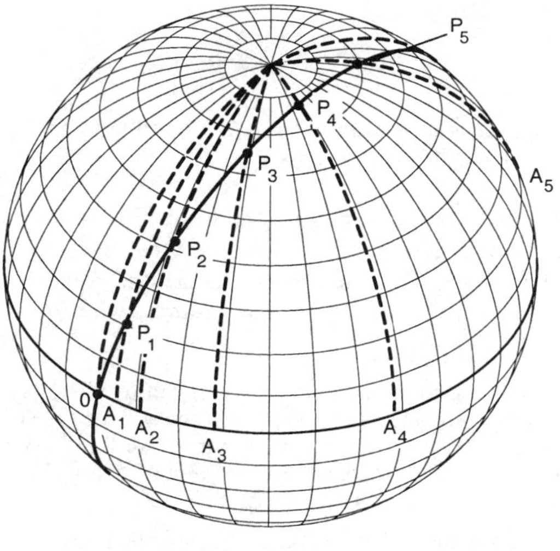

Fig. 4-7. Variation in Azimuthal Rate for a Satellite Moving Uniformly in its Orbit. A_1, A_2,...,A_5 are azimuthal projections of the orbital points P_1, P_2,...,P_5 and are equally spaced in time.

To provide a more uniform time than the real Sun, a fictitious *mean Sun*, which moves along the equator at a constant rate equal to the average annual rate of the Sun, has been introduced. *Mean solar time* is defined as the *HA* of the mean Sun. The difference between mean and apparent solar time is called the *equation of time*. This is often represented by an analemma, or figure 8, which frequently shows up in the middle of the Pacific ocean on globes of the world. This is the correction that is applied to a sundial to determine mean solar time.

In contrast to solar time, *sidereal time, ST*, is based on the rotation of the Earth relative to the stars and is defined as the *HA* of the vernal equinox, ♈.† The *local sidereal time, LST*, is defined as the local *HA* of ♈, *LHA* ♈. The *Greenwich sidereal time, GST*, (also called the *Greenwich HA of the vernal equinox, GHA* ♈) is the hour angle of the vernal equinox for an observer on the Earth's prime meridian, which goes through the Royal Greenwich Observatory.

The *right ascension, RA*‡, of any star or other celestial object is the azimuthal component of the star's position measured eastward from ♈. It is the celestial equivalent of longitude measured on the surface of the Earth.

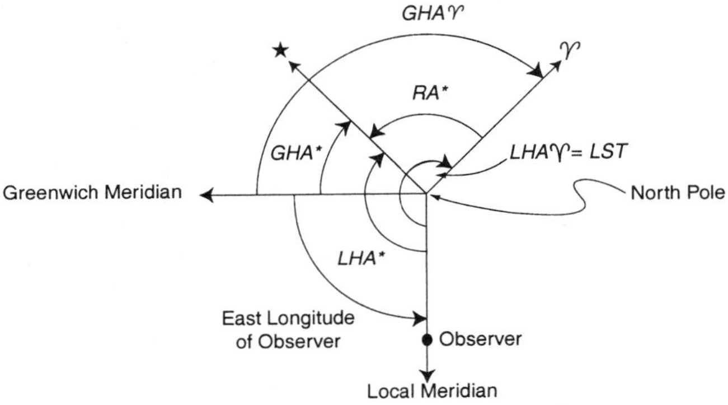

Fig. 4-8. Relationship Between Position on the Earth and Sidereal Time. View looking down from the Earth's North Pole.

Figure 4-8 shows the azimuthal angular relationships between ♈, a star or other celestial object, the Greenwich meridian, and the local meridian of the observer. All of these are azimuthal angles projected onto the celestial equator. From this figure we can determine a variety of relationships. For example, the *local sidereal time, LST,*

† The *vernal equinox* is the location of the Sun in the sky on the first day of spring. It is located at one of the two intersections between the ecliptic plane and the celestial equator. The symbol for the vernal equinox (♈) is the astronological symbol for the constellation Aries, the Ram, because the vernal equinox is also called the First Point of Aries. (The vernal equinox was in Aries when the name was given to that region of the sky.)

‡ The units here can be particularly confusing. Throughout this book we will use deg and decimal fractions of a deg for most angular measurements, although radians will occasionally be used. In astronomical work, angles, and particularly declination (the latitude-like measurement on the celestial sphere), are often measured in deg, min, and sec of arc, which are written as, $10°$, $10'$, and $10''$, where 1 min of arc is 1/60th deg, and 1 sec of arc is 1/60th of a min. Very small angles such as the resolution of optical instruments, are frequently measured in sec of arc. Because right ascension also corresponds to time, it is often measured in hours, min, and sec, written as 10^h, 10^m, 10^s. Here 1 hr corresponds to 15 deg, 1 min corresponds to 0.25 deg, and 1 sec is 1/60th of a min, or 1/240th of a deg. Thus, min and sec of right ascension are **not** the same as min and sec of declination. We avoid this confusion by using deg and decimal fractions of a degree for all angles.

may be determined from the *RA* and observed *HA* of any star:

$$LST = LHA\ \Upsilon = [LHA^* + RA^*]\text{mod}_{24\text{ hrs}} \quad (4\text{-}12)$$

where *LHA** and *RA** are the *HA* and *RA* of the star, both converted to time. In the example in Fig. 4-8, *LHA** is 135 deg or 9 hours, *RA** is 90 deg or 6 hours and *LST* is 15 hours. Similarly, we can determine the *Greenwich sidereal time, GST,* from:

$$GST = GHA\ \Upsilon = [GHA^* - RA^*]\text{mod}_{24\text{ hrs}} \quad (4\text{-}13)$$

*GHA** is the *GHA* of any star, converted to time. Again in the example figure, *GHA** is 45 deg or 3 hours; thus *GST* is 9 hours. Note that the sidereal time at Greenwich is equal to the right ascension of the Greenwich meridian. The difference between *LST* and *GST* (6 hours in the example of the figure) corresponds to the observer's east longitude (90 deg in the example). In general,

$$LST = GST + EL/15 \quad (4\text{-}14)$$

where *EL* is the observer's east longitude in deg and *LST* and *GST* are in hours.

From the definition of mean solar time, the Greenwich mean time, *GMT*, or universal time, *UT*, equals the *GHA* of the fictitious mean Sun plus 12 hours:

$$UT = GMT = GST - RA_0 + 12\text{ hours} \quad (4\text{-}15)$$

where RA_0 is the right ascension of the mean Sun. For a given *UT* on any calendar date, the expression for the *GST* is given by

$$\begin{aligned} GST &= RA_0 - 12\text{ hours} + UT \\ &= 6^h38^m45^s.836 + 8{,}640{,}184^s.542T + 0^s.092\,9T^2 + UT \end{aligned} \quad (4\text{-}16)$$

where *T* is the number of Julian centuries of 36,525 days which have elapsed since noon (GMT) on January 0, 1900. The corresponding equation for *GST* expressed in degrees is

$$GST = 99^\circ.690\,983 + 36{,}000^\circ.768\,925T + 0^\circ.000\,387T^2 + UT \quad (4\text{-}17)$$

where *UT* is in degrees and *T* is again in Julian centuries.

The Julian date, *JD,* defined in Sec. 4.1.1 provides a convenient mechanism for determining *T* in Eqs. (4-16) and (4-17). The *JD* for Greenwich mean noon on January 0, 1900 (i.e., January 0.5 1900) is 2,415,020.0. The *JD* for any date in the current era may be obtained by adding the day number of the year to the date *JD* for January 0.0 *UT* of that year as listed in Table 4-2. For example, to find the *GST* for 3 hours *UT* on July 4, 2026:

Day number of July 4.125 (3^h *UT* July 4)	186.125
+ *JD* for January 0.0, 2026	+2 442 777.500
= *JD* for July 4.125, 2026	= 2 442 963.625
– *JD* for January 0.5, 2000	– 2 415 020.000
= *T* in days	27 943.625
÷36,525 = *T* in Julian centuries	0.765054757
8,640,184.542 *T*+0.0929 T^2	6 610 214.340 sec
	$=76^d12^h10^m14^s.340$
+ first term Eq. (4-16)	6 38 45.836
+ *UT*	300.000
GST	$=21^h49^m0^s.176$

Given the Greenwich sidereal time, we can finally compute the longitude of the subsatellite point for a spacecraft whose ephemeris is known. Specifically from Eqs. (4-2a and b) we have

$$EL_{spc} = RA_{spc} - GST \text{ (in degrees)} \tag{4-18}$$

where RA_{spc} is the right ascension in degrees of the spacecraft at the time in question and EL is the East longitude of the subsatellite point.

Note that the Greenwich sidereal time defined by these equations is a uniformly flowing time whereas the actual rotation of the Earth on its axis has a very low amplitude wobble as described in the front of the chapter. Consequently, the accuracy of the resulting longitude from the general equations above will be about 0.005 deg (= 500 m at the equator) if the spacecraft ephemeris is known precisely.

4.1.5 Relativistic Time

On the whole, relativity is not something to worry about in space missions, except for spacecraft designed specifically to test relativistic theories. Nonetheless, we need to understand the boundaries of Newtonian physics so that we can understand the magnitude of the errors that occur and under what circumstances they become relevant. Consequently, this section summarizes the relativistic effects most important for work with spacecraft clocks and the level of error that results when relativistic effects are ignored. A mathematical summary of relativistic time as it applies to the generation of ephemerides is given by Seidelmann [1992]. A detailed mathematical and physical explanation of most effects in special and general relativity is provided by Misner et al. [1973]. A detailed explanation of relativistic effects applied to spacecraft and an extensive reference list are given by Ashby and Spilker in Parkinson and Spilker [1996]. However, this volume does not cover the relativistic time systems adopted by the IAU which are discussed by Seidelmann [1992]. More popular and readable explanations of the physical phenomenon in special and general relativity are provided by a wide variety of texts including, for example, Einstein [1950], Mermin [1968], and Kaufmann, III [1973].

The fundamental relativistic effect that is important for time systems is that the rate at which time flows depends on the observer. In *special relativity* the most important effect, known as *time dilation*, is that moving clocks run slow, i.e., any clock in motion with respect to me runs slower than my clock. Here the concept of a "clock" is a very general way of expressing the flow of time, and applies to clocks as fundamental as those which are inside an atom. One of the most compelling demonstrations of time dilation is associated with the radioactive decay of atomic particles. When cosmic rays interact with the Earth's upper atmosphere, they produce streams of very high velocity mesons. These mesons undergo radioactive decay, but do so far more slowly than do mesons produced in experiments "at rest" with respect to us on the surface of the Earth.

In general, if we have a collection of observers in motion with respect to each other (for example, observers with very precise clocks on a collection of spacecraft in different orbits) each observer will determine that all of the other observers' clocks run slow. (It is not just that they **see** the clocks run slow due to the finite velocity of light. They take the velocity of light into account and **calculate** that all of the other clocks actually are running slow.) This leads to a wide variety of apparent paradoxes, in terms of different observers comparing the results of timing experiments. Most of these are resolved by a second important phenomenon in relativity—the *lack of absolute simultaneity*, which states that whether two distant events are simultaneous (occur at the same time) does not have an absolute meaning, but depends upon the state of motion of the observer.

In the *general theory of relativity*, an effect similar to time dilation is that clocks run slower in a gravitational field.† Thus, clocks on the surface of the Earth run more slowly than those away from any of the planets, even if they are not moving relative to the Earth. Similarly, clocks run slower as they approach any massive object.

Time dilation, the slowing of clocks in a gravitational field, and related relativistic effects are discussed in detail in the references above. The important issue for spacecraft is that the flow of time in its most basic sense is not an absolute thing but depends on both the gravitational field and the state of motion of the clock. Clocks in orbit, even atomic clocks, don't behave like clocks on the surface of the Earth, although the differences are remarkably small.

As summarized in Table 4-6, relativistic effects are dramatically small and are of no consequence for most space missions. For example, a clock on a spacecraft in low-Earth orbit, moving at 8 km/s relative to an observer on the Earth, runs slow by 11 msec per year or a fractional shift of 3.5×10^{-10}. A clock sitting on the "surface" of Jupiter runs slow by 1 part in 5×10^7 which changes a 10 MHz signal from a spacecraft there by 0.2 Hz.

The effects of relativity are extremely small, even by the standards of precise spacecraft measurements. Nonetheless, they are measurable and do have an impact on our basic understanding of time systems and, perhaps more importantly, what we mean by time. In 1991 the general theory of relativity was explicitly adopted as the theoretical framework for defining space-time reference frames.‡ The implication is that time is no longer defined in an absolute sense, i.e., as so many ticks of an atomic clock, but only as so many ticks **in a specific coordinate frame**. The key issue for spaceflight is that no matter how you measure it—the decay of subatomic particles, the clicks of a Cesium clock, or the number of old movies you can watch—time flows at a different rate on board spacecraft than it does on the Earth. We need to tie our definition of time to the coordinate frame which we are using. This in turn leads to the two remaining types of time, both of which fall into the category of dynamic time, or time which depends on orbital motion in the Solar System.

Terrestrial Time (TT)

The fundamental unit of *Terrestrial Time* is the *SI* second, as kept by a perfect atomic clock at mean sea level on the surface of the Earth. Here the second is the same

---

† Effects in general relativity are tied to those in special relativity by the *Principal of Equivalence* which states that the effects of a gravitational field are equivalent to those of an accelerating frame of reference. This also implies that a freely falling, non-rotating body is equivalent to one which is not in a gravitational field at all. Thus, if an object has fallen from infinity to near the surface of a gravitating body, its "clock" is equivalent to one that is not in a gravitational field. Therefore, the slowing of clocks in a gravitational field is equivalent to the time dilation of a "stationary" clock near the celestial body when compared with one which is moving at the velocity it would have when falling from being at rest at infinity (i.e., the escape velocity of the celestial body).

‡ For both historical and practical reasons, the astronomical community has been the caretaker of fundamental clocks and the definition of time. The definitions of time systems given here and Sec. 4.1.1 are those adopted by resolutions of the general assembly of the International Astronomical Union.

TABLE 4-6. Typical Relativistic Time Effects. Relativistic effects are not important for normal spacecraft operations, but may become relevant if extreme precision is required. Note that for the Doppler shift, the first term is the ordinary (Newtonian) Doppler shift and the second term is the relativistic correction.

Effect	Basic Formulas	Examples
Time Dilation (Moving clocks run slow)	Time delay: $\frac{\Delta t}{t} = \frac{1}{\sqrt{1 - v^2/c^2}} \approx \frac{1}{2}$	In Low-Earth orbit = 11 ms/yr In Earth's orbit about Sun = 158 ms/yr On Fastest Spc (60 km/s) = 632 ms/yr
	Doppler shift (frequency shift) due to spacecraft velocity: $\frac{\Delta f}{f} \approx \frac{v}{c} \cos\theta + \frac{1}{2}\frac{v^2}{c^2}$	Effect on signal at 10.23 MHz (GPS): In Low-Earth orbit = 269.747 + 0.004 Hz In Earth's orbit about Sun = 1023.708 + 0.051 Hz On Fastest Spc = 2047.416 + 0.205 Hz
	Sagnac effect (time delay due to rotating frame): $\frac{\Delta t}{t} \approx \frac{\omega^2 R^2}{2c^2}$	On Earth's surface = 0.038 ms/yr On Jupiter's surface = 28 ms/yr
Gravitational Time Dilation (Clocks run slow in a gravitational field)	Gravitational frequency shift: $\frac{\Delta f}{f} \approx \frac{\mu}{Rc^2}$	Effect on signal at 10.23 MHz (GPS): At surface of Earth = 0.007 Hz At surface of Jupiter = 0.202 Hz At surface of Sun = 21.702 Hz At Earth distance (due to Sun's gravitational field) = 0.101 Hz

Definition of Variables:

c = velocity of light (299,792,458 m/s)
v = velocity of clock relative to the observer
θ = angle between velocity vector and line of sight
R = radius of the celestial body
μ = GM = gravitational constant of the celestial body
ω = angular rotation rate
t = time
Δt = time difference
f = frequency
Δf = frequency shift

as that defined by International Atomic Time, *TAI*, but is given a more precise definition by being attached to a specific reference frame. Because the units are identical, *TT* is equal to *TAI* time plus an offset of 32.184 sec. The offset comes about for historical reasons having to do with the evolution of time systems. In a series of actions from 1950 to 1958, *Ephemeris Time*, *ET*, was adopted by the international community as the most fundamental definition of time based on the motion of the planets as defined by Simon Newcomb's tables of the Sun published in 1900. In 1967, the atomic clock definition of the second was introduced, which led to very small variations in the rate of time and small offsets in differently defined time systems. In 1984, *ET* was abandoned in favor of *terrestrial dynamic time*, *TDT*. Finally, in 1991 when relativity was adopted as the appropriate analytical framework, *TDT* was renamed *terrestrial time*, *TT*. This is currently the time scale in use for generating ephemerides for the motion of celestial objects as seen from the surface of the Earth.

Barycentric Dynamic Time (TDB)

Barycentric dynamic time is the independent variable in the orbital equations of motion with respect to the barycenter of the solar system. Thus, *TDB* transforms time as measured on the surface of the Earth to time as kept by the motion of the planets (thus, in a different coordinate frame). *TDB* and *TT* are very close to each other (i.e., to within less than 2 msec), with the differences between them being determined by means of mathematical expressions. An approximate formula for converting *TT* to *TDB* that is sufficient for all practical applications is:

$$TDB = TT + 0.001\,658 \sin g + 0.000\,014 \sin 2g \tag{4-19}$$

where the times and coefficients are in SI seconds and g, expressed in deg, is given by

$$g = 357.53 \text{ deg} + 0.985\,600\,3\,(JD - 2{,}451{,}545.0) \tag{4-20}$$

and *JD* is the Julian date expressed to two decimals of a day.

4.2 The Global Positioning System

The *Global Positioning System* (GPS), also called *NavStar*, is a navigation system using 6 planes of 4 satellites each in circular orbits at an altitude of 20,184 km (half GEO) and inclination of 55 deg. By processing the simultaneous signals from multiple GPS satellites, a GPS receiver can determine its instantaneous position anywhere on the surface of the Earth to an accuracy of approximately 30 m (3 σ). In addition, the GPS receiver solves for the time to an accuracy of about 10 nsec and can determine the velocity to an accuracy of about 1 cm/s. Kaplan [1996], Leick [1995], Hofmann-Wellenhof [1997], and the two volume set by Parkinson and Spilker [1996] provide excellent technical summaries of GPS technology and applications.

In 1964, the United States Navy navigation satellite system called *Transit* first became operational. Transit provided a 2-D position fix (i.e., for objects on the Earth's surface) based on processing 10 to 15 min of satellite data with fixes available every 30 min to 2 hours depending on the user's location. This process worked well for ship navigation but was inappropriate for aircraft or other rapidly moving vehicles which require position fixes more often and with far less processing time.

At approximately this same time, the Naval Research Laboratory was experimenting with highly stable space-based clocks in order to obtain precision time transfer. This program was called *Timation*. By the early 1970s, the Air Force had created a project known as 621B intended to create a higher accuracy truly global system for military navigation. In 1973, the general concept for what was to become GPS was developed based on combining elements of the technology from Transit, Timation, and the 621B programs. The first operational prototype GPS satellite was launched in February 1978 with substantial testing throughout the 1980s. The initial operating capability for GPS, with 24 satellites operating simultaneously, occurred on December 8, 1993. With the deployment of the full complement of GPS satellites, the system has gained widespread acceptance for civil and military applications and is in use worldwide for cars, planes, spacecraft, and individuals. This served to both expand the technology and substantially lower the cost of GPS receivers.

The GPS satellite itself, shown in Fig. 4-9, is basically a flying atomic clock.† Each satellite broadcasts the time and its own orbital elements on a carrier with two precisely controlled frequencies—1,575.42 MHz (called L1) and 1,227.60 MHz (L2). Dual frequencies allow the receiver to solve for atmospheric delays which are different for the two.

---

† Because the atomic clock is both critical and subject to on-orbit failures, each of the initial GPS satellites carried two Cesium and two Rubidium atomic clocks. Subsequent production satellites reduced the number of clocks but are still redundant.

Fig. 4-9. The GPS Satellite. (Courtesy of the GPS Program Office.)

TABLE 4-7. Orbit Parameters of the GPS Constellation. ID = plane/slot; a = semimajor axis; i = inclination; Ω = right ascension of ascending node; M = mean anomaly; *lan* = longitude of ascending node; ΔM = phase difference in mean anomaly to adjacent satellite in the same plane [Parkinson, et al., 1996].

	ID	a (km)	i (deg)	Ω (deg)	M (deg)	ΔM (deg)	*lan* (deg)
1	A3	26561.75	55.0	272.847	11.676	103.55	179.63
2	A4	26561.75	55.0	272.847	41.806	31.13	14.69
3	A2	26561.75	55.0	272.847	161.786	119.98	74.68
4	A1	26561.75	55.0	272.847	268.126	106.34	127.85
5	B1	26561.75	55.0	332.847	80.956	130.98	94.27
6	B2	26561.75	55.0	332.847	173.336	92.38	140.46
7	B4	26561.75	55.0	332.847	204.376	31.04	155.98
8	B3	26561.75	55.0	332.847	309.976	105.60	28.78
9	C1	26561.75	55.0	32.847	111.876	100.08	169.73
10	C4	26561.75	55.0	32.847	241.556	129.68	54.57
11	C3	26561.75	55.0	32.847	339.666	98.11	103.62
12	C2	26561.75	55.0	32.847	11.796	32.13	119.69
13	D1	26561.75	55.0	92.847	135.226	100.07	61.40
14	D4	26561.75	55.0	92.847	167.356	32.13	77.47
15	D2	26561.75	55.0	92.847	265.446	98.09	126.51
16	D3	26561.75	55.0	92.847	35.156	129.71	11.37
17	E1	26561.75	55.0	152.847	197.046	130.98	152.31
18	E2	26561.75	55.0	152.847	302.596	105.55	25.09
19	E4	26561.75	55.0	152.847	333.686	31.09	40.63
20	E3	26561.75	55.0	152.847	66.066	92.38	86.82
21	F1	26561.75	55.0	212.847	238.886	103.54	52.23
22	F2	26561.75	55.0	212.847	345.226	106.34	106.40
23	F3	26561.75	55.0	212.847	105.206	119.98	166.39
24	F4	26561.75	55.0	212.847	135.346	30.00	1.46

In order to accurately measure the position, the GPS receiver must solve for both its position and the time, i.e., 4 unknown quantities. To do this, it must process simultaneous signals from 4 non-coplanar GPS satellites. Consequently, the GPS constellation is designed to provide fourfold, non-coplanar coverage of the entire world on a continuous basis. The constellation pattern is illustrated in Fig. 4-10 and the orbit parameters are given in Table 4-7. For satellite applications, it is important to note that having a GPS satellite in view is not the same as being able to receive the signal as illustrated in Fig. 4-11. The transmit antenna on the GPS satellite is intended to provide coverage of the Earth and, therefore, broadcasts in a cone toward the Earth's

Fig. 4-10. GPS Constellation Structure. There are 4 satellites in each of 6 planes at an inclination of 55 deg. The orbit period is 12 hours.

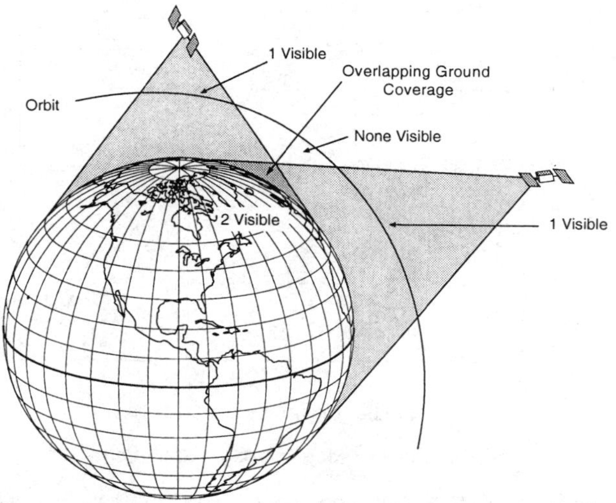

Fig. 4-11. Viewing Geometry for GPS Satellites. Although there is spill-over, GPS satellites are designed to broadcast signals only in the direction of the Earth's surface.

surface. To be within the standard GPS broadcast cone, a receiver in orbit must be between the GPS satellite and the surface of the Earth. The extent to which the "spill-over" signal can be received outside this cone depends on the antenna pattern, the attitude of the GPS satellite, the range, and the sensitivity of the GPS receiver. If we make the conservative assumption that the satellite using GPS for navigation must be inside the GPS Earth cone, then the number of usable GPS satellites drops rapidly as the spacecraft altitude increases, as shown in Fig. 4-12.

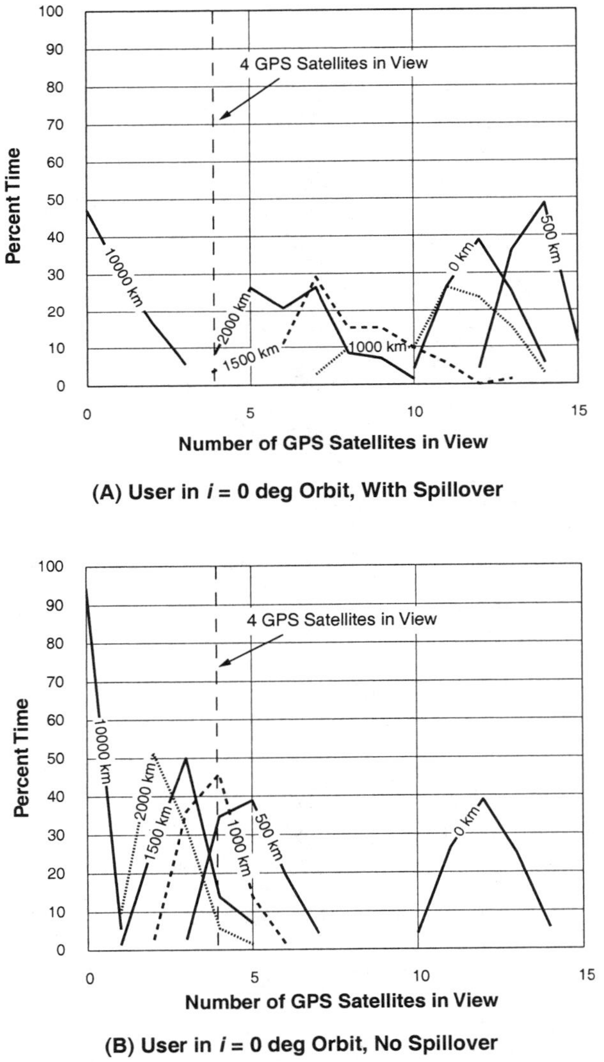

Fig. 4-12. Number of Usable GPS Satellites from Varying Altitudes. Even though many GPS satellites may be in view in low-Earth orbit the user satellite may be outside of the usable signal area. (See Fig. 4-11.)

The fundamental GPS measurement is the 3-D position and the time. These parameters are solved for in the GPS receiver using the time and orbit elements for the GPS satellites contained in the GPS message. The basic structure of this message is shown in Fig. 4-13. Each of the GPS satellites continuously transmits this navigation message on both L1 and L2 at a rate of 50 bps. The complete message consists of 25 frames of 1500 bits each. Each frame is further subdivided into five 300-bit subframes and each subframe is divided into 10 words of 30 bits. At 50 bps, it requires 6 sec to transmit a subframe, 30 sec for each frame, and 12.5 min for transmission of the complete navigation message. However, subframes 1, 2, and 3 which contain all of the necessary clock information and satellite ephemeris data are transmitted in each frame. Consequently, the information needed to compute the position and the time is repeated every 30 sec. The content of the GPS ephemeris message is shown in Table 4-8A and the defined set of equations used to process this data to determine the user position and the time is given in Table 4-8B. Note that these parameters and equations are closely related to the Keplerian elements discussed in Chap. 2, with a harmonic expansion for the principal orbit perturbations at the GPS satellite altitude.

In addition to position and time, many GPS receivers can also solve for velocity. In principle, we can determine velocity by successive differences in position measurements but the accuracy would be poor. Much better accuracy is achieved by measuring the Doppler shift of the carrier signal which provides a measurement of the radial velocity toward or away from the GPS satellite. These velocity components toward the 4 GPS satellites can then be processed directly (along with the known velocities of the GPS satellites in their orbits) to solve for the velocity of the GPS receiver.

Finally, the GPS signal can also be used to solve for the attitude of the vehicle on which the receiver is located. This is done by using multiple GPS antennas which are a known distance apart and which are attached to a rigid element of the vehicle. By measuring the phase difference between the signal from one GPS satellite arriving at two antennas, the GPS receiver serves as an interferometer measuring the angle between the line of sight to the GPS satellite and the line joining the two antennas. See Fig 3-24 in Sec 3.3.2. The wavelength of the GPS carrier signal is about 20 cm. Therefore, accuracy of the attitude is limited by both the long wavelength and multipath effects which cause confusion in the identification of the signal coming directly from the GPS satellite. In practice, spacecraft have been able to achieve on-orbit attitude accuracies on the order of 0.3 to 0.5 deg. Of course, the attitude accuracy and the availability of an attitude signal depends on the availability of appropriate GPS satellites which varies continuously with time.

As shown in Table 4-9, the number of satellites required and the amount of equipment needed on board the spacecraft depend on the functions to be performed. If a solution can be obtained, then the actual accuracy depends upon both the accuracy of the individual measurements and the geometry of the satellites being observed. For example, if the GPS receiver happens to be coplanar with all of the GPS satellites being used, then the out-of-plane component of the position of the receiver will be essentially unknown and the resulting position measurement will be singular (i.e., will have a very large error even if the individual measurements themselves are very good). This geometric component of the precision is measured by what is called the *geometric dilution of precision* or *GDOP*. By definition

$$\sigma \equiv GDOP\ \sigma_0 \tag{4-21}$$

where σ_0 is the standard deviation of the observed range measurements and σ is the standard deviation of the resulting position measurements.

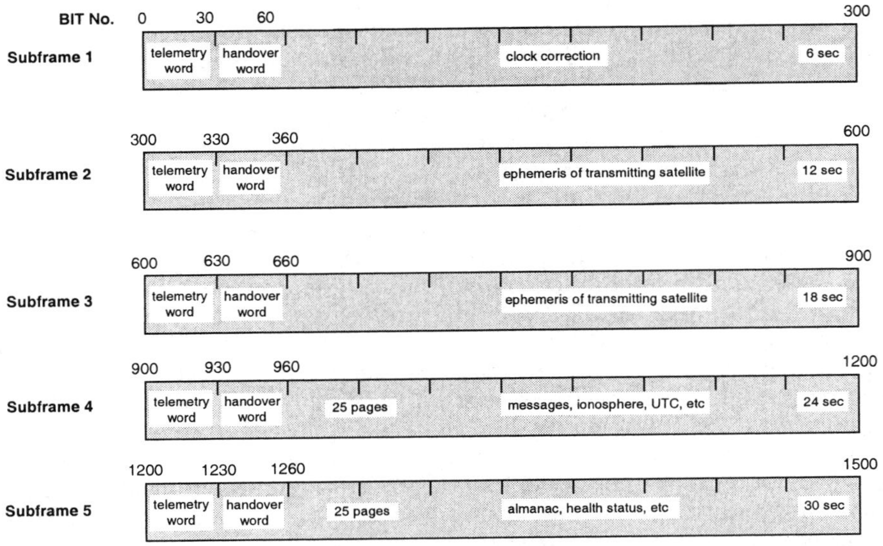

Fig. 4-13. Structure of the GPS Message. See text for discussion.

TABLE 4-8. GPS Navigation Message and Processing Algorithms. The parameters in the navigation message are intended to be used with these specific algorithms.

A. Ephemeris Parameterization of the Navigation Message	
M_0	Mean anomaly at reference time
Δn	Mean motion difference from computed value
e	Eccentricity
$\sqrt{a}$	Square root of the semimajor axis
Ω_0	Longitude of ascending node of orbit plane at weekly epoch
i_0	Inclination angle at reference time
ω	Argument of perigee
$\dot{\Omega}$	Rate of change of right ascension
IDOT	Rate of change of inclination angle
C_{uc}	Amplitude of the cosine harmonic correction term to the argument of latitude
C_{us}	Amplitude of the sine harmonic correction term to the argument of latitude
C_{rc}	Amplitude of the cosine harmonic correction term to the orbit radius
C_{rs}	Amplitude of the sine harmonic correction term to the orbit radius
C_{ic}	Amplitude of the cosine harmonic correction term to the angle of inclination
C_{is}	Amplitude of the sine harmonic correction term to the angle of inclination
t_{oe}	Ephemeris reference time
IODE	Issue of Data (Ephemeris)

TABLE 4-8. GPS Navigation Message and Processing Algorithms. The parameters in the navigation message are intended to be used with these specific algorithms.

B. Ephemeris Algorithms	
$\mu = 3.986\,005 \times 10^{14}\ m^3/s^2$	WGS 84 value of the Earth's universal gravitational parameter
$\dot{\Omega}_E = 7.292\,115\,146\,7 \times 10^{-5}$ rad/s	WGS 84 value of Earth's rotation rate
$a = \left(\sqrt{a}\right)^2$	Semimajor axis
$n_0 = \sqrt{\mu / a^3}$	Computed mean motion (rad/sec)
$t_k = t - t_{oe}$†	Time from ephemeris reference epoch
$n = n_0 + \Delta_n$	Corrected mean motion
$M_k = M_0 + n t_k$	Mean anomaly
$\pi = 3.141\ 592\ 653\ 589\,8$	GPS standard value for π
$M_k = E_k - e \sin E_k$	Kepler's equation for eccentric anomaly
$\cos f_k = (\cos E_k - e)/(1 - e\cos E_k)$ $\sin f_k = \left(\sqrt{1-e^2}\,\sin E_k\right)/(1 - e\cos E_k)$	True anomaly
$E_k = \cos^{-1}\left[(e + \cos f_k)/(1 + e\cos f_k)\right]$	Eccentricity anomaly
$\phi_k = f_k + \omega$	Argument of latitude
$\delta u_k = C_{us} \sin 2\phi_k + C_{uc} \cos 2\phi_k$	Argument of latitude correction (2nd harmonic perturbations)
$\delta r_k = C_{rc} \cos 2\phi_k + C_{rs} \sin 2\phi_k$	Radius corrections (2nd harmonic perturbations)
$\delta i_k = C_{ic} \cos 2\phi_k + C_{is} \sin 2\phi_k$	Correction to inclination (2nd harmonic perturbations)
$u_k = \phi_k + \delta u_k$	Corrected argument of latitude
$r_k = a\,(1 - e\cos E_k) + \delta r_k$	Corrected radius
$i_k = I_0 + \delta i_k + (\text{IDOT})t_k$	Corrected Inclination
$x'_k = r_k \cos u_k$ $y'_k = r_k \sin u_k$	Positions in orbital plane
$\Omega_k = \Omega_0 + \left(\dot{\Omega} - \dot{\Omega}_e\right)t_k - \dot{\Omega}_e\, t_{oe}$	Corrected longitude of ascending node
$x_k = x'_k \cos\Omega_k - y'_k \cos i_k \sin\Omega_k$ $y_k = x'_k \sin\Omega_k + y'_k \cos i_k \cos\Omega_k$ $z_k = y'_k \sin i_k$	Earth fixed coordinates

† t is GPS system time at time of transmission, i.e., GPS time corrected for transit time (range/speed of light). Furthermore, t_k shall be the actual total time difference between the time t and the epoch time t_{oe}, and must account for beginning or end of week crossovers. That is, if t_k is greater than 302,400 sec, subtract 604,800 sec from t_k. If t_k is less than −302,400 sec, add 604,800 sec to t_k.

TABLE 4-9. Number of GPS Satellites Required to be Simultaneously in View for Various Functions. (Note that all position solutions require that the GPS receiver solve simultaneously for the time.)

Function	Requirement
Position determination if altitude known (*2-D position*) + time	3 GPS satellites noncoplanar with the target
Position + altitude determination (*3-D position*) + time	4 GPS satellites noncoplanar with the target
3-D Position + altitude + time	3 noncollinear antennas on the spacecraft + sufficient GPS satellites in view for the position determination

GDOP measures the effect of the geometry of the satellites, much as the correlation coefficient determines the accuracy of attitude and position measurements in satellite attitude and navigation as described in Sec. 7.2. *GDOP* is a composite measure taking into account the geometrical impacts on both time and position. It is evaluated geometrically by determining the uncertainties on the range measurements to the satellites and then transforming coordinates to compute the uncertainties in three mutually perpendicular Earth referenced axes (represented by the subscripts n for north, e for east, and h for height) and the time, t. *GDOP* is then given by

$$GDOP = \sqrt{\sigma_n{}^2 + \sigma_e{}^2 + \sigma_h{}^2 + c^2\sigma_t{}^2} \tag{4-22}$$

where σ_n, σ_e, and σ_h are the measurement uncertainties in the north, east, and height directions, σ_t is the uncertainty in the time measurement, and c is the velocity of light.

We can use a similar process to define dilution of precision factors for specific components as well. Thus, the *vertical dilution of precision, VDOP*, is given by

$$VDOP = \sigma_h \tag{4-23}$$

the *horizontal dilution of position, HDOP*, is:

$$HDOP = \sqrt{\sigma_n^2 + \sigma_e^2} \tag{4-24}$$

the 3-D *position dilution of position, PDOP*, is:

$$PDOP = \sqrt{\sigma_n^2 + \sigma_e^2 + \sigma_h^2} \tag{4-25}$$

and the *time dilution of precision, TDOP*, is:

$$TDOP = \sigma_t \tag{4-26}$$

In general, the dilution of precision can range from 1 to about 100. The mean value for the GPS constellation is about 2.7. A *DOP* of over 6 is typically regarded as poor performance for that measurement.

4.2.1 The Russian Global Navigation Satellite System

The *global navigation satellite system*, GLONASS, is a Russian space-based navigation system that provides 3-D position, velocity determination, and time dissemination on a worldwide basis. As shown in Table 4-10. GLONASS is very similar to GPS. It consists of a 24 satellite constellation at approximately half geosynchronous altitude and provides accuracies very similar to those of GPS. There are several manufacturers of GLONASS receivers, some of which are combined GPS/GLONASS receivers. As shown in Table 4-10, GLONASS is operated by Russia's Ministry of Defense. Like GPS, it was initiated in the mid-1970s with military design goals. Also like GPS, the civilian applications became apparent rapidly and the system is now in use for both civilian and military purposes. While the end results are very similar, the GLONASS signal structure is significantly different than that of GPS. Both GLONASS and GPS are available for use by spacecraft, and many satellite manufacturers are considering the use of either or both systems for onboard determination of position, velocity, time, and sometimes attitude.

TABLE 4-10. Comparison of GPS and GLONASS.

	GPS	GLONASS
Number of Satellites	24	24
Number of Orbital Planes	6	3
Satellites per Plane	4 (uneven)	8 (even)
Inclination	55 deg	64.8 deg
Nominal Eccentricity	0	0
Semimajor Axis	26,560 km	25,510 km
Period	≈11 h 58 m	≈11 h 15 m
	SIGNALS	
Signal Separation Technique	CDMA	FDMA
Carrier	L1:1575.42 MHz	L1:1602.5625-1615.5 MHz
	L2:1227.60 MHz	L2:1246.4375-1256.6 MHz
C/A-code (L1)	1.023 MHz	0.511 MHz
P-code (L1, L2)	10.23 MHz	5.11 MHz
	NAVIGATION MESSAGE	
Duration	12.5 min	2.5 min
Capacity	37,500 bits	7,500 bits
Word Duration	0.6 s	2.0 s
Word Capacity	30 bits	100 bits
Number of Words Within a Frame	50	15
Ephemeris	Modified Kepler elements	Geocentric Cartesian coord., velocities, and accelerations
	GENERAL	
Time Reference	UTC (USNO)	UTC (Russian)
Geodetic Datum	WGS 84	SGS 85
Selective Availability	Yes	Not planned
Antispoofing of P-codes	Yes	Possible
	ACCURACY (95% = 2 × RMS)	
Precise Constricted Service		
Horizontal Position	22 m	comparable to GPS
Vertical Position	28 m	comparable to GPS
Velocity	0.2 m/s	comparable to GPS
Time	200 ns	comparable to GPS
Standard Service		
Horizontal Position	100 m	100 m
Vertical Position	156 m	150 m
Velocity		0.04 m/s
Time	340 ns	5 ns

4.3 Autonomous Navigation Systems

Section 2.7 introduced both the techniques and terminology for spacecraft navigation (recall that navigation and orbit determination are used interchangeably). In some respects autonomous navigation, i.e., doing the orbit determination on board the spacecraft, is straightforward, since it can be done by any sequence of observations which establish the position of the spacecraft as a function of time. Nonetheless, there are some issues which serve to make the problem significantly more complex. Orbit determination requires knowing both the position and the velocity of the spacecraft. Determining the velocity by looking at differences in the position with large position errors results in extremely poor velocity measurements. However, measuring the velocity directly is also difficult. In addition, nearly all types of measurements are subject to both outages and a variety of singularities which produce either divergence or very large errors in both deterministic solutions and state estimation methods. Given an appropriate set of non-singular observations, actually computing the orbit on board is technically easy with the introduction of advanced spacecraft computers that handle high level languages. The fundamental problem is to provide orbit determination that is reliable, robust, and economical in terms of both cost and weight.

Autonomous navigation is inherently real time; thus, definitive orbit solutions and payload data are available simultaneously, which means that we can generate ground look points or target positions and immediately associate them with the payload data. In addition, measurements can be less accurate than those for systems that work on old data, because solutions propagated forward in time lose accuracy. To do accurate orbit maneuvers, for instance, we need a greater accuracy from a definitive solution based on old data that must be propagated forward to meet real-time requirements. With a real-time system, highly accurate orbit propagation is less critical, although we will still need some forward propagation for prediction and planning. To date, this potential for relaxing orbit determination requirements has typically been superseded by an ever-increasing demand for navigation accuracy for payload purposes.

As summarized in Tables 4-11 and 4-12, several systems have been proposed for spacecraft navigation. Other alternatives are also possible. For example, the New Millennium Program uses asteroid tracking with respect to the background of stars to determine the position of interplanetary spacecraft, and target relative tracking (e.g., tracking craters during an asteroid fly-by) has also been proposed. In practice, solutions proposed for any given mission need to be addressed in terms of both nonrecurring and recurring costs and the robustness and testing of the final navigation product.

In practice, most orbit determination is done by very large software systems using some type of filtering to smooth a large quantity of over-determined data. Traditionally, this has been a function for large ground processing computers. However, with modern onboard processors, navigation from the satellite itself is both possible and may be significantly more robust at lower cost.

Onboard navigation may be broadly divided into two categories. *Semi-autonomous systems*, such as GPS, depend on signals received from outside the spacecraft. While they may not require ground processing, they do nonetheless depend on whatever system is generating the observation signals. In contrast, *fully autonomous systems* make use of observations of the world around them so as to be as nearly independent as possible of external support requirements. However, achieving complete autonomy is probably neither possible nor particularly useful. As discussed in Sec. 4.1, irregular-

TABLE 4-11. Alternative Autonomous Navigation Methods. (See also Table 4-12.)

System	Basis	Status	Determines	Typical Accuracy (3σ)	Operating Range	Comments	Manufacturer
Global Positioning System (GPS)	Network of navigation satellites	Operational	Orbit†	15 m–100 m in LEO	LEO only	Semiautonomous; see Sec. 4.2	Motorola, Rockwell
Microcosm Autonomous Navigation System (MANS)	Observations of Earth, Sun, and Moon	Flight tested in 1993	Orbit, attitude, ground look point, Sun direction	100 m–400 m in LEO (using only Earth, Sun and Moon)	LEO to GEO, lunar and planetary orbits	Can use other instruments (GPS receiver, star sensor, IMUs) to improve accuracy	Microcosm
Space Sextant	Angle between stars and Moon's limb	Flight tested	Orbit and attitude	250 m	LEO to GEO	Not being actively marketed for space at the present time	Lockheed Martin
Stellar Refraction	Refraction of starlight passing through the atmosphere	Proposed; some ground tests done	Orbit and attitude	150 m–1 km	Principally LEO	Could use attitude sensor data	
Landmark Tracking	Angular measurements of landmarks	Proposed; observability conditions are uncertain	Orbit and attitude	Several kilometers	Principally LEO	Could, in principle, use observation payload data	
Satellite Crosslinks	Range and range rate or angle measurements to other satellites in a constellation	Proposed; may be used on communication constellations	Orbit‡	Theoretically as good as 50 m	Principally LEO	Operation with less than full constellation can be a problem; has no absolute position reference	
Earth and Star Sensing	Observe direction and distance to Earth in inertial frame	Proposed	Orbit and attitude	100 m–400 m in LEO	LEO to GEO, planetary orbits	Similar to MANS with higher accuracy and availability	

† Attitude determination using GPS receivers has been demonstrated. Accuracy is ~ 0.3 to 0.5 deg.
‡ Could, in principle, be used for attitude determination as well.

ities in the rotational motion of the Earth cause the position of a ground station in inertial space to be knowable with only limited precision long times in advance. Thus, even in fully autonomous navigation systems, the onboard clock or the rotational position of the Earth represented by occasional leap seconds must be updated from time to time to maintain the system accuracy.

Among the specific systems which have been proposed or are in use, ground tracking methods have been discussed in Sec. 2.7, and GPS in Sec. 4.2. The other approaches listed in Tables 4-11 and 4-12 are briefly described below.

TABLE 4-12. Advantages and Disadvantages of Alternative Navigation Methods. (See also Table 4-11.)

System	Advantages	Disadvantages
Ground Tracking	Traditional approach Methods and tools well established	Accuracy depends on ground-station coverage Can be operations intensive and expensive
TDRS Tracking	Standard method for NASA spacecraft High accuracy Same hardware for tracking and data links	Not autonomous Available mostly for NASA missions Requires TDRS tracking antenna
Global Positioning System (GPS); GLONASS	High accuracy Provides time signal as well as position	Semi-autonomous Depends on long-term maintenance and structure of GPS Orbit only (see text for discussion) Must initialize some units
Microcosm Autonomous Navigation System (MANS)	Fully autonomous Uses attitude-sensing hardware Provides orbit, attitude, ground look-point, and direction to Sun	Flight-tested prototype only Initialization and convergence speeds depend on geometry and Moon availability
Space Sextant	Could be fully autonomous	Flight-tested prototype only—not a current production product Relatively heavy and high power
Stellar Refraction	Could be fully autonomous Uses attitude-sensing hardware	Still in concept and test stage
Landmark Tracking	Can use data from observation payload sensor	Still in concept stage Landmark identification may be difficult May have geometrical singularities
Satellite Crosslinks	Can use crosslink hardware already on the spacecraft for other purposes	Unique to each constellation No absolute position reference Potential problems with system deployment and spacecraft failures
Earth and Star Sensing	Earth and stars available nearly continuously in vicinity of Earth	Cost and complexity of star sensors Not yet flown

Space Sextant

The *Space Sextant* was developed and flight tested in the late 1970s as a means of autonomous navigation by accurately measuring the angle between a star and the limb of the Moon [Martin Marietta Aerospace, 1977; Booker, 1978]. The Space Sextant provides both orbit and attitude information and can work over a very large regime, including geosynchronous orbit. The Space Sextant unit was flight qualified; however, the need for very precise telescope measurements makes the instrument heavy and expensive, and therefore limits its usefulness in many space applications

Microcosm Autonomous Navigation System

The Microcosm Autonomous Navigation System (MANS) uses observations of the Earth, Moon and Sun from a single sensor to provide real-time position and attitude data [Tai and Noerdlinger, 1989; Anthony, 1992; Hosken and Wertz, 1995]. The MANS flight software can also make use of, but does not require, data from a GPS receiver, star sensors, gyros, and accelerometers. The addition of other data sources provides added accuracy and robustness. In addition to orbit and attitude, MANS provides ground look point and Sun direction information (even when the Sun is not visible). It can work in any orbit from LEO to beyond GEO. The MANS system was flight tested on the TAOS mission in 1994 and 1995. Although the software system executed successfully on board, sensor and computer hardware problems prevented sufficient data from being collected to allow system-level calibration and bias determination. This, in turn, limited the accuracy of the test results [Hosken and Wertz, 1995]. Difficulties in accurately sensing the Sun and Moon combined with recent advances in star sensor technology imply that future implementations of the MANS technology should make use of star and central body sensing, rather than Sun, Moon, and Earth sensing. The MANS autonomous algorithms worked successfully and demonstrated that accuracies that be obtained with currently available star and central body sensors should allow navigation errors on the order of a few hundred meters or less. This technology would then be applicable near essentially any central body, i.e. Earth, Moon, planets, planetary moons, or larger asteroids.

Earth and Star Sensing

An alternative to using the Earth, Moon and Sun for autonomous navigation is to use the Earth and stars. The fundamental approach is to measure the direction to the Earth with respect to the background stars, and potentially the distance, which then implies the direction and distance to the spacecraft in inertial space. The principal advantage is that the Earth and stars should be available nearly continuously in the general vicinity of the Earth. The principal disadvantage is the cost and complexity of star sensors. However, smaller, lower cost, and far more capable star sensors are becoming available, such that this solution may become both economical and robust in the future. In addition, Honeywell has been working for some time on a single sensor to identify both the Earth and stars in UV wavelength. This has the advantage of eliminating the problem of intersensor mounting angle biases, which would otherwise limit the accuracy or require on-orbit calibration for systems using separate sensors.

Stellar Refraction Systems

A number of approaches for orbit and attitude determination have been proposed based on the interaction of starlight with the Earth's atmosphere [Hummel, 1984]. Specifically, as stars approach the edge of the Earth as seen from the spacecraft, refraction will cause their position relative to other stars to shift, producing an effect which can be measured with considerable accuracy. Theoretical accuracies for such systems are projected to be in the vicinity of 100 m. However, none of these systems has been fully developed for flight as yet.

Landmark Tracking

Landmark tracking has also been proposed for orbit determination [Markley, 1981]. This has been established as feasible by using data returned from satellite payloads. However, it has not been used as a normal method for satellite navigation due in part to the difficulty of establishing automatic, unambiguous identification of landmarks to ensure that tracking accuracy can be maintained in the presence of adverse weather or poor seeing conditions.

Satellite Crosslinks

A number of proposals have been made for using satellite crosslinks to provide orbit determination. (For a summary of initial work in this area see Chory et al., [1984].) This is of interest because it can be done with crosslink equipment used for intersatellite communications, and, therefore, requires minimal additional hardware. Crosslink tracking has been proposed for a number of constellations, and will probably be implemented in some of the low-Earth orbit communications constellations. Nonetheless, there are several practical problems with crosslink tracking. One is that satellite tracking provides only the relative positions of satellites. This means that if the absolute position is needed for mission planning or data reduction, then an additional system must be provided to establish the orbit relative to the Earth's surface. The second problem is that the satellites become interdependent, so satellite-to-satellite tracking may not work well for the first satellites, or may degrade if one or more satellites in the constellation stops working. Therefore, an alternative system not based on satellite-to-satellite tracking is required. If additional systems must be provided, there is less benefit from the satellite-to-satellite tracking.

4.3.1 Semiautonomous Navigation

There are three types of semiautonomous navigation systems:

- A sequence of navigation satellites (GPS, GLONASS, or a similar system around the Moon or planets)
- *Inverse GPS*, i.e., a set of beacons on the ground or on the surface of the Moon or planets
- *Intersatellite navigation,* where the goal is to maintain the relative satellite parameters.

The principal advantage of semiautonomous systems is that they allow high precision with relatively modest equipment on the target satellite. The beacons or GPS satellites themselves may be expensive, but in principle, the cost can be shared by multiple users. Another key advantage is that, like ground radar tracking, beacon or GPS tracking can determine both the position and velocity of the target satellite. Consequently, we have high-accuracy information immediately available, which can then be filtered for additional accuracy.

There are two principal disadvantages to beacons or navigation satellites. The first is that they must be maintained over time and the satellite user is dependent on this maintenance activity. Thus, commercial users may be reticent to rely on government or military systems for commercial communications navigation. Any system built for this purpose, such as a GPS-like system around the Moon, must be maintained and therefore, forms another potentially serious failure mode for any lunar navigation activity.

The second principal problem is a practical issue of implementation and sensor coverage. As shown previously in Fig. 4-11, GPS signals are meant to completely cover only the surface of the Earth and will cover smaller areas on any sphere which is at an altitude above the surface of the Earth. In the extreme, a satellite which is above the altitude of the GPS constellation may have a line of sight to a large number of GPS satellites but will be outside the nominal signal cone for all of them. There is the potential for using "spillover" from the GPS system for navigation at high altitudes such as geosynchronous orbit. However, this depends on the amount of spillover and the design of the specific GPS satellite. Since the GPS system itself is designed to cover only the surface of the Earth, more advanced GPS satellites will presumably have narrower cones of coverage to minimize the spillover and the "wasted energy" from the perspective of the GPS constellation. As shown in Fig. 4-12 in Sec. 4.2, if we assume that only the GPS signal that is in the nominal direction (i.e., toward the surface of the Earth) can be used, then the number of usable GPS satellites drops rapidly as the spacecraft altitude increases. In addition, both the GPS constellation and the target satellite are moving relative to each other and, therefore, coverage patterns will be continuously changing. All of this implies that both GPS and beacon navigation will typically not be continuous. This means that there is a need for orbit propagation on board the target satellite to fill in the gaps in coverage or outages due to the loss of a ground beacon or GPS satellite. Typically this orbit propagation would be combined with some level of Kalman filtering to improve the inherent accuracy of the original measurements and maintain the system overall accuracy during modest periods of outage. The actual computations on board the spacecraft are essentially equivalent to those using GPS for terrestrial navigation as discussed in Sec. 4.2.

The third type of semiautonomous navigation is navigation relative to another spacecraft, as would be required for a flying interferometer, or as might be considered for use in communications constellations. Here measurements are made relative to the other spacecraft, and thruster firings are used to maintain the satellite separations. The achievable accuracy depends on a number of factors, including whether the absolute positions are important or only the relative positions, and on the accuracy of the measurements themselves. The achievable accuracy for relative stationkeeping also depends on the separation between the satellites because of the impact of higher order perturbations in the geopotential field (see Sec. 2.5 and Chap. 10).

4.3.2 Fully Autonomous Satellite Navigation

GPS navigation is a mature field with a variety of manufacturers making onboard GPS receivers. In contrast, the process of fully autonomous navigation, in which satellites use measurements of their external environment for orbit determination, is largely a new field which has come about primarily because of the availability of large onboard processors. Consequently, it is not clear how this process will work in the long term, either for Earth-orbiting spacecraft or interplanetary missions.

The most fundamental problem with fully autonomous navigation is that there is no convenient mechanism for autonomously measuring the satellite velocity. Optical Doppler measurements are not sufficiently accurate to be useful for this purpose, and natural radio sources, such as quasars, are too weak to be detected by small spacecraft antennas. This is one of the reasons that beacon tracking can be a very useful supplement to autonomous navigation systems.

On the positive side, so long as the spacecraft is not in too low an Earth orbit, the forces on the spacecraft can be modeled with considerable precision and long-term measurements can be used to determine the orbit period and, therefore, the total spacecraft energy and its velocity at any given time. Consequently, although challenging, fully autonomous navigation is still feasible and potentially very low cost, because it can use the same sensors that are on board the spacecraft for attitude determination. This lack of accurate velocity measurements is a problem particularly for satellite targeting required for interplanetary missions. In order to be efficient in fuel utilization, I would like to make correction maneuvers well in advance of arriving in the vicinity of the target, i.e., it is much easier to change the orbit to arrive at a specific location on Mars when I am leaving the vicinity of the Earth than when I am arriving in the vicinity of Mars. However, knowing what correction to make requires a highly accurate velocity estimate so that I can propagate the orbit forward in time. Since the velocity is only poorly known, we could allow the spacecraft to fly for a long period in order to determine the velocity accurately, but this prevents us from making the correction early as we would prefer for fuel efficiency. In addition, any thruster firing has a significant uncertainty with it that effectively decouples the previous measurements from those made after the firing, such that a series of small correction maneuvers makes it extremely difficult to determine the velocity profile along the way.

The basic principle of *optical autonomous navigation* is to measure the position of the spacecraft with respect to some nearby object, e.g., the Earth, the Moon, or Mars. This is done by measuring the position of the nearby object with respect to the background stars (or other celestial objects) and by some process for measuring the distance. Alternatively, we can measure the direction to two nearby objects or two points on the same object, and then use triangulation to determine the spacecraft's location. Several key issues are important in this process:

- There is no navigation information in star measurements by themselves. Stars are sufficiently far away that their apparent positions remain unchanged as the satellite moves. Consequently, there is no navigation content in any combination of measurements of star positions alone.

- Direction measurements will produce position errors directly proportional to the distance to the reference object. Directions are fundamentally angular measurements. Thus the position error of the spacecraft is the distance to the object times the sine of the angular error, which for small angles is equal to the angle itself in radians. Thus, high accuracy position measurements require that they be made with respect to objects which are relatively close. (Once again, stars provide the inertial frame but do not provide navigation by themselves.)

- A single direction/distance pair is sufficient to determine the position of the satellite in inertial space. The direction of a nearby object with respect to the background stars determines its direction relative to the satellite in inertial space and implies that the satellite is in the opposite direction with respect to the object. This, combined with the distance, uniquely determines the position of the spacecraft in inertial space.

- Multiple position measurements can be used to determine the orbit using traditional filtering or deterministic methods. A sequence of position observations such as direction/distance pairs can be used just as radar measurements are used in ground-based processing. All of the analytic and numerical techniques which have been developed for general orbit determination can be applied to the problem of onboard autonomous navigation. While deterministic processes are available, the most likely approach for an autonomous navigation system would be some form of Kalman filter where our sequence of position observations is processed to provide increasingly accurate estimates of the spacecraft position and velocity.

The direction measurement is relatively simple and requires two components. We need a *local reference sensor* (i.e., an Earth sensor or target sensor) and an *inertial sensor*, such as a star sensor. Gyroscopes can also be used for the inertial sensing component, but must be calibrated from time to time relative to an absolute inertial source such as the stars, the Sun, or distant planets. As described previously, the Microcosm Autonomous Navigation System uses the Earth, Sun and Moon, or the Earth and stars. In both cases, the Earth provides the local reference and either the stars or the Sun and the Moon provide the inertial frame of reference against which the position of the Earth is measured. The space sextant uses stars for the inertial frame and the limb of the Moon for the local reference. Because of the distance to the Moon, this measurement must be much more accurate than the corresponding Earth measurement to achieve comparable position accuracies.

Distance measurements to nearby celestial objects are substantially more difficult than direction measurements, although a number of options are available. The general techniques are summarized in Table 4-13, and the approximate ranges of applicability are shown in Fig. 4-14. Very close to the surface of an object, we can make use of parallax as seen from two sensors on the sensing spacecraft or the target size on another spacecraft in a docking maneuver, for example. Because of the short baseline, this process only works for distances that are extremely close.

TABLE 4-13. Methods for Autonomous Distance Measurements.

Measurement	Potential Instruments	Typical Range	Assumed Sensing Accuracy for Fig. 4-13
Target Parallax (as seen from 2 locations on the spacecraft)	• Payload sensors • Star cameras • Possibly with mirrors for 2nd image	Contact to 100 km	1 arc sec for spacecraft sites 1 m apart
Angular Diameter of the Planet	• Payload sensors • Star cameras • Horizon sensors	10 km to 100,000 km	0.001 deg for planet radius of 7,000 km
Angular Separation between Moons	• Payload sensors • Star cameras	50 km to 10^8 km	1 arc sec for moons 30,000 km apart
Apparent Magnitude of Target or Moon	• Payload sensors • Star cameras	$> 10^6$ km	0.01 magnitudes (=1% in intensity)

For planets such as the Earth which are nearly spherical, the size of the planet provides a very sensitive measure of distance in a low orbit above the surface. The individual measurements themselves are good, and these can be substantially improved by long-term averaging in orbit around the planet. For example, at 400 km altitude, the angular diameter of the Earth is approximately 140 deg. If this can be measured to an accuracy of 0.05 deg, this corresponds to an altitude accuracy of 1 km. Independent measurements of this accuracy can be made continuously throughout the orbit such that the ultimate altitude accuracy can be quite good. As we get further away from the target planet, the angular diameter of the planet becomes less sensitive. In geosynchronous orbit, the same accuracy of 0.05 deg on the diameter of the Earth corresponds to an altitude accuracy of about 120 km, which is sufficiently coarse to be of very little use in most autonomous navigation systems.

At large distances from the Earth or other planets, the best distance measurement is the angular separation between the primary planet and one of its natural moons or, alternatively, between two moons such as Phobos and Deimos at Mars. These measurements can typically be made with high precision using a star sensor and provide both accurate measurements and changing geometric conditions which allows us to average out many of the systematic errors. As described further in Chap. 7, the measurement of the angular separation between two nearby objects puts the spacecraft on a "donut of position" which is a figure that is rotationally symmetric about the line joining the two target bodies.

As we recede further and further from our "nearby" target, it becomes increasingly difficult to measure distance. Ultimately, the only measurement left is the apparent magnitude or brightness of the object in question. This can be used to estimate distance but is both difficult to measure with precision and is a relatively insensitive measurement. Nonetheless, it is the optical information that is available from the greatest distance

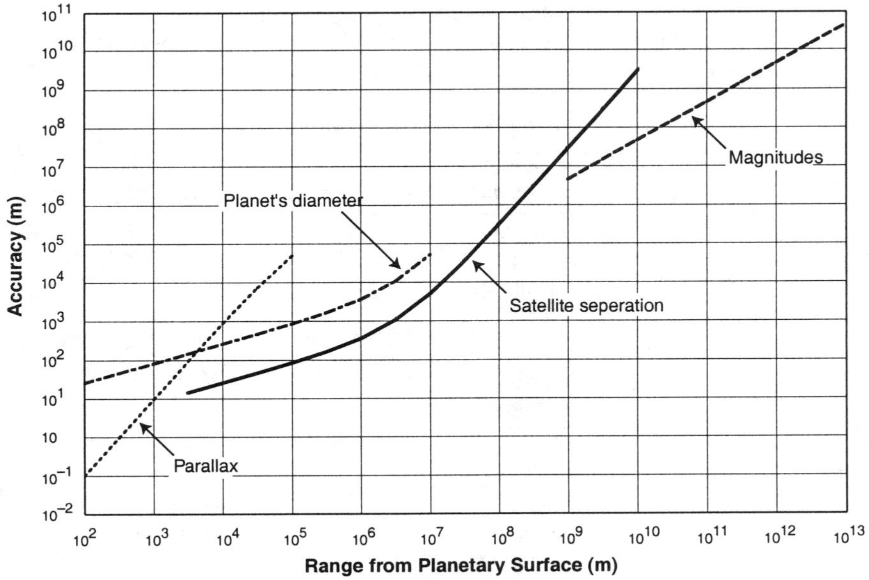

Fig. 4-14. Approximate Ranges and Accuracies for the Autonomous Distance Measurements from Table 4-13.

4.4 Autonomous Orbit Maintenance and Control

Section 2.7.2 discussed the need for doing orbit maintenance and control, the circumstances under which some type of control is required, and the implementation of orbit control in a traditional ground-based process. This section examines the implementation of autonomous on-board orbit control, particularly with respect to constellation maintenance. Section 4.5 then summarizes the advantages and disadvantages of onboard vs. ground control and sets out a common architecture for spacecraft orbit and attitude control systems. Results of the first on-orbit demonstration of autonomous on-board orbit control on UoSAT-12 are given by Gurevich, Bell, and Wertz [2000].

A key difference between traditional ground-based orbit control and autonomous onboard orbit control† is that the ground-based process as described in Sec. 2.7.2 is intended primarily to maximize the time between orbit maneuvers and therefore minimize the amount of commanding and interaction with the spacecraft that is required in order to minimize the cost. In contrast, onboard orbit control is much less concerned with the number of commands sent to the control system or the time interval between maneuvers and consequently will optimize some other aspect of the orbit control problem, such as minimizing propellant utilization or minimizing the size of the stationkeeping box. Consequently, onboard orbit control is typically not simply moving the logic that was previously on the ground to the spacecraft computer. It entails a somewhat different set of objectives and therefore may use different logic to achieve these objectives.

The least stringent orbit control requirements is typically simple altitude maintenance in order to keep the satellite from reentering the Earth's atmosphere. This can be done at very long intervals, and places very few restrictions on the accuracy with which maneuvers are accomplished. The most stringent requirements come principally from the need for some type of formation flying, such as a spaceborne interferometer in which we may wish to control the relative positions between satellites to small fractions of a meter. However, the most common reason for orbit control is constellation maintenance in low-Earth orbit or, equivalently, geostationary stationkeeping. Here the accuracy requirements are typically moderate, ranging from a fraction of a kilometer to several kilometers or tens of kilometers for high altitude orbits.

Long-term orbit maintenance and control for constellations is required to maintain global coverage and avoid collisions among satellites. The system objective is to maintain the same **relative** position among the satellites. We want to minimize both the propellant utilization and the cost and complexity required to do this.

For both formation flying and constellation maintenance, the need for stationkeeping arises from two sources. First, at any given time each satellite will be in an orbit slightly different than intended. If left uncorrected, these small differences accumulate with time to destroy the overall structure of the formation or constellation. For example, a satellite whose period is 1 sec off the nominal value will, if uncorrected for one month, drift by 4,000 km relative to its desired position.

The second reason for orbit control arises from perturbations. Without orbit maintenance, atmospheric drag will eventually bring down a low-Earth orbit constellation and the satellites will reenter the atmosphere. Other perturbations result in differential

---

† Throughout Sec. 4.4, we will use *autonomous* and *onboard* as being synonymous. See the beginning of Sec. 4.5 for a discussion of the distinction between these two types of control.

satellite motion with respect to a Keplerian orbit which has components which are cyclic with the orbit period and, also, ones which result in continuous secular drift. In general, we can treat each perturbation separately in deciding how best to deal with it and its level of importance to the control problem being addressed. Ultimately, the implementation will be divided into the two major categories of in-track and cross-track stationkeeping.

In general, we can treat each individual perturbation in any of three ways:

- **Leave the Perturbation Uncompensated**—In this case, we increase the stationkeeping box size to incorporate variations resulting from the perturbation. This has no cost and uses no propellant. It is the best method for accommodating short period variations

- **Negate the Perturbing Force**—This maintains the orbit characteristics over time. However, it requires continuous propellant consumption and should be used only when necessary.

- **Control the Perturbing Force to be the Same for All Satellites in the Constellation**—In this case, the satellites maintain the same relative positions but will not follow a perfectly circular or Keplerian orbit. This can be done for much less propellant usage than negating the disturbance and is the best approach if perturbations cannot be left uncompensated.

The principal orbit perturbations affecting low-Earth orbit constellations and the recommended treatment for each are shown in Table 4-14. Note that the differential effect of these perturbations puts a limit on the level of control that can be achieved in intersatellite spacing as a function of the distance between satellites. This is critical to the formation flying problem for systems such as a space-based interferometer.

There are two principal stationkeeping trades involved in constellation maintenance:

- Whether to maintain the system altitude or allow the constellation to slowly "fall" to lower altitudes due to atmospheric drag.

- Whether to maintain an **absolute pattern** or only the **relative** locations of all satellites.

Allowing the system to fall reduces the propellant requirement in the short term. Replacement satellites would be launched at a lower altitude. However, drag would continually increase as the altitude decreases and coverage holes would begin to appear or grow as the altitude decreases and the coverage of each satellite is reduced. Maintaining the altitude is the only way to give the system long-term viability without having performance degradation grow with time. Consequently, for most constellations the only realistic approach is to maintain the system altitude over time.

If the decision is made to maintain the altitude of the constellation, then the principal remaining trade is whether to maintain each satellite in a well-defined stationkeeping box, as is done for geosynchronous satellites, or whether to maintain only the relative orientation among the satellites. The goal of constellation maintenance is only relative stationkeeping. However, in looking at the implementation, there are substantial advantages to absolute stationkeeping and no significant advantages to relative stationkeeping [Wertz, 1997, 1999]. These merits and demerits are summarized in Table 4-15.

TABLE 4-14. Principal Perturbations in Low-Earth Orbit that Impact Constellation Structure and Recommended Treatment for Each. See text for discussion.

Perturbation	Impact	Recommended Treatment
Atmospheric Drag	• Secular decay highly dependent on altitude	• Negated by in-track orbit maintenance
J_2 (Oblateness)	• Secular node rotation proportional to cosine of the inclination • Secular phase rotation (perigee rotation for an eccentric orbit) • Changes shape of the orbit resulting in up to 5 km variation between satellites in a global constellation	• Controlled to be the same for all satellites by cross-track orbit maintenance • Controlled as part of the in-track maintenance • Uncompensated
Higher Order Harmonics (Zonal)	• Small eccentricity oscillation	• $e = 0.0013$ can be maintained naturally (frozen orbit); can also be controlled as part of in-track maintenance
Solar/Lunar	• Small secular drift in inclination and node • Low amplitude oscillation in inclination and node	• Negated by cross-track maintenance or compensated by inclination change • Uncompensated
Solar Radiation Pressure	• Small eccentricity growth	• Negated as part of in-track maintenance

For in-track stationkeeping, each satellite must ultimately put back the ΔV which atmospheric drag takes out. The only question is how this ΔV is applied. With absolute stationkeeping it is provided by a large number of small burns, such that the phase in the orbit is continuously maintained. In relative stationkeeping, only the relative orientation between two or more satellites is maintained and the entire group is, from time-to-time, returned to its original altitude. Note, however, that atmospheric density decreases exponentially with increasing altitude. Therefore, continuously maintaining the satellite at the higher altitude results in lower drag and, therefore, a small but noticeable propellant savings for absolute stationkeeping. For example, dropping the satellite altitude from 500 km to 490 km increases the atmospheric density and therefore losses due to drag by 20% to 35%, depending on the level of solar activity.

In addition, there is an inherent complexity to relative stationkeeping because each satellite must know not only its own orbit, but also that of the other satellites with respect to which it is maintaining itself. This represents both high operations cost and a complex stationkeeping logic with the potential danger of breaks in coverage, satellite collisions, or other problems associated with the failure of a complex, interacting system. In absolute stationkeeping, constellation buildup is greatly simplified. Each satellite has an assigned slot defined before launch. The satellite is placed in that slot just as orbit rendezvous is done and as geosynchronous satellites are put in their assigned location. Orbit maintenance is then begun, irrespective of whether the satellite is the first or last in the constellation.

With absolute stationkeeping the constellation pattern itself is fully deterministic. The intended position of each satellite at all future times is known. Consequently, we

TABLE 4-15. Advantages and Disadvantages of Relative vs. Absolute Stationkeeping. Assumes that the constellation is ultimately kept at a given altitude. If constellation is allowed to continuously decay, relative stationkeeping can reduce propellant utilization.

	Advantages	Disadvantages
Relative Stationkeeping	• Minimizes maneuver frequency	• Stationkeeping depends on interrelationship between all related satellites • Complex commanding may lead to command errors and greater collision risk • High operations cost • Different logic for system buildup than operations • Requires information transfer between satellites
Absolute Stationkeeping	• Minimizes propellant utilization • Simple commanding • Satellite positions known in advance • Satellites can autonomously maintain themselves in the pattern • Position of all other satellites known without requiring intersatellite communication • Easily monitored from the ground • Same logic for constellation buildup as normal operations • Fewer failure modes • Constellation pattern is purely deterministic	• More frequent stationkeeping burns

know in advance when they will pass over any given ground station, target, or communications location. The basic geometric conditions such as Sun angles, ground station angles, or intersatellite angles are all fully known in advance, so that activities can be planned at the convenience of the operations group and do not need to be updated repeatedly as the constellation changes. We can, for example, pre-establish pattern boundaries as a function of time so that we know precisely which satellite will cover any ground location at any future time. This also makes the job of spacecraft requirement specification much easier. Each spacecraft needs only to meet its pre-assigned ground coverage pattern.

4.4.1 System Configuration and Implementation Requirements

As shown in Fig. 4-15, constellation maintenance requires some type of onboard orbit control system consisting of sensing, logic, and actuation. Fortunately, the logic required for fully autonomous absolute orbit control is straightforward. It is less complex than that required for relative stationkeeping, and far less complex than that used in a typical attitude control system. Consequently, an autonomous orbit control system requires significantly less computer throughput than would be required for attitude determination, attitude control, or orbit determination. Although they have a number of characteristics in common, the specific orbit control strategies and algorithms can be implemented in a variety of ways. (See, for example, Wertz et al. [1997], Glickman [1994].)

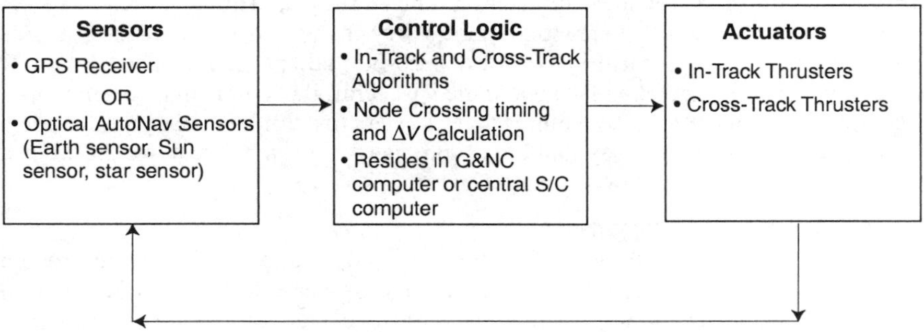

Fig. 4-15. Structure of an Autonomous Orbit Control System.

One of the most interesting characteristics of autonomous orbit control is that it can make use of, but does not necessarily require, onboard orbit propagation. We have become accustomed to thinking of orbit determination, control, and orbit prediction in terms of a precision orbit propagator; it is easy to overlook the fact that it may not be necessary. Essentially, we use a sensor to determine when the satellite is correctly positioned in its stationkeeping box and apply the appropriate corrections to maintain the satellite there. This is equivalent to the attitude control process in which we sense the deviation from the desired attitude and apply the appropriate control torque. The typical attitude control system does not fly an attitude propagator. While attitude propagators are used on the ground to simulate and verify performance, they are only rarely used on board the spacecraft. Similarly, we use precision orbit propagators to validate the performance of the orbit control system on the ground but may or may not choose to use them on board, depending upon the details of our particular application.

While orbit propagation is not required, some type of position sensing is needed in order to provide the error signal for orbit control. For satellites in low-Earth orbit, this error signal can be provided either by a GPS or GLONASS receiver, or by optical autonomous navigation. (In principle, ground tracking can also be used for autonomous orbit control, but this obviously negates many of the advantages of an otherwise autonomous system.) Whatever sensor we choose, the error signal is simply the time difference between when a satellite is anticipated to cross a reference plane and the measured time when it crosses that plane. An obvious choice for satellites at moderate to high inclinations is the time at which the satellite is at the ascended node, i.e., crossing the equator from south to north. Note that the node crossing time is a precisely defined mathematical function which is attached to some type of internal spacecraft clock which, from time to time, is synchronized with ground-based civil clocks, such as those provided by GPS or other standard time sources. Consequently, when a leap second is inserted during some years, the orbit control logic will automatically correct for the additional 1 sec on the appropriate orbit just as though there were additional drag during that orbit and the spacecraft was running a bit slow. This will cause a very small hiccup in the constellation pattern which will correct itself such that the constellation pattern continues to precisely follow the civil clock.

For absolute stationkeeping, the only actuators currently available are thrusters. However, either very low thrust chemical or electric propulsion can be used. The key characteristic is that the thruster impulse should be low enough that thrusting can be applied on a very regular basis (every few orbits or every few days). This requires a low level of thrust and is an ideal application for electric propulsion, although a variety of alternatives are available. In practice, another key characteristic is to make the thrust levels low enough such that they do not disturb normal spacecraft operations. This means that thrusting can take place while the spacecraft payload is in its normal operating mode. This of course also requires that thrusters for stationkeeping be positioned on the spacecraft in such a way that an attitude maneuver is not required in order to fire the thrusters for normal orbit maintenance.

Thruster Sizing and ΔV Requirements

In low-Earth orbit, both the size of the thrusters and the total propellant requirement are dominated by the requirement to overcome atmospheric drag. To provide margin thruster firings at solar maximum should cover a small fraction (< 1%) of a full orbit. On the other extreme, the firing must be long enough that the thruster is able to maintain reasonable efficiency when it is providing a ΔV every few orbits. Thus, a maximum thruster size should be such that the smallest efficient thruster pulse provides a ΔV that is no more than 2–3 times the minimum ΔV per orbit at solar minimum (at altitudes over 800 km an upper limit of 20 to 100 times the minimum ΔV is reasonable). Similarly, the minimum thruster size should be such that the ΔV applied over 1 min (approximately 1% of the orbit period) is larger than the maximum ΔV expected at solar maximum. Representative values of these ΔV parameters and range of thruster size are given in Table 4-16.

TABLE 4-16. ΔV Estimates for Thruster Sizing and Propellant Budgets for Autonomous Orbit Control. In-track numbers assume a ballistic coefficient of 100 kg/m^2. In-track range is from solar minimum to solar maximum. Data based on Wertz and Dawson [1996].

Altitude (km)	ΔV per Orbit		ΔV per Year	
	In-Track (m/s)	Cross-Track (m/s)	In-Track (m/s)	Cross-Track (m/s)
200	2.9×10^{-1} to 5.7×10^{-1}	N/A	1.7×10^{3} to 3.4×10^{3}	small
400	1.2×10^{-3} to 1.2×10^{-2}	N/A	6.8×10^{0} to 7.0×10^{1}	small
600	2.8×10^{-5} to 8.1×10^{-4}	N/A	1.5×10^{-1} to 4.4×10^{0}	small
800	5.0×10^{-6} to 8.3×10^{-5}	N/A	2.6×10^{-2} to 4.3×10^{-1}	small
1,000	2.0×10^{-6} to 1.5×10^{-5}	N/A	1.0×10^{-2} to 7.5×10^{-2}	small
1,500	4.1×10^{-7} to 2.2×10^{-6}	N/A	1.8×10^{-3} to 9.8×10^{-3}	small

The total propellant budget for constellation maintenance will be the total ΔV required over the life of the spacecraft plus margin and *ullage* (unusable propellant in the tanks). In low-Earth orbit, this is fixed nearly entirely by the ΔV loss due to drag over the spacecraft lifetime. If the total spacecraft life is a few years or less, than the worst case would be for the satellite to be active entirely at solar maximum. If the satellite lifetime is ten years or more, then it is reasonable to average the propellant utilization over both solar maximum and solar minimum. Representative values are provided in Table 4-16.

The situation for cross-track orbit control is very different than in-track control in terms of propellant utilization. There is no fundamental cross-track disturbance to be overcome. Consequently, the cross-track component oscillates slowly with very small errors, due to both measurement and thrust errors and low-level cyclic perturbations. Propellant utilization is no longer fixed by the environment itself, but depends on the measurement system, the thruster used, the control requirements, and the initial orbit insertion error. Consequently, there is considerably more variability in determining the exact value. However, because there is no fundamental perturbation to be overcome, the cross-track propellant utilization can be made small.

Navigation and Attitude Requirements

Autonomous orbit control systems have an inherent accuracy constrained by higher order perturbations on the order of 0.1 to 0.5 sec. In order to achieve this accuracy, we need a navigation accuracy on the order of 20% of the stationkeeping accuracy or better. This implies a navigation (i.e., node crossing time) accuracy requirement of better than 0.02 to 0.1 sec, which corresponds to an in-track position requirement of 150 m to 1 km. This is well within the capability of both GPS and autonomous navigation systems.

Orbit maintenance requires that in-track thruster firings be made in the direction of the velocity vector and that cross-track firings be made at right angles to this direction, i.e., toward the orbit poles. For the individual firings, the ΔV values are extremely small (typically ~ 1 mm/sec). Consequently, small variations in the direction of the firings are equivalent to a small unmodeled perturbation and are corrected on subsequent firings. Thus, the only substantial attitude requirement is to maintain the efficiency of thruster firings by providing them in approximately the correct direction. Fortunately, the thrust component along the desired axis is proportional to the cosine of the error and, consequently, is relatively insensitive to small errors in the thrust direction. A random fluctuation in attitude of less than 1 deg is very adequate to ensure high efficiency and even larger errors could be tolerated, if necessary.

Finally, it is important to understand the consequences of an orbit control failure. This is best done by comparing orbit and attitude control systems. Typically, we must control the attitude nearly continuously (i.e., at rates of 1 to 10 Hz) if we are to avoid serious consequences. Loss of attitude control will usually result in the spacecraft tumbling, which in turn can result in loss of the payload function, power in the solar arrays, and contact with the ground. It could also point sensitive instruments at the Sun, or create substantial thermal problems. Consequently, even a brief attitude control failure can seriously damage the spacecraft or destroy the mission entirely. For example, several key interplanetary missions including the Viking Lander on Mars were terminated by inadvertently pointing the communications antenna away from the Earth. Once this had occurred, it was impossible to communicate with the spacecraft and regain control.

In contrast, orbit control maneuvers occur infrequently and have very modest consequences if they fail or even occur in entirely the wrong direction. As long as we control the orbit with low thrust systems (i.e., burns of a few mm/sec or less), a short-term failure causes no damage. Gravity takes care of short-term orbit control very well. If the orbit control system fails, the ground or onboard navigation system will determine that the satellite is slowly drifting from its assigned slot, and a warning can be issued with adequate time to fix the problem or implement a backup before adverse consequences occur. This is dramatically different from the case of very large thruster firings in which errors can destroy the spacecraft or change the orbit such that there is no potential for recovery. In low thrust orbit control systems, the consequences of individual maneuvers are nearly imperceptible and the system is inherently fail-safe. If the orbit control system can be recovered by any process, such as a software upload or changing to backup hardware, the consequences of a single failure or even a sequence of failures are very minor.

4.5 Combined Orbit, Attitude, and Timing System Architecture

It is clear from the last three chapters that orbit, attitude, and timing systems are highly interrelated. Although there are clearly strong differences between them, they use many of the same sensors and actuators, much of the same logic, and are frequently required to interact to provide accurate information for both payload and spacecraft operations. The purpose of this section is to create the architecture for a combined orbit, attitude, and timing measurement and control system. Irrespective of whether this system is implemented entirely on board the spacecraft, it is clear that an objective of the system designer should be to reduce the cost and complexity of all of these functions taken together, rather than viewing them as independent and separate systems.

First, note that autonomous and onboard systems are related but not synonymous. An autonomous system can, for example, be computer controlled from the ground station. Similarly, onboard logic is often used to carry out orbit maneuvers in interplanetary spacecraft, although these maneuvers are computed on the ground and sent to the spacecraft such that the resulting system is implemented on board, but not autonomous in the traditional sense. Most practical systems are a mix of both. Even ground-based processes need to become highly automated in order to reduce both cost and risk. Space-based systems need some level of ground update from time to time, if nothing else, to correct the onboard clock and synchronize it with Earth-based timing systems.

Whether to use autonomous, onboard, or autonomous onboard systems will depend upon the specific mission applications. The advantages and disadvantages of the various alternatives are shown in Table 4-17. A key issue in this process is determining where data is generated and where it is to be used. For example, attitude determination data is generated on board the spacecraft and used on the spacecraft for attitude control. Transmitting the attitude information to the ground for computation of attitude control commands would represent excessive delay and dramatically increase the risk of system failure in the case of even a short-term communications problem. Although timing is not as critical in the case of orbit determination and control, much the same logic applies. If the orbit determination data is available on board the spacecraft, then in most cases the lowest risk and cost would be to compute the orbit control commands on board the spacecraft. On the other hand, if the spacecraft orbit is determined entirely by ground processing of Earth-based tracking data, then it would be relatively low cost to compute the orbit control commands on the ground and upload simply the commands rather than all of the data that would be required for onboard orbit control computations. In addition, this process would minimize the required bandwidth and reduce the probability of communications errors, since a relatively small number of orbit control commands could be validated by re-transmitting the commands to the ground for verification. With the increasing use of GPS or GLONASS for orbit determination, and the introduction of very substantial processing capability on board the spacecraft, it is reasonable to consider spacecraft in which the entire orbit, attitude, and timing determination and control processes are contained on board the spacecraft in a single functional unit. Although there is not yet enough on-orbit experience to determine how this process will evolve, it is clear that this has the potential for dramatically reducing both the cost and risk of future spacecraft systems.

TABLE 4-17. Advantages and Disadvantages of Onboard and Autonomous Systems. While onboard and autonomous systems are often thought of as synonymous, they need not be. See text for discussion.

Approach	Advantages	Disadvantages	Typical Applications
Non-Autonomous, Ground-Based	• Minimizes nonrecurring development cost	• High recurring cost • Error prone • Requires satellite contact to execute	• Orbit control for unique, experimental satellites
Autonomous, Ground-Based	• No onboard computing required	• High development cost • Requires active communication link • More failure modes than onboard	• Used for TDRS single access antenna pointing
Non-Autonomous, Onboard (i.e., Stored Commands)	• Low development cost • Can verify that commands were sent	• Requires all computations done in advance	• Typically used for orbit maneuvers
Autonomous, Onboard	• Low recurring cost • Robust (reduces failure modes) • Can usually be made fail-safe	• Highest nonrecurring cost • Requires onboard computer	• Nearly always used for attitude control • Good for orbit control, but non-traditional

One of the key objectives of this book is to clearly establish the interrelationship (both similarities and differences) between orbit and attitude systems on modern spacecraft. Traditionally, these have been very separate systems with attitude done on board the spacecraft by a group concerned principally with spacecraft systems. Orbit has traditionally been determined and controlled on the ground by a group whose principal concern has been ground-based operations and analysis activities. In fact, both orbit and attitude systems have a great deal in common. This leads to substantial advantages for combining both orbit and attitude determination and control:

- Both sensors and actuators have substantial overlap between orbit and attitude (see Figs. 4-16 and 4-17)
- Can obtain backup of one with sensors and actuators of the other (this provides functional redundancy which is significantly more robust than physical redundancy)
- Can more easily control and minimize the interaction and the impact on the rest of the spacecraft by having both orbit and attitude elements of a common system
- Orbit and attitude together are what is needed as an end output

I would like to emphasize the importance of the last bullet. We tend to think of orbit and attitude separately, because they are treated in part as separate technologies. For example, Chap. 2 is on orbits and Chap. 3 on attitude, with only a few paragraphs comparing and contrasting them. However, orbit and attitude independently are ultimately of very little use to the end user. By and large, the person who will use the data, either a scientist evaluating observations, a user with a cellular communications system, or a military officer pointing a space-based laser at a missile target, is not interested in either the orbit or the attitude of the spacecraft; rather, they are interested in where their particular payload is pointed, or the geolocation of some target identified in a frame of data. Thus, photographs from space of the surface of the Earth, or the Moon, or Mars do not indicate the position and attitude of the spacecraft that took them but simply the location that is being photographed and perhaps the resolution or altitude if more detail is appropriate. Similarly, the operator of a direct broadcast satellite wants to point his transmitting antenna at France or at the United States, but uses the orbit and the attitude only as intermediate variables to achieve this objective. In order to fire thrusters to get to Mars, I need to know both when and in what direction to fire them. The pieces of information apart from each other are of little use.

By far the most compelling reason for viewing orbit attitude and timing as a single system is that ultimately they must be brought together to satisfy the needs of the mission.

Thus, our objective is to achieve this at the minimum cost and risk for the system as a whole.

What this implies is the need for a common **system** solution for the orbit/attitude problem. This does not mean that they need to be done together, nor that they both need to be done on board the spacecraft. But the combined solution should minimize the cost and risk of the system as a whole, while providing the highest level of robustness and reliability.

We want the orbit and attitude systems to work together. This does not mean that we necessarily want to solve simultaneously for both orbit and attitude in a single "grand Kalman filter." This may or may not be a good approach. At least some experiments in this direction have been done, typically with very poor results. When you try and solve for the entire world in a single unified filter, the most likely result is that the filter will diverge.

A combined orbit/attitude system does not imply that we have a single software system solving for all variables simultaneously. Even if the orbit and attitude data are separated within the software system, they can still use a great many elements in common. All of the data validation and checking, much of the communication, and much of the data will be the same between the two systems. Thus, even if orbit and attitude are solved for entirely separately, there are significant advantages to doing this work in the same computer and potentially in the same software system.

Figure 4-16 shows an example of combined orbit and attitude control system architecture. It is drawn specifically to show the parallel with the general attitude ystem architecture, shown in Fig. 3-1 at the front of Chap. 3. There are differences in essentially all of the elements, and in the frequency at which the processes occur. Nonetheless, there are also very substantial similarities with much of the data and some of the actuators being appropriate for both aspects of the problem. Thus, it is certainly a reasonable and realistic alternative to think in terms of a spacecraft control system which both determines and controls the orbit and attitude of the spacecraft, establishes the timing of both spacecraft and payload events, and ultimately computes as output those elements of interest to the end user such as the pointing orientation of an antenna, or the geographic coordinates of the center of the field of view of a payload optical sensor.

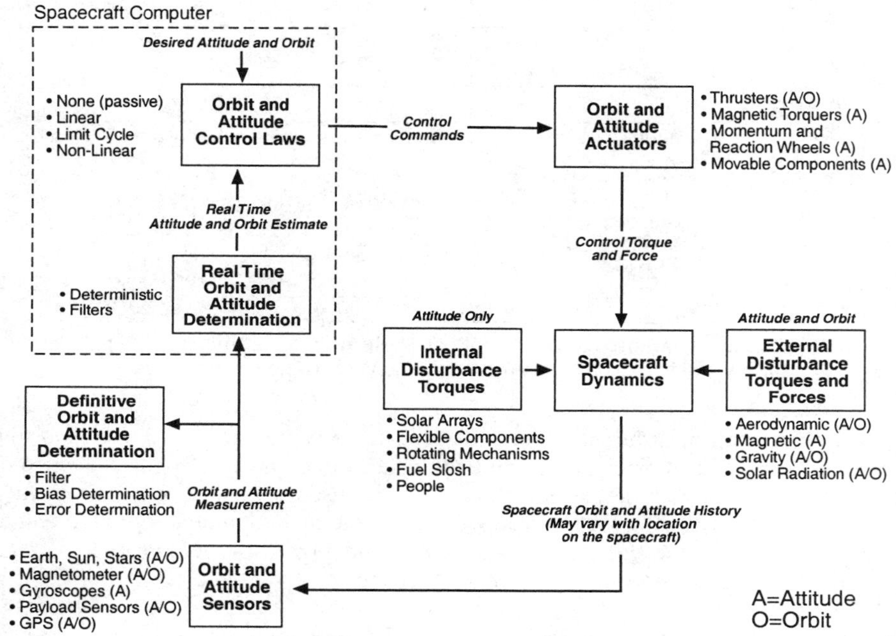

Fig. 4-16. Representative Example of Combined Orbit and Attitude Control System Architecture.

Figure 4-17 shows some of the typical components that we might use for a combined orbit and attitude system. A key issue here is that while the accuracies are not necessarily the same, it is very reasonable for primary systems on one side to serve as backup systems for the other. For example, GPS provides a relatively low-cost, high-accuracy orbit determination system for low-Earth orbit spacecraft. Because of inherent limitations in the system and the potential for short-term outages, GPS typically provides a very poor source of primary information for attitude. Nonetheless, it can provide coarse attitude for a wide variety of spacecraft orientations and therefore provides excellent backup to optical onboard attitude determination systems. It could also be used for attitude system initialization, or as a fail-safe mode. Similarly, standard attitude sensors such as a combination of Earth and star sensors, or Earth sensors, Sun sensors and magnetometers, can provide high-accuracy attitude solutions. Using autonomous navigation methods as described in Sec. 4.3, they can also provide an excellent backup to a GPS system being used as the primary onboard navigation system. A second level of backup for orbit is simply to propagate the existing solution maintained on board. Orbit propagation can normally cover outages in even an extended period until such time as additional data is available.

	System Function	Primary	Back-Up
System Engineering (Stationkeeping) Requirements and Constraints	Navigation	LEO: GPS	LEO: Optical Navigation
		GEO: Optical Navigation or GPS	GEO: Onboard Propagation
	Attitude Determination	Standard Attitude Sensors	GPS
	Orbit Control	Thrusters	
	Attitude Control	Wheels/Thrusters for momentum dumping	
	Software (Orbit, Attitude, Thruster, Commanding, Collision Avoidance)	Autonomous Navigation System Autonomous Navigation and Orbit Control Constellation System Database Satellite Replacement, Satellite Rephasing (Due to Loss of Member)	

Fig. 4-17. Typical Components for Combined Orbit/Attitude Architecture. Final selection will depend in part on requirements accuracy, cost, and redundancy.

For orbit control, differential drag can be used to some degree. Nonetheless, the principal orbit control mechanism will be thrusters either using a chemical system or electric propulsion. These same thrusters can be used for either primary attitude control or, in the case of a system with wheels, for momentum unloading. Momentum unloading can also be done using magnetic torqueing. However, magnets cannot provide the forces appropriate for orbit maintenance.

Finally, the combined orbit/attitude software will have a large number of elements in common. Frequently, attitude information will depend upon where the spacecraft is, and may require, for example, a magnetic field model, or in the case of star sensors, an orbit model in order to relate inertial attitude to pointing locations on the surface of the Earth. Similarly, orbit control will require issuing attitude commands to maintain thrusters pointed correctly for orbit maintenance. Pointing a cross-link antenna at another communications satellite requires working simultaneously with the positions and attitude of both spacecraft. While the configuration of the resulting system will depend upon the differing requirements of each mission, there are substantial advantages to considering the potential for combining orbit, attitude, and timing determination and control.

4.6 Annotated Bibliography

Bibliography includes time systems, GPS, autonomous navigation and orbit control, and evolution of orbit/attitude/timing systems.

Farrell, Jay A. and Matthew Barth. 1999. *The Global Positioning System and Inertial Navigation.* NY: McGraw-Hill. 340 p.

Provides a general mathematical introduction and reference on GPS, inertial navigation, GPS-aided inertial navigation, and optimal estimation.

Hofmann-Wellenhof, Bernard, Herbert Lichtenegger, and James Collins. 1997. *GPS: Theory and Practice* (4th ed). New York: Springer-Verlag Wien. 389 p.

Good mathematical introduction to GPS and its applications.

Kaplan, Elliot D. (ed.). 1996. *Understanding GPS: Principles and Applications.* Boston, MA: Artech. 554 p.

Good technical discussion of GPS, GLONASS, and INMARSAT navigation services. Discusses principally marine, air, and land applications, but general techniques are applicable to all systems.

Leick, Alfred. 1995. *GPS Satellite Surveying* (2nd ed). NY: John Wiley and Sons. 560 p.

Intended primarily for terrestrial surveying, this volume provides an excellent technical overview of GPS, GPS signal processing, and error analysis.

Logsdon, Tom. 1992. *The Navstar Global Positioning System.* NY: Van Nostrand Reinhold. 256 p.

A non-technical, but extensive discussion of GPS and its applications. Intended to help potential users of GPS learn what they need to know to evaluate the potential of GPS systems, select appropriate applications and hardware to support those applications, and obtain the maximum benefit from its use.

Logsdon, Tom. 1995. *Understanding the Navstar, GPS, GIIS, and IVHS* (2nd ed) . NY: Chapman and Hall. 330 p.

This book provides a general description and comparison of modern radio-navigation system. Includes discussion of geographic information systems (GIS) and intelligent vehicle highway systems (IVHS). Discusses both military and civil applications.

Parkinson, Bradford W., and James J. Spilker. 1996. *Global Positioning System: Theory and Applications.* Washington, DC: AIAA. 2 vols., 1,436 p.

An extremely complete treatment of GPS theory and applications, including detailed technical discussion of topics not normally covered, such as wide area differential GPS and use in land, air, and space systems—including spacecraft orbit and attitude determination.

Seidelmann, P. Kenneth. 1992. *Explanatory Supplement to the Astronomical Almanac.* Mill Valley, CA: University Science Books. 600 p.

Not really casual reading. Contains a clear, well-written explanation of essentially all time frames and coordinate systems used in astrodynamics; an excellent reference. Very economical for what it contains.

Wertz, J. R., and W. J. Larson. 1996. *Reducing Space Mission Cost.* Dordrecht, The Netherlands and Torrance, CA: Kluwer Academic Publishers and Microcosm Press. 617 p.

Presents both processes and technology for reducing cost in spacecraft manufacturing, launch, and operations. Includes discussion of cost modeling, reliability, and implementation strategies. Has detailed case studies of 10 missions (with actual dollar costs) which have reduced cost by factors of 2 to 10 relative to tradition expectations.

References

Anthony, Jack. 1992. "Autonomous Space Navigation Experiment." Paper No. AIAA 92-1710, presented at the AIAA Space Programs and Technologies Conference, Huntsville, Alabama, March 24–26.

Booker, R. A. 1978. "Space Sextant Autonomous Navigation and Attitude Reference System—Flight Hardware Development and Accuracy Demonstration." Rocky Mountain Guidance and Control Conference, Paper AAS 78–124.

Chory, M. A., D. P. Hoffman, C. S. Major, and V. A. Spector. 1984. "Autonomous Navigation—Where We Are in 1984." Paper presented at AIAA Guidance and Control Conference, Seattle, Washington, August 20–22.

Einstein, Albert. 1950. *Relativity: The Special and the General Theory.* Translated by Robert W. Lawson. NY: Crown Publishers.

Fliegel, Henry F. and Thomas C. Van Flandern. 1968. "A Machine Algorithm for Processing Calendar Dates." *Communications of the ACM*, Vol. II, p. 657.

Glickman, R. 1994. "The Timed-Destination Approach to Constellation Formation-keeping." AAS paper 94-122.

Gurevich, Gwynne, Robert Bell, and James R Wertz. 2000. "Autonomous On-board Orbit Control: Flight Results and Applications." Paper No. 2000-5226 presented to the AIAA 2000 Conference and Exposition. Long Beach, CA, September 19–21.

Hofmann-Wellenhof, Bernard, Herbert Lictengegger, and James Colins. 1997. *GPS: Theory and Practice* (4th ed). NY: Apringer-Verlag Wien.

Hosken, R. W. and J. R. Wertz. 1995. "Microcosm Autonomous Navigation System On-Orbit Operation." Paper AAS 95-074, presented at the 18th Annual AAS Guidance and Control Conference Keystone, CO, February 1–5.

Hummel, S. G. 1984. "Spacecraft Autonomous Navigation Using Stellar Refraction Measurements." Paper presented at AIAA Guidance and Control Conference, Seattle, Washington, August 20–22.

Kaplan, Elliot D. (ed). 1996. *Understanding GPS: Principles and Applications.* Boston: Artech.

Kaufmann III, William J. 1973. *Relativity and Cosmology*. NY: Harper and Row Publishers.

Leick, Alfred. 1995. *GPS Satellite Surveying* (2nd ed). NY: John Wiley and Sons.

Markley, F. Landis. 1981. "Autonomous Satellite Navigation Using Landmarks." Paper No. 81-205 presented to the AAS/AIAA Astrodynamics Specialist Conference, Lake Tahoe, Nevada, August 3–5.

Martin Marietta Aerospace. 1977. *Design and Laboratory Testing of Self-Contained High Altitude Navigation System, Phase 1—The Space Sextant Autonomous Navigation Attitude Reference System (SS-ANARS).* Phase 1 Final Report, MCR-77-196. Denver, CO.

Mermin, N. David. 1968. *Space and Time in Special Relativity*. NY: McGraw-Hill.

Misner, Charles W., Kip S. Thorne, and John Archibald Wheeler. 1973. *Gravitation*. San Francisco: W.H. Freeman and Company.

Parkinson, B. W., J. J. Spilker Jr., P. Axelrad, and P. Enge (eds.) 1996. *Global Positioning System: Theory and Applications*, Vol. 1, p. 183. Washington, D.C.: American Institute of Aeronautics and Astronautics.

Seidelmann, P. Kenneth (ed.) 1992. *Explanatory Supplement to the Astronomical Almanac.* Mill Valley, CA: University Science Books.

Tai, Frank and Peter D. Noerdlinger. 1989. "A Low Cost Autonomous Navigation System." Paper No. AAS 89-001, presented to the 12th Annual AAS Guidance and Control Conference, Keystone, CO, Feb. 4–8.

Wertz, James R., John T. Collins, Simon Dawson, Hans J. Koenigsmann and Curtis W. Potterveld. 1997. "Autonomous Constellation Maintenance." Presented at the IAF Workshop on Satellite Constellations, Toulouse, France, Nov. 18–19.

Wertz, James R. 1999. "Guidance and Navigation." In *Space Mission Analysis and Design* (3rd ed), James R. Wertz and Wiley J. Larson (eds.) Torrance, CA and Dordrecht, The Netherlands: Microcosm Press and Kluwer Academic Publishers.

Chapter 5

Definition of Requirements

Space missions begin with a broad set of subjective, typically fuzzy, mission requirements—we want to explore Mars, provide better, cheaper telephone communications for Africa, or improve navigation for military forces. Ultimately these objectives flow by a somewhat mystical process called *systems engineering* or *requirements definition* into a set of specific numerical requirements on various components of the space system—i.e., the spacecraft must have 2 star sensors, each weighing less than 1.8 kg, using less than 3 W of power, with an 8 × 8 deg field of view, capable of detecting 6th magnitude stars with an angular accuracy of 0.005 deg (3σ).

Experience has shown that by the time this requirements definition process is complete, on the order of 90% of the cost and complexity of the space system will have been determined. This implies that the process of requirements definition is by far the most important single aspect of space system design in terms of establishing the performance, cost, and risk of the system. Consequently, we need to put as much or more thought and care into defining the requirements as we do into the process of designing the system or equipment to fulfill these requirements.

If, at the end of requirements definition most of the cost of the system is fixed, then the requirements definition process itself must be the principal focus in the process of reducing cost. Within this phase, cost reduction comes about principally by the process of *trading on requirements*. This is the name given to the overall process of defining and revising the requirements in an iterative process in order to minimize the cost and risk of the system as a whole. Our broad objective may be to explore Mars, whereas the ultimate requirement will be to map 95% of the surface of Mars in one year at a resolution of 50 m. It is this translation of objectives into requirements that determines the performance, cost, and risk of the system. Will the scientific return of our mission be significantly degraded by a resolution of 55 m, 75 m, or 200 m? What are the cost implications of each of these changes? In the end, requirements definition should not be done in a vacuum.

> **Just like anything else that we buy or build, the detailed requirements should represent some reasonable compromise between what we want and what we can afford.**

Only when we have truly understood the nature of this compromise, i.e., what we are paying in terms of cost in order to achieve a given level of performance, can we begin to make intelligent decisions on defining the system requirements.

Too often the requirements definition process is left to the end user of the system or to the people or organization that are originally defining it. Thus, the government or organization which is financing the mission establishes the requirements and then asks prime contractors to bid on meeting these requirements at the lowest cost. However, this process means that the requirements will have been largely fixed before the impact on cost has been understood. If a better process is to let the requirements evolve as the system definition evolves, then we should always be looking for ways to reduce the requirements in order to drive down cost. This chapter introduces that process. Additional details can be found in Wertz and Larson [1999], and details specifically oriented toward reducing cost are given by Wertz and Larson [1996].

Requirements definition consists of two distinct but interrelated functions:

- A process associated with people and organizations and the division of responsibility among them; and,
- A mathematical process in which requirements are broken down into constituent components and error budgets, performance budgets, and cost budgets are created to track progress and ensure that the system objectives are met.

Beginning with Sec. 5.2, this book focuses primarily on the mathematical process. Nonetheless, to be successful at obtaining the best possible product for the lowest possible cost and risk, we need to work both parts of the problem. The organizational process is the subject of Sec. 5.1.

5.1 The Requirements Definition Process

The *system requirements* are the quantitative expression of how well the objectives are met and are recorded in the *systems specifications*. The way these are most often determined by organizations which purchase space systems is by creating a straw man mission design, that is, a hypothetical design for the mission which the defining organization believes is fundamentally capable of meeting the overall objectives. Thus, if the broad goal is to explore Mars, we may create a hypothetical system of satellites to provide mapping and magnetic field measurements over some defined period of time. If the objective is to create global communications, we may define a constellation consisting of a specific number of low-Earth orbit satellites each with a number of communications channels capable of meeting our broad objectives. The characteristics of this straw man design are then used to create the system specifications, i.e., we must have so many satellites at a specific altitude over the surface of Mars with instruments capable of a certain angular resolution. The fundamental problem with this approach is that although the original system designers may have been very clever and very knowledgeable, they do not necessarily have all of the necessary or appropriate knowledge to determine how best to do this job at the lowest possible cost. Consequently, if the system requirements are expressed in terms of the specific parameters of the straw man mission, i.e., so many satellites or star sensors with a specific field of view or limiting magnitude, then any further trades are effectively eliminated. The defining organization has basically created the system design and fixed the system cost such that it becomes nearly impossible to reduce that cost.

On the other hand, if the system requirements at all levels go back and specify **what** it is that is to be achieved rather than **how** it is to be achieved, then it is possible for the system trade process to continue and to take advantage of new knowledge, new developments, or clever techniques from throughout the astronautics community. For example, we may choose to specify, rather than the altitude and resolution of an instrument, the resolution on the ground we wish to achieve. This leaves open the trade for using a large number of satellites at a lower altitude or a smaller number at higher altitudes or perhaps even a smaller number at lower altitudes and taking longer to achieve the results. Similarly for the star camera, we should not in general specify the field of view or resolution required, but simply the end result; that is, we wish to have an attitude accuracy of so many degrees. Even better, as described at the end of Chap. 4, attitude is of little interest to the end user. In the end it is simply geopositioning knowledge or pointing knowledge. Consequently, the requirements should be specified in these terms, pointing and mapping, rather than in terms of how they are to be achieved (orbit and attitude). By using this process of specifying what we want, not how it is to be achieved, we can leave open other options which have the potential of reducing cost, reducing risk, or perhaps improving performance at minimal increase in cost or risk, in order to obtain the best system at the lowest cost. These and other critical issues in the requirements development process are summarized in Table 5-1.

TABLE 5-1. Critical Issues in Requirements Development. Note that the reason is rarely included in the specification, but must be documented if requirements trades are to be performed. See text for discussion.

Critical Features of System or Subsystem Requirements:

- Should be based on the fundamental mission objectives
    1. Mission or payload derived
    2. Flow down from basic requirements
- Should be part of the system trade process
- Should state what is to be done (i.e., pointing, mapping, and timing), rather than how to do it (orbit, attitude, and onboard clock)
- Are the quantitative expressions of how well the objectives are met, recorded in the system specification

Types of Requirements:

- *Functional requirements* = how well it must perform
- *Operational requirements* = how it is to be used
- *Constraints* = what limitations are imposed on the system

Elements which Should be Documented for Each Requirement in the System or Subsystem Specification:

- *Function* = what is to be done
- *Performance requirement* = how well it has to be done
- *Verification* = how the performance is to be verified

    1. Inspection 2. Test 3. Analysis

Key Element which Should be Documented (though typically omitted from the system specification):

- *Reason* = <u>why</u> it is required

Requirements should be based on the fundamental mission objectives. What is it the mission must do in order to satisfy these objectives? As discussed in Sec. 1.2, attitude, orbit and timing requirements flow from two basic sources: the mission itself (*payload requirements*) and from the remainder of the spacecraft bus (*housekeeping requirements*). For nearly all spacecraft, attitude, orbit, and timing systems are a part of the spacecraft bus. That is, they provide support to the payload that is doing the real work for which the spacecraft was built. However, the end user normally does not care where the spacecraft is at any given moment or what the attitude is, or when a particular measurement was made. The end user cares about the impact on the overall system performance, i.e., the impact on the payload and subsequent mission data processing. What is the latitude and longitude of the object seen in the photo? What is the time difference between two photos of the same event? These values are associated with pointing, mapping, and synchronization which are the fundamental contributions of orbit attitude and timing systems to the overall mission performance.

The second source of requirements is the spacecraft itself or the housekeeping functions, i.e., the ability to point the solar arrays at the Sun, communicate with the ground station, or get within 2 km of a distant asteroid. These housekeeping requirements are typically, though not necessarily, less stringent than the mission or payload-derived requirements. However, housekeeping requirements usually apply to all mission phases, whereas payload requirements frequently apply only to the operational phase. Thus housekeeping requirements, though less stringent, may drive the range over which orbit and attitude systems must operate or the various conditions under which data must be provided. For example, a typical housekeeping function would be to regain control of the spacecraft if it tumbles. This implies the need to have low accuracy attitude in a variety of orientations such that it is possible to recover the system when it is in a non-nominal mode. This might, for example, imply the use of very coarse Sun sensors covering a large fraction of the sky, or an Earth sensor that is capable of picking up the Earth as the spacecraft tumbles.

There are three basic types of requirements:

- *Functional requirements* define how well the system must perform
- *Operational requirements* define how it is to be used
- *Constraints* define what limitations are imposed on the system

These types of requirements apply both at the system level of pointing and mapping budgets and at the more detailed subsystem or allocated level of orbit and attitude systems and hardware. Specific examples are shown in Table 5-2.

In the case of each requirement, we want to define it so as to minimize the cost and risk of the system as a whole. Once again, this implies that the requirements themselves should be a part of the system trade process. There are two basic types of trades which can be done:

- Trades on the overall level of performance
- Trades on how the performance is achieved

Most often the level of performance is defined as a specific number, such as attitude accuracy or resolution on the ground, or position knowledge accuracy. These tend to be fixed by the nature of the requirements definition process. That is, in order to be fair to the various contractors, the defining agency picks a number which they believe to be appropriate and then asks contractors to achieve this value at minimum cost. Neither the customer nor the contractor wants to change the number. The customer has

TABLE 5-2. Examples of Requirements Typically Placed on Orbit, Attitude, and Timing Systems. Specific requirements may be classified as different types depending on the need and the implementation.

System Requirements	Pointing	Mapping	Timing and Synchronization
Functional Requirements	• Pointing accuracy • Stability • Target acquisition and tracking	• Geolocation accuracy • Target ID	• Timing accuracy • Data synchronization
Operational Requirements	• Duration • Availability • Acquisition time	• Coverage • Rate • Data form and content	• Time between clock updates
Constraints	• Cost • Signal spill over	• Cost • Policy and regulation	• Cost • Synchronization with civil time
Subsystem or Allocated Requirements	**Orbit**	**Attitude**	**Timing**
Functional Requirements	• Orbit definition • Position accuracy (determination and control) • Targeting accuracy	• Accuracy (determination and control) • Range • Jitter • Settling time	• Clock accuracy • Onboard output rate • Data synchronization
Operational Requirements	• Orbit maintenance • Mission lifetime • Stationkeeping box size • Maneuver frequency • Collision avoidance	• Autonomous operation • Safe mode • Solar array or antenna pointing • Slew rates	• Update mechanism • Time between clock updates (allowed drift rate) • Clock frequency
Constraints	• Launch vehicle • Eclipse times and duration • Environment • Propellant budget • Spacecraft disposal	• Cost • Size, mass, and power limitations • Level of payload disturbance	• Cost • Use (or non-use) of GPS

gone to some lengths to specify this number, and would like to have it achieved, although of course at very low cost. The contractor doesn't want to appear unresponsive to the customer's needs, and therefore will go to great lengths to achieve the specified performance, even if it drives up the cost or risk of the end system. The implication is that there needs to be an ongoing dialog on the implications of specific requirements on performance, cost, and risk. It is this dialog and trading back and forth which too often are omitted in the requirements definition process.

The trades on how the performance is achieved are also critical. Ideally, these should allow the use of alternative design options to reduce cost or to meet other elements of the system performance. Thus a high-accuracy system may specify the use of star sensors to achieve the required attitude accuracy. On the other hand, it may be possible to achieve an acceptable level of accuracy using a combination of Earth sensors and gyros to average the noise from the Earth's horizon. This is an example of a trade process that may be able to achieve the fundamental objectives of the mission at lower cost and risk. Figure 1-16 in Sec. 1.3 shows a typical example of this trade process in which a given geolocation accuracy can be obtained either with a tight attitude budget and a loose position budget, or vice versa.

Most people in the space business recognize that in order to minimize cost the requirements should be part of the overall system trade process, and yet this is rarely done for several reasons. As discussed above, contractors do not wish to be unresponsive. Typically, you do not become a general officer or a captain of industry by arguing with the people who have given you an assignment, that the assignment is too difficult or too complex. It is much better to salute, say "Yes, Sir" and imply that there is no problem in meeting the requirements which have been specified. But driving down the cost of the system implies that we need to have this basic debate between the desired performance and the cost.

A second reason for not trading on requirements is that it frequently entails moving requirements, and therefore budget, between organizations or between various elements of the system. In the geolocation accuracy example that we have talked about, changing from tight attitude requirements and loose orbit requirements to the other way around implies putting additional requirements on the orbit, and therefore the ground system, in order to save money on the spacecraft. However, these are most typically done by different organizations operating in different ways. Therefore, to save money we need to take money from one organization, and give it to another. For obvious reasons, this can prove to be an unpopular process.

If it is politically difficult to trade on requirements, how do we go about doing it? The best approach is to make it a very explicit and open process. Almost every mission is divided into a series of phases as the definition of the system becomes more concrete. Each of these phases usually begins with a briefing or technical meeting defining the status of the system at the present time. Thus, we might have a Phase A briefing or a kick-off for Phase C/D defining the status of the program. This can occur at the system level, subsystem level or component level. The key issue for requirements trades is to have the first portion of each such briefing devoted explicitly to requirements trades. Ask the system engineer either for the prime contractor or the component manufacturer to explicitly define the source of the requirements that they are working to and indicate which of those requirements are principally responsible for impacting performance, cost, risk, and schedule. This allows the customer to at least examine explicit trades on the key requirements with the objective of reducing the overall system cost. The key point is that this process makes trading on requirements an open and defined engineering process subject to review and detailed examination in much the same fashion as the system design itself is examined and reviewed.

To do good system trades we need to identify the *critical requirements*, i.e., those which are principally responsible for performance, cost, risk, and schedule. These critical requirements will depend on the specific implementation which is being considered. Wertz and Larson [1999] set out in detail the process for defining the critical requirements. Basically, we do this by looking at the impact of changing each of the fundamental requirements. However we define them, the objective is to let the requirements evolve in order to achieve the mission objectives at minimum cost and risk. To do this we need to concentrate our system trades around the critical requirements, so that we are continuously examining and re-examining those requirements which in fact have the highest impact on performance, cost and risk. The boxed example provides representative samples of good and bad requirement trades in orbit, attitude and timing systems.

Specifications

Specifications are the documentation of requirements. Every requirement that is documented must include three things:

- *Function* = what is to be done
- *Performance requirements* = how well it is to be done
- *Verification* = how the performance is to be verified

In the end, we verify the performance of the system as a whole by allocating our top-level requirements and then verifying each of the components such that we can say that, in the end, the final system will work as designed. In perhaps the simplest example, we may have a top-level requirement to use a specific launch vehicle of a total spacecraft weight. This total weight is then allocated to each of the various subsystems and, in turn, to the various components within those subsystems. This will be reflected in the specification documents for the components, and all of the weights will be added up in a single weight budget. The weights of the various components will first be verified by analysis, and ultimately by weighing all of them as the spacecraft is built. In doing this, we will determine that the final spacecraft will in fact meet its weight requirement.

There is one major element missing from the typical specification document. This is:

- *The reason* = why it is to be done

Specification documents tend to be a demand from the customer to the supplier and therefore generally do not reflect the reasons why specific requirements are imposed. Nonetheless, if we are to continue the system trade process and make it a part of the overall process of system design, then we must know why specific requirements are imposed. Otherwise there is no way to go back and determine if a less stringent or more stringent requirement is appropriate. Consequently, even though it does not fit well within the contractual hierarchy, providing the reasons for the various requirements given in the specification is extremely important to the process of trying to drive down system cost.

In order to be useful in terms of whether the system can meet its broad requirements, each individual requirement must be capable of being verified. This verification is typically done in one of three ways: inspection, test, or analysis. Thus, we may determine that a particular system has redundant components simply by inspection. Alternatively, we may test the star sensor to determine the resolution, or we may verify adequate performance of a structural element by analysis. Whatever method we choose, we need to specify how specific requirements are to be verified.

The general classes of system specifications are shown in Fig. 5-1. In newer, smaller programs, many of these specification documents are no longer created in order to reduce the very substantial cost associated simply with documentation. On the other hand, failure to document those issues of the system which are critical to determining

Good and Bad Requirements Trades in Orbit, Attitude, and Timing Systems

Our end goal is to achieve the overall mission objectives at the minimum cost and risk. Trades done at a low level to reduce the cost and risk of specific elements may end up driving the costs much higher in other parts of the system. This occurs most often when the broader implications of the trade are not taken into account. Specific examples of potentially good and bad requirements trades are shown below.

Potentially Good Trades

Use of Autonomous Navigation

There is a basic trade between providing navigation data in real time on board the spacecraft vs. providing it after the fact by processing ground station data. Frequently, this will be done on the basis of the cost to achieve a specified level of performance.

System-Level Discussion—Real-time data may not need to be as accurate as data generated after the fact. Suppose, for example, that we need a position accuracy of 1 km at the time of firing an engine to put a spacecraft into the proper orbit around Mars. For a real-time (i.e., autonomous, onboard) system, the required accuracy is 1 km. For the ground-based system operating on older data, we will need a greater accuracy, say 100 m, in order to do the orbit determination, then propagate the position forward to the time of the maneuver. Thus, if done for purposes of maneuver accuracy or event planning, real-time systems should have a less stringent accuracy requirement than those which use historical data and propagate forward in time.

Measuring Relative Time Rather than Absolute Time

We may wish to know the time between two scientific observations, to an accuracy of, say, 100 ms. One way to do this is to specify the absolute accuracy for all observations to within 50 ms such that the time between any two can be determined to 100 ms.

System-Level Discussion—Measuring the absolute time of individual events to within 50 ms may prove to be extremely expensive because of the need to continuously synchronize the onboard clock with some absolute reference. On the other hand, measuring the relative time between two events using an onboard clock can prove to be a much more economical approach. This would require that the onboard clock not be reset to the absolute time between the two observations. This could be easily accomplished by, for example, maintaining a continuing register of the difference between the time as measured by the onboard clock and the absolute time such that relative time could be measured on board, and the absolute time of specific observations would be determined by reading the offset register.

Potentially Bad Trades

Selection of Sun-Synchronous Orbit for Housekeeping Reasons

Putting a spacecraft in a Sun-synchronous orbit rather than a moderate inclination prograde orbit can reduce the cost of the spacecraft by providing a more uniform thermal environment and by eliminating the need for a second gimbal on the solar arrays. Thus in a Sun-synchronous orbit the solar arrays can have only a single gimbal, and simply rotate at a fixed angle relative to orbit normal.

System-Level Discussion—Depending on the choice of launch vehicle, going to a Sun-synchronous orbit rather than a moderate inclination prograde orbit may reduce the on-orbit mass by as much as 30%. Consequently, the system level cost of choosing a Sun-synchronous orbit for housekeeping reasons is extremely high. In addition, by choosing the Sun-synchronous orbit we've introduced a new failure mode. If we designed our spacecraft to be able to work in non-Sun-synchronous orbits, then, of course, there was no need for the Sun-synchronous orbit in the first place. If we designed the spacecraft such that it can only work in Sun-synchronous orbits, then any error in the orbit insertion, or excessive drift during the mission lifetime such that the orbit becomes non-Sun-synchronous, will result in a mission failure. In most cases, it would be substantially less expensive and lower risk to simply design the spacecraft to operate in a general prograde orbit rather than specify a Sun-synchronous orbit for housekeeping purposes.

Use of a Line Scanner Rather than Array Sensor to Reduce Payload Cost

Spacecraft provide continuous coverage by sweeping across the ground. One way to provide continuous coverage is to have a line scanner which covers the full width of the ground swath and is extremely narrow, such that the sequence of line scans perpendicular to the ground track provides a continuous scan of the world underneath. This significantly reduces the cost relative to a large array processor which must have a much greater number of array elements.

System-Level Discussion—Typically one of the key objectives in creating a scan of the world is to reconstruct a "picture" of the world such that we can measure the relative positions between different objects which we have seen, or to define a specific location on the Earth associated with a specific observation. Using a large array, the relative positions between the various pixels in the array are fixed and known with considerable precision. Using an array processor we can determine the angular separation, and therefore, the real separation between observed objects with good precision at low cost. Given that we know the attitude of the sensor at the time the image was taken, we can provide geolocation for all of the various elements. In contrast, reconstructing an image from a line scanner requires that we either control or know the attitude of the spacecraft on a continuing basis to very high accuracy. The angular separation between two objects which are very close together but separated in the along-track direction will be determined both by the orbital characteristics of the spacecraft and by its attitude motion. Any rotation or yaw of the spacecraft between successive observations will result in either a blurring or a displacement or some combination of both on various components of the image. This, in turn, places very stringent (and therefore, very costly) requirements on the attitude determination and control system. It will be nearly impossible to reconstruct an image with the same level of precision which could be easily achieved using an array processor. Consequently, use of a line scanner will typically represent a substantially more expensive system level solution, although it may reduce the cost of the payload element itself.

performance can ultimately drive up the cost very dramatically. Particularly important is the Interface Control Document, because it typically represents an interface between people or organizations that may not be working closely together. For example, it may be the job of the navigation computer to compute the position and velocity of the spacecraft. How that computation is done is typically of little consequence to the end user. Nonetheless, it is important to specify how that information will be communicated to those systems which need it. The interface control document could specify, for example, the data rates, units, and word characteristics associated with the information generated by the navigation system.

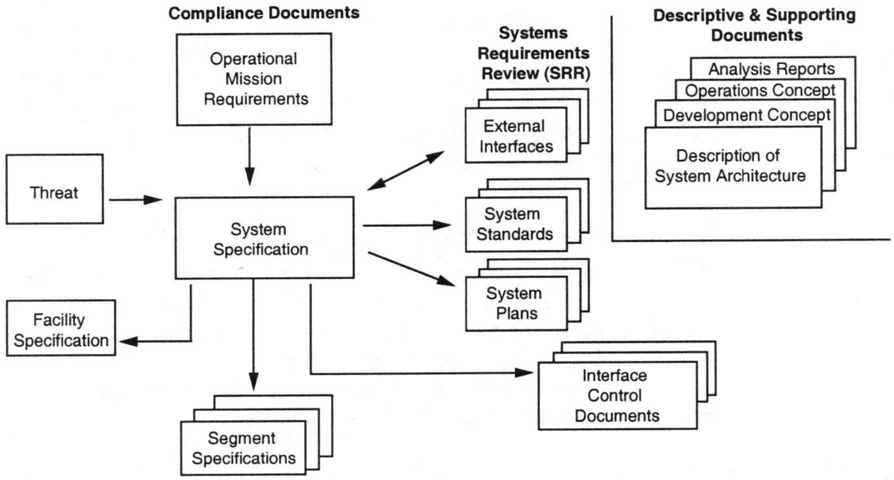

Fig. 5-1. Typical Specification Documents. While not all documents exist for all programs, the information contained in each should be recorded so that it is available for review and is agreed to by everyone involved in the project.

As we have stressed above, a key issue in requirements definition, and therefore in creating specification documents, is to specify what is to be done and not how it is to be done. No mission requires star cameras. Missions simply require accurate attitude data or, more likely, accurate mapping and pointing data. How this is achieved should reasonably be left to the organizations or individuals assigned the responsibility of achieving it.

5.2 Budgeting, Allocation, and Flow-Down

Having established the top-level system requirements, the next step in the requirements definition process is to *budget*, *allocate*, or *flow-down* these requirements to the components which make up the overall system. This section summarizes the broad process of doing that, and Sec. 5.3 provides a detailed numerical example for mapping and pointing budgets which are the principal area of interest for spacecraft orbit and attitude systems.

The *budget* is the numerical list of the components into which the top-level resource or requirement is divided along with the rules on how the components are to be combined to meet the system requirement. The *margin* is the planned difference between the system requirement and the sum of the components. Margin should be tracked and controlled at the system level to be available to meet implementation needs. Table 5-3 provides a list of items frequently budgeted in space missions. Generally almost anything that should be budgeted represents either a scarce resource or an element that is necessary to make the mission successful. For example, weight, power, and propellant are scarce commodities that are budgeted on virtually all missions. Communications systems would have a pointing budget to ensure that the communication antennas are correctly pointed and a link budget to ensure that there is adequate margin in the data transmission. An observation mission would add a mapping budget to establish the accuracy with which the location of identified targets could be established. If the time limit for obtaining data is critical, as might be the case for military surveillance or emergency data processing, then a time budget would be established to monitor and control this.

TABLE 5-3. Items Frequently Budgeted in Space Missions. Overall budgets are typically established at the systems level and flow-down or allocated to the subsystems. See Wertz and Larson [1999] for a discussion of each of the budgets listed here.

Primary	Secondary
Weight	Subsystem Weight Power Propellant
Geolocation or System Pointing Errors	Pointing and Alignment Mapping Attitude Control Attitude Determination Position Determination
Timing	Coverage Communications Operations Processing
Availability	Reliability Operational Availability
Cost	Development Cost Deployment Cost Operations and Maintenance Cost

There are two basic types of space system budgets. *Commodity budgets* allocate any of the finite resources available on the spacecraft, such as weight, power, propellant, or data rate. These budgets are straightforward; there exists a certain amount and that amount is allocated in some appropriate fashion among the subsystems that need it. Thus, the spacecraft mass will be allocated to all of the subsystems, including, for example, the attitude control system. The attitude control mass budget will then be allocated to the various components, which will in turn be allocated to the elements which make up the components. Verification of the commodity budgets is also straightforward. We weigh each component and ultimately the spacecraft. Commodity budgets are often broken down further. For example, the weight budget may be broken down into different weights during different mission phases, and the power budget is frequently broken down into orbit average and peak power requirements.

The second and more complex type of budget is the *error budget* which breaks down the required accuracy on any measurement or control requirement, such as the mapping errors, pointing errors, or absolute timing errors. These are discussed in more detail in Secs. 5.3 and 5.4. The principal cause of the complexity for these budgets, and a potential major cost driver for the system as a whole, is the process of how error budgets are to be added. If the elements that make up the error budget are random and uncorrelated then a root sum square (RSS) is the correct approach. If the error components are fully correlated, or if they are components that will physically add, then they should be added linearly. For attitude systems, the most common result is to RSS the short-term noise, RSS the bias sources and then add the two results. However, in a worst-case situation the bias terms would add linearly. The correct approach to doing this is a mathematical question, discussed in more detail in Sec. 5.4.

TABLE 5-4. Simplified Pointing Error Budget for a Space Telescope. (All values in degrees.) In reality, there would be substantially more elements in the pointing budget as shown, for example, in Fig. 5-2. Note that if the errors had been summed literally, the total of 0.0155 deg would exceed the requirement and a major design enhancement would be required.

Random Errors:	
Star sensor noise	0.002
Star centroid calculation	0.003
Pixel-to-pixel variations	0.002
Thermal variations	0.0015
RSS of random errors	0.0044
Bias Errors:	
Star sensor mounting errors	0.002
Payload mounting error	0.002
Payload detector mounting error	0.003
RSS of bias errors	0.0041
Sum of Random and Bias Errors	0.0085
Requirement	0.010
Margin	0.0015

Table 5-4 shows a simplified pointing error budget for a space telescope. In a real mission there would be substantially more elements in the budget, as shown in Fig. 5-2 on geopositioning error. However, this simple example illustrates one of the fundamental problems in error budgets. The user wishes to point the telescope to within 0.01 deg. If we RSS the random terms and bias terms separately, and then add the results, we're able to meet this requirement with some margin. On the other hand, if all of the terms were simply added linearly, the requirement would not be met, and we would have to either change the requirement or change the system design, presumably at significantly higher cost. In the end, how we treat error budgets depends on what it is the mission is trying to achieve. Is it a scientific mission in which we are trying to establish confidence levels? A military mission, where we are looking for the worst case that might be taken advantage of by an opponent? Or a commercial mission, in which we are trying to provide a customer with services of a given quality? In each case, we need to work with the user or the customer in order to determine what is really intended by the error budget and budgeting process.

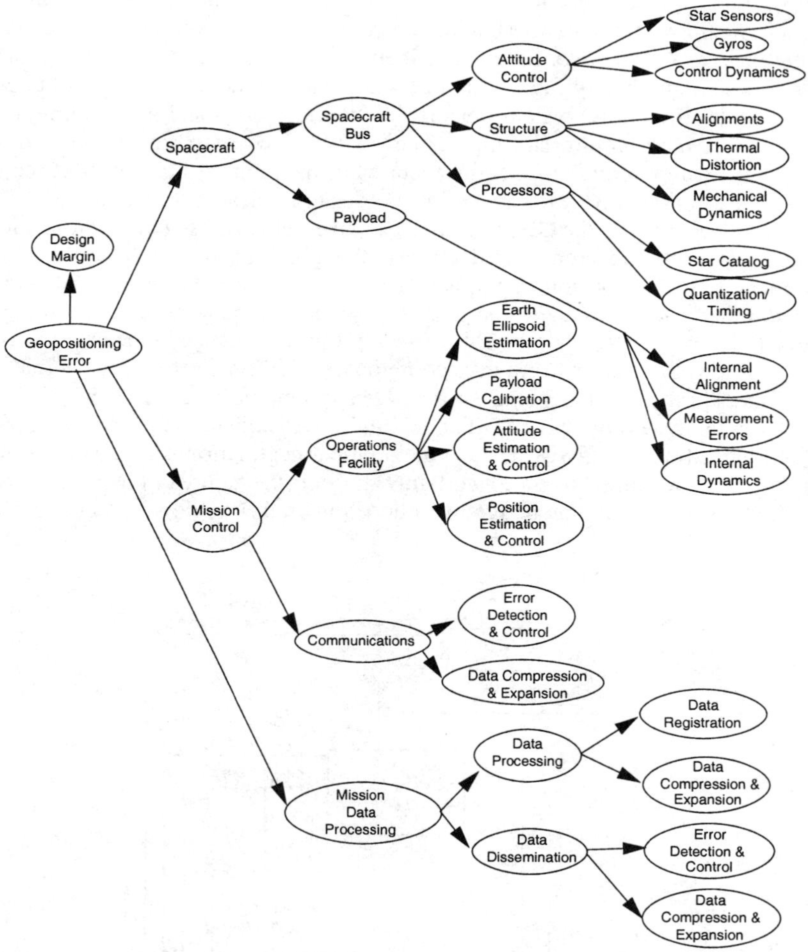

Fig. 5-2. Allocation of Geopositioning Error from Mission Requirements Down to Component Design Level.

Figure 5-2 shows an example of the allocation of a geopositioning error from a top-level mission requirement down to detailed component designs. As can be seen from the figure, this allocation is both complex and involves both the spacecraft and the mission control or data processing segments. As described in Sec. 3.7 for attitude budgets, each step of the operation includes at least a small source of additional error. This may be round-off errors in the computer, errors in the uncertainty of coordinate transformation, or errors in physical hardware or their calibration. The importance of the budgeting process itself is to reach agreement on the list of error sources such that we can then find numerical values appropriate to each source, to ensure ourselves that the ultimate mission requirement will be met

Budgeting is both a mathematical process, as discussed in Secs. 5.3 and 5.4, and a political process in which various individuals and organizations agree on how much of any of the budgeted elements is to be incorporated within their particular subsystem. Each subsystem would of course like to have as much of the weight, power and precision budgets as possible in order to make their job less expensive and less complex. In principle we should be willing to change the allocation among the various budgets in order to make the entire system perform as well as possible for a minimum cost. However, this may require shifting resources between competing organizations or making changes to contractual requirements. For example, it may be possible to do additional calibration on an Earth sensor in order to improve its accuracy to make up for a lack of accuracy in the GPS receiver. However, since these two components will typically be built by different manufacturers, changing this allocation could represent a contractual change for both manufacturers which could make it expensive for the prime contractor to achieve the end goal. Consequently, most system and subsystem engineers will work hard to both achieve an appropriate balance in the original budget and to provide sufficient margin to accommodate additional error sources that arise. This political process of balancing error budgets is summarized in Fig. 5-3. This chart was originally created by Mike Williams [1992], who coined the phrase "negotiation of terrible injustices" to give a sense of the political negotiations that go on during the budgeting and allocation process. It certainly suggests the nature of the political battles that can often ensue from the budgeting, allocating, and flow-down process.

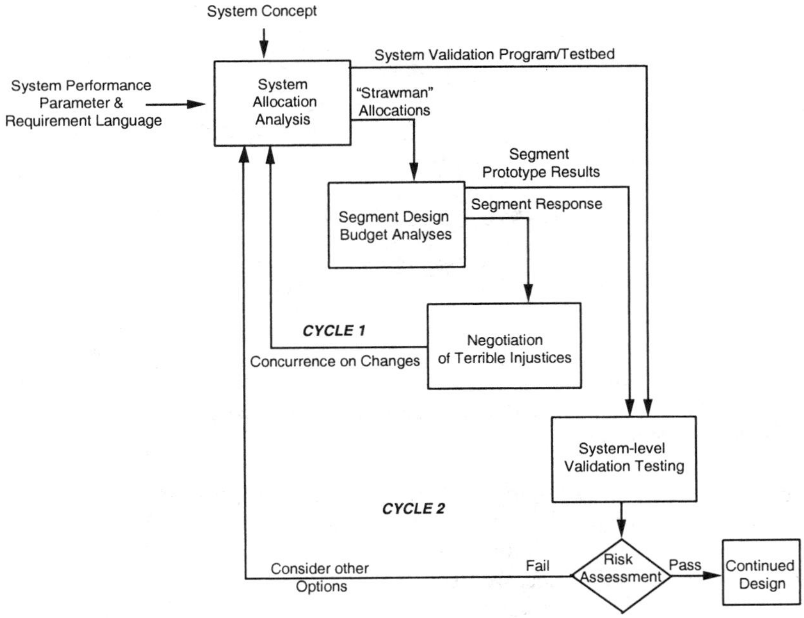

Fig. 5-3. Iterative Process for Budgeting and Validation. In practice, the budget is resolved by negotiations between those who must actually build the equipment or carry out the process of meeting the requirement. (From Williams [1992].)

Figure 5-4 provides a summary of a time budget for providing data on forest fires for a forest fire detection mission. Here it is clear that timeliness is critical to the end user. Information on the fire's location is of very little interest a week after the data was collected. On the other hand, millisecond accuracy is also not necessary. This implies that there is a time-span in which data must be provided to be useful to the user, and that we can allocate this time to the various components of the system, including the orbital coverage of the spacecraft, the identification of the forest fire data, and the delivery of this data to the end user. Note also that there may be more than one timeline involved. For example, we may have one timeline from the time that a detectable fire starts until it is first seen by the system, and a second, probably much shorter, timeline from when a fire is detected by the system until that data is reported to a firefighter on the ground. Even here, there can be substantial contractual questions such as whether "detection" of a forest fire represents appropriate data being collected on board the spacecraft, or the process of identifying a specific forest fire which may occur somewhat later. The critical issue for system design is to create this budget such that issues can be defined and resolved as early in the process as possible. Consequently, the detailed budgeting process is an important one for the organizations involved, as well as for the system engineering process of ensuring that the mission objectives can be met.

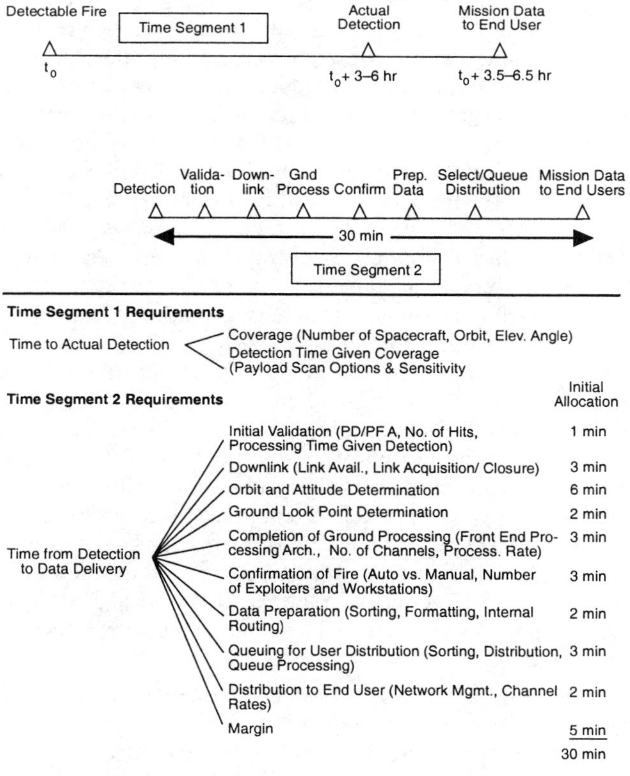

Fig. 5-4. Allocation of Data Timeline. Note that there are separate time requirements for how soon an event is detected (Segment 1) and how soon after detection the information is provided to an end user (Segment 2).

5.3 Introduction to Mapping and Pointing Budgets

As discussed in Sec. 1.3, most space missions are not concerned with orbit, attitude, and timing per se, but rather with the more fundamental aspects of mapping and pointing. In this context, *pointing* means orienting the spacecraft, camera, sensor, or antenna to a target having specific geographic coordinates or inertial direction. *Mapping* is determining the coordinates of the *look-point* of a camera, sensor, or antenna. Satellites used only for communications will generally require only pointing. Satellites having some type of viewing instrument, such as weather, ground surveillance, or Earth resource satellites, will ordinarily require both pointing (point the instrument at Los Angeles) and mapping (determine the geographic location of the feature in pixel 1096).

In order to create a mapping and pointing budget, we must first understand the sources of error in determining the mapping and pointing, and then evaluate how to quantify these error sources, and how the errors should be added to create the final budget. The components of pointing and mapping budgets for an Earth-oriented observation mission are shown in Fig. 5-5 and defined in Table 5-5.* Mapping and pointing errors are related to the knowledge of the spacecraft position and attitude in space. However, even if these are known precisely, other errors will be present. For example, an error in the observation time will result in an error of the computed location of the target, because the target frame of reference moves relative to the spacecraft. A target fixed on the Earth's equator will rotate with the Earth at 464 m/s. A 10 sec error in the observation time would produce an error of 5 km in the computed geographic location of the target. Errors due to the target altitude come about because of the projection of the direction of the target onto a location on the surface of the Earth. For example, if the spacecraft has an elevation angle of 45 deg as seen from the target, and if the assumed altitude of the target is off by 1 km, then there will be a 1 km error in "placing" the target on the geographic surface of the Earth. Since the roughness of the surface of the Earth has a variation of several kilometers relative to a perfect spheroid, this implies that observations must be made nearly vertically, or if we wish geographic accuracies much greater than this, the target altitudes must be well known.

Pointing errors differ from mapping errors in the way they include inaccuracies in attitude control and angular motion. The pointing error must include the entire control error for the spacecraft. On the other hand, the only control-related component of the mapping error is the angular motion during the exposure or observation time. This short term jitter results in a blurring of the look-point of the instrument or antenna. Except for this blur, it is attitude knowledge, rather than attitude control that is important for observation missions and therefore mapping. As discussed in Sec. 1.3, we may achieve an accuracy goal for either pointing or mapping in many ways. For example, we may know the position of the spacecraft precisely, and the attitude only poorly. Or we may choose to allow a larger error in the position, and make the requirements for determining the attitude more stringent. The ideal mathematical process for minimizing the cost is as follows:

> **If the components of an error budget are continuously variable then the minimum system cost is obtained by adjusting each component until the differential cost of improvement is the same for all components.**

---

* Errors associated with an inertially pointed mission are similar, but do not include any of the error sources associated with projecting the position onto the Earth.

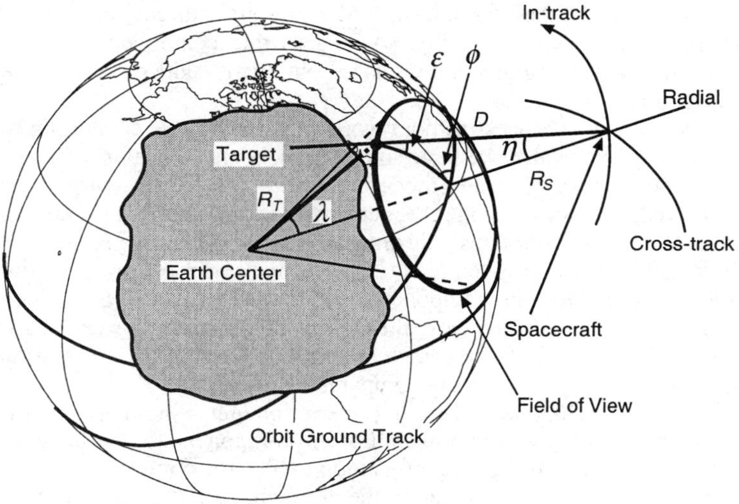

Fig. 5-5. Definition of Pointing and Mapping Error Components.

TABLE 5-5. Sources of Pointing and Mapping Errors.

Spacecraft Position Errors:		
ΔI	In- or along-track	Displacement along the spacecraft's velocity vector
ΔC	Cross-track	Displacement normal to the spacecraft's orbit plane
ΔR_S	Radial	Displacement toward the center of the Earth (nadir)
Sensing Axis Orientation Errors (In polar coordinates about nadir):		
$\Delta\eta$	Elevation	Error in angle from nadir to sensing axis
$\Delta\phi$	Azimuth	Error in rotation of the sensing axis about nadir
Sensing axis orientation errors include errors in (1) attitude determination, (2) instrument mounting, and (3) stability for mapping or control for pointing.		
Other Errors:		
ΔR_T	Target altitude	Uncertainty in the altitude of the observed object
ΔT	Clock error	Uncertainty in the real observation time (results in uncertainty in the rotational position of the Earth)

Assume, for example, that we wish to minimize the cost of achieving a given pointing accuracy, and that with the current design, we can improve the pointing accuracy by adjusting the orbit accuracy at a cost of \$100,000/mrad. Also assume that we could improve the pointing accuracy by improving the attitude accuracy at a cost of only \$50,000/mrad. In this case, we should adjust our error budgets so as to be less stringent in terms of orbit accuracy and more stringent in terms of attitude accuracy until the differential cost of improvement for both was \$75,000/mrad. In a sense, we are selling orbit accuracy for \$100,000/mrad, in order to buy attitude accuracy for only \$50,000/mrad. Continuing to do this so long as one component costs more than another in terms of improvement allows us to continually reduce the cost of achieving a given level of performance.

In practice the above process seldom works. Ordinarily, we cannot improve accuracy continuously. Normally, we have some components for which very little adjustment in accuracy is possible, and others for which there are very large steps in both performance and cost as we change the methods or techniques that we are using. Even if we can make nearly continuous adjustments, we seldom know precisely how much money it costs to achieve a given level of performance. In practice, the mission designer attempts to balance the components, often by relying on experience and intuition as much as analysis. In any case, the overall goal remains correct. We should try to balance the error budget so the incremental cost of improvement in any of the components results in approximately comparable cost.

A more practical technique for creating an error budget is summarized in Table 5-6. We begin the process by writing down all of the components of the budget. We then spread the total available budget equally among all of the components. For example, if there are five error sources relevant to the problem, then if we are going to add the errors linearly we would assign each source 1/5 of the error and if we are going to use a root sum square then we would assign each source the square root of 1/5 of the error. This provides a starting point for allocating the errors. Our next step is to look at the range of options available to us and divide the error sources into the following categories:

A. Those allowing very little adjustment

B. Those easily meeting their error allocation

C. Those allowing increase accuracy at increased cost

TABLE 5-6. Construction of Mapping and Pointing Error Budgets. This process is essentially the same for all types of spacecraft error budgets. (See also Table 5-8 for rules on mathematically combining error terms.)

Optimal Solution (How It Should be Done)	Practical Solution (How it Works in Practice)
Adjust each error component until the differential cost of improvement (\$ per milliradian or \$ per km) is the same for each Doesn't work in practice because performance improvements are not continuously variable.	Allocate the budget equally among all components Divide the components into three categories A. Those allowing very little adjustment (e.g., position) B. Those that easily meet the allocation (e.g., time) C. Those allowing increased accuracy at increased cost (e.g., attitude) Adjust both the requirement and category (C) components to meet the cost vs. performance trade

For example, determining the position of the spacecraft is a normal spacecraft operational function, done either by the ground station or perhaps by GPS. Whichever method is chosen, the level of accuracy is essentially fixed and cannot be adjusted without a dramatically high cost. (Launching a new and more accuracy GPS constellation is not a practical solution for most missions). Consequently, we assign these errors to category A and accept whatever error is inherent in the process. Timing errors frequently fall into category B, since modern spacecraft clocks can easily maintain an accuracy of tens of milliseconds which represents a small motion on the part of the spacecraft. Therefore, the error associated with the timing will typically be much smaller than the allocation and we will again accept the more accurate values in order to allow a looser budget in another category. Attitude determination errors ordinarily fall into category C. Here, we could use a gravity-gradient stabilized system at low cost, but accurate to only a few degrees, or a horizon sensor system, accurate to 0.05–0.10 deg at moderate cost, or a very expensive star sensor system, accurate to better than 0.01 deg.

This process not only allows us to balance cost between appropriate components, but also to go back to the mission definition process and find the real requirements. For example, achieving a mapping accuracy of 100 m on the ground might triple the cost of the space mission, by requiring highly accurate attitude determination, a new system for orbit determination, and a detailed list of target altitudes. Reducing this accuracy requirement to 500 m might lower the cost enough to make the mission possible within established budget constraints. This is an example of trading on mission requirements as discussed in more detail in Sec. 1.3, and Sec. 5.1. Requirements trading is extremely important to a cost-effective mission, but we often omit this step in the normal process of defining and allocating mission requirements. However, it is this evaluation of the cost of achieving a particular level of performance that allows technical information and technical decision-making to flow back into the requirements definition process.

To carry out the trade process defined above, we need to know how an error in each of the components listed in Table 5-5 relates to the overall mapping and pointing errors. Table 5-7 gives the formulas relating the errors in each of the seven basic components to the overall mapping and pointing errors. The notation here is the same as in Fig. 5-5. For any specific mission conditions, these formulas relate the errors in the fundamental components to the resulting pointing and mapping accuracies. This set of formulas provides the basic algebraic information which we use to transform attitude, position, and other error sources into specific mapping and pointing requirements for a given mission.

Representative Mapping Budget

To illustrate the process of constructing detailed mapping and pointing budgets, we will look at specific numerical examples of a moderate accuracy satellite, flying at an altitude of 1,000 km.

The errors associated with mapping, depend strongly on how close to the horizon we choose to work. Working in a very small region directly under the spacecraft gives excellent mapping accuracy and resolution, but provides very poor coverage, as shown in Fig. 5-6. On the other hand, working near the horizon provides very wide coverage, but poor mapping accuracy. Thus, we must trade resolution and mapping accuracy for coverage. The mapping accuracy for a particular mission will depend on the spacecraft's elevation angle at the edge of the coverage region. In almost all cases the mapping accuracy would be much better looking straight down, and the limiting accuracy will be closest to the horizon. To assess satellite coverage, we look at the satellite's swath width, that is we assume the spacecraft could work directly below itself, and at all angles out to a limiting spacecraft elevation angle as seen from a target on the ground. To see how this works in practice, Table 5-8 provides representative mapping

TABLE 5-7. Mapping and Pointing Error Formulas. ε is the observation angle of the spacecraft as seen from the target, *lat* is the latitude of the target, ϕ is the target azimuth relative to the ground track, λ is the Earth central angle from the target to the satellite, D is the distance from the satellite to the target, R_T is the distance from the Earth's center to the target (typically ~ R_E, the Earth's radius), and R_S is the distance from the Earth's center to the satellite. See Fig. 5-5.

Error Source	Error Magnitude (units)	Magnitude of Mapping Error (km)	Magnitude of Pointing Error (rad)	Direction of Error
Attitude Errors:(1)				
Azimuth	$\Delta\phi$(rad)	$\Delta\phi D \sin\eta$	$\Delta\phi \sin\eta$	Azimuthal
Nadir Angle	$\Delta\eta$ (rad)	$\Delta\eta\ D / \sin\varepsilon$	D*h*	*Toward nadir*
Position Errors:				
In-Track	ΔI (km)	$\Delta I\ (R_T/R_S) \cos H$(2)	$(\Delta I/D) \sin Y_I$(5)	Parallel to ground track
Cross-Track	ΔC (km)	$\Delta C\ (R_T/R_S) \cos G$(3)	$(\Delta C/D) \sin Y_C$(6)	Perpendicular to ground track
Radial	ΔR_S (km)	$\Delta R_S \sin\eta / \sin\varepsilon$	$(\Delta R_S/D) \sin\eta$	Toward nadir
Other Errors:				
Target Altitude	ΔR_T (km)	$\Delta R_T / \tan\varepsilon$	—	Toward nadir
S/C Clock	ΔT (s)	$\Delta T\ V_e \cos(lat)$(4)	$\Delta T\ (V_e / D) \cos(lat) \cdot \sin J$(7)	Parallel to Earth's equator

Notes:

(1) Includes attitude determination error, instrument mounting error, stability over exposure time (mapping only), and control error (pointing only). The formulas given assume that the attitude is measured with respect to the Earth.

(2) $\sin H = \sin\lambda \sin\phi$.

(3) $\sin G = \sin\lambda \cos\phi$.

(4) V_e = 464 m/s (Earth rotation velocity at the equator).

(5) $\cos Y_I = \cos\phi \sin\eta$.

(6) $\cos Y_C = \sin\phi \sin\eta$.

(7) $\cos J = \cos\phi_E \cos\varepsilon$, where ϕ_E = azimuth relative to East.

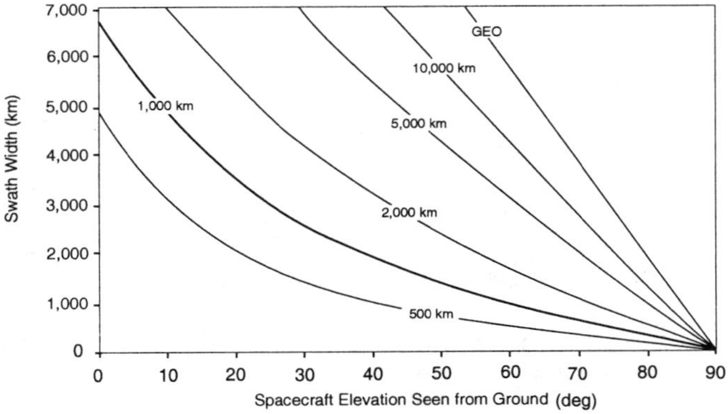

Fig. 5-6. Swath Width vs. Elevation Angle for a Spacecraft at Various Altitudes. The *swath width* is the width of the coverage band on the surface of the Earth and is a direct measure of how much coverage each spacecraft will have. Note that the swath width increases dramatically at small elevation angles where the mapping errors become very large.

and pointing error budgets which are then plotted for an altitude of 1,000 km in Fig. 5-7 as a function of spacecraft elevation angle as seen from the ground, using the equations listed in Table 5-7. The total mapping error is the RSS of the individual components. Generally, uncertainty in target altitude and attitude determination contribute the most to the errors in mapping accuracy. In most cases, improving the other factors will have only a second-order effect. Consequently, determining the target altitude and spacecraft attitude are high priorities in assessing a mission's mapping performance and cost.

TABLE 5-8. Representative Mapping and Pointing Error Budgets. See Figs. 5-7 and 5-8 for plots corresponding to this data.

Source	Error in Source	Error Budgets			
		Mapping Error (km)		Pointing Error (deg)	
		ε = 10 deg	ε = 30 deg	ε = 10 deg	ε = 30 deg
Attitude Errors:					
Azimuth	0.06 deg	2.46	1.33	0.051	0.045
Nadir Angle	0.03 deg	8.33	1.78	0.030	0.030
Position Errors:					
In-Track	0.2 km	0.17	0.17	0.002	0.005
Cross-Track	0.2 km	0.16	0.17	0.004	0.007
Radial	0.1 km	0.49	0.15	0.002	0.003
Other Errors:					
Target Altitude	1 km	5.67	1.73	—	—
S/C Clock	0.5 sec	0.23	0.23	0.005	0.008
Root Sum Square		10.39	2.84	0.060	0.055

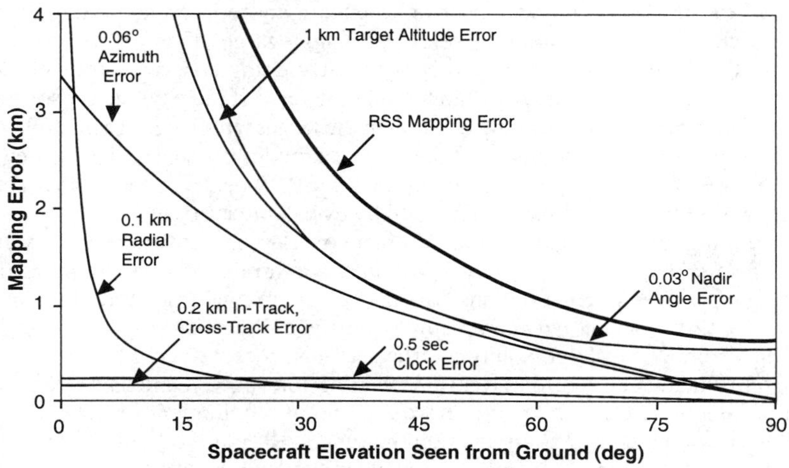

Fig. 5-7. Mapping Error as a Function of Elevation Angle for a Spacecraft at 1,000 km Altitude. The errors are those from Table 5-8.

The uncertainty in target altitude typically contributes most to determining a geographic location on the Earth. The oblateness of the Earth has the largest effect on target altitude. It causes a variation in distance from the center of the Earth of approximately 25 km between the poles and the equator. However, we can account for this factor analytically at a very low cost, so it does not usually contribute to the error. The next plateau is for airplanes, clouds or other atmospheric features. The uncertainty in target altitude for these will typically be 10 km or larger, unless we have some a priori estimate of the altitude. For features fixed on the Earth's surface, the uncertainty in target altitude reduces to approximately 1 km, unless data analysis includes a detailed map of target altitudes. Figure 5-7 incorporates this 1 km error in target altitude as the dominant source of error. To do significantly better would require one of two options. First, the spacecraft could work only very near nadir and therefore have very poor coverage. Alternatively, it could include the elevation of the target region as a part of the data reduction process, therefore requiring a very large database and making the data processing much more complex.

Representative Pointing Budget

Unlike mapping, pointing depends only weakly on the spacecraft's elevation angle. This can be seen in Fig. 5-8, which is based on the same parameters as Fig. 5-7. For missions which require only pointing, working in a region near the horizon is almost as easy as pointing to a target or ground antenna at nadir. In this case the working limit on the spacecraft's elevation angle will depend on other factors, such as the transmission of the atmosphere for a selected wavelength, or possible obstruction by local geography. For example, ground stations ordinarily limit their work to approximately 5 deg above the horizon because of the reduced transmission of the atmosphere at lower elevation angles.

Pointing requirements normally arise from the spacecraft's housekeeping function, or from the need to point a particular instrument or antenna toward a ground target. Housekeeping requirements, such as solar array pointing and orbit maneuvers ordinarily demand pointing accuracies of 0.25–1 deg. Consequently, for most missions, the need to point the mission sensor or antenna is more important. Here again, two cases exist. If we wish to point the sensor at a single target, then we will generally try to point the center of the sensor at the target. By doing so, we establish a pointing requirement to place the target within the field of view. If the payload sensor's field of view is four times the 3σ pointing error, then the target will lie within the field of view with a 6σ probability, or virtual certainty. For example, if a sensor has a 1 deg square field of view, an overall pointing requirement of 0.25 deg will assure that the target will be within the field of view on essentially every observation.

In pointing, we may also want to eliminate overlapping coverage. For example, if we wish to take a series of pictures, we must overlap the pictures by more than the pointing error to ensure continuous coverage of the ground. This requirement in turn implies that the spacing between pictures must equal the field of view size, less the pointing error. With a large pointing error, we must accept having fewer pictures in a given time, an increased resource cost in terms of time, power, and data rate for a given level of coverage. It is common to have a pointing requirement of 10%–20% of the field of view diameter. Driving the pointing under 10% of the field of view diameter will only slightly improve overall coverage. On the other hand, a pointing error worse than 20% of the field of view size can require substantial overlap, thus significantly diminishing the system's coverage and resource utilization.

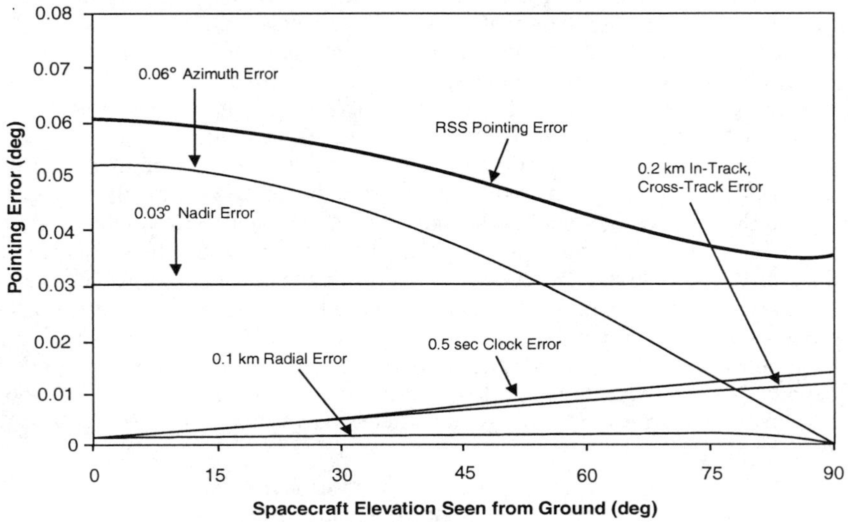

Fig. 5-8. Pointing Error as a Function of Elevation Angle for a Spacecraft at 1,000 km Altitude. Compare with Fig. 5-7. Note that mapping error is very sensitive to elevation angle while pointing error is not.

Minimizing Cost

The first approach for minimizing cost is to eliminate entirely elements from the overall budget, thereby improving performance at essentially no cost. The key issue here is to look at the budget components and see which ones could be eliminated. For example, consider the pointing budget for a spacecraft whose goal is to remain nadir pointed. We can do this by using either star sensors or Earth sensors. However, star sensors are sensing the orientation with respect to inertial space, and therefore require an additional coordinate transformation which includes uncertainties in the position of the spacecraft in order to determine where nadir is and, therefore, remain nadir pointed. This is eliminated by using an Earth sensor to provide measurements directly with respect to the item we would like to be pointed toward. This implies that I could end up with a system that achieves lower accuracy using the high-cost star sensors than using low-cost Earth sensors. In general, I can both maximize accuracy and minimize cost by using sensors that detect directly the object that I am interested in measurements with respect to.

The second principal way to reduce cost is to look at the overall problem of system requirements specification. If you do not meet the initial requirement, then the classic response is to go back and tighten up on the specifications. However, in a cost-conscious system, this is the wrong answer. The process needs to involve an iterative trade between what we want (the initial requirement) and what we can afford (what the engineering budget comes back with). In the end, whatever organization is putting up the money must come up with a decision on how to proceed and whether or not meeting the accuracy objectives is worth the differential cost of doing so.

A key issue is to look for creative mechanisms for defining accuracy that may be able to meet the needs of the end user while still holding down cost. For example, as discussed above, accuracy is a strong function of elevation angle for a mapping error budget. This results in a very undesirable trade. If we increase the elevation angle to improve the accuracy, we will dramatically reduce coverage, which could drive up the number of spacecraft that are required. On the other hand, working at low elevation angles to achieve wide coverage with a small number of spacecraft provides extremely poor mapping accuracy at the edges of the swath. In cases such as this, a possible alternative is a "flexi-spec" in which different accuracies are required at different elevation angles. For example, in examining Fig. 5-7, we might set a mapping requirement of 3 km at an elevation angle of 25 deg, and 1 km at an elevation angle of 60 deg. This means that the user will get very wide and frequent coverage, with limited accuracy, and much higher accuracy, but at a less frequent rate, from the narrow swath. Certainly, this is less desirable than achieving high accuracy at all times. However, we may be able to reduce the number of spacecraft required by a factor of two or three and, therefore, dramatically drive down the cost of the system, if we can find way to make use of poorer accuracy data at a higher frequency, and more accurate data at a lower frequency. This is representative of the types of trade that need to be made in modern systems, in order to drive down the overall system cost and maximize the performance.

5.4 Introduction to Error Analysis

Geoffrey N. Smit, *The Aerospace Corporation*

In this section we discuss how error budgets are to be handled numerically—i.e. how component errors are to be "summed" to yield the total error or *system error.** System error analysis involves the following steps:

(1) Modeling the system and identifying the *error sources* i.e., the places where errors are introduced,

(2) Determining the sensitivity of the system error to each of the error sources,

(3) Characterizing the distribution for each of the error sources, and

(4) Combining the sources to determine the system error.

Accomplishing Step 1 adequately is crucial and is system specific. Because this topic is better discussed via examples than in the abstract, most of this section will be devoted to examples. In realistic systems, the models for error analyses can be dismayingly complex. Our examples will be as simple as possible, to bring out the main features.

Step 2 is really an integral part of Step 1, but we have separated it out for emphasis. Step 1 normally gives us a deterministic relationship between error sources and the system error. For want of a better term, we shall call this relationship the *error equation*. Typically, the system error will not be dominated by the effects from a single source. Usually, there are numerous error sources, and an efficient design will tend to balance their effects as discussed in Sec. 5.2 and App. C. In some situations, a system may have singularities leading to high sensitivity to a particular input. (See Sec. 7.2 and Example 3 below.) In the normal situation (no singularities, reasonably balanced

* The error budgeting problem described in Secs. 5.2 and 5.5 is, in a sense, the inverse of the summation problem. The budget allocates to each component an allowable error. Here we want to know how to combine the errors to check that the resulting system error meets requirements.

response to the various errors), the error equation can be represented as a sum in which the output error is the algebraic sum of the inputs. This is discussed in more depth in the examples and App. C. (See also Taylor [1997].)

Step 3 involves a knowledge of the types of components being used, and of the operating environment. Since many errors are inherently random, some sort of probabilistic characterization must be given. Usually, the component errors are specified in terms of standard deviations. For example, a star tracker may be accurate to 30 arcseconds ("3σ"), implying that the distribution is Gaussian and that about 99% of all readings will be within 30 arcseconds of the true direction. Ideally, the probability distribution of the errors could be given, but this level of information is usually not available.

From the error equation, we can easily bound the system error. If $e = e_1 + e_2 + \ldots + e_n$, where e is the system error and $e_1, e_2, \ldots$ are the component errors, then $|e| \leq |e_1| + |e_2| + \ldots + |e_n|$. This bound can form the basis for an error budget. Normally, however, it will be too conservative, i.e. it will demand that we keep the e_i considerably smaller than is necessary to achieve a given bound on e. We must exploit the statistical nature of the errors to make the design affordable while still meeting the error budget.

Step 4 addresses the mathematical problem of estimating the statistical properties of the system error, given those of the components and the error equation connecting them. The summation calculation can be approached in various ways. The actual analysis undertaken and the degree of detail included will depend on the system and on the amount of information available:

- In some cases (e.g., when the probability distribution of the e_i are normal or uniform), the distribution of the sum can be evaluated analytically. (See Feller [1957], Meyer [1972], Papoulis [1965], and Parzen [1960].)
- When this is not possible (or efficient) the output distribution can be generated using a Monte Carlo simulation as described in Table 5-10 below.
- In many cases, generation of the system probability distribution may not be necessary or feasible, e.g., when the component distributions are unknown. It is possible to estimate the system standard deviation directly in terms of the component standard deviations. This not only makes fewer demands for detail in the input data, it is also far simpler computationally. For most error budgeting, this is the preferred approach.*

---

* It is shown in App. C (where the terminology is defined) that if $e = e_1 + e_2 + \ldots + e_n$, then

$$\sigma^2 = \sum_i \sigma_i^2 + 2\sum_{i>j}\left[\mathrm{Cov}\left(e_i, e_j\right)\right]$$

where σ is the standard deviation of e, σ_i is the standard deviation of e_i, and $\mathrm{Cov}(e_i, e_j)$ is the covariance between e_i and e_j. If the covariances are zero (i.e. if the errors are independent), this reduces to

$$\sigma = \left(\sigma_i^2 + \cdots \sigma_n^2\right)^{1/2}$$

This is called the *root sum square*, or RSS. If the correlations are unity, so that the covariances equal the products of the corresponding standard deviations, then σ reduces to the sum of the σ_i. If the correlations are partial, we get a combination rule between the RSS and the sum. This is a standard result for the combination of standard deviations, and it forms the basis for most error analyses. (See Feller [1957], Meyer [1972], Papoulis [1965], and Parzen [1960].)

The procedure for undertaking an error analysis for the purpose of error budgeting is summarized in Table 5-9. A related procedure for a Monte Carlo error analysis is given in Table 5-10.

TABLE 5-9. Creating Error Budgets. RSS = "Root Sum Square" = Square root of the sum of the squares of the individual components.

Step	Comments	Where Discussed
1. Define the end-to-end measurement process.	Start with basic orbit, attitude, and payload measurements and compute the final output. See Table 5-15 and Fig. 5-9.	Secs. 5.2, 5.4.1, 7.2; Table 5-15 in Sec. 5.5
2. Identify sources of error in each step.	Break down each step into its lowest constituents. See Tables 5-9 to 5-14 and Fig. 5-9.	Secs. 5.4.1, 5.5, Chap. 7
3. Identify the statistical distribution of each error source.	Typically Gaussian or uniform if the measurements are quantized.	Secs. 5.4.2, 7.2
4. Assign a preliminary error value to each error source	If Gaussian, use 3σ error; if quantized use full range.	Secs. 5.4.2, 5.5, Table 5-15
5. Estimate the maximum probable error by adding all error terms in worst case end-to-end geometry.	If this meets the requirement, quit and go to Step 12. If singularities occur, calculation and implementation may need refinement.	Sec. 7.6 for effect of singularities
6. Estimate the minimum probable error by RSSing all error terms.	If this doesn't meet the requirement, then need to find a way to reduce error sources or find another solution	Sec. 5.4.2
7. If the requirement lies between (5) and (6), proceed to more accurate summation techniques.	Steps 8–11.	App. C, also Sec. 5.4
8. Determine the frequency associated with each of the error sources.	Over what time span is one measurement set not correlated with the previous one?	Sec. 5.4.4
9. Divide the error sources into frequency regimes.	Typically, Gaussian noise at the sampling frequency, most error sources at orbit frequency, and some at other frequencies (for example, weather sampling or magnetic field errors).	Sec. 5.4.4
10. Determine the error within each frequency regime as follows:	Within each frequency regime, there is the potential for errors to be correlated.	Sec. 5.4.4
10a. Add the correlated errors*.	Look explicitly for where singularities can occur†.	Sec. 7.6
10b. RSS the uncorrelated errors and the sums of the correlated errors	Assumes these are statistically independent.	Sec. 5.4.2
11. RSS the errors for different frequency regimes; this gives an analytic estimate of the total error.	Errors at different frequencies are orthogonal (cf Fourier analysis) and can be RSS'd.	Sec. 5.4.4
12. Review the steps looking for missing sources of error, such as uncertainty in coordinate transformations. Also conduct an independent search for singularities.	Every coordinate transformation includes an error associated with the definition of the new coordinate frame in terms of the old one.	Table 5-15 in Sec. 5.5; Sec. 7.6
13. Document and Iterate.		Sec. 5.1

* For partial correlations, summing is conservative, RSS is optimistic. For more accurate formulas, see App. C.

† A key measurement problem is that correlated error sources can lead to singularities in the measurement process for which the error in the result can become unbounded (i.e., very large). For a geometrical discussion of the source and treatment of measurement correlation, see Secs. 7.2 and 7.6.

TABLE 5-10. Monte Carlo Error Analysis. This is a numerical approach requiring a large number of runs. Singularities become evident due to a dramatic increase in the spread of the solutions when noise or biases are added to the data. (See Sec. 7.6.)

Step	Comments	Where Discussed
1. Do steps 1–4 of the analytic approach	See Table 5.4-1	Chaps. 5, 7
5. Assign a representative value for each of the variables involved	Pick both representative values and extremes where singularities can occur	Sec. 5.4.1
6. Execute the computation, from initial measurements to final answer; adding error to each computation according to the assigned probability distribution	Near singularities, computations may fail due to an illegal operation (e.g., arc sin of a number greater than 1)	Secs. 5.4.1, 7.2; Table 5-15 in Sec. 5.5
7. Evaluate the statistical results of multiple runs*	The statistical distribution of the result is the best estimate of the final error	Sec. 5.4.3
8. Check carefully for singularities, correlated measurements, and missing error sources†	Must cover the full range of measurements. If this is done, singularities become evident in the data due to very high noise levels.	Sec. 7.6
9. Iterate and document		Sec. 5.1

* For ways to enhance the efficiency of this process. For example, see Robert et al. [1999].

† As in the case of an analytic assessment, measurement singularities can dramatically impact the final error and cause divergence in numerical solutions. (See Secs. 7.2 and 7.6.)

We have been describing the error addition process as though the system and the errors were static. In most cases this is not true, and the dynamics of the system and the time structure of the component errors should be accounted for to obtain an accurate error estimate. At the simplest level, this involves looking at the frequency spectra of the various errors, and noting that in some cases this allows us to reduce the effective system error variance. (See App. C.) On a more sophisticated level, the system dynamical equations can be manipulated to provide an equation for the propagation of the system error covariance matrix which is then optimized. The error budget is then formulated in terms of this optimal error. The degree of sophistication adopted will depend on how far along in the program we are and the program's financial budget.

Note that there are two distinct "flows" in the error analysis and budgeting process:

(a) The desire for less conservatism, and hence more accuracy, leads us to increasing levels of sophistication in our modeling of the system, and

(b) The need to keep the calculations manageable leads us to simpler ways of characterizing the errors. This aspect of the flow is often driven by a lack of data on the error performance of the components.

Errors sources can be categorized in various ways: *random* vs. *systematic* (or *deterministic*), *additive* vs. *multiplicative*, *modeled* vs. *unmodeled*. Some of the classifications commonly used, such as noise vs. bias, are often subjective. The basic idea is to distinguish between effects which can be removed by calibration or filtering and those which cannot and which must therefore be added to the error budget. This distinction will depend on several factors. Some error sources are inherently random (such as thermal noise in electronic systems and optical detectors), while others, such as misalignments, are systematic. In principle, the systematic part can be calibrated out. In practice there are always residuals due to limitations in the calibration technique or due to the myriad of details in the system behavior. The ability to compensate for error sources will depend on how accurately they have been modeled. In very high precision systems, we may be prepared to take into account a large number of details which would simply be ignored and lumped into "noise" in other systems. For example, a star tracker may distort under temperature changes. To some extent we can measure this effect and use an open loop calibration curve to take it out based on a temperature measurement. However, there are also hysteresis effects, so the distortion is not exactly repeatable. This would contribute to the residuals. A more complex model accounting for the thermal time history might be used to further reduce the residuals. There will always be a bound to the degree of detail that can be justified, and the unmodeled effects will usually be treated as "random."

The time scale over which measurements are being taken will also influence how we view different sources. What may appear as a slowly varying bias on one time scale, may look like noise on another. With this in view, the distinction between noise and bias is really based more on how they are ***treated*** in a given system. Normally, bias is estimated, either via a separate calibration procedure or some sort of filter, and subtracted out. Noise is usually filtered via a low pass filter. In general, error sources that are outside the frequency band being used for measurements can be removed by various kinds of filters. Error sources within the measurement band can sometimes be removed, provided we understand the system well enough. The errors which would be summed, as described in the rest of this section, would be those which cannot be removed or which are not economical to remove.

Finally, combinations of sensors, and the corresponding combinations of their errors, do not always result in a system error larger than that of the components. In fact, many configurations are set up to allow sensors to complement each other. A simple example would be to put several identical sensors in parallel and take their average. The variance of the output would be $(1/N)$ times the variance of an individual sensor reading. A more realistic example would be combining a gyro with a star sensor.

We now proceed to specific examples illustrating the types of error equations which arise, and some of the related error summation issues.

Example 1: Direction to Target

Consider the system described in Table 5-15 in Sec. 5.5—i.e. a spacecraft looking at something on the Earth. The location of the target is determined by (1) estimating the spacecraft location, and (2) estimating the direction to the target.* Focusing on the problem of finding the direction to the target, the configuration implied in Table 5-15 is shown schematically in Fig. 5-9 and Table 5-11.

---

* If the target is at nadir, we have enough information to calculate its location. Otherwise we need more information (e.g. the range to the target or its altitude) or we need to incur additional errors related to ignoring these factors.

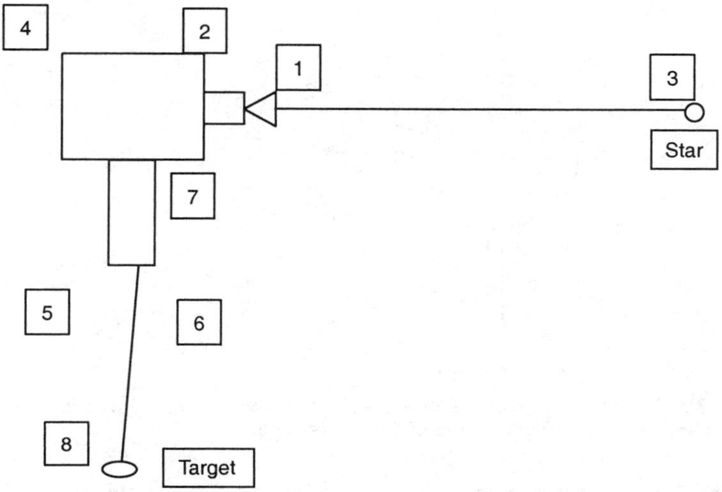

Fig. 5-9. Schematic of Measurements Implied in Table 5-15 in Sec. 5.5. Numbers give the location of the various error sources in both Table 5-15 and Table 5-11.

TABLE 5-11. The Estimated Errors for the Measurements Shown in Fig. 5-9. See text for discussion.

Star sensor measurement error (1)	0.0015 deg
Star sensor mounting error (2)	0.0020 deg
Star catalog error (3)	0.0001 deg
Attitude computation error (4)	0.0001 deg
Payload sensor measurement error (5)	0.0010 deg
Target centroid error (6)	0.0020 deg
Payload sensor mounting error (7)	0.0010 deg
Coordinate transformation error (8)	0.0001 deg

To see how the contributions of the various components combine, note that the implied calculation of the direction to the target is:

(a) Measure the direction to the star as seen by the star tracker. (1).

(b) Compare with star catalog data.

(c) Compute the inertial orientation of the star tracker. (3).

(d) Compute the inertial attitude of the spacecraft. (2) and (4).

(e) Compute the inertial attitude of the payload. (7).

(f) Measure the direction to the target as seen by the payload. (5) and (6).

(g) Compute the inertial direction to the target. (8).

Assume for the moment that we are only interested in rotations about one axis, then the estimate of the direction to the target is simply the algebraic sum of these angles. To see this, consider a single axis version of Fig. 5-9 as shown in Fig. 5-10.

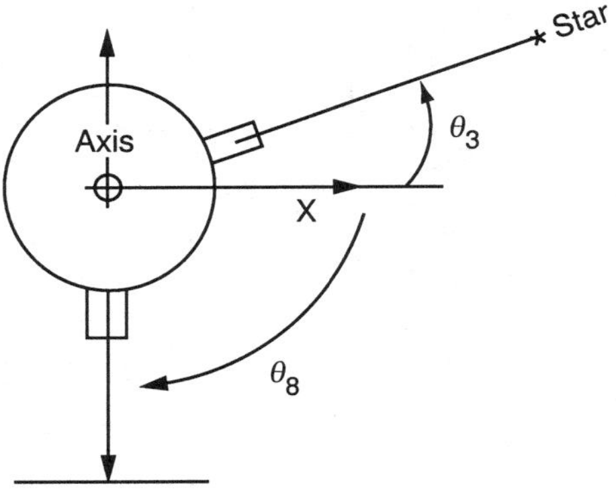

Fig. 5-10. Single Axis Version of the Measurement Shown in Fig. 5-9. The total error is simply the algebraic sum of the error of the components.

The sequence of measurements effectively determine the angle θ_3, the direction to the star in spacecraft coordinates and the angle θ_8, the direction to the target in spacecraft coordinates. These angles are actually computed in several steps, as outlined above.

If we now contaminate the nominal values with errors, we can decompose the actual contribution from each item into a sum of the true value, d_i, and an error, e_i. The system measurement, x, is then

$$\begin{aligned} x &= d + e \\ &= (d_1 + e_1) + (d_2 + e_2) + \ldots + (d_n + e_n) \\ &= (d_1 + d_2 + \ldots + d_n) + (e_1 + e_2 + \ldots + e_n) \end{aligned} \qquad (5\text{-}1)$$

Hence, the system error is the algebraic sum of the component errors.

If we allow rotations in two dimensions, the same considerations apply with the exception that we now have two orthogonal axes ("sideways" and "up-and-down"). With several gimbals, and several opportunities for structural and mounting misalignment, the actual geometrical evaluation of the errors can get quite complex. Although for some types of mechanism the two axes may be coupled, usually the **error** coupling is higher order, so that small errors are independent. This geometrical independence has some aspects of statistical independence, as will be discussed in Example 5.

Equation 5-1, or its 2D or 3D counterpart, represents a linear "error equation." In fact, error equations of practically any functional form can occur: i.e., the system error can be given by ratios, products, trigonometrric functions or any other functions of the component errors.

Example 2: Target Geolocation

If we extend Example 1 to include finding the location of the target on the surface of the Earth we have the situation shown in Fig. 5-11. The target is located by (1) determining the spacecraft location and (2) inferring the target location via the target angle (discussed in Example 1) and some trigonometry. The error in the target position is then the sum of the error in the subsatellite point estimate and the error in the estimate of the relative position of spacecraft and target, which, in turn, is a complex function of the angle to the target and the spacecraft altitude.

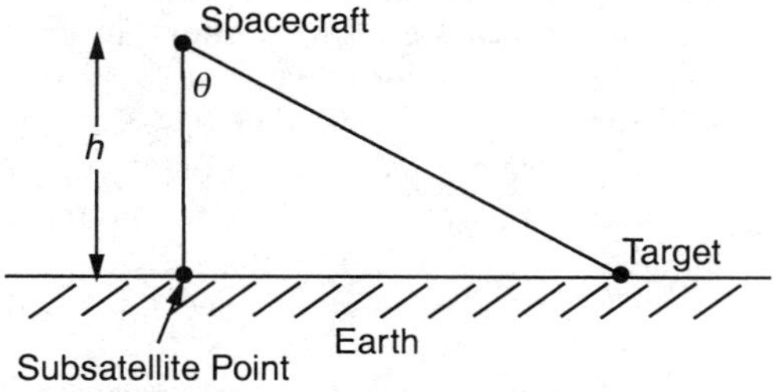

Fig. 5-11. Measuring the Location of a Target by Measuring Altitude, *h*, and Nadir Angle, *θ*.

It is standard procedure in the theory of errors to expand the system error as a Taylor series in the errors about the nominal value, and keep only the linear terms [Taylor, 1997]. This yields the total error as a weighted sum of the component errors. If desired, this can be converted to a pure sum by rescaling the variables. The assumption of small errors is natural (and usually well justified), because measurement errors usually represent a small fraction of the value of the measurand. Hence, the error equation can usually be reduced to an algebraic sum.

In our current example we have (assuming a flat Earth):

$$r = h\tan\theta \tag{5-2}$$

Assume h and θ have errors ε_h and ε_θ respectively, i.e.,

$$h = h_0 + \varepsilon_h \tag{5-3}$$

$$\theta = \theta_0 + \varepsilon_\theta \tag{5-4}$$

we then have

$$\begin{aligned} r &= (h_0 + \varepsilon_h)\tan(\theta_0 + \varepsilon_\theta) \\ &\approx (h_0 + \varepsilon_h)\left[\tan\theta_0 + \varepsilon_\theta(\sec^2\theta_0) + \ldots\right] \\ &= h_0\tan\theta_0 + \varepsilon_h\tan\theta_0 + h_0\,\varepsilon_\theta\sec^2\theta_0 + \mathcal{O}(\varepsilon^2) \\ &= r_0 + \delta r_h + \delta r_\theta + \mathcal{O}(\varepsilon^2) \end{aligned} \tag{5-5}$$

The geometric meaning of δr_h and δr_θ is shown in Fig. 5-12.

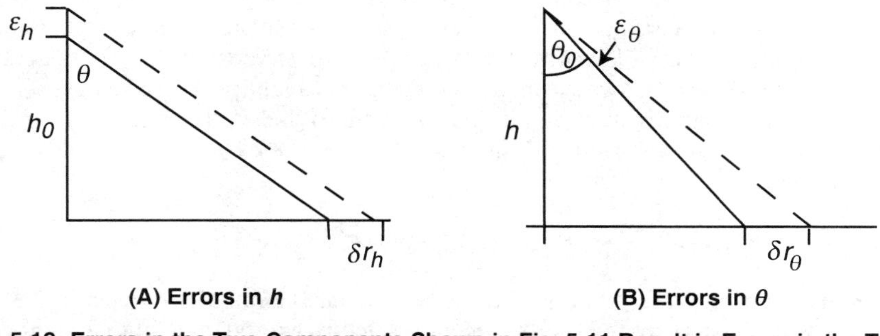

Fig. 5-12. Errors in the Two Components Shown in Fig. 5-11 Result in Errors in the Target Location.

In this way we can reduce most error equations to linear combinations. By rescaling the variables, this can then be expressed as a simple sum. The exception to this is when we have a singularity such that the Taylor expansion is no longer valid. In this example, we clearly have a singularity at $\theta = 90$ deg. This represents a poorly chosen mission geometry—i.e., trying to determine the position of a target right at the horizon. (Actually, $\theta = 90$ deg represents a point above the horizon, indicating a shortcoming of the flat Earth approximation.)

Example 3: Singular Solutions

Suppose that in Example 1, instead of using a star sensor, we used a combination of Earth sensor and Sun sensor. Each sensor will determine the spacecraft attitude up to a rotation around the line of sight to the reference, i.e., each determines two of the three degrees of attitude freedom. Combined, they will give all three axes. Ideally, the two reference objects should be 90 deg apart. As the angle between them decreases (or goes to 180 deg) we lose accuracy. When the spacecraft and the two references are collinear, we effectively have only a single reference, the error sensitivity becomes infinite, and the solution is singular. (See, for example Fig. 7.3 in Sec. 7.1.) Another situation in which a simple Taylor series approach does not work is illustrated in Example 5.

Example 4: Correlated Measurements

Referring to the data in Table 5-15, we note that the standard deviation of the system error has been computed as the RSS of the inputs. This implies the assumption of independence. This would apply for the component errors given as standard deviations, or any multiple of the standard deviation. (So long as a consistent convention is used for all entries the output will be the same number of standard deviations.) Had the component errors been correlated, a more conservative system estimate would have been required. For example, the RSS of the pointing items tabulated above yields 0.003 degrees whereas the sum (appropriate for perfect correlation) yields over 0.007 degrees. A partial correlation would have yielded an intermediate estimate. This discussion is strictly valid only for pointing about a single axis. In Example 5, we introduce more degrees of freedom.

Example 5: Coordinate Singularities

Let us continue consideration of the example in Table 5-15, but now in two dimensions. Consider a system which must point at a target on the celestial sphere—i.e. with two degrees of freedom. For small excursions from the target, we can use cartesian coordinates, x and y. Assume that the x and y motions are distinct inputs (e.g. the two axes of a gimbal system). Normally, the system error of interest in this problem is the total angular displacement away from the target, r. This quantity is given by $\sqrt{x^2 + y^2}$.

Assume that we are given σ_x and σ_y and we want to find σ_r. (σ_x and σ_y may be derived from chains of errors as in Example 1.)

Clearly, we have

$$\sigma_r^2 = E\left(r^2\right) = E\left(x^2 + y^2\right) = E\left(x^2\right) + E\left(y^2\right) = \sigma_x^2 + \sigma_y^2 \tag{5-6}$$

Note, however, that $E(r)$ is not quite so easily calculated along these lines. It is worth looking at this problem more closely since its structure is fundamental to a number of error combination problems. In the general formulation, we noted that the output, r, would normally be given as a smooth function of the inputs x and y, and that this function could then be expanded as a Taylor series to yield a linear sum, which could then be analyzed in a standard way. Here, the Taylor series about $(x, y) = (0, 0)$ is undefined. The reason is that r is not smooth in x and y at $r = 0$. For example, if we look at the $x - r$ plane, we have Fig. 5-13 (B).

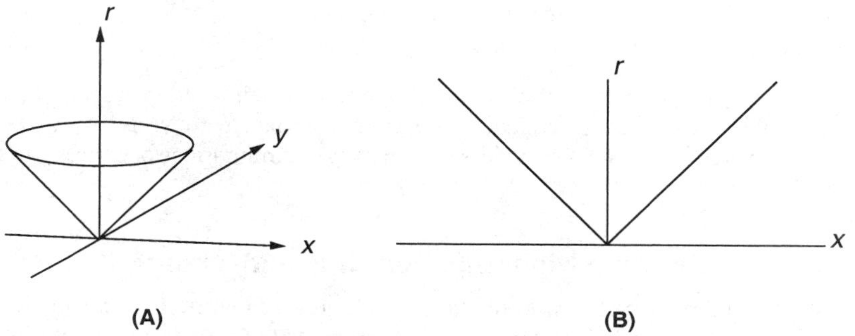

Fig. 5-13. (A) Graph of $r = \sqrt{x^2 + y^2}$ vs. x and y. (B) Section of (A) in the $x - r$ Plane. Note the discontinuity in the derivative at the origin.

This is a peculiarity of the coordinate system and could be handled by expanding about some other point in the x/y plane. However, it is better to exploit the multidimensional geometry of the situation and to use vector variables. In this formulation the vector $\mathbf{r}$ is given by the sum of the vectors $\mathbf{x}$ and $\mathbf{y}$, i.e.

$$\mathbf{r} = \mathbf{x} + \mathbf{y} \tag{5-7}$$

We can now square and take expectations:

$$E(r^2) = E(\mathbf{r} \cdot \mathbf{r}) = E((\mathbf{x} + \mathbf{y}) \cdot (\mathbf{x} + \mathbf{y})) = E(x^2) + E(y^2) + 2E(\mathbf{x} \cdot \mathbf{y}) \tag{5-8}$$

Now $E(\mathbf{x} \cdot \mathbf{y}) = 0$ since $\mathbf{x}$ and $\mathbf{y}$ are orthogonal. Thus we have

$$E(r^2) = E(x^2) + E(y^2) \tag{5-9}$$

as expected. Also note that

$$E(\mathbf{r}) = E(\mathbf{x}) + E(\mathbf{y}) = 0 \tag{5-10}$$

is evaluated simply. This approach readily generalizes to three or more dimensions.

Note that the fact that $\mathbf{x}$ and $\mathbf{y}$ are orthogonal causes them to contribute to $E(r^2)$ as though they were statistically independent. This is true even if they are correlated when regarded as real variables (instead of vectors). For example, suppose that $x = y$ (i.e. perfect correlation). We would then have $E(r^2) = 2\ E(x^2)$, i.e. $\sigma_r = \sqrt{2\sigma_x}$, a we would expect.

Referring again to Table 5-15, if we suppose that each of the entries is a standard deviation in a radial direction, and we assume that x and y displacements are equally likely and independent, then we can RSS the table entries to obtain the system standard deviation. Various other assumptions are also possible. For example, we could tabulate x and y standard deviations separately and RSS the end results. We could also introduce various intermediate degrees of correlation.

Example 6: Summing Errors with Different Frequencies

The error sources affecting a system may have widely differing characteristic frequencies. For example, an Earth sensor has at least four different disturbance frequencies:

(1) Fixed biases (static)

(2) Radiance errors (orbital frequency)

(3) Weather effects (10 to 100 × orbital frequency)

(4) Electronic noise (high frequency)

Errors at different frequencies can be treated as being independent based on the orthogonality of different frequency sine waves and, hence, their effects can be RSS'd. Under some circumstances even less conservative summation procedures can be used. (See App. C.)

5.5 Creating Mapping, Pointing, and Timing Budgets

Section 5.3 provided an introduction to mapping and pointing budgets. Section 5.4 then provided the mathematical basis for creating error budgets and combining terms. This section gave a detailed list of the components for typical error budgets for mapping, pointing and timing and for attitude and orbit determination and control. For any specific mission, these budgets provide the glue which holds together the mathematical evaluation of the ultimate accuracy the system will achieve.

The principal error sources for mapping, pointing, timing and orbit, and attitude determination and control are listed in a tree structure in Tables 5-12 through 5-17. The interrelationship among these tables is illustrated in Fig. 5-14. The tables provide both a summary budget and a reference guide to the remainder of the book.

TABLE 5-12. Top-Level Error Budgets. See Tables 5-13 to 5-17 for lower levels. See text for discussion.

Function	Subsystem (Level I)
P. Pointing Error (Sec. 5.3)	P.1 Payload Pointing Control [Table 5-14]
	P.2 Attitude Control [Table 5-14]
	P.3 Orbit Determination [Table 5-13]
	P.4 Timing System [Table 5-17]
M. Mapping Error (Sec. 5.3)	M.1 Payload Orientation Determination [Table 5-13]
	M.2 Attitude Determination [Table 5-13]
	M.3 Orbit Determination [Table 5-13]
	M.4 Timing System [Table 5-17]
	M.5 Projection [Table 5-18]
T. Timing Error (Sec. 4.1)	T.1 Event Time Measurement [Table 5-17]
	T.2 Timing System [Table 5-17]

There are two ways to construct error budgets for any specific mission. One is to follow the process laid out in Tables 5-12 through 5-17, listing all of the errors which are relevant to the specific mission being addressed. The second process is to determine the top-level information which is of interest, such as the latitude and longitude for items observed in images taken by a low-Earth orbit satellite. The algorithms or formulas for computing that information are then written down in detail and each term in these algorithms can be considered a source of error and should be included in the error budget. In practice, it is possible to overlook sources of error in both approaches. Consequently, I recommend a combined approach in which the computations are evaluated in detail and then Tables 5-12 through 5-17 are examined to determine if any components or elements have been left out. In any case, we always begin with the top-level question of what is to be determined and then proceed to break this down into the elements required to compute it. Each of these elements is then a source of error and is further broken down into its constituent parts. This process proceeds until we have developed the full algorithm for computing the quantities of interest based on the observations made by the satellite system.

The final error budget depends not only on the mission and the observations, but also on the process that is used to compute and calibrate mission parameters. For example, a common practice is to align attitude instruments with a coordinate frame defined by the spacecraft structure. The payload instruments are then similarly aligned to the spacecraft structure. Both sets of alignments contain errors which must be included in the error budget for payload pointing and mapping. However, this introduces more error than is necessary by incorporating an intermediate reference frame, namely that of the spacecraft. An alternative approach is to calibrate the orientation of the attitude sensors directly with respect to the payload sensors. In this approach, I now have only a single alignment error to take into account, and I have eliminated the intermediate spacecraft frame of reference. This provides improved accuracy for payload pointing and mapping. It is important to note that the improvement here is real, and not simply a mathematical fiction. By aligning the payload sensors and attitude sensors directly with respect to each other, I can reduce the number of alignment measurements which must be made, and provide a higher level of accuracy for payload measurements. A similar physical approach to improving accuracy would be to mount the attitude sensors and payload sensors both on the same base plate or, even better, mount small attitude sensors directly on the payload instrument. This process eliminates not only measurements, but also mechanical and thermal distortions and bending brought on by launch loads, vibration, and thermal bending and relaxation while in orbit.

In our error budget, the payload is simply another sensor or actuator with its full complement of internal and external errors. However, since it is the payload that we want to know the orientation of, it is important to make the measurements as directly as possible with respect to the payload instrument and, in turn, with respect to the object in the spacecraft sky which is being sensed.

In most cases the error budgets for orbit and attitude are numerically different, but conceptually similar. However, Table 5-14 shows a significant difference between the two due to the timescales over which control operates. For a single observation or pointing event, we may control the attitude of the spacecraft or of the payload or both, but we will ordinarily not control the orbit. We simply measure the orbit and use that to determine the correct pointing or mapping. Therefore, orbit determination shows up in both pointing and mapping, and orbit control does not. The requirement for orbit control flows from the need to maintain a constellation structure or to put the system

TABLE 5-13. Attitude and Orbit Determination Error Budget. See text for discussion. Specific values and entries will be different for orbit and attitude systems, but the general form of the error budget is similar.

Level I	Level II	Level III	Level IV	Level V	Level VI
D. Attitude Determination [also applies to Payload Orientation Determination and Orbit Determination]	D.1 Reference Frame Error Table 5-16				
	D.2 Observation Error	D.2.1 Measurement Error	D.2.1.1 High Frequency Noise	D.2.1.1.1 (See Note)	
			D.2.1.2 Low Frequency Noise	D.2.1.2.1 Alignment	
				D.2.1.2.2 Drift	
				D.2.1.2.3 Bias	
				D.2.1.2.4 Calibration	
		D.2.2 Modelling Error	D.2.2.1 Environmental Model	D.2.2.1.1 Earth Model	D.2.2.1.1.1 Oblateness
					D.2.2.1.1.2 Atmospheric Height
					D.2.2.1.1.3 Lighting Conditions
				D.2.2.1.2 Sun Model	
				D.2.2.1.3 Star Catalog	
				D.2.2.1.4 GPS Model	
				D.2.2.1.5 Clock Model	
				D.2.2.1.6 Ground Stn. Mode & Propagation Model	
				D.2.2.1.7 Magnetic Model	
				D.2.2.1.8 Inertial Space Model	
				D.2.2.1.9 Planetary & Small Body Ephemerides	
			D.2.2.2 Sensor Model	D.2.2.2.1 Earth Sensor	
				D.2.2.2.2 Sun Sensor	
				D.2.2.2.3 Star Tracker	
				D.2.2.2.4 GPS Receiver	
				D.2.2.2.5 Clocks	
				D.2.2.2.6 Ground Stn.	
				D.2.2.2.7 Magnetometer	
				D.2.2.2.8 IMU's	D.2.2.2.8.1 Gyroscopes
					D.2.2.2.8.2 Accelerometers
				D.2.2.2.9 Planetary & Small Body Sensor	
		D.2.3 Measurement Density			
	D.3 Correlation Error				
	D.4 Timing Error Table 5-17				
	D.5 Filter Error	D.6.1 Propagation Error			
		1.1.6.2 Process Noise			
		D.6.3 Computational Error			

TABLE 5-14. Attitude and Orbit Control Error Budget. Note that attitude determination can be either a subset or superset of attitude control (see Table 5-15).

Level I	Level II	Level III	Level IV	Level V
Attitude Control [also applies to Payload Orientation Control and Orbit Control]	C.1 Determination (Table 5-15 or 5-13)			
	C.2 Control Law	C.2.1 Bandwidth		
		C.2.2 Computation		
		C.2.3 Quantization	C.2.3.1 Computation	
			C.2.3.2 Time Steps	
		C.2.4 Feedback	C.2.4.1 Error Signal	
			C.2.4.2 Transfer Function	C.2.4.2.1 Magnitude
				C.2.4.2.2 Model Error
			C.2.4.3 Gain	
	C.3 Actuation	C.3.1 Quantization		
		C.3.2 Transients		
		C.3.3 Misalignments		
	C.4 Modelling	C.4.1 Dynamics	C.4.1.1 Orbit	C.4.1.1.1 Keplerian or Multi-Body
				C.4.1.1.2 Cyclic Perturbations
				C.4.1.1.3 Secular Perturbations
			C.4.1.2 Attitude	C.4.1.2.1 Rigid Body Model
				C.4.1.2.2 Articulated Components
				C.4.1.2.3 Flexible Components
				C.4.1.2.4 Other Internal
		C.4.2 Environments	C.4.2.1 Gravitational Field	
			C.4.2.2 Magnetic Field	
			C.4.2.3 Solar Radiation Pressure	
			C.4.2.4 Orbital Debris	
			C.4.2.5 Atmosphere	
		C.4.3 Actuation	C.4.3.1 Orbit Maneuvers	C.4.3.1.1 Thrust Alignment
				C.4.3.1.2 Thrust Magnitude
			C.4.3.2 Attitude Control Torques	C.4.3.2.1 Momentum & Reaction Wheels
				C.4.3.2.2 Magnetic Coils
				C.4.3.2.3 Gas Jets
		C.4.4 Computation		
	C.5 Delays	C.5.1 Transmission	C.5.1.1 Measurement Control	
			C.5.1.2 Control Actuation	
		C.5.2 Control Computation		
		C.5.3 Response Time	C.5.3.1 Orbit Maneuvers	
			C.5.3.2 Attitude Maneuvers	
			C.5.3.3 Payload Commanding	

into the necessary position to do the work that is required. Section 5.3 provided a discussion of the top-level mapping and pointing errors shown in Table 5-12. Here we provide a brief discussion of the top-level components for both determination and control budgets.

TABLE 5-15. Interrelationship Between Attitude Determination Error and Attitude Control Error. Depending on the application, attitude determination can be a sub level of attitude control or vice versa.

Level A	Level B	Level C
Definitive Attitude Determination (filtering)	Dynamics and Control Errors	Real Time Attitude Determination [Table 5-13] Attitude Control System [Table 5-14]
	Other Attitude Determination Errors [Table 5-13]	

TABLE 5-16. Reference Frame Error Budget. Each separate sensor or each coordinate frame transformation carries with it an error budget corresponding to mounting errors and coordinate frame definition errors.

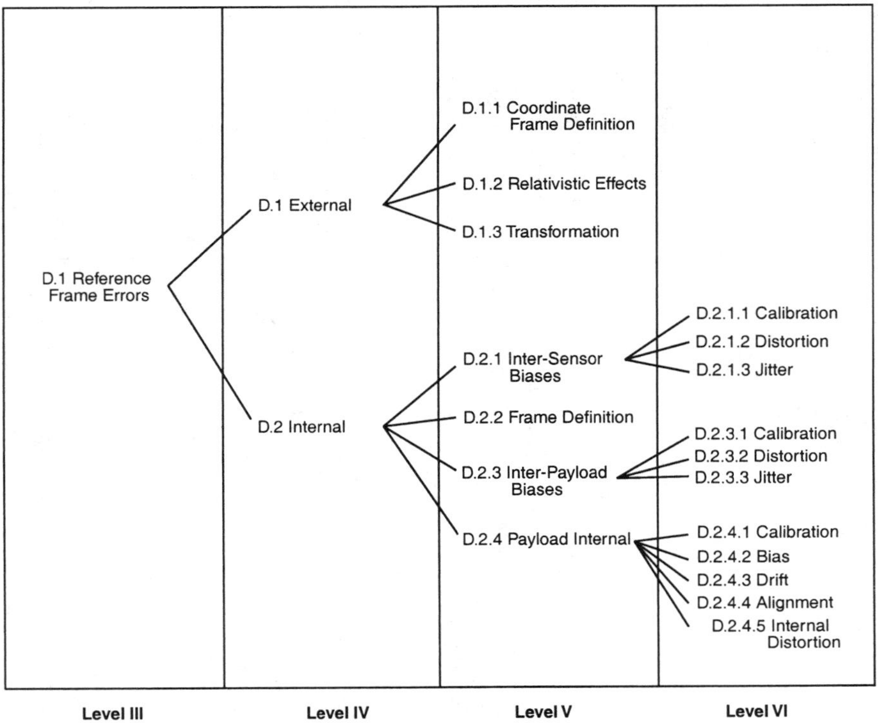

TABLE 5-17. Timing Error Budget. See text for discussion. Errors for the event timing have the same form and components as those for the clock system. See Sec. 4.1 for a more detailed discussion of time systems.

Function	Subsystem (Level I)	Level II Errors	Level III Errors
T. Timing Error	T.1 Event Time Measurement	T.1.1 Event Synchronization	T.1.1.1 Event definition
			T.1.1.2 Uncompensated travel compensation delays
			T.1.1.3 Instrument
		T.1.2 Smear and Quantization	T.1.2.1 Event duration
			T.1.2.2 Instrument
	T.2 Timing System	T.2.1 Clock Synchronization	T.2.1.2 Error in update clock
			T.2.1.2 Uncompensated travel propagation delays
			T.2.1.3 Synchronization errors
		T.2.2 Propagation	T.2.2.1 Uncompensated
			T.2.2.2 Clock resets
		T.2.3 Smear and Quantization	T.2.3.1 Clock pulse width
			T.2.3.2 Bus synchronization
		T.2.4 Relativistic Effects (4.1)	T.2.4.1 Gravity effects
			T.2.4.2 Velocity effects
			T.2.4.3 Reference frame effects

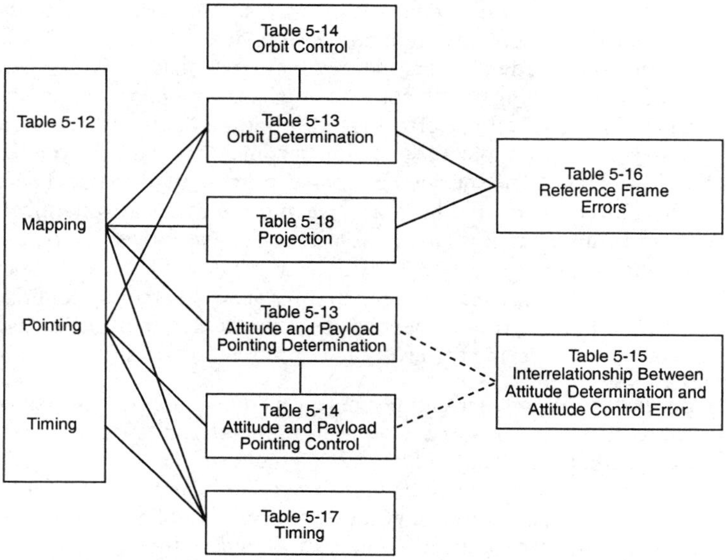

Fig. 5-14. Development of Orbit, Attitude, and Timing Related Error Budgets in Tables 5-12 to 5-17. The requirement for orbit control comes from mission aspects other than pointing, mapping, and timing. (See Secs. 2.7.2 and 4.4.) Attitude determination and attitude control can each be a component of the other as shown in Table 5-15.

We normally think of orbit and attitude determination errors as being primarily observation errors. However, as shown in Table 5-13 there are significant additional components to this error budget. The errors for both orbit and attitude determination fall into six major categories as listed in Table 5-13 and discussed below.

1. **Observation errors**. These are the errors normally thought of as being most important and they include all of the errors associated with the orbit and attitude sensors. Both low frequency and high frequency noise or quantization errors are characteristic of essentially all sensing processes. In addition, each sensor is subject to two distinct types of modeling errors: environment models, and sensor models. *Sensor models* are mathematical representations of the physical sensor hardware such as, the location of individual pixels, a model of the lens, or the rotational position over time for a scanning sensor. *Environmental models* are models of what it is that is being sensed, such as star catalog errors, errors in modeling the Earth or its atmosphere, or errors in our knowledge of what inertial space really means. Volume 2 in this series presents mathematical models for all of the fundamental hardware types and for the environment. Both types of errors must be included for each sensor. For example, attitude measurements using a star sensor must include errors due to the lack of mathematical precision in the specification of the star sensor, and also our lack of knowledge of the position of the stars themselves.

2. **Reference frame errors.** These are errors associated with the differences between the reference frame of the orbit and attitude observations and the ultimate reference frame in which these observations are being interpreted, or to which the data is to be applied, such as the Earth's surface. For example, a sensor may be on a different part of the spacecraft from where the payload is located and therefore have mounting errors due to the measurement of where it is mounted plus added errors induced by launch loads, relaxation in zero g and any thermal bending due to solar heating and cooling during eclipses. Another source of reference frame errors is the definition of the reference frame itself. In our star sensor example, the question becomes, "What is the reference frame of the fixed stars?" The stars are, of course, moving with respect to each other and with respect to the Earth. Thus, we must turn to astronomical systems to determine an average frame of reference for the "fixed" stars, and then must take into account the varying positions of whatever stars we happen to observe with respect to this average frame of reference. Whether or not this is important for our particular problem depends both on the nature of the measurements we are trying to make and the level of accuracy we are trying to achieve.

3 **Correlation errors**. This represents errors due to multiple measurements of the same component of an observation rather than independent components, as described in more detail in Sec. 7.2.1. Whenever measurements are not orthogonal, correlation errors will be introduced. For example, consider the process of measuring the position of a point on the surface of a desk, by measuring the distance from two adjacent corners of the desk. If the point we are trying to measure is out on the center of the desk such that the angle at that point between the two corners is approximately a right angle, then the two arcs represented by the measurement will intersect at nearly right angles, and we will have a very good measurement. On the other hand, if the two reference points get closer

together, for example, by moving one from a corner along the edge toward the second corner, then the quality of the measurement becomes poorer and poorer until in the extreme the two reference points lie on top of each other, and although we have made two measurements, it has been the same measurement twice, rather than two independent ones. The principal impact of a high correlation is to magnify the impact of systematic errors or unmodeled biases. Since these are always present at some level, two highly correlated measurements will have errors that become extremely large.

4. **Measurement density**. This represents the sensitivity of the observation to the measurement as described in Sec. 7.2.1. Either very low or very high measurement densities can cause problems. As discussed in Sec. 5.3, mapping targets near the limb of the Earth is essentially impossible, because even small errors are greatly magnified by the foreshortening of the limb. Conversely, using observations of stars or distant planets to do navigation is also nearly impossible, because the position of the spacecraft simply isn't sensitive to the measurement, i.e., the observed positions of the stars are the same no matter where we are in the orbit.

5. **Timing errors**. Timing errors determine both our capacity to use multiple measurements carried out at slightly different times, and our capacity to know where our target is. Not only is the spacecraft moving, but typically, so is the target, even if it is fixed on the surface of the Earth—so we must know what time it is to know where the target is.

6. **Filter errors**. Long term filtering or averaging of data can drive down noise and other high frequency random errors. However, filtering cannot remove fixed alignment biases or calibration errors. In addition, it introduces a whole new set of errors, due to both the computational process, and errors in the dynamic model of the observation system. For example, long duration filtering of attitude data will couple any orbit errors into the attitude observations. It is the model of the dynamics of the system which allows us to use data at different times to determine both the position and the attitude at any one time. Consequently, errors in this dynamic model result directly in errors in the end measurements.

Control errors summarized in Table 5-14 are more easily understood than measurement errors, because they tend to be introduced by the control system itself. Here, a key distinction is between the tightness of the control and the accuracy of what it is we are controlling with respect to. For example, we may be controlling the pointing of the spacecraft to within a noise or jitter of 0.01 deg, but have the centroid of the control box be 0.50 deg from the desired target because of errors in the measurement system or biases in the control process.

This interrelationship between determination and control leads to another conceptual problem as shown in Table 5-15. Depending on the circumstance, the attitude control budget may be an element of the attitude determination budget, or vice versa. For example, definitive attitude determination comes about by long term filtering of a sequence of attitude data. This in turn depends on accurately modeling both the attitude dynamics and on the control errors introduced over the course of time. The capacity to provide accurate control in turn, depends on the real time attitude determination process as discussed previously in the discussion of Fig. 3-1. Thus, most commonly, real time attitude determination is an element of the control budget which in turn is an element of the definitive attitude determination budget.

As described above, a key feature of error budgets is that each reference frame and each coordinate transformation introduces additional error terms. Typically, both the payload and each spacecraft sensor is aligned relative to some arbitrary spacecraft axes. However, there are measurement errors, fixed biases, and time varying errors in the alignment of each of these sensors. These are frequently called intersensor mounting angle biases and occur between each pair of attitude and payload sensors. They occur between sensors (due to misalignments and thermal distortions) internal to sensors (due to component misalignments and electronic errors) and within the environment models (ephemeris errors and Earth rotation rate errors). The various components of these are summarized in Table 5-16.

Table 5-17 provides a timing error budget. These are frequently among the most subtle errors in the system. Timing is important not only as an end element of interest to the user, but to tie together the observations at different times—both payload observations and the attitude and orbit observations which will be used to interpret them. By some process, all of these observations must be brought to a common epoch or defined event time, which represents the time that will be recorded as the event having occurred. In practice, real events are spread out over time, just as the process of taking a photograph of the Earth requires sampling a sequence of pixels, or opening and closing a shutter over the course of time.

In using space systems for scientific, military or commercial purposes, we are fundamentally dealing with remote systems that we can measure and use only indirectly. The engineering challenge for these systems is not only to control errors, but to know what they are. This is one of the biggest challenges of space systems engineering.

The two subsections below provide examples of a detailed error budget for mapping and pointing. These also illustrate the two approaches to constructing error budgets—going step-by-step, through the computations, or beginning with the tables of error sources earlier in this section. It is convenient to use one of the two approaches to construct the budget, and the other approach to verify that no error terms have been inadvertently omitted.

5.5.1 Representative Mapping Error Budget

As an example of a mapping error budget we will follow the example introduced in Table 3-18 (Sec. 3.3.3) of using an optical sensor in space to find the geographic location of a rock formation, found in one of the images. We will use the budget from Table 3-18 and the sensitivity (measurement density) formulas provided in Table 5-7. In this case we develop the budget by going through each of the computations, and finding the errors associated with each. The results are shown in Table 5-18.

Note that many of the errors listed in the table have a preferential direction. For example, the largest errors in a star sensor are in the rotation about the star sensor axis and in the ephemeris of the spacecraft the largest errors are in the along-track direction along the orbit. This or course, introduces an asymmetry in the errors associated with the final measurement. This asymmetry may or may not be important, depending upon the uses to which the data is being put.

5.5.2 Representative Pointing Error Budget

As discussed at the beginning of Sec. 5.5, there are two ways to construct error budgets. Sec. 5.5.1 demonstrated the process of going through the computation from

TABLE 5-18. Projection Error Budget. See text for discussion. See Table 5-7 in Sec. 5.3 for formulas.

Error Source	Assumed Error Value	Impact on Mapping Budget (m)	Comments
Star Sensor Measurement Error	0.0015 deg	193.1	Typically larger error in rotation about sensor axis
Star Sensor Mounting Error	0.0020 deg	257.5	May vary from sunlight to eclipse
Star Catalog Accuracy	0.0001 deg	12.9	Have to eliminate double stars
Attitude Computation Error	0.0001 deg	12.9	Computation errors typically small
Payload Sensor Measurement Errors	0.0010 deg	128.8	Sum of many internal error sources
Target Centroiding Error	0.0020 deg	257.5	Depends on size and shape of target
Payload Sensor Mounting Error	0.0010 deg	128.8	Payload sensor opposite side of spacecraft from star sensor
Transformation of Target Location to Inertial Coordinates	0.0001 deg	12.9	Only small arithmetic error (attitude errors accounted for above)
Orbit Determination Error	100 m	100.0	Along-track component much larger than others
Timing Error	50 ms	367.5	LEO spacecraft moving at 7.35 km/s (1,000 km altitude)
Total Pointing Error With Respect to Nadir	—	**590.5**	RSS of pointing components above; worst in radial direction
Projection Error Due to Altitude	700 m	700.0	All in radial direction
Error in Subsatellite Point	450 m	450.0	Orbit determination plus timing error — almost all in along-track direction
Total Geolocation Error	—	**1020.4**	RSS of last 3 terms

basic observations to desired output and identifying the errors in each step. Here we construct a pointing budget by going through the alternative process of using the tables in Sec. 5.5 to identify the elements of the error budget. In practice we should use a mix of both approaches—creating a top level budget by looking at the flow of the computations and then looking at the tables and discussion earlier in Sec. 5.5 to find elements that have been overlooked.

For our example, we assume a satellite in a medium altitude Earth orbit with an antenna fixed to the body of the spacecraft that is to be pointed at a target on the Earth. Attitude determination is done using an Earth sensor and Sun sensor. We have constructed the pointing error budget by the table look-up process, beginning with Table 5-12. The results are shown in Table 5-19. For example, the 4 top level entries (P.1 to P.4) in Table 5-12 are the bold first level entries in Table 5-19. To keep the table from getting excessively long, we have taken the observation errors (D.2) down to a low level, but left the rest at a higher level.

TABLE 5-19. Pointing Error Budget Based on Tables 5-10 to 5-14. See text for discussion.

Error Source	Assumed Error	Pointing Budget Impact (m)	Table	Level
Payload Pointing Control			5-12	
Determination				
Reference Frame Error			5-16	3
Internal			5-16	4
Frame Definition (Spc to P/L)	0.001 deg	175	5-16	5
Modeling	0.003 deg	524	5-14	2
Delays	0.01 sec	49	5-14	2
Attitude Control			5-14	
Determination			5-13	1
Reference Frame Error	0.001 deg	175	5-13	2
Observation Error (Sun)			5-13	2
Sun Measurement Error	0.03 deg	5,236	5-13	3
Modeling Error			5-13	3
Sun Model	0.004 deg	698	5-13	5
Sun Sensor Model	0.001 deg	175	5-13	5
Sun Angle Measurement Density	0.167	873	5-13	3
Observation Error (Earth)			5-13	2
Earth Measurement Error	0.03 deg	5,236	5-13	3
Modeling Error			5-13	3
Earth Model			5-13	5
Oblateness	0.02 deg	3,491	5-13	6
Atmospheric Height	0.05 deg	8,727	5-13	6
Earth Sensor Model	0.001 deg	175	5-13	5
Nadir Angle Measurement Density	0.167	873	5-13	3
Correlation Error (Earth/Sun Sensors)	0.116	10,472	5-13	2
Timing Error	0.005 sec	25	5-13	2
Filter Error	0.000 2 deg	35	5-13	2
Control Law	0.003 deg	524	5-14	2
Actuation	0.001 deg	175	5-14	2
Modeling	0.005 deg	873	5-14	2
Delays	0.2 sec	987	5-14	2
Orbit Determination			5-13	
Reference Frame Error	0.001 deg	175	5-13	2
Observation Error	0.002 deg	349	5-13	2
Correlation Error (GDOP)	0.008	698	5-13	2
Timing Error	0.005 sec	25	5-13	2
Filter Error	0.005 deg	873	5-13	2
Timing System			5-17	
Event Time Measurement			5-17	1
Event Synchronization	0.001 sec	5	5-17	2
Timing System			5-17	1
Clock Synchronization	0.005 sec	25	5-17	2
Total Error with Respect to Nadir		**16,084**		

Table 5-19 clearly shows the role of the measurement process. We are used to the concept of an observation error or measurement error. However, every observation is based on constructing a mathematical model of the environment (the thing we are measuring) and of the sensor (our measuring instrument). Each of these elements introduce error. If we use a ruler to measure the height of this book, there will be an error in the measurement itself. In addition, there is an assumption that the book is a constant height across the pages and this will only be true to some level. Finally, there is an error in the calibration of the ruler used to make the measurement. All of these errors will contribute to the overall inaccuracy of the measurement.

The error sources which dominate any particular mapping, pointing, or timing problem tend to be unique to each situation. Nonetheless, Tables 5-12 to 5-17 provide a starting point for identifying error sources that might otherwise be overlooked.

5.6 Annotated Bibliography

This section provides a bibliography of systems engineering, requirements definition process, and legal political limitations on system design as well as references to the mathematical details of error analysis and budgeting.

AIAA Special Project Report. 1999. *MEO/LEO Constellations: U.S. Laws, Policies, and Regulations on Orbital Debris Mitigation.* SP-016-2-1999. Reston, VA: AIAA. 22 p.

An excellent very short summary of laws, policy, and regulation from multiple U.S. government organizations (NASA, DoD, FAA, FCC, and others) on orbital debris. Important to any program considering launching satellites into LEO or MEO.

AIAA Special Project Report. 1992. *Orbital Debris Mitigation Techniques: Technical, Legal, and Economic Aspects*. SP-016-2-1992. Reston, VA: AIAA. 53 p.

Discusses technical, economic, and legal aspects of the orbital debris problem. Relatively brief, but provides a good overall summary of the debris issues and approaches for dealing with it from various perspectives.

Bender, R. 1998. *Launching and Operating Satellites: Legal Issues.* Dordrecht, The Netherlands: Kluwer International Law. 350 p.

A practical guide to the legal aspects of satellite systems. Principal emphasis is on satellite operations. Also discusses acquisition of orbital slots and frequencies, responsibility and liability, and the use of radioisotope power.

Churchill, Suzanne E. 1997. *Fundamentals of Space Life Sciences.* 2 vols. Malabar, FL: Krieger Publishing Co. 364 p.

A detailed presentation of practical aspects of human spaceflight. Covers nearly all aspects of physiological response to spaceflight, including areas such as food and nutrition, health care delivery, and countermeasures to 0 g. Also includes related topics such as design for habitability, extended duration missions, EVA, and many similar topics. Applicable to both mission design and requirements definition. 2 volume set, but each volume is only 170 pages.

Goldman. 1996. *American Space Law: International and Domestic* (2nd ed). San Diego, CA: Univelt, 488 p.

An excellent, single volume treatment of both national law and international treaties on space. Includes complete text of major space laws and treaties.

Greenberg, J. S., and H. R. Hertzfeld. 1994. *Space Economics*. Washington, DC: AIAA. 438 p.

The only current treatment of economic analysis and methodology for space systems; includes cost analysis, cost effectiveness models, standard cost elements, and implications of economics for space programs and major programmatic issues.

Kay, W. D. 1994. *Can Democracies Fly in Space?* Westport, CT: Praeger. 244 p.

As the author points out, the U.S. government made a decision in the 1960's to support space exploration on a large scale. This book contends that the present institutional arrangements and political practices prevent that decision from being effectively carried out. This implies we need to change the process or rethink the initial decision. An interesting, provocative, and very well researched discussion.

Przemieniecki, J. S. 1993. *Acquisition of Defense Systems*. Washington, DC: AIAA. 336 p.

A thorough, well-organized discussion of the acquisition, management, and control of large defense systems.

Rechtin, E. 1991. *Systems Architecting*. Englewood Cliffs, NJ: Prentice Hall. 333 p.

This book presents a methodology for the design of large, complex systems by the former Director of NASA's DSN, Director of DARPA, Assistant Secretary of Defense, and President of the Aerospace Corp. Presents a top-level, yet very practical view of the systems engineering process and the problems encountered in designing and building complex systems.

Reynolds, G. H. and Robert P. Merges. 1997. *Outer Space: Problems of Law and Policy* (2nd ed). Boulder, CO: Westview Press. 446 p.

An excellent introduction to space law. Broad coverage. Easily read by those who are engineers or managers rather than law students.

Shishko, R. 1995. *NASA Systems Engineering Handbook*. Washington, DC: NASA. 154 p.

A clear and well-written explanation of the NASA systems engineering process. Discusses management, systems analysis and modeling, and engineering specialties as a part of systems engineering. Available free as NASA SP-6105.

Simpson, John A. 1994. *Preservation of Near-Earth Space for Future Generations*. Cambridge: Cambridge University Press. 250 p.

This discusses orbital debris from a broad perspective. It discusses technical, legal, economic, and political issues including both current and future debris environments, the effects of the debris population, methods for mitigation and risk reduction, insurance and regulatory issues, and a recommended multilateral treaty on space debris. An excellent overall summary of the issues involved.

Taylor, J. R. 1997. *An Introduction to Error Analysis: The Study of Uncertainties in Physical Measurements,* 2nd ed. Sausalito, CA: University Science Books. 270 p.

An excellent introductory manual in error analysis. Provides a good introduction, but insufficient depth to allow preparation of a detailed error budget.

Wertz, J. R. and W. J. Larson. 1996. *Reducing Space Mission Cost.* Torrance, CA, and Dordrecht, the Netherlands: Microcosm, Inc. and Kluwer Academic Publishers. 670 p.

Presents both processes and technology for reducing cost in spacecraft manufacturing, launch, and operations. Includes discussion of cost modeling, reliability, and implementation strategies. Has detailed case studies of 10 missions (with actual dollar costs) which have reduced cost by factors of 2 to 10 relative traditional expectations.

Wertz, J. R. and W. J. Larson. 1999. *Space Mission Analysis and Design* (3rd ed). Torrance, CA, and Dordrecht, the Netherlands: Microcosm, Inc. and Kluwer Academic Publishers. 970 p.

Has become a standard reference for space mission engineering and the mission analysis and design process. Process-oriented with many data tables. Broad coverage of all mission aspects—including topics not covered in other volumes, such as mission engineering, requirements definitions, legal limitations, orbit selection and design, cost modeling, and low-cost spacecraft.

Williamson, M. 1990. *The Communications Satellite.* NY: Adam Hilger. 420 p.

A largely non-mathematical, yet technical introduction to satellites with an emphasis on communications satellites. Aimed primarily at undergraduates and young engineers. Discusses all of the spacecraft subsystems plus Earth stations and launch vehicles. Discussion of space insurance not found in most books. Includes an extensive case study on the design of a geosynchronous direct broadcast satellite.

References

Feller, W. *An Introduction to Probability Theory and its Applications.* Vol. 1 (1957), Vol. 2 (1966). New York: Wiley.

Meyer, P. L. 1972. *Introductory Probability and Statistical Applications.* Redding, MA: Addison-Wesley.

Papoulis, A. 1965. *Probability, Random Variables and Stochastic Processes.* New York: McGraw-Hill.

Parzen, E. 1960. *Modern Probability Theory and its Applications*. New York: Wiley.

Robert, C. P., G. Casella. 1999. *Monte Carlo Statistical Methods.* New York: Springer Verlag.

Taylor, J. R. 1997. *An Introduction to Error Analysis: The Study of Uncertainties in Physical Measurements,* 2nd ed. Sausalito, CA: University Science Books.

Wertz, J. R. and W. J. Larson. 1996. *Reducing Space Mission Cost*. Torrance, CA, and Dordrecht, the Netherlands: Microcosm, Inc. and Kluwer Academic Publishers.

Wertz, J. R. and W. J. Larson. 1999. *Space Mission Analysis and Design,* (3rd ed). Torrance, CA, and Dordrecht, the Netherlands: Microcosm, Inc. and Kluwer Academic Publishers.

Williams, M. 1992. "Requirements Definition," Chap. 4 in Larson, W. J., and J. R. Wertz (eds.) *Space Mission Analysis and Design* (2nd ed). Dordrecht, Netherlands and Torrance, CA: Kluwer Academic and Microcosm.

PART II

SPACE MISSION GEOMETRY

Part II provides the most extensive discussion available of the mission analysis and design topics listed below. Many of the mathematical expressions have not been previously available and substantially simplify the computation of fields of view, ground coverage, relative motion of satellites, and related mission engineering issues.

Chapter 6

Geometry on the Celestial Sphere

Most spacecraft observations including both payload and orbit and attitude systems are angles—i.e. they are measurements made on the sky as seen by the spacecraft, called the celestial sphere. Unfortunately, there is no general introduction to this topic other than astronomical literature which deals with measurements made from the surface of the Earth. (Limited discussions occur in Wertz [1978] and Wertz and Larson [1999].) Nonetheless, a thorough understanding and good formal techniques for evaluating angular measurements are critical to the process of orbit and attitude determination and control.

This chapter provides an introduction to measurements and observations on the celestial sphere. It begins by explaining why spherical geometry is important and establishes the relationship between spherical geometry and vector analysis with which many analysts are more familiar. It then introduces basic algorithms and provides several sample applications. Wherever possible in this and subsequent chapters, we provide summary formulas in both vector and spherical forms that can be readily applied to practical problems. Readers thoroughly familiar with the analysis of measurements on the celestial sphere may wish to skip this chapter. Note, however, that Chap. 8 provides substantial new material on measurement theory on the celestial sphere that has not been previously been published.

As referenced in Chaps. 2 and 3, there is a substantial literature base on orbit and attitude dynamics and the general equations of motion for spacecraft. There is no comparable literature base for the theory of measurements made by spacecraft. Consequently, background information must be assembled from a variety of sources. *Spherical Astronomy* [Green, 1985] provides a good summary of spherical geometry but only from an astronomical perspective. Similarly, the precursor to this volume, *Spacecraft Attitude Determination and Control* [Wertz, 1978], provides the most detailed previous discussion of mission geometry but only for attitude analysis. (These techniques are broadly applicable, however, and form the basis for much of Chaps. 6–12 in this volume). *Space Mission Analysis and Design, 3rd edition* [Wertz and Larson, 1999] gives an overview of the application of spherical geometry to problems of space mission analysis but provides only a top-level introduction. Shuster [1993] gives an excellent and complete assessment of coordinate transformations and their applications. Similarly, Seidelmann [1992] provides a very complete discussion of both coordinate frames and time systems used in essentially all astronomical and astronautical measurement systems. From a historical perspective, Nathaniel Bowditch's *American Practical Navigator* [1966] provides one of the most complete discussions of spherical geometry as applied to terrestrial navigation. A large number of authors from the mid-twentieth century [Brink, 1942; Palmer et al., 1950; Small, 1952; and Newcomb, 1960] provide derivations of the general rules of spherical geometry. Note, however, that these rules are less complete and substantially less useful for computer implementation than those which are introduced in Chap. 8 and given in detail in App. A.

6.1 Introduction to Geometry on the Celestial Sphere

As listed in Table 6-1, many space mission analysis problems (orbit, attitude, and payload related) are fundamentally geometrical. In analyzing the behavior of spacecraft sensors and the data they produce, we are more interested in what they see than the forces which move either the spacecraft or the objects that we are looking at. For example, in analyzing star camera data, we are interested in where the stars are relative to some object we are observing, but have little interest in their distances or the forces that keep the stars moving about the center of the galaxy.*

TABLE 6-1. Representative Topics in Space Mission Geometry. Most spacecraft observations measure angles only. (See Sec. 7.5 for distance measurements.)

- Earth coverage
- Sensor and antenna coverage and placement
- Mapping and pointing error budgets
- Earth geometry viewed from space (e.g., ground station and target viewing parameters)
- Sun interference, eclipses, thermal and power analysis
- Satellite ground traces
- Relative and apparent motion of other satellites
- Constellation design and analysis
- Spacecraft-to-spacecraft viewing
- Measurement singularities and accuracy analysis
- Autonomous navigation techniques and analysis

* I apologize to our astronomy customers and colleagues. We really are interested in the motion of the stars. It's just that this motion makes relatively little difference for most practical problems in orbit and attitude analysis. Note, however, that the assumption that the stars are essentially fixed begins to break down as we try to achieve more accurate measurements. As high accuracy becomes more and more important, the relative motion of the stars themselves and of the inertial coordinate frame becomes a critical part of orbit and attitude analysis.

Most spacecraft sensors measure only angles. Fundamental to this angles-only geometry is the concept of the *celestial sphere*, illustrated in Fig. 6-1, which is the apparent bowl of the sky, such as that seen by anyone on a dark starry night in a large open area. We know that the distances to the Moon, planets, and stars are dramatically different. But this is not relevant to looking at them with our eye or a camera nor to building clock drives for telescopes or analyzing astronomical photographs. Points on the celestial sphere such as stars, planets, or the outline of the horizon, represent directions in space irrespective of distance. Just as unit vectors, which are also used to represent direction, have a length of one, the celestial sphere is assumed to have a radius of one so that only the angular coordinates on the sphere are relevant.

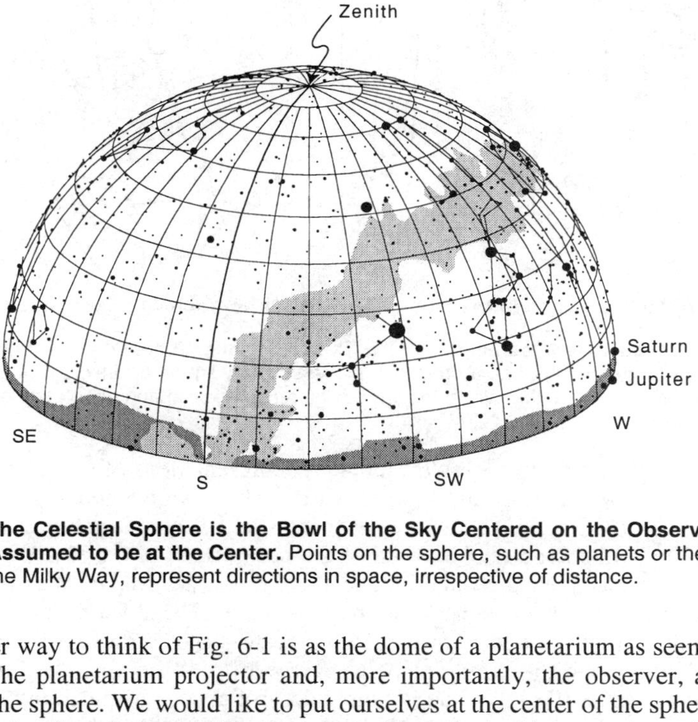

Fig. 6-1. The Celestial Sphere is the Bowl of the Sky Centered on the Observer who is Assumed to be at the Center. Points on the sphere, such as planets or the outline of the Milky Way, represent directions in space, irrespective of distance.

Another way to think of Fig. 6-1 is as the dome of a planetarium as seen from the outside. The planetarium projector and, more importantly, the observer, are at the center of the sphere. We would like to put ourselves at the center of the sphere as well but that is significantly more difficult to draw. The principal inconvenience in looking at the celestial sphere from the outside is that east and west are reversed in orientation. Thus, in Fig. 6-1, east is to the right of south and, for those who are amateur astronomers, Orion and Canis Major are reversed in their orientation as we would see them from "inside" the celestial sphere.

How we choose to display the celestial sphere, the Earth, or any spherical surface depends on our objectives. No representation is perfect. Figure 6-2 illustrates the two most common alternatives. On the left is a typical latitude-longitude plot of the Earth's surface common in many ground station displays. On the right is an orthographic projection which we refer to as a *globe plot*. We have drawn the same satellite ground trace on both. The lat-long plot has the advantage of allowing us to see the entire Earth at one time but the disadvantage of distorting shapes and sizes. Is the ground trace on the left a circle? In looking at it, we cannot easily tell because of the distortions introduced by the plot itself. The shapes of figures in a lat-long plot tell us more about the plot projection than about the shapes we're looking at. In the globe plot on the right, we only see half of the surface of the world. But shapes and directions are much more easily distinguished. It is clear in the plot on the right that the orbit is basically circular and we can easily envision the Earth rotating under the orbit in inertial space such that the orbit traces out a slowly moving spiral over the Earth's surface.

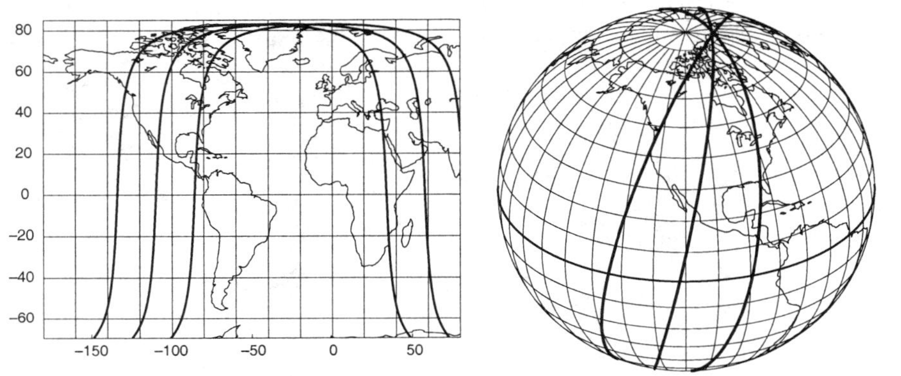

(A) Latitude-Longitude Plot (B) Orthographic Projection or Globe Plot

Fig. 6-2. Alternative Representations of the Earth's Surface. Our objective is to use the globe plot on the right not as a projection of the surface, but as a "drawing" of a globe. We want to do our arithmetic on the surface of the globe itself and not on any projection.

Figure 6-3 illustrates comparable alternative representations of the celestial sphere showing a rainbow in the sky and a large, nearby balloon with a gondola attached. As always, the observer is assumed to be at the center of the sphere such that he or she is looking at the balloon and rainbow against the background of the sky. On the upper plot, it is clear that both the rainbow and the balloon are round. We could easily measure both the diameter and the location of the center. The lower figure contains the identical information plotted in an azimuth-elevation plot such that the horizon is along the bottom, and the zenith, or point overhead, is at the top. The fundamental problem with the Az-El plot is that it simply doesn't convey as much information to the person who is looking at it. Is the balloon round? Which has the larger diameter, the balloon or the rainbow? We could, of course, analyze the lower figure to determine at least some of the answers. The arc of the rainbow is 100 deg across; the diameter of the balloon, if we believe it to be round goes from an elevation of 20 deg to 90 deg and, therefore, is only 70 deg in diameter. Thus, the rainbow is larger. Nonetheless, this is not immediately apparent from the plot and it takes some work to find what we can see immediately by simply looking at the picture in the upper plot.

The key issue is that we don't want to use a projection at all. We want to work directly on the curved surface of the Earth or of the celestial sphere. This allows us to avoid completely both the conceptual and arithmetic distortions associated with projections. Consequently, we want to think of the globe plot as a "picture" of a sphere and work directly on a sphere itself. For example, look at the intersections of the

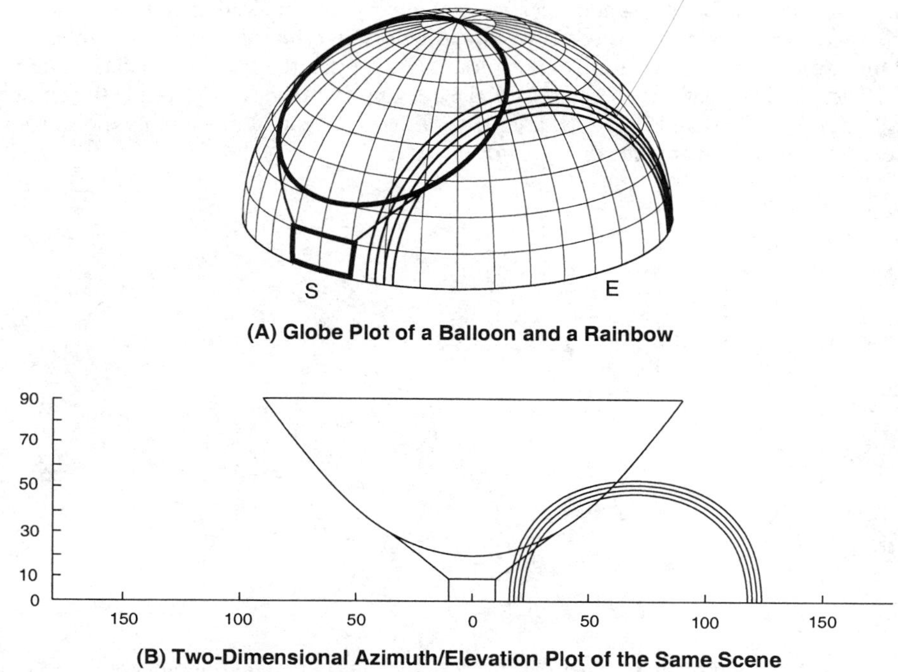

Fig. 6-3. The Celestial Sphere Provides Distortion-Free Geometry on the Sky. The key to using the plot in (A) is to think of it as a sphere with the observer at the center and to work on the curved surface of the sphere.

latitude and longitude lines in Fig. 6-2B. In the center of the drawing they are at right angles to each other. At the edges, they intersect at very oblique angles. However, if we think of this figure not as a flat projection, but as a drawing of a globe, and see it as round and three dimensional, then it is easy to perceive that on the curved surface of the globe, the intersections are still at right angles at the edge, and will appear that way when we rotate the globe to move them nearer the center of the figure. Working on the globe itself provides truly distortion free geometry, and is the **only** way to achieve this.*

Most scientists and engineers are familiar with vector analysis and the use of unit vectors to represent directions. Two such unit vectors are shown in a typical representation of a three dimensional Cartesian coordinate frame in Fig. 6-4A. One of the difficulties with this type of representation is that it is difficult to interpret unambiguously. For example: What is the radius of the small circle, and is it centered to the left or the right of the X-Z plane? Given the coordinates of the points, we could find the answer, but it is difficult to interpret from the drawing. Another way to conceptualize the celestial sphere is to think of it as a plot of the tips of all possible unit vectors centered on the origin of a coordinate frame. This idea of the celestial sphere is illustrated in Fig. 6-4B where the coordinate axes and vectors are identical to those in

* For a discussion of alternative projections, see, for example, Canters and Decleir [1989].

Fig. 6-4A, but we have now added a sphere of unit radius centered on the origin. In the spherical plot, we are interested only in the points on the surface representing the tips of the axes and the unit vectors. In this plot, it is clear that the small circle has a radius of 10 deg, and its center is 15 deg over and 30 deg up from the X axis. While the points plotted in Fig. 6-4A and Fig. 6-4B are identical, we can learn considerably more from the spherical coordinate plot in Fig. 6-4B.

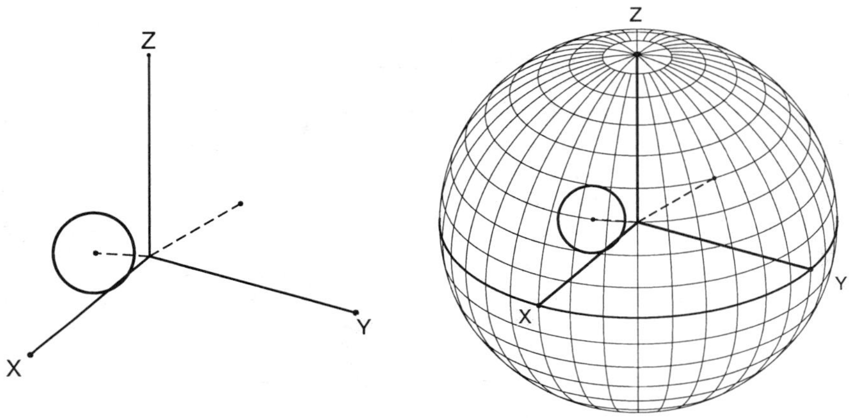

(A) Unit Vector in 3-D Space **(B) Point on Unit Sphere**

Fig. 6-4. Alternate Representations of Unit Vectors. Global geometry plots provide an unambiguous interpretation of directional geometry.

We will use globe plots frequently throughout the subsequent chapters. However, in most cases, we will omit the origin, the axes and other lines inside the sphere and draw simply the points on the surface of the sphere itself. Nonetheless, these points represent directions in space just as the unit vectors do. The celestial sphere is simply a good way to think about directional geometry much as vectors are a good way to think about forces and velocity. Doing the mathematics as vectors or in spherical geometry gives the same results. We are interested here in the angular measurements themselves, and the information they contain, not in how they are processed.

Finally, we have discussed thus far principally the celestial sphere as seen by an observer on the ground. However, our principal interest is what is seen from space. Consequently, as illustrated in Fig. 6-5, we need to introduce the concept of the *spacecraft-centered celestial sphere*, showing the direction to objects seen from a spacecraft. The principal difference between this and one for an observer on the ground is that on the ground we are looking only at the sky overhead, and the celestial "sphere" is really just a hemisphere overhead. Spacecraft, on the other hand, see the entire sky, although portions of it may be blocked by the Earth or another planet. While the globe plot approach eliminates the distortion of map projections, it only shows half the sky. Therefore, in most of our plots, we will try and show the half of the sky containing the objects of most interest for the problem at hand. But we need to keep in mind that there is always a second half as well and that for the spacecraft, the celestial sphere is the sky both "above" and "below" the spacecraft.

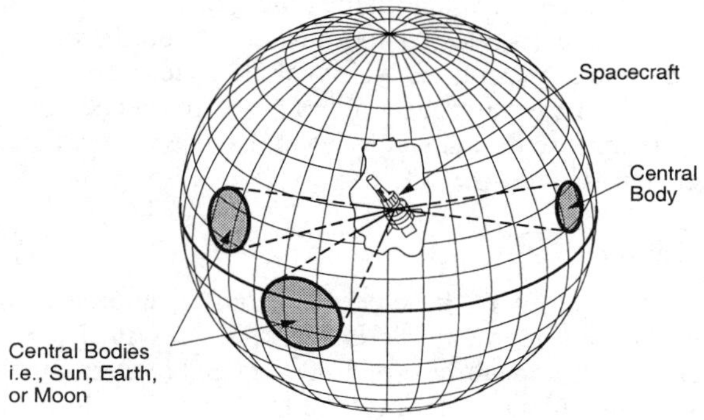

Fig. 6-5. The Spacecraft-Centered Celestial Sphere is the Bowl of the Sky Centered on the Spacecraft. The "observer" at the center may be an instrument, the center of the spacecraft, or any point in space.

The differences between the spacecraft-centered celestial sphere and the tradition Az-El plots can be seen in Fig. 6-6. The figures on both the left and the right show the Earth as seen from a low-Earth orbiting spacecraft. How large is the Earth? Is it round? Where is the center? Both plots contain the same information, but these questions are not easily answered from an Az-El plot because of the distortion of the plot itself. In effect, we are seeing the consequences of the plot rather than the reality of what is seen. In the globe plot, these problems go away. We have eliminated the distortion by plotting directly on the sphere. Here it is clear that the disk of the Earth is indeed round, has a radius of approximately 60 deg, and is centered about 35 deg above the equator of the plot.

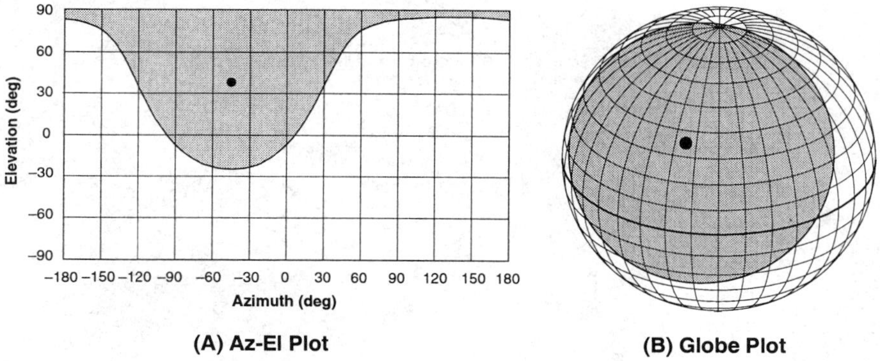

Fig. 6-6. The Disk of the Earth as Seen From Low-Earth Orbit. Globe plots of the sky provide distortion-free geometry as seen from the spacecraft.

As with unit vectors, the underlying coordinate frame for globe plots can represent a variety of coordinate frames, either fixed or moving, depending on the problem we are interested in analyzing. For the celestial sphere for an observer on the Earth, the two most common coordinate frames are one with the equator along the horizon and the pole at the zenith, or one which is aligned with celestial coordinates with the North

Star at the pole and the celestial equator along the globe's equator. Both of these can be used in spacecraft-centered celestial coordinates as well. In addition, common coordinate frames for space mission analysis include spacecraft-fixed coordinates, in which the axes are fixed in the spacecraft frame of reference, and axes which are momentarily fixed relative to the stars, relative to the direction of the Earth, or relative to some target being observed.

6.1.1 Eclipse Duration

As an example of the utility of the spherical geometry approach, we will calculate the eclipse duration for a satellite in low-Earth orbit. Specifically, assume we have a satellite in a circular orbit at an altitude of 1,000 km and inclination of 32 deg relative to the equator. We would like to determine the frequency and duration of eclipses for the satellite. Figure 6-7A shows a standard isometric view of the eclipse problem. This type of approach would allow us to set up a simulation using the various equations introduced in Chap. 2. We could then run the simulations for different seasons and node crossing times, and determine a statistical distribution. However, we get no numerical estimates from the drawing itself, and no physical insight into what is happening until we have completed the simulation and subsequent analysis.

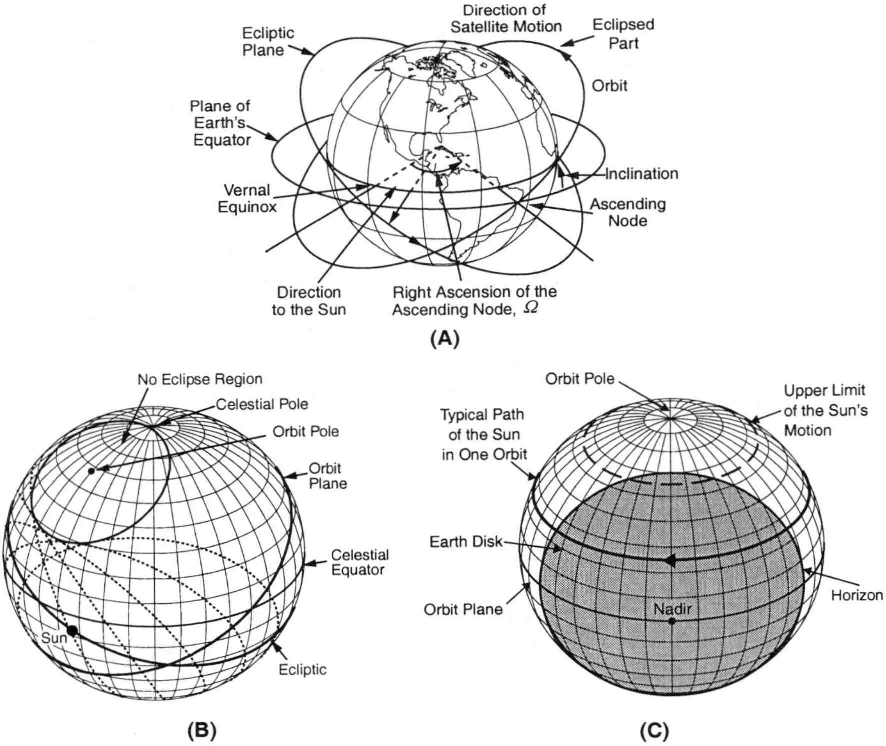

Fig. 6-7. Eclipse Geometry. (A) Traditional representation of eclipse geometry. (B) Eclipse geometry on spacecraft-centered celestial sphere improves results. (C) Eclipse geometry on Earth-referenced spacecraft-centered celestial sphere. See text for discussion.

Figure 6-7B provides better insight by plotting the problem on the spacecraft-centered celestial sphere in inertial coordinates. By inertial coordinates we mean that the sphere is attached to the fixed stars, such that the celestial pole (near the North Star) is at the pole of the coordinate system and the celestial equator is along the coordinate equator. The ecliptic, or path of the Sun in the sky, is inclined 23.5 deg to the equator, and is also shown on the plot. The orbit plane is inclined at 32 deg to the equator. Note that the orbit plane is the plane of the spacecraft's orbit for an observer at the center of the Earth. However, for an observer on the spacecraft, it can also be thought of as the orbit of the Earth around the spacecraft.

If I am sitting on the spacecraft, I see the Earth going around me relative to the background stars, in the same path as an observer at the center of the Earth would see the spacecraft move against the same stars, only 180 deg out of phase. At any given time the apparent disk of the Earth is a circle on the celestial sphere, centered at a point along the orbit plane. As we will determine in Chap. 9, the angular radius of the Earth as seen from 1,000 km altitude is approximately 60 deg [see Eq. (9-2)]. The outline of the disk of the Earth at a series of locations along the orbit is shown by the sequence of dotted circles of 60 deg radius centered on the orbit plane. As the Earth moves around the spacecraft (as seen from the spacecraft) it will sweep across the sky and from time to time cover the Sun, thus causing an eclipse to occur from the perspective of the spacecraft. It is the frequency and duration of these eclipses that we would like to determine. Notice on Fig. 6-7B that as the Earth moves along the orbit plane, there will be a region in the vicinity of the orbit pole which is never covered by the disk of the Earth. This "no eclipse region" centered on the orbit pole and a similar one, centered at the opposite pole, will be 30 deg in radius, because the angular diameter of the Earth is 60 deg at this altitude. Whatever is in either of these "polar caps" will not be eclipsed, including the Sun, Moon, and some set of stars. For the sample plotted in Fig. 6-7B, the Sun is not in the no eclipse region, and therefore, an eclipse will occur at some period during the orbit.

We can learn somewhat more from Fig. 6-7B. The Sun moves along the ecliptic which is inclined 23.5 deg to the celestial equator. The orbit plane is at 32 deg to the equator but may be oriented with the node at various places along the equator, depending both on how the spacecraft was launched and the motion of the node as described in Sec 2.3. Wherever the node is, the orbit plane will still be inclined at 32 deg to the equator. Since the ecliptic is inclined at 23.5 deg to the equator, the most that the ecliptic can be inclined to the orbit plane will be 55 deg. The Earth's angular radius at the assumed altitude is 60 deg. Consequently, at this altitude and inclination, the Sun can never be in the no eclipse region surrounding either orbit pole. Thus, at 1,000 km and 32 deg inclination, there will **always** be an eclipse on every orbit, at all seasons, irrespective of the longitude at which the satellite is launched. Although it would still be difficult to calculate the duration of a particular eclipse, we have gained substantial insight just by the way we have constructed the figure.

We can further increase our insight into the eclipse problem by making the simple coordinate transformation shown in Fig. 6-7C. Here, we plot the Earth and Sun on the spacecraft centered celestial sphere in Earth referenced coordinates, i.e., in coordinates centered on the spacecraft in which the direction of the Earth remains fixed. Many spacecraft fly with one axis fixed in the direction of the Earth, and one axis toward the orbit pole. This is the coordinate frame we would like to use, although, since we are only interested in eclipse geometry, we don't care whether the spacecraft itself is in this attitude or not. On the figure, the orbit pole is at the pole of the plot, and the orbit plane is along the equator. *Nadir*, or the direction of the center of the Earth, is marked by a dot on the plane. Because our coordinate frame is fixed in the direction of the Earth, the apparent disk of the Earth is fixed and has been shaded in the figure.

In this figure we are sitting on the spacecraft, facing the Earth, and watching the Sun and the stars go by behind it. The coordinate frame we have chosen has an axis fixed in inertial space in the direction of the orbit pole. In order to maintain the other axis in the direction of the Earth, the coordinate frame is rotating in inertial space, at one rotation per orbit in order to keep the Earth's disk fixed in the coordinate frame. This in turn means that in this coordinate frame, objects fixed in space will appear to rotate once per orbit as seen in the coordinate frame of Fig. 6-7C. The stars, the Moon and the Sun will all move in small circles centered on the orbit pole as the coordinate frame rotates to follow the Earth. The typical path of the Sun in one orbit is shown as the heavy solid line. The Moon and the stars all follow similar paths. Depending on where the Sun is along the ecliptic, and the orientation between the ecliptic and the orbit plane, the Sun will move slowly (over the course of months) up and down on the plot but can never get more than 55 deg above or below the orbit plane, as shown by the dashed line at 35 deg from the orbit pole.

As the Sun moves in this coordinate frame, eclipses occur whenever the Sun is behind the disk of the Earth, i.e., within the shaded region. The maximum eclipse occurs when the Sun is along the orbit plane and will cover 120 deg of the orbit or 1/3 of the orbit period. Since the orbit period at this altitude is approximately 105 min, the maximum eclipse duration for 1,000 km satellite will be 35 min. The minimum eclipse will occur when the Sun is at the upper limit of the Sun's motion, at the dashed line. Here, the Sun covers 60 deg in azimuth as can be seen by the figure. Consequently, the minimum eclipse duration will be approximately half of the maximum duration or about 17 min.

Using Fig. 6-7C, we can calculate not only the maximum and minimum duration of the eclipses, but also get substantial physical insight into how they occur. Notice that in the vicinity of the orbit plane, the eclipses remain long and only get to be shorter as we get very close to the extremes. Therefore, if we were to ask for the average eclipse duration, we would not be far off by indicating that it was 35 min. The average eclipse duration is very close to the maximum. We have now gained substantial physical insight into the problem. If we were to increase the orbit inclination by 5 deg, the minimum eclipse would drop to zero, but there would be little impact on the average eclipse. Simply by constructing the plot, we are able to gain considerable insight into the problem, and to provide at least some quantitative estimates. We will use a plot very similar to this to calculate eclipse durations in the second example in Sec. 6.3, after we've introduced spherical geometry computations.

6.1.2 Coordinate Systems

In principle, any coordinate system will work for space mission geometry problems. However, as we have seen in the previous section, selection of the proper reference coordinates is often critical to developing a good physical understanding, obtaining analytic expressions for key mission parameters, and reducing the probability of error.

To define a *coordinate system* for space applications, we must first specify two characteristics: the location of the origin (i.e., its motion) and what the coordinate system is fixed with respect to (i.e., its attitude and attitude rate). Typically, we choose the Earth's center as the origin for problems in orbit analysis or geometry on the Earth's surface and the spacecraft's position for problems concerning the apparent position and motion of objects as seen from the spacecraft. Occasionally, coordinates are centered on a specific spacecraft instrument when we are interested not only in viewing the outside world but also in obstructions of the field of view by other spacecraft components. Typical ways to fix the rotational orientation of a coordinate system are with respect to inertial space, to the direction of the Earth or some other object being viewed, to the spacecraft, or to an instrument on the spacecraft. Table 6-2 lists the most common coordinate systems in space mission analysis and their applications. These are illustrated in Fig. 6-8. If you are uncertain of the coordinate system to select, I recommend beginning with the following:

- Earth-centered inertial for orbit problems
- Spacecraft-centered local horizontal for missions viewing the Earth
- Spacecraft-centered inertial for missions viewing anything other than the Earth

For a more detailed discussion of coordinate systems and a complete set of coordinate transformations, see App. A.

TABLE 6-2. Common Coordinate Systems Used in Space Applications. Figure 6-8 shows the most common ones. See Table 6-5 in Sec. 6.3 for further information on the first two rows.

Coordinate Name	Fixed with Respect to	Center	Z Axis or Pole	X Axis or Ref. Point	Applications
Celestial (Inertial)	Inertial space*	Earth† or spacecraft	Celestial pole	Vernal equinox	Orbit analysis, astronomy, inertial motion
Earth-Fixed	Earth	Earth	Earth pole = celestial pole	Greenwich meridian	Geolocation, apparent satellite motion
Spacecraft-Fixed	Spacecraft	Defined by engineering drawings	Spacecraft axis toward nadir	Spacecraft axis in direction of velocity vector	Position and orientation of spacecraft instruments
Local Horizontal‡	Orbit	Spacecraft	Nadir	Perpendicular to nadir and orbit pole (toward velocity vector)	Earth observations, attitude maneuvers
Ecliptic	Inertial space	Sun	Ecliptic pole	Vernal equinox	Solar System orbits, lunar/solar ephemerides

* Actually rotating slowly with respect to inertial space. See text for discussion.
† Earth-centered inertial coordinates are frequently called *GCI (Geocentric Inertial).*
‡ Also called *LVLH (Local Vertical/Local Horizontal), RPY (Roll, Pitch, Yaw)* or *Local Tangent Coordinates.*

Unfortunately, the inertial coordinate system which everyone uses, called *celestial coordinates*, is not truly fixed with respect to *inertial space*—that is, the mean position of the stars in the vicinity of the Sun. Celestial coordinates are defined by the direction in space of the Earth's pole, called the *celestial pole*, and the direction from the Earth to the Sun on the first day of spring, when the Sun crosses the Earth's equatorial plane going from south to north. This fundamental reference direction in the sky is known

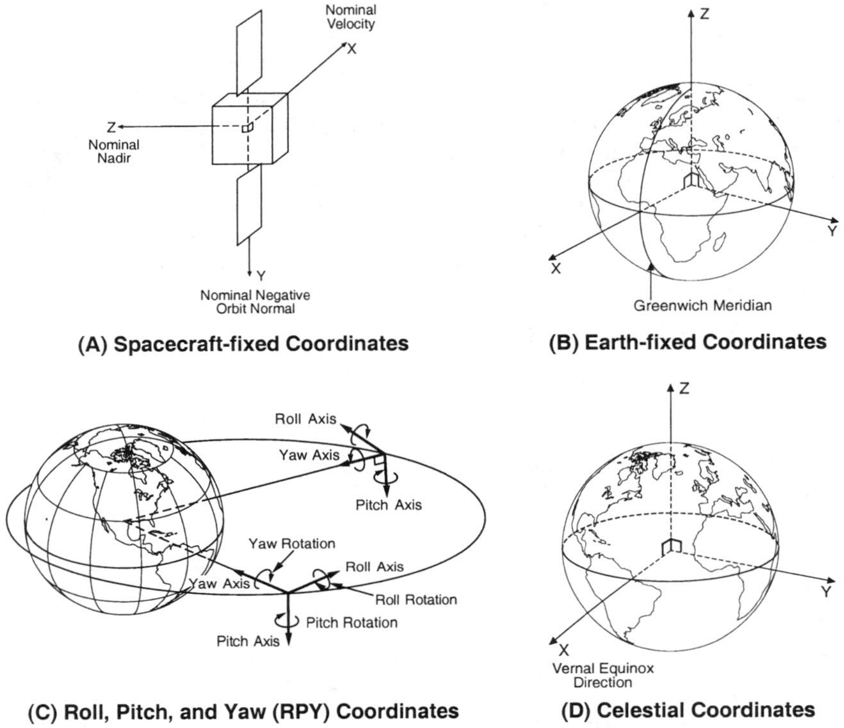

Fig. 6-8. Coordinate Systems in Common Use. See Table 6-3 for characteristics.

as the *vernal equinox* or *First Point of Aries.** Unfortunately for mission analysts, the Earth's axis and, therefore, the vernal equinox precesses around the ecliptic pole (the pole of the Earth's orbit) with a period of 26,000 years. This *precession of the equinoxes* results in a shift of the position of the vernal equinox relative to the fixed stars at a rate of 0.014 deg/yr. Because of this slow drift, celestial coordinates require a date to accurately define the position of the vernal equinox. The most commonly used systems are *1950 coordinates, 2000 coordinates*, and *true of date*, or *ToD*. The latter coordinates use the same epoch as the orbit parameters and are traditionally used for spacecraft orbit analysis. The small corrections required to maintain ToD coordinates are conveniently done by standard computer subroutines. They are important for precise numerical work, but are not critical for most problems in mission analysis.

Once the underlying coordinate system has been defined most work is done in either rectangular (x, y, z) or spherical (ϕ, θ) coordinates or some combination of the two. A given problem may be easier in one or the other, but so long as the computa-

---

* The position of the vernal equinox in the sky has been known since before the naming of constellations. When the zodiacal constellations were given their current names several thousand years ago, the vernal equinox was in Aries, the Ram. Consequently the zodiacal symbol for the Ram, ♈, or sometimes a capital T (which has a similar appearance), is used for the vernal equinox. Since that time the vernal equinox has moved through the constellation of Pisces and is now slowly entering Aquarius, ushering in the "Age of Aquarius."

tions are done correctly and we do not introduce added singularities, the accuracy of the solution will be the same in either set of coordinates. Transforming between them is both conceptually and numerically straightforward. As shown in Fig. 6-9, the +X axis is normally toward the reference point on the equator, and the +Z axis is toward the positive or North pole. The great circles through the poles and perpendicular to the equator are called *meridians*. The meridian through any point on the sphere determines the *azimuth coordinate* of that point. *Azimuth* is the equivalent of longitude on the Earth's surface, and is measured along the equator. The azimuth is also equivalent to the rotation angle measured counterclockwise about the pole from the reference point to the point in question. The second coordinate which determines the position of any point on the sphere is the *elevation* or latitude component. It is the arc-length distance above or below the equator. The *co-latitude* or *co-elevation* is the arc length from the pole to the point in question. Small circles at a constant elevation are called *parallels*. Because a parallel of constant elevation is not a great circle (except at the equator), the arc length along a parallel will be larger than the arc-length separation between two points. As Table 6-3 shows, several spherical coordinate systems in common use have special names for the azimuth and elevation coordinates.

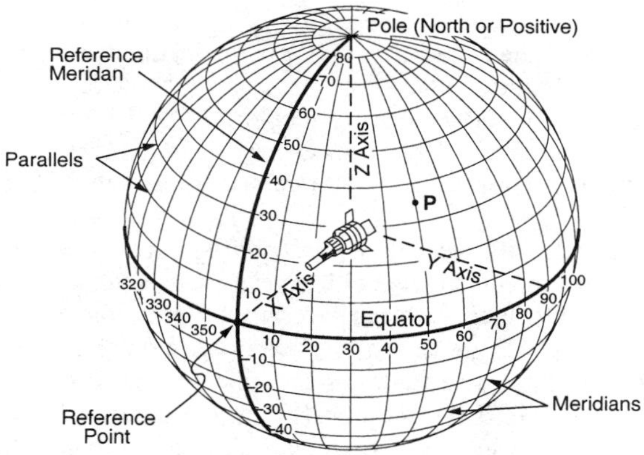

Fig. 6-9. Definition of a Spherical Coordinate System on the Unit Sphere. The point **P** is at an azimuth of 50 deg and elevation of 35 deg, normally written as (50°, 35°).

TABLE 6-3. Coordinate Names in Common Spherical Systems.

Coordinate System	Azimuth Coordinate	Elevation Coordinate (Z Axis)	Applications
Celestial Coordinates	Right ascension	Declination	Inertial measurements, astronomy
Earth-Fixed	Longitude	Latitude	Earth applications
Spacecraft-Fixed	Azimuth or clock angle	Elevation	Spacecraft measurements, attitude analysis
Local Horizontal	Azimuth	Elevation*	Directions relative to central observer
Ecliptic Coordinates	Celestial longitude	Celestial latitude	Planetary motion

* Also used are *zenith angle* = angle from point directly overhead to point in question = 90 deg minus elevation angle; and *nadir angle* = angle at the observer from the center of Earth to point in question = 90 deg plus elevation angle.

The following equations transform the azimuth, ϕ, and elevation, θ, to the corresponding unit vector coordinates (x, y, z):

$$x = \cos\phi \cos\theta \tag{6-1a}$$

$$y = \sin\phi \cos\theta \tag{6-1b}$$

$$z = \sin\theta \tag{6-1c}$$

Similarly, to transform from unit vectors to the corresponding spherical coordinates, use:

$$\phi = \text{atan2}\,(x, y) \tag{6-2a}$$

$$\theta = \text{asin}\,(z) \tag{6-2b}$$

where atan2 is the FORTRAN function with output defined over 0 to 360 deg and the asin function is evaluated over –90 deg to +90 deg.

6.2 Basic Spherical Geometry and Unit Vector Formulas

Section 6.1 discussed the broad concept of the celestial sphere and explained why we want to use it. This section reintroduces the celestial sphere as a formal mathematical construct, and describes how we go about working on it. App. A provides the specific rules for spherical geometry. We discuss here the major differences between plain and spherical geometry, and introduce spherical triangles as the principal computation tool.

Figure 6-10 illustrates the use of the celestial sphere to represent directions to objects in space. These objects may be either very close, such as other components of the spacecraft, or very far, such as the surface of the Earth, planets, or stars. As can be seen from the spherical triangle in Fig. 6-10, there are three types of objects on the celestial sphere. Points, lines, and angles on the sphere represent directions, arc lengths and rotations angles as seen from the observer at the center. *Points on the celestial sphere* represent directions in space, such as the direction to the Sun, Moon, or the rotation axis of the spacecraft. The direction opposite a given direction is called the *antipode* or *antipoint* and frequently has a –1 superscript. Thus S^{-1} is the direction opposite the Sun, and is called the *antisolar point*. *Nadir* is the direction to the center of the Earth. The direction opposite nadir is called the *zenith*. Points on the sphere may represent either directions to real objects or simply directions in space with no object associated with them, such as the direction parallel to the axis of the Earth (the *celestial pole*) or parallel to the +Z axis of the spacecraft coordinate system.

Recall from Chap. 3, that specifying a direction requires two independent numbers. From our perspective, these are the azimuth and elevation in a spherical coordinate system. In contrast, orientation or attitude requires three numbers—the direction to the center, and the rotation about that axis.*

---

* This explanation is easy, but not exactly correct. "Direction to center" tells us where the pole of the second coordinate system is, but not how it is oriented. More precisely, I can convert any one spherical coordinate system into any other, by specifying the orientation of the pole (two numbers for this) plus the rotation angle about that pole between two reference points (one number).

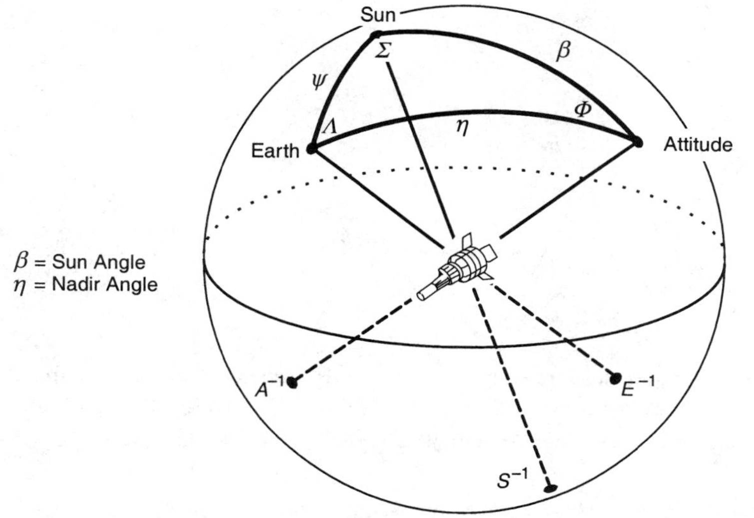

Fig. 6-10. The Spacecraft-Centered Celestial Sphere Specifies Direction in Space. The sides of the triangle are arc lengths. The angles of the triangle are rotation angles.

A *great circle* on the celestial sphere is any circle which divides the sphere into two equal hemispheres. Any part of a great circle is called an *arc* or *arc segment* and is equivalent to a straight line segment in plane geometry. Thus, the shortest path connecting two stars on the celestial sphere is the *great circle arc* connecting the stars. Any two points which are not antipoints of each other determine a unique great circle arc on the celestial sphere.

Given three points in the sky, such as the direction to the Sun, the Earth and the spacecraft spin axis attitude, we can connect them with great circle arcs (η, β, and ψ in Fig. 6-10) to construct a *spherical triangle.* The angles Λ, Σ, and Φ at the vertices of the spherical triangle are called *rotation angles* or *dihedral angles*. The lengths of arc segments and the size of rotation angles are both measured in degrees. However, as shown in Fig. 6-11, these are distinctly different measurements. The arc length represents the side of the spherical triangle, and is equal to the angular separation between two points as seen on the sky, such as the angle between the Sun and the Earth. The rotation angle, which is always measured about a point on the sphere represents the angle in a spherical triangle and is equal to the dihedral angle between two planes for the observer in the center. For example, assume that we see the Earth, Sun, and Moon on the spacecraft sky. The arc length between the Sun and the Moon is the angular separation between them as seen by the observer at the spacecraft. The rotation angle about the Earth between the Sun and the Moon is equal to the angle between two planes. The observer, Earth, and Sun form the first plane, and the observer, Earth and Moon form the second. An alternative way to think about the difference, is that a rotation angle is the angle between the hour hand and the minute hand on a clock, or about 90 deg at 12:15. The angular length of the minute hand or the hour hand as I look at the clock are both arc length measurements. Both types of angles are important in mission geometry problems, and we must clearly understand the distinction between them. Table 6-4 lists the properties of these two basic measurement types.

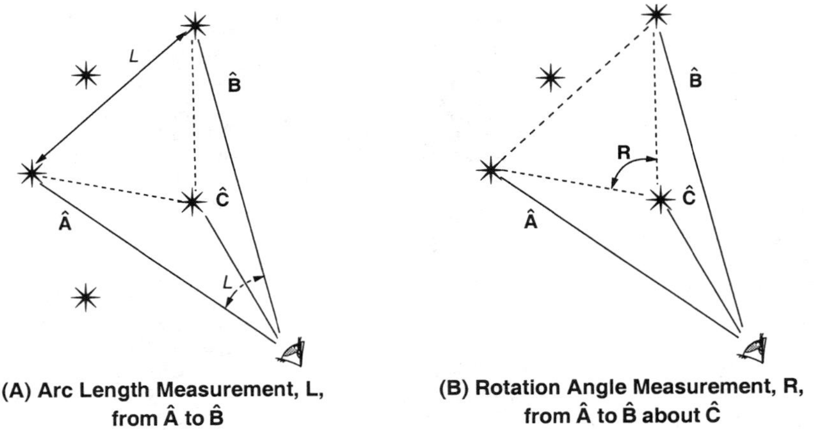

Fig. 6-11. Distinction between Arc Length and Rotation Angle Measurements.

TABLE 6-4. Properties of Arc Lengths and Rotation Angles. See also Fig. 6-11.

ARC LENGTHS

- Angle between two directions
- Segment of a great circle on the celestial sphere
- Side of a spherical triangle
- Measured in degrees
- Equivalent to a distance measurement in plane geometry
- For unit vectors $\hat{\mathbf{A}}$ and $\hat{\mathbf{B}}$, arc length = arc cos ($\hat{\mathbf{A}} \cdot \hat{\mathbf{B}}$)
- Examples:
  - — Angular distance from Sun to Earth
  - — Measurement from a 1-axis Sun sensor
  - — Angle from spin axis to center of Earth or Sun
- Expressed as "Angle from **A** to **B**" or "Arc length between **A** and **B**"

ROTATION ANGLES

- Angle about a point on the sky from one arc to another
- Dihedral angle between two planes
- Angle in spherical triangle
- Also measured in degrees
- Equivalent to an angular measurement in plane geometry
- For unit vectors $\hat{\mathbf{A}}$, $\hat{\mathbf{B}}$, and $\hat{\mathbf{C}}$, rotation angle from $\hat{\mathbf{A}}$ to $\hat{\mathbf{B}}$ about $\hat{\mathbf{C}}$ = $\arctan\left[\dfrac{\hat{\mathbf{C}}\cdot(\hat{\mathbf{A}}\cdot\hat{\mathbf{B}})}{\hat{\mathbf{A}}\cdot\hat{\mathbf{B}}-(\hat{\mathbf{C}}\cdot\hat{\mathbf{A}})(\hat{\mathbf{C}}\cdot\hat{\mathbf{B}})}\right]$
- Examples:
  - — Earth width from a conical Earth sensor
  - — Any phase or azimuthal measurement
  - — Angle measured by a dithering GEO Earth sensor
- Expressed as "Rotation angle from **A** to **B** about **C**"

The arc length and rotation angle between two points are equal if and only if the rotation angle axis is 90 deg from both points.

Most work in spherical geometry is done with great circle arcs which are the equivalent of straight lines in plane geometry. However, another important figure on the celestial sphere is the *circle* which is the locus of all points equidistant from a given point. (The center and all of the points on the circle are assumed to be on the celestial sphere). If the radius of the circle is 90 deg, the circle divides the sphere into two equal *hemispheres* and the circle is a great circle. Otherwise it is a *small circle*. In this context a "small circle" is not necessarily small. It could have a radius of 89.9 deg, for example. We could also construct a small circle with a radius of 110 deg, which would be the same as a small circle centered on the antipode of the center with a radius of 180 – 110 = 70 deg. The lines of constant latitude on the surface of the Earth are small circles, except for the equator which is a great circle, and the poles themselves which are points.

In plane geometry, there exist parallel straight lines which do not intersect. However, this is not possible with great circle arcs on the sphere. Consider, for example, the equator on a globe and any two lines of constant longitude, which are great circle arcs perpendicular to the equator. Irrespective of the separation between the lines of longitude, they always intersect at the two poles. Any two great circles on the sphere will either lie on top of each other, or intersect at two points 180 deg apart. The orange slice-shaped figure formed by the intersection of two great circles is called a *lune*. The lune has two sides, both of which are 180 deg long. The rotation angle between the sides, at either of the intersection points is equal to the angle between the two planes that form the great circles and pass through the center of the sphere.

Because great circle arcs (which are the spherical equivalent of straight lines) always intersect, triangles in spherical geometry are substantially more common than in plane geometry problems, and take a more important role in computations on the sphere. Nearly all problems in spherical geometry can be reduced to the solution of spherical triangles. Thus, spherical trigonometry becomes the principal computational method for most mission geometry problems. These computations are described further in Sec. 6.3, and the detailed rules of spherical trigonometry are given in App. A. Note that one of the most common errors in spherical trigonometry is to construct a "triangle" in which one of the sides is a small circle arc rather than a great circle arc. Just as all of the sides of a plane triangle must be straight lines, all of the sides of a spherical triangle must be great circle arcs. We cannot apply plane trigonometry directly to a piece of pie. Similarly,

The sides of spherical triangles can ***not*** *be small circles.*

Although most of the work in mission geometry is done with spherical triangles and small and great circles, there are other more complex figures as well. The rhumb line is introduced in the boxed example at the end of this section, the dual-axis spiral is described in Chap. 8, and the analemma is introduced in Chap. 10.

Another concept in spherical geometry that is different from plane geometry is illustrated in Fig. 6-12, in which we have constructed a spherical triangle using the equator and two lines of longitude. The intersections of the longitude lines with the equator are both right angles, such that the sum of the angles of the triangle exceeds 180 deg by an amount equal to the angle at the pole. The sum of the angles of any spherical triangle is always larger than 180 deg. The amount by which this sum exceeds 180 deg is called the spherical excess and is directly proportional to the area of the spherical triangle. Thus, small triangles on the sphere have a spherical excess near zero, and are very similar to plane triangles. Large spherical triangles, however, are very different as in Fig. 6-12 with two right angles.

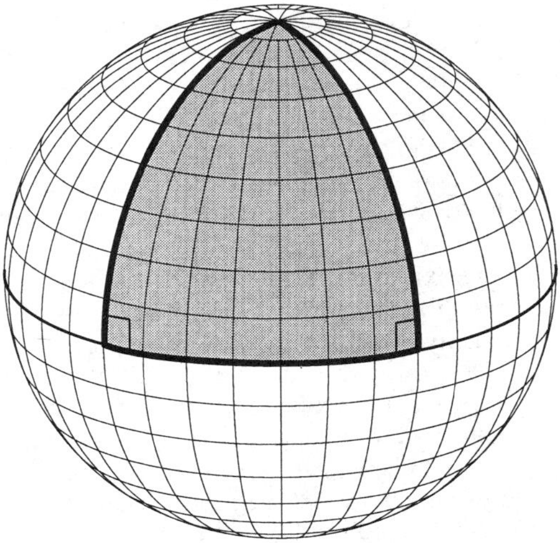

Fig. 6-12. The Sum of the Angles in a Spherical Triangle is Always Greater than 180 deg. The sum of the angles minus π radians is called the *spherical excess* and equals the area of the triangle in steradians.

A *radian* is the angle subtended if I take a string equal in length to the radius of a circle, and stretch it along the circumference. Similarly, if I take an area equal to the square of the radius, and stretch it out on the surface of a sphere (which requires some distortion, since the surface of a sphere cannot fit on a flat sheet), the resulting area is called a *steradian.* Since the area of a sphere is $4\pi r^2$, there are 4π steradians in a full sphere, and 2π steradians in a hemisphere. These units are convenient for area problems, because in any spherical triangle the spherical excess, expressed in radians, is equal to the area of the triangle expressed in steradians. In general, the area, A, of any spherical polygon (a figure with sides which are great circle arcs) expressed in steradians is given by:

$$A = \Sigma - (n - 2)\pi \tag{6-3}$$

where n is the number of sides, and Σ is the sum of the rotation angles expressed in radians.

Figure 6-13 shows a variety of spherical triangles. Note that all of the triangle sides are great circle arcs. Figure 6-13A is a nearly plane triangle, for which the sum of the angles is approximately 180 deg and plane geometry is a close approximation. Figure 6-13B is called a *right spherical triangle* because the angle at B is a right angle. Just as right plane triangles have particularly simple relationships among the angles and sides, right spherical triangles also have exceptionally simple relationships between the sides and angles. These are expressed by *Napier's rules* which are written out in App. A. Right spherical triangles are common in mission geometry problems, and provide simple, straightforward solutions for many problems associated with angular measurements.

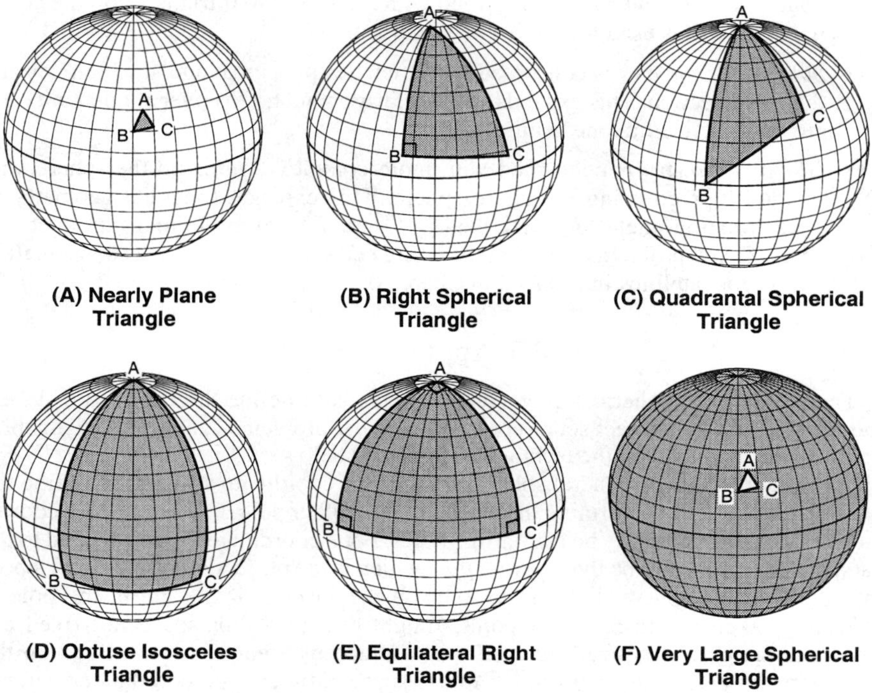

Fig. 6-13. Types of Spherical Triangles. See text for discussion.

In spherical trigonometry, there is a second type of special and particularly simple spherical triangle shown in Fig. 6-13C. Here, side A-B has an arc length of 90 deg. This is called a *quadrantal spherical triangle*. An equally simple set of rules applies to the relationship among the angles and sides in quadrantal spherical triangles. These are also summarized in App. A. Between them, right and quadrantal spherical triangles provide solutions to most of the problems encountered in mission analysis.

Figure 6-13D shows an *obtuse isosceles triangle* with two equal rotation angles larger than 90 deg. Clearly, this cannot exist in plane geometry. A similar strange triangle for plane geometry is Fig. 6-13E which shows an *equilateral right triangle* in which all three angles and all three sides are 90 deg. This triangle represents 1/8 of the surface of the celestial sphere, and has an area of 0.5 π steradians, which can be seen either by examination or from the spherical excess rule. Finally, Fig. 6-13F shows a very large spherical triangle. Note that this triangle is remarkably similar in appearance to the small triangle in 6-13A. This is because the triangle can be thought of either as a small triangle with three angles of approximately 60 deg, or as a very large one, with three angles of approximately 300 deg. That is, the area between A, B, and C can be thought of either as the inside of a small triangle or as the outside of a large one which covers all of the surface of the sphere except for the small area between A, B, and C. In this large spherical triangle, the rules of spherical geometry still apply and can be used in very convenient fashions as described further by Wertz, [1999].

The ideas above lead to defining three major areas of geometry on the surface of the sphere:

- *Spherical trigonometry* is concerned with the solution of triangles on the celestial sphere. It is used for almost all computations
- *Spherical geometry* is concerned with triangles plus great and small circles and their intersection. This expands spherical trigonometry to cover angular area and circles contained in one hemisphere.
- *Global geometry* is concerned with more complex figures on the sphere, and relationships covering the entire sphere. This expands spherical geometry to cover rotation angle loci described in Chap. 7, dual angle loci introduced in Chap. 8, and problems covering the entire celestial sphere, such as constellation design for satellites introduced in Chap. 10.

6.3 Applications

The key to most spherical geometry problems is to define the coordinate system correctly. Given the correct set of coordinates, most problems can be solved algebraically very quickly, using the techniques described below.

Figure 6-14 shows a general spherical geometry coordinate system. To define the coordinates, we start by defining the orientation of either pole. For geographic coordinates, this would ordinarily be the Earth's poles. For a coordinate frame attached to the stars, it is often taken to be the *celestial pole* which is the projection of the Earth's pole onto the celestial sphere. For an observer on the surface of the Earth, the pole is frequently taken as the *zenith* or point straight overhead. For spacecraft-fixed coordinates, the pole is typically the +Z axis defined by some mark inscribed on the spacecraft body. It is also convenient to use spacecraft-centered coordinates defined relative to the orbit plane, such that the pole is in the direction of the angular momentum of the spacecraft in its orbit, i.e., the positive orbit pole.

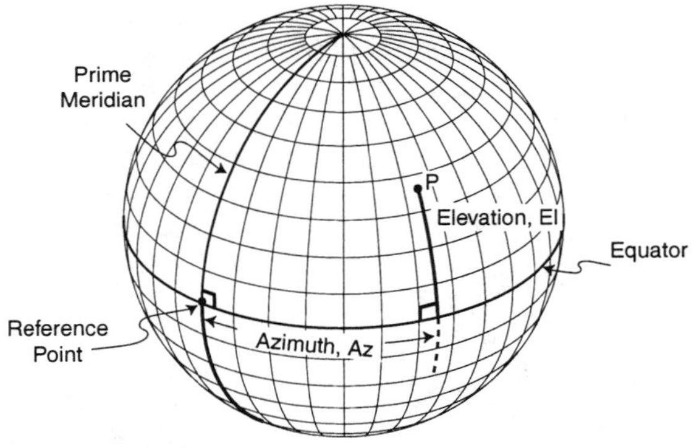

Fig. 6-14. The Spherical Geometry Coordinate System. See Table 6-5 for definitions of principal components. (See also Fig. 6-9.) P is at (65°, 35°).

The *equator* of the coordinate system is the great circle which is 90 deg from the two poles. In order to fully define the coordinates we need to define where to start our azimuthal coordinate measured along the equator. This is determined by a *reference point* along the equator, or equivalently, by a *prime meridian,* which is one of the lines of constant azimuth going through a well-defined point, not necessarily on the equator.

Rhumb Lines and the Mercator Projection

A *rhumb line* is a curve on the surface of the sphere which makes a constant angle relative to North. Figure 6-15 illustrates a rhumb line between Miami and northern Russia on the surface of the Earth. Rhumb lines are nearly great circle arcs in the vicinity of the equator, and become more of a spiral as they approach the pole, ultimately spiraling around the pole and never reaching it.

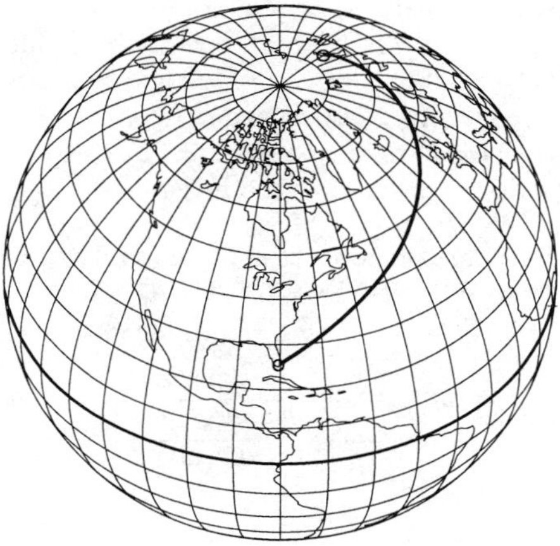

Fig. 6-15. Rhumb Line Path.

Rhumb lines are a remarkably convenient way to navigate when I know where I started and where I'm going, but don't necessarily know where I am now. For example, in Fig. 6-15, the rhumb line beginning in Russia makes an angle of approximately 230 deg relative to north. Thus, if I set out from northern Russia, at a compass heading of 230 deg, and maintain that compass heading long enough, then even though I don't know where I am along the route, I will eventually wind up in Miami Beach. Obviously, this was an extremely important characteristic for navigation, prior to the introduction of inertial navigation systems and GPS.

It was the rhumb line that led to the development of one of the most famous of all map projections by Flemish geographer, Gerhardus Mercator in 1568. The Mercator projection is frequently thought of as being simply latitude vs. longitude, but it is not. The horizontal scale is the longitude, but the vertical scale is the log tangent of the latitude. This tends to substantially exaggerate the size of features near the poles (often called the Greenland effect in maps). However, it has one very important characteristic—a straight line drawn between any two points on a Mercator projection is a rhumb line on the surface of the Earth. If I take a Mercator projection of the world, and draw a straight line from New York to London, then measure on the map the angle relative to North, I will have the compass heading I need. If I set sail from New York with that compass heading, I will eventually arrive in London. I haven't quite followed the shortest path, which would be a great circle arc connecting the two, but I have made the navigation easy and eliminated the requirement to know where I am along the way.

The rhumb line doesn't deviate too much from a great circle arc in low and moderate latitudes, where it is most important for practical purposes. On the whole, relatively few people are interested in taking ships to the North or South poles, which tends to be inconvenient for other reasons. Rhumb lines are also used from time to time for attitude maneuvers on spacecraft where, for example, we might fire our thrusters at a constant angle relative to the Sun to change the orientation of a spinning spacecraft.

In geographic coordinates, the prime meridian goes through the Royal Greenwich Observatory, near downtown London, and is often called the *Greenwich meridian*. It represents the starting point for longitude on the surface of the Earth. On the celestial sphere, relative to the stars, we use one of the two *equinoxes*, or intersections between the ecliptic (the path of the Sun) and the equator. As discussed in Sec. 6.1.2, the one chosen as the zero point on the sky is the *vernal equinox*, which is the location of the Sun on the first day of spring. (The other intersection is called the *autumnal equinox*.) See Table 6-2 for other common systems.

The two coordinates in a general spherical coordinate system are called *azimuth*, measured along the equator, and *elevation*, measured above and below the equator. In geographic coordinates, these are called *longitude* and *latitude*, and in celestial coordinates on the sky, they are *right ascension* and *declination*. *Meridians* are the arcs of great circles running from pole to pole, and latitude lines are small circles at a constant latitude. Naming conventions are summarized in Table 6-5.

TABLE 6-5. Names of Principal Components in Common Spherical Coordinate Systems. See Table 6-2 for other coordinate systems.

Component	Coordinate System		
	Generic	**Geographic**	**Celestial**
Fixed with Respect to	Various	Earth	"Fixed" stars
Pole	Pole	North and South poles	Celestial poles (projection of Earth's poles onto the sky)
Equator	Equator	Equator	Celestial equator
Reference Meridian	Prime meridian	Greenwich meridian	0 of right ascension
Reference Point	Not named	Not named	Vernal equinox
Azimuthal Coordinate	Azimuth	Longitude	Right ascension
Vertical Coordinate	Elevation	Latitude	Declination

Virtually all problems in spherical geometry are done by solving spherical triangles. These are significantly more powerful than plane triangles, both because great circles always intersect, and because any three components, including the three rotation angles provide a solution. The specific algebraic rules for solving all types of spherical triangles are summarized in App. A. The rules to be applied to specific types of figures are as follows.

- **Right spherical triangles**: If one of the rotation angles is a right angle, and any two of the remaining components (rotation angles or sides) are known, then the three unknown components can be determined immediately by Napier's rules* which are a very simple set of relationships between the sines and cosines of the various components. These are explicitly defined for all possible combinations of right spherical triangles in App. A.

---

* Not too surprisingly, Napier's rules were introduced by the Scottish mathematician and Baron of Merchiston, John Napier, who also invented logarithms and in 1617 introduced the decimal system as it is used today. During the early part of the 20th century Napier's rules for spherical triangles were taught as a part of high school mathematics and a variety of convenient mechanisms for memorizing them were introduced. Needless to say, relatively few of today's high school students are required to do so.

- **Quadrantal spherical triangles:** If one of the sides is equal to 90 deg, and any two of the remaining components are known, then the three unknown components can be determined by rules analogous to Napier's rules for right spherical triangles.
- **Oblique (general) spherical triangles**: Use either the law of cosines or law of sines set out in App. A. The law of cosines is preferred, since the inverse cosine is uniquely defined between 0 and 180 deg.
- **Area of any figure**: Use the spherical excess rule for polygons and the formulas in App. A for the areas of small circles or fractions of small circles.

To illustrate the applications of spherical geometry, we will present four sample problems:

- The field of view of a "square" Sun sensor
- Eclipse duration in a circular orbit (corresponding to the sample problem set out conceptually in Sec. 6.1)
- Computation of the Sun angle on an arbitrary spacecraft face
- The shape of a circular orbit viewed from nearby

6.3.1 Example 1: Field of View of a "Square" Sun Sensor

Sensors used on spacecraft are often said to have square or rectangular fields of view, i.e., an "8 × 8 deg star sensor" or "128 × 128 Sun sensor." Unfortunately, "square" and "rectangular" are not as well defined as we might like in terms of sensor fields of view on the sky. If the edge of a sensor field of view is defined by a straight line, such as an array of pixels on a focal plane, then this straight line will be projected onto the spacecraft sky as an arc of a great circle. Two parallel edges on the field of view will be projected as two great circle arcs on the sky. We can, for example, think of these two edges as being projected out along two meridians, or lines of longitude in a celestial coordinate system. However, since these are great circle arcs, they do not remain the same distance apart, and would ultimately intersect if extended far enough. Thus, a square or rectangular field of view when projected onto the spacecraft sky does not have edges which remain a fixed distance apart. In this section we define what is meant by a "square" field of view, and determine the parameters of such a field of view projected onto the sky. Rectangular fields of view are discussed in Sec. 9.1.4.

To make our example 1 specific, we will look at a 128 deg square field of view Sun sensor, and ask what is the actual field of view projected onto the sky. Figure 6-16 shows how such a sensor could be constructed.

We begin with a flat square array 8.2 cm on a side. We mount the array parallel to an opaque sheet and 2 cm behind it. As shown in the figure, we will put a pinhole in the center of the opaque sheet such that it is directly above the center of the array. We use a pinhole because this provides perfect geometrical optics, i.e., there are no distortions introduced by the pinhole itself and we are interested in creating a "perfect" sensor, although, perhaps, not a very practical one. As the array looks through the pinhole out into the sky, the angle from the central axis to the center of any one of the edges will be equal to atan(2.05) = 64 deg, such that the field of view of the sensor is 128 deg across as measured through the center, perpendicular to the edge. This is what we traditionally mean by "128 deg square" field of view. What we would like to determine for this perfect sensor is:

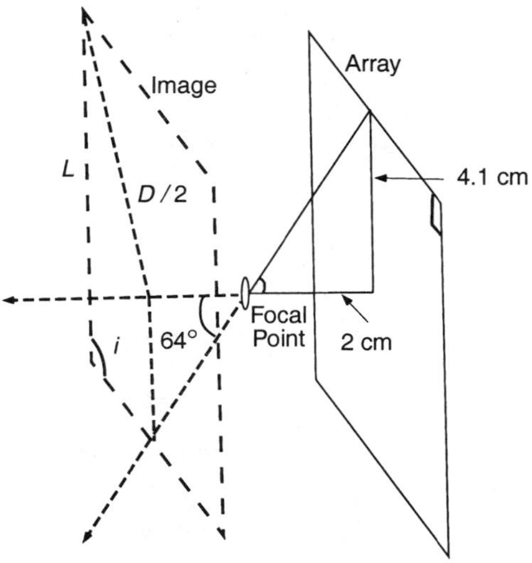

Fig. 6-16. Construction of a "128 × 128 deg" Sun Sensor. The "128 deg" is measured between opposite sides, through the center.

- The length, *L,* of each side
- The angle of intersection, *i,* between two adjacent sides
- The length of the diagonal, *D*, and
- The projected area, *A,* of the sensor on the sky.

To show how the problem is done, we will solve it using plane geometry, vectors, and spherical geometry.

The plane geometry solution is shown in Fig. 6-17. Here the arithmetic is particularly simple. In the plane geometry approximation, the distance across the center is 128 deg. Therefore the length of each side, *L,* is 128 deg. The angle of intersection at the corners is 90 deg, the area, *A,* is $128^2 = 16{,}384\ \text{deg}^2$ (equals 39.7% of the celestial sphere) and the diagonal, *D,* is $128\sqrt{2} = 181.0$ deg. Clearly, there is a very fundamental problem with this solution. Although our sensor may not be a practical one, it is certainly capable of being constructed. And yet, if it is constructed, it is highly unlikely that the field of view on the sky would be more than 180 deg across, since this means that the sensor would be seeing behind itself. The solution using plane geometry is simple to compute, but, unfortunately, wrong.

Figure 6-18 illustrates a vector solution to the Sun sensor problem illustrated on Fig. 6-16. Here we construct unit vectors to the center of the edge of the field of view, and to one of the corners. We then use the vector algebra illustrated in the figure to determine the angles among the various vectors and the rotation angle formed at the corner of the sensor. The solution presented in the figure is computationally correct, but is both awkward and complex. In addition, the area of the field of view is not easily computed using vectors. Finally, the solution provides us with almost no physical insight into the shape of the field of view, or the implications of the shape for either measurements or creating overlapping fields of view with other sensors.

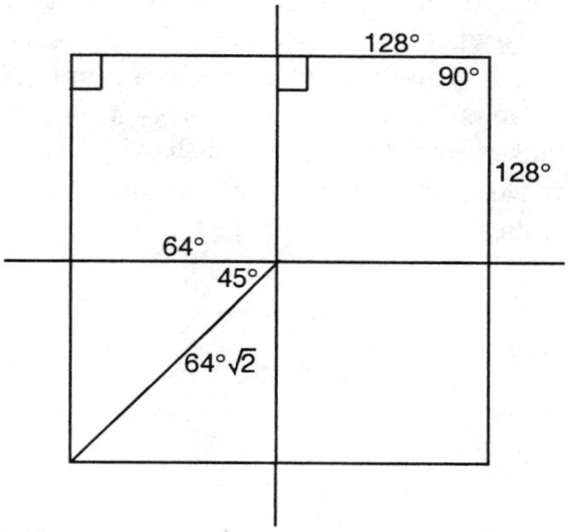

Fig. 6-17. Plane Geometry Solution to Sun Sensor Problem. The answer is simple, but, unfortunately, wrong.

$$\frac{L}{2} = \text{angle between } (\vec{\mathbf{V}}_4, \vec{\mathbf{V}}_5)$$

$$\frac{D}{2} = \text{angle between } (\vec{\mathbf{V}}_1, \vec{\mathbf{V}}_5)$$

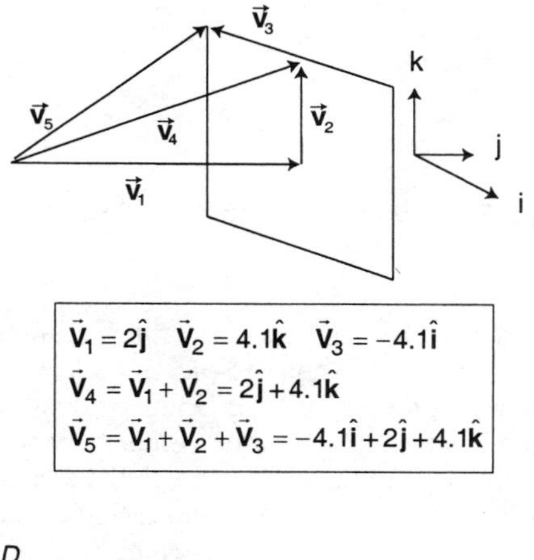

$$\vec{\mathbf{V}}_1 = 2\hat{\mathbf{j}} \quad \vec{\mathbf{V}}_2 = 4.1\hat{\mathbf{k}} \quad \vec{\mathbf{V}}_3 = -4.1\hat{\mathbf{i}}$$
$$\vec{\mathbf{V}}_4 = \vec{\mathbf{V}}_1 + \vec{\mathbf{V}}_2 = 2\hat{\mathbf{j}} + 4.1\hat{\mathbf{k}}$$
$$\vec{\mathbf{V}}_5 = \vec{\mathbf{V}}_1 + \vec{\mathbf{V}}_2 + \vec{\mathbf{V}}_3 = -4.1\hat{\mathbf{i}} + 2\hat{\mathbf{j}} + 4.1\hat{\mathbf{k}}$$

$$\cos\left(\frac{L}{2}\right) = \frac{\vec{\mathbf{V}}_4 \cdot \vec{\mathbf{V}}_5}{\left|\vec{\mathbf{V}}_4\right|\left|\vec{\mathbf{V}}_5\right|}$$
$$= \frac{(2)\cdot(2) + (4.1)(4.1)}{\sqrt{(2)^2 + (4.1)^2}\sqrt{(-4.1)^2 + 2^2 + (4.1)^2}}$$
$$= 0.7437$$

$$\frac{L}{2} = 41.95 \text{ deg}$$
$$L = 83.9 \text{ deg}$$

$$\cos\left(\frac{D}{2}\right) = \frac{\vec{\mathbf{V}}_1 \cdot \vec{\mathbf{V}}_5}{\left|\vec{\mathbf{V}}_1\right|\left|\vec{\mathbf{V}}_5\right|}$$
$$= \frac{4}{(2)\sqrt{(-4.1)^2 + (2)^2 + (4.1)^2}}$$
$$= 0.3261$$

$$\frac{D}{2} = 70.97 \text{ deg}$$
$$D = 141.9 \text{ deg}$$

$$I = \text{vector}\left\{\frac{\left|\vec{\mathbf{V}}_5\right| \cdot \vec{\mathbf{V}}_5\left(\vec{\mathbf{V}}_3 \times \vec{\mathbf{V}}_2\right)}{\left|\vec{\mathbf{V}}_5\right|^2\left(\vec{\mathbf{V}}_3 \cdot \vec{\mathbf{V}}_2\right) - \left(\vec{\mathbf{V}}_5 \cdot \vec{\mathbf{V}}_3\right)\left(\vec{\mathbf{V}}_5 \cdot \vec{\mathbf{V}}_2\right)}\right\}$$

$I = 143.9$ deg

A = not normally computed with vectors

Fig. 6-18. Vector Solution to Sun Sensor Problem. The answer is correct, but both incomplete (since the area cannot be computed) and complex.

Figure 6-19 shows the spherical geometry solution to the Sun sensor problem. The sphere represents the celestial sphere as seen by the sensor. We construct the edges of the field of view by first defining the center axis as a point on the equator, then going 64 deg along the equator in either direction and drawing the meridians at right angles to the equator. These lines represent the sides of the field of view. The top and bottom are produced by rotating about the center by 90 deg and constructing two similar lines. This is the real shape of the field of view projected onto the sky.

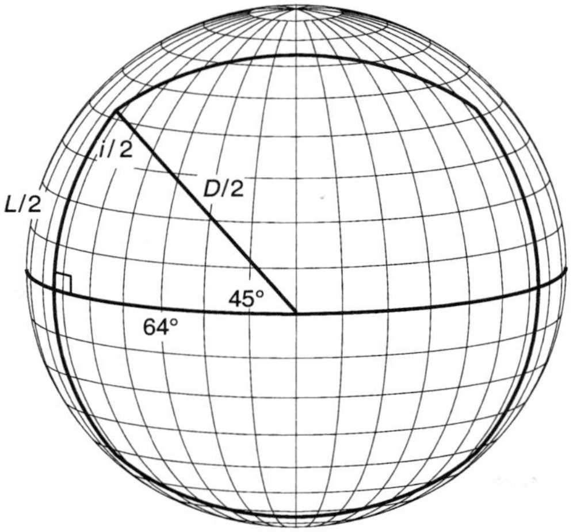

Fig. 6-19. Spherical Geometry Solution to Sun Sensor Problem. Solution is complete, correct, and simple.

To determine the values of the parameters of interest, we first construct the diagonal going from the center to one of the corners, and the line from the center to the middle of one of the edges. The length of this line is 64 deg by the definition of our problem. The rotation angle at the center between the two edges of the triangle is 45 deg by symmetry, and the line through the center to the middle of the edge intersects the edge at a right angle, again by definition of our problem. Consequently, we have formed a right spherical triangle in which two of the components are known. Using Napier's rules from App. A, we simply write down the formulas for the various components:

$$\tan(L/2) = \sin 64° \tan 45° \qquad L = 83.9° \tag{6-4}$$

$$\cos(i/2) = \cos 64° \sin 45° \qquad i = 143.9° \tag{6-5}$$

$$\tan(D/2) = \tan 64° \cos 45° \qquad D = 141.9° \tag{6-6}$$

$$\text{Spherical Excess} = 4 \times 143.9° - 360° = 215.6° = 3.763 \text{ rad} \tag{6-7}$$

$$A = 3.763 \text{ steradians} = 29.9\% \text{ of the sphere} \tag{6-8}$$

Here the solution is exact, simple, and gives us good physical insight into how the solution will vary with different defining parameters. The sensor is 128 deg across at the middle, but the edges are only 84 deg long. In addition, two edges which are at right angles on the focal plane array intersect at an angle of 144 deg on the celestial sphere. While the rows and columns of the physical array may be orthogonal, the projected fields of view onto the sky are not orthogonal and indeed, are highly correlated.* Rows and columns near the edge of the sensor are no longer independent measurements. The large scale of the Sun sensor exaggerates the size of the effect. Nonetheless, sensors with smaller fields of view typically require much higher accuracy which may require the spherical geometry of the sensor field of view be taken into account. Typical magnitudes of plane geometry errors for various size fields of view are given in Table 6-6. Whether the differences between plane and spherical geometry are important for any given application will depend upon the required accuracies. This table allows us to judge whether a plane geometry approximation is appropriate. In any case, the correct computations in spherical geometry are extremely simple.

TABLE 6-6. Representative Errors Using Plane Geometry Approximation for Sensor Fields of View. The subscript "plane" means a plane geometry approximation. The subscript "true" means the actual spherical geometry value.

FOV size (deg)	128 × 128	64 × 64	32 × 32	20 × 20	8 × 8	1 × 1
Application	Sun sensor; Earth at LEO	Sun sensor	General photographs	Earth at GEO	Star sensor	Telescope
Equivalent 35 mm Camera Lens	7 mm	25 mm	50 mm	85 mm	200 mm	1,700 mm
$SIDE_{plane}$ (deg)	128.00	64.00	32.00	20.00	8.00	1.00000
$SIDE_{true}$ (deg)	83.89	55.84	30.82	19.70	7.98	0.99996
$ANGLE_{plane}$ (deg)	90.00	90.00	90.00	90.00	90.00	90.0000
$ANGLE_{true}$ (deg)	143.88	106.31	94.36	91.73	90.28	90.0044

The solution here is applicable to any square field of view, which corresponds to a relatively large number of instruments flown in space. The complete expressions can be easily derived from Fig. 6-19. However, they are also provided in detail in Sec. 7.4.1 for any sensor with a rectangular field of view.

---

* As discussed in detail in Sec. 7.2, *independent* or *uncorrelated* measurements are ones that do not depend on each other. In an ordinary rectangular coordinate frame, such as the layout of array sensor, the x and y measurements are orthogonal and uncorrelated — changing the value of x has no impact on the value of y. When this same array coordinate frame is projected onto the celestial sphere, that is no longer true and the measurements are said to be *correlated* or related to each other. As we move along the top row of the array for example, both the x and y values on the celestial sphere will change. If two measurements are *fully correlated*, they are simply two different ways of measuring the same thing, such as specifying a location on the Earth by giving the latitude and the distance from the North Pole. This gives us two measurements of the north-south location and no measurement of the East-West location.

6.3.2 Example 2: Eclipse Duration for Circular and Non-Circular Orbits

This example returns to the eclipse problem illustrated in Fig. 6-7 in Sec. 6.1. The computational geometry is shown in Fig. 6-20. Recall that the altitude of the satellite was 1,000 km, which implies that the angular radius of the Earth ρ = 59.8 deg (see Eq. (9-2) in Sec. 9.1). For specificity we will calculate the duration of the eclipse when the Sun is 25 deg out of the orbit plane, i.e., β = 25 deg in Fig. 6-20.

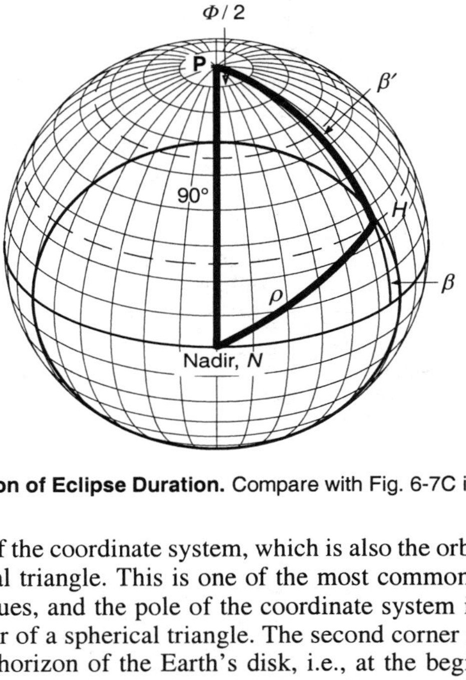

Fig. 6-20. Computation of Eclipse Duration. Compare with Fig. 6-7C in Sec. 6.1.

We use the pole of the coordinate system, which is also the orbit pole, as one of the corners of a spherical triangle. This is one of the most common spherical geometry computation techniques, and the pole of the coordinate system is often chosen such that it can be a corner of a spherical triangle. The second corner is the point at which the Sun crosses the horizon of the Earth's disk, i.e., at the beginning or end of the eclipse, and the third point is the direction to nadir or the center of the Earth. The angle from the orbit pole to nadir is 90 deg by definition, so we have constructed a quadrantal spherical triangle. The angular radius of the Earth, ρ= 59.8 deg, is known. Similarly, the side β'= 90 deg – β = 65 deg is also known. Consequently, we can use Napier's rules for quadrantal triangles to determine any of the three rotation angles. In particular, we would like to determine $\Phi/2$ at the orbit pole, which is given by:

$$\cos(\Phi/2) = \cos\rho / \sin\beta' \tag{6-9}$$

If β'= 65 deg, then $\Phi/2$ = 56.3 deg and Φ = 112.6 deg. This is the rotation angle covered by the Sun as it passes behind the disk of the Earth. Since the orbit is assumed to be circular with the spacecraft moving at a constant angular rate, the eclipse duration will be 112.6/360 = 31.3% of the orbit. With an orbit period of 105 min, this gives an eclipse duration of 32.9 min for this example. The formulation is extremely simple, and can be easily evaluated for other angles of the Sun out of the orbit plane. In addition, we could take into account the 0.5 deg diameter of the Sun itself, or the angular height of the Earth's atmosphere, and calculate, for example, the time at which eclipse begins, when it reaches full darkness, or the length of twilight at either end. None of these computations requires complex simulations or detailed orbit analysis. Simple geometrical calculations give us good insight into both the duration and character of eclipses seen from space.

For eccentric orbits the situation is more complex, because the eclipse fraction varies depending upon where the eclipse occurs relative to apogee and perigee. Nonetheless, we can relatively easily determine the eclipse extremes that occur at apogee and perigee. First, note that even though the orbit is noncircular, the projection of the orbit plane onto the celestial sphere, and therefore, the apparent path of the Earth will still be a great circle. The differences from a circular orbit are twofold. The Earth moves at a nonuniform rate along this great circle and the apparent size of the Earth's disk changes with changing altitude. As shown in Fig. 6-21 the no-eclipse region about either pole will change from circular to an approximately oval shape with a much larger no-eclipse region in the direction of apogee. The maximum eclipse at both apogee and perigee will, of course, occur when the Sun is in the orbit plane, and is given by:

$$E_{A/P} \approx \left(\frac{\rho_{A/P}}{180}\right)\left(\frac{\mathrm{R_E} + H_{A/P}}{a}\right) \tag{6-10}$$

$$a = \mathrm{R_E} + (H_A + H_P)/2 \tag{6-11}$$

where $E_{A/P}$ is the fraction of the orbit period spent in eclipse at apogee and perigee when the Sun is in the orbit plane, $\rho_{A/P}$ is the angular radius of the Earth at apogee or perigee in degrees, $\mathrm{R_E}$ is the radius of the Earth, $H_{A/P}$ is the height of apogee and perigee and a is the semimajor axis. The angular radius of the Earth can be evaluated using Eq. (9-2) in Sec. 9.1. The effect of the Sun not being in the orbit plane can be determined using Eq. (6-9), just as for circular orbits. Note that the excursion range is not as large as one might anticipate, since at apogee the Earth's disk is much smaller, but the spacecraft is moving more slowly, thus providing some compensation. For example, in an extremely elliptical orbit with perigee at 500 km and apogee at geosynchronous altitude of 35,768 km, the maximum eclipse at perigee is 10.6% of the orbit period, vs. 8.3% at apogee. However, as the Sun moves out of the orbit plane, it will enter the no-eclipse region at apogee far more quickly than at perigee.

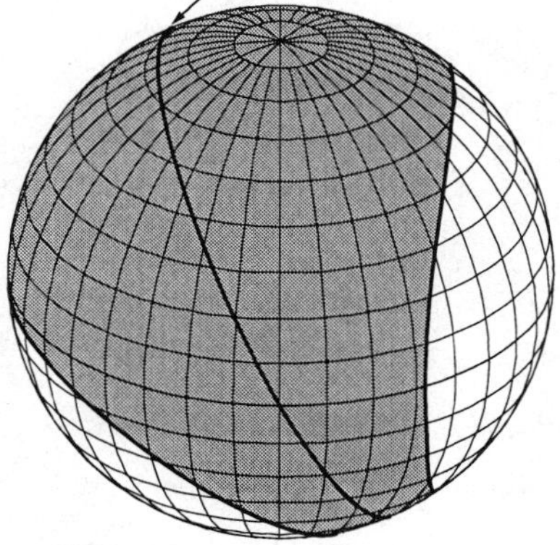

Fig. 6-21. Motion of the Disk of the Earth in an Eccentric Orbit. Shaded area is the portion of the celestial sphere blocked by the disk of the Earth.

6.3.3 Example 3: Sun Angle on an Arbitrary Spacecraft Face

The previous example computes the motion of the Sun as seen from the spacecraft. Now we will extend this to compute the Sun angle as a function of time on an arbitrary spacecraft face. This is of use for problems such as Sun interference or the total heat input on a particular face or instrument.

There are many possible orientations of the spacecraft relative to the Sun. The most common are:

- *Inertially fixed*: Sun angle doesn't change significantly over an orbit
- *Earth-fixed*: Sun angle oscillates as the spacecraft rotates once per orbit about the orbit pole
- *Spinning spacecraft*: Same geometry as for Earth-fixed spacecraft, except that the spacecraft rotates much faster about a spin axis arbitrarily fixed in inertial space.

Sun angles for an inertially fixed spacecraft are simple to calculate since the Sun remains fixed in spacecraft coordinates. Specifically, the Sun angle, β, on any face is given by:

$$\beta = \operatorname{acos}(\hat{\mathbf{N}} \cdot \hat{\mathbf{S}}) \tag{6-12}$$

where $\hat{\mathbf{N}}$ is the unit vector normal to the face in question and $\hat{\mathbf{S}}$ is the unit vector to the Sun.

The more complex case occurs with an Earth-fixed spacecraft (or equivalently a spinning spacecraft) where any spacecraft-fixed component continuously changes its orientation with respect to the Sun. We will continue with the sample problem of Example 2 with a spacecraft in a circular orbit at 1,000 km and the Sun 25 deg out of the orbit plane. In this case, the computational geometry is shown in Fig. 6-22, in which the coordinate system and the solar motion are the same as shown previously in Fig. 6-20. This coordinate system is fixed in the spacecraft. Therefore, we can represent an arbitrary spacecraft surface by a point, **N**, on the celestial sphere normal to the given face. **N** remains fixed in spacecraft coordinates, as does the orientation of nadir, and the orbit pole. The Sun moves once per orbit along a small circle of radius γ_s. This radius remains essentially fixed for a single orbit. γ_N is the angle from **N** to the orbit pole. The rotation angle ΔAz is the azimuthal difference between the Sun and **N**. It varies uniformly once per orbit from 0 to 360 deg. If I is the incident energy on the face with area A, K is the solar constant in the vicinity of the Earth = 1,367 W/m^2, and β is the angle between the Sun and the normal, **N**, to the face, then at any given moment when the Sun is shining on the face:

$$I = AK \cos\beta \tag{6-13}$$

and, from the law of cosines for sides:

$$\cos\beta = \cos\gamma_N \cos\gamma_s + \sin\gamma_N \sin\gamma_s \cos(\Delta Az) \tag{6-14}$$

By inspection, the maximum and minimum angles between the Sun and N are:

$$\beta_{max} = \gamma_s + \gamma_N \quad \text{and} \quad \beta_{min} = |\gamma_s - \gamma_N| \tag{6-15}$$

γ_s and γ_N are both constants for a given orbit and spacecraft face, whereas ΔAz

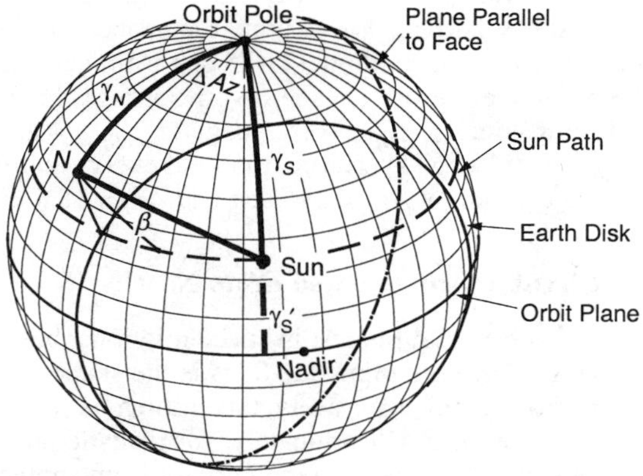

Fig. 6-22. Geometry for Computing Sun Angle on an Arbitrary Spacecraft Face. The coordinate system and solar motion are the same as in Fig. 6-20.

changes throughout the orbit. Equations (6-13) to (6-15) apply to either circular or elliptical orbits. If the orbit is circular with period P and angular frequency $\omega = 2\pi/P$, then Eqs. (6-13) and (6-14) can be integrated directly to determine the total energy, E, incident on the face between azimuths Az_1 and Az_2:

$$E_{Az_1 \text{ to } Az_2} = (AK/\omega)\,[(Az_2 - Az_1)\cos\gamma_N \cos\gamma_s + (\sin Az_2 - \sin Az_1)\sin\gamma_N \sin\gamma_s] \tag{6-16}$$

In Eq. (6-16), the 0 azimuth is in the direction of **N** and the angles are in radians. In a full orbit, the Sun will shine on the face, except for two periods: (a) during eclipse, and (b) when β is greater than 90 deg, and therefore the Sun is on the "back side" of the face. These conditions can be seen in Fig. 6-22. The spacecraft is in eclipse whenever the Sun lies behind the disk of the Earth and is on the back side of the face, whenever it is beyond the dashed great circle perpendicular to **N.** This great circle represents the plane of the surface projected onto the celestial sphere. In Fig. 6-22, the Sun is currently in eclipse. As it moves to the left in the diagram, it first goes out of eclipse, and then comes as close as possible to **N** such that the Sun is highest in the sky relative to that spacecraft face. It then becomes lower in the sky, going to the back side of the spacecraft face on the other side of the globe plot and continuing on the back side until the spacecraft again enters eclipse on the right side of the figure. Somewhat later, still on the right of Fig. 6-22, the Sun would have risen over the forward face, but is in eclipse behind the Earth. It then returns to its original position, and the process repeats.

Numerically, we can determine the conditions for eclipse from Eq. (6-9) as:

$$Az_{eclipse} = Az_0 \pm \arccos(\cos\rho / \sin\gamma_s) \tag{6-17}$$

where Az_0 is the azimuth of nadir relative to **N**. To determine when the Sun will be on the back side, we use a quadrantal triangle with $\beta = 90$ deg to find:

$$Az_{back} = \pm \arccos[-1/(\tan\gamma_N \tan\gamma_s)] \tag{6-18}$$

The problem now reduces to determining whether conditions (a) or (b) or both will occur, and the relative order of the azimuth limits. Section 11.2 extends this example to compute the average solar radiation intensity over the orbit.

As an example, consider the geometry illustrated in Fig. 6-22 for which $\rho = 60$ deg, $\omega = 0.0010$ rad/sec and $\gamma_s = 25$ deg. We assume the spacecraft face has an area of 0.5 m^2 with its normal vector at an azimuth of –75 deg from nadir ($Az_0 = 75$ deg) and an elevation of 35 deg above the orbit plane ($\gamma_N = 55$ deg). From Eqs. (6-17) and (6-18) the azimuthal limits are: $Az_{1eclipse} = 18.5$ deg, $Az_{2eclipse} = 131.5$ deg, $Az_{1back} = 109.0$ deg, and $Az_{2back} = 251$ deg. Therefore, the total energy input on the face over one orbit is between the azimuth of $Az_1 = 251$ deg and $Az_2 = 18.5$ deg.

6.3.4 Example 4: A Circular Orbit Viewed From Nearby

One other shape is of substantial interest in space missions, but is somewhat more complicated than those we have seen thus far. This is the shape of a circular orbit as seen from nearby. Seen from a long ways away, the problem is simple. A circular orbit viewed from an angle is an ellipse. Unfortunately, for realistic problems, such as the motion of a satellite seen from the surface of the Earth or from another nearby satellite, this approximation is not realistic. Figure 6-23 shows the shape of a circular, equatorial orbit seen from somewhat above and outside of point A. The reason the orbit is not a perfect ellipse is that the near edge of the orbit is magnified much more than the far edge. If we were able to stand next to an orbit as the satellite goes by, we would see the satellite moving through large angular arcs in a very short time as it zipped past our location, then slow down and move through small angles as it recedes into the distance. This has several practical effects on the appearance of an orbit seen from the Earth or from space. Although the orbit will appear to be approximately elliptical, the center of that apparent ellipse will **not** be in the same direction as the center of the Earth, but will be below it (i.e., in the direction toward the closest point on the orbit). Consequently, the circumstance illustrated in Fig. 6-23 can occur often, in which the satellite disappears behind the Earth, but on the front side does not pass over the disk of the Earth, but rather outside it.

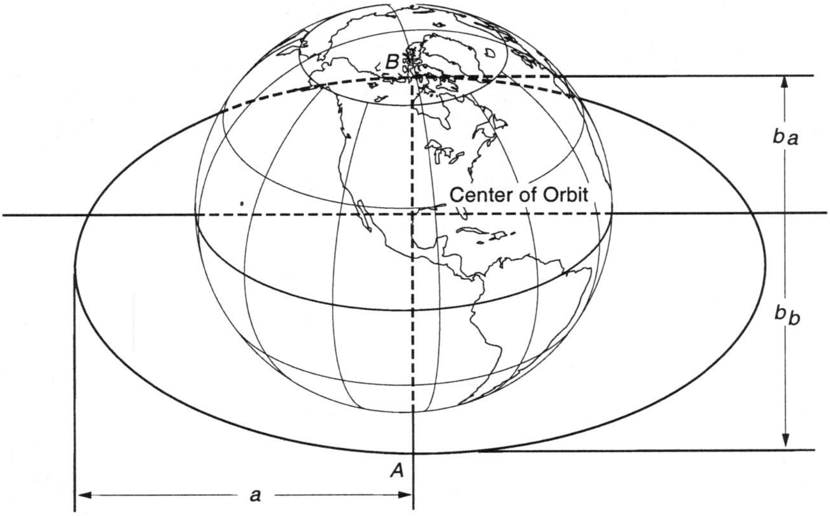

Fig. 6-23. Appearance of a Circular Orbit Viewed Obliquely from Near Point A.

Although the shape itself is somewhat complex, it is straightforward to compute the extrema of the motion as seen from nearby. Specifically, the angular height, b_a, of the apparent ellipse above the Earth's center (on the far side of the orbit), and the angular distance, b_b, below the Earth's center (for the point on the orbit nearest the observer) are given by:

$$\tan b_a = \frac{R \sin I}{D + R \cos I} \tag{6-19}$$

$$\tan b_b = \frac{R \sin I}{D - R \cos I} \tag{6-20}$$

where R is the radius of circular orbit being viewed at distance D from the center of the Earth and at an angle I measured at the center of the Earth between the orbit plane and the observer. The quantity b_b and the implied atan function in Eq. (6-20) should be evaluated over the range 0 to 180 deg. When $\tan b_b > 0$, then the observer is "outside" the apparent orbit and the nearest point on the orbit is within 90 deg of nadir. When $\tan b_b < 0$, the nearest point is more than 90 deg from nadir, the observer is "inside" the orbit, and the satellite appears to go around the observer as well as around the Earth. The minor axis of the apparent ellipse will be along the great circle arc perpendicular to the orbit plane and through the center of the Earth.

The semimajor axis, a, of the apparent ellipse is given by:

$$\sin^2 a = 2R^2 / \left(D^2 + R^2 + \sqrt{K}\right) \tag{6-21a}$$

where:

$$K = (D^2 + R^2)^2 - 4\, D^2 R^2 \cos^2 I \tag{6-21b}$$

For simplified computations, note that a falls in the range:

$$\text{asin}\,(R/D) \geq a \geq \text{atan}\,(R/D) \tag{6-22}$$

which is adequately narrow for most applications.

The azimuthal position along the apparent orbit is most conveniently measured by the rotation angle, α', measured about the orbit pole. (The orbit pole is a direction in space projected onto the celestial sphere, just as the celestial pole is in the direction of the Earth's rotation axis projected onto the celestial sphere. There is no parallax in either case.) To determine α', we first determine D_p, the projection of D into the orbit plane:

$$D_p = D \cos I \tag{6-23}$$

Then:

$$\tan \alpha' = (R \sin \alpha) / (D_p - R \cos \alpha) \tag{6-24}$$

where α is the angular position along the orbit (i.e., the rotation angle measured at the center of the orbit) from the point on the orbit nearest the observer to the point in question.

References

Bowditch, Nathaniel. 1966. *American Practical Navigator.* Washington, DC: Government Printing Office.

Brink, Raymond W. 1942. *Spherical Trigonometry.* New York: Appleton-Century-Croft, Inc.

Canters, Frank, and Huge Decleir. 1989. *The World in Perspective: A Directory of World Map Projections.* New York: John Wiley & Sons.

Green, R.M. 1985. *Spherical Astronomy.* Cambridge: Cambridge University Press.

Newcomb, Simon. 1960. *A Compendium of Spherical Astronomy.* New York: Dover.

Palmer, C.I., C.W. Leigh, and S.H. Kimball. 1950. *Plane and Spherical Trigonometry.* New York: McGraw-Hill, Inc.

Seidelmann, P. Kenneth (ed.). 1992. *Explanatory Supplement to the Astronomical Almanac.* Mill Valley, CA: University Science Books

Shuster, Malcolm D. 1993. "A Survey of Attitude Representations." *Journal of Astronautical Sciences*, Vol. 41, No. 4, pp. 439–517.

Small, Lloyd Lenny. 1952. *Trigonometry: Plane and Spherical.* New York: McGraw-Hill, Inc.

Wertz, James R. (ed.). 1978. *Spacecraft Attitude Determination and Control.* Dordrecht, The Netherlands: D. Reidel Publishing Company.

Wertz, James R. and Wiley J. Larson (eds.). 1999. *Space Mission Analysis and Design* (3rd ed). Torrance, CA and Dordrecht, The Netherlands: Microcosm Press and Kluwer Academic Publishers.

Chapter 7

Spacecraft Position and Attitude Measurements

This chapter provides both physical interpretation and quantitative analysis for position and attitude measurements made on board the spacecraft. The purpose of the chapter is to provide the understanding and formulas needed to interpret and evaluate attitude, orbit, and payload measurements. Specific sensors that we will consider are:

- Conical scanner (Earth width, and nadir angle measurement)
- Vector magnetometer
- Earth/Sun rotation angle measurement
- Array processors (Sun sensor, star sensor, or CCD camera)

Most measurements made on board the spacecraft are inherently geometrical and most involve angular measurements. This is the case for CCD arrays, photographs, Earth sensors, Sun sensors, star sensors, and interferometers. Some measurements, such as those from a GPS receiver, radar, or radio ranging, are direct range measurements. These measurements are used for a variety of purposes:

- Position and orbit determination
- Attitude and attitude rate determination
- Instrument pointing
- Mapping (i.e., determining where the object we see is located)

The purpose of this chapter is to determine the meaning and information content of the individual measurements. By *information content*, we have a specific mathematical definition in mind—i.e., what is the measurement telling us about the possible location, direction, or orientation of a point or object. This is critical for correctly interpreting the measurements in terms of the desired outputs.

The most important message in this chapter is:

> **What matters most in analyzing, interpreting, and determining the errors in measurements and combinations of measurements is the information content of the individual measurements, not how they are processed or how the computations are done.**

We can illustrate this general rule with an example of trying to determine a location on the surface of the Earth. Suppose, for example, we make two measurements of a point's location with different instruments, one which determines its distance, south of the Washington Monument, and a second measurement which determines its latitude. I can repeat these measurements many times and collect an enormous amount of statistical data. Nonetheless, no amount of clever processing or Kalman filtering will tell me where I am. The reason is that the two measurements are *correlated*, i.e., they are two separate numbers but both are measuring the same thing. They have the same information content. Both tell me about north-south distance and neither tells me about east-west distance. The best answer that I can give is that the point in question is at a specific latitude and, presumably, is somewhere in the vicinity of Washington, D.C., since I have measured the north-south distance with respect to the Washington Monument. With each measurement, and with each combination of measurements, I want to understand what it is telling us about the quantity that we are interested in, and I need to know when to abandon my Kalman filter and start looking for an "east-west sensor."

It is also critical to note that the information content of a measurement is independent of how the measurement is processed. Computations can add error by, for example, introducing singularities (or even mistakes) in the computation process, but cannot get out more information than is contained in the measurements themselves. What we want is to break measurements down into their constituent components and then reassemble them so that we can understand the source of the irreducible error (i.e., the errors inherent in the measurements themselves) and how these errors accumulate. We will assume throughout the chapter that we are careful in the processing so as not to introduce additional errors.

Unfortunately, relatively few references provide a thorough assessment of spacecraft measurements and their interpretation. Attitude measurements are described in some detail in Wertz [1978]. Other types of measurements are described at a top level by Wertz and Larson [1999].

7.1 Introduction to Angular Measurements

This section discusses the general problem of making and interpreting angular measurements made by spacecraft instruments. The physical interpretation will be done in terms of points and loci on the spacecraft-centered celestial sphere introduced in Chap. 6.

7.1.1 Measurements as Loci on the Celestial Sphere

Recall from Chap. 3 that measuring a direction in space requires two numbers, and measuring the attitude or orientation requires three numbers. This implies that a single number or single measurement corresponds to a one-dimensional locus along the celestial sphere. It is convenient to consider an analogy on the surface of the Earth. Specifying the latitude is a single number or measurement and corresponds to a fixed angle from the Earth's pole, i.e., an object at a given latitude lies on a small circle centered on the pole. Specifying the longitude puts the point on a *meridian* or arc of a great circle running between the poles. The intersection of these determines the location of the point. There are, of course, many ways to specify a single locus. It could, for example, be 3 miles north of some identified location or 2 miles off the coast of Florida, which would be a locus with a rather complex shape. As shown in Fig. 7-1A, the intersection of 2 loci then determines a direction in space which has a clear and unambiguous interpretation.*

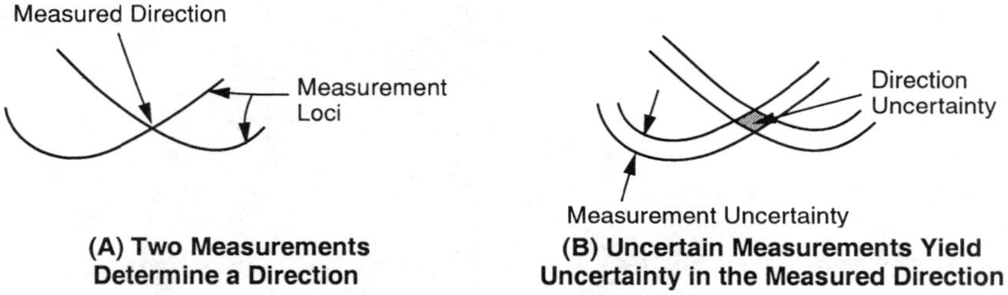

Fig. 7-1. Measurements as Loci on the Celestial Sphere. The intersection of two loci determines a direction in space.

As illustrated in Fig. 7-1B, each measurement also has an uncertainty associated with it. Consequently, the full measurement represents not a single line across the celestial sphere, but rather a band representing the measurement plus the uncertainty. (This band could be either an absolute value, as would be appropriate for quantized measurements, or a statistical value, such as the 1σ or 3σ uncertainties.) This affects how we interpret the final measurement but does not affect the loci and uncertainty regions themselves. The intersection of the two bands corresponding to the measurements provides the uncertainty region for the direction which is being determined.

Position measurements behave similarly with two numbers required to specify a position on the surface of the Earth and three numbers required in three-dimensional space. In three dimensions, a single measurement specifies a surface, or with uncertainty, a surface with some thickness. The intersection of two surfaces produces a line, and the intersection of three surfaces reduces the position determination to a point surrounded by its uncertainty region.

Unfortunately, there is not a comparably clean geometrical definition for the meaning of 3-axis attitude. There are several methods for specifying 3-axis attitude, as described in Chap. 3, but none of them are as simple and as clean as specifying either a direction or 3-dimensional position. One reason is that specifying the attitude typi-

* This is not entirely true. For example, 3 miles north then 2 miles west is not quite the same as 2 miles west then 3 miles north. See the boxed example in Sec. 6.1 for a further discussion.

cally gives different accuracies for different points. For example, suppose we attempt to find the celestial coordinates for a star that is directly overhead some location on the Earth, but the time of the sighting is only poorly known. The resulting coordinates on the celestial sphere would be more accurate over the poles than over Los Angeles, because Los Angeles is moving more rapidly in inertial space than the pole is.

The easiest direction measurement in space to understand is the arc length. The *Sun angle* or angle between the Sun and an unknown point in the sky is a good example of an *arc length measurement*. The unknown point could be the direction of the spacecraft spin axis or the direction to some object seen by a spacecraft instrument. Assuming that we know the time of the measurement and the ephemeris of the Earth's orbit about the Sun (or, in any case, the position of the spacecraft in the solar system), we then know the location of the Sun in spacecraft-centered celestial coordinates. Measuring the Sun angle implies that the unknown object or direction lies on a small circle with a radius equal to the angular measurement and centered on the celestial coordinates of the Sun, as shown in Fig. 7-2.

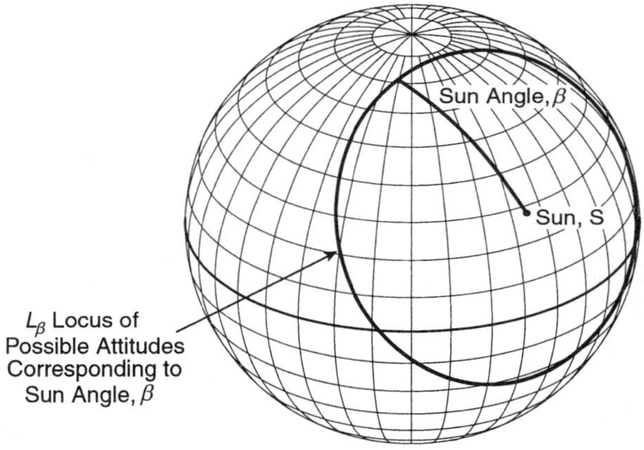

Fig. 7-2. Locus of Points Corresponding to a Measured Sun Angle, β. The direction to the Sun is assumed to be known. Consequently, the unknown direction must lie on a small circle centered on the Sun.

Let us now assume that we have a second arc length measurement for the same unknown point, say, its angular distance from the center of the Earth, again assuming that we know where the Earth is relative to us. This gives us two loci which then define the direction to the point in inertial space.

This simple case illustrates several important features of measurement loci. As shown in Figs. 7-3 A, B, and C, there are three possible outcomes for these measurement loci:

1. The loci intersect at two discrete locations (Fig. 7-3A)
2. The loci are nearly tangent (Fig. 7-3B)
3. The loci do not intersect (Fig. 7-3C)

Each of these cases is both possible and important. In the first case, I have two valid solutions that must be resolved by, for example, a third measurement or an apriori estimate of the unknown direction. Case 2, where the curves are nearly tangent, will arise whenever the two reference vectors and the unknown lie approximately along a great circle. In this case, there will be a singularity in determining the unknown direction, just as there is a singularity in having one measurement of the latitude and one of the distance south of the Washington Monument. I have very nearly the same information in both measurements such that I am getting the same information twice, rather than two distinct pieces of information.

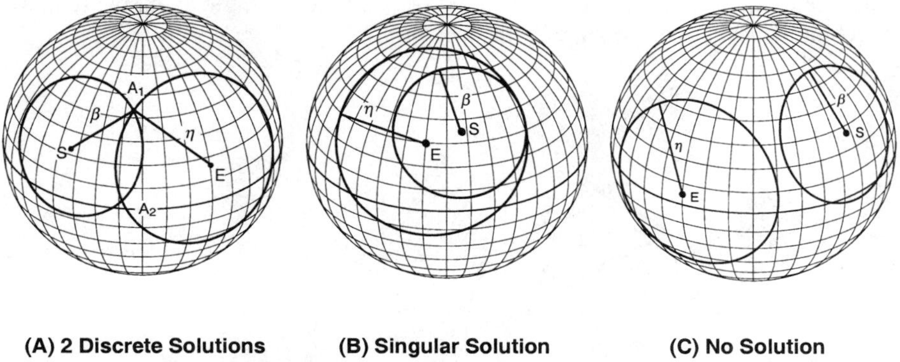

Fig. 7-3. Two Arc Length Measurements Used to Define the Direction to a Point in Space. In (A), the solution is well determined, to within an ambiguity. In (B), the solution is not well determined because the measurements are not independent, but duplicate each other. In (C), the loci do not intersect due to, for example, measurement noise.

It is easy to ignore Case 3, in which the two solutions do not intersect, but it is important not to do so, because of the uncertainty in each of the measurements. If they are nearly tangent, then a small error in either measurement can result in nonintersecting solutions. The critical point is that in any large collection of data, this **will** occur, and, therefore, cannot be allowed to bomb the processing software. We must be able to handle this case when it arises.

It is important to stress again that it does not matter how I process the measurements. The uncertainty regions, ambiguities, singularities, and lack of intersections are inherent in the measurements themselves. I cannot remove them by clever processing or data averaging. Processing can remove information from the measurements, but it cannot create it. Once we have determined the true information content of the measurements themselves, then we have obtained all the information that is available.

Finally, in this example we have assumed that we know where the Earth is with respect to the spacecraft. This is illustrative of a coupling between orbit and attitude that frequently occurs. Errors in the spacecraft position knowledge will ultimately transform into errors in my capacity to point toward objects of interest or map the surface of the Earth.

7.1.2 Basic Measurement Types

Nearly all angular measurements can be classed as one of three basic measurements types—the arc length measurement described above, or one of two types of rotation angles. These three types of measurements are illustrated in the spherical triangle in

Fig. 7-4. Here we assume that there are two reference directions for which the positions on the celestial sphere are known and, consequently, the arc length between them is also known. This leaves us with five components in the spherical triangle—two arc lengths and the three rotation angles. Any of these five unknowns represent realistic angular measurements. The arc length measurements are both similar to those described in Sec. 7.1.1. However, there are two different types of rotation angles. Both R_1 and R_2 in the figure are measurements about a known point from a known reference direction to the unknown direction. These are called *Type I rotation angles*. On the other hand, S, called a *Type II rotation angle*, is a rotation angle about the unknown direction between two known reference vectors.

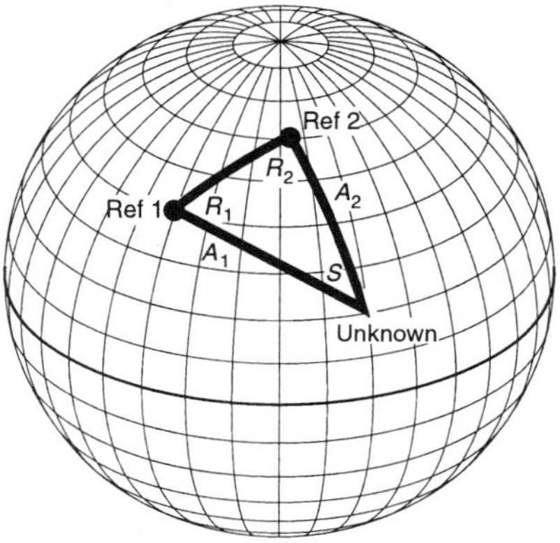

Fig. 7-4. Illustration of Basic Measurement Types. The measurement type, and the corresponding measurement locus, depends on which angles in the spherical triangle are measured. See Fig. 7-5 for the loci corresponding to the rotation angle measurements.

For any given measurement, the type is determined not by what is being measured but by the shape of the resulting loci on the celestial sphere. Thus, if the locus of possible solutions is a small circle, the measurement **is** an arc length measurement. It is this basic measurement type that determines how the data should be processed, where singularities occur, and how errors accumulate. To correctly process data from any sensor, we need to determine the loci on the celestial sphere corresponding to the measurements, and then determine how best to evaluate and process these measurements.

The loci corresponding to the three basic measurement types are shown in Fig. 7-5. For the arc length measurement, the locus is simply a small circle centered on the reference direction. For a Type I rotation angle (R_1 or R_2), the unknown must lie along a great circle arc with one end on the reference vector that the rotation angle was measured about. The Type II rotation angle (S in Fig. 7-4), has a much more peculiar locus shaped approximately like a double horseshoe on the celestial sphere. The ends of the horseshoe lie on the two reference directions and the antipodes of these reference directions. Except in the special case in which the measured rotation angle is equal to the arc length between the reference directions, the two horseshoes do not intersect. This measurement will be described in more detail in Sec. 7.4.2.

The basic measurement for any rotating mechanism is a rotation angle. If the direction of the rotation axis is known, such that the measurement is between a reference

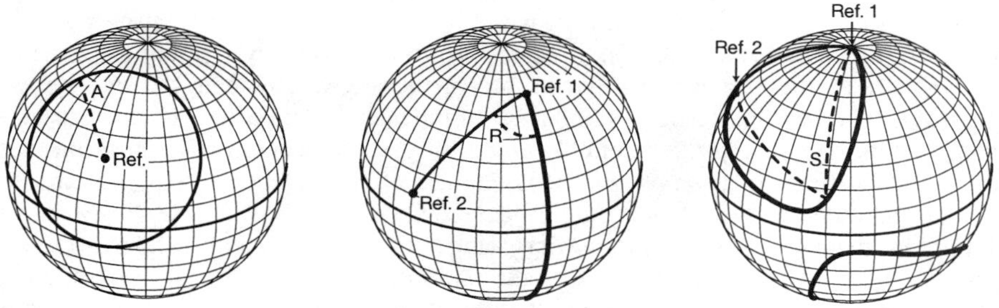

(A) Arc Length, A (B) Type I Rotation Angle, R (C) Type II Rotation Angle, S

Fig. 7-5. Loci Corresponding to the Basic Measurement Types Illustrated in Fig. 7-4. The second lobe of the Type II rotation angle curve occurs because of the unique character of spherical geometry. (See Sec. 7.4.2.).

direction and an unknown, then it will be a Type I rotation angle. If the rotation axis itself is the unknown, and we measure the rotation angle between two known targets, it is a Type II measurement. In practice, both occur often in space missions.

Table 7-1 provides a classification in terms of measurement types for the most common angular measurements made by spacecraft. While there is a wide variety of reference vectors, unknowns, and sensors to provide celestial measurements, nearly all of the measurements fall into one of the three categories we have discussed. Each of these sensors will be discussed in more detail later in the chapter.

TABLE 7-1. Classification of Most Common Measurements Made by Spacecraft. RA = rotation angle, AL = arc length. (See Figs. 7-4 and 7-5.)

Object Sensed	Sensor	Measurement Technique	Measurement Type
Sun/Stars	Single slit on spinning spacecraft	Measure RA from Sun to spacecraft reference	Type I RA
Sun/Stars	Single axis array or calibrated slit	Measure "vertical" position of Sun when it crosses a ref slit	AL
Sun/Stars	Two inclined slits on rotating sensor or spinning spacecraft	Measure midpoint and separation between crossings	Separation = AL Midpoint = Type I RA
Sun/Stars	2-axis array	Measure x/y coordinates	Both are Type I RAs
Earth Horizon	Conical scanner	Measure midpoint and separation between crossings	Separation = AL Midpoint = Type I RA
Earth Horizon	Static sensor	Measure 1 or more individual edge crossings	Each pair = a conical scanner
Earth/Sun	Earth and Sun sensor on a spinning spacecraft	Measure rotation angle between Earth and Sun	Type II RA
Magnetic Field	3-axis magnetometer	Measure 3 components of the field	All 3 are AL
Inertial Space	Gyroscope	Measure cumulative rotation about a "known" axis	Type I RA
GPS	GPS receiver (attitude)	Use as interferometer to measure angle with respect to a given GPS satellite	AL

An interesting example of a sensor which makes two different measurement types is either a conical Earth horizon sensor (i.e., a sensor that uses a rotating mirror or prism to scan out a small circle in the sky), or a static sensor on a spinning spacecraft. In both cases, the sensor scans out an arc in the sky and detects the two horizon crossings when the scan crosses onto or off of the disk of the Earth. The two measurements could be taken as the azimuthal angles of the two horizon crossings, but these are highly correlated. However, as discussed in Sec. 7.2.1, a better interpretation of the two measurements results from combining them into an *Earth width measurement* (the azimuthal distance between the two crossings) and a *mid-scan rotation angle* (the rotation angle from some reference to the midpoint between the two horizon crossings). The mid-scan and Earth width are independent measurements. The Earth width measurement determines how far down onto the disk of the Earth the scan is crossing, and, therefore, is a measure of the angle from the nadir to the center of the sensing cone. Consequently, the Earth width is an arc length measurement. On the other hand, the mid-scan rotation angle measures the rotation angle about the unknown axis of rotation from the direction to the center of the Earth to some other reference direction, such as the Sun. Because the direction to the measurement axis is the unknown, this is a Type II rotation angle measurement. Thus, the conical scanner provides an arc length measurement and a Type II rotation angle. If we choose to use instead the "raw" measurements of the azimuthal orientation of the two horizon crossings, we have a significantly more complex measurement type.

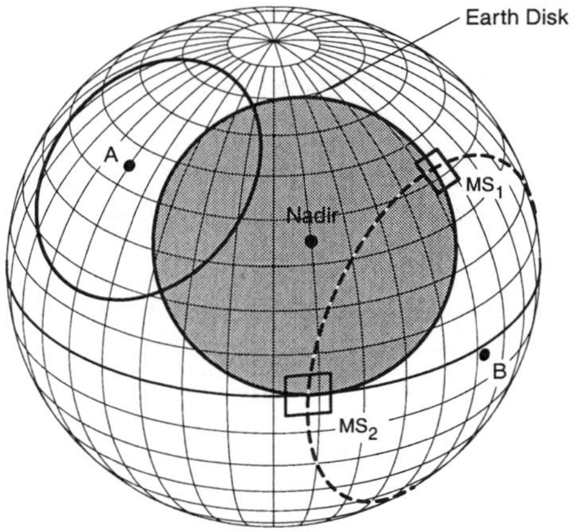

Fig. 7-6. Alternative Interpretations of Horizon Crossing Measurements. Measurements can be made either by a single scanning sensor centered at A or by 2 mini-static sensors, MS_1 and MS_2. The information content is the same for both and, hence, the processing should be the same. The 2 mini-static sensors provide the same information as a conical scanner at B.

In many spacecraft, conical scanners are being replaced by simpler and lower-cost mini-static sensors. Each mini-static sensor determines the location of the horizon of the Earth along a sensitive axis as illustrated in Fig. 7-6. Although the sensors themselves are physically very different, the resulting measurements are essentially the same for a pair of mini-static sensors as for a conical scanner. The two mini-static sensors represent a segment of the conical scan produced by a scanning sensor. They can be thought of as the active portion of an imaginary conical scanner whose axis is at the intersection of the two great circle arcs perpendicular to the sensitive axis of the two mini-statics. Once again, what is important is not how the measurement is made but rather the information content of the measurement—that is, what is the locus on the celestial sphere of the possible directions corresponding to a given measurement or set of measurements. We will return to this issue in Sec. 7.3, after examining the numerical evaluation of measurement uncertainties and combining measurements.

7.2 Evaluation of Measurement Uncertainty

All measurements have associated with them an uncertainty which can be represented by a *probability distribution*, which is the likelihood that the measured quantity has a specific value. Most measurements fall into one of two general types:

- **Quantized measurements** such as a digital clock. If the clock is well calibrated, then there is a uniform probability that the actual time lies between the previous time step and the next step on the digital clock and zero probability that it lies outside this range.
- **Continuous measurements** such as an analog meter, in which the most likely value is the one read by the meter and there is a typically Gaussian probability distribution defined by 1σ or 3σ errors about the most-likely value.

In practice, many measurements will be a mix of both, such as when an analog level in a sensor is digitized and processed through a computer. While this can make the probability arithmetic more complex, it doesn't change the fundamental nature of uncertainty as a probability distribution.

There are two critical points to keep in mind during the process of evaluating measurement uncertainties:

- **The error in the final value (such as the direction to a target) <u>is</u> the probability distribution on the celestial sphere.** We may choose to approximate that probability distribution by a variety of numbers or combinations of numbers such as a circular error probability or by the 1σ or 3σ value along some particular axis. Nonetheless, it is the probability distribution itself which is the error in the measurement.
- In general, errors do not depend on the method by which the data is processed. We may introduce additional error by processing the data poorly or going through incorrect intermediate steps. However, we cannot by any amount of clever processing reduce the error inherent in the measurements themselves.

The last point is particularly important. We may choose to process measurements as unit vectors or angles in spherical triangles. We may average them to reduce the level of noise, or filter them to obtain a better statistical combination. Multiple measurements may be combined to provide better answers than individual measurements. However, no amount of processing can reduce or eliminate errors inherent in the data itself. Whether we process the data as vectors or angles in spherical triangles does not matter, so long as we do the processing correctly. The measurements tell us something about the world, such as the direction to a star or target. Our objective is to find out what they are telling us—i.e., what the measurement and the uncertainties in the measurement mean in terms of the final value we wish to compute.

7.2.1 Correlation Angle and Measurement Density

For simplicity, we begin by assuming that the measurement errors are quantized and therefore, the probability distribution lies between two well defined limits. Section 7.2.2 deals with the results for nonquantized measurements. For ease of discussion, we will assume that the measurements are two arc lengths—the *Sun angle*, or angle from the Sun to an unknown direction, and the *nadir angle*, or angle from the center of the Earth to the same unknown direction. However, the general rules which we develop apply equally well to other reference vectors, such as angles relative to two stars, or other measurement types, such as rotation angles.

Figure 7-7 shows both of our measurements as bands on the sky, representing the measured value and the uncertainty about it. For quantized measurements, the unknown point must lie in one of the two intersection areas. We frequently determine which area by using either another crude measurement type or an apriori estimate of the value based, for example, on the value at a slightly earlier time. Once we have resolved the ambiguity, we know that the unknown point must lie in the *error parallelogram*, which is the area of intersection between the two measurement bands. We may approximate this error parallelogram in various ways, but the actual measurement **is** the intersection area.

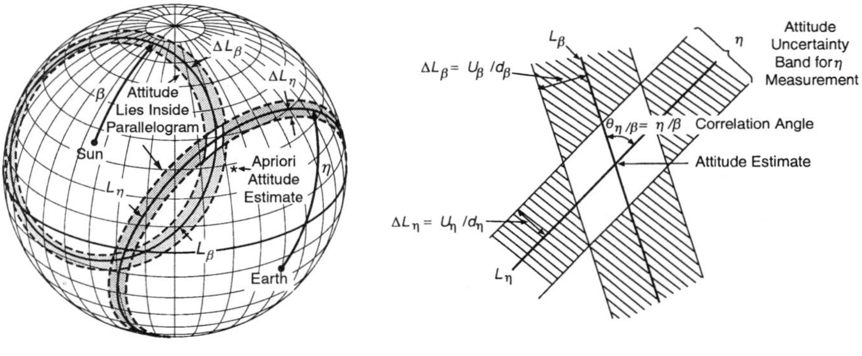

(A) (B)

Fig. 7-7. Uncertainty in the Direction on the Celestial Sphere Resulting from Uncertainty in Individual Measurements. (B) is an expanded view of the intersection shown in (A).

The size and shape of the error parallelogram is determined by two factors: the width of the individual measurement uncertainty regions and the angle at which these bands intersect, called the *correlation angle.* For a given uncertainty band on individual measurements, it is the correlation angle which determines how these measurements combine to produce an uncertainty in the final measurement. If the correlation angle is 90 deg or 270 deg, then the measurements are said to be *independent* or *uncorrelated*, in that they measure components of the final direction which do not depend on each other. For example, a given latitude can correspond to any longitude. On the other hand, if the correlation angle is 0 deg or 180 deg, the measurements are said to be *fully correlated* or *singular*. Here the two measurements are both measuring the same quantity, such as the distance south of a given reference and a second measurement of the latitude. Both measurements correspond to the distance from the pole or the equator and neither tells us the longitude.

The implication of this for two arc length measurements on the celestial sphere is shown in Fig. 7-8. We have defined the reference frame such that the Sun is at one pole and, consequently, the latitude lines on the figure correspond to constant Sun angle measurements. The Earth is at some other location in this coordinate frame, and constant nadir angle measurements are represented by a series of small circles centered on the Earth. As can be seen by inspection, whenever the unknown direction lies on the great circle defined by the directions to the Sun and the Earth, the correlation angle between the Sun angle and nadir angle measurements will be 0 deg or 180 deg, and the corresponding solution will be singular. Whenever the unknown direction is well away from this great circle, it will have an accurate solution and two well defined intersections of the two measurement bands.

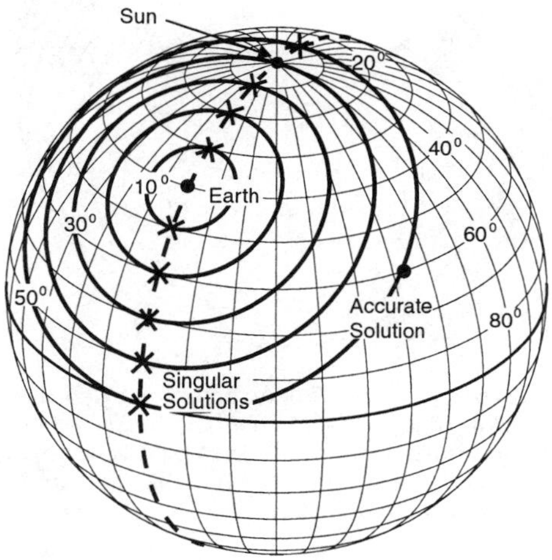

Fig. 7-8. For Two Arc Length Measurements, the Correlation Angle will be Zero and the Results Singular when the Measured Direction Lies Along the Great Circle Through the Reference Vectors.

The second factor which determines the uncertainty is the width of the uncertainty band in the two or more measurements that are being combined. The width of these bands depends on both the uncertainty in the original measurement and in how that uncertainty projects onto the celestial sphere. For example, suppose we have some type of sextant or space protractor which measures the Sun angle to an accuracy of ± 1 deg, irrespective of the value of the Sun angle. In this case, the uncertainty band for the Sun angle would be a band 2 deg wide, centered on the measured value.

In reality, most measurements are more complex than this and do not measure directly the angles on the celestial sphere. For example, one of the simplest ways to measure the Sun angle is by using what is commonly called a *cosine detector*, which is just a solar cell facing out into space. The intensity of the illumination is proportional to the amount of sunlight falling on the cell, which, in turn, is proportional to the area of the cell and the cosine of the angle from the Sun to the vector normal to the cell's surface (hence the term cosine detector). If we assume that the cell measures constant steps in solar intensity, it does **not** measure constant steps in the Sun angle because the cosine function itself is nonlinear. When the Sun is nearly perpendicular to the cell, the angle relative to the normal will be small, the cosine will be approximately 1, and the cosine detector is very insensitive to the actual value of the angle. Consequently, the cosine detector is a very poor measuring device when the Sun is nearly overhead. On the other hand, when the Sun is at reasonably large angles relative to the normal, the sensitivity can be good and the cosine detector is a good measuring device.

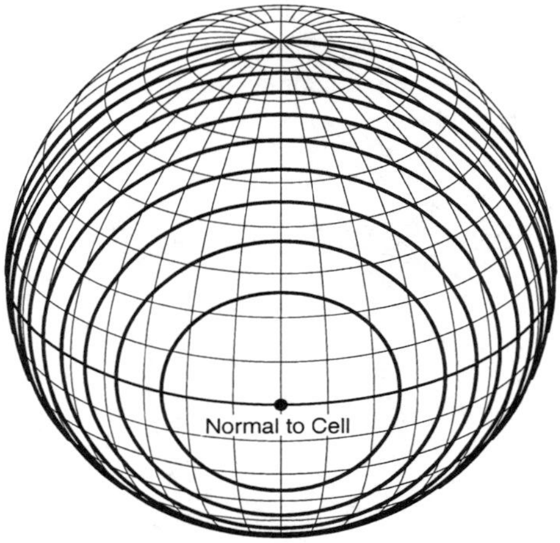

Fig. 7-9. Equal Steps in Intensity of Light Falling on a Solar Cell. This *cosine detector* can be used as a coarse Sun angle measurement. The *measurement density* reflects the degree to which the end direction is sensitive to the particular measurement. For an intensity detector, such as a single solar cell, the measurement itself is the cosine of the angle between the detector and the Sun.

Figure 7-9 shows a series of Sun angle curves at equal steps in the intensity for a cosine detector. These curves illustrate the impact of what we call the *measurement density*, which is a measure of the sensitivity of the unknown to changes in the measured value. More formally, the measurement density can be thought of either as the gradient of the direction on the celestial sphere with respect to the measurement in question, or as the change in measurement per unit arc length change between adjacent loci measured perpendicular to the loci. Thus, the *measurement density*, d_m, is:

$$d_m \equiv U_m / \Delta L_m \tag{7-1}$$

where U_m is the uncertainty in the measurement and ΔL_m is the width of the measurement band on the celestial sphere. If the measurement density is near 0, then the loci of possible positions for the unknown on the celestial sphere will be far apart, small differences in the measurement will correspond to very large differences in the orientation of the unknown, and the resulting determination of the orientation of the unknown will have large uncertainties. This is the case near the center of the concentric circles in Fig. 7-9, where we are normal to the solar cell. As the Sun angle gets larger, the measurement density gets higher, the loci come closer together, and the measurement becomes inherently more accurate. More formal definitions of the measurement density and of the correlation angle are given in the inline footnote at the end of this section. The derivation of various values are given by Wertz [1978].

There are two ways in which variations in the measurement density occur:

- Nonlinear measurements (such as the cosine detector for Sun intensity sensing)
- Nonlinearities introduced by transforming one measurement into another (measuring the Earth width to determine the nadir angle, as defined in Sec. 7.1).

The distinction between these two is somewhat arbitrary. For example, a nonlinear Sun angle measurement could be treated as a linear intensity measurement followed by a nonlinear transformation. Nonetheless, the result is the same. The direction loci on the celestial sphere are not evenly distributed, and consequently, the measurement is better in some parts of the sky than in other parts. As a consequence of both variations in measurement density and correlation angle, the accuracy of measurements in terms of the direction to an unknown depends on the orientation of the unknown relative to the reference vectors being used. On the whole, these are purely geometric issues which are a function of the measurement type and the orientations of the various vectors involved. Table 7-2 summarizes both the measurement densities and correlation angles for combinations of various measurement types. The definitions of the variables involved are shown in Fig.7-10.

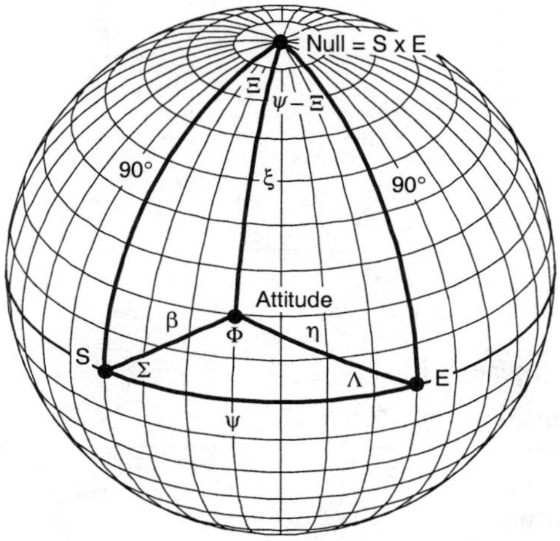

Fig. 7-10. Definitions of the Variables Defined in Table 7-2.

In practice, most observables are overdetermined and will be evaluated by some sort of least squares averaging or filtering process. This complicates the arithmetic but not the basic result. In the end, we cannot get more from the measurements than the information contained in them. One of the most common reasons for filter divergence is that we run into singularities in the principal measurements. If the fundamental measurements are singular, no amount of processing nor filtering will help us to achieve an accurate solution.

TABLE 7-2. Summary of Single-Axis Accuracy for Arc-Length and Rotation Angle Measurements. Here Φ is a Type II rotation angle, β and η are arc length measurements, and Ω is an Earth width measurement that is transformed into an arc length.

Method	d_m	d_n	$\Theta_{m/n}$
β/η	1	1	Φ
β/Ω	1	$2\left\|\dfrac{\cot\gamma}{\sin\frac{\Omega}{2}} - \cot\eta\cot\frac{\Omega}{2}\right\|$	Φ
β/Φ	1	$\left\|\dfrac{\sin\Phi}{\sin\beta}\right\|\sqrt{\cos^2\beta+\cot^2\Sigma}$ or $\left\|\dfrac{\sin\Phi}{\sin\eta}\right\|\sqrt{\cos^2\eta+\cot^2\Lambda}$ or $\left\|\dfrac{\sin\Phi\sin\xi}{\sin\beta\sin\eta}\right\|$	$\tan^{-1}\left[\dfrac{\tan\eta}{\tan\beta\sin\Phi}-\cot\Phi\right]$ or $\tan^{-1}\left[\dfrac{\cot\Lambda}{\cos\eta}\right]$
η/Φ	1	Same as above	$\tan^{-1}\left[\dfrac{\tan\beta}{\tan\eta\sin\Phi}-\cot\Phi\right]$ or $\tan^{-1}\left[\dfrac{\cot\Sigma}{\cos\beta}\right]$
Ω/Φ	$2\left\|\dfrac{\cot\gamma}{\sin\frac{\Omega}{2}} - \dfrac{\cot\eta}{\tan\frac{\Omega}{2}}\right\|$	Same as above	Same as above

NOTE:

$$(U_A)_{m/n} = \frac{1}{\sqrt{2}\left|\sin\Theta_{m/n}\right|}\left[\left(\frac{U_m}{d_m}\right)^2 + \left(\frac{U_n}{d_n}\right)^2 - 2\left(\frac{C_{m/n}}{d_m d_n}\right)\cos\Theta_{m/n}\right]^{1/2}$$

where U_m, U_n, and $C_{m/n}$ are as given in Eq. (7-26).

In summary, the measurement density or *geometrical gain, d*, determines the information content of a single measurement:

- Mathematically, it is the gradient of the measurement on the celestial sphere.
- Physically, it is the sensitivity of the measurement to changes in what is being measured.
- It relates the uncertainty in the unknown component being measured, U_{unk}, to the measurement uncertainty, U_m, by $U_{unk} = d \times U_m$.

The correlation angle, θ, determines how well two measurements combine to define a given direction in space:

- It is the angle, θ, at which the loci of the two measurements intersects.
- The ultimate measurement accuracy is inversely proportional to $\sin\theta$.

Correlation angles and measurement densities determine the information content of measurements. This does not depend on how the unknown is computed numerically. We cannot improve our uncertainties by processing as either unit vectors or spherical triangles. The uncertainties are contained in the measurements themselves. We are interested in determining what these uncertainties are, assuming that our processing is perfect.

Formal Definitions of Measurement Density and Correlation Angle

To obtain a more formal definition of the measurement density, let m_1 and m_2 be two values of the measurement m (e.g., β_1 and β_2), and let σ_{m_1,m_2} be the arc length separation between loci L_{m_1} and L_{m_2} measured perpendicular to the loci. Then the measurement density, d_m, is the two-dimensional gradient of m on the celestial sphere for a fixed position of the reference vectors (i.e., Sun vector, nadir vector), that is,

$$d_m \equiv \left|\vec{\mathbf{V}}_m\right| \quad \text{for fixed reference vectors}$$
$$\equiv \lim_{\sigma_{m_1 m_2} \to 0} \left|m_2 - m_1\right| / \sigma_{m_1 m_2} \tag{7-2}$$

If we let m_1 and m_2 be the limits of uncertainty in measurement m, then σ_{m_1,m_2} corresponds to the width, ΔL_m, of the attitude uncertainty band on the celestial sphere. (See Fig. 7-7B.) Thus,

$$\Delta L_m = U_m / d_m \tag{7-3}$$

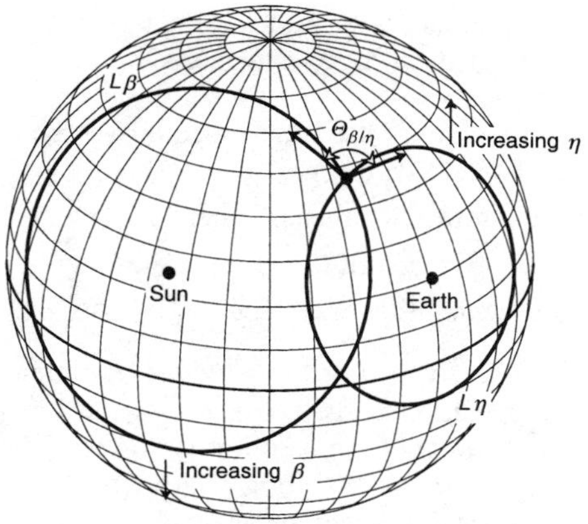

Fig. 7-11. Definition of the Correlation Angle, $\Theta_{\beta/\eta}$.

To specify the correlation angle or the angle of intersection between two loci, several choices are available. Physically, it is convenient to think of the correlation angle as the acute angle between the tangents to the loci as was done in the text above. However, for computer work or algebraic manipulation, this involves continuous tests on the range of an angle, and adjustments when it falls outside the range of 0 deg to 90 deg. Consequently, for algebraic use, it is more convenient to define a unique correlation angle covering the range 0–360 deg. Given two arbitrary loci, L_i and L_j, we formally define the correlation angle between them, $\Theta_{i/j}$, as the rotation angle at the intersection of the loci from the positive gradient of L_i counterclockwise (as viewed from infinity toward the spacecraft) to the positive gradient of L_j, as illustrated in Fig. 7-11. This is equivalent in its effect on attitude uncertainties to defining $\Theta_{i/j}$ as the acute angle between the tangents to L_i and L_j. Note that from this formal definition we have $\Theta_{j/i} = 360$ deg $- \Theta_{i/j}$.

As an example of a correlation angle for two arc length measurements, consider the Sun angle-nadir angle correlation angle, $\Theta_{\beta/\eta}$ shown in Fig. 7-11. $\Theta_{\beta/\eta}$ equals the angle between the radii of the two small circles at their intersection, however, this is also equal to the Sun-Earth rotation angle, Φ. Thus,

$$\Theta_{\beta/\eta} = \Phi. \tag{7-4}$$

When the correlation angle is 0 deg or 180 deg, the unknown lies along the great circle connecting the Sun and the Earth, the two small circles are tangent, and the two measurements give essentially the same information about the unknown. Thus, when the correlation angle is small (or near 180 deg), the uncertainty in the unknown is largest because the component of its position tangent to two circles is essentially unknown. In contrast, when the correlation angle is near 90 deg or 270 deg, the two measurements are independent, and the uncertainty in the position of the unknown is smallest.

7.2.2 Calculation of Direction Uncertainties

In general, deterministic solutions for the direction to any point in space are the result of two measurements made with respect to two distinct reference directions, such as the Earth and Sun, two stars, or in terms of the spacecraft, two axes of a CCD array or star camera. Of course, redundant measurements are typically available. These can be handled either as multiple independent deterministic solutions, or preferably, by some least squares algorithm that weights the accuracy of the individual measurements. This makes the arithmetic more complex, but does not change the fundamental issue of measurement accuracy and the implications for combining measurements. In this chapter, we will ignore these issues of multiple measurements and concentrate on the information content in each individual measurement and measurement pair.

For any single measurement pair used to determine a direction in space, the uncertainty in the result depends on three things:

- Uncertainty for each of the two measurements
- Measurement density for each of the two measurements
- Correlation angle at which they intersect

As discussed in Sec. 7.2.1 and illustrated in Fig. 7-9, the measurement density indicates the sensitivity of the position of the unknown vector to changes in the measured quantity. For example, we could determine our position on the surface of the Earth by measuring the apparent position of the Moon relative to the background stars. (This was done by the *Space Sextant* developed by Martin Marietta.) However, the apparent position of the Moon is very insensitive to our position on the Earth and consequently small errors in the measurement will result in large errors in our latitude and longitude.

The problem of small correlation angles is related to singularities in measurement pairs. A singularity occurs whenever two measurements which were assumed to be independent are, in fact, measuring the same thing, i.e., their loci on the celestial sphere are parallel. When this occurs, the measurements are said to be fully *correlated* or *singular* and the correlation angle is 0 deg.

What constitutes good or bad pairs of measurements depends on the application for which they are being used? While there are no absolute rules, we can assign general rules of thumb for bad measurements as follows:

- Measurement densities of less than 0.2 for angular measurements
- Correlation angles less than 11 deg.

If either of the above conditions holds, then the uncertainty in the resulting direction measurement will be more than five times larger than the uncertainties in the measured quantities. This, in turn, means that the measurement geometry is beginning to strongly impact the accuracy of the results. If the uncertainties in the unknown become more than a factor of 10 worse than the measurement uncertainties (i.e., measurement density less than 0.1 or correlation angle less than 6 deg), then accurate results become extremely difficult and the solution will be very sensitive to noise, biases, and other systematic errors. The following sections provide fundamental formulas for uncertainty in direction, in terms of correlation angle and measurement density. (See also Sec. 7.6 and the boxed example in Sec. 7.4.)

7.2.2.1 Quantized Measurements

As described in Sec. 7.2.1, quantized measurements are the easiest to interpret physically. Each measurement corresponds to a distinct error band with a uniform probability distribution across that band. As shown in Fig. 7-7, the intersection of the bands corresponds to the resulting attitude estimate. The probability density for the resulting direction in space is uniformly distributed across the *error parallelogram* illustrated in the figure. The probability of the measured direction being in any small area of the parallelogram is proportional to the ratio of the small area to that of the parallelogram itself and is the same regardless of location within the parallelogram. For example, the probability of the unknown direction being in a small circle at the tip of the parallelogram is the same as the probability of the unknown being in the same small circular area at the center of the parallelogram. The *probability density*, or probability per unit area on the celestial sphere, is constant inside the parallelogram, and 0 outside.

The *direction uncertainty* for quantized measurements **is** the error parallelogram. To fully specify this uncertainty requires stating both the size and the orientation of the parallelogram, which depends on four independent parameters. For example, we could give the width of both bands and the azimuthal orientation of each band relative to some arbitrary reference direction.

It is frequently convenient to characterize the direction uncertainty by a single number. Clearly this cannot be done in any precise sense because no one number completely defines the error parallelogram. However, we can define three convenient error parameters which may be used, depending on the nature of the uncertainty requirements and the problem being solved. The *component uncertainty* is the distance from the center to the edge of the parallelogram along some specified direction, e.g., uncertainty in right ascension. The *maximum uncertainty*, U_{max}, is the semilength of the longest diagonal, or, equivalently, the radius of a circle circumscribed about the parallelogram.

$$\begin{aligned} U_{max} &= \frac{1}{\sin\Theta_{m/n}}\left[(\Delta L_m)^2 + (\Delta L_n)^2 + 2(\Delta L_m)(\Delta L_n)\left|\cos\Theta_{m/n}\right|\right]^{1/2} \\ &= \frac{1}{\sin\Theta_{m/n}}\left[\left(\frac{U_m}{d_m}\right)^2 + \left(\frac{U_n}{d_n}\right)^2 + 2\left(\frac{U_m}{d_m}\right)\left(\frac{U_n}{d_n}\right)\left|\cos\Theta_{m/n}\right|\right]^{1/2} \end{aligned} \tag{7-5}$$

If no other definition has been specified, U_{max} should typically be taken as the direction uncertainty for quantized measurements. Finally, we define the *mean uncertainty*, U_{mean}, as the radius of a circle with area equal to that of the parallelogram.

$$\begin{aligned} U_{mean} &= 2\left[\frac{\Delta L_m \Delta L_n}{\pi \left|\sin \Theta_{m/n}\right|}\right]^{1/2} \\ &= 2\left[\frac{U_m U_n}{\pi d_m d_n \left|\sin \Theta_{m/n}\right|}\right]^{1/2} \end{aligned} \tag{7-6}$$

While the mean uncertainty is a convenient average value, it fails to take into account the very large uncertainties which can occur in highly correlated measurements where the error parallelogram can become extremely long.

7.2.2.2 Continuous Measurements

If the uncertainty in a measurement is due to either Gaussian-distributed random noise or any unknown systematic error which is assumed to have a Gaussian probability distribution, then the direction uncertainty corresponds to an *error ellipse* on the celestial sphere. For illustration, we first consider the simplest case in which the two independent measurements, m and n, correspond to loci which are orthogonal on the celestial sphere, as shown in Fig. 7-12. Let x be the direction component perpendicular to L_m and σ_x be the standard deviation in x resulting from the uncertainty in m; i.e., $\sigma_x \equiv U_m / d_m$, where U_m is now the standard deviation of the measurement m. By the definition of a Gaussian distribution, the probability of the x-component of the direction lying between x and $x + \delta_x$ is given by

$$\rho(x)\delta x = \left(\frac{1}{\sigma_x \sqrt{2\pi}}\right) \exp(-x^2/2\sigma_x^2)\delta x \tag{7-7}$$

where $\rho(x)$ is the *probability density* for x. Similarly, if y is the component perpendicular to L_n, then the y-component probability is

$$\rho(y)\delta y = \left(\frac{1}{\sigma_y \sqrt{2\pi}}\right) \exp(-y^2/2\sigma_y^2)\delta y \tag{7-8}$$

The probability that both the x-component lies between x and $x + \delta x$ and that the y-component lies between y and $y + \delta y$ is

$$\begin{aligned} \rho(x)\delta x\, \rho(y)\delta y &= \left(\frac{1}{2\pi\sigma_x\sigma_y}\right) \exp\left[-\frac{1}{2}(x^2/\sigma_x^2) - \frac{1}{2}(y^2/\sigma_y^2)\right]\delta x \delta y \\ &\equiv \rho(x,y)\delta x \delta y \end{aligned} \tag{7-9}$$

$\rho(x,y)$ is the two-dimensional probability density on the celestial sphere. From Eq. (7-9) it is clear that the lines of constant probability density are ellipses defined by $(x^2/\sigma_x^2) + (y^2/\sigma_y^2) = \mathrm{K}$, where K is a constant. The standard deviations of x and y are just the semimajor and semiminor axes of the K = 1 ellipse. As shown in Fig. 7-12, the standard deviation of any arbitrary component, x', is the perpendicular projection of the K = 1 ellipse on the X' axis. That is,

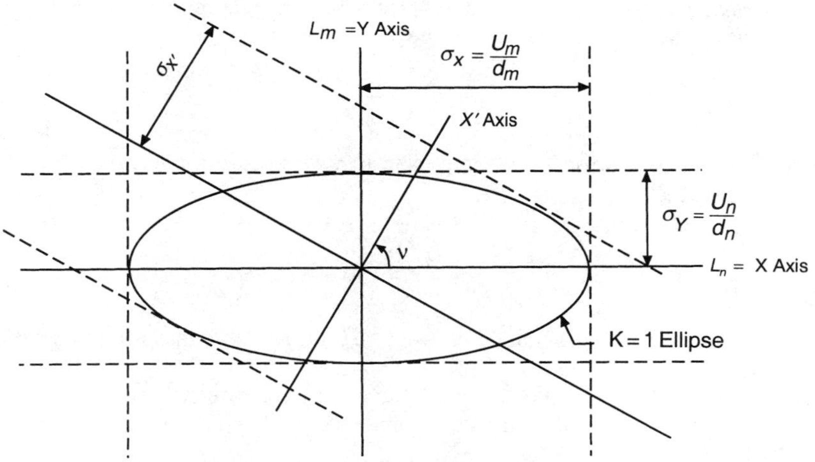

Fig. 7-12. Error Ellipse for Orthogonal Measurements. See text for discussion.

$$\sigma_{x'} = \frac{1}{\sqrt{2}}\left[(\sigma_x^2 + \sigma_y^2) + (\sigma_x^2 - \sigma_y^2)\cos 2v\right]^{1/2} \tag{7-10}$$

where v is the angle between the X′ axis and the major axis of the ellipse. The same relationship holds for the Kσ uncertainties in any measurement component.

In general, we would like to consider the independent measurements, m and n, corresponding to nonorthogonal loci, as shown in Fig. 7-13. For computation, we choose

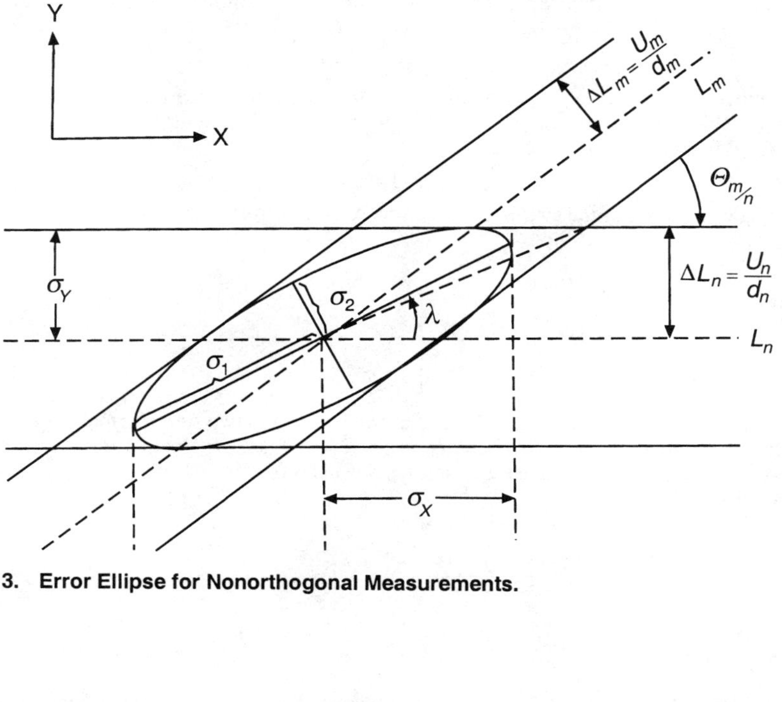

Fig. 7-13. Error Ellipse for Nonorthogonal Measurements.

an orthogonal coordinate system, x and y, for which the y-component is perpendicular to L_n. Thus, the standard deviation for the y-component is

$$\sigma_y = \frac{U_n}{d_n} \tag{7-11}$$

The standard deviation for the x-component is now more complex. As we will show later [Eq. (7-18b)]:

$$\sigma_x = \frac{1}{\left|\sin\Theta_{m/n}\right|}\sqrt{\left(\frac{U_n}{d_n}\right)^2 \cos^2\Theta_{m/n} + \left(\frac{U_m}{d_m}\right)^2} \tag{7-12}$$

where $\Theta_{m/n}$ is the correlation angle between L_m and L_n. Note that for $\Theta = 90$ deg, the previous result is recovered.

Because L_m and L_n are not orthogonal, the x and y components are not independent. A measure of the degree of their interdependence is the correlation coefficient, $\tilde{C}_{xy}$, given by Eq. (7-18d).

$$\tilde{C}_{xy} = \tilde{C}_{yx} = -\frac{\left(\frac{U_n}{d_n}\right)^2 \cot\Theta_{m/n}}{\sigma_x\,\sigma_y} \tag{7-13}$$

$$= -\frac{\frac{U_n}{d_n}\cos\Theta_{m/n}}{\sqrt{\left(\frac{U_m}{d_m}\right)^2 + \left(\frac{U_n}{d_n}\right)^2 \cos^2\Theta_{m/n}}}$$

Note that $\tilde{C}_{xy} = 0$ (measurements m and n are independent) when $\Theta_{m/n} = 90$ deg or 270 deg, and $\left|\tilde{C}_{xy}\right|$ is a maximum when $\Theta_{m/n} = 0$ deg or 180 deg.

The above results may also be established by use of a covariance analysis. The covariance matrix, P, which defines the direction uncertainty determined from measurements m and n, can be obtained from the following equation:

$$P^{-1} = M^{-1} + G^T U^{-1} G \tag{7-14}$$

where M and U are the initial estimates of the square of the errors in direction and measurements, respectively, and G is given by

$$G = \begin{bmatrix} \dfrac{\partial m}{\partial x} & \dfrac{\partial m}{\partial y} \\ \dfrac{\partial n}{\partial x} & \dfrac{\partial n}{\partial y} \end{bmatrix} \tag{7-15}$$

where m and n are the two measurements and x and y are any two orthonormal components on the celestial sphere (such as $\alpha\cos\delta$ and δ where α and δ are the right ascension and the declination of the direction). Because U_m and U_n are uncorrelated, the uncertainty matrix, U, is diagonal. By definition,

$$U = \begin{bmatrix} U_m^2 & 0 \\ 0 & U_n^2 \end{bmatrix} \tag{7-16}$$

If we assume $M^{-1} = 0$ and let (x, y) be the two perpendicular coordinates shown in Fig. 7-13, then

$$\frac{\partial m}{\partial x} = -d_m \sin \Theta_{m/n} \tag{7-17a}$$

$$\frac{\partial m}{\partial y} = d_m \cos \Theta_{m/n} \tag{7-17b}$$

$$\frac{\partial n}{\partial x} = 0 \tag{7-17c}$$

$$\frac{\partial n}{\partial y} = d_n \tag{7-17d}$$

By substituting Eqs. (7-15) through (7-17a) into Eq. (7-14), we obtain

$$P = \begin{bmatrix} P_{xx} & P_{xy} \\ P_{yx} & P_{yy} \end{bmatrix} \tag{7-18a}$$

where

$$P_{xx} = \frac{\left(\frac{U_n}{d_n}\right)^2 \cos^2 \Theta_{m/n} + \left(\frac{U_m}{d_m}\right)^2}{\sin^2 \Theta_{m/n}} = \sigma_x^2 \tag{7-18b}$$

$$P_{yy} = \left(\frac{U_n}{d_n}\right)^2 = \sigma_y^2 \tag{7-18c}$$

$$P_{xy} = P_{yx} = -\left(\frac{U_n}{d_n}\right)^2 \cot \Theta_{m/n} = \tilde{C}_{xy} \sigma_x \sigma_y \tag{7-18d}$$

The semimajor axis, σ_1; semiminor axis, σ_2; and the orientation, λ, of the error ellipse in Fig. 7-13 can be expressed in terms of σ_x, σ_y, and $\tilde{C}_{xy}$ by the following equations:

$$\sigma_1^2 = \frac{1}{2}\left[\sigma_x^2 + \sigma_y^2 + \sqrt{\left(\sigma_x^2 - \sigma_y^2\right)^2 + 4\tilde{C}_{xy}^2 \sigma_x^2 \sigma_y^2}\right] \tag{7-19a}$$

$$\sigma_2^2 = \frac{1}{2}\left[\sigma_x^2 + \sigma_y^2 - \sqrt{\left(\sigma_x^2 - \sigma_y^2\right)^2 + 4\tilde{C}_{xy}^2 \sigma_x^2 \sigma_y^2}\right] \tag{7-19b}$$

$$\tan 2\lambda = -\frac{2\tilde{C}_{xy} \sigma_x \sigma_y}{\sigma_x^2 - \sigma_y^2} \tag{7-19c}$$

By substituting Eqs. (7-11) through (7-13) into Eq. (7-19), the following expressions for σ_1, σ_2, and λ in terms of U_m, U_n, d_m, d_n, and $\Theta_{m/n}$ are obtained:

$$\sigma_1^2 = \frac{1}{2}\frac{A+B}{\sin^2\Theta_{m/n}}\left[1+\sqrt{1-\frac{4AB}{(A+B)^2}\sin^2\Theta_{m/n}}\right] \tag{7-20a}$$

$$\sigma_2^2 = \frac{1}{2}\frac{A+B}{\sin^2\Theta_{m/n}}\left[1-\sqrt{1-\frac{4AB}{(A+B)^2}\sin^2\Theta_{m/n}}\right] \tag{7-20b}$$

$$\tan 2\lambda = \frac{B\sin 2\Theta_{m/n}}{A+B\cos 2\Theta_{m/n}} \tag{7-20c}$$

where

$$A \equiv \frac{U_m^2}{d_m^2} \qquad B \equiv \frac{U_n^2}{d_n^2} \tag{7-20d}$$

Note that the long axis of the error ellipse is **not**, in general, aligned with the long diagonal of the error parallelogram. The uncertainty of the direction component along any specific direction making an angle v with respect to the semimajor axis of the error ellipse, or making an angle $v+\lambda$ with respect to L_n, can then be obtained by substituting Eq. (7-20) into Eq. (7-10), with σ_x replaced by σ_1 and σ_y replaced by σ_2. That is,

$$\sigma_v^2 = \frac{1}{2}\frac{A+B}{\sin^2\Theta_{m/n}}\left[1+\sqrt{1-\frac{4AB}{(A+B)^2}\sin^2\Theta_{m/n}}\cos 2v\right] \tag{7-21}$$

where A and B are defined in Eq. (7-20d).

The physical interpretation of the error ellipse in Fig. 7-13 is different in several respects from that of the quantized error parallelogram of Fig. 7-11. As shown in Eq. (7-9) and Fig. 7-14, the probability density is no longer uniform, but is a maximum at the center and falls off continuously away from the center. The boundaries of the error ellipses are lines of constant probability density. The $n\sigma$ uncertainty along any arbitrary axis is given by the perpendicular projection of the $n\sigma$ error ellipse onto that axis. Thus, the 1σ uncertainty along the Y' axis is the distance from the origin to the point A in Fig. 7-14; that is, the probability that the y'-component of the direction lies between A and A' is 0.68.

Although the probability of any one component being within the 1σ uncertainty boundary is 0.68, the probability of both direction components in any orthogonal coordinate system being within the 1σ error ellipse is less than 0.68.* Specifically, the probability of the direction lying somewhere inside the 1σ error ellipse is 0.39. Table 7-3 gives the probability for the direction to lie within various error ellipses and for any one component to be within the boundary of the error ellipse.

A precise statement of the direction uncertainty for Gaussian errors requires the specification of three independent numbers, e.g., the size and eccentricity of the error

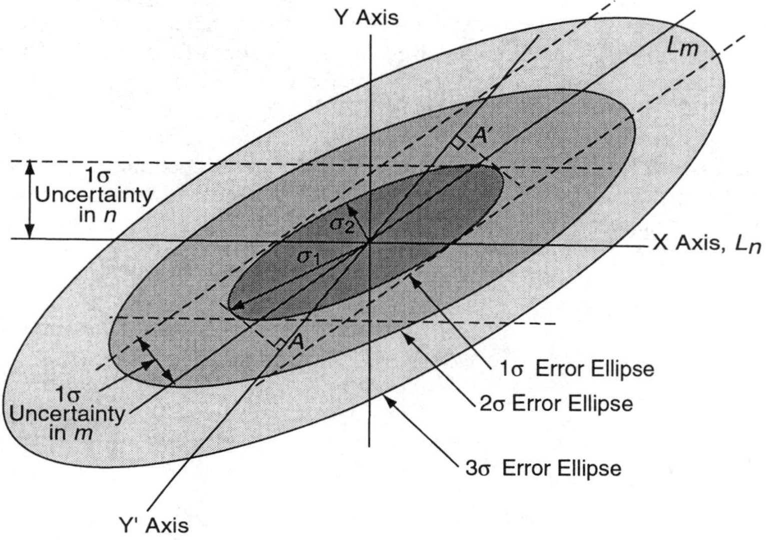

Fig. 7-14. Probability Interpretation of Error Ellipse from Fig. 7-13.

TABLE 7-3. Probabilities Associated with Gaussian Measurement Errors.

Uncertainty Level, K	Probability or Confidence Level		
	Single Component	Two Components (Single-axis Direction)	Three Components (Three-axis Direction)
1σ	0.6827	0.3935	0.1987
2σ	0.9545	0.8647	0.7385
3σ	0.9973	0.9889	0.9707
4σ	0.99994	0.99966	0.9989
Confidence Level	**Uncertainty Level, K**		
0.50	0.675σ	1.177σ	1.538σ
0.68	0.994σ	1.510σ	1.872σ
0.90	1.645σ	2.146σ	2.500σ
0.95	1.960σ	2.448σ	2.795σ
0.99	2.576σ	3.035σ	3.368σ
0.995	2.807σ	3.255σ	3.583σ

* This is easily visualized by considering a two-component error rectangle. If the two components, x and y, have upper limits at the boundary of the rectangle of B_x and B_y, then four possibilities exist: $x \le B_x$ and $y \le B_y$, $x > B_x$ and $y > B_y$, $x \le B_x$ and $y > B_y$, and $x > B_x$ and $y \le B_y$. However, only the first combination results in the point defined by (x, y) being inside the box. The probability of this occurring is clearly less than either the probability of $x \le B_x$ or the probability of $y \le B_y$.

ellipse and the orientation of the long axis relative to some arbitrary direction. As in the case of quantized measurements, we would like to characterize the uncertainty by a single number. Again, there is no precise way to do so, because specifying the ellipse is the only unambiguous procedure. One option for a single accuracy parameter would be to use Eq. (7-20a) to obtain σ_1. This is then the long axis of the error ellipse and corresponds approximately to U_{max} for quantized measurements.

An alternative one-parameter estimate for the direction uncertainty would be the radius of a small circle on the celestial sphere which had the same integrated probability as the corresponding error ellipse. A numerically convenient approximation to this radius is given by

$$\begin{aligned} U_A &= \sqrt{(\sigma_1^2 + \sigma_2^2)/2} \\ &= \sqrt{(P_{xx} + P_{yy})/2} \\ &= \frac{1}{\sqrt{2}\,|\sin\Theta_{m/n}|}\left[\left(\frac{U_m}{d_m}\right)^2 + \left(\frac{U_n}{d_n}\right)^2\right]^{1/2} \end{aligned} \tag{7-22}$$

This approximation is good for $\sigma_1 \approx \sigma_2$. That is, if U_m and U_n are the 3σ uncertainties in m and n, then the probability that the direction will lie within U_A of the estimated value, if $\sigma_1 \approx \sigma_2$, is 0.989. If $\sigma_1 >> \sigma_2$, then the approximation of Eq. (7-22) is less accurate, being a 37% overestimate for the 1σ uncertainty radius and a 16% underestimate for the 3σ uncertainty radius. As σ_1 becomes much larger than σ_2, the error ellipse becomes very elongated and any single number representation becomes less meaningful. In this case, the best choice for the one-parameter direction uncertainty would be the semimajor axis of the error ellipse, which is approximately

$$U_A' \approx \frac{1}{|\sin\Theta_{m/n}|}\left[\left(\frac{U_m}{d_m}\right)^2 + \left(\frac{U_n}{d_n}\right)^2\right]^{1/2} \tag{7-23}$$

as can be obtained from Eq. (7-20) when σ_2 approaches zero. An alternative physical interpretation of U_A, as defined by Eq. (7-22), is to note that U_A is the exact formula for the direction component inclined at 45 deg to both the semimajor and semiminor axes of the error ellipse [see Eq. (7-10)].

Another option for a single accuracy parameter would be to use the radius of a circle with the same geometrical area as the error ellipse. That is,

$$\begin{aligned} U_{mean} &= \sqrt{\sigma_1 \sigma_2} \\ &= \left[\frac{U_m U_n}{d_m d_n |\sin\Theta_{m/n}|}\right]^{1/2} \end{aligned} \tag{7-24}$$

Equation (7-24) is analogous to Eq. (7-6) for the quantized measurements. Note that this representation also gives a poor estimate of the direction uncertainty when $\sigma_1 >> \sigma_2$ because $U_{mean} \to 0$ when $\sigma_2 \to 0$. Again, when $\sigma_1 >> \sigma_2$, Eq. (7-23) should be used for one-parameter direction uncertainty. Throughout the rest of this chapter, we will use U_A as defined by Eq. (7-22) as our one-parameter estimate of the direction uncertainty, unless stated otherwise.

7.2.2.3 *Direction Accuracy for Measurements with Correlated Uncertainties*

Whenever there exists a systematic error which can introduce uncertainties in both measurements m and n, then the measurement uncertainties contain a *correlated component*. When a direction is determined from two measurements with a correlated uncertainly component, the measurement uncertainty matrix given in Eq. (7-16) will contain off-diagonal terms. That is,

$$U = \begin{bmatrix} U_m^2 & C_{m/n} \\ C_{m/n} & U_n^2 \end{bmatrix} \tag{7-25}$$

where

$$U_m^2 = R_m^2 + \sum_i \left(\frac{\partial m}{\partial S_i}\right)^2 (\Delta S_i)^2 \tag{7-26a}$$

$$U_n^2 = R_n^2 + \sum_i \left(\frac{\partial n}{\partial S_i}\right)^2 (\Delta S_i)^2 \tag{7-26b}$$

$$C_{m/n} = \sum_i \left(\frac{\partial m}{\partial S_i}\right)\left(\frac{\partial n}{\partial S_i}\right)(\Delta S_i)^2 \tag{7-26c}$$

In Eq. (7-26), U_m and U_n are the total uncertainties in measurements m and n; R_m and R_n are the random errors in measurements m and n; ΔS_i is the ith systematic error existing in either measurement; $\partial m / \partial S_i$ and $\partial n / \partial S_i$ are the partial derivatives of m and n with respect to the ith systematic error; and $C_{m/n}$ is the correlated uncertainty component between the two measurements.

In this case, the direction uncertainty can be obtained from the covariance matrix approach given in Sec.7.2.2.2 with Eq. (7-16) replaced by Eq. (7-25). The result is:

$$U_A = \frac{1}{\sqrt{2}\left|\sin \Theta_{m/n}\right|}\left[\frac{U_m^2}{d_m^2} + \frac{U_n^2}{d_n^2} - 2\frac{C_{m/n}}{d_m d_n}\cos\Theta_{m/n}\right]^{1/2} \tag{7-27}$$

Equation (7-27) gives the general expression for the direction uncertainty determined by two measurements with total uncertainties U_m and U_n, and correlated uncertainty component $C_{m/n}$. This equation can be applied to any single-axis direction determination procedure regardless of the type of measurements and processing methods.

Equation (7-27) shows that the direction accuracy in general is determined by three factors: the measurement uncertainties U_m, U_n, and $C_{m/n}$; the measurement densities, d_m and d_n; and the correlation angle, $\Theta_{m/n}$. Note that the direction uncertainty goes to infinity (i.e., a singularity occurs) whenever d_m, d_n, or $\sin \Theta_{m/n}$ is zero.

7.3 Applications: Earth Sensors, Magnetometers, V-Slit Scanners

This section provides specific applications of the measurement geometry techniques introduced in Secs. 7.1 and 7.2 to some of the more common types of spacecraft sensors. Table 7-1 at the beginning of the chapter lists where each type of sensor is discussed. In particular, Sec. 7.4 discusses rotation angle measurements in more detail and provides a discussion of the array processor, which is one of the more common modern applications of rotation angle measurements.

7.3.1 Earth Sensors

This section provides a detailed analysis of the measurement geometry for both static and scanning Earth horizon sensors. We provide the computation of the nadir angle, Earth-Sun rotation angle, and Earth mid-scan from the Earth horizon crossing data. Volume II provides detailed discussions of Earth horizon sensing hardware, analytical models of the hardware, and models of the Earth horizon and Earth sensing environment. In general, the purpose of the spacecraft's Earth sensor is to determine the orientation of nadir, i.e., the direction to the center of the Earth, with respect to the sensor coordinates, which are assumed to be well known in the spacecraft. For this section, we will assume a spherical Earth; oblateness adds somewhat to the complexity of the computation but doesn't change the basic process. A particularly clever technique for handling oblateness is provided by Collins [1992].

We begin by looking at a scanning horizon sensor and then analyze other sensors as special cases. Note that the scanning sensor is geometrically equivalent to two ministatic horizon sensors or to a single scan line in a multidetector static sensor. As shown in Fig. 7-15, the fundamental measurement made by a horizon sensor consists of two horizon crossings which are determined in sensor or spacecraft coordinates. Unfortunately, the individual horizon crossings are not independent. Given a single horizon crossing, there are a number of possible locations for the other horizon crossing that depend on both the altitude and attitude of the spacecraft. However, it is very convenient to construct two independent measurements from this pair, which are significantly easier to evaluate and use for attitude sensing. The independent measurements correspond effectively to the sum and the difference of the two horizon crossing values.

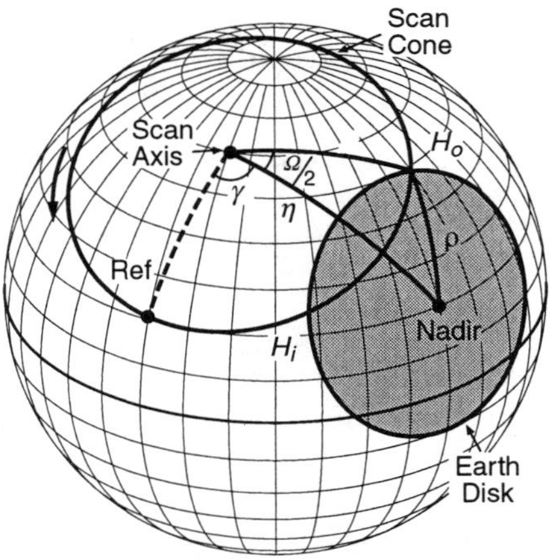

Fig. 7-15. Horizon Crossing Measurement Geometry. The triangle shown is used to compute the scan width and azimuth offset.

The first of the two constructed measurements is the *Earth mid-scan angle*, which is the rotation angle about the scan axis from an arbitrary reference to the center of the two horizon crossings. For a spherical Earth, the center of the two horizon crossings defines the direction to nadir on the Earth. Consequently, the Earth mid-scan angle defines the azimuthal direction to nadir in spacecraft coordinates irrespective of any properties of the apparent disk of the Earth, such as the altitude of the spacecraft. The errors in the measurement are well behaved; that is, errors in the two horizon crossings translate directly into errors in the azimuthal orientation of the Earth in sensor coordinates.

The *Earth width measurement* is also easy to compute; it is the difference in azimuthal orientation between the Earth in-crossing and the out-crossing, which is the rotation angle about the scan axis subtended by the Earth (see Fig. 7-15). However, what we are interested in computing is the nadir angle, i.e., the angle from the scan axis to nadir. This is somewhat more complex to compute and substantially more involved in terms of error propagation than the Earth mid-scan measurement.

The formula for the Earth mid-scan angle in terms of the rotation angles to the horizon in-crossing, H_i, and the horizon out-crossing, H_o:

$$\Phi = (H_o + H_i) / 2 \tag{7-28}$$

To compute the nadir angle, we first compute the Earth width, Ω, as:

$$\Omega = H_o - H_i \tag{7-29}$$

and the intermediate variable K:

$$K = \sin m \cos \Omega/2 \tag{7-30}$$

We then apply the law of cosines for sines to the spherical triangle shown in Fig. 7-15 to compute the nadir angle as follows:

$$\frac{\cos\gamma \cos\rho \pm \sin\gamma \cos(\Omega/2)\sqrt{\sin^2\gamma \cos^2(\Omega/2) + \cos^2\gamma - \cos^2\rho}}{\sin^2\gamma \cos^2(\Omega/2) + \cos^2\gamma} \tag{7-31}$$

where γ is the radius of the scan cone, ρ is the angular radius of the Earth, and Ω is the Earth width.

Figure 7-16 shows the sensing geometry for the case in which the scan cone radius is smaller than the radius of the Earth. In this case, the solutions are accurate and well behaved over the entire region in which the scan cone crosses the Earth horizon. The scan of the Earth width can range from approximately 0 deg when $\eta = \gamma + \rho$ through 180 deg when $\eta \approx \rho$ to nearly 360 deg when $\eta = \rho - \gamma$. Thus, even with the scan cone nearly entirely on the disk of the Earth, a good measurement of the nadir angle is possible. Figure 7-17A shows the Earth width measurement as a function of the nadir angle for a 70 deg radius Earth, typical of the size of the Earth as seen from very low Earth orbit. The measurement density or geometrical gain for the nadir angle measurement is simply the derivative of this curve with respect to the nadir angle and is shown in Fig. 7-17B.

The Earth width/nadir angle geometry becomes substantially more complex when the scan cone is larger than the size of the disk of the Earth, as is more typically the case. This geometry is illustrated in Fig. 7-18. First note that there are two distinct solutions for the nadir angle for a given Earth width measurement. These correspond to the scan crossing the disk of the Earth either above or below nadir. The nadir angle

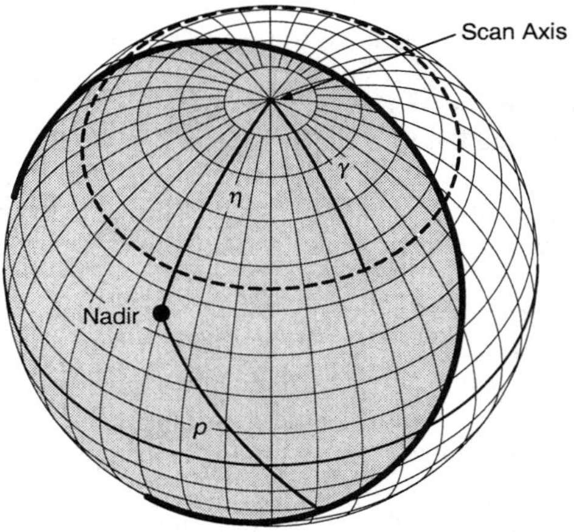

Fig. 7-16. **Earth Scanner Sensing Geometry for Scan Cone Smaller than the Disk of the Earth.**

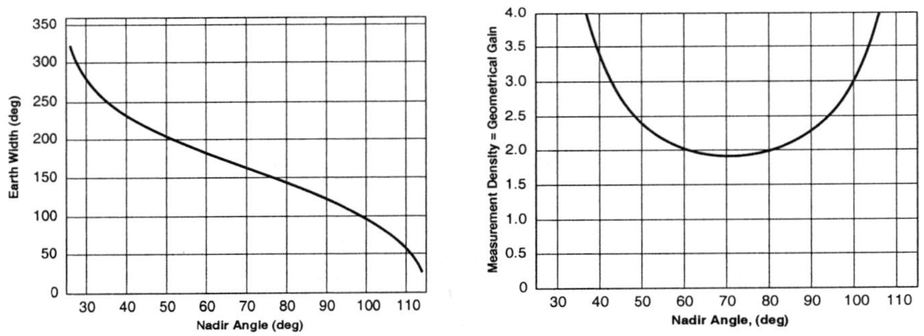

(A) Earth Width vs. Nadir **(B) Geometrical Gain vs. Nadir Angle**

Fig. 7-17. **Earth Width and Geometrical Gain for Sensor Configuration in Fig. 7-16.** Assumed values are scan cone radius of 45 deg and Earth angular radius of 70 radius.

is a function of Earth width and measurement density plots are also significantly more complex as shown in Fig. 7-19. Note in particular that the figure is asymmetric and that there is a midway point at which the measurement density goes to zero. This corresponds to the geometry of Fig. 7-18B, in which the scan cone is crossing the diameter of the disk of the Earth. (Because of the curvature of the scan cone, this occurs when η is slightly less than γ.) Figure 7-18B shows clearly what is happening in this case. The Earth width scan is crossing the diameter of the Earth such that if the nadir angle is changed slightly, i.e, the sensor axis moved up or down a bit, the value of the Earth width measurement doesn't change because we are crossing the diameter. The sensor is fully on the disk of the Earth, the mid-scan rotation angle is well behaved, but the nadir angle is only very poorly defined because the measurement density for this parameter goes to zero. If the motion of the spacecraft around the Earth carries a scan line across the diameter of the Earth, the value of the nadir angle measurement will become very ambiguous and errors will become extremely large, i.e., we will encounter a singularity in the middle of a set of otherwise acceptable measurements.

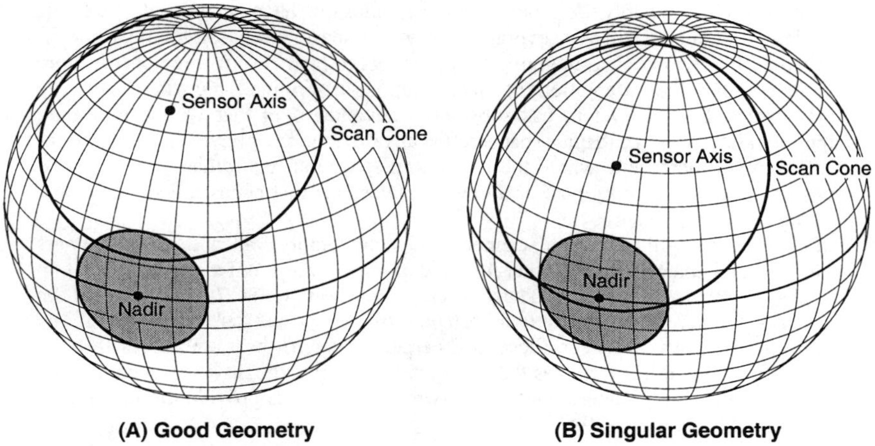

Fig. 7-18. Earth Scanner Sensing Geometry for Scan Cones Larger than the Disk of the Earth.

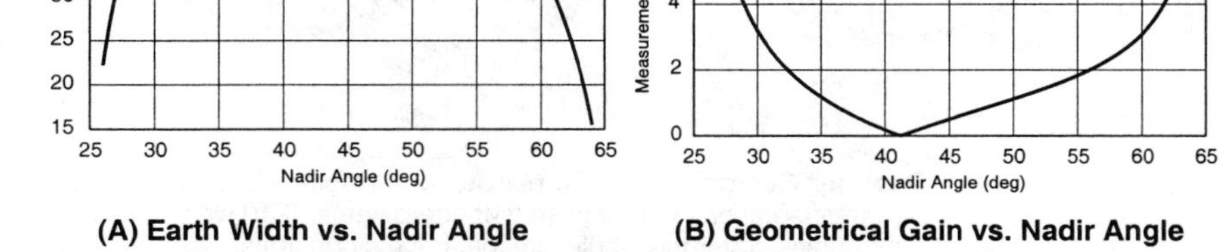

Fig. 7-19. Earth Width and Geometrical Gain for Sensor Configuration in Fig. 7-18. Assumed values are scan cone radius of 45 deg and Earth angular radius of 20 deg.

Another interesting characteristic of the Earth width measurement is that although it is physically a rotation angle which is being measured, we classify the measurement as an arc length because of the shape of the loci on the celestial sphere. That is, a given Earth width implies a given nadir angle, which in turn implies that the direction to the center of the Earth is at a fixed arc length from the axis of the scan cone. Consequently, this measurement corresponds to an arc length measurement in terms of how it behaves geometrically.

Using Two Planar Scanners to Achieve Full-Sky Earth Coverage

We would like to apply the general geometry rules that have been developed to the problem of obtaining full sky coverage with as few sensors as possible. In particular, we would like two conical scanning Earth sensors to provide coverage of the entire sky, such that the orientation of nadir can be determined anywhere with no singularities. Such a system has substantial advantages in that with a minimum amount of hardware, I can put a spacecraft at any orientation or have it generally tumbling and still determine where the Earth is in spacecraft coordinates, as might be appropriate for a space lifeboat or a low-cost telescope that needs full sky coverage but only moderate accuracy.

To do this, we will use planar scanners, which are simply conical horizon scanners with a 90 deg cone angle, such that the field of view sweeps out a great circle arc in the sky. The measurements from such a sensor are show in Fig. 7-20A. As in all the conical scanners, we determine two horizon crossings on the disk of the Earth. The great circle midway between these and perpendicular to the scan passes through nadir, the scan width determines the nadir angle such that the distance of nadir from the scan plane can be determined; these two measurements provide the location of nadir as shown in Fig. 7-20A.

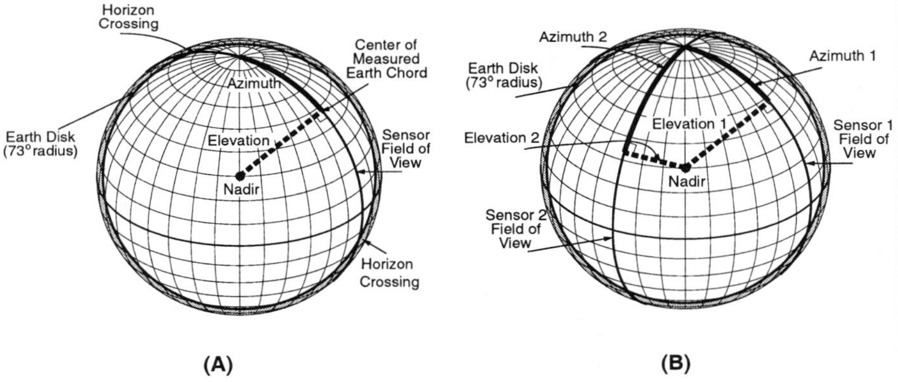

Fig. 7-20. Planar Scanner Geometry in LEO. (A) Use of a single planar scanner to determine the orientation of nadir in sensor coordinates. (B) Two such sensors at right angles cover the whole sky, but have singularities.

Our first approach to using two scanners to provide full-sky coverage is shown in Fig. 7-20B, in which the two scanners are oriented in right angles to each other, such that the disk of the Earth is always on at least one of the two scans and frequently on two. Unfortunately, although we provide full sky coverage with this arrangement, the solutions are singular in several places. Specifically, consider the areas of the sky where a single scanner will not work well. If nadir is in the direction of the scan axis (i.e., perpendicular to the scan lines), then the scanner will miss the disk of the Earth entirely and there will be no measurement. At the other extreme, if nadir lies in the plane of the scan, then the scan will cross the diameter of the Earth, and the measurement density will be zero for the nadir angle component of the measurement. In this case, the mid-scan angle and therefore the direction to nadir will be well defined, but the nadir angle itself, i.e., how far nadir is on either side of the plane, will be very poorly determined. In Fig. 7-20B, if the direction to nadir lies in the direction of the pole of either of the scanners, it will lie very close to the scan plane of the second scanner. When nadir is in this direction, one scan will miss the Earth entirely and the second scan will have a good rotation angle measurement but a poor nadir angle measurement and we will have a singular solution.

The solution to this problem, as shown in Fig. 7-21A, is to place the two scans at an angle of approximately 60 deg with respect to each other, rather than at right angles. Although this at first seems strange, it serves to eliminate the singularities as shown in Fig. 7-21B. Whenever nadir is in the direction of one of the two sensor axes, it is in a region in which two good measurements are provided by the other sensor, that is, when only one sensor can see the Earth, it is in a position to provide two good measurements for the orientation of nadir. When nadir is in the direction of either of the two places where the two scans cross, the nadir angle measurement for both sensors is poor. However, there remain two valid rotation angle measurements which are nonparallel and which determine the direction to nadir. These two measurements will cross at a well defined location and therefore provide an accurate, nonsingular measurement for the direction of nadir.

Irrespective of where the Earth is in the spacecraft sky, two planar scanners at 60 deg to each other will provide high accuracy measurements for the direction to the center of the Earth. In addition, three planar scanners, each at 60 deg to the other, would provide fully redundant, full-sky coverage such that with any one of the scanners nonfunctioning, complete full-sky coverage without singularities would still be available. By looking at singularities, covered regions, and measurement densities, we can determine how specific sensor configurations will work, and design the configurations to provide the accuracy and range of coverage that we need for the mission at hand.

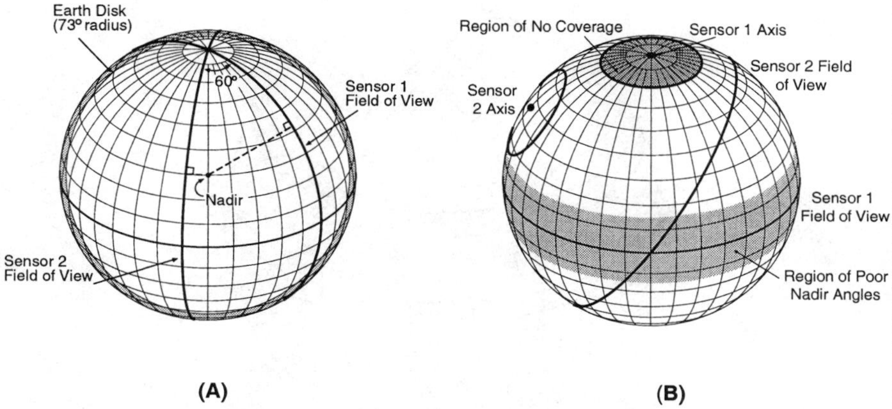

Fig. 7-21. Better Solution Alternative. (A) Alternate solution in which the scanners are at 60 deg to each other. (B) Non-overlapping singular regions show that this solution provides coverage over the whole sky without singularities.

7.3.2 Magnetometers

A *vector magnetometer* for spacecraft applications typically consists of three orthogonal sensors, each of which measures the field strength along an individual axis. For simplicity in analyzing magnetometers, we assume that there is a fixed accuracy in terms of field strength measurement for each of the three sensors. What we would like to determine is the accuracy of the magnetometer as a function of orientation relative to the orthogonal axes. Are there any regions of singularities, or regions in which the direction of the magnetic field is particularly good? If either were the case, we could use this information to orient our magnetometer correctly on the spacecraft, so that we have accurate measurements at times when they are most needed.

To determine the direction of the field in sensor coordinates, each axis measurement represents a small circle centered on that axis. The three components together provide the magnitude of the field, which is then used to normalize each of the vectors such that we have the three components of a unit vector. With this normalization, any two measurements provide the direction to the magnetic field in spacecraft coordinates to within a twofold ambiguity. The third measurement resolves this ambiguity.

What is the accuracy of the field measurement with respect to the orientation of the sensor? For simplicity, assume that we have a quantized magnetometer that has only 10 steps over the entire field strength. Figure 7-22 is a plot of lines at every 10% of the total field strength. Where the enclosed area is the smallest, the measurement density will be high, and the field measurement will be the most accurate. Where the enclosed area is large, the measurement density will be low, and the field measurement will be the poorest. In looking at Fig. 7-22, we see that the field measurement is nearly uniform over the entire celestial sphere, but slightly worse at 45 deg to all of the axes. Even though the measurement of a single axis is poor along that axis, this is compensated by accurate measurements from the other two. Consequently, the vector magnetometer does an excellent job of determining the direction of the magnetic field in spacecraft coordinates irrespective of the field direction.

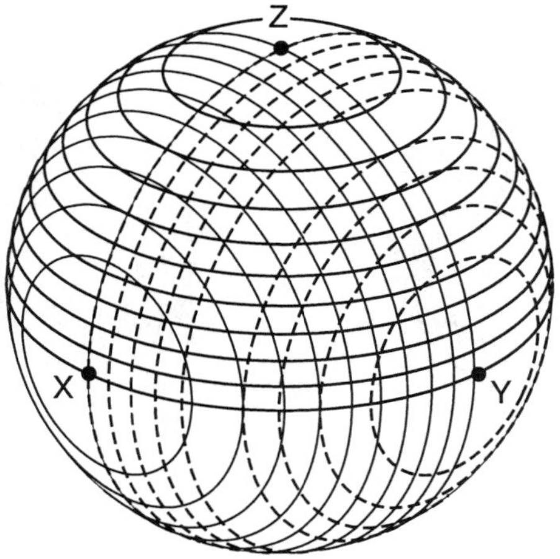

Fig. 7-22. Accuracy of Magnetic Field Measurements with Respect to Magnetometer Axes. The field measurement is best near one of the axes due to the improved accuracy from the other two axes.

7.3.3 V-Slit Sensors

A particularly simple arrangement for measuring directions is called the *V-slit scanner*, which consists of one or more approximately vertical slits rotating about a common axis. The rotation can come about either because the slits are rigidly mounted to a rotating spacecraft or mounted as part of a scanning sensor. For purposes of analyzing the geometry, both of these are the same. The V-slit sensor has been used to measure the orientation of stars on spinning spacecraft and the Earth, Sun and Moon on both spinning and 3-axis stabilized spacecraft.

Some of the more common types of rotating slit sensors are shown in Fig. 7-23. In Fig. 7-23A, there is a single vertical slit, where "vertical" means that the great circle forming the slit includes the rotation axis. This type of sensor is useful only for measuring the azimuthal orientation of a sensed object and the rotation period for the spacecraft by timing successive crossings of the Sun or an identified star. In Fig. 7-23B, the V-sensor consists of two slits with equal and opposite inclinations relative to the spin plane. Here the time is measured for an object crossing both of the slits. The midway point between these times is equivalent to measuring the crossing of a vertical slit and gives the azimuthal orientation of the object. The time between the slit crossings is approximately equal to the Earth width measurement described in Sec. 7.1, and provides the elevation component for the object.

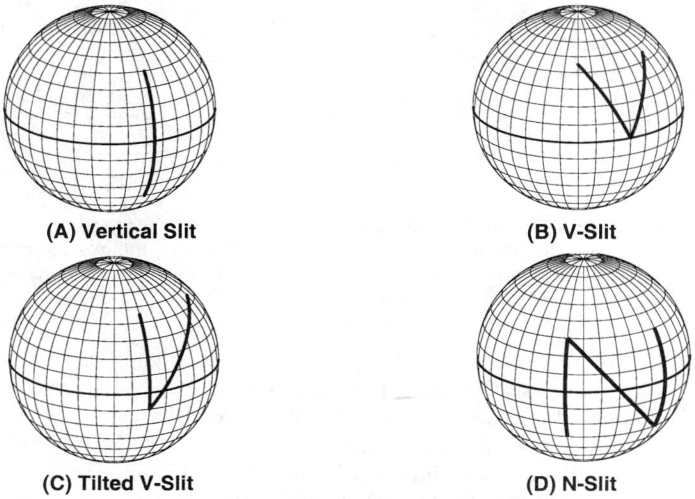

Fig. 7-23. Typical Slit Sensor Configurations. The configuration shown in (A) is used only for measuring the rotation period.

An alternative configuration is shown in Fig. 7-23C, in which one of the slits is vertical to provide azimuth and rotation period directly, and the second slit is inclined to provide the elevation measurement. The advantage of this arrangement is that the azimuth component and the rotation period are now measured by a single slit. The disadvantage, is that the inclined slit must be tilted further to obtain a comparable sensitivity to the configuration in (B). Finally, Fig. 7-23D shows a sensor design used for star sensing on a number of spinning spacecraft with an N configuration. In this case, the time between the two vertical bars of the N depends only on the rotation period and the intermediate time of crossing the center slit depends on the elevation component of the star.

Figure 7-24 shows two alternative configurations of a general V-slit sensor. In order to obtain coverage of the pole, it is tempting to orient the V-slit with the point of the V toward the pole as shown in Fig. 7-24A. Unfortunately, this is not a functioning sensor because the rotation angle between the two components of the V does not change with elevation angle. Consequently, the measurement density is near zero and we don't have a useful elevation sensor. Turning the V upside down as shown in Fig. 7-24B, with the point along the "equator" of the sensor, provides an accurate elevation measurement, but leaves a hole without coverage in the vicinity of the sensor axis. In general, a slit which is inclined at an angle i relative to the spin plane cannot provide coverage in a circle of radius 90 deg – i centered on the spin axis.

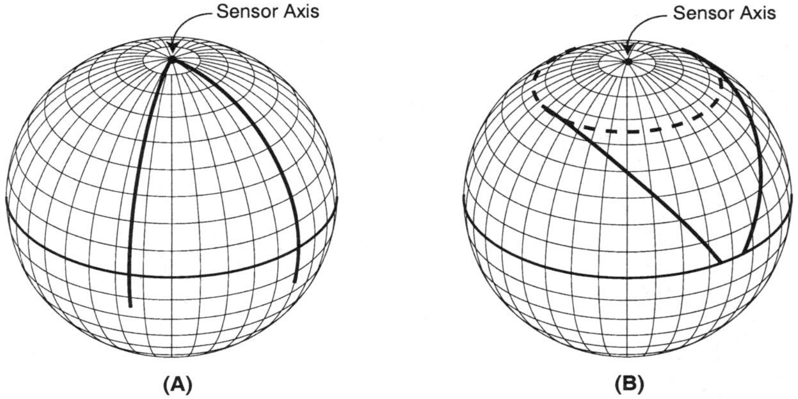

Fig. 7-24. Alternative V-Slit Sensor Configurations. (A) is not a functional sensor—i.e., it doesn't provide useful elevation information because the measurement doesn't change as the elevation changes. (B) provides good elevation, but has a region of no coverage in the vicinity of the pole.

The analysis of measurements made with rotating slits is extremely straightforward. The azimuth measurement is particularly simple and is given directly either by the crossing time of a vertical slit or the center time of two slits at the same inclination, but opposite sense. The elevation measurement is also straightforward but requires some care. We begin as shown in Fig. 7-25 by mathematically extending the great circle arc of any of the slits to cross the spin plane or "equator" of our rotating coordinate system. Note that this may or may not occur in the center of the V-slit and may require some additional azimuthal adjustment. We then form the quadrantal triangle from this intersection to the pole of the sensor to the horizon crossing point. We then take the rotation width w corresponding to the time between the crossings of the two slits and divide by 2 or make whatever additional adjustment is necessary to construct w', the reduced crossing time representing the time from crossing the slit to crossing the vertical which intersects the slit in the equator. From this we determine the angle to the pole, θ, from:

$$\tan\theta = \frac{\tan i}{\sin w'} \tag{7-32}$$

where i is the inclination of the slit relative to the spin plane. If, for example, we have a geometry such as that in Fig. 7-25, with two equal but opposite inclined slits, separated by a distance s at the spin plane, then $w' = 0.5(w - s)$. The same measurement technique and basic formula is used for all the sensors with slits which project as great circle arcs (i.e., any straight slits on a focal plane).

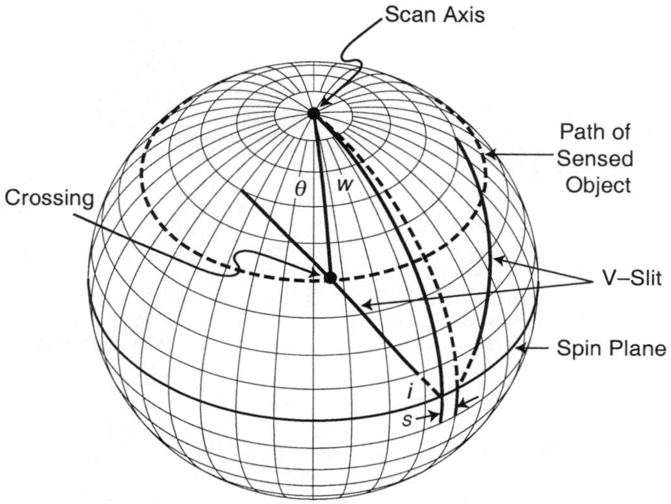

Fig. 7-25. Analysis of V-Slit Measurements. The key is to form a quadrantal triangle between the pole, the crossing, and the intersection of the slit with the spin plane (which is typically not the center of the V-slit).

Figure 7-26 shows two different slit configurations that have been used historically and the substantial advantages that can be obtained by the use of computer technology. Figure 7-26A shows the tilted-V configuration used on the SIRIO spacecraft. The output of such a sensor is fundamentally a set of trig functions as given in Eq. (7-32) and therefore produces the nonlinear output shown in Fig. 7-26B. To remove this nonlinearity, the SMS spacecraft created a curved mask for the second slit as shown in Fig. 7-26C in order to produce the linear output of Fig. 7-26D. Of course the shape of the sensor for SMS had to be carefully computed and machined into the focal plane and would need to be carefully calibrated to ensure that it was the correct shape at each point along the curved mask. This is a worthwhile process if there is a strong need for linear output as, for example, a control system which is implemented entirely in analog electronics. On the other hand, once we have a general purpose computer doing the measurement processing, then the SIRIO design is far superior. We can construct one or more linear slits both more economically and more accurately than curved slits. In addition, the only calibration is the angle of each slit, since the straightness of the slit can usually be assured to a high degree of precision. Consequently, we have a far easier and, therefore, lower cost calibration procedure, lower cost manufacturing, and a simpler design at the cost of output evaluation that requires trig functions. With the current spacecraft processors, this is a very modest price to pay for significantly simplifying the sensor design.

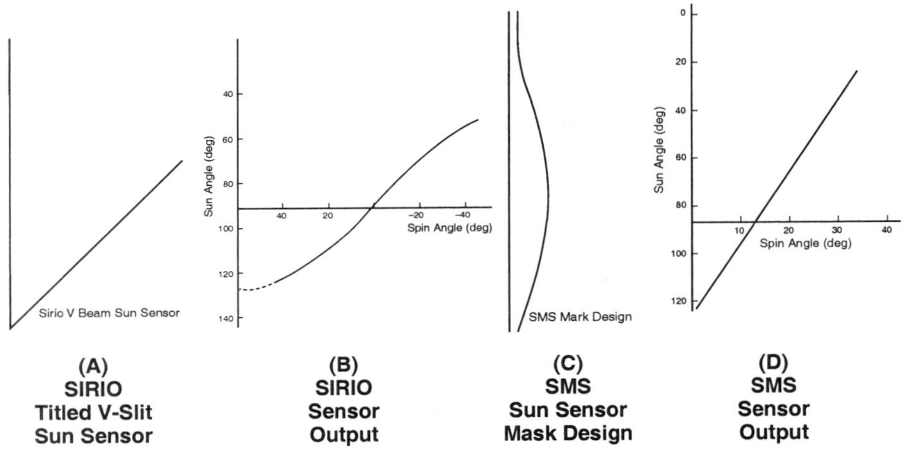

Fig. 7-26. Straight vs. Curved Slits for a V-Slit Sun Sensor. Options (A) and (B) show the linear slit with a non-linear response used on SIRIO. Options (C) and (D) show the curved slit with the linear response used on SMS. With modern processing, Option A/B is far better.

7.4 Rotation Angle Measurements

As introduced in Sec. 7.1, and illustrated in Fig. 7-27, there are two basic types of rotation angle measurements:

- Type I—rotation about a known axis from a known reference direction to the unknown direction
- Type II—rotation about an unknown axis between two known points

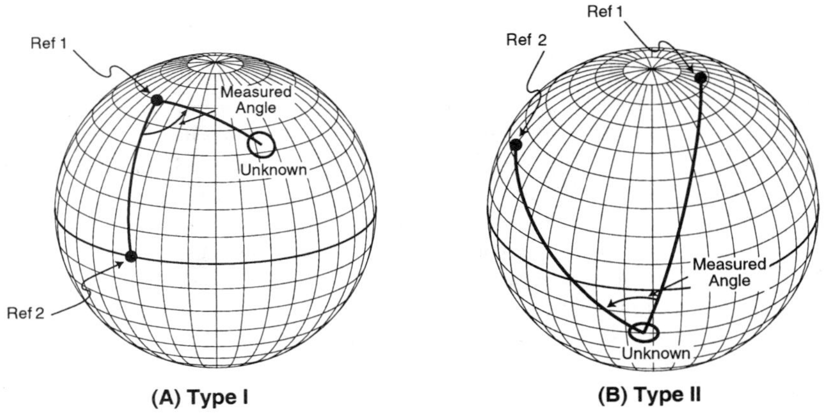

Fig. 7-27. Two Types of Rotation Angle Measurements. (A) In Type I the measurement is made about a known reference axis from a second reference to the unknown direction. (B) In Type II the measurement is made about the unknown axis from one known reference to another.

A remarkably large number of sensors produce rotation angle measurements—rotating sensors, nearly all sensors on spinning spacecraft, and many fixed 3-axis sensors such as a two-dimensional array. Note that a two-dimensional slit Sun sensor measures two arc lengths, whereas a two-dimensional array sensor measures two rotation angles. As discussed in Sec. 7.1, the type of measurement is determined by the solution loci on the celestial sphere. It is the shape of the loci that determines how the measurements should be processed, the arithmetic associated with analyzing and combining measurements, and the impact of sensor or mission geometry on the accuracy.

7.4.1 Type I—Rotation Angle About a Known Axis (Array Sensors)

As we will demonstrate shortly, the Type I rotation angle is the basic measurement made by an array processor. In Sec. 6.3.1, we showed the projection of 128×128 deg field of view Sun sensor onto the celestial sphere, largely because the size of the sensor dramatically increased the impact of the spherical geometry effects and therefore made the nature of the results more apparent. Nonetheless, the same fundamental geometry and formulas apply to star sensors, payload array sensors, cameras, and any other instrument which uses a generally rectangular array with its field of view projected onto the sky. Because this is such a fundamental type of instrument, we will provide all the relevant formulas for a generic rectangular array.

As illustrated in Fig. 7-28, the basic assumption throughout is that the array is perfectly rectangular, i.e., has straight edges on the focal plane, and that the optical system itself is perfect, i.e., it behaves like a pinhole camera. Of course, a real camera adds distortion and absorbs light differently in various parts of the field of view. The effects that we are concerned with here are purely geometrical, i.e., taking a flat focal plane and projecting it onto the "curved" surface of the celestial sphere. Consequently, these effects apply to any sensor that uses a flat focal plane. This should be the starting point for any systematic calibration because it will minimize the magnitude of the variations. Larger arrays will be used to illustrate the effects more clearly, but numerical values will also be given for smaller fields of view.

Figure 7-29 shows the view projected onto the celestial sphere for the rectangular physical array illustrated in Fig. 7-28. Specifically, we assume that the focal plane array is perfectly rectangular and flat, with dimensions $2x_a$ by $2x_b$; that is, x_a is the distance from the center of the array to the edge of the array along the long axis, and x_b is the distance from the center to the edge along the short axis. Since our camera or detector is assumed to be focused at infinity, the array is at a distance from the camera's focal point equal to the focal length, FL. Consequently, we can determine the angular dimensions of the array on the celestial sphere, a and b, by:

$$\tan a = x_a / FL \tag{7-33a}$$

$$\tan b = x_b / FL \tag{7-33b}$$

where a and b are now the angular dimensions projected onto the sky corresponding to the linear dimensions x_a and x_b. For example, a normal 35 mm camera produces a negative on the focal plane with an image size 36 mm $\times$24 mm. (It is called a 35 mm camera because the film is 35 mm wide, including the sprocket holes.) This means that $x_a = 18$ mm and $x_b = 12$ mm. Projected onto the sky using a normal 50mm focal length lens, a = atan (18/50) = 20 deg and b = atan (12/50) = 13.5 deg such that the total field of view on the sky is 40 deg wide by 27 deg high, measured through the center perpendicular to the edges.

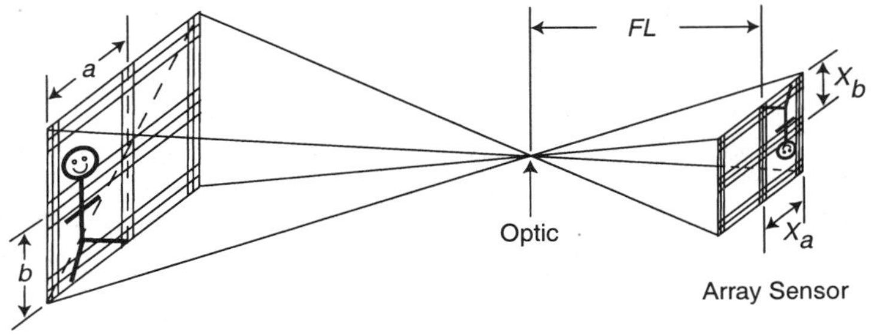

Fig. 7-28. Geometry of an Array Sensor. A rectangular sensor on the right looks through a perfect optical system. Pixels on the right are projected into space on the left and the stick figure in space is projected onto its corresponding location on the array. The projection onto the celestial sphere is shown in Fig. 7-29.

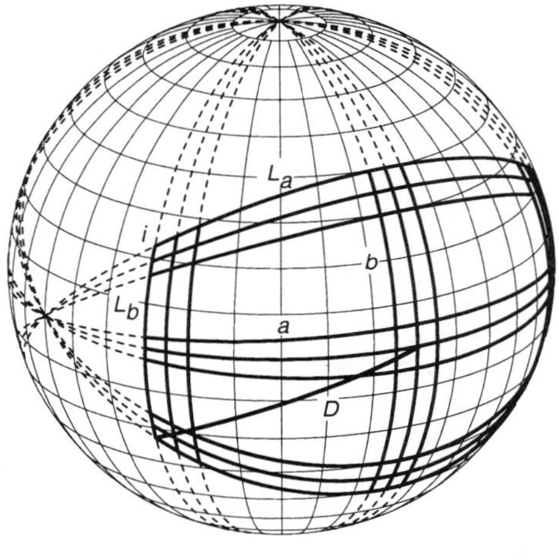

Fig. 7-29. Projection of a Rectangular Array onto the Celestial Sphere. Assumption here is that the projection is a perfect optical system. This is the image seen on the left in Fig. 7-28.

Given a and b, we want to determine the formulas for the edge lengths L_a and L_b, the angle of intersection of the edges at the corner, i, the distance from the corner to the center (i.e., half the diagonal), D, and the area of the rectangular array. We also wish to calculate the basic parameters for the pixel size and shape at any place within the array. **Note**: Depending upon our application, we may think of a and b either as the dimensions of the entire array or as the coordinates of a given point on the array. Thus, x_a and x_b can be either the size of the physical array on the focal plane or can be the two coordinates of some pixel within that array whose position, size and shape we are trying to calculate.

Section 6.3.1 provided the geometry and formulas for a square array. Here we will describe the general formulas for a rectangular array with the notation shown in Fig. 7-30. The important characteristic here is that a straight line on the focal plane projects onto the sky as a great circle arc. Thus the rows and columns in our perfectly rectangular array project onto the sky as a series of great circle arcs. The rows are all orthogonal to the middle column in the array and will project onto the sky as orthogonal to the great circle going vertically through the sensor, as shown in Fig. 7-29. Consequently, extending these great circle arcs on either side, they will all meet at a pole 90 deg on either side of the center of the sensor. Similarly, the columns on the physical focal plane array project as great circle arcs which meet at two poles, 90 deg above and below the projection of the center of the camera. By identifying a particular row in the array, we are identifying one of the horizontal great circle arcs. A particular column represents one of the vertical great circle arcs. Consequently, the row-column specification on the focal plane array corresponds to specifying two great circle arcs on the sky. The angle b represents the angular displacement of the point in question above or below the horizontal center line. The angle a represents the angular displacement of the column right or left of the vertical center line. These angles are measured along the two central axes and, therefore, are equal to the rotation angle measured at the pole of those central axes. Consequently, the measurement b implies that the pixel in question lies at a rotation angle b about the horizontal sensor pole upward from the reference axis. Similarly, a specification of a for the point in question means that the point lies along the great circle arc at rotation angle a, measured about the top or bottom pole relative to the reference axis. Thus, a and b are Type I rotation angle measurements.

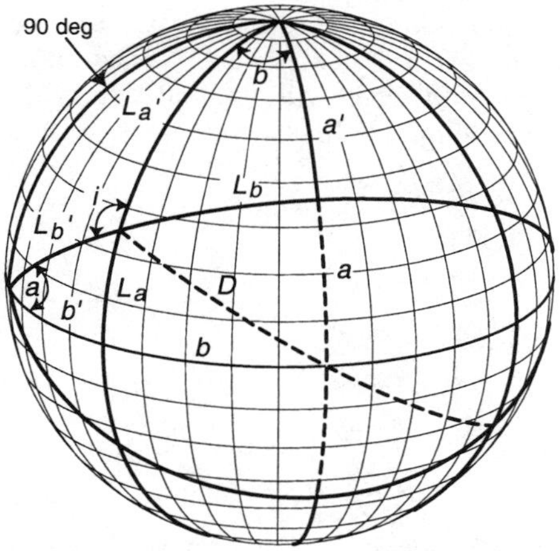

Fig. 7-30. Definition of Parameters for a Rectangular Array.

Once we have recognized the nature of the array processor geometry, doing the arithmetic to calculate the various values is straightforward. First, note that we have constructed a quadrantal spherical triangle since the arc length between the horizontal and vertical poles is 90 deg. Given the known quantity a, the angle in the quadrantal triangle, a', is just 90 deg – a, and similarly, $b' = 90$ deg – b. Consequently, we know two of the three rotation angles in the quadrantal triangle, and the remaining rotation angle and sides can be easily computed. We can then use the right spherical triangle between the corner of the rectangle and the center to determine the length of the diagonal. Given this triangle, we simply write down by inspection the formulas for the various components as follows:

$$\cos i = \sin a \sin b \tag{7-34}$$

$$\tan L_a = \tan a \cos b \tag{7-35}$$

$$\tan L_b = \tan b \cos a \tag{7-36}$$

$$\cos D = \cos L_a \cos b = \cos L_b \cos a \tag{7-37}$$

$$A = 4I - 2\pi \text{ (steradians)} \tag{7-38}$$

For an array processor, we are interested not only in the general coordinates of various components in the array, but also in the size, shape, and area of individual pixels projected onto the sky. Here the geometry is shown in Fig. 7-31. Because the spherical geometry effects are very small near the center, pixels near the center of the array have the shape that one would expect from plane geometry. However, this becomes more distorted as pixels get further from the center. In particular, the angular height of a pixel **along the central axes** is given by:

$$\Delta a = (\Delta x_a / FL) \cos^2 a \tag{7-39}$$

$$\Delta b = (\Delta x_b / FL) \cos^2 b \tag{7-40}$$

where Δa and Δb are the angular dimensions of the pixel in radians along the a and b directions, respectively, Δx_a and Δx_b are the linear dimensions of the pixels on the array, and FL is the focal length of the optical system. This is due simply to each pixel covering a smaller and smaller angle as it gets further from the optical axis; i.e., when I am in the center horizontally and move above or below the central horizontal axis, the angular height of each pixel will get shorter. If, in addition, I also move horizontally along a row the height of the pixel will get shorter still (by the cosine of the angle off the central axis) just as longitude lines come closer together as I move from the equator to the pole.

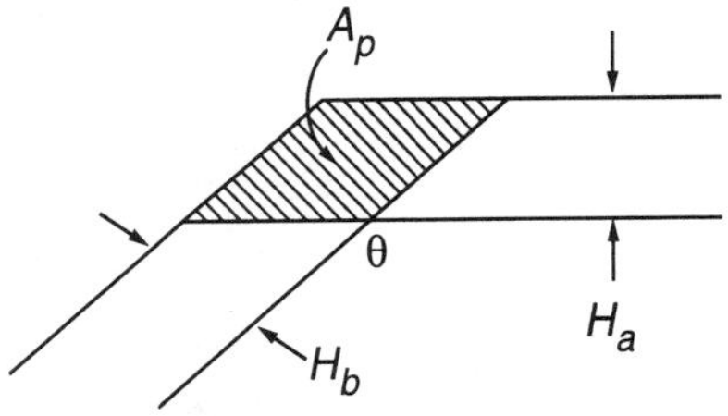

Fig. 7-31. Field of View of a Single Pixel Within a Rectangular Array.

In addition, the angle at which the edges of the pixel intersect gets further from a right angle as I approach the diagonal corners. In this case, the correlation angle, Θ, or angle at which the edges of the pixel intersect is the same angle at which the sides of the image intersect. It is therefore equal to the angle i above. The area of the pixel, A_p, can be computed with a plane geometry approximation. Thus the pixel equations are as follows:

$$H_a = H_{a_0} \cos^2 a \cos L_b \tag{7-41}$$

$$H_b = H_{b_0} \cos L_a \cos^2 b \tag{7-42}$$

$$\cos \theta = \cos i = \sin a \sin b \tag{7-43}$$

$$A_p = H_{a_0} H_{b_0} \cos L_a \cos L_b \cos^2 a \cos^2 b / \sin\theta \quad (7\text{-}44)$$

where H_a is the angular height of the pixel in the a direction, H_{a_0} is the angular height of the pixel along the reference axis through the center of the sensor, and A_p is the area of the pixel.

Table 7-4 gives both the array size and pixel size and shape for a variety of rectangular arrays. This gives a sense of the geometric distortion that comes about, not from any optical irregularities, but simply from the process of projecting the celestial sphere onto a flat image plane.

Note that by the time I've gotten to the corner of a 60 deg × 60 deg sensor, the half-length of the sides is only 41 deg and the correlation angle at which the sides intersect is nearly 140 deg, such that a "rectangular" pixel is very distinctly diamond shaped. The distance from the center of the sensor is only 68 deg. Equally important, the pixel that was 1 deg by 1 deg at the center is now only 0.2 deg × 0.2 deg. In addition to its rather elongated shape, the angular area has now been reduced to 5% of the area of one of the pixels at the center.

Whether or not the spherical geometry calculations are necessary for your particular problem can be determined by examining the size of the effects shown in Table 7-4. Notice, however, that the correct spherical geometric equations in Eqs. (7-41) through (7-44) are extremely simple, such that doing the computation correctly, rather than incorrectly in plane geometry, is very straightforward.

It is important to clearly understand what is meant by "distortion" in this context. Assume that we take a picture of a brick wall from some distance away with the optical axis of the camera pointed precisely perpendicular to the wall. In our "perfect" camera with no "optical irregularities," the picture we take of the brick wall will be an exact, though reduced, duplicate of the wall itself. The rows of bricks will line up precisely with the edges of the film. On the print, each brick will have the same area, and so on. However, for a brick that is 45 deg off the central axis both horizontally and vertically the angular area subtended by that brick, from the right hand column in Table 7-4, is 19.2% of the angular area of a brick on the optical axis. This means that I will have less than 20% of the light and less than 20% of the image intensity relative to those bricks directly in front of the camera. Another way to think of it is that the light coming from a brick in the corner of the field-of-view, which appears very small when we look at it, must be spread out to cover the same area on the negative as the light from a brick right in front of us that covers a much larger angular area.

That parallel lines get "closer together" as they get further away is known to anyone that does much drawing or photography. This is usually expressed as "parallel lines converge at infinity" and is most easily seen in railroad tracks or the edges of a highway. Again, this is expressed mathematically in the columns labeled H_a and H_b in Table 7-4.

Finally, the correlation between "orthogonal" directions seen off-axis is much less apparent in everyday life, but can be observed. Try standing very close to a wall and looking at the corner where two walls and the ceiling come together. This intersection represents three orthogonal axes. As your eye gets very close to the wall, the two perpendicular edges of the wall you're next to begin to form nearly a straight line at the corner. A bug walking at the corner will appear to be moving in nearly the same direction if he is going up the seam between the two walls or toward you along the seam between the wall and the ceiling. This is a manifestation of the correlation between orthogonal components expressed in the "I" column in Table 7-4.

Although these effects are apparent only in extreme cases, they are still present in any array image. Whether they are important depends on the precision required. Thus, Table 7-4 should be used as a guide to the size of the effects so that you determine what needs to be taken into account in any given problem.

TABLE 7-4. Coordinates and Dimensions on the Celestial Sphere for a 1 deg × 1 deg Pixel (Measured at the Center of the Array). See Fig. 7-30 and Fig.7-31 for the definition of variables. The most important parameters are *i* for which a value different from 90 deg indicates a correlation between the sensor rows and columns and A_p (the projected area of the pixel) which shows the reduction in coverage by pixels away from the center. Note that this assumes a pixel size that gives a 1 deg × 1 deg field of view on the optical axis of the sensor. The dimensions and area in the 3 right columns can be proportionally adjusted for other pixel sizes.

a (deg)	b (deg)	L_a (deg)	L_b (deg)	D (deg)	$\theta = i$ (deg)	H_a (deg)	H_b (deg)	A_p (deg^2)
0	0	0.00	0.00	0.00	90.00	1.00	1.00	1.000
5	0	5.00	0.00	5.00	90.00	0.99	1.00	0.989
5	5	4.98	4.98	7.05	90.44	0.99	0.99	0.977
10	0	10.00	0.00	10.00	90.00	0.97	0.98	0.955
10	5	9.96	4.92	11.14	90.87	0.97	0.98	0.945
10	10	9.85	9.85	14.00	91.73	0.96	0.96	0.913
15	0	15.00	0.00	15.00	90.00	0.93	0.97	0.901
15	5	14.95	4.83	15.74	91.29	0.93	0.96	0.892
15	10	14.78	9.67	17.78	92.58	0.92	0.94	0.863
15	15	14.51	14.51	20.75	93.84	0.90	0.90	0.818
30	0	30.00	0.00	30.00	90.00	0.75	0.87	0.650
30	5	29.91	4.33	30.28	92.50	0.75	0.86	0.644
30	10	29.62	8.68	31.12	94.98	0.74	0.84	0.627
30	15	29.15	13.06	32.48	97.44	0.73	0.81	0.600
30	30	26.57	26.57	39.23	104.48	0.67	0.67	0.465
45	0	45.00	0.00	45.00	90.00	0.50	0.71	0.354
45	5	44.89	3.54	45.11	93.53	0.50	0.70	0.352
45	10	44.56	7.11	45.44	97.05	0.50	0.69	0.345
45	15	44.01	10.73	45.99	100.55	0.49	0.67	0.335
45	30	40.89	22.21	49.11	110.70	0.46	0.57	0.281
45	45	35.26	35.26	54.74	120.00	0.41	0.41	0.192
60	0	60.00	0.00	60.00	90.00	0.25	0.50	0.125
60	5	59.91	2.50	60.03	94.33	0.25	0.50	0.125
60	10	59.62	5.04	60.13	98.65	0.25	0.49	0.124
60	15	59.13	7.63	60.29	102.95	0.25	0.48	0.122
60	30	56.31	16.10	61.29	115.66	0.24	0.42	0.111
60	45	50.77	26.57	63.43	127.76	0.22	0.32	0.089
60	60	40.89	40.89	67.79	138.59	0.19	0.19	0.054

7.4.2 Type II—Rotation Angle Between Two Known Points

In the Type I rotation angle, the position of the axis was known, so that the locus of unknown points was simply a great circle arc and the geometry was straightforward. However, it is also possible for the axis to be the unknown point. This Type II rotation angle occurs whenever we measure the rotation angle about an unknown axis between two known points, such as two stars, or the Sun and the center of the Earth. Typically, although not always, this type of measurement is made by a rotating or scanning sensor, for example, almost any sensor or combination of sensors on a spinning spacecraft will make Type II rotation angle measurements when the orientation of the spin axis itself is the unknown parameter. Similarly, on a three-axis stabilized spacecraft, any rotating sensor or scanner used for attitude determination will create a Type II measurement because it is the orientation of the rotation axis on the celestial sphere which is unknown. Recall, however, that it is the shape of the loci which determines the measurement type, and not the instrument. Thus, it is also possible for various static sensors to produce Type II rotation angle measurements.

The fundamental question for this measurement type is to determine the possible loci for the axis, given a fixed rotation angle between two known points. The answer is shown in Fig. 7-32 for plane geometry and in Fig. 7-33 for geometry on the celestial sphere. (Here we use the plane geometry principally to motivate the spherical geometry plots. We will use the plane curves in three-dimensional measurements in Sec. 7.5). In Fig. 7-32, the various loci are simply circles with the two known points being the endpoints of a common chord. In plane geometry, all angles inscribed in a circle whose endpoints lie on a common chord are equal. If the chord is a diameter of the circle, then the inscribed angle will be a right angle. Thus, in plane geometry, the locus of all points for which the rotation angle between two given points is a right angle will be a semicircle with its end on the two known points. For rotation angles less than 90 deg, the loci will be arcs of semicircles greater than 90 deg, and for rotation angles greater than 90 deg, the loci will be arcs of less than 90 deg, as illustrated in the figure.

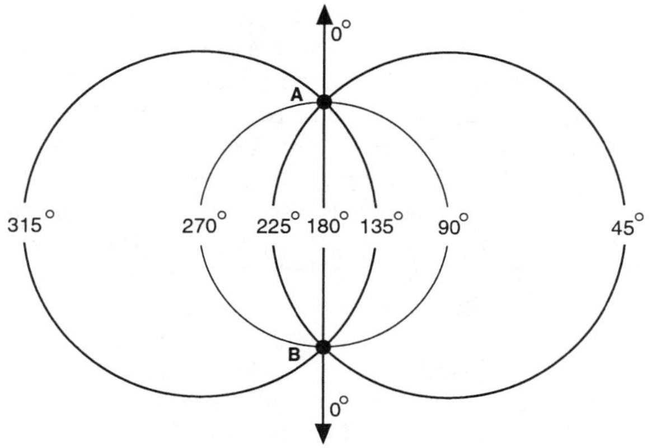

Fig. 7-32. Plane Geometry Locus of Possible Points for Which the Rotation Angle from A to B is a Fixed Angle, α. The locus is simply a circular arc beginning and ending on **A** and **B**. Note that the rotation angle is measured in a right-handed sense from 0 to 360 deg.

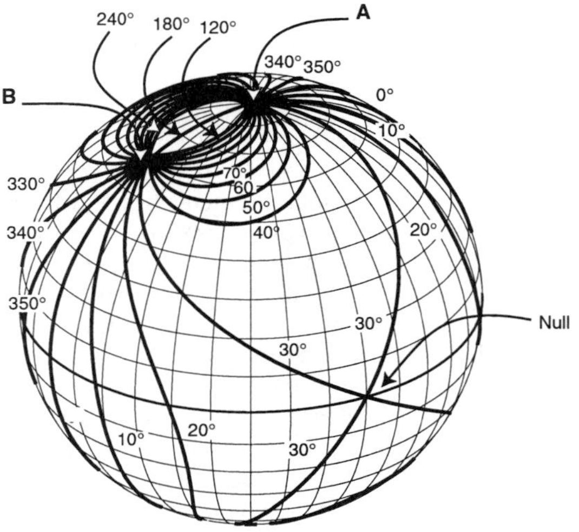

Fig. 7-33. Spherical Geometry Locus of Possible Points for Which the Rotation Angle from A to B is a Fixed Angle, α. The loci here are somewhat more complex than in Fig. 7-32. Each locus has two distinct branches and each branch begins or ends on one of the points or anti-points. (See Fig. 7-34 for other views of the same geometry.)

Although conceptually similar, the shapes become significantly more complex when we switch to geometry on the celestial sphere. Figure 7-33 shows the family of loci with a fixed rotation angle α, measured between two known reference vectors, **A** and **B**, which are 30 deg apart. ("30 deg apart" means that the arc length separation between them is 30 deg.) The rotation angle between them will of course depend upon where on the celestial sphere the rotation axis is located. Because the geometry over the entire celestial sphere is of interest, Fig. 7-34 shows four other views of the same set of loci on which different aspects of the geometry can be more clearly seen. As can be seen most clearly in Fig. 7-34C, each rotation angle locus consists of two distinct branches. Each branch begins and ends on one of the two reference points, or their antipoint. If the measured rotation angle is equal to the arc length separation (30 deg in the case of the figure), then the two independent loci intersect in an approximate X shape. The ends of the X are at the reference directions and their antipoints, and the intersection is at the pole of the great circle formed by these four points called the *null*, for reasons that will be apparent shortly. For rotation angles larger than the arc length separation, the loci will have branches which are approximately semicircular, and which start and end on either **A** and **B** or $\mathbf{A^{-1}}$ and $\mathbf{B^{-1}}$. For rotation angles less than the angular separation, the loci will be longer, less strongly curved arcs, which have one end on **A** and the other end on $\mathbf{B^{-1}}$, or one end on **B** and the other on $\mathbf{A^{-1}}$. As can be seen most clearly in Fig. 7-34A and Fig. 7-34D, all of the rotation angles between 0 and 180 deg lie in one hemisphere and all the rotation angles between 180 deg and 360 deg lie in the other hemisphere. These hemispheres are separated by the great circle defined by the two reference vectors.

One of the most striking characteristics of the rotation angle loci is the strongly varying density in different regions of the celestial sphere. In the general vicinity of the two reference vectors and their antipoints, the loci are very close together and the

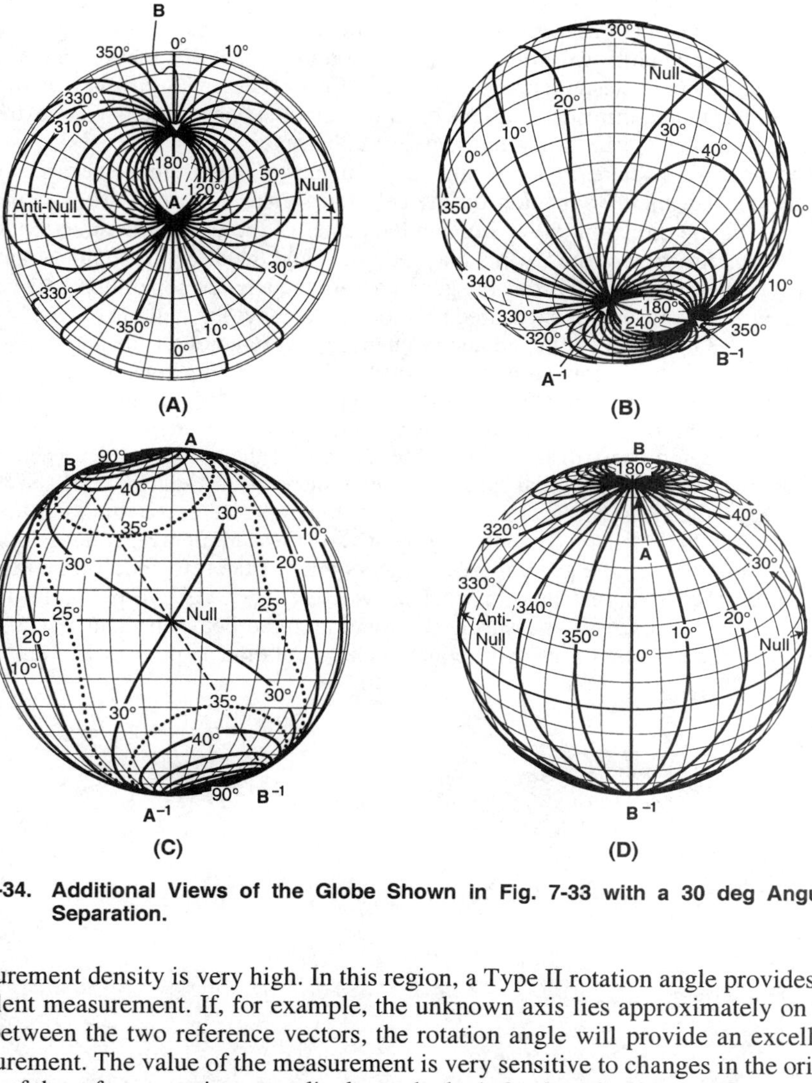

Fig. 7-34. Additional Views of the Globe Shown in Fig. 7-33 with a 30 deg Angular Separation.

measurement density is very high. In this region, a Type II rotation angle provides an excellent measurement. If, for example, the unknown axis lies approximately on the line between the two reference vectors, the rotation angle will provide an excellent measurement. The value of the measurement is very sensitive to changes in the orientation of the reference axis perpendicular to the loci. On the other hand, in the general direction of the *null*, or the cross product between the two reference vectors, the measurement density is extremely low. To give some sense of this, we have included, as a dotted line, the 35 deg and 25 deg rotation angle loci in Fig. 7-34C. Notice that these are still quite some distance from the null. Although the measurement is perfectly well defined at the null, it has very little information content. If our unknown axis is the general direction of the null, then as it moves around in any direction, there are only very small changes in the measurement and, consequently, the measurement provides very little information about where the unknown axis is located. No matter how we process the rotation angle measurements, the end result will be the same. There is simply almost no information in the region where the measurement density goes to zero. Consequently noise or small systematic errors will produce very large variations in the answer and the uncertainties for all of the computations will be large. Without the rotation angle plots, we would have no reason to suspect that measurements made on this part of the celestial sphere were bad. However, we would find that in using them, either in deterministic solutions or filters, that the uncertainties were extremely large and the results very noisy and sensitive to biases.

The conclusions here do not depend on the nature of the reference vectors, simply on the fact that their orientation on the celestial sphere is known. They could, for example, be the direction to the Sun and the center of the Earth, the direction to two stars, or the direction of the Earth's magnetic field and the direction to the Moon. The two parameters which determine the geometry are the angular separation between the two known vectors and the measured rotation angle about the unknown axis.

Figure 7-35 shows how the geometry changes as a function of the angular separation between the two known reference vectors. Figure 7-35A shows the results for an angular separation of 90 deg. The null still remains an area of zero measurement density; however, throughout most of the rest of the celestial sphere, the rotation angles become more uniformly distributed. In the vicinity of the two reference vectors, the curves behave much like radial spokes as we would expect. Figure 7-35B shows, the geometry as the reference vectors come closer together. Here, the region around the null is substantially enlarged and the region of good measurement densities gets smaller, confining itself to the general area in the vicinity of the reference vectors or their antipoints. This is consistent with what we would expect. As two points in the sky come very close together, measuring the rotation angle between them tells us very little about the location of the axis about which the rotation angle is measured.

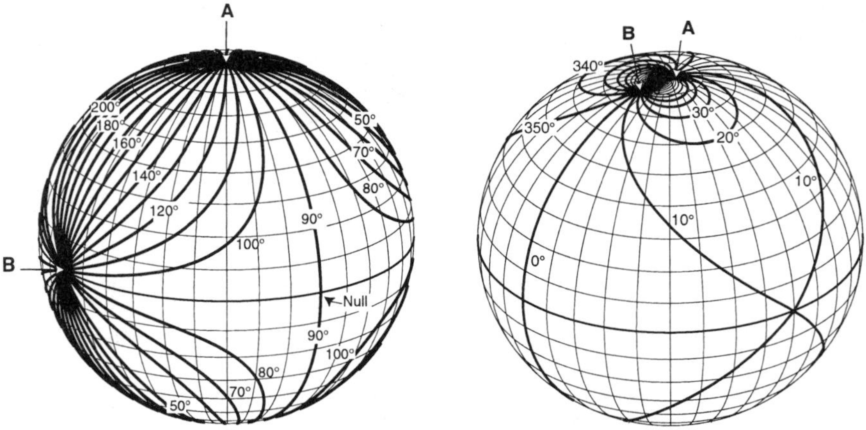

(A) 90 deg Angular Separation (B) 10 deg Angular Separation

Fig. 7-35. Constant Rotation Angle Plots for Angular Separations Between the Reference Vectors of 90 deg and 10 deg.

7.4.3 Combining Arc Length and Rotation Angle Measurements

Many spacecraft are spin stabilized, either during operations or during orbit transfer, in which the spacecraft is put into a "barbecue mode" in order to provide reasonable thermal input for all of the spacecraft surfaces. During spinning portions of the mission, a Sun sensor and Earth sensor are commonly used for attitude determination. The three independent measurements available from this combination of sensors are the *Sun angle*, or the angle from the Sun to the spin axis, the *nadir angle*, or angle from the center of the Earth to the spin axis, and the Type II rotation angle from the Sun to nadir. Any two of the three can provide a deterministic attitude solution. It is tempting to use the Sun angle and nadir angle to provide attitude solutions, since both are arc lengths and are somewhat easier to understand and analyze than the rotation angle measurement. However, leaving out the rotation angle introduces unnecessary singularities which often occur at times when measurements are most critical. The reason is that the nadir angle-Sun angle solutions will be singular whenever the attitude of the spin axis lies on the great circle connecting the Sun and the center of the Earth. For any short period of time, the Sun and the spin axis attitude will be fixed in inertial space and the direction to nadir will move around the celestial sphere on a great circle once per orbit as the spacecraft goes around the Earth. (Recall that the projection of the orbit plane onto the celestial sphere is a great circle, irrespective of whether the orbit itself is circular or elliptical.) This implies that singularities will occur twice per orbit whenever the Earth passes through the great circle containing the spin axis and the Sun. In addition, if the Sun happens to lie in or near the orbit plane, then the singular conditions will occur essentially continuously and it will be extremely difficult to use the Sun angle and nadir angle to determine the spin axis attitude at any time.

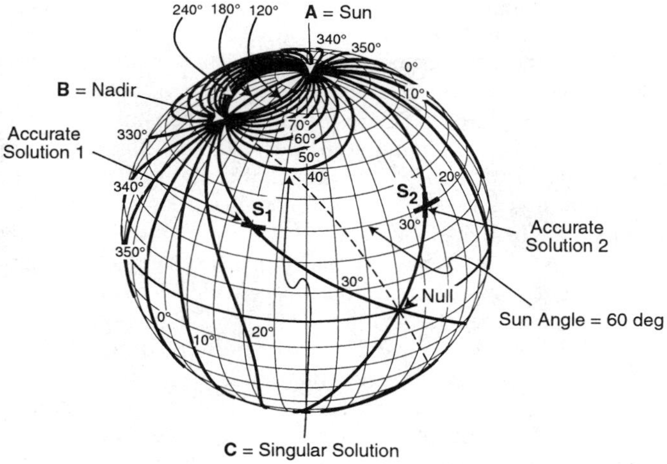

Fig. 7-36. Solution to the Problem of Spin Axis Determination when the Sun Angle and Sun-to-Earth Rotation Angle are Known. See text for discussion of singularities.

The singularity problems associated with using two arc length measurements can be resolved by using an arc length and the Type II rotation angle measurement. The geometry for this combination is shown in Fig. 7-36, where we have assumed the Sun to be one of the two reference vectors and the nadir direction the other. Note that the solution geometry here is the same as that previously shown in Fig. 7-33. The Sun is assumed to be at the pole of the underlying coordinate system. Consequently, constant Sun angle solutions are represented by the small circles centered on the Sun, or the latitude lines on the coordinate grid. Thus, a measured Sun angle is represented by one of the underlying lines of equal latitude. The loci drawn on the plot represent constant rotation angles and, therefore, are the solution curves for any specific rotation angle measurement. The intersection between the rotation angle loci and the underlying latitude lines represent various solutions for the spin axis attitude for a given Sun angle and rotation angle.

In general, just as two arc length measurements provide two discrete solutions corresponding to the intersection of two small circles, an arc length and a rotation angle measurement also provide two discrete solutions. In the figure, the points S_1 and S_2 represent the two solutions with a 60 deg Sun angle and 30 deg Sun-Earth rotation angle. These solutions are separated by a reasonable distance and are both accurate solutions in terms of the correlation angle, because they intersect the underlying latitude lines at a reasonably steep angle. Note however, that there are two regions in which these solutions become very inaccurate. As the Sun angle goes toward 90 deg, the solution will get closer to the region of the null, the measurement density of the rotation angle measurement will go to zero, and the solutions will become very inaccurate. The other possibility is for the correlation angle between the two measurements to go to zero. This occurs whenever the two sets of loci are parallel, as in solution C. By inspection, we can determine that the rotation angle loci will be parallel to the underlying latitude lines whenever the spin axis attitude lies along the great circle through the Earth perpendicular to the Earth-Sun line, i.e., between the Earth and the null. Note that this is a somewhat peculiar result. The solutions based on combining the Sun angle with the rotation angle about the attitude between the Sun and the Earth will be singular where the attitude lies along a great circle defined by the Earth and the null. Although the results seem strange, it can be clearly seen in the figure and verified with the algebraic solutions defined in Sec. 7.4.1.

Recall that the Sun angle-nadir angle solution will be singular when the rotation axis lies along the great circle containing the Earth and the Sun, i.e., on the 0 deg and 360 deg rotation angle curves in Fig. 7-36. Along this region, however, the Sun angle-rotation angle solution is very well defined and has a correlation angle of 90 deg because the rotation angle loci are perpendicular to the underlying latitude lines. Consequently, as shown in Fig. 7-37, the singularity in the Sun angle-nadir angle solutions can be broken and high accuracy measurements provided by using Sun angle-rotation angle solutions in this regime. On the other hand, the Sun angle-nadir angle solutions will be more accurate both in the vicinity of the null and along the line joining the Earth and the null, in which the Sun angle-rotation angle solution is singular.

Table 7-5 summarizes the characteristics of arc length-rotation angle solution combinations. Figure 7-39A shows the singularities for the various solution combinations with respect to two fixed reference vectors. Each of the three combinations has a great circle in which the solutions are singular. In addition, any solution using the rotation angle will be poor in the vicinity of the null or the direction of the cross product to the two reference directions. From this figure, it is clear that no single pair is ideal for all possible geometric conditions.

The Earth of course is one of the most common reference vectors since we are frequently interested in the general direction to the Earth for communications. However, during the course of an orbit, the Earth moves around the entire sky, while the orientation of the spin axis attitude will remain approximately fixed in inertial space. Figure 7-39B shows the conditions of singular geometry if the unknown vector and one of the two reference vectors are approximately fixed and the second reference vector is changing. This figure shows the possible positions on the celestial sphere for

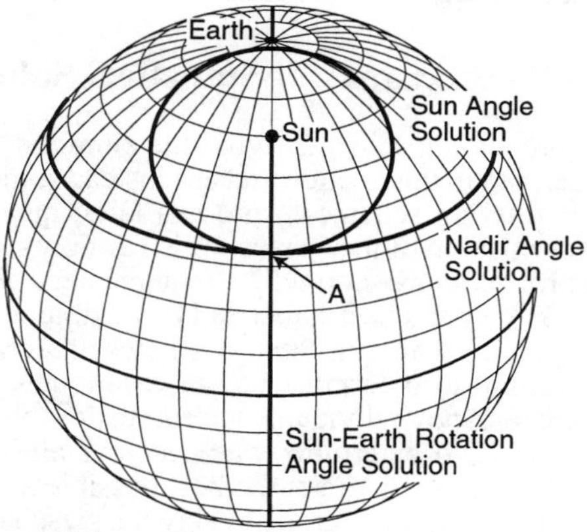

Fig. 7-37. Resolution of Singularities by Using Different Measurement Types. A point A combining the Sun Angle measurement and nadir angle measurement will result in a singularity. However, using either of these in combination with the Sun-Earth rotation angle measurement will result in a good, non-singular solution. If all measurements are treated as dot products during processing (i.e., rotation angle measurements are ignored), then singularities will be present that could be avoided by making use of the rotation angle measurements.

TABLE 7-5. Arc Length/Rotation Angle Solution Characteristics. S is the angular separation between the two known reference vectors, **A** and **B**. **U** is the unknown attitude vector or direction being determined. *R* is the measured rotation angle about the unknown vector **U** from **A** to **B**. *a* is the measured arc length from **U** to **A.**

Rotation Angle Solution Loci

- All solution loci begin and end on **A**, **B**, $\mathbf{A}^{-1}$, or $\mathbf{B}^{-1}$ which all lie on a single *reference great circle*
- All loci for $R < 180$ deg fall into one of the two hemispheres created by the reference great circle; all loci for R > 180 fall into the other hemisphere
- If $R = S$ or $R = 360 - S$, the loci are an X between the end points
- If $R > S$ and $R < 360 - S$, the loci are in two nonintersecting segments, one segment connecting **A** and **B** and the other connecting $\mathbf{A}^{-1}$ and $\mathbf{B}^{-1}$
- If $R < S$ or $R > 360 - S$, the loci are in two nonintersecting segments, one segment connecting **A** and $\mathbf{B}^{-1}$ and the other connecting $\mathbf{A}^{-1}$ and **B**

Arc Length/Rotation Angle Singularity Conditions

- Measurement density is 0 at the *null* = pole of the reference great circle
- For rotation angle + arc length from **A**, correlation angle is 0 or 180 deg (i.e., solution is singular) on the great circle through **B** and the null

Number of Solutions

- If $a < S$ or $a > 180 - S$, there is a single, unique solution
- If $a > S$ and $a < 180 - S$, there are either two solutions, a singular solution, or no solutions

Solution Quality

- Solution quality is best near the reference vectors, between **A** and **B**, and between $\mathbf{A}^{-1}$ and $\mathbf{B}^{-1}$
- Solution quality is poor in the vicinity of the null (measurement density for R is low) and in the vicinity of the singularity great circle (measurements are highly correlated)

Testing the Accuracy of Statistical Solutions

Most "modern" processing schemes avoid the simple deterministic solutions which are described in this section and use instead some type of weighted least squares or filtering scheme to process large quantities of data in which the attitude or position of the spacecraft is strongly overdetermined. If these filtering approaches are correctly implemented, they will indeed provide good answers with the best statistically available information. However, such filters typically deal with the coordinates of sensed objects and it is difficult or impossible to determine how measurement singularities are handled, since there are no individual deterministic solutions. Here, we provide two simple tests to determine whether your algorithm or filter is correctly handling the data so as to get the best possible answer in the presence of systematic errors and measurement singularities. The best filter will get out all of the information contained in the data. On the other hand, no amount of clever processing or sophisticated filtering can get out more.

The geometry for the tests for processing accuracy is shown in Fig. 7-38. We assume for purposes of the test that S_1 and S_2 are known stars and we wish to determine the direction to a new planet, P, which is observed to be directly between the two stars. We assume that the real coordinates of the two stars are known exactly. We measure the x and y position of all three objects which are assumed to all lie along a line at 45 deg to the x and y axes. (Note: both tests can be done equally well in either plane or spherical geometry, depending upon the processing algorithms that are being used.)

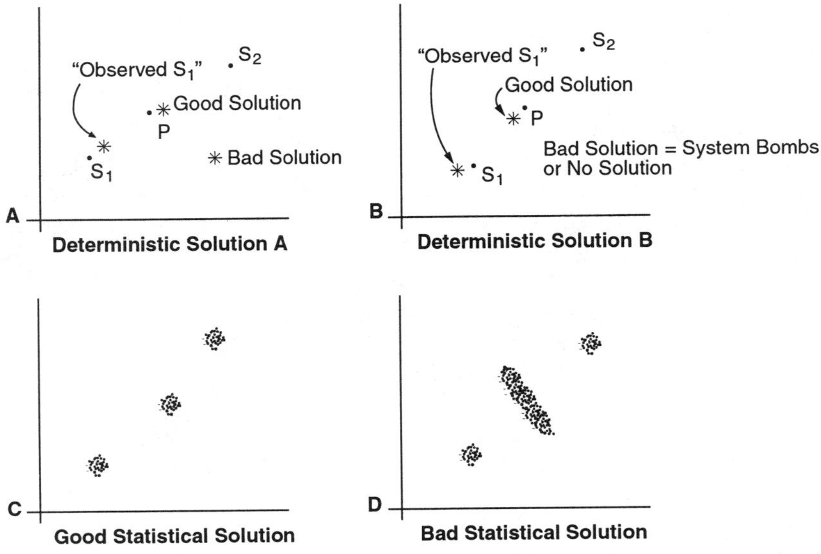

Fig. 7-38. Tests for Processing Accuracy. (A) and (B) are the test for processing a single observation. (C) and (D) are the test for processing a collection of data with random noise. See text for discussion.

Single Observation Test

In this test, we give the processing algorithm the exactly correct coordinates for all three objects, except that the "observed" coordinates for S_1 are shifted toward S_2 by 10% of the distance between them. A good algorithm will estimate P as being on or near the line joining S_1 and S_2 and shifted toward S_2 by about 5% of the spacing. A bad algorithm will push the estimate of P off the line separating them by a substantial amount.

In a related test, shift the "observed" coordinates for S_1 away from S_2, while keeping the other observations correct. A good algorithm will do approximately the same as above, and shift the estimated solution 5% of the way from S_2 toward S_1. A poor algorithm will not return a solution at all, since the data is inconsistent.

Both of the above tests depend on whether or not the algorithm actually makes use of all of the information contained in the measurements. If the algorithm ends up processing nothing but arc lengths or dot products, then it will behave as though the solutions are arc length measurements and will encounter singularities along the line joining S_1 and S_2. These singularities will create strongly incorrect results whenever noise or biases are present. A good algorithm will use the information contained in the rotation angle data and will not suffer from either singularities or large errors in the presence of noise or biases. It is the presence of singularities and large errors which are being observed in this test.

Statistical Tests

If the algorithm employed is inherently statistical and requires an overdetermined solution to work, then a statistical test comparable to the single observation test above can also be done. In this test, we add random noise to all of the observed coordinates and look at the distribution of the computed positions. In virtually any algorithm, the observed distribution should be centered on the real location of P. If the distribution about this point is consistent with the amount of noise that has been added and is nearly circular, or even better, elongated along the line joining S_1 and S_2, you have a very robust algorithm that will provide accurate solutions under almost all conditions. If the distribution is elongated at right angles to the line joining S_1 and S_2, then your algorithm is fundamentally losing information along the way. You have lost information in the processing, and therefore do not have as robust a solution as the data is capable of providing.

If noise were the only problem, then a poor algorithm would not be a significant difficulty, since the center of the noisy data would still be a good estimate of what is being measured. However, in reality, almost all multiply overdetermined observation problems are dominated by systematic errors and not random noise. (Typically enough measurements will be taken to drive the noise contribution in the error to near zero, leaving behind the error contribution due to systematic variations.) In this case, a poor algorithm will in some cases strongly shift the solution away from the correct value. Thus a poorly defined algorithm which does not make use of all of the information content of the data can provide significant errors in the presence of systematic biases under conditions in which singularities would occur in deterministic solutions.

the second reference vector (i.e., the Earth) such that a singularity will occur in measuring the unknown when using the two reference vectors. The singularity region for the nadir angle-Sun angle solution is the great circle connecting the Sun and the attitude. The singularity for the Sun angle-rotation angle curve is a great circle through the Sun at right angles to the attitude-Sun great circle. Finally, the nadir angle-rotation angle singularity occurs along a 90 deg rotation angle curve between the attitude and the Sun.

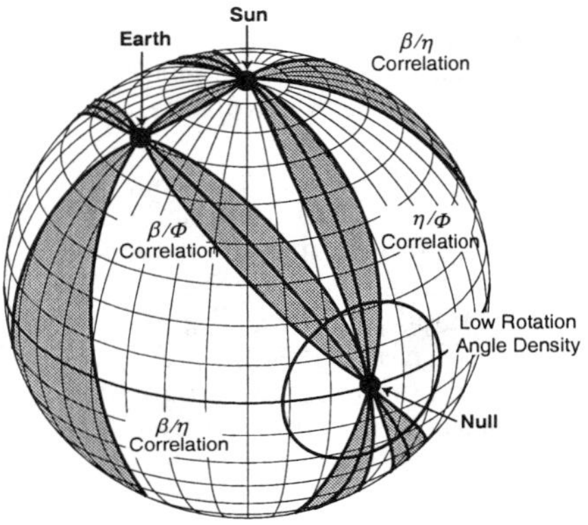

(A) Poor geometry regions for the attitude given fixed locations for the Earth and Sun.

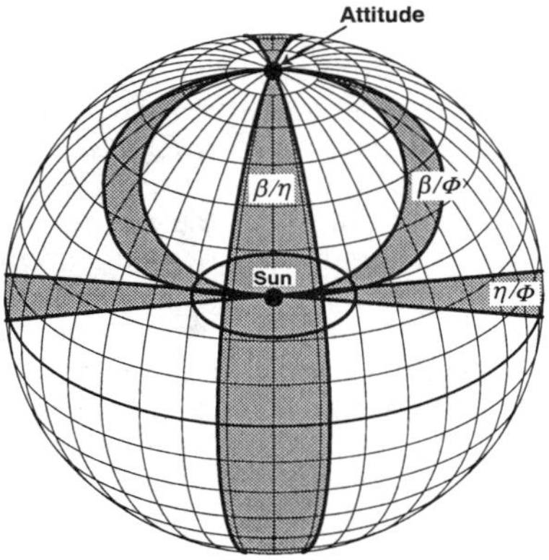

(B) Poor geometry regions for the direction to the Earth given fixed locations for the Sun and the attitude.

Fig. 7-39. Regions of Poor Solutions When Using the Sun and the Earth as Reference Vectors for a Spinning Spacecraft. β = Sun angle, η = nadir angle, Φ = Sun/Earth rotation angle.

Similar plots can be constructed for any combination of reference vectors, with either arc lengths or rotation angles. The basic objective is to determine in advance where solutions will be good and where they will be poor, so that mission planning can be done and sensors can be positioned so as to provide accurate, stable solutions during critical portions of the mission timeline.

7.5 Distance Measurements

Thus far, we have treated only angular relationships as seen by the spacecraft. In addition, there are a number of methods by which spacecraft make direct measurements of distance. In approximate order of increasing distance and applicability (and decreasing accuracy), these are:

- Radar and radio ranging (including tracking antennas and GPS receivers)
- Triangulation or parallax, either instantaneously or over time
- Size of observed objects, such as planets
- Angular separation between two nearby objects (the "donut of position")
- Intensity or apparent magnitude

In *radar* and *radio ranging*, the fundamental measurement is the light travel time between the source of the emission and the spacecraft. To provide sufficient timing accuracy, the measurement is frequently made by using a two-way signal from the source to the target and back again, so that the total travel time can be measured using the same clock. In the case of the GPS receiver, additional observations are used to solve simultaneously for the time as well as the distance, and therefore eliminate the need for turnaround range measurements. The advantage of this type of tracking is that the range determination is extremely good, usually in the range of several centimeters to several meters. The principal disadvantage is that it requires either very high power or cooperative electronics on both ends. In radio ranging, a signal is sent from one location to another and then retransmitted back to the original location. This, of course, requires active electronics on both ends which are cooperating in the measurement process. Thus, this mechanism is only useful in measuring distances to a ground station or to an appropriately equipped satellite or target. Radar, in which the signal simply reflects off of the target, does not require cooperative electronics. Unfortunately, the radar signal falls off as $1/r^4$ where r is the separation between the objects. (See Sec. 11.7) Consequently, using radar to detect spacecraft requires extremely high power or short distances or both. One way to overcome the $1/r^4$ losses and maintain a significant signal strength is to use a corner reflector on the target such that a much higher percentage of the incoming incident energy is directed back toward the transmitter. This mechanism was used during Apollo, where a number of corner reflectors were placed on the surface of the Moon. These were then used in conjunction with lasers on the surface of the Earth to provide very precise measurements of the distance to the Moon and how it changed over time in order to study both the stability of the lunar surface and the astrodynamics of the Moon's motion.

The results of radar and radio ranging methods are a direct measurement of the distance between two objects. Consequently, the locus of position for the unknown object is a spherical shell centered on the known object. The thickness of the shell is, of course, the uncertainty in the range measurement. The intersection of two shells centered at different locations forms a circular tube in three-dimensional space. The intersection of this tube with the shell of a third measurement from a third location which is noncollinear with the first two provides a measurement of the position of the spacecraft. There is a twofold ambiguity in this position corresponding to the spacecraft being on either side of the plane formed by the three reference locations. Usually this ambiguity is easily resolved because the three reference locations can see only about a hemisphere, as for example, when they are located on the surface of the Earth.

This type of measurement works best when the three reference objects are mutually orthogonal, as seen from the spacecraft. As the spacecraft moves further away from the three objects, the references are more nearly aligned in the same direction and the surfaces of the three shells are more nearly parallel. This means that the measurements become highly correlated, and therefore, the uncertainties become larger. The correlation angle between any two of the measurements will be equal to the arc length between the two reference locations as seen from the spacecraft. Thus, while the ranging itself may be accurate over extremely long distances, the combination of distance measurements becomes very inaccurate at measuring the component of the position perpendicular to the direction between the spacecraft and the reference sources.

Both triangulation and parallax measurements are fundamentally trigonometric, as shown in Fig. 7-40. In *triangulation*, I carefully measure the angles at A and B to an unknown point C, and then calculate the distance using straightforward plane geometry. A and B will typically be two points fixed on the spacecraft such as two sensors looking into two mirrors. Triangulation will typically be used to measure the distance to a very nearby spacecraft with which I am docking, or a point on the surface of the planet. The locus of possible positions corresponding to two angular measurements A and B is a circle for which the axis of the circle is the line joining A and B. We can then use either a third single measurement or second angular pair to provide additional measurement and determine the three-dimensional location of the distant object with respect to us. Much like the radar ranging method, triangulation only works when the distance to the object is comparable to the space between the points from which the measurement is made. As the distance to the object becomes larger with respect to the spacing between the measurements, the uncertainty grows rapidly, the measurements become highly correlated, and the distance to the target becomes effectively unknown.

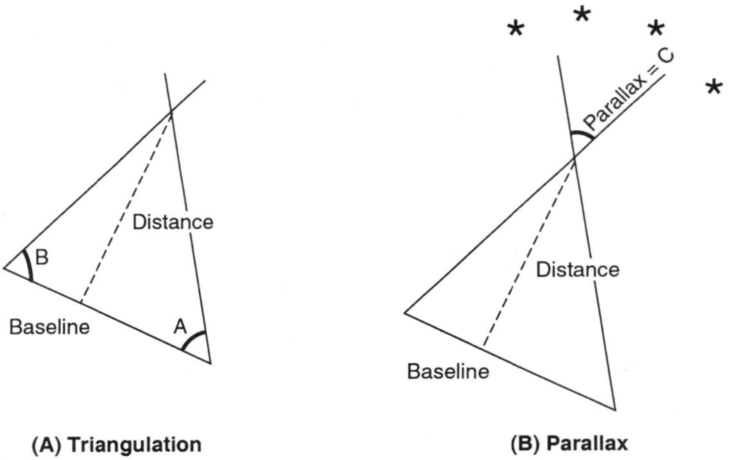

Fig. 7-40. Triangulation and Parallax. Both methods are essentially trigonometric. Triangulation relies on measuring the angles within the instrument itself. Parallax relies on measuring angles by looking at the apparent shift relative to the background stars.

An alternative approach which can extend the range of triangulation measurements to substantially longer distances is known as *parallax* and is illustrated in Fig. 7-40B. Instead of measuring the angles at A and B directly, I measure the angular orientation of the target with respect to the background stars. This can be done by making measurements either simultaneously from two distant sites (such as locations on opposite sides of the Earth) or from a single site at different times, such that I can determine the baseline by knowing the time separation and velocity of the site from which the measurement was made. In any case, I use the angular position with respect to the background stars to infer the *parallax*, which is the angle C at the target between the two sources. If the distance between the sources is known, this infers the distance from the source to the target, again with a straightforward plane geometry computation.

Because the background stars are effectively point sources, angles can be measured relative to these with high precision. Consequently, parallax measurements can be used for measuring distances that are quite large with respect to the angular separation of the two observations. In fact, parallax has been used to determine the distances of nearby stars with respect to the more distant background stars and is the only direct measurement of interstellar distances available to us. All of the rest of the interstellar and intergalactic measurement scales depend on calibration using parallax measurements made to nearby stars. The baseline is the diameter of the Earth's orbit with measurements made 6 months apart. For spacecraft purposes I can use parallax measurements either by seeing the shifting position of the spacecraft against the background stars from two different observing sites, or alternatively, if the orbit and therefore velocity of the spacecraft are known, I can use measurements from the spacecraft of some object with respect to the background stars to determine the distance to that object.

The third class of distance measurement is the observation of the angular size of objects whose physical dimensions are known, such as planets or other spacecraft. The geometry for determining the distance from the size of a planet is shown in Fig. 7-41. A line from the spacecraft tangent to the surface of the planet will be perpendicular to the radius vector of the planet at the point of tangency. Consequently, the angular size of the planet is given by

$$\sin \rho = R_E/D \equiv R_E/(R_E + H) \tag{7-45}$$

where ρ is the angular diameter of the planet of radius R_E, D is the distance from the center of the planet, and H is the distance from the surface. This measurement is a sensitive measure of altitude in low orbit over the planet but is less useful as we get farther away. Thus, at 500 km over the Earth, measuring the angular radius of the Earth to 0.01 deg provides a distance measurement accurate to 500 m. At geosynchronous orbit measuring the angular radius of the Earth to this same accuracy provides an accuracy in the distance measurement of 50 km. Distance measurements based on the angular size of a planet can be improved over time by the use of filtering to significantly reduce noise levels. Consequently, this can be an accurate distance measurement for autonomous navigation techniques. This is, once again, a direct distance measurement. Therefore, just as in the case of radar or radio ranging techniques, this measurement puts the spacecraft on a shell centered on the center of the planet, with a thickness of the shell equal to the uncertainty in the altitude.

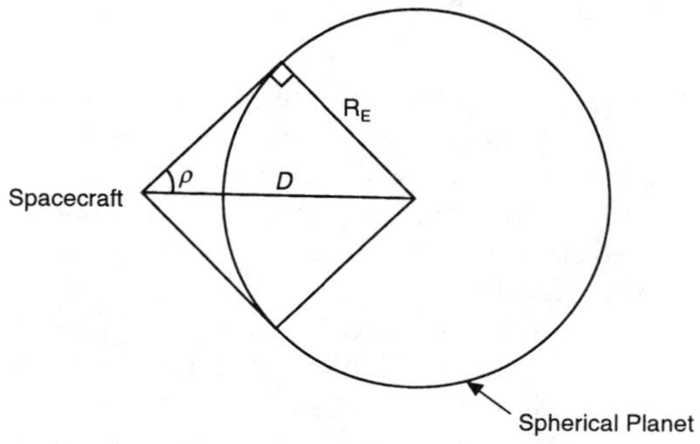

Fig. 7-41. Measuring Distance Based on the Size of a Planet.

In addition to measuring the size of a planet or moon, we can also measure the angular separation between two nearby objects, such as the Earth and the Moon, or two satellites of Mars, Jupiter, or Saturn. Recall from Sec. 7.4.3 that measuring the angle between two points puts us on the arc of a circle for which those two points are a chord. In three dimensions, we do not know our angular orientation about the line joining the two objects. As a consequence, the arc length measurement between the two puts the observer on a circle containing the two objects and then rotated about the line joining them as shown in Fig. 7-42. This "*donut of position*" gives us a shape which is approximately a torus, but which has no hole in the center of the donut. As can be seen from the figure, this measurement behaves like an angular measurement when I am near either of the two objects, and as a distance measurement when the observer is near the "equator" of the axis joining the two objects. The range measurement is directly proportional to the separation between the two objects and inversely proportional to the tangent of the apparent angular separation. The two objects which we are measuring could be, for example, a planet-moon pair, two moons, the Earth and Moon seen from near the Earth, the Earth and some target, or two asteroids.

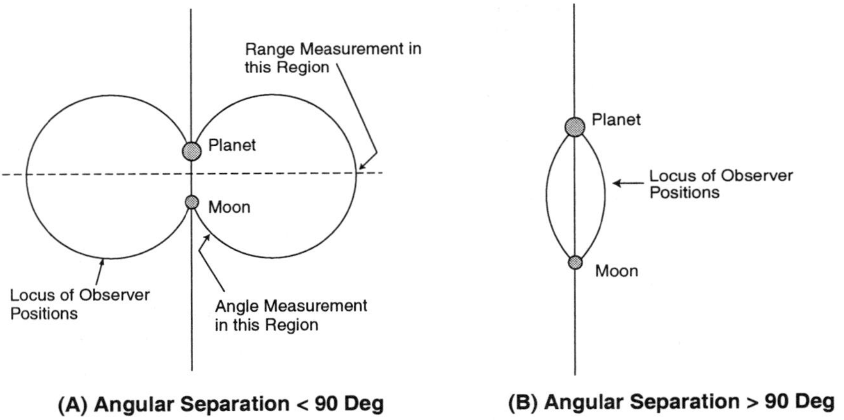

Fig. 7-42. The Donut of Position. Measuring the angular separation between two known objects such as the Earth and Moon or the two satellites of Mars, puts the observer on a torus of revolution about the line joining the objects. A) Angular separation less than 90 deg. B) Angular separation greater than 90 deg. As is apparent, this shape was determined during a late morning discussion that extended into lunch time.

Given the angular separation between two nearby objects, I can then determine my three-dimensional position by measuring the angular position of either of the objects relative to the background stars. This puts me on a narrow cone or pencil centered on the planet, with a radius equal to the uncertainty in the angular measurement with respect to the background stars. The intersection of this cone and the donut of position provides an estimate of the location.

If I measure the angular position with respect to the background stars for one of the two objects, I could do the same for the other object as well. I should, in principle, achieve a similar result to using our donut solution. However, two pencil solutions may or may not intersect in three dimensional space and therefore may yield no solution or have significant ambiguities. An advantage of using the donut solution is that the intersection between that and the cone is very well defined, at least for objects which are near the equator of the line joining the reference objects.

Finally, if the reference object is very distant, the only property that I can measure is its intensity or apparent magnitude which is directly related to the distance of the object. A detailed discussion of brightness as a function of both distance and phase angle is provided in Sec. 11.6. Here we note simply that the intensity of distant objects falls off as $1/r^2$. Typically measuring the intensity with high accuracy is difficult and, therefore, range measurements by measuring apparent magnitude have inherently poor accuracy. Nonetheless, it is the only measurement available for distant objects which are just a point source of light.

The range accuracy vs. range for the various measurements described above are shown in Fig. 4-13 in Sec. 4.3 and the assumptions and instruments used are listed in Table 4-13. While the radar or radio ranging technique is by far the most accurate at essentially all distances, it requires some type of cooperative target at long distances and, therefore, is only applicable when used between ground stations or spacecraft which are intended to communicate with each other. This technique would be applicable to docking with another spacecraft or for measuring precise ranges in a formation flying interferometer or between satellites in a constellation. The other measurements are inherently less accurate but are more appropriate for range measurements in purely autonomous navigation systems in which the spacecraft is attempting to determine its own position based on observations of the outside world.

7.6 Good and Bad Measurement Sets

The fundamental problem of space geometry is: I see a target and want to measure where it is with respect to me, or equally, where I am with respect to it. In some cases, this will involve a two-dimensional measurement which may be used directly, or combined with other two-dimensional measurements for three-axis attitude or position determination. Alternatively, 2D measurements may be projected onto the surface of the Earth or planet, in other cases a three-dimensional measurement is desired. Irrespective of the end application, the basic objective is to create orthorgonal measurement sets in either two dimensions or three dimensions, depending on whether I'm interested in direction or position. By orthogonal, I do not mean that the measurements themselves are in some sense perpendicular but that the loci, either in three-dimensional space or projected onto the celestial sphere, intersect at right angles.

In two-dimensional measurements on the celestial sphere, the best combination is an arc length measurement combined with a Type I rotation angle about the central reference direction. This provides loci which are a small circle and a radial arc extending out from the center. Thus, the measurement loci will be orthogonal everywhere on the sky and will have no singularities or ambiguous solutions. This measurement combination is particularly strong for purposes of determining a direction in space. If I use two arc length measurements, then I will have good results with orthogonal solutions whenever the rotation angle measured about the unknown between the two reference directions is 90 deg. When this angle is either 0 or 180 deg, i.e., when I'm on the great circle connecting the two reference directions, then I'll have a singularity and the measurements will be very poor. Similarly, when combining an arc length measurement and a Type II rotation angle measurement, a singularity arises whenever I'm on the great circle connecting the null and the second reference vector. With these two measurements, I will have orthogonal solutions in the vicinity of either of the two reference vectors or their antipoints.

An example of the use of good and bad measurement sets is shown in Fig. 7-43 which illustrates alternative approaches for measuring the position of an asteroid with respect to the background stars. In Fig. 7-43A, I measured two arc lengths which gives a solution singularity when the asteroid is on the line connecting the two stars. In Fig. 7-43B, I measure the arc length plus a rotation angle about one of the stars between the planet and the other star. In this case, the result is two orthogonal measurements with no ambiguity, no singularity for collinear objects, and maximum measurement accuracy.

Similarly, to the two arc length measurements, two Type I rotation angles provide a good solution only when the angle measured at the target between the two reference directions is nearly orthogonal. When the object lies on the line joining the reference directions, both the pair of arc lengths and the pair of Type I rotation angles will provide poor results.

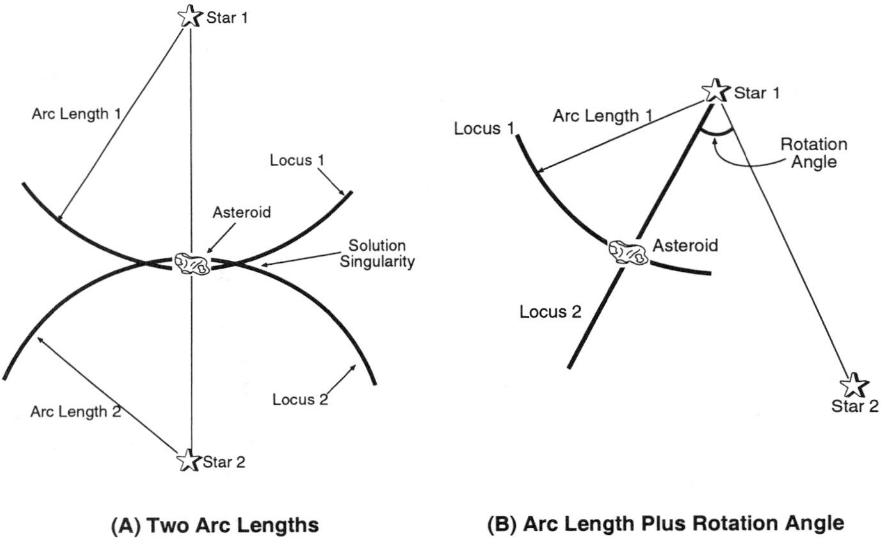

Fig. 7-43. Alternative Approaches for Measuring the Position of an Asteroid with Respect to the Background Star. Solution A has large potential errors that aren't present in solution B.

In three dimensional measurements, the best solution is to provide a range measurement combined with an arc length and a Type I rotation angle. These solutions are orthogonal over the entire sky and do not have any singularities or ambiguities. Specifically,

> ***Any measurement triad consisting of one arc length measurement, one Type I rotation angle measurement, and one range measurement, creates a mutually perpendicular measurement set that avoids singularities.***

This process is illustrated in Fig. 7-44 and summarized in Table 7-6. In general, I would like to measure distance to nearby objects rather than far away ones, to avoid subtracting large numbers and thereby creating large errors. Similarly, angular measurements made with respect to nearby objects provide smaller errors than those with respect to more distant ones. For example, measuring the angular positions of asteroids against the background stars has been proposed for interplanetary autonomous navigation. The fundamental problem is that asteroids are at very large distances from the spacecraft most of the time. Consequently, I need to make angular measurements which are remarkably precise in order to avoid generating large errors by the intersection of cones which are extremely long.

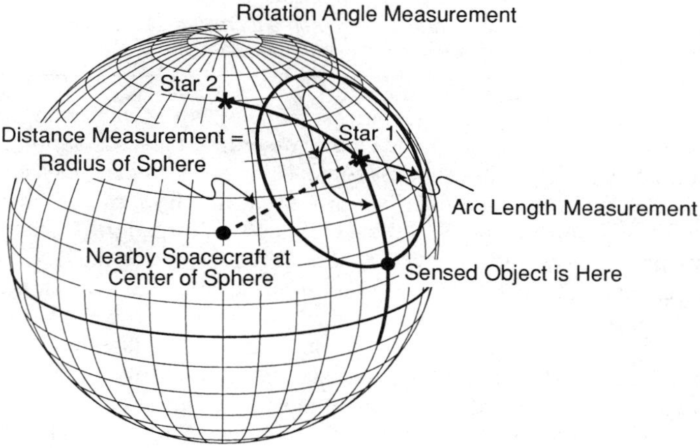

Fig. 7-44. The Best Measurement Set Involves a Distance Measurement, an Arc Length, and a Rotation Angle. The solutions are orthogonal and have no singularities or ambiguous solutions. The distance measurement defines the radius of the sphere. The arc length measurement from a reference direction (Star 1) defines the radius of a small circle centered on the star. The rotation angle about Star 1 from Star 2 to the unknown object defines a Type I rotation angle measurement that determines where on the small circle the sensed object is located.

Similarly, I would like to make measurements in the final coordinate system that I am interested in, in order to avoid additional errors as the result of coordinate transformations. An example here would be the use of star sensors vs. Earth sensors for Earth-based measurements. Star sensors are inherently much more accurate than Earth sensors. Nonetheless, in order to transform the attitude measured in a star sensor coordinate system to a position on the Earth, I must ultimately use the spacecraft orbit information to transform from inertial coordinates to Earth-fixed coordinates. This transformation introduces additional error, which, depending on the accuracy with which the orbit is known, may be significantly larger than the accuracy of the star sensor itself. Similarly, if I use the Earth width measurement to determine nadir, I do so based on a knowledge of the angular size of the Earth, which requires that I know the altitude of the spacecraft. Once again, I've introduced additional error by not being able to directly measure the angle to the center of the Earth.

TABLE 7-6. Interplanetary Autonav Preferred Measurement Sets.

• 2 asteroids with respect to background stars—measure either: – Both asteroids with respect to background stars (gives one redundant measurement) – Arc length between asteroids, 1 star-asteroid arc length, and 1 star-asteroid-asteroid rotation angle • 2 stars and target – measure 1 arc length, 1 rotation angle, and 1 range measurement via luminosity or angular size • Planet, moon, and 1 star (same as 2 moons and sun or 2 moons and distant planet) - measure angular separation between planet and moon and between planet, and star, measure rotation angle about planet between moon and star.
Any measurement triad consisting of 1 arc length measurement, 1 rotation angle measurement, and 1 range measurement creates a mutually perpendicular measurement set that avoids singularities

As we have pointed out previously, measurements will normally be filtered or go through some data averaging technique in order to reduce the level of noise. However, it is important that the information content in the original measurements be maintained. This will only be done if we process all the information, making use of both rotation angle information as well as arc length information. Tests to determine whether any particularly algorithm will do this were provided in the boxed example at the end of Sec 7.4. Note that if the observations are formulated as vectors and we use only the dot products between vectors as measurements, then we are restricting our solutions to arc length measurements and losing information inherent in the basic data.

The formulas provided throughout this chapter give all of the basic data that is needed to evaluate the information content of most space measurements. Our principal result is that it is the information content of the measurement more than the processing technique that determines how accurate the final results will be. I can lose information by processing poorly, but cannot in the end provide any additional information beyond that inherently present in the data itself. This basic information content can be determined by looking at either the attitude or position loci on the celestial sphere or three dimensional space. It is these loci and their intersections that determine what the actual measurements are. The processing is simply a means of computing the intersections or reducing the noise associated with the measurements themselves.

References

Collins, Steve. 1992. "Geocentric Nadir and Range from Horizon Sensor Observations of the Oblate Earth." AIAA Paper No. 92-176, presented at the AAS/AIAA Spaceflight Mechanics Meeting, Colorado Springs, CO, Feb. 24-26.

Wertz, James R., ed. 1978. *Spacecraft Attitude Determination and Control*. Dordrecht, The Netherlands: D. Reidel Publishing Company.

Wertz, James R. and Wiley J. Larson, eds. 1999. *Spacecraft Mission Analysis and Design (Third Edition)*. Torrance, CA and Dordrecht, The Netherlands: Microcosm, Press. and Kluwer Academic Publishers.

Chapter 8

Full-Sky Spherical Geometry

As described in Chaps. 6 and 7, the basic measurements for most spacecraft observations consist of angles on the celestial sphere. The typical analytical approach is to transform these angular measurements into an alternative representation (e.g., unit vectors, quaternions, or Euler angles), process the data, and then transform back into angular output as needed for interpretation or display. This indirect or nongeometrical approach has several potential problems because it can

- Introduce singularities but not eliminate ones inherent in the data
- Obscure the basic meaning of the measurements
- Be difficult to interpret
- Make solutions difficult for problems having no convenient solution outside of spherical geometry, such as
  —Representation of solution loci
  —Angular area computations for field-of-view, thermal, or intensity analysis

The main advantage of the nongeometrical formulation is that a convenient and complete formalism exists for handling the mathematics. At one time, it was also computationally faster. Both of these disadvantages to a direct geometrical approach have now been overcome. The increased computer speed (particularly for trig functions) has made spherical geometry solutions as fast or faster than vector solutions for many problems. In addition, computer advances over the last decade have made computation time less important and put a greater emphasis on being able to interpret and verify intermediate and final solutions.

The other main disadvantage of the geometrical approach has been the problem of quadrant ambiguities that, in the past, has made completely general solutions to mission geometry problems almost impossible. Spacecraft measurements inherently range over the full sky and both angles and arc lengths can vary from 0 to 360 deg. When doing a single problem by hand, keeping track of quadrant ambiguities is not difficult. However, in doing multiple, diverse, and automated solutions, keeping track of quadrants, quadrant ambiguities, and multiple solutions becomes nearly impossible, particularly in trying to verify and validate all of the solution options.

This technical problem has now been fully resolved. This chapter and App. A provide complete solutions for all spherical triangles in which any of the sides or angles range from 0 to 360 deg.* Consequently, these solutions can now be implemented in computer programs and operational systems such that complete and correct solutions will be provided irrespective of the quadrants of any of the measurements. There are, of course, multiple solutions to many problems. This occurs whenever the multiple solutions are inherent in the data itself. No extra solutions or solution ambiguities are introduced by the full-sky processing. In addition, as we will show shortly, there are several cases where the full-sky solutions are both physically and mathematically simpler than those which restrict angles and sides to lie within a single hemisphere.

This chapter reports on work done at Microcosm over the last decade. So far as I am aware, there are no other references in the literature to full-sky geometry theory or applications. We provide the analytic basis and then present results that can be easily implemented without continually returning to the basic theory. If you're not interested in the geometrical formulation, simply use the full-sky trigonometric solutions presented in App. A. Given any three components of a spherical triangle, the remaining three components can be determined using these solutions. The three known components can take on any arbitrary real value and the three determined components will all fall in the range of 0 to 360 deg.

If you skip Sec. 8.1 on the analytical foundation for full-sky geometry, you should review Secs. 8.2 and 8.3 on applications to see how applying the geometric solutions can simplify some practical problems. Specifically, Sec. 8.2 introduces a curve called the dual-axis spiral, which closely approximates attitude and orbit motion for several common spacecraft problems. This simplifies, for example, the analysis of the spacecraft ground trace in circular orbits, the relative motion of spacecraft, the motion of a point on a nutating spacecraft, or a spinning sensor on a rotating spacecraft.

The full-sky geometry results are sometimes strange—sides cross each other between vertices, and some triangles look more like starfish covering the entire sky than traditional triangles. Still, the results are extremely practical for analyzing problems involving a spacecraft's orbit and attitude. I hope you find the results as intriguing to consider as we did to derive them.

8.1 Introduction to Full-Sky Spherical Geometry

Unfortunately, even relatively simple problems in spherical geometry can be complex to solve with the traditional approaches of unit vectors or classical spherical geometry. For example, consider the "airplane problem" illustrated in Fig. 8-1. An airplane is initially at an arbitrary location on the Earth's surface. It flies an arbitrary distance, D_1, in a straight line (i.e., a great circle path), changes direction through an

* Angles and arc lengths outside this range simply repeat, so that in practice, arc length and rotation angle measurements can take on any positive or negative real value.

arbitrary angle, ϕ_1, in a counterclockwise (right-handed) sense, and again flies an arbitrary distance, D_2. What we would like to determine is:

- What is the distance home, D_3?
- In what direction, ϕ_2, must the airplane turn to get home?
- Once home, what direction, ϕ_3, must the airplane turn to get to its initial heading?

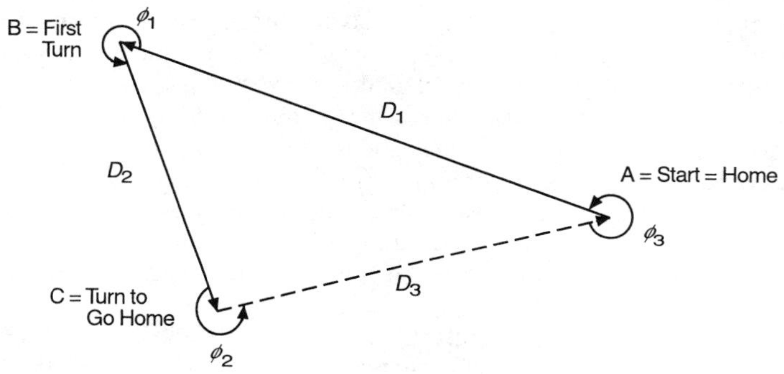

Fig. 8-1. The Airplane Problem. This exemplifies a problem that is conceptually simple yet computationally complex for both vectors and traditional spherical geometry because any of the sides or angles can range from 0 to 360 deg.

To convert from a change in direction to an angle in a spherical triangle, we must add or subtract 180 deg depending on the quadrant. For example, going "straight ahead" is a 0 deg change in direction or a 180 deg angle in the triangle in Fig. 8-1. The problem then seems straightforward and is conceptually easy. No matter where we end up on the Earth (point C), the distance home (D_3) and direction to get there are well defined, unless of course we end up either back home or 180 deg from home, in which case the direction is arbitrary.

Unfortunately, this conceptually simple problem becomes remarkably inconvenient to do on the computer. In most solutions, we need to keep track of whether we go more or less than 180 deg and whether we turn through more or less than 180 deg (equivalent to turning to the left or to the right). The result is a tree structure for the solution that is quite complex for such a simple problem. If we have only two quadrant ambiguities each time, we still end up with 16 solutions to keep track of. In general, because four quadrants are available for each arc and angle, we could have as many as 256 possible options—far too many for convenience, either in vectors or classical spherical geometry. (At the end of this section, we will return to the airplane problem and solve it using vectors, classical spherical trig, and full-sky geometry.)

The regime of classical spherical trigonometry, as discussed in Chap. 6, covers only triangles with sides and angles less than 180 deg. This works for all problems in spherical geometry because any three arbitrary vertices can always be contained in a single hemisphere. The sides which connect these vertices can all be shorter than 180 deg and contain rotation angles less than 180 deg. Thus, we can use the classical approach to do all problems in spherical trigonometry. However, as in the airplane problem, the real world isn't always limited to measurements of sides or angles that range only through 180 deg. Even the basic spherical geometry coordinate system has an azimuth angle that ranges from 0 to 360 deg. Similarly, rotating mechanisms measure angles through 360 deg and arc lengths can, and in many cases do, cover a range of 0 to 360 deg or larger. (Angles larger than 360 deg also pose no problem because each is numerically equivalent to an angle less than 360 deg.) In principle, we can solve the airplane problem simply by keeping track at each stage of whether we've gone more or less than 180 deg around the world and turned through angles of more or less than 180 deg (i.e., left or right). This works fine for a single problem done by hand, but is remarkably inconvenient to automate.

Fortunately, this bookkeeping problem has been resolved. Solutions are given in App. A for all possible spherical triangles in which any sides and angles can cover the full range of 0 to 360 deg. These are called *complete spherical triangles*. Because angles beyond 0 to 360 deg in either direction are equivalent to ones within this range, we can solve triangles in which the sides and angles take on any arbitrary real value. Given any combination of 3 sides or angles (including 3 angles), we can solve for all of the remaining parts. In some cases, the resulting triangles "look funny," but are nonetheless extremely practical. In addition, the full-sky solutions are analytically simpler than the solutions which constrain all sides and angles to the range 0 to 180 deg.

I've mentioned that a single hemisphere can always contain any three arbitrary vertices. However, in full-sky geometry there are many ways to connect these vertices, resulting in 16 unique triangles with 8 possible shapes. These are drawn on the celestial sphere in Fig. 8-2 and in "flat" sketches in Fig. 8-3. The simplest way to think of the possible shapes is that any of the 3 sides may be constructed by going either the short way (less than 180 deg) or the long way (greater than 180 deg). This gives us 4 options with either 0, 1, 2, or 3 of the sides longer than 180 deg. In addition, for a given set of sides, inside and outside may be interchanged, resulting in 2 distinct triangles for each combination of sides. The taxonomy of complete spherical triangles is shown in Figs. 8-2 and 8-3 and summarized in Table 8-1.

TABLE 8-1. Taxonomy of Complete Spherical Triangles. For 3 arbitrary vertices, each of the 3 sides can be either less than 180 deg (short arc) or greater than 180 deg (long arc). For a single set of sides, each triangle can be either small or large (i.e., the angle inverses of each other). The table is a complete list of the 16 possible spherical triangles and their properties. See Figs. 8-2 and 8-3 for illustrations.

Sides	Area	Number	Angles
3 short arcs (Regular)	small#	1	3 lesser angles
	large	1	3 greater angles
2 short arcs, 1 long arc (irregular Notch)	small	3	2 lesser angles 1 greater angle*
	large	3	1 lesser angle** 2 greater angles
1 short arc, 2 long arcs (irregular Fish)	small	3	2 lesser angles 1 greater angle†
	large	3	1 lesser angle‡ 2 greater angles
3 long arcs (irregular Star)	small	1	3 lesser angles
	large	1	3 greater angles

\# Called a *proper* triangle
* Greater angle is opposite the long arc
** Lesser angle is opposite the long arc
† Greater angle is opposite the short arc
‡ Lesser angle is opposite the short arc

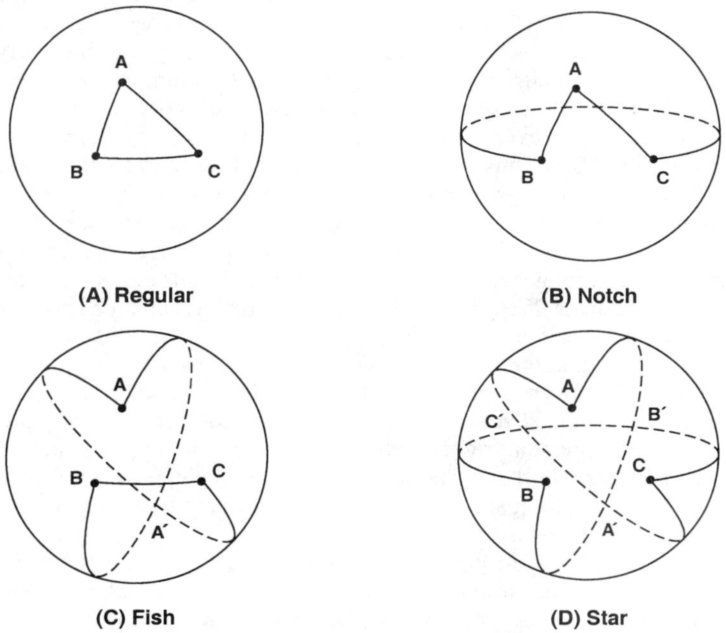

Fig. 8-2. Any 3 Vertices Define 8 Possible Shapes for Spherical Triangles. Each pair of vertices can be connected by going either the short way (< 180 deg) or the long way (> 180 deg). Either 0, 1, 2, or 3 sides can be longer than 180 deg and the "inside" and "outside" are interchangeable. This results in 8 possible types of triangles and in 16 unique shapes because for the notch and fish any of the 3 sides can be the one which is a short or long arc.

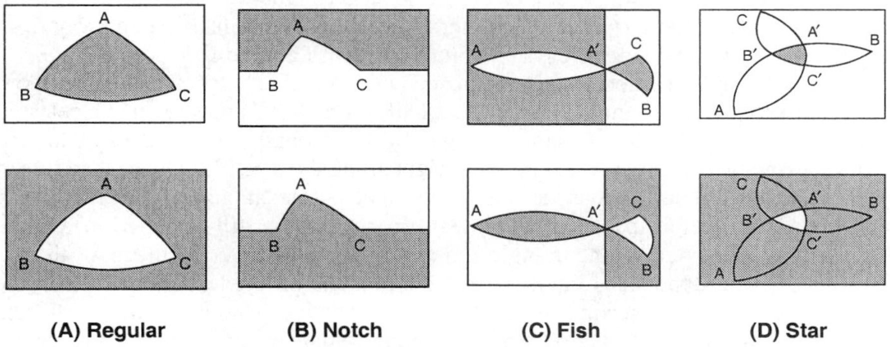

Top Row = Small Triangle, Bottom Row = Large Triangle

Fig. 8-3. An Alternative "Flat" Sketch of the 8 Possible Spherical Triangles. In the notch any of the 3 sides can be greater than 180 deg and in the fish any of the sides can be less than 180 deg. This results in the 8 possible sets of sides and 16 possible shapes because either area defined by a particular shape can be taken as the inside. In traditional spherical geometry only the shaded triangle in the top diagram of (A) is allowed.

Figures 8-2A and 8-3A show a *regular* spherical triangle in which all of the vertices are connected with arcs less than 180 deg. For convenience, we call any arc shorter than 180 deg a *short arc* and any greater than 180 deg a *long arc*. Similarly, we use *lesser angle* for one smaller than 180 deg and *greater angle* for one greater than 180 deg. Thus, Fig. 8-2A has 3 short arcs and 3 lesser angles of approximately 60 deg. However, we could also reverse what we think of as inside and outside, as shown by the shading in Fig. 8-3A. Thus, the triangle with the 3 short arcs could have 3 lesser angles of about 60 deg, or 3 greater angles of about 300 deg. We call the result of flopping the triangle inside-out an *inverse-angle spherical triangle* because all of the sides remain the same, but each of the angles becomes 360 deg minus its previous value. The sum of the areas of a triangle and its inverse-angle triangle fills the sky and must, therefore, cover 4π steradians. We will call the triangle which has an area less than a hemisphere (i.e., $< 2\pi$ steradians) a *small spherical triangle*; the other is then a *large spherical triangle* because it has an area larger than a hemisphere.

The small regular spherical triangle in Fig. 8-3A has all sides and angles less than 180 deg. This *proper spherical triangle* (all short arcs and lesser angles) represents the domain of classical spherical trigonometry. However, the more general class of regular spherical triangles (short arcs and lesser or greater angles) is also of considerable practical use because spherical coordinate systems have arc lengths less than 180 deg and rotation angles which cover 0 to 360 deg.

The next option, shown in Figs. 8-2B and 8-3B, has 2 short arcs and 1 long arc, reaching more than 180 deg around the sphere. This is called a *notch spherical triangle* because it has the appearance of a hemisphere with a notch in it. If the top part of Fig. 8-2B is the inside, it will be a small triangle with 1 greater angle and 2 lesser angles. If the bottom part is the inside, it will be a large triangle with 1 lesser angle and 2 greater angles. In addition to having two ways to think of inside and outside, any of the 3 sides can become the long arc in a notch triangle. Consequently, there are 6 different notch triangles for a single set of vertices.

If 2 of the sides of the spherical triangle are long arcs, then we create a *fish*, as shown in Figs. 8-2C and 8-3C. This triangle is somewhat strange in that the 2 arcs which are longer than 180 deg intersect in 2 locations. One of these (point **A**) is, of course, the vertex of the triangle. The other (point **A′**) is the point 180 deg away from that vertex. Thus, the 2 sides cross at a point which isn't a vertex.

In a fish triangle the definitions of "inside" and "outside" also are unusual. Consider, for example, the triangle in the bottom half of Fig. 8-3C and shown in a celestial sphere drawing in Fig. 8-4. Assume that we "walk" around the boundary of the triangle, starting on the left at **A** and going to right along the top side. The dashed line in Fig. 8-4 remains on our right as we walk. (The shaded area on our right is the interior, and, as we pass **A′**, the shaded area below us on our right is still the interior.) On the first part, our left is outside the triangle and our right is inside. As we cross **A′**, the antipode of **A**, where the sides intersect, outside remains on the left and inside on the right. As we come to the second vertex, **B**, the interior angle is now a greater angle and the exterior angle (unshaded area) is a lesser angle. What appears to be the outside has now become the inside. Following along, keeping the inside on our right, we come to vertex **C** in the upper right, where again the greater angle is inside and the lesser angle is outside. We now turn at this vertex and follow the third side back toward where we started, still keeping inside to the right and the outside to the left. As we again cross **A′** where the sides intersect, we still have the inside on the right and the outside on the left. Although we can logically keep track of the inside and outside, the result seems strange. As with the notch, there are 6 possible fish spherical triangles, corresponding to any of the 3 sides being the short arc, and each of the sets of sides having inside and outside interchanged

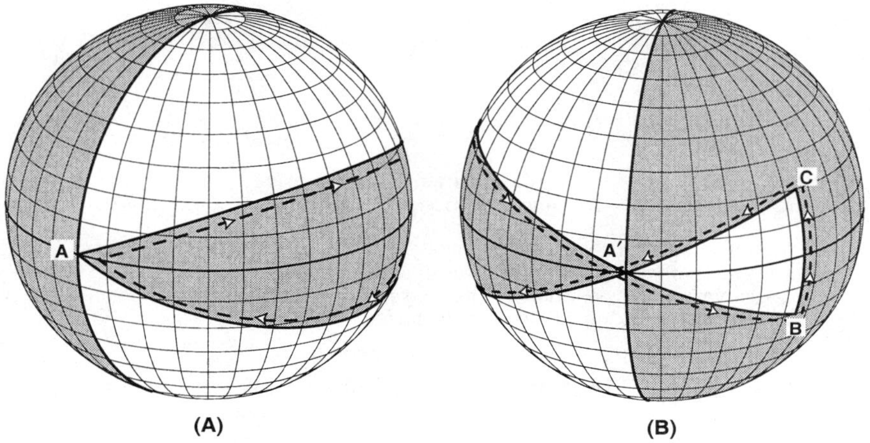

Fig. 8-4. The Fish Spherical Triangle. If we "walk around" the triangle keeping the dashed line on our right, this will define the interior of the triangle as shown by the shaded area.

Finally, Figs. 8-2D and 8-3D illustrate the shape if all 3 sides are long arcs. Now, there are 3 locations where the sides intersect, at the 3 antipodes 180 deg from the vertices. This triangle, called a star, seems to wrap around the entire sphere like a starfish holding an oyster. In the star, the inside is the area within the proper spherical triangle formed with the 3 intersections which are not vertices. The exterior of the star is, of course, the remaining area on the sphere and again, the role of inside and outside can be reversed, as shown in Fig. 8-3D. I have no intuitive explanation for this definition of inside and outside other than this result is consistent with the spherical excess rule. There is only one way to connect all 3 vertices with long arcs. Consequently, there are only 2 star triangles. This gives us a total of 16 possible spherical triangles formed with any arbitrary set of 3 vertices. The complete list of these 16 triangles and their properties is given in Table 8-1.

The vocabulary of complete spherical triangles is summarized in Table 8-2. We've seen in Figs. 8-2 and 8-3 examples of the inverse angle spherical triangle in which we interchange the inside and the outside. A computationally convenient special case is the inverse angle triangle of a right spherical triangle, called a *right three-quarter spherical triangle* (Fig. 8-5A). The negative of the right angle is a 270 deg angle. Similarly, we can replace the 90 deg arc in a quadrantal triangle with a long arc of 270 deg, forming a *quadrantal three-quarter spherical triangle*. If we replace the sides in any spherical triangle with their negatives, we have an *inverse side spherical triangle*. The inverse side triangle for a regular triangle would be a star, and vice-versa. Similarly, the inverse side triangle of a notch would be a fish, and the inverse side of a fish would be a notch.

One other special case is of interest. If one angle in a spherical triangle is 180 deg, then the triangle becomes a two-sided figure called a *lune*. A lune has 2 sides 180 deg

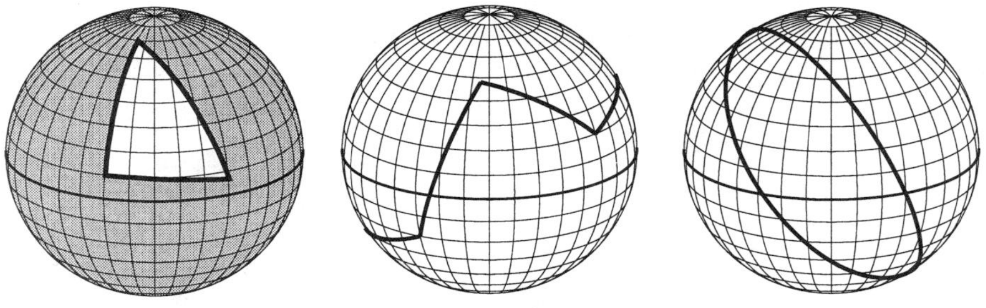

(A) Right Three-Quarter Spherical Triangle **(B) Quadrantal Three-Quarter Spherical Triangle** **(C) Lune**

Fig. 8-5. Special Cases of Full-Sky Spherical Triangles (A) A right three-quarter spherical triangle (shaded). (B) A quadrantal three-quarter spherical triangle. (C) A *lune*—a degenerate case in which one of the angles is 180 deg. Note that in both (B) and (C), either area can be the "inside" of the triangle.

long and 2 equal angles. An example of a lune is the figure created by any 2 lines of constant longitude on the Earth or by the intersection of any 2 great circles, as shown in Fig. 8-5C.

Clearly, there are far more complete triangles than there are in the constrained case of classical spherical geometry. However, there are two important points to keep in mind:

- While there are many triangles, the solutions to complete spherical geometry problems are **equally simple or simpler*** than for the classical case and they neither introduce nor remove any extraneous solutions.

- The multiple triangles are "real," in that they represent real solutions to practical problems, such as the airplane problem discussed at the beginning of the section.

Nothing (other than a fuel shortage or tired pilot) prevents our hypothetical airplane from flying more than 180 deg, turning through an angle of more than 180 deg, flying more than 180 deg again, and asking "how should I turn to get home?" The resulting spherical triangle is a fish, and we would like to answer the problem without resorting to the type of logic which says, "Oh, the pilot went more than 180 deg on the first leg, so we need to change the triangle problem we're solving." We want to simply put the values into a spherical-trig formula and get the results, no matter how far the pilot flew.

It is often important to determine the angular area of figures on the celestial sphere, such as when we are computing thermal input, radiation intensity, or field of view blockage. Fortunately, this is straightforward for any spherical triangle, or, more generally, any polygon on the celestial sphere. For any *spherical polygon* (i.e., any figure with two or more sides, all of which are great circle arcs), the area, expressed in steradians, equals the spherical excess when the angles are expressed in radians. The *spherical excess* is the sum of the angles minus $(n-2)\,\pi$ (see Chap. 6), where n is the number of sides or angles in the polygon. Note that the area of the angle inverse of any

* See the discussion following Fig. 8-6.

TABLE 8-2. Basic Definitions for Complete (Full-Sky) Spherical Triangles.

Spherical Triangle (ST): Any triangle on the surface of a sphere with all sides and all angles between 0 and 360 deg. Also called *a complete spherical triangle (CST),* to distinguish it from the subset of proper spherical triangles.

Proper Spherical Triangle (PST): One with all angles and all sides less than 180 deg. This is the domain of traditional spherical trigonometry.

Improper Spherical Triangle (IST): One with one or more sides or angles greater than 180 deg.

Small Spherical Triangle (SST): One with area less than 2π steradians.

Large Spherical Triangle (LST): One with area greater than 2π steradians.

Regular Spherical Triangle (RegST): One with all sides less than 180 deg. A *proper spherical triangle* is one which is both regular and small.

Irregular Spherical Triangle (IregST): One with one or more sides greater than 180 deg.

Notch (N): An irregular spherical triangle with one side longer than 180 deg.

Fish (F): An irregular spherical triangle with two sides longer than 180 deg.

Star (S): An irregular spherical triangle with all three sides longer than 180 deg.

Inverse Angle Spherical Triangle (IAST): The spherical triangle with the sides of a given triangle and angles equal to the negative of each of the angles of the given triangle.

Inverse Side Spherical Triangle (ISST): The spherical triangle with the angles of a given triangle and sides equal to the negative of each of the sides of the given triangle.

Polar Triangle (PT): The proper spherical triangle for which the vertices are the poles of the three great circles which form the sides of a given spherical triangle.

Right Spherical Triangle (RST): Any spherical triangle in which at least one of the angles is a right angle.

Quadrantal Spherical Triangle (QST): Any spherical triangle in which at least one of the sides is 90 deg in length.

Lune: A figure formed by two intersecting great circle arcs. A lune is a singular spherical triangle, i.e., a triangle in which one of the sides and one of the angles is 180 deg.

Right Three-Quarter Spherical Triangle (R3QST): An improper spherical triangle in which one of the angles is 270 deg.

Quadrantal Three-Quarter Spherical Triangle (Q3QST): An improper spherical triangle in which one of the sides is 270 deg in length.

Complement of an angle (A′) or side (a′): 90 deg minus the given angle or side.

Supplement of an angle (A″) or side (a″): 180 deg minus the given angle or side.

Negative of an angle (–A) or side (–a): 360 deg minus the given angle or side.

Spherical Excess (SE): The amount by which the sum of the angles in any spherical triangle, expressed in radians, exceeds π.

Short Arc (SArc): One which is less than 180 deg in length.

Long Arc (LArc): One which is greater than 180 deg in length.

Lesser Angle (LAng): One which is less than 180 deg.

Greater Angle (GAng): One which is greater than 180 deg.

spherical triangle (or polygon) will be the remaining area in the full sphere, or 4π minus the area of the original triangle. This also equals the angle-inverse triangle's spherical excess because the sum of all 3 angles and their negatives will be 6π. See Table 8-3 for a summary of these formulas.

TABLE 8-3. Area Formulas in Spherical Geometry. Angles are expressed in radians and area in steradians.

Figures with Sides that Are Great Circle Arcs
Area of any Spherical Polygon:
Area = Spherical Excess (SE) = Σ angles − $(n-2)\,\pi$ where n is the number of sides (or angles) in the figure
Area of the angle inverse of any Spherical Polygon:
Area = SE of the angle inverse polygon = 4π − Area of original polygon
Area of a Lune with angle of intersection, Θ:
Area = SE = 2Θ
Area of any Spherical Triangle:
Area = SE = Σ angles − π
Area of any Spherical Quadrilateral:
Area = SE = Σ angles − 2π
Figures with One or More Sides that Are Small Circle Arcs
Area of a small circle of radius λ:
Area = $2\pi\,(1-\cos\lambda)$
Area of a segment of rotation angle ϕ in a small circle of radius λ:
Area = $\phi(1-\cos\lambda)$
Area of an annulus of inner radius λ_1 and outer radius λ_2:
Area = $2\pi\,(\cos\lambda_1-\cos\lambda_2)$
Area of a segment of rotation angle ϕ of an annulus of inner radius λ_1 and outer radius λ_2:
Area = $\phi\,(\cos\lambda_1-\cos\lambda_2)$
Area of intersection = Overlap area between two small circles of radii λ_1 and λ_2 separated by a center-to-center distance α:
$\text{Area} = 2\pi - 2\cos\lambda_1 \,\text{acos}\left[\frac{\cos\lambda_2-\cos\lambda_1\cos\alpha}{\sin\lambda_1\sin\alpha}\right] - 2\cos\lambda_2\,\text{acos}\left[\frac{\cos\lambda_1-\cos\lambda_2\cos\alpha}{\sin\lambda_2\sin\alpha}\right] - 2\,\text{acos}\left[\frac{\cos\alpha-\cos\lambda_2\cos\lambda_1}{\sin\lambda_2\sin\lambda_1}\right]$ $\quad\lvert\lambda_1-\lambda_2\rvert \le \alpha \le \lambda_1+\lambda_2$

A note of caution: The spherical excess rule works only for figures in which all of the sides are great circle arcs. One of the more common mistakes to watch out for is forming a "triangle" with a "curved" side that isn't a great circle arc. Many spherical geometry figures have one or more sides which are small circle arcs. Table 8-3 includes formulas for several of them for completeness. In this case, neither the area formulas nor the standard rules of spherical trigonometry work.

Spherical triangles can be defined either by the coordinates of the 3 vertices (for which there are 16 solutions) or by specifying any 3 components. This is different from plane geometry in which the specified components must include at least one side, because angle-angle-angle triangles in plane geometry are all similar and can be various sizes. Because of the spherical excess rule, this is not the case in spherical trigonometry and angle-angle-angle triangles have unique solutions. In general, any 3 components of the spherical triangle can be used to solve for the rest. Thus, the 6 possible ways of solving spherical triangles are s-s-s, s-a-s, s-s-a, a-a-s, a-s-a, and a-a-a, where a and s are known angles and sides, respectively. The number of solutions depends on which components are specified and which types of triangles are considered, as summarized in Table 8-4. App. A gives all six sets of full-sky solutions, including complete solutions for all means of specifying spherical triangles where the sides and angles can each take on any value. I'll describe here two specific solutions that are interesting and useful for many space mission applications.

TABLE 8-4. Methods of Specifying Spherical Triangles. Spherical triangles can be specified either by the coordinates of the vertices or by giving any 3 components (i.e., sides or angles). Because of the spherical excess rule, 3 angles fully specify a spherical triangle, unlike a plane triangle in which 3 angles result in either no solution (if they do not add to 180 deg) or an infinite number of solutions.

Method of Specification	Number of Proper Spherical Triangles*	Number of Regular Spherical Triangles*	Number of Complete Spherical Triangles*	Number of Plane Triangles*
Coordinates of 3 Vertices	1	2	16†	1
Side-Side-Side (s-s-s)	0 or 1	0 or 2	0 or 2	0 or 1
Side-Side-Angle (s-s-a)	0, 1, or 2	0, 1, or 2	0 or 2	0 or 2
Side-Angle-Side (s-a-s)	1	1	2	1
Angle-Angle-Side (a-a-s)	0, 1, or 2	0, 1, or 2	0 or 2	0 or 1
Angle-Side-Angle (a-s-a)	0 or 1	0 or 1	2	0 or 1
Angle-Angle-Angle (a-a-a)	0 or 1	0 or 1	0 or 2	0 or infinite

*Excludes singular solutions. Assumes specified components fall within the allowed range.
†Listed in Table 8-1.

A case that illustrates the simplicity of full-sky solutions is the angle-side-side spherical triangle, shown in Fig. 8-6. Without loss of generality, we can assume that the unknown third side lies along the equator of a coordinate system, to the right of the known angle, A. The first known side, S_1, takes us to a well defined point, B, in this coordinate system. The possible solutions for the second known side are represented by a small circle centered on B, with radius, S_2, equal to length of the second known side. Wherever this small circle intersects the equator is a solution for the spherical triangle. If S_2 is less than the perpendicular distance from B to the equator, then the small circle does not intersect the equator and there are no solutions. If S_2 is equal to the perpendicular distance, then the circle will be tangent to the equator, and there will be a single, unique solution. If S_2 is larger than the perpendicular distance from B to the equator, then the small circle intersects the equator twice, and there should be two distinct solutions. In the case of full-sky spherical geometry, this is indeed the case. Ignoring the special case of a single solution, all angle-side-side triangles have either no solutions or two solutions, i.e., values of the remaining variables that represent real triangles that we can construct.

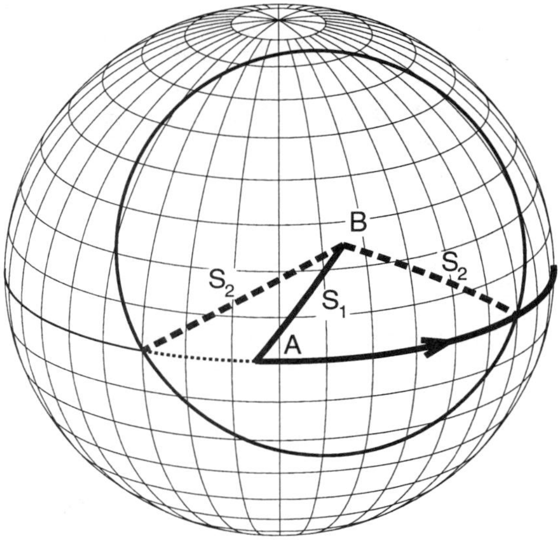

Fig. 8-6. Illustration of the Angle-Side-Side Problem. Assume that the unknown third side lies along the equator. The known angle is A and the first known side is S_1. The length of side S_2 is known, but not the direction. Thus, the end of S_2 not at B must be where the circle intersects the equator. Classical spherical geometry would allow only solutions within 180 deg to the right of A. This could be either 0, 1, or 2 of the intersections. This makes the problem more complex by having to keep track of which solutions are allowed Full-sky spherical geometry includes the solution where the third side (on the equator) is a long arc.

This problem is more complex if we restrict ourselves to proper triangles. By the definition of our problem and the value of the known angle A, the third side is to the right of A. Both intersections of the small circle with the equator may also lie to the right of A, allowing two proper spherical-triangle solutions. On the other hand, as shown in Fig. 8-6, one or both of the intersections may also lie to the left of A, so the unknown third side can be a long arc of greater than 180 deg. This solution is disallowed because it violates our definition of a proper triangle.

In dealing with full-sky triangles, we are free to select all of the intersections, and construct triangles from them. In proper spherical triangles, we need to test whether any of the solutions create sides or angles larger than 180 deg. Because we don't have to deal with "acceptability tests," the complete solutions are simpler to compute and keep track of than the solutions for the more restricted traditional spherical triangles.

One of the most often used triangles in space mission geometry is the side-angle-side, in which 2 sides and the included angle are known. As shown in Fig. 8-7, there are always exactly 2 full-sky solutions, except for the singular cases of returning to the starting point or its antipode. The side-angle-side case corresponds to our airplane problem at the beginning of the section. No matter where the pilot ends up on the Earth's surface, there are always two ways home—the short arc or, by turning in the opposite direction, the long arc. Our goal is to write down the solutions so they are convenient to compute and provide a way to eliminate the quadrant ambiguities common to classical spherical trig. (Of course, multiple solutions may exist, as in the side-angle-side triangle, but we want to include only real solutions).

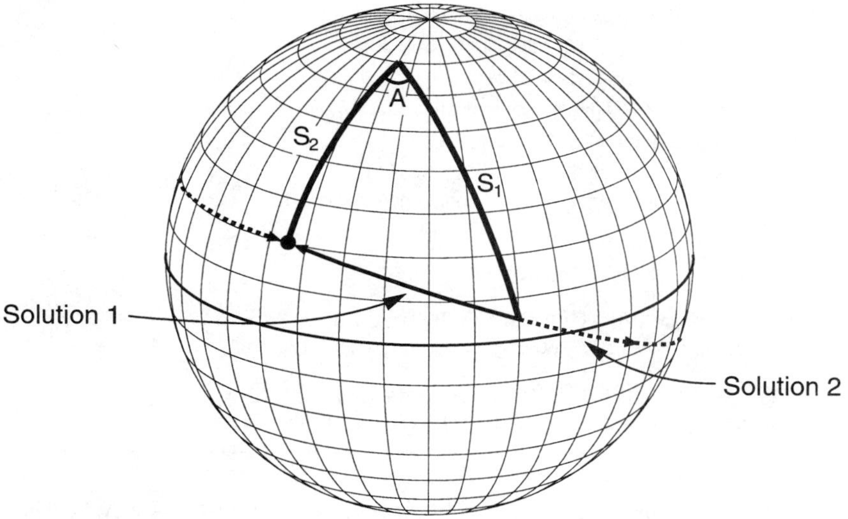

Fig. 8-7. The Two Solutions to the Side-Angle-Side Triangle Correspond to Returning to the Starting Point Going Either the Short Way or the Long Way. This solution is one of the most common applications of full-sky spherical trigonometry.

In working with full-sky triangles, we need to have a mechanism for evaluating inverse trigonometric functions over the full range of 0 to 360 deg. For the arc tangent, the computer function atan2 is convenient. With the angle's sine and cosine specified, atan2 uniquely specifies the angle. In general, any inverse trig function covering the full range of 0 to 360 deg must be a function of two arguments, because all of the trig functions have two solutions over this range. For many triangles, it is convenient to define an acos2 function that plays a role similar to that of atan2. To do this, we first define the hemisphere function, $H(\phi)$:

$$\begin{aligned} H(\phi) &\equiv +1 && \text{if } 0 \text{ deg} \le \phi \bmod_{360 \text{ deg}} < 180 \text{ deg} \\ H(\phi) &\equiv -1 && \text{if } 180 \text{ deg} \le \phi \bmod_{360 \text{ deg}} < 360 \text{ deg} \end{aligned} \tag{8-1}$$

The acos2 function is then defined by:

$$\begin{aligned} &\text{acos2}[\cos\phi, H(\phi)] \equiv [H(\phi)\, \text{acos}(\cos\phi)] \bmod_{360 \text{ deg}} \\ &\text{where } 0 \text{ deg} \le \text{acos}(\phi) < 180 \text{ deg} \end{aligned} \tag{8-2}$$

Thus, over the range of 0 to 360 deg, acos2, and the set (cos, H) are inverse functions:

$$\text{If } 0 \text{ deg} \le \phi < 360 \text{ deg, then } \phi = \text{acos2}[\cos(\phi), \text{H}(\phi)] \qquad (8\text{-}3)$$

Additional properties of the acos2 function are summarized in Table 8-5.

TABLE 8-5. Properties of the acos2 Function. The acos2 function serves the same purpose as atan2—i.e., it is a function of two variables rather than one so that it can return an angle over the range 0 to 360 deg.

- First define the hemisphere function, $H(\phi)$:
  - $H(\phi) \equiv +1$ if $0 \text{ deg} \le \phi \bmod_{360 \text{ deg}} < 180 \text{ deg}$
  - $H(\phi) \equiv -1$ if $180 \text{ deg} \le \phi \bmod_{360 \text{ deg}} < 360 \text{ deg}$
- Then the acos2 function is defined by:
  - $\text{acos2}[\cos(\phi), H(\phi)] \equiv [H(\phi)\, \text{acos}(\cos\phi)] \bmod_{360 \text{ deg}}$
  - where $0 \text{ deg} \le \text{acos}(\phi) < 180 \text{ deg}$
- Thus:
  - If $0 \text{ deg} \le \phi < 360 \text{ deg}$, then $\phi = \text{acos2}\,[\cos(\phi), H(\phi)]$
- Also:
  - $\text{acos2}\,[\cos(\phi), -H(\phi)] = 360 \text{ deg} - \phi$
  - $\text{acos2}\,[\cos(\phi), -H(\phi)] = (180 \text{ deg} - \phi) \bmod_{360 \text{ deg}}$
    $= 180 \text{ deg} - \phi$, if $\phi < 180$ deg, or $360 \text{ deg} - (\phi - 180 \text{ deg})$, if $\phi > 180$ deg
  - $\text{acos2}\,[-\cos(\phi), -H(\phi)] = (180 \text{ deg} + \phi) \bmod_{360 \text{ deg}}$
    $= 180 \text{ deg} + \phi$, if $\phi < 180$ deg, or $\phi - 180$ deg, if $\phi > 180$ deg

Using the acos2 function, we can easily solve the side-angle-side spherical triangle. Given two sides (a, b) and the included angle C, there are always exactly two solutions except in the singular cases of returning to the origin or anti-origin. The first solution is:

$$c = \text{acos2}[(\cos a \cos b + \sin a \sin b \cos C), \text{H}(C)] \qquad (8\text{-}4a)$$

$$A = \text{acos2}\left[\frac{\cos a - \cos b \cos c}{\sin b \sin c\, H(a)}\right] \qquad (8\text{-}4b)$$

$$B = \text{acos2}\left[\frac{\cos b - \cos a \cos c}{\sin a \sin c\, H(a)}\right] \qquad (8\text{-}4c)$$

And the second solution is:

$$c^* = 360° - c \qquad (8\text{-}5a)$$

$$A^* = [A + 180 \text{ deg}]\text{mod}_{360 \text{ deg}} \qquad (8\text{-}5b)$$

$$B^* = [B + 180 \text{ deg}]\text{mod}_{360 \text{ deg}} \qquad (8\text{-}5c)$$

Whether the resulting triangles have angles or sides greater or less than 180 deg will depend on the general taxonomy of the spherical triangle, as previously summarized in Table 8-1. For computations, it simply doesn't matter. We have a set of formulas which return results over the full range of 0 to 360 deg. If we input the known values, the correct, complete results are returned.

There is also a convenient subset of the full-sky side-angle-side problem in which all of the angles are allowed to range over 0 to 360 deg, but the sides are restricted to 0 to 180 deg (i.e., the triangle is a regular spherical triangle). This is convenient because it corresponds to spherical coordinate systems, in which the latitude or elevation component is confined to 0 to 180 deg, but the azimuthal component, or rotation about the pole, covers the full range of 0 to 360 deg. Within the restricted set of regular spherical triangles, there is one and only one solution to the side-angle-side problem. For the airplane example, this corresponds to finding the shortest way home. No matter where the pilot ends up on the Earth's surface, there's only one answer (except for the second point being home or 180 deg from home). This unique solution for regular triangles is

$$c^1 = \text{acos}\,(\cos a \cos b + \sin a \sin b \cos C) \tag{8-6a}$$

$$A^1 = \text{acos}\left[\frac{\cos a - \cos b \cos c}{\text{H}(c)\sin b \sin c}\right] - 90^\circ\left[\text{H}(c) - 1\right] \tag{8-6b}$$

$$B^1 = \text{acos}\left[\frac{\cos b - \cos a \cos c}{\text{H}(c)\sin a \sin c}\right] - 90^\circ\left[\text{H}(c) - 1\right] \tag{8-6c}$$

Here the acos function is the normal inverse cosine evaluated over the range of 0 to 180 deg and the "1" superscript is used for the single solution.

The Airplane Problem Revisited

Finally, we would like to return to the airplane problem and provide complete solutions in plane geometry, unit vector geometry, and full-sky spherical geometry. These solutions were coded and the computations timed with the results given in Table 8-6. Both the unit vector and spherical trigonometric solutions are equally correct, but for this particular problem, the spherical trig solution is both simpler and computationally faster.

TABLE 8-6. Computation Time and Complexity for Alternative Solutions to the Airplane Problem. The computation time listed is for 100,000 iterations on a personal computer. The implication is **not** that one approach is better than another, but that both vector and spherical geometry solutions are potentially appropriate for working directions-only geometry.

Solution Method	Time for 100,000 Iterations	Complexity
Plane Geometry	5 sec	Problem simpler because there is only one right answer; still have one branch depending on whether turn is to the right or left.
Unit Vectors	21 sec	Requires special functions to keep track of the direction of motion plus substantial analysis time to complete.
Full-Sky Spherical Trigonometry	10 sec	Solution is trivial, once the full-sky spherical trig rules are known.

Plane Geometry Solution for the Airplane Problem

All of the solutions use the notation of Fig. 8-1. In plane geometry, we use the Law of Cosines for Plane Triangles to define the length of the third side as

$$D_3 = \sqrt{D_1^2 + D_2^2 - 2D_1 D_2 \cos\phi_1} \tag{8-7}$$

If 180 deg $\le \phi_1 \le$ 360 deg, then:

$$\phi_2 = 360\text{ deg} - \text{acos}\left[\frac{D_2^2 + D_3^2 - D_1^2}{2D_2 D_3}\right]$$

$$\phi_3 = 360\text{ deg} - \text{acos}\left[\frac{D_1^2 + D_3^2 - D_2^2}{2D_1 D_3}\right] \tag{8-8a}$$

If 360 deg $\le \phi_1 \le$ 540 deg, then:

$$\phi_2 = 180\text{ deg} + \text{acos}\left[\frac{D_2^2 + D_3^2 - D_1^2}{2D_2 D_3}\right]$$

$$\phi_3 = 180\text{ deg} + \text{acos}\left[\frac{D_1^2 + D_3^2 - D_2^2}{2D_1 D_3}\right] \tag{8-8b}$$

The solution here is relatively simple because it allows only one right answer, whereas in fact there are two. (Going around the world is not an option in plane geometry.) But the solution still includes one branch depending on whether the initial turn is to the right or to the left. Of course for spherical problems, the plane geometry solution is incorrect.

Unit Vector Solution

To work the airplane problem with unit vectors, we must find a way to rotate a vector through a given angle and determine a rotation angle between two vectors. Rotating a vector, **r**, through an angle, θ, about the rotation axis defined by a unit vector, $\hat{\mathbf{u}}$, creates a new vector:

$$\text{ROT}(\mathbf{r},\theta,\hat{\mathbf{u}}) = (\hat{\mathbf{u}}\times\mathbf{r})\times\hat{\mathbf{u}}\cos\theta + \hat{\mathbf{u}}\times\mathbf{r}\sin\theta + \hat{\mathbf{u}}(\hat{\mathbf{u}}\cdot\mathbf{r}) \tag{8-9}$$

The angle between two vectors, **a** and **b**, is given by:

$$\text{VANG}(\mathbf{a},\mathbf{b}) = \text{acos}\frac{\hat{\mathbf{a}}\cdot\hat{\mathbf{b}}}{ab} \quad \text{where } a = |\mathbf{a}| \text{ and } b = |\hat{\mathbf{b}}| \tag{8-10}$$

Finally, the rotation angle from **a** to **b** about the rotation axis $\hat{\mathbf{c}}$ is given by:

$$\text{RANG}(\mathbf{a},\mathbf{b},\hat{\mathbf{c}}) = \begin{cases} \text{acos}\left[\dfrac{(\mathbf{a}\times\hat{\mathbf{c}})\cdot(\mathbf{b}\times\hat{\mathbf{c}})}{|\mathbf{a}\times\hat{\mathbf{c}}|\,|\mathbf{b}\times\hat{\mathbf{c}}|}\right] & \text{if } (\mathbf{a}\times\mathbf{b})\cdot\hat{\mathbf{c}} \ge 0 \\ 360\text{ deg} - \text{acos}\left[\dfrac{(\mathbf{a}\times\hat{\mathbf{c}})\cdot(\mathbf{b}\times\hat{\mathbf{c}})}{|\mathbf{a}\times\hat{\mathbf{c}}|\,|\mathbf{b}\times\hat{\mathbf{c}}|}\right] & \text{if } (\mathbf{a}\times\mathbf{b})\cdot\hat{\mathbf{c}} < 0 \end{cases} \tag{8-11}$$

With these definitions, we can work the airplane problem in unit vectors.

Let $\hat{\mathbf{r}}_1$, $\hat{\mathbf{r}}_2$, and $\hat{\mathbf{r}}_3$ be the positions of the airplane at the start and at the second and third corners of the spherical triangle, respectively. Let $\hat{\mathbf{p}}_1$, $\hat{\mathbf{p}}_2$, and $\hat{\mathbf{p}}_3$ be the polar vectors of the first, second, and third sides. The polar vector of a side is the unit vector perpendicular to the plane containing the side and related to the direction of travel by the right-hand rule. For this problem, the Earth's radius and the triangle's orientation on the surface of the Earth are irrelevant, so we may assume for convenience:

$$\hat{\mathbf{r}}_1 = \begin{bmatrix} 1 \\ 0 \\ 0 \end{bmatrix} \qquad \hat{\mathbf{p}}_1 = \begin{bmatrix} 0 \\ 0 \\ 1 \end{bmatrix} \tag{8-12}$$

We then have:

$$\hat{\mathbf{r}}_2 = \text{ROT}\left(\hat{\mathbf{r}}_1, D_1, \hat{\mathbf{p}}_1\right) \tag{8-13a}$$

$$\hat{\mathbf{p}}_2 = \text{ROT}\left(\hat{\mathbf{p}}_1, \phi_1 - 180\text{ deg}, \hat{\mathbf{r}}_2\right) \tag{8-13b}$$

$$\hat{\mathbf{r}}_3 = \text{ROT}\left(\hat{\mathbf{r}}_2, D_2, \hat{\mathbf{p}}_2\right) \tag{8-13c}$$

where the D's are from Fig. 8-1 and the $\hat{\mathbf{p}}$'s are the polar vectors corresponding to these sides.

If $\hat{\mathbf{r}}_3 \times \hat{\mathbf{r}}_1 = \hat{\mathbf{0}}$, then the triangle is indeterminate. This corresponds to returning to the starting point or the antipode of the starting point. Otherwise, as we have seen, the triangle has two solutions. The first is:

$$D_3 = \text{VANG}\left(\hat{\mathbf{r}}_3, \hat{\mathbf{r}}_1\right) \tag{8-14a}$$

$$\hat{\mathbf{p}}_3 = \frac{\hat{\mathbf{r}}_3 \times \hat{\mathbf{r}}_1}{\left|\hat{\mathbf{r}}_3 \times \hat{\mathbf{r}}_1\right|} \tag{8-14b}$$

$$\phi_2 = \left[\text{RANG}\left(\hat{\mathbf{p}}_2, \hat{\mathbf{p}}_3, \hat{\mathbf{r}}_3\right) + 180\text{ deg}\right] \text{mod}_{360\text{ deg}} \tag{8-14c}$$

$$\phi_3 = \left[\text{RANG}\left(\hat{\mathbf{p}}_3, \hat{\mathbf{p}}_1, \hat{\mathbf{r}}_1\right) + 180\text{ deg}\right] \text{mod}_{360\text{ deg}} \tag{8-14d}$$

The second solution, going the long way around, is:

$$D_3^* = 360\text{ deg} - D_3 \tag{8-15a}$$

$$\hat{\mathbf{p}}_3^* = -\hat{\mathbf{p}}_3 \tag{8-15b}$$

$$\phi_2^* = \left(\phi_2 - 180\text{ deg}\right) \text{mod}_{360\text{ deg}} \tag{8-15c}$$

$$\phi_3^* = \left(\phi_3 - 180\text{ deg}\right) \text{mod}_{360\text{ deg}} \tag{8-15d}$$

This solution is correct but cumbersome, and takes substantial analysis time to formulate. In addition, although all of the various intermediate variables have well-defined meanings, they are inconvenient to evaluate and verify.

Full-Sky Geometry Solution

In the case of full-sky spherical geometry, we simply apply Eqs. (8-4) and (8-5), and write down the first solution as:

$$D_3 = \text{acos2}\left[\cos D_1 \cos D_2 + \sin D_1 \sin D_2 \cos \phi_1, \text{H}(\phi_1)\right] \tag{8-16a}$$

$$\phi_2 = \text{acos2}\left[\frac{\cos D_1 - \cos D_2 \cos D_3}{\sin D_2 \sin D_3}, \text{H}(D_1)\right] \tag{8-16b}$$

$$\phi_3 = \text{acos2}\left[\frac{\cos D_2 - \cos D_1 \cos D_3}{\sin D_1 \sin D_3}, \text{H}(D_2)\right] \tag{8-16c}$$

And the second solution as:

$$D_3^* = 360 \text{ deg} - D_3 \tag{8-17a}$$

$$\phi_2^* = (\phi_2 + 180 \text{ deg}) \bmod_{360 \text{ deg}} \tag{8-17b}$$

$$\phi_3^* = (\phi_3 + 180 \text{ deg}) \bmod_{360 \text{ deg}} \tag{8-17c}$$

Once we know the rules for full-sky spherical trigonometry, the solution is easy to write down and fast to compute. The interpretation is also straightforward. From any endpoint on the Earth, we can turn one way and go home or turn the other way and go around the world to get home. Whether this solution computes faster or slower than the corresponding unit-vector solution will depend on how you formulate the problem, how the input is specified, and what output you want. Our point from this example is that the full-sky geometry solution is conceptually simple and may compute as fast as, or faster than, the more commonly used vector alternatives.

8.2 The Dual-Axis Spiral

A small circle is the locus of points equidistant from a fixed axis, i.e., the path swept out by a point rotating at a fixed distance about a fixed point on the sphere. A dual-axis spiral occurs whenever the previously fixed center is itself moving in a small circle about a different axis. More formally, a *dual-axis spiral* is the locus of points on a sphere swept out by rotating at a fixed distance about an axis called the *secondary axis*, which itself is rotating at a fixed distance about a fixed axis called the *primary axis*. (See Fig. 8-8.) In general, the motion is a spiral across the sky.

As listed in Table 8-7, there are many unrelated applications for dual-axis spirals in orbit and attitude analysis. This spiral represents the motion of a satellite with respect to the Earth's surface, the relative motion of satellites, the relative motion of planets, nutating spacecraft, and a spinning sensor on a rotating spacecraft. One of the most convenient examples for discussion is the ground trace of a satellite in a low-Earth orbit. As shown in Fig. 8-9, the subsatellite point follows a dual-axis spiral, as does a point 30 deg to the left of the subsatellite point. The primary axis is the Earth's pole or the celestial pole and the secondary axis is the satellite orbit pole. In reality, the satellite's orbit is approximately fixed in inertial space as the Earth rotates underneath it.

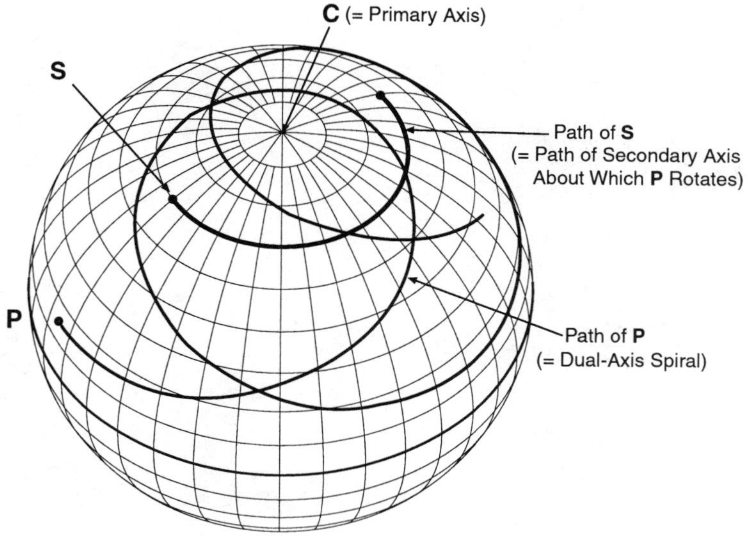

Fig. 8-8. The Dual-Axis Spiral. The spiral is created by a point, **P**, rotating about a secondary axis, **S**, which is itself rotating about a primary or central axis, **C**.

TABLE 8-7. Dual-Axis Spiral Applications. In cases such as orbital motion the real motion is made complex by both the elliptical shape of real orbits and orbit perturbations. Nonetheless, the dual-axis spiral provides simple, closed-form analytic solutions that can provide quick, moderate accuracy approximations for mission, attitude, and orbit analysis.

Application	Primary Axis	Secondary Axis	Comments	Where Discussed
Satellite Ground Track	Earth pole	Orbit pole	First axis is Earth rotation	Sec. 8.3.3, Sec. 9.3
Satellite Relative Motion	Observer orbit pole	Pole of observed orbit	First axis "derotates" reference satellite	Chap. 10
Apparent Planetary Motion	Ecliptic pole	Planetary orbit pole	First axis "stops" Earth orbital motion	Sec. 2.2
Satellite Nutation	Angular momentum vector	Principal axis	Shows direction of any spacecraft axis in inertial space	Sec. 8.3.2
Rotating Sensor on a Spinning Spacecraft	Spacecraft spin axis	Sensor rotation axis	Shows FOV motion in inertial space	Sec. 8.3.1

However, from a geometrical perspective, it is equally convenient to think of the rotation of the Earth as carrying the satellite's orbit pole around once per day while the satellite itself is rotating in a frame of reference with the orbit pole as the axis.

The characteristics of small circles or *single-axis spirals* are simple and well known. Applications in spacecraft analysis include sensor scans, the apparent disk of

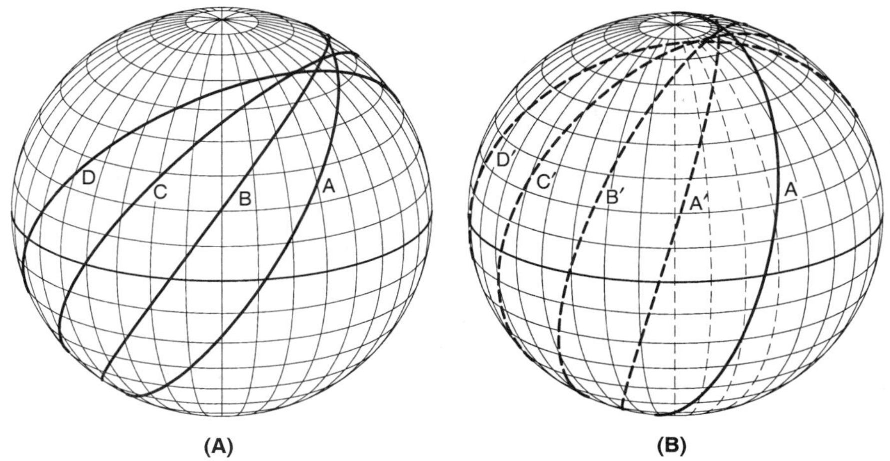

Fig. 8-9. The Satellite Ground Trace is an Example of a Dual-Axis Spiral. The subsatellite point, shown in (A), follows a dual-axis spiral, as does a point 30 deg to the "left" of the subsatellite point, as shown in (B).

celestial bodies, and the fields of view of many instruments and antennas. The characteristics of the dual-axis spiral are generally not well known and analytical approximations are extremely difficult because of quadrant ambiguities. The difficulty is that practical applications of the dual-axis spiral include rotations forward and backward at diverse relative rates with widely varying arc lengths and curves covering the entire sky. There is no simple solution without having to worry about quadrant ambiguities. In addition, quadrants cover the full range of 0 to 360 deg. In analyzing dual-axis spirals, arc lengths can be constrained to the range of 0 to 180 deg, but rotation angles inherently cover 0 to 360 deg. Thus, it is the full-sky spherical geometry solutions in the preceding section which make the dual-axis spiral analytically tractable. In this section, we develop the basic formulas for the dual-axis spiral. Specifically, for the point **P** in Fig. 8-8 we wish to compute the position (α, δ), the velocity, v, and the direction of motion, ψ, as a function of the time, t, and the defining variables for the dual-axis spiral. Sec. 8.3 then applies these formulas to several practical applications in orbit and attitude motion.

We first use our new spherical trig expressions to analyze the motion of a single-axis spiral to obtain closed form expressions for the position, direction, and velocity on the sky. We do this to establish nomenclature and assumptions. We then apply these results to the dual-axis spiral to obtain similar closed form expressions.

Consider the locus formed by a point, **P**, at a fixed distance, ρ_2, and rotating at a uniform angular velocity, ω_2, about a fixed axis, $\mathbf{S} = (\alpha_2, \delta_2)$, as shown in Fig. 8-10. We want to obtain formulas for the position (α, δ) the direction of motion, ψ, and the velocity, v of **P**. The coordinates will be the azimuth, α, and elevation, δ, equivalent to longitude and latitude on the surface on the Earth. We also use the co-elevation, $\delta' \equiv 90$ deg $- \delta$. Unless otherwise noted, all angles are in deg. All azimuth angles and rotation angles are measured counterclockwise and cover the range 0 to 360 deg. Arc lengths can also cover the range 0 to 360 deg. Elevation angles, however, are restricted to -90 to $+90$ deg and co-elevation angles to 0 to 180 deg. The direction of motion, ψ, is defined as the instantaneous angle between the tangent to the path and "north," which is the direction toward the celestial pole. The velocity, v, is defined as the rate of change of arc length along the locus. Lastly, we define the difference in azimuth between the center of the circle, **S**, and the point on the circle, **P**, as $\Delta\alpha = (\alpha - \alpha_2)$ $\text{mod}_{360\text{ deg}}$.

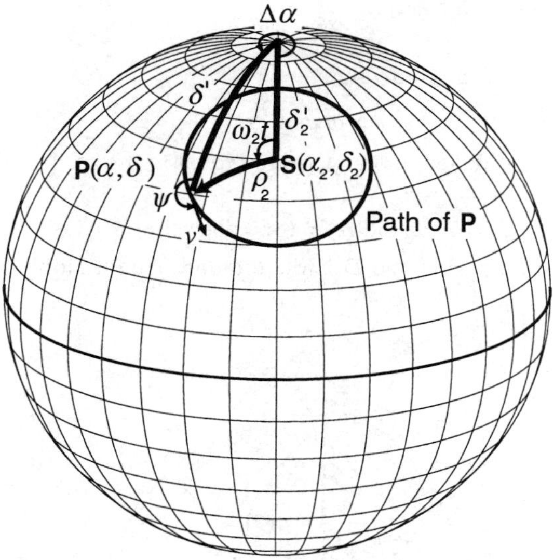

Fig. 8-10. Analysis of a "Single-Axis Spiral," i.e., a Small Circle.

In Fig. 8-10, consider the spherical triangle formed by the pole of the coordinate system, the center of the small circle, and an arbitrary point, **P**, on the small circle. For this circle, δ_2' and ρ_2 are fixed arc lengths. The rotation angle between them is the amount by which point **P** has rotated at any time, t, which is simply $\omega_2 t$. Therefore, we have a general side-angle-side spherical triangle and the results can be applied immediately to provide expressions for the position **P** as follows:

$$\cos\delta' = \cos\delta_2' \cos\rho_2 + \sin\delta_2' \sin\rho_2 \cos(\omega_2 t) \tag{8-18a}$$

$$\cos\Delta\alpha = \frac{\cos\rho_2 - \cos\delta_2' \cos\delta'}{\sin\delta_2' \sin\delta'} \tag{8-18b}$$

Therefore:

$$\delta = 90\text{ deg} - \text{acos}\left[\sin\delta_2 \cos\rho_2 + \cos\delta_2 \sin\rho_2 \cos(\omega_2 t)\right] \quad -90 \le \delta < 90 \tag{8-19a}$$

$$\Delta\alpha = \text{acos2}\left[\frac{\cos\rho_2 - \sin\delta_2 \sin\delta}{\cos\delta_2 \cos\delta}, -\text{H}(\omega_2 t)\right] \quad 0 \le \Delta\alpha < 360 \tag{8-19b}$$

The direction relative to north is the remaining rotation angle in the triangle minus 90 deg. Therefore:

$$\Delta\psi = \text{acos2}\left[\frac{\sin\delta_2 - \cos\rho_2 \sin\delta}{\sin\rho_2 \cos\delta}, -\text{H}(\omega_2 t)\right] \quad 0 \le \Delta\psi < 360 \tag{8-20a}$$

$$\psi = [\Delta\psi - 90 \text{ deg}] \text{mod}_{360 \text{ deg}} \tag{8-20b}$$

Finally, the velocity, v, is a fixed value

$$v = \omega_2 \sin\rho_2 \tag{8-21}$$

and the total distance traveled in one period is equal to the arc length along the small circle:

$$D = T\,\omega_2 \sin\rho_2 = (360 \text{ deg}) \sin\rho_2 \tag{8-22}$$

where T is the rotation period and D is the total arc length along the small circle of radius ρ_2.

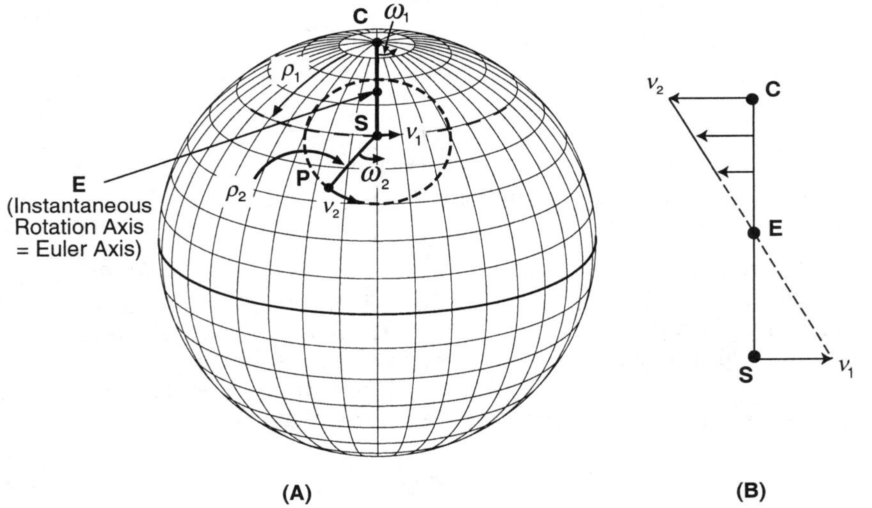

Fig. 8-11. Geometry of the Dual-Axis Spiral. (A) The point **P** rotates with angular velocity ω_2 about the axis **S** which, in turn, is rotating with angular velocity ω_1 about axis **C**. In the combined rotation of the two coordinate frames, there is one point, the instantaneous rotation axis or Euler axis, **E**, where the two rotations cancel and which is instantaneously at rest as shown by figure (B).

We now want to extend the results to the case in which the center of the small circle, **S**, is itself rotating with angular velocity, ω_1, about the pole, **C**, as shown in Fig. 8-11. Again, we wish to find the general equations for the position, direction, and velocity of the point, **P**. However, we will begin by looking at a key general characteristic of the motion. Throughout the motion there is a point along the great circle connecting **S** and **C** called the *Euler axis* or *instantaneous rotation axis*, **E**, which will be instantaneously at rest.* This is where the rotations ω_1 and ω_2 cancel each other. Relative to **S**, the instantaneous rotation axis, **E**, will be toward **C** if ω_1 and ω_2 rotate in the same sense and away from **C** if they rotate in opposite sense (i.e., one clockwise and the other counterclockwise). Because this axis is instantaneously fixed and the coordinate frames themselves are rigid, then the motion at that instant must be simply a rotation about the Euler axis itself. This will let us determine the direction of motion and velocity at any given time.

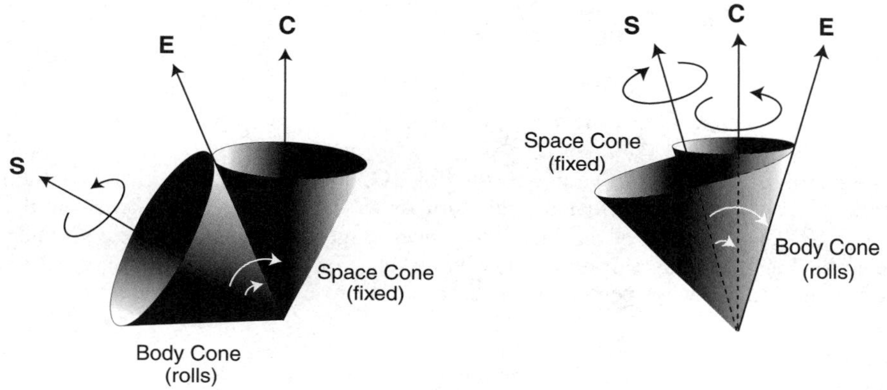

Fig. 8-12. Alternative View of One Axis Rotating About Another. The rotation of the coordinate frames in the dual-axis spiral can be viewed as a cone rolling without slipping on another cone. The instantaneous rotation axis, **E**, is the point of contact between the cones on the great circle joining **C** and **S**; (A) both rotations in the same sense. (B) Rotations in the opposite sense. Note that the cones represent the rotation of the coordinate frames. The point **P** is at a distance ρ_2 from **S** and does not in general lie on the rim of the cone.

A convenient way to visualize the general rotation about the instantaneous rotation axis is shown in Fig. 8-12, which is commonly used to describe spacecraft nutation. (See Fig. 3-8 in Sec. 3-2.) We can think of the motion as one cone rolling on another without slipping on each other. The cone centered on the pole, **C**, has a radius equal to the co-elevation of the Euler axis or instantaneous rotation axis, δ_E'. The radius of the second cone is equal to $\rho_1 - \delta_E'$, such that the axis of the second cone is the center of rotation, **S**. The second cone rotates on the first carrying the point **P** along with it. The instantaneous rotation axis lies on both cones but is not fixed on either. It moves at angular velocity, ω_1, about **C** and also at angular velocity ω_2 about **S**. If the two coordinate frames are rotating in the same sense, then the cones will be outside each

* *Euler's Theorem* states that the most general displacement of a rigid body with one point fixed (such as a spherical coordinate frame) is a rotation about some axis. The *Euler axis* is the rotation axis and the *Euler angle* is the amount of the rotation. At any given instant, the Euler axis will be fixed and the frame containing **P** will appear to be rotating about it. (In the case of the dual-axis spiral, this motion represents the instantaneous sum of the rotations ω_1 and ω_2.) This work, and quite a bit more, was done by the remarkably prolific 18th century Swiss mathematician Leonhard Euler who fathered 13 children and was the author of 886 mathematical books and articles.

other, as in Fig. 8-12A. If they are rotating opposite each other, then one cone will be inside the other, as in Fig. 8-12B

To determine the orientation of **E** and rotation rate, $\omega_{\mathbf{E}}$, about this axis, note that the instantaneous rotation is simply the vector sum of the two rotations, ω_1 and ω_2. Using the plane geometry shown in Fig. 8-13, we get

$$\tan\delta_{\mathbf{E}}' = \frac{\omega_2 \sin\rho_1}{\omega_1 + \omega_2 \cos\rho_1} \qquad 0 \le \delta_{\mathbf{E}}' \le 180 \text{ deg} \tag{8-23a}$$

$$\omega_{\mathbf{E}} = \frac{\omega_2 \sin\rho_1}{\sin\delta_{\mathbf{E}}'} \tag{8-23b}$$

or

$$\omega_{\mathbf{E}}^2 = \omega_1^2 + \omega_2^2 + 2\omega_1\omega_2\cos\rho_1 \qquad \omega_{\mathbf{E}} \ge 0 \tag{8-23c}$$

As shown in Fig. 8-14, we use **E**, the pole, **C**, and the point, **P**, on the dual-axis spiral to construct a spherical triangle similar to that for the single-axis spiral in Fig. 8-10. The direction of motion is no longer tangent to the small circle around **S** because **P** is also being carried by the rotation ω_1. For the dual-axis spiral, the direction of motion is always perpendicular to the arc from **E** to **P**.

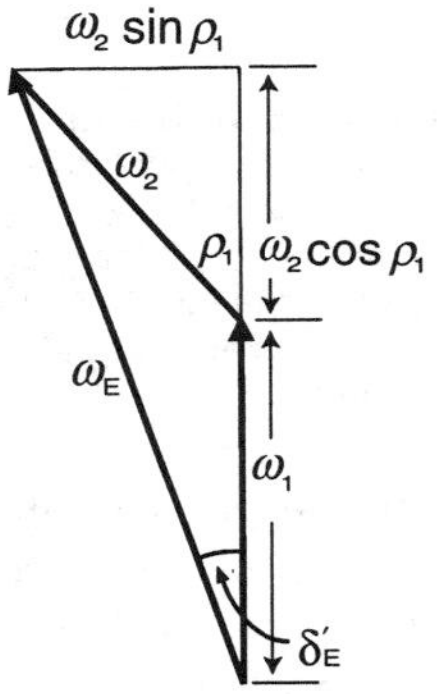

Fig. 8-13. The Addition of Rotation Vectors. The instantaneous rotation axis is the vector sum of the two individual rotation vectors.

We first solve for the distance, $\rho_{\mathbf{E}}$, from **E** to **P**:

$$\cos\rho_{\mathrm{E}} = \cos\delta_{\mathbf{E}}'\sin\delta + \sin\delta_{\mathbf{E}}'\cos\delta\cos\Delta\alpha \qquad 0 \le \rho_{\mathbf{E}} \le 180 \text{ deg} \tag{8-24}$$

We then solve for the direction, ψ:

$$\Delta\psi = \text{acos2}\left[\frac{\cos\delta_{\mathbf{E}}' - \cos\rho_{\mathbf{E}}\sin\delta}{\sin\rho_{\mathbf{E}}\cos\delta}, \mathrm{H}(\Delta\alpha)\right] \qquad 0 \le \Delta\psi < 360 \text{ deg} \tag{8-25a}$$

$$\psi = [\Delta\psi - 90 \text{ deg}]\text{mod}_{360 \text{ deg}} \tag{8-25b}$$

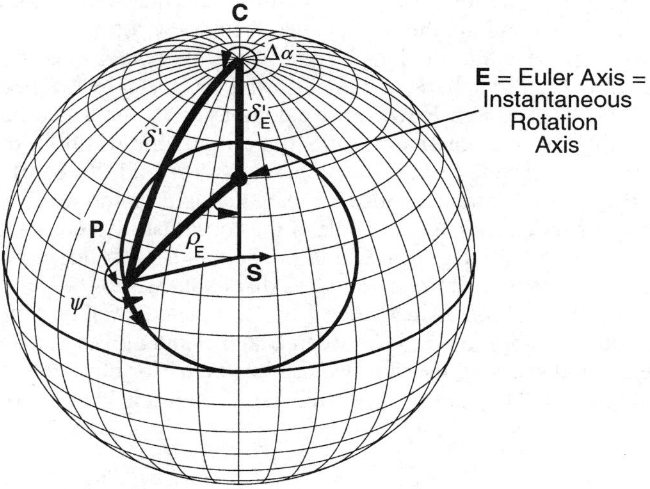

Fig. 8-14. Geometry for Computing the Instantaneous Direction and Velocity. These are based on the concept of the instantaneous rotation axis.

and the velocity, v:

$$v = \omega_E \sin \rho_E \qquad 0 \le v \le \omega_E \qquad (8\text{-}26)$$

To compute the position at any time, t, we first compute the azimuth angle about the pole, ϕ_1, and about the center of the small circle, ϕ_2:

$$\phi_1 = \phi_{1_0} + \omega_1 t \qquad \phi_2 = \phi_{2_0} + \omega_2 t \qquad (8\text{-}27)$$

where ϕ_{1_0} is the initial orientation of the center of the small circle in the base (α, δ) coordinate frame and ϕ_{2_0} is the azimuthal starting orientation of the point **P** relative to **C**. We now have a problem equivalent to the single-axis spiral, and the general solutions for the position are given by the ***equations of motion for the dual-axis spiral***:

$$\Delta\alpha = \mathrm{acos2}\left[\frac{\cos\rho_2 - \cos\rho_1 \sin\delta}{\sin\rho_1 \cos\delta}, -\mathrm{H}(\phi_2)\right] \qquad 0 \le \Delta\alpha < 360 \text{ deg} \qquad (8\text{-}28a)$$

$$\alpha = [\phi_1 + \Delta\alpha]\mathrm{mod}_{360 \text{ deg}} \qquad 0 \le \alpha < 360 \text{ deg} \qquad (8\text{-}28b)$$

$$\delta = 90 \text{ deg} - \mathrm{acos}(\cos\rho_1 \cos\rho_2 + \sin\rho_1 \sin\rho_2 \cos\phi_2) \qquad -90 \text{ deg} \le \delta < 90 \text{ deg} \qquad (8\text{-}28c)$$

The full solution to the dual-axis spiral is summarized in Table 8-8. These equations of motion are relatively simple. The complexity arises from the fact that the point **P** can move all across the celestial sphere, as previously shown in Fig. 8-8. This makes the appearance complex, linear approximations impossible, and the solutions analytically very difficult if there isn't some way to continuously resolve the quadrant ambiguity. The full-sky trig solutions allow us to do this, such that we no longer need to be concerned with which quadrant the result is in, whether the rotation has taken us over the pole, or whether we are to the left or right of any particular axis. As the point **P** moves across the sky, the spherical triangles take on many of the peculiar shapes illustrated in Figs. 8-2 and 8-3. However, we do not need to be concerned with these shapes. We simply use the algebraic results to compute the position, direction, and velocity as a function of time from Eqs. (8-25a-b), (8-26), and (8-28a-c).

Many of the general characteristics of the dual-axis spiral can be seen from Fig. 8-15. The primary axis, **C**, is at the pole of the coordinate system. In this example, the secondary axis, **S**, is 50 deg from **C** and the point we are following, **P**, is 45 deg from **S**. Rotation about **S** is 12 times as fast as that about **C**, ($\omega_2 / \omega_1 = 12$), such that the secondary axis has moved 30 deg when P has completed a full revolution about **S**. The instantaneous rotation axis, **E**, is between **C** and **S** and moves in azimuth with **S**. For convenience in discussing the plot, we use "vertical" for motion toward or away from **C** and "horizontal" for motion around **C**, i.e., "longitude" motion on the plot.

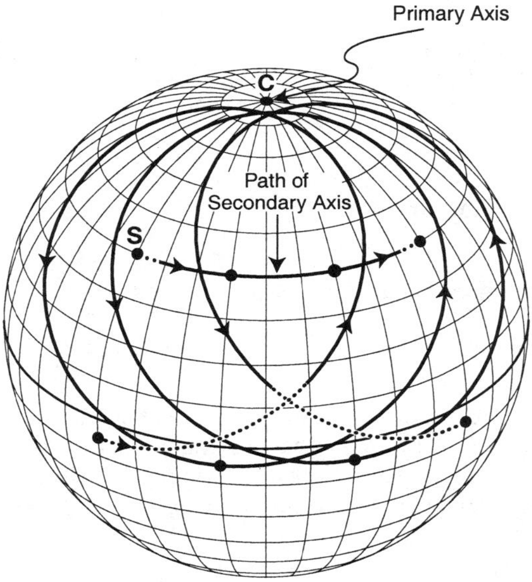

Fig. 8-15. General Characteristics of the Dual-Axis Spiral. The vertical motion (i.e., toward the pole) simply repeats itself on each spiral pass. The horizontal motion is offset from one spiral to the next by the rotation about the primary axis in one rotation period about the secondary axis, 30 deg in the example shown.

Notice in Fig. 8-15 that the vertical motion repeats itself after every revolution about the secondary axis, **S**. The horizontal motion also repeats itself but shifts horizontally by $360 \times (\omega_1 / \omega_2)$, which is exactly 30 deg in the example. Thus, successive spirals are simply displaced from one another by 30 deg in a horizontal or azimuth sense. Note that 30 deg in rotation is a smaller arc length near **C** than near the equator. Consequently, the spirals are closer together in arc length in the vicinity of **C** and farther apart near the equator, but in all cases are separated by 30 deg in azimuth. Thus,

TABLE 8-8. Summary of Equations for the Dual-Axis Spiral.

	Variable	Equations or Definitions	Conditions	Where Discussed
Definitions	*Defining Parameters*	The Point **P** with coordinates (α, δ) is rotating with angular velocity ω_2 about the secondary axis, **S**, which in turn is rotating with angular velocity ω_1 about the primary or central axis, **C**. **P** is at an angular distance ρ_2 from **S** and **S** is at an angular distance ρ_1 from **C**.	$0 \le \rho_1 \le 180°$ $0 \le \rho_2 \le 180°$ **C** at (0°, 90°) **P**, **S** anywhere ω_1, ω_2 arbitrary	Fig. 8-13
Intermediate Variables	ϕ_1 = *Azimuth of* **S** *about* **C** relative to $\alpha = 0$	$\phi_1 = \phi_{1_0} + \omega_1 t$	no constraints	Eq. (8-27)
	ϕ_2 = *Azimuth of* **P** *about* **S** relative to **C**	$\phi_2 = \phi_{2_0} + \omega_2 t$	no constraints	Eq. (8-27)
	$\Delta\alpha$ = *Change in Azimuth of* **P** *about* **C**,	$\Delta\alpha =$ $\text{acos2}\left[\dfrac{\cos\rho_2 - \cos\rho_1 \sin\delta}{\sin\rho_1 \cos\delta}, \; -H(\phi_2)\right]$	$0 \le \Delta\alpha < 360°$	Eq. (8-28a)
	ρ_E = *Angle from* **P** *to Euler Axis* **E** *(=Instantaneous Rotation Axis)*	$\rho_E =$ $\text{acos}\left(\cos\delta_E' \sin\delta + \sin\delta_E' \cos\delta \cos\Delta a\right)$	$0 \le \rho_E \le 180°$	Eq. (8-24)
	ω_E = *Rate of Rotation about* **E**	$\omega_E = \dfrac{\omega_2 \sin\rho_1}{\sin\delta_E'}$ $= \sqrt{\omega_1^2 + \omega_2^2 + 2\omega_1\omega_2 \cos\rho_1}$	$\omega_E \ge 0$	Eq. (8-23b) Eq. (8-23c)
	δ_E' = *Angle from* **C** *to* **E**	$\delta_E' = \text{atan}\,[\omega_2 \sin\rho_1 / (\omega_1 + \omega_2 \cos\rho_1)]$	$0 \le \delta_E' \le 180°$*	Eq. (8-23a)
	$\Delta\psi$ = *Change in Direction of Motion of* **P**	$\Delta\psi =$ $\text{acos2}\left[\dfrac{\cos\delta_E' - \cos\rho_E \sin\delta}{\sin\rho_E \cos\delta}, \; H(\Delta\alpha)\right]$	$0 \le \Delta\psi < 360°$	Eq. (8-25a)
Results	α = *Azimuth of* **P** *about* **C**	$\alpha = [\phi_1 + \Delta\alpha]\text{mod}_{360\text{ deg}}$	$0 \le \alpha < 360°$	Eq. (8-28b)
	δ = *Elev. of* **P** *relative to* **C**	$\delta = 90° - \text{acos}\,(\cos\rho_1 \cos\rho_2$ $+ \sin\rho_1 \sin\rho_2 \cos\phi_2)$	$-90° \le \delta$ $\le 90°$	Eq. (8-28c)
	v = *Velocity of* **P**	$v = \omega_E \sin\rho_E$	$0 \le v \le \omega_E$	Eq. (8-26)
	ψ = *Direction of Motion of* **P**	$\psi = (\Delta\psi - 90°)\,\text{mod}_{360\text{ deg}}$	$0 \le \psi < 360°$	Eq. (8-25b)

*The output of the atan function should be converted to the range 0 to 180 deg.

the entire pattern repeats itself, shifted continuously in azimuth by the rotation about **C**. After one complete rotation about **C**, the curves may repeat precisely or may shift, depending on whether the ratio of ω_2 to ω_1 is an integral value.

Motion in the dual-axis spiral occurs in an annulus centered on the primary axis, **C**. The boundaries of the annulus are:

$$\text{inner radius} = |\rho_1 - \rho_2|$$
$$\text{outer radius} = 180 \text{ deg} - |180 \text{ deg} - \rho_1 - \rho_2| \tag{8-29}$$

The motion will actually touch **C** only if $\rho_1 = \rho_2$.

While the range of motion is determined by the 2 radii, the direction and velocity is best described in terms of the instantaneous rotation axis, **E**. The point **P** is rotating at a constant angular speed about **E**. Consequently, the direction of the curve will always be perpendicular to **E** and the velocity will be proportional to the sine of the angular distance from **E**. The slowest velocity along the curve will occur at the point closest to **E**. As we go farther from **E**, the velocity increases until the arc length from I is 90 deg; after that, the linear velocity will decrease, having reached "over the equator" of the instantaneous rotation frame. The minimum value of the velocity will occur when **P** crosses the plane containing **C** and **S**. This will occur at:

$$\rho_{lim\,1} = |\rho_1 - \rho_2 - \rho_{\mathbf{E}}| \tag{8-30a}$$

or

$$\rho_{lim\,2} = |\rho_1 + \rho_2 - \rho_{\mathbf{E}}| \tag{8-30b}$$

The value of the minimum velocity will be the smaller of either $\omega_{\mathbf{E}}\sin\rho_{lim\,1}$ or $\omega_{\mathbf{E}}\sin\rho_{lim\,2}$. The maximum velocity will depend on whether $\rho_{\mathbf{E}}$ reaches 90 deg. If this occurs, then the value of the maximum velocity will equal $\omega_{\mathbf{E}}$. If it does not occur, then the maximum velocity will again occur when the locus crosses the plane containing the 2 axes, and the value of the maximum velocity will be the larger of $\omega_{\mathbf{E}}\sin\rho_{lim1}$ or $\omega_{\mathbf{E}}\sin\rho_{lim2}$.

Lastly, it is of interest to determine the separation between successive "up" and "down" curves at a fixed co-elevation, δ', relative to the primary axis. This will be the sum of the azimuth separation in the small circle defined by the secondary rotation plus the rotation about the primary axis during the time it takes to come back to the same co-elevation. Using the spherical triangle in Fig. 8-16, the total horizontal separation, $\Delta\phi_{\text{down/up}}$, is:

$$\begin{aligned}\Delta\phi_{\text{down/up}} &= 2\Delta\phi_1 + 2\Delta\phi_2 \\ &= 2\Delta\phi_A(\omega_1 / \omega_2) + 2\Delta\phi_2\end{aligned} \tag{8-31a}$$

where

$$\cos\Delta\phi_2 = \frac{\cos\rho_2 - \cos\delta'\cos\rho_1}{\sin\delta'\sin\rho_1} \tag{8-31b}$$

and

$$\text{os}\,\Delta\phi_A = \frac{\cos\delta' - \cos\rho_1\cos\rho_2}{\sin\rho_1\sin\rho_2} \tag{8-31c}$$

Note that $\Delta\phi_2 = \omega_2 t/2$ and $\Delta\phi_1 = \omega_1 t/2 = \Delta\phi_A(\omega_1/\omega_2)$,where t is the time between crossings at co-elevation δ' . The rotational spacing between two successive "up" or two successive "down" crossings is just the rotation about the primary axis during one secondary rotation period. Thus,

$$\Delta\phi_{up/up} = \Delta\phi_{down/down} = 360 \text{ deg } (\omega_1 / \omega_2) \tag{8-32}$$

With these expressions, we can determine the basic characteristics of any dual-axis spiral and can apply them to practical problems in orbit and attitude analysis.

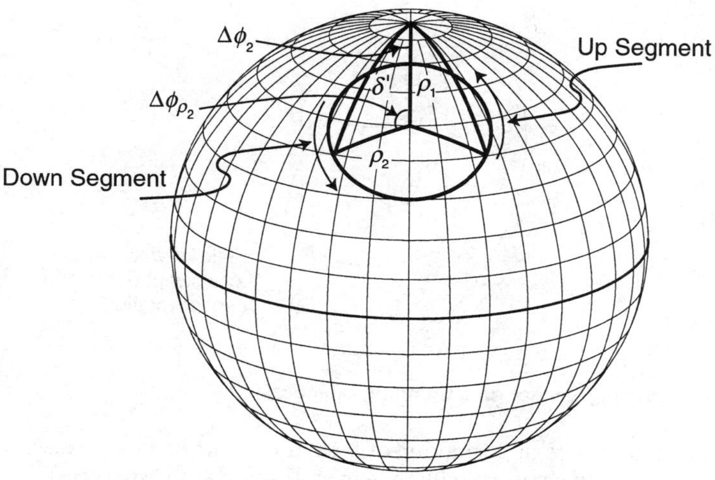

Fig. 8-16. Separation Between the "Up" and "Down" Segments of the Dual-Axis Spiral. See text for equations.

8.3 Dual-Axis Spiral Applications

Table 8-7 at the front of Sec. 8.2 gives the principal space applications for the dual-axis spiral. This section describes sample applications for the spinning and nutating spacecraft and analyzing the ground track of satellites in circular orbits. Our interest here is describing the kinematics of the motion—not the forces or dynamic equations which bring about that motion. Providing an accurate, detailed model of the spacecraft motion typically requires numerical simulation and integration of the equations of motion for either the attitude or orbit. Unfortunately, that detailed analysis can, at times, obscure the broader characteristics important to designing and placing sensors, analyzing missions, designing orbits and constellations, planning missions, or evaluating on-orbit data and data anomalies. For these functions, we're often better served by the following less precise, but easier to analyze, formulation.

8.3.1 Rotating Sensor on a Spinning Spacecraft

Rotating sensors are often used on 3-axis stabilized spacecraft to expand the field of coverage available from a static sensor. Spinning spacecraft typically use fixed sensors and allow the spacecraft's rotation to sweep the sensor's field-of-view across the sky and provide coverage. However, an interesting option is a rotating sensor on a spinning spacecraft, as shown in Fig. 8-17. This option allows the sensor to sweep out not simply a small circle in space but the entire sky. In other words, it has a field-of-view of 4π steradians. In this mode a single sensor can achieve what typically requires 5 to 10 sensors. This configuration also has a number of advantages in error analysis, bias determination, and coverage of the celestial sphere.

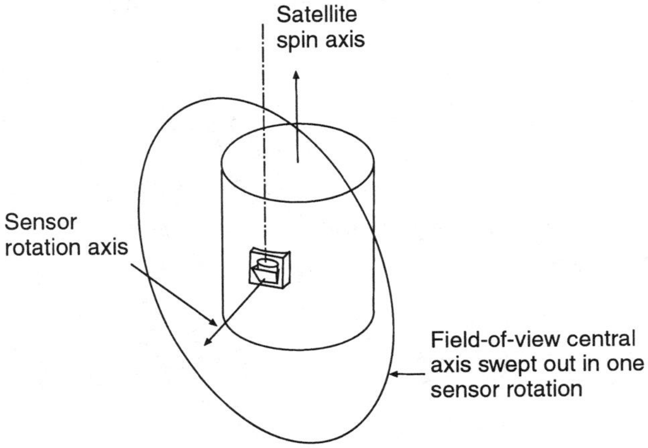

Fig. 8-17. A Rotating Sensor on a Spinning Spacecraft.

We're interested here in the motion of the field-of-view on the spacecraft centered celestial sphere, i.e., what is the motion in inertial space as the spacecraft spins and the sensor rotates? The full-sky algorithms provide a straightforward tool for achieving this. The primary axis is the spacecraft spin axis and the secondary axis is the sensor rotation axis. Both the sensor and the spacecraft are assumed to be rotating uniformly, but typically at different rates. The general equations of motion are those previously described in Sec. 8.2, Eqs. (8-24) to (8-28a–c).

A wide variety of sensor configurations are possible. However, a particularly simple one uses a planar scanner ($\rho_2 = 90$ deg) mounted with its rotation axis in the spacecraft spin plane ($\rho_1 = 90$ deg). In this case, the only remaining variable is the relative rotation rates of the sensor and the spacecraft. Several examples are illustrated in Fig. 8-18. In Fig. 8-18A, the rotation rate of the sensor, ω_{sensor}, is just equal to the spin rate of the spacecraft, ω_{spc}. Here the sensor field-of-view travels in an analemma or figure 8 on the sky. When the field-of-view crosses the spacecraft spin plane, the horizontal and vertical components of the velocity are equal and the curve crosses the spin plane at 45 deg. Half of a rotation period later, the sensor will have rotated 180 deg as will the spacecraft, such that the field-of-view returns to the same point with both velocities reversed such that the field-of-view center crosses the spin plane at right angles to the original path. The process repeats itself on the other side of the spin plane and the curve closes after 360 deg when both the sensor and the spacecraft have made one complete revolution. If the two periods are exactly equal, the pattern will repeat over and over and the sensor will scan out a figure 8 covering a relatively small component of the celestial sphere (Fig. 8-18A). Mechanically this type of motion can

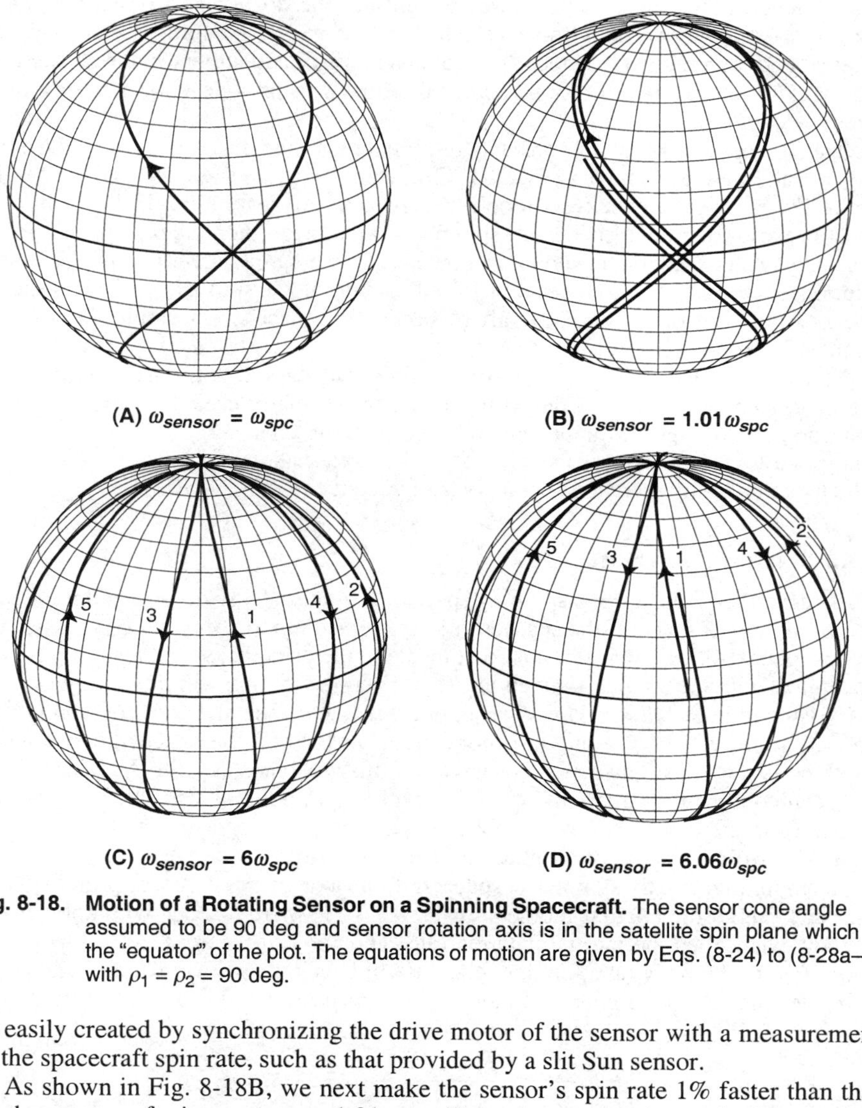

Fig. 8-18. Motion of a Rotating Sensor on a Spinning Spacecraft. The sensor cone angle is assumed to be 90 deg and sensor rotation axis is in the satellite spin plane which is the "equator" of the plot. The equations of motion are given by Eqs. (8-24) to (8-28a–c) with $\rho_1 = \rho_2 = 90$ deg.

be easily created by synchronizing the drive motor of the sensor with a measurement of the spacecraft spin rate, such as that provided by a slit Sun sensor.

As shown in Fig. 8-18B, we next make the sensor's spin rate 1% faster than that of the spacecraft, i.e., $\omega_{\text{sensor}} = 1.01\omega_{\text{spc}}$. Here the pattern is nearly identical to Fig. 8-18A, except that when the sensor has returned to the spacecraft spin plane after one complete revolution, the spacecraft is just short of having one revolution. Thus, the pattern will shift "backward" by 1% or 3.6 deg. As time passes, the pattern will shift with each spacecraft revolution by 1% and will sweep out the entire sky in 100 revolutions. (More precisely, in 100 revolutions the sensor will sweep out the entire sky twice—once on the upward part of the curve and again on the downward part. However, after 50 revolutions, it will have scanned half the sky twice, not covered the entire sky.) The key characteristic of this motion is that we can cover the entire sky, 4π steradians, with only a single sensor. What's more, we can do this with very small adjustments in the sensor rotation rate and can slice the sky as finely or coarsely as we like. For example, we could take very large steps while searching for an object of interest and then reduce the step size with a very small adjustment in the sensor rotation rate to take many fine steps across the object to provide good imaging or an accurate centroid.

The 100 spacecraft revolutions may require longer than desirable to scan the entire sky. An alternative is shown in Fig. 8-17C in which $\omega_{\text{sensor}} = 6\omega_{\text{spc}}$. We now cover the entire sky at a very coarse resolution in each spacecraft revolution. If the ratio of the sensor revolution rate to spacecraft spin rate is an integer, then the pattern will repeat precisely. Alternatively, as shown in Fig. 8-17D, we can again adjust the pattern to slide across the sky. Now however, a 1% adjustment in the spin rate will cover the entire sky twice in only 16 spacecraft revolutions because of the multiple coverage achieved in each spin.

Many additional configurations of rotating sensors and spinning spacecraft are possible, such as using a 45 deg conical scanner normally used on 3-axis stabilized spacecraft. Although the appearance of the patterns changes, the basic method of analysis follows the same process as above. In all cases, it is a simple dual cone spiral which can be easily modeled and analyzed by the techniques of Sec. 8.2.

8.3.2 Nutating Spacecraft

As described in Chap. 3, a spinning spacecraft rotates about the angular momentum vector in inertial space. If the spacecraft is axially symmetric, the axis of symmetry is a principal axis. If the spacecraft is rotating about the principal axis, then this axis will be aligned with the angular momentum vector and the motion will be a simple spin as was assumed in Sec. 8.3.1. However, in practice, the principal axis is frequently misaligned slightly from the angular momentum vector and the spacecraft nutates or wobbles as it rotates. The general character of this wobble is described in Chap. 3 and the detailed dynamic equations of motion will be provided in Vol. III. Here, we are interested in the motion of a sensor field-of-view in inertial space when the spacecraft nutates or wobbles about the angular momentum vector.

In a nutating, axially symmetric spacecraft, the axis of symmetry or principal axis, **P**, rotates about the angular momentum vector, **L**, in inertial space with angular frequency, wL, called the inertial nutation rate. The body of the spacecraft then rotates about **P** with the body nutation rate, ω_P. As will be shown in Vol. III, the ratio of ω_P to ω_L depends on the moments of inertia of the spacecraft and is given by:

$$\frac{\omega_P}{\omega_L} = \left(\frac{I_T - I_S}{I_S} \right) \cos\theta \tag{8-33}$$

where I_T is the transverse moment of inertia perpendicular to the symmetry axis, I_S is the moment of inertia along the symmetry axis, and θ is the nutation angle between **P** and **L**. If $I_S > I_T$ then the object is *oblate* (like a disc), the motion is stable, and ω_P and ω_L rotate in the same sense. If $I_T > I_S$ then the object is *prolate* (like a pencil), the motion is unstable, and ω_P and ω_L are in the opposite sense, i.e., rotating in opposite directions with respect to each other. (See Sec. 3.2 for further discussion.)

The detailed dynamics of this process will be discussed later. Here we're interested only in the kinematics, i.e., the motion of the field of view of a sensor across the sky. For this purpose, the angular momentum vector, **L**, corresponds to the primary axis and the principal axis, P, is the secondary axis. In the terminology of Sec. 8.2, $\omega_L = \omega_1$ and $\omega_P = \omega_2$. With this notation the motion of any point on a nutating axially symmetric spacecraft is simply a dual-axis spiral with all the properties we have discussed. Here, the nutation angle, $\theta = \rho_1$, is typically small, while ρ_2 is the angle from the principal axis to the direction of field-of-view of the sensor in spacecraft coordinates and can take on any value depending upon where the sensor is pointed. Fig. 8-19 shows the general motion for various axes on both prolate and oblate nutating spacecraft.

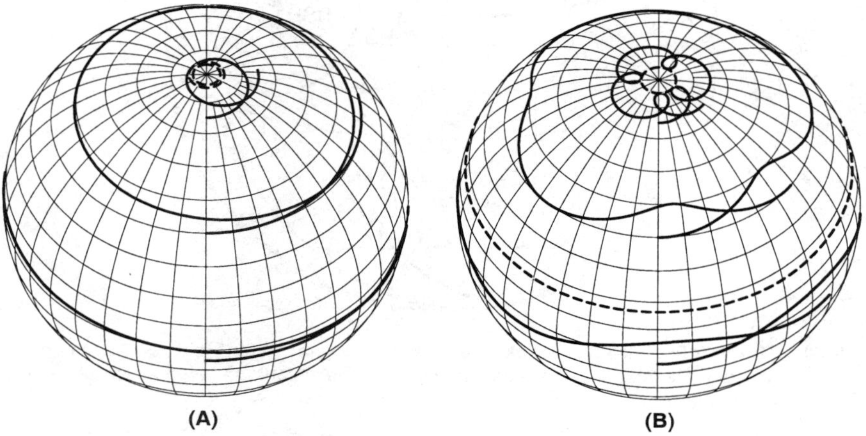

Fig. 8-19. Motion of a General Axis on a Nutating Spacecraft. (A) Oblate spheroid (stable). (B) Prolate spheroid (unstable) with $I_T/I_S = 4.5$.

We can apply all the equations and general conclusions of Sec. 8.2 directly to this motion. For example, if we define the cone angle, γ, as the angle from the principal axis to the direction of a sensor field-of-view, F, then the general motion of F in inertial space is contained within an annulus centered on the angular momentum vector, **L**, with an inner radius $\gamma - \theta$ and outer radius $\gamma + \theta$. Similarly, we can determine the range of velocities and directions of motion of F in inertial space. These are of interest in analyzing whether and how the sensor detects an object. If Eq. (8-33) results in rotation rates which are integer multiples of each other, then the motion will be repetitive and the field-of-view will not sample all of the directions within the viewing annulus. This means the observations will repeat themselves, which may serve to mask the spacecraft nutation. This will make it difficult to determine the nutation parameters or find the correct orientation of the angular momentum vector. On the other hand, if the ratio of the rotation frequencies is not a ratio of small integers, then the field-of-view of the sensor will fill the observation annulus over time. In this case, statistical techniques can be used to determine both the amplitude of the nutation and the orientation of the angular momentum vector with high accuracy.

8.3.3 The Satellite Ground Track

The dual-axis spiral results can also be applied directly to the motion of a satellite in a circular orbit over the Earth's surface. Fig. 8-9 in Sec. 8.2 showed the general appearance of the ground track. Fig. 8-20 shows the same motion with the various axes labeled.

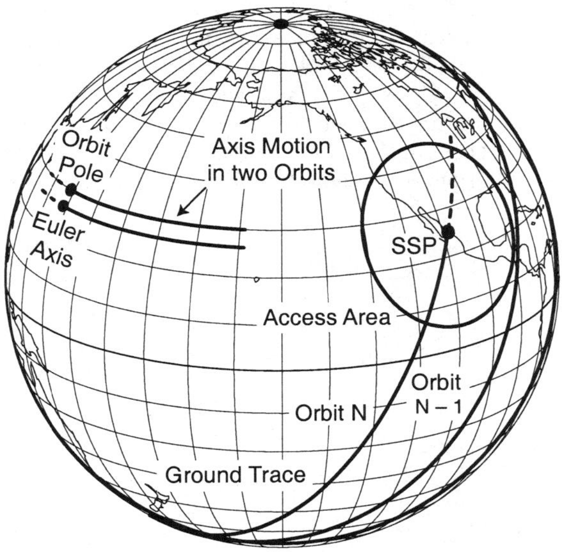

Fig. 8-20. The Satellite Ground Track is a Dual-Axis Spiral. The Earth's pole is the primary axis and the orbit pole is the secondary axis. The instantaneous rotation axis, **E,** is between them.

For the satellite ground track, we define the primary axis as the rotation axis of the Earth (i.e., the Earth's pole) and ω_1 as the negative of the Earth's rotation rate, ω_{day} (i.e., $\omega_1 \equiv -\omega_{day}$). The rotation about the pole at $-\omega_{day}$ effectively "de-rotates" the Earth so the secondary axis remains approximately fixed in inertial space. The primary radius, ρ_1, equals the orbit inclination, i. The secondary axis is the satellite orbit pole. The secondary rotation rate, ω_2, is just n, the mean angular motion of the satellite in its orbit and the secondary radius, $\rho_2 = 90$ deg. Because of this, the equations of motion for the dual-axis spiral can be further simplified. Doing this and changing notation gives the equations of motion for the satellite ground track shown in Table 8-9. Here α and δ are the longitude and latitude of the satellite and α_O and δ_O are the longitude and the latitude of the orbit pole at any time, t, after an arbitrary start time. δ' is the satellite co-latitude and the intermediate variable, ϕ_S is the azimuth of the satellite relative to north at the time, t. As defined in Sec. 8.2, n_G is the ground track velocity and ψ is the direction of satellite motion at time t. Note that i is the inclination and **E** as a subscript refers to the instantaneous rotation axis or Euler axis for the orbit.

The instantaneous rotation axis, **E**, plays an interesting role in the ground track analysis. We frequently think of a first order approximation for an orbit over a short arc as being a great circle centered on the orbit pole. This approximation is very good in inertial space, but ignores the Earth's rotation when looking at the ground track. The instantaneous rotation axis, **E**, is the real axis about which the satellite is rotating **with respect to the Earth's surface**. The axis **E** maintains a fixed latitude and the same longitude as the orbit pole and, thus, rotates about the Earth's pole along with the orbit pole at the negative of the Earth rotation rate. The satellite then rotates about **E** at a fixed angular rate, $\omega_{\mathbf{E}}$. Consequently, if we use **E** as the center of a small circle of radius $\rho_{\mathbf{E}}$, which may be greater or less than 90 deg, this small circle arc will provide

TABLE 8-9. Satellite Ground Track Equations. Equations for the ground track position, direction, and ground track velocity as a function of time for a satellite in a circular orbit at inclination i and with mean motion, n. Based on the dual-axis spiral equations with $\rho_1 = i$, $\rho_2 = 90$ deg, $\omega_1 = -\omega_{day}$, $\omega_2 = n$. See text for discussion. Compare with Table 8-8 for dual-axis spiral equivalent.

	Variable	Equations or Definitions	Conditions
Definitions	*Defining Parameters*	The subsatellite point, **S,** with (longitude, latitude) = (α, δ) is rotating with mean angular velocity, n, about the orbit pole, **O**, which in turn is rotating with angular velocity, $-\omega_{day}$, about the Earth's pole, **P**. The inclination of the orbit is i.	$0 \le i \le 180°$ **P** at (0°, 90°) **O, S** anywhere n, ω_{day} arbitrary
Intermediate Variables	α_O = *Longitude of* **O**	$\alpha_O = \alpha_{O_0} - \omega_{day}\, t$	no constraints†
	ϕ_S = *Azimuth of* **S** *about* **O** relative to north	$\phi_S = 270 \text{ deg} + \phi_{S_0} + nt = 270 \text{ deg} + \omega_0 + \nu(t)$	no constraints*
	$\Delta\alpha$ = *Change in Longitude of* **S**	$\Delta\alpha = \text{acos2}\left[\dfrac{-\tan\delta}{\tan i},\ -H(\phi_S)\right]$	$0 \le \Delta\alpha < 360°$
	ρ_E = *Angle from* **S** *to Euler Axis* **E** *(=Instantaneous Rotation Axis)*	$\rho_E =$ $\text{acos}(\sin\delta_E \sin\delta + \cos\delta_E \cos\delta \cos\Delta\alpha)$	$0 \le \rho_E \le 180°$
	ω_E = *Rate of Rotation about* **E**	$\omega_E = \dfrac{n \sin i}{\cos\delta_E}$	$\omega_E \ge 0$
	δ_E = *Latitude of* **E**	$\delta_E = \text{atan}\left(\dfrac{-\omega_{day} + n\cos i}{n \sin i}\right)$	$-90° \le \delta_E \le 90°$
	$\Delta\psi$ = *Change in Direction of Motion of* **S**	$\Delta\psi =$ $\text{acos2}\left[\dfrac{\sin\delta_E - \cos\rho_E \sin\delta}{\sin\rho_E \cos\delta},\ H(\Delta\alpha)\right]$	$0 \le \Delta\psi < 360°$
Results	α = *Longitude of* **S**	$\alpha = (\alpha_O + \Delta\alpha) \text{mod}_{360 \text{ deg}}$	$0 \le \alpha < 360°$
	δ = *Latitude of* **S**	$\delta = 90° - \text{acos}(\sin i \cos\phi_S)$	$-90° \le \delta \le 90°$
	n_G = *Ground track angular velocity of* **S**	$n_G = \omega_E \sin\rho_E$	$0 \le n_G \le \omega_E$
	ψ = *Direction of Motion of* **S** *relative to North*	$\psi = [\Delta\psi - 90°]\text{mod}_{360 \text{ deg}}$	$0 \le \psi < 360°$

*Here ϕ_{S_0} is measured from the ascending node, ω_0 is the argument of perigee, and $\nu(t)$ is the true anomaly at time t.

†For a more accurate expression that includes the rotation of the orbit pole due to J_2, see Eq. (9-66) in Sec. 9.3.1.

the correct velocity and direction of motion of the satellite at any point along the ground track. Thus, we can fit the ground track much more accurately in the vicinity of a ground station or target by using a small circle centered on **E** rather than a great circle centered on the orbit pole. The differences will be small in low-Earth orbit, where the satellite's rotation velocity is much greater than the Earth's. However, the effect will become larger as we go to higher altitudes, where the two rotation rates are more nearly the same. This is illustrated in Fig. 8-21, which shows the ground track, a great circle centered on the orbit pole, and a small circle centered on the instantaneous rotation axis for both a satellite in low-Earth orbit and a GPS satellite at approximately half geosynchronous.

TABLE 8-10. Location of the Instantaneous Rotation Axis, E, and Value of the Rotation Rate about E for a 500-km Orbit and a 20,000-kim Orbit at Various Inclinations. The satellite rotation rate is 3.805 deg/min at 500 km and 0.507 deg/min at 20,000 km.

	Altitude = 500 km		Altitude = 20,000 km	
Inclination (deg)	Co-latitude of Instantaneous Rotation Axis, δ_E' (deg)	Instantaneous Rotation Rate, ω_E (deg/min)	Co-latitude of Instantaneous Rotation Axis, δ_E' (deg)	Instantaneous Rotation Rate, ω_E (deg/min)
0	0.00	3.554	0.00	0.256
10	10.70	3.558	19.51	0.263
20	21.38	3.570	37.55	0.284
30	32.00	3.590	53.41	0.315
40	42.55	3.616	67.12	0.353
50	53.02	3.649	79.07	0.395
60	63.38	3.686	89.66	0.439
70	73.62	3.727	99.24	0.482
80	83.76	3.769	108.06	0.525
90	93.77	3.813	116.33	0.565
100	103.67	3.856	124.17	0.603
110	113.47	3.898	131.69	0.637
120	123.16	3.936	138.96	0.668
130	132.77	3.971	146.05	0.695
140	142.31	4.000	152.99	0.717
150	151.79	4.024	159.83	0.734
160	161.22	4.041	166.59	0.747
170	170.62	4.052	173.31	0.755
180	180.00	4.056	180.00	0.757

As shown by the equations in Table 8-9, the latitude of the instantaneous rotation axis, δ_E, is a function of both the inclination of the orbit and the satellite angular rotation rate, n ,which is a function of the altitude. (The "counter-rotation" that transforms the Earth frame into the inertial frame is opposite the direction of the satellite rotation in its orbit. Therefore, the orbit pole is between the Euler axis and the celestial pole.) Table 8-10 provides the co-latitude of **E** and the value of ω_E for 500 km and 20,000 km orbits at various inclinations. Recall that the longitude of **E** will be the same as the

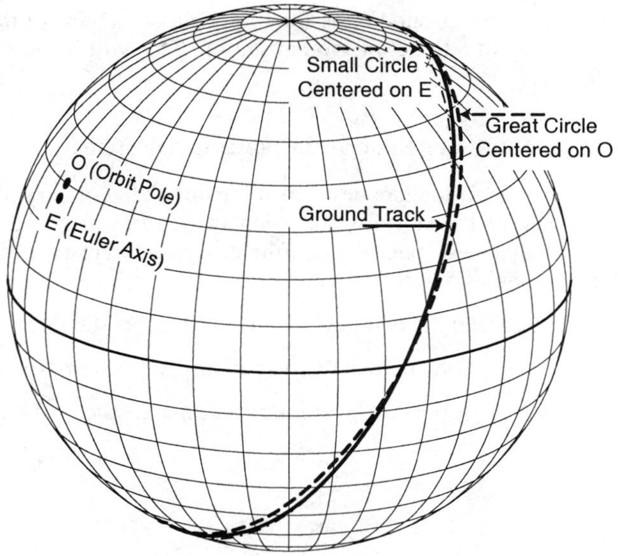

(A) Low-Earth Orbit

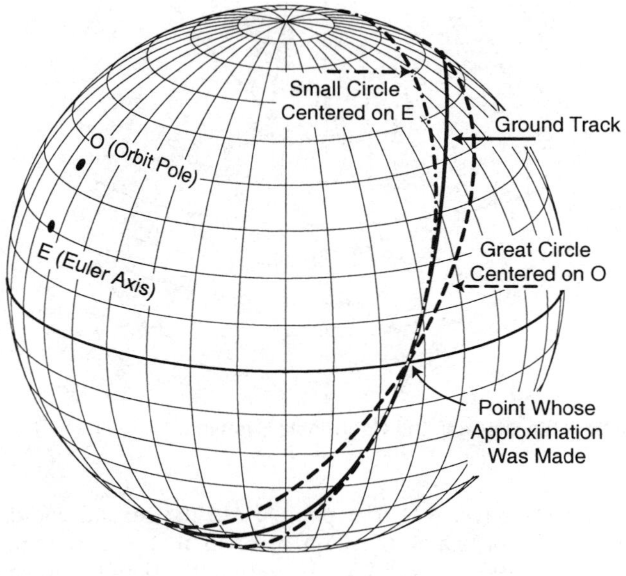

(B) GPS

Fig. 8-21. For Earth Satellites the Orbit Pole, O, is Between the Earth's Pole, P, and the Instantaneous Rotation Axis, E. The satellite motion at any time is best represented by small circle centered on **E**. Because **E** is on the great circle containing the orbit pole and the Earth's pole, the satellite will be 90 deg from the **E** when it crosses the equator and its velocity relative to the surface of the Earth will be a maximum.

longitude of the orbit pole. This table can be used to provide a more accurate fit to both the velocity and slope of the ground track for analytic assessments of the behavior of a satellite in the vicinity of a target or ground station. This will be described in more detail in Chap. 9.

8.3.4 Transformation Between Spherical Coordinate Systems

Finally, we can use the formalism developed for full-sky geometry to significantly reduce the complexity of transforming between two spherical coordinate systems. Specifically, assume that two spherical coordinate systems are related as shown in Fig. 8-22, with the variables defined as follows:

$\rho \equiv$ arc length between the two positive poles ($0 < \rho < 180$ deg)

$\psi_1 \equiv$ azimuth of the second pole in the first coordinate system ($0 < \psi_1 < 360$ deg)

$\psi_2 \equiv$ azimuth of the first pole in the second coordinate system ($0 < \psi_2 < 360$ deg)

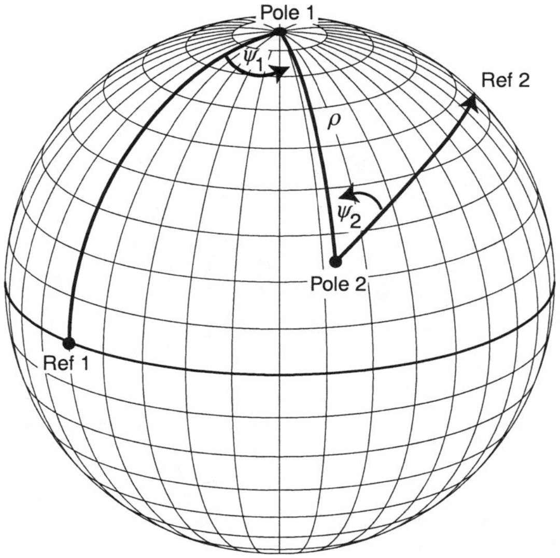

Fig. 8-22. Relationship Between the Coordinate Systems.

Given the coordinates (ϕ_2, δ_2') of a point, **P**, in the second coordinate system, we wish to find the coordinates (ϕ_1, δ_1') of **P** in the first system, where δ' is the co-elevation angle = 90 deg − δ. We first define the triangle shown in Fig. 8-23, with:

$$\Delta\phi_1 = \psi_1 - \phi_1 \qquad (8\text{-}34)$$

and

$$\Delta\phi_2 = \phi_2 - \psi_2 \qquad (8\text{-}35)$$

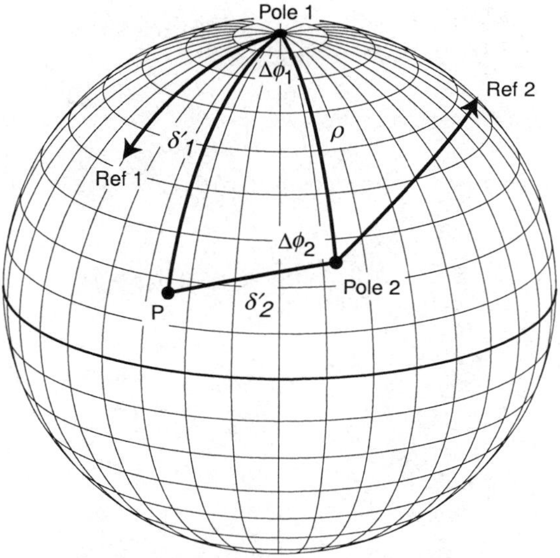

Fig. 8-23. Definition of the Spherical Triangle for Coordinate Transformations.

From the general solution for spherical triangles, we have:

$$\delta_1' = \text{acos}\,2[\cos\rho\cos\delta_2' + \sin\rho\sin\delta_2'\cos\Delta\phi_2, \text{H}(\Delta\phi_2)] \tag{8-36}$$

$$\Delta\phi_1 = \text{acos}\,2\left[\frac{\cos\delta_2' - \cos\rho\,\cos\delta_1'}{\sin\rho\,\sin\delta_1'}, \text{H}(\delta_2')\right] \tag{8-37}$$

or

$$\delta_1'^{*} = 360 \text{ deg} - \delta_1' \tag{8-38}$$

$$\Delta\phi_1^{*} = \Delta\phi_1 + 180 \text{ deg} \tag{8-39}$$

If we allow the angles to range from 0 to 360 deg, but restrict the sides to the range of 0 to 180 deg, then we have a unique solution, except in the singular case in which the poles are identical or 180 deg apart:

$$\delta_1' = \text{acos}[\cos\rho\cos\delta_2' + \sin\rho\sin\delta_2'\cos\Delta\phi_2] \tag{8-40}$$

$$\phi_1 = \text{acos}\left[\frac{\cos\delta_2' - \cos\rho\cos\delta_1'}{\text{H}(\Delta\phi_2)\sin\rho\sin\delta_1'}\right] - 90\,\text{deg}[\text{H}(\Delta\phi_2) - 1] \tag{8-41}$$

This can be further reduced to the normal coordinate expressions (α, δ), as:

$$\delta_1 = \text{acos}(\cos\rho\,\sin\,\delta_2 + \sin\rho\,\cos\,\delta_2\cos\,\Delta\phi_2) - 90 \text{ deg} \tag{8-42}$$

$$\Delta\phi_1 = \text{acos}\left[\frac{\sin\delta_2 - \cos\rho\sin\delta_1}{H(\Delta\phi_2)\sin\rho\cos\delta_1}\right] - 90\text{ deg }[H(\Delta\phi_2) - 1] \tag{8-43}$$

By symmetry, the reverse transformation will be:

$$\delta_2 = \text{acos}(\cos\rho\sin\delta_1 + \sin\rho\cos\delta_1\cos\Delta\phi_2) - 90\text{ deg} \tag{8-44}$$

$$\Delta\phi_2 = \text{acos}\left[\frac{\sin\delta_1 - \cos\rho\sin\delta_2}{H(\Delta\phi_1)\sin\rho\cos\delta_2}\right] - 90\text{ deg}[H(\Delta\phi_1) - 1] \tag{8-45}$$

Chapter 9

Earth Coverage

This chapter is intended as a cookbook for Earth coverage. Our goal is to provide a complete, practical set of formulas and algorithms for analyzing Earth coverage from space. We will use the preceding chapters for both motivation and derivations as appropriate. We provide both static and dynamic formulas, i.e., formulas for both instantaneous coverage and coverage over time.

Throughout the chapter, we give vector formulations wherever they are significantly different from the spherical geometry formulation. To make the text easier to follow, the vector formulations have been put in inline notes, separated from the remainder of the text by a rule at the top and bottom, and a substantial philosophical gulf. Those who have reviewed the preceding two chapters may safely ignore the inline notes. On the other hand, those who remain staunchly unconverted (direct descendants of those who refused to look through Galileo's telescope, no doubt) will find the necessary formulas in the inline notes and can ignore the rest of the text.

A spherical Earth model is used throughout the chapter. For problems which represent pure coordinate transformations, the spherical approximation to the Earth's surface is exact so long as geocentric coordinates are used for the Earth. For problems involving the physical surface of the Earth, Earth's oblateness may need to be taken into account, depending upon the accuracies required. In low-Earth orbit, Earth oblateness can shift the position of the horizon by as much as a few tenths of a degree on an angular radius of 60 to 70 deg. Consequently, oblateness may be important for data analysis, but is rarely of concern for mission analysis or planning. Alternative methods for taking oblateness into account are discussed in Sec. 9.1.5.

9.1 Geometry of the Earth's Surface Seen from Space

9.1.1 Transforming Between Earth and Spacecraft Perspectives

The most common problem in space mission geometry is to transform back and forth between Earth coordinates and the view as seen from the spacecraft. This section provides all of the fundamental formulas in both spherical geometry and vector forms for making this transformation. An example of problems of this type is to use the given coordinates of a target on the Earth to determine its coordinates in the spacecraft field of view. Another is to determine the intercept point on the surface of the Earth corresponding to a given direction in spacecraft coordinates or a given location in the field of view of a spacecraft camera.

Figure 9-1 shows the relationship between geometry on the Earth's surface and as seen from the spacecraft. A vector from the spacecraft will be tangent to the surface of the Earth at the *true* or *geometric horizon.* (The *effective horizon* introduced in Sec. 9.4 will be nearer to the spacecraft due to both foreshortening and atmospheric absorption.) The area inside the horizon is called the *access area*; it represents all of the surface of the Earth that the spacecraft can communicate with or look at, at this time. For a spherical Earth, the true horizon will be a small circle. The angular radius of this circle is called the *maximum Earth Central Angle*, λ_0, when measured from the center of the Earth, and the *angular radius of the Earth*, ρ, when measured from the spacecraft. The axis of the two cones formed by the horizon and either the Earth's center or the spacecraft is the *spacecraft position vector* when it goes from the center of the Earth to the spacecraft, and the *nadir vector* when it goes from the spacecraft to the center of the Earth. This line intersects the surface of the Earth at the *subsatellite point, SSP*. Finally, the direction toward the center of the Earth is called *nadir*, and the opposite direction is called *zenith.* Thus, for an observer standing at the subsatellite point, the center of the Earth is in the nadir direction and the spacecraft is at the zenith. (Nadir and zenith are well defined for an observer on the spacecraft or on the Earth's surface, but not for an observer at the center of the Earth).

For both conceptual and computational purposes, it is convenient to define an access area coordinate frame on the Earth's surface corresponding to the nadir coordinate frame on the spacecraft. As shown in Fig. 9-2, the elevation component is the Earth Central Angle, λ, measured from the SSP and the azimuthal angle, Φ_E, is the rotation angle measured about SSP from a reference direction to the point in question. Depending upon the particular problem, the reference direction may be either North or the projection of the velocity vector down onto the Earth's surface. The transformation between latitude and longitude and access area coordinates is straightforward and is

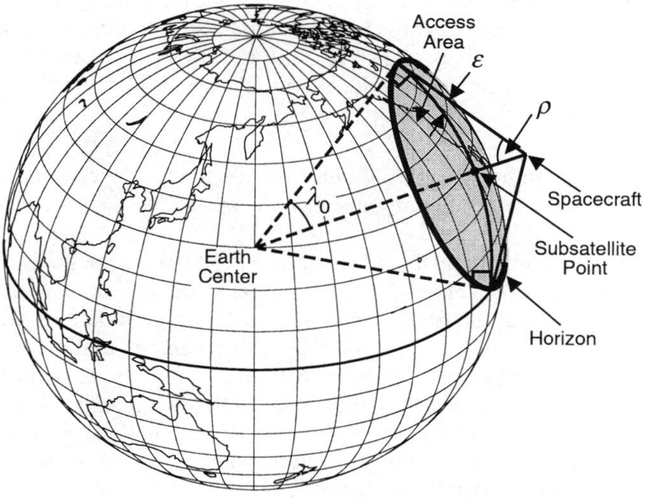

Fig. 9-1. Relationship Between Geometry as Viewed from the Spacecraft and from the Center of the Earth.

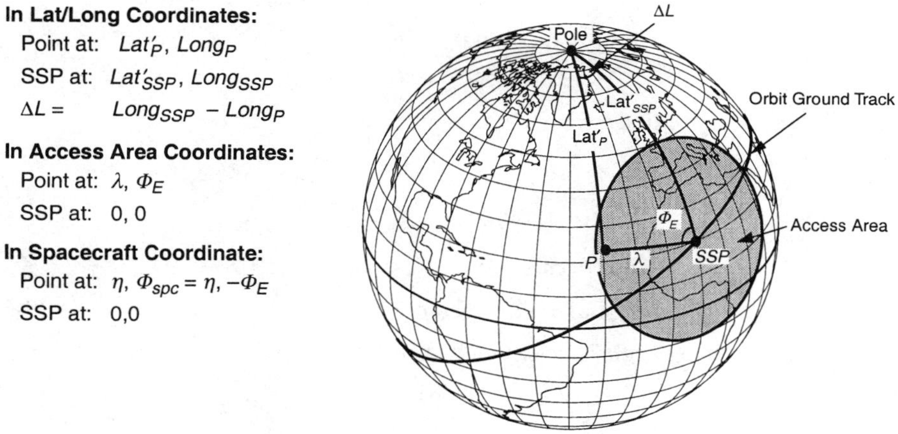

Fig. 9-2. Definition of the Access Area Coordinate Frame. See the box at the end of Sec. 9.1.1 for transformation equations.

given in the boxed example at the end of this section. (This transformation would be substantially more complex without the full-sky geometry introduced in Chap. 8).

Our fundamental geometry problem has now been reduced to transforming back and forth between access area coordinates on the surface of the Earth and spacecraft coordinates centered on nadir. This is particularly easy to do for the azimuthal component, since it is the same azimuth angle measured in either frame of reference, i.e., the azimuth is the angle between two planes—one containing the spacecraft, the center of the Earth, and the pole, and the other containing the spacecraft, the center of the Earth, and the target. In order to keep the rotation right handed, as seen from the spacecraft and on the Earth's surface, we introduce a minus sign so that:

$$\Phi_{spc} = -\Phi_E \tag{9-1}$$

where Φ_{spc} is the azimuthal angle about nadir from the reference direction to the target point, and Φ_E is the same angle measured on the surface of the Earth about the subsatellite point.

The remaining problem is to transform the radial component. Depending on the problem at hand, it is convenient to measure this radial component either in terms of angles at the satellite, at the Earth's center, or at the target point on the surface of the Earth. As shown in Fig. 9-3, the *nadir angle,* η, is measured at the spacecraft from the subsatellite point (= nadir) to the target. The Earth central angle, λ ,is measured at the center of the Earth from the subsatellite point to the target, and the *grazing angle* or *spacecraft elevation angle*, ε, is the angle measured at the target between the spacecraft and the local horizontal. First, we find the angular radius of the Earth, ρ, and the maximum Earth Central Angle, λ_0, from:

$$\sin\rho = \cos\lambda_0 = \frac{R_E}{R_E + H} \tag{9-2}$$

Next, if λ is known, we find η from:

$$\tan\eta = \frac{\sin\rho\sin\lambda}{1 - \sin\rho\cos\lambda} \tag{9-3}$$

Or, if η is known, we find ε from:

$$\cos\varepsilon = \frac{\sin\eta}{\sin\rho} \tag{9-4}$$

Or, if ε is known, we find η from:

$$\sin\eta = \cos\varepsilon\ \sin\rho \tag{9-5}$$

Finally, the remaining angle is determined from:

$$\eta + \lambda + \varepsilon = 90\text{ deg} \tag{9-6}$$

The distance D, to the target, is:

$$D = R_E\,(\sin\lambda/\sin\eta) \tag{9-7}$$

and the distance to the true horizon D_0 is given by:

$$D_0 = R_E/\tan\rho \tag{9-8}$$

Vector Formulation

For the corresponding vector equations, see Eqs. (9-16) to (9-75) in the boxed example at the end of this subsection.

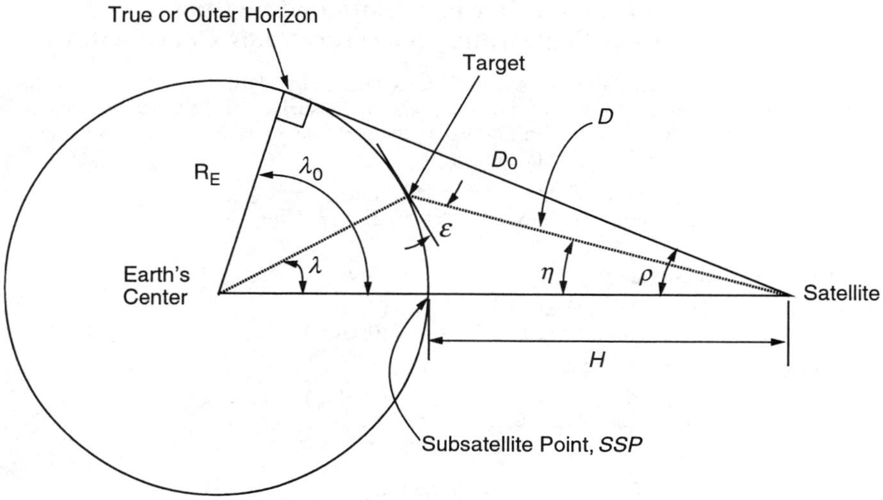

Fig. 9-3. Definition of Angular Relationships Between the Satellite, Target, and Earth's Center.

As an example, consider a satellite at an altitude of 1,000 km. From Eq. (9-2), the angular radius of the Earth, $\rho = 59.8$ deg. From Eqs. (9-3) and (9-6), the horizon is 30.2 deg in Earth Central Angle from the subsatellite point and is at a line-of-sight distance of 3,709 km from the satellite. We will assume a ground station at Hawaii ($D_r = 22$ deg, $L_r = 200$ deg) and a subsatellite point at $\delta_s = 10$ deg, $L_s = 185$ deg. From Eqs. (9-7) and (9-8), the ground station is a distance $\lambda = 18.7$ deg from the subsatellite point, and has an azimuth relative to North = 48.3 deg. Using Eqs. (9-3) and (9-8) to transform into spacecraft coordinates, we find that from the spacecraft to the target is 56.8 deg up from nadir (η) at a line of sight distance, D, of 2,444 km. From Eq. (9-7), the elevation of the spacecraft as seen from the ground station is 14.5 deg. The substantial foreshortening at the horizon can be seen in that at $e = 14.5$ deg we are nearly half way from the horizon to the subsatellite point ($\lambda = 18.7$ deg vs. 30.2 deg at the horizon).

The spherical Earth approximation is adequate for most mission geometry applications. However, for precise work, we must apply a correction for oblateness as described in Sec. 9.1.5. The Earth's oblateness has two distinct effects on the shape of the Earth as seen from space. First, the Earth appears slightly oblate rather than round, and second, the center of the visible oblate Earth is displaced from the true geometric center of the Earth. Except when we are specifically dealing with oblateness, we will use spherical coordinates throughout this chapter, both on the Earth and in the spacecraft frame. Computationally, we can treat both oblateness and surface irregularities as simply the target's altitude above or below a purely spherical Earth. That the Earth's real surface is both irregular and oblate is immaterial to the computation and, therefore, the results are exact.

Transformations Between Latitude/Longitude, Access Area Coordinates, and Spacecraft Nadir Coordinates

To transform between the various coordinate sets, we first define coordinates for the subsatellite point and for the *target* (i.e., the point on the surface of the Earth we wish to determine or point at). As shown in Fig. 9-2 in the text, the geocentric coordinates (latitude and longitude) for these points are:

Target Point, **P**, at	$(Lat_P, Long_P)$
Subsatellite Point (SSP), **P**, at	$(Lat_{SSP}, Long_{SSP})$
$\Delta L \equiv Long_{SSP} - Long_P$	

In Area Access coordinates:

Target Point, **P**, at	(λ, Φ_E)
Subsatellite Point, **S**, at	(0, 0)

and, in spacecraft nadir coordinates:

Target Point, **P**, at	$(\eta, \Phi_{spc}) = (\eta, -\Phi_E)$
Subsatellite Point, **S**, at	(0,0)

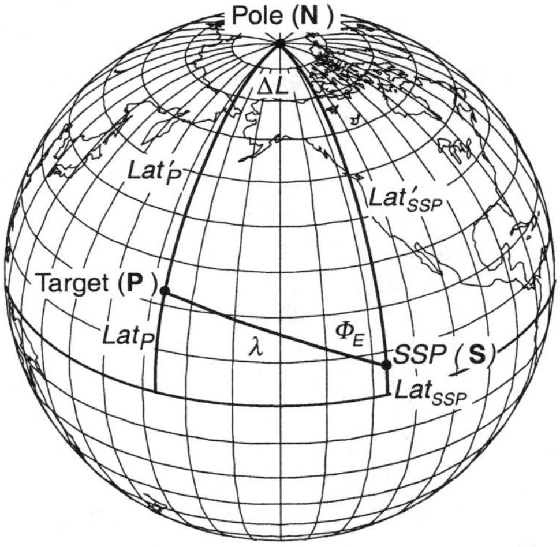

Fig. 9-4. Relationship Between the Target and the Subsatellite Point on the Earth's Surface.

Using spherical coordinates on both the Earth's surface and the spacecraft, and given the latitude and longitude for the target and SSP, we have:

$$\lambda = \text{acos}\left[\cos Lat'_P \cos Lat'_{SSP} + \sin Lat'_P \sin Lat'_{SSP} \cos \Delta L\right] \tag{9-9}$$

$$\Phi_E = \text{acos}\left[\frac{\cos Lat'_P - \cos Lat'_{SSP} \cos\lambda}{2(0.5 - H(\Delta L)) \sin Lat'_{SSP} \sin\lambda}\right] + H(\Delta L) \cdot 180 \text{ deg} \tag{9-10}$$

where $Lat' \equiv (90 \text{ deg} - Lat)$ is the angle measured from the pole and is frequently more convenient to use. The acos function is evaluated over range 0 to 180 deg, and the *hemi-*

sphere function, H, is defined by Eq. (8-1) in Sec. 8.1. Given the area access coordinates (λ, Φ_E), we have:

$$\eta = \text{atan}\,[\sin\rho \sin\lambda / (-\sin\ \rho \cos\lambda)] \quad \text{point is on visible side if } \lambda < (90\text{ deg} - \rho) \tag{9-11}$$

$$\varepsilon = \text{acos}\,(\sin\eta / \sin\rho) \tag{9-12}$$

$$\lambda = 90\text{ deg} - \eta - \varepsilon \tag{9-13}$$

$$Lat'_P = \text{acos}\left[\cos\lambda \cos Lat'_{SSP} + \sin\lambda \sin Lat'_{SSP} \cos\Phi_E\right] \tag{9-14}$$

$$\Delta L = \text{acos}\left[\frac{\cos\lambda - \cos Lat'_P \cos Lat'_{SSP}}{2(0.5 - H(\Phi_E))\sin Lat'_{SSP} \sin Lat'_P}\right] + H(\Phi_E)\cdot 180\text{ deg} \tag{9-15}$$

Vector Formulation

To do the problem using vectors, we first define the vector quantities shown on Fig. 9-4 as follows:

P = target vector from the center of the Earth to the target point
S = spacecraft position vector from the center of the Earth to the spacecraft, and
O = observation vector from the spacecraft to the target.

Given **P** and **S**, we determine the observation vector, **O**, from the spacecraft by:

$$\mathbf{O} = \mathbf{P} - \mathbf{S} \tag{9-16}$$

Given the observation unit vector, $\hat{\mathbf{O}}$, from the spacecraft, first determine the distance to Earth's surface, D:

$$D = -(\mathbf{S}\cdot\hat{\mathbf{O}}) \pm \sqrt{(\mathbf{S}\cdot\hat{\mathbf{O}})^2 - |\mathbf{S}|^2 + R_E^2} \tag{9-17}$$

where R_E is the Earth radius (6,378.14 km), and the smaller value of D corresponds to the intersection on the visible portion of the Earth. Then,

$$\mathbf{O} = (D\cdot\hat{\mathbf{O}}) \tag{9-18}$$

$$\mathbf{P} = \mathbf{S} + \mathbf{O} \tag{9-19}$$

To compute the observability parameters, ρ, η, ε, λ, and Φ_E.

$$\eta = \text{acos}(-\hat{\mathbf{S}}\cdot\hat{\mathbf{O}}) \tag{9-20}$$

$$\rho = \text{asin}\,(R_E / |\mathbf{S}|) \tag{9-21}$$

$$\varepsilon = \text{acos}\,(\hat{\mathbf{P}}\cdot\hat{\mathbf{O}}) - 90\text{ deg} \tag{9-22}$$

$$\lambda = \text{acos}\,(\hat{\mathbf{S}}\cdot\hat{\mathbf{P}}) \tag{9-23}$$

The point is visible if $\lambda < (90\text{ deg} - \rho)$. Finally,

$$\Phi_E = \text{acos}\left[\left(\hat{\mathbf{S}}\times\hat{\mathbf{N}}\right)\cdot\left(\hat{\mathbf{S}}\cdot\hat{\mathbf{P}}\right) / \left|\hat{\mathbf{S}}\times\hat{\mathbf{N}}\right|\cdot\left|\hat{\mathbf{S}}\cdot\hat{\mathbf{P}}\right|\right] \tag{9-24}$$

where $\hat{\mathbf{N}}$ is the unit vector from the center of the Earth to the celestial pole.

9.1.2 Earth Features Viewed from Space

What does the surface of the Earth look like from space? This is a key question, not only for understanding what an astronaut sees, but for developing an understanding of how to design space missions and analyze data from them. We are so used to looking at projections onto the Earth that it is easy to forget that it is the geometry as seen from the spacecraft that has a major impact on the capacity of the spacecraft to fulfill its objectives.

Figure 9-5 is a photo of the Earth taken by the Apollo 17 astronauts on their way to the Moon. Northern Africa, Arabia, the Red Sea, and the Mediterranean are all clearly visible at the top of the photo. The Antarctic polar ice cap is visible at the bottom although it blends in with the clouds somewhat. The brightest feature by far is the cloud tops such that weather patterns become much more visible than features on the surface. There is also good contrast between the desert in northern Africa and the vegetation in central Africa. Although this view is nearly a "full Earth," the terminator, or sunrise/sunset line, can be seen by the slightly fuzzier, right-hand edge of the Earth's disk. Finally, notice the bright spot in the clouds just above and to the left of center. This is the specular reflection of the Sun off the clouds where the angle of incidence equals the angle reflection.

Fig. 9-5. Photo of the Earth from Apollo 17 on the Way to the Moon. See text for discussion. (Photo courtesy of NASA.)

To clearly illustrate the geometrical effects, Fig. 9-6 shows the geometry on the surface of the Earth and as seen from spacecraft for a satellite at 1,000 km over Mexico's Yucatan Peninsula at the southern edge of the Gulf of Mexico. The left side shows the geometry on the surface of the Earth. The right side shows the geometry as seen by the spacecraft projected onto the spacecraft-centered celestial sphere. As computed above, the maximum Earth central angle will be approximately 30 deg from this altitude such that the spacecraft can see from northwestern South America to

Maine on the East Coast of the U.S. and Los Angeles on the West Coast. The angular radius of the Earth as seen from the spacecraft will be 90 – 30 = 60 deg as shown in Fig. 9-6B. Because the spacecraft is over 20 North latitude, the direction to nadir in spacecraft-centered celestial coordinates will be 20 deg south of the celestial equator. (The direction from the spacecraft to the Earth's center is exactly opposite the direction from the Earth's center to the spacecraft.)

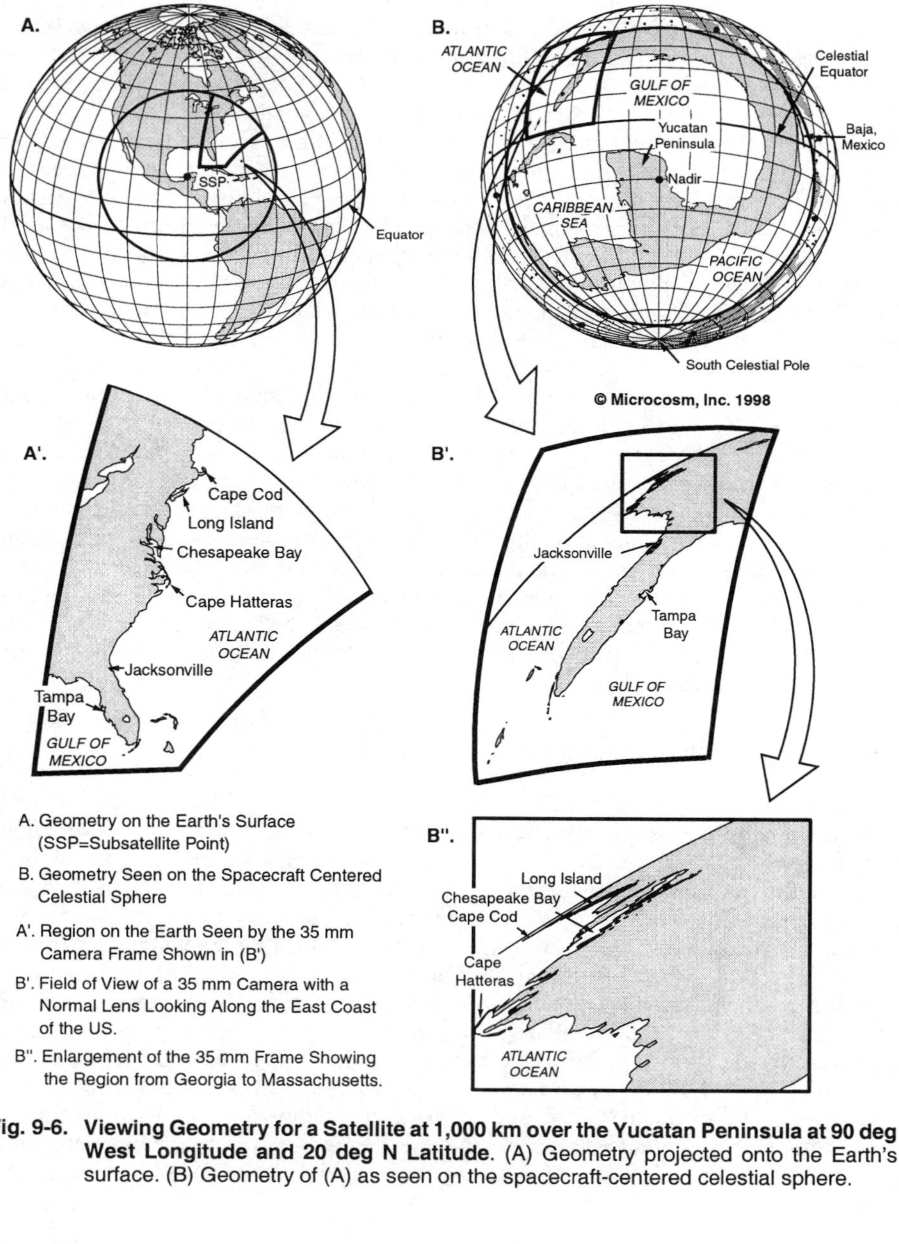

Fig. 9-6. Viewing Geometry for a Satellite at 1,000 km over the Yucatan Peninsula at 90 deg West Longitude and 20 deg N Latitude. (A) Geometry projected onto the Earth's surface. (B) Geometry of (A) as seen on the spacecraft-centered celestial sphere.

Even after staring at it a bit, the view from the spacecraft in Fig. 9-6B looks strange. First, recall that we are looking at the spacecraft-centered celestial sphere **from the outside**. The spacecraft is at the center of the sphere. Therefore, the view for us is reversed right-to-left relative to the view as seen by the spacecraft. Consequently, the Atlantic is on the left and the Pacific on the right. Nonetheless, there still appear to be distortions in the view. Mexico has an odd shape and South America has almost disappeared. All of this is due to the very strong foreshortening at the edge of the Earth's disk. Notice, for example, that on the Earth Jacksonville, FL, is about halfway from the subsatellite point to the horizon. This means that only 1/4th of the area seen by the spacecraft is closer to the subsatellite point than Jacksonville. Nonetheless, as seen from the perspective of the spacecraft, Jacksonville is 54 deg from nadir, i.e., 90% of the way to the horizon with 3/4ths of the visible area beyond it.

The rectangle in the upper left of Fig. 9-6B is the field of view of a 35 mm camera with a 50 mm focal length lens (a normal lens that is neither wide angle nor telephoto). The cameraperson on our spacecraft has photographed Florida and the eastern seaboard of the U.S. to approximately Maine. The region photographed on the Earth is shown in Fig. 9-6A′ and 9-6B′ and an enlargement of a portion of the photo from Georgia to Maine is shown in Fig. 9-6B″. Note the dramatic foreshortening as Long Island and Cape Cod become little more than horizontal lines, even though they are some distance from the horizon. This distortion does not come from the plotting style, but is what the spacecraft sees. We see the same effect standing on a hilltop or a mountain. (In a sense, the spacecraft is simply a very tall mountain.) Most of our angular field of view is taken up by the mountain top we are standing on. For our satellite, most of what is seen is the Yucatan and Gulf of Mexico directly below. There is plenty of real estate at the horizon, but it appears very compressed.

As shown quantitatively in Fig. 5-8 in Sec. 5-3, we can point an antenna approximately equally well at Cancun on the Yucatan below us or at Boston, on the horizon. However, as shown in Fig. 5-7, mapping can be done extremely well directly below us, but is nearly impossible near the horizon. From the perspective of the satellite, we can draw an excellent map of the Yucatan or the Gulf of Mexico. We can point our antenna at Boston. But we can not realistically map Boston or Massachusetts from the current location of the satellite.

9.1.3 Directions, Shapes, and Areas

Figure 9-6 in Sec. 9.1.2 provides a good conceptual view of the geometry as seen from space. However, for analysis and computation, it is most convenient to work in terms of points, directions, shapes and areas on the Earth's surface, and to ask how these are viewed from the spacecraft. The formulation for transforming points was given in Sec. 9.1.1. Directions, shapes and areas are described below. For viewing geometry computations, it is very convenient to introduce horizontal and vertical to refer to directions when looking at the Earth. Specifically, *horizontal* refers to the direction parallel to the Earth's horizon, either in the spacecraft coordinate frame, or on the surface of the Earth. Similarly, *vertical* refers to the direction perpendicular to the horizontal, i.e., toward or away from nadir or radial with respect to the subsatellite point. With these definitions, horizontal and vertical mean the same for the spacecraft, the access area coordinate system, and an observer standing at the subsatellite point.

Although horizontal and vertical remain the same as seen from the spacecraft and in the access area coordinate system, angular directions relative to horizontal and vertical do not. As shown in Fig. 9-7, directions are most conveniently described relative to the horizontal. If we define θ as the angle relative to the horizontal on the surface of the Earth and θ' as the angle relative to the horizontal as seen from the spacecraft, then these are related by:

$$\tan \theta' = \tan \theta \sin \varepsilon \tag{9-25}$$

where ε is the elevation angle at the point in question. We can see from this equation another effect of foreshortening. As ε goes to 0 near the horizon, any direction other than purely horizontal becomes nearly vertical. Thus, essentially all curves on the spacecraft centered celestial sphere, when projected onto the Earth, will intersect the horizon nearly perpendicular to it. Similarly, essentially all curves on the surface of the Earth near the horizon will become nearly horizontal when seen from the spacecraft. This can be seen clearly by looking at the shape of the coastline near the horizon in Fig. 9-6B″.

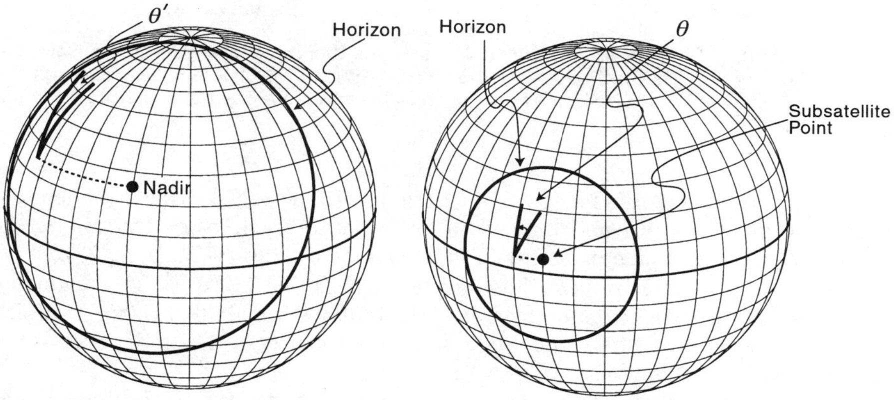

(A) On the Spacecraft-Centered Celestial Sphere **(B) On the Earth**

Fig. 9-7. Directions are Most Conveniently Described Relative to the Horizontal, or Equivalently, with Respect to the Subsatellite Point or Nadir.

Figure 9-8 shows the same geometry as Fig. 9-6 with the Earth's latitude and longitude lines and several geometrical figures as seen from the spacecraft. Generally, circles on the spacecraft's celestial sphere will project onto the surface of the Earth as elongated in the vertical direction, just as a flashlight beam is elongated when shone along a table top. If the projected beam goes all the way to the Earth's horizon, the elevation angle there will be 0 and the edges of the beam will be very nearly vertical. The projection of circles, rectangles, and straight lines onto the surface of the Earth is discussed in more detail in Sec. 9.1.4.

The primary shape of interest on the surface of the Earth is a circle, since both great circles and small circles on the Earth are actually circles in 3-dimensional space as seen from the spacecraft. The discussion of the shape of circles as seen from nearby was given in Sec. 6.3.4. When viewed from infinity, these circles are ellipses. When viewed from the finite distance of a LEO spacecraft, they are distorted ellipses with the shape and dimensions given in Sec. 6.3.4. Of course, any portion of the curve that

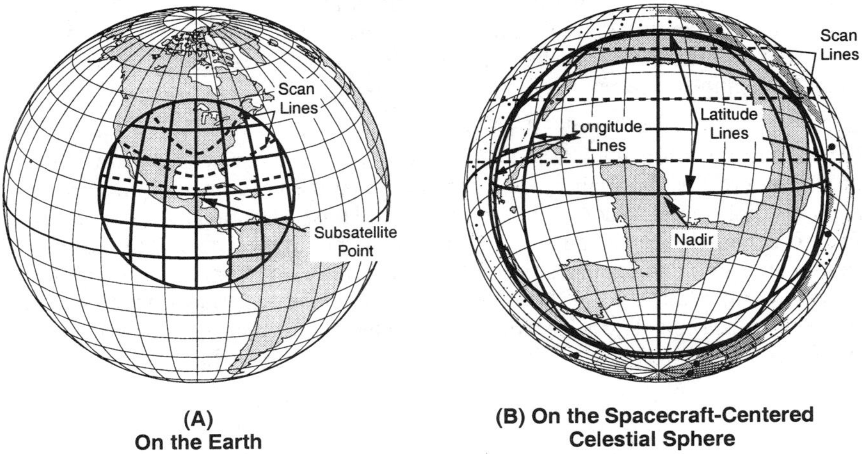

Fig. 9-8. Common Shapes on the Earth (A) and on the Spacecraft-Centered Celestial Sphere (B). The dashed lines are sensor scan lines which are small circles on the spacecraft sky. The solid lines are lat/long lines which are great or small circles on the Earth.

goes over the true horizon is hidden by the Earth itself. The actual shape is moderately complex to project. However, the general limits and characteristics are well established and easy to compute in a closed form, as given by Eqs. (6-24) to (6-27). Short segments are most easily projected as directions according to Eq. (9-25). Segments either tangent or perpendicular to the radial direction will remain that way. All circles will be symmetric about the vertical line through the center of the circle, even if the center is beyond the horizon.

Finally, the projection of area is also of interest. Given a number of deg^2 on the Earth's surface, what angular area in deg^2 does this represent as seen from the spacecraft? In general, the only solution is to integrate the projected area. This is done by looking at area elements on the ground and transforming these into area elements as seen by the spacecraft, where the horizontal component expressed in radians is just x/d and the vertical component is $y/(d \sin \varepsilon)$, where d is the distance to the point in question.

Fortunately, there are several convenient approximations that make estimating the angular area reasonably easy. For shapes which have a high degree of symmetry about nadir, exact formulas are readily available. These formulas are given in Table 9-1 with the definition of variables shown in Fig. 9-9.

Finally, there is a convenient approximation that can be made as accurate as desired for odd shaped areas. Angular segments, i, on the Earth centered on nadir, project into annular segments as seen from the spacecraft and the exact area, A_i, of each is easily computed.

$$A_i = \Phi_i (\cos \lambda_i - \cos \lambda_{i+1}) \tag{9-26a}$$

where Φ_i defines the width of the segment, λ_i is the inner radius, and λ_{i+1} the outer radius. The total area, A, is then simply

$$A = \Sigma A_i \tag{9-26b}$$

TABLE 9-1. Formulas for the Areas of Shapes Symmetric About Nadir. See Fig. 9-9 for the definition of variables. See Eqs. (9-3) to (9-6) for transformation between η and λ. For area computations, $\Phi_{Earth}=\Phi_{spc} = \Phi$. **Note that for area formulas, all angles should be expressed in radians and angular areas in steradians.**

Shape	Area on the Surface of the Earth	Area on the Spacecraft-Centered Celestial Sphere
Entire Access Area	$2\pi\,(1 - \cos\lambda_0)$ $= 2\pi\,(1 - \sin\rho)$	$2\pi\,(1 - \cos\rho)$ $= 2\pi\,(1 - \sin\lambda_0)$
Area within Effective Horizon	$2\pi\,(1 - \cos\lambda)$	$2\pi\,(1 - \cos\eta)$
Pie Shaped Piece	$\Phi\,(1 - \cos\lambda)$	$\Phi\,(1 - \cos\eta)$
Annulus Centered on Nadir	$2\pi\,(\cos\lambda_1 - \cos\lambda_2)$	$2\pi\,(\cos\eta_1 - \cos\eta_2)$
Annular Segment Centered on Nadir	$\Phi\,(\cos\lambda_1 - \cos\lambda_2)$	$\Phi\,(\cos\eta_1 - \cos\eta_2)$

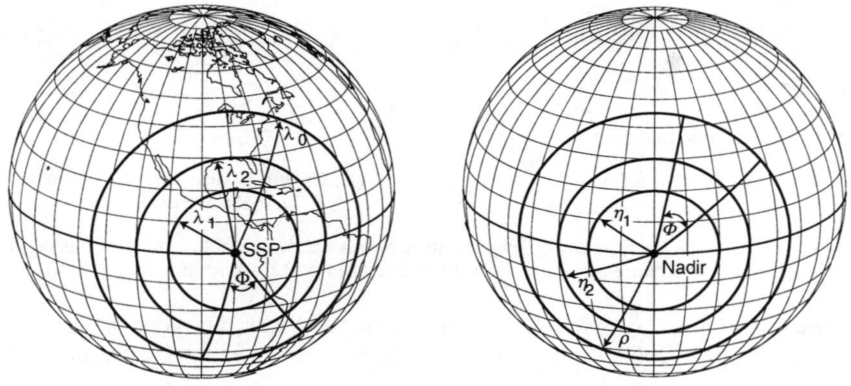

(A) On the Surface of the Earth **(B) On the Spacecraft-Centered Celestial Sphere**

Fig. 9-9. Definition of Variable for Annular Shapes Centered on Nadir. See Table 9-1 for area formulas.

Since Φ_i will be the same on the Earth and as seen from the spacecraft, the comparable formulas for the angular area on the spacecraft centered celestial sphere, A_i, is:

$$A_i' = \Phi_i\,(\cos\eta_i - \cos\eta_{i+1}) \tag{9-27a}$$

$$A' = \Sigma A_i' \tag{9-27b}$$

where η_i is related to λ_i by the previously derived equations:

$$\tan\eta_i = \frac{\sin\rho\sin\lambda_i}{1-\sin\rho\cos\lambda_i} \tag{9-28}$$

If η_i is known, we find ε_i from:

$$\cos\varepsilon_i = \frac{\sin\eta_i}{\sin\rho} \tag{9-29a}$$

If ε_i is known, we find η_i from:

$$\sin \eta_i = \cos \varepsilon_i \sin \rho \tag{9-29b}$$

Finally, the remaining angle is obtained from:

$$\eta_i + \lambda_i + \varepsilon_i = 90 \text{ deg} \tag{9-30}$$

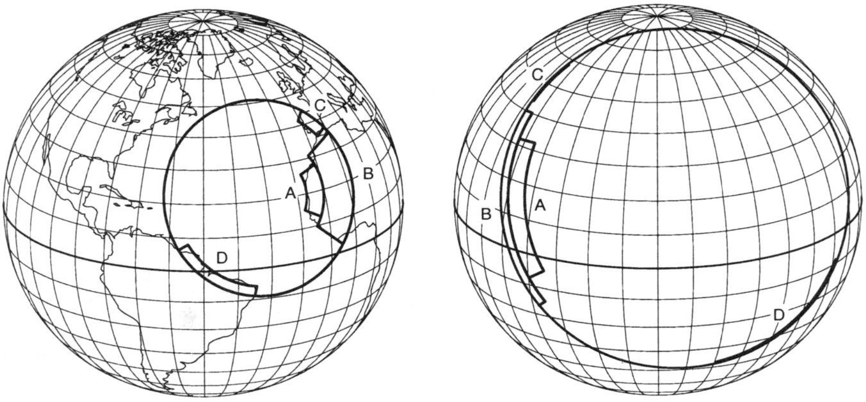

Fig. 9-10. Areas are Conveniently Transformed From Earth to Spacecraft Coordinates by Using Annular Segments for Which the Area can be Transformed Exactly.

Consequently, as shown in Fig. 9-10, any arbitrary area can be conveniently transformed by simply breaking it down into appropriately sized annular segments.

Vector Formulation

In the unit vector formulation, there is no convenient method for working with directions shapes, or areas on the celestial sphere except as collections of points. Consequently, all of the computational work in a vector approach would be done using the point transformations given in Sec 9.1.1. The only additional computational element required is to determine when a point on the Earth is beyond the horizon. This occurs whenever:

$$\hat{\mathbf{x}} \cdot \hat{\mathbf{s}} < \sin \lambda \tag{9-31}$$

where $\hat{\mathbf{x}}$ is the unit vector from the Earth's center to the point in question, $\hat{\mathbf{s}}$ is the unit vector from the Earth's center to the subsatellite point, and λ is the angular radius of either the true horizon or the effective horizon, as appropriate.

9.1.4 Projection of Sensor Fields of View onto the Earth

We now wish to work the Earth geometry problem the other way from Sec. 9.1.2, and project shapes as seen from the spacecraft (i.e., on the spacecraft-centered celestial sphere) down onto the Earth. Once again, points transform as given in Sec. 9.1.1, and directions transform as given in Sec. 9.1.2. For convenience, the transformation equations used for projecting onto the surface of the Earth are as follows:

Cutting the Viewing Area Into Equal Parts

It is frequently conceptually convenient to cut the area viewed by the satellite into approximately equal parts to divide the coverage between multiple sensors or antennas. However, foreshortening serves to make this task difficult. As an example, consider the problem of trying to cut the viewing region into 5 equal areas. One option would be to cut the Earth into 5 "pie slices," each covering an azimuthal angle of 72 deg. This clearly provides equal areas but does not provide a particularly convenient process for covering the area near nadir.

Another alternative is shown by the solid lines in Fig. 9-11A in which the subsatellite area seen from 1,000 km is cut into 5 equal parts on the Earth's surface, with one area centered on the subsatellite point and the remaining annulus cut into 4 equal segments, each with an area equal to the center small circle. However, if we project this same area onto the spacecraft centered celestial sphere, we obtain the figure shown by the solid lines in Fig. 9-11B, in which the effects of foreshortening become very apparent. The antenna assigned to the central area will need to cover virtually all of the apparent disk of the Earth, as seen from the spacecraft, while the remaining antennas will each cover very narrow arcs.

In Fig. 9-11B the dashed lines divide the visible dish of the Earth into equal areas as seen by the spacecraft. Projecting these equal areas onto the Earth gives the dashed lines in Fig. 9-11A. In this case the center circle is a small portion of access area.

Depending on the application, we may want equal areas as seen from the spacecraft, or equal areas projected onto the Earth. In any case, the two will be significantly different.

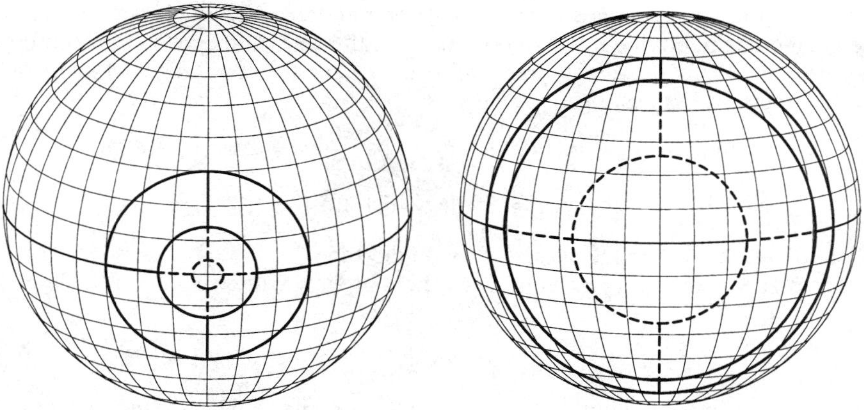

(A) On the Earth

(B) On the Spacecraft-Centered Celestial Sphere

Fig. 9-11. The Subsatellite Area Cut into 5 Equal Parts. (A) On the Earth's surface, (B) as seen from the spacecraft. In both cases, the solid lines are the boundaries of equal areas on the Earth's surface and the dashed lines are equal areas as seen from the spacecraft.

$$\Phi_{spc} = \Phi_{Earth} = \Phi \tag{9-32}$$

$$\cos \varepsilon = \sin \eta \,/\, \cos \rho \tag{9-33}$$

$$\lambda = 90 \text{ deg} - \eta - \varepsilon \tag{9-34}$$

$$\tan \theta = \tan \theta' / \sin \varepsilon \tag{9-35}$$

where Φ is the azimuthal orientation of the point in question and is the same both from the spacecraft and on the surface of the Earth, ε is the elevation angle at the target point from the horizontal up to the spacecraft, η is the nadir angle measured at the spacecraft from the subsatellite point to the target, ρ is the angular radius of the Earth determined from Eq. (9-2), λ is the Earth Central Angle measured at the center of the Earth from the subsatellite point to the target, θ is the direction relative to the horizontal measured on the Earth's surface, and θ' is the direction relative to the horizontal measured on the spacecraft-centered celestial sphere. The equations in vector form are given in the box at the end of Sec. 9.1.1; there is no convenient vector form for determining the direction relative to the horizontal.

Most practical shapes (i.e., instrument fields of view and antenna patterns) are lines, circles, or rectangles, as seen from the spacecraft. Examples include the field of view of a conical scanner, a circular antenna pattern, or a 35 mm camera with a 50 mm lens pointed at the horizon and tilted. The edge of any rectangular or linear field of view from a spacecraft instrument projects onto the sky as a great circle arc and projects into space as a plane surface. The pole of the great circle on the celestial sphere is in the direction of the vector normal to the plane in space. This great circle is characterized by two numbers: the azimuthal orientation, Φ, of the pole relative to some reference and either θ_p, the angle from nadir to the pole, or θ_E, the angle from nadir to the arc of the great circle (= the edge of the field of view). Note that θ_E is measured along the great circle arc connecting nadir and the pole and is perpendicular to the great circle in question. If the coordinates of the pole of the great circle representing the edge in any coordinate frame are (α_p, δ_p) and the coordinates of nadir in the same coordinate frame are (α_N, δ_N) then:

$$\sin \theta_E = \cos \theta_p = \sin \delta_p \sin \delta_N + \cos \delta_p \cos \delta_N \cos (\alpha_p - \alpha_N)$$

$$\theta_E = | 90 \text{ deg} - \theta_p | \tag{9-36}$$

where θ_E is the angle to the nearest point on the edge.

The plane representing the edge of the field of view will miss the Earth altogether if:

$$\theta_E > \rho \qquad \text{(great circle misses Earth)} \tag{9-37}$$

where ρ is the angular radius of the Earth. If $\theta_E = 0$, then the plane passes through nadir and the projection of the plane onto the surface of the Earth will be a great circle through the subsatellite point. If $0 < \theta_E < \rho$, then the plane intersects the spherical surface of the Earth in a small circle. Therefore, in general, the edges of a rectangular field of view from the spacecraft will intersect the surface of the Earth in a set of four intersecting small circles. A small circle on the surface of the Earth is fully defined by the center and radius. As always, the azimuthal orientation of the center of the small circle is the same as seen from the spacecraft and as projected onto the surface of the Earth. (Note that the azimuth changes sign if we wish to maintain a right-handed coordinate system in both cases.) The distance λ_{pole} from the pole of the small circle to nadir is given by:

$$\lambda_{pole} = 90 \text{ deg} - \theta_E = \theta_p \tag{9-38}$$

and finally, the radius of the small circle, ξ, is given by:

$$\cos\xi = \frac{(R_E + H)\sin\theta_E}{R_E} \tag{9-39}$$

where R_E is the radius of the Earth and H is the altitude of the spacecraft. These variables are defined in Fig. 9-12.

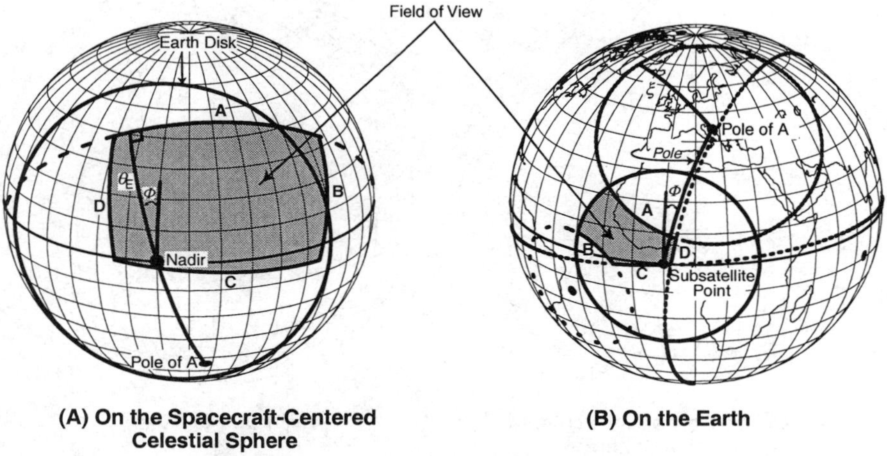

Fig. 9-12. Projection of a Rectangular Field of View as seen from the Spacecraft onto the Earth. The field of view is equivalent to that of a 50 mm lens on a 35 mm camera. (A) as seen from the spacecraft, (B) as projected onto the Earth's surface.

An alternative approach to projecting the field of view is to project the corners of the field of view onto the Earth using the point transformation equations at the end of Sec. 9.1.1 and the radius of the small circle defined by Eq. (9-39) to construct the four sides. We could also use any three points along the small circle such as two of the corners and either the nearest point to nadir or the point at which the small circle intersects the horizon.

The equations above were used to construct Fig. 9-12, which shows the projection of a rectangular field of view down onto the surface of the Earth. Note that the azimuthal orientation of all of the points remains the same on both the spacecraft-centered celestial sphere and on the surface of the Earth (to within the sign change for opposite directions), but that the radial distortion caused by projection onto the surface of the Earth transforms the great circle arcs on the spacecraft-centered celestial sphere into small circle arcs on the surface of the Earth.

Most sensors will have fields of view which are more symmetric with respect to nadir than that in Fig. 9-12, and the angular parameters with respect to nadir can frequently be determined by inspection. The approximately rectangular shape is largely retained when the field of view is oriented toward nadir. The more strongly curved edges occur when the edge of the sensor lies near or crosses the edge of the disk of the Earth. Figure 9-13 shows the projection of a "line scan" as seen from the spacecraft down onto the Earth. The shape appears approximately rectangular, because the radius of the small circle edges on the Earth are nearly 90 deg. Table 9-2 shows the angular radius for various small circles and the distance from the edge of the small circle to the subsatellite point for straight lines projected onto the surface of the Earth from an altitude of 1,000 km. As we approach the edge of the disk of the Earth, the curvature of the projection becomes very strong.

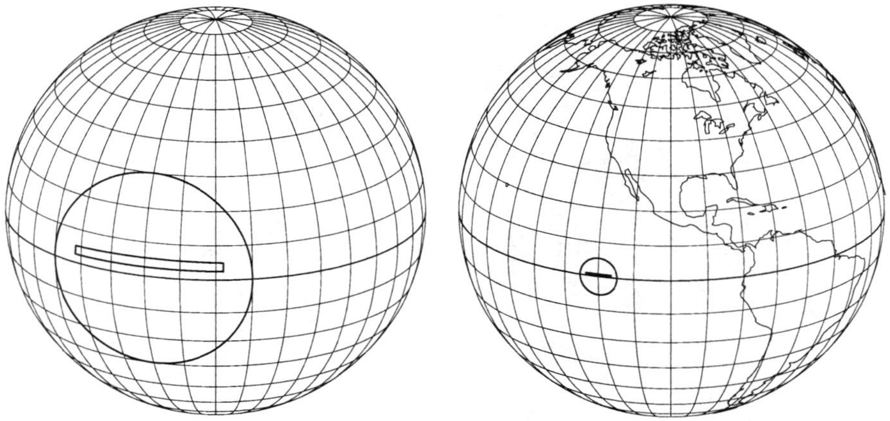

(A) On the Spacecraft-Centered Celestial Sphere

(B) On the Earth

Fig. 9-13. Projection of a "Line Scan" as seen from the Spacecraft onto the Earth. (A) As seen from the spacecraft, (B) as projected onto the Earth's surface.

Unfortunately, circular fields of view as seen from the spacecraft are both relatively common (for example, from conical scanners or antenna patterns) and are more difficult to compute exactly than rectangles. The circular field of view on the spacecraft-centered celestial sphere represents a cone in space, which projects into an elongated, roughly elliptical shape on the surface of the Earth.

While the edge is not a simple function, the extrema are easily computed. Given a circular field of view on the spacecraft-centered celestial sphere of radius ρ_{FOV} and centered η_{FOV} from nadir, we can compute the extremes as:

$$\eta_{max} = \eta_{FOV} + \rho_{FOV} \tag{9-40}$$

$$\eta_{min} = |\eta_{FOV} - \rho_{FOV}| \tag{9-41}$$

$$\sin(\Delta\Phi/2) = \sin\rho_{FOV} / \sin\eta_{FOV} \tag{9-42}$$

where η_{max} and η_{min} are the maximum and minimum nadir angles on the perimeter of the field of view and $\Delta\Phi$ is the width of the field of view measured in rotation angle

TABLE 9-2. Planes or Edges Projected onto the Surface of the Earth. Altitude = 1,000 km. Therefore, ρ = 59.8 deg and λ_0 = 30.2 deg. All values in deg.

On Spc Dist. to Edge (θ_E)	On Spc. Dist. to Pole (θ_p)	On Earth Radius (ξ)	On Earth Dist. to SSP (λ_{Pole})	On Earth Dist. to Horizon ($\lambda_0 - \lambda_{Pole}$)
0	90	90.00	0.00	30.18
5	85	84.21	0.79	29.39
10	80	78.41	1.59	28.59
15	75	72.58	2.42	27.76
20	70	66.69	3.31	26.87
25	65	60.73	4.27	25.91
30	60	54.66	5.34	24.84
35	55	48.43	6.57	23.61
40	50	41.96	8.04	22.14
45	45	35.12	9.88	20.30
50	40	27.61	12.39	17.79
55	35	18.63	16.37	13.81
56	34	16.46	17.54	12.64
57	33	14.03	18.97	11.21
58	32	11.18	20.82	9.36
59	31	7.45	23.55	6.63
59.5	30.5	4.64	25.86	4.32

about nadir. If $\rho_{FOV} > \eta_{FOV}$, then the field of view covers the nadir direction and $\Delta\Phi$ is undefined. Projecting these variables down onto the surface of the Earth using Eqs. (9-2) to (9-6), we have:

$$\Delta\Phi_{Earth} = \Delta\Phi_{spc} = \Delta\Phi \tag{9-43}$$

$$\cos \varepsilon_i = \sin \eta_i / \sin \rho \tag{9-44}$$

$$\lambda_i = 90 \text{ deg} - \eta_i - \varepsilon_i \tag{9-45}$$

where, as usual, the rotation angle is the same on the Earth as on the spacecraft and the radial components are elongated due to the foreshortening of the projection. The i subscript can refer to either the maximum angle, minimum angle, or angle to the center of the beam, which will of course no longer be midway between the extrema. The area, A, of the elongated projection on the Earth can be determined approximately from:

$$\xi_{max} = \lambda_{max} - \lambda_{FOV} \tag{9-46}$$

$$\xi_{min} = |\lambda_{max} - \lambda_{FOV}| \tag{9-47}$$

$$A \approx 2\pi\,(1 - \cos\,[(\xi_{max} - \xi_{min}) / 2]) \tag{9-48}$$

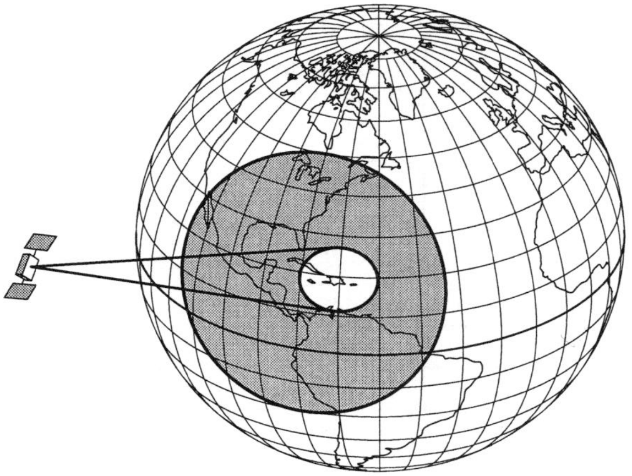

Fig. 9-14. Circular Antenna Beam Projected onto the Earth's Surface.

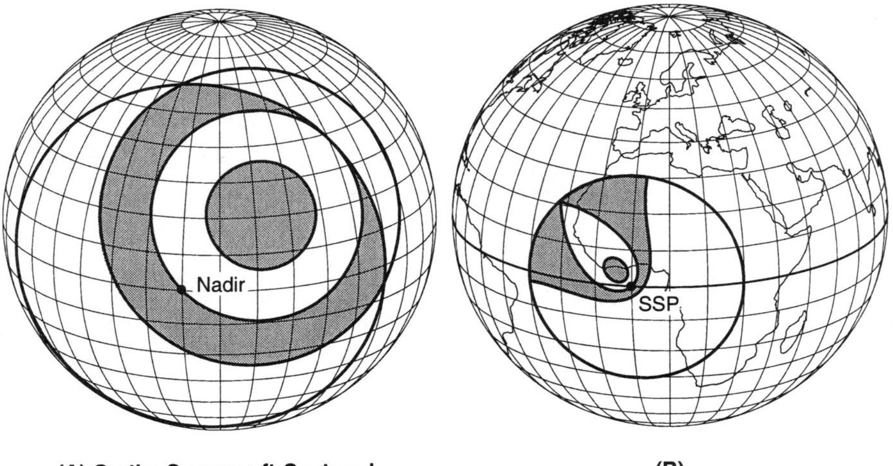

(A) On the Spacecraft-Centered Celestial Sphere

(B) On the Earth

Fig. 9-15. Projection of Several Circular Fields of View as Seen from the Spacecraft onto the Earth. (A) As seen from the spacecraft, (B) as projected onto the Earth's surface.

where ξ_{max} is the maximum value of the radius of the projected cone and ξ_{min} is the minimum value of the radius of the projected cone. The general appearance of a beam projected on the surface of the Earth is shown in Fig. 9-14 and the projections of several different sized cones are shown on both the spacecraft-centered celestial sphere and projected onto the Earth in Fig. 9-15. Finally, the area of various figures on the surface of the Earth are provided by formulas equivalent to those provided in Sec. 9.1.2 for areas on the celestial sphere (see Table 9-1 and Fig. 9-8). Explicitly, these are:

Entire Access Area:	$2\pi\,(1-\cos\lambda_0) = 2\pi\,(1-\sin\rho)$
Area within Effective Horizon:	$2\pi\,(1-\cos\lambda)$
Pie Shaped Piece:	$\Phi\,(1-\cos\lambda)$
Annulus Centered on Nadir:	$2\pi\,(\cos\lambda_2-\cos\lambda_1)$
Annular Segment Centered on Nadir:	$\Phi\,(\cos\lambda_2-\cos\lambda_1)$

Again, the area projection rule in Sec. 9.1.2 can be used to provide high accuracy approximations for any areas that are irregular figures. As previously, the best approach is to cut the area into annular segments centered on nadir for which the exact area formulas are available.

9.1.5 Earth Oblateness

Most analysis of Earth coverage is based on assuming a spherical model for the shape of the Earth. However, the Earth is much closer to an oblate spheroid which is the equilibrium shape of a rotating, gravitating fluid. The general characteristics of this shape are defined by a number of parameters:

Equatorial radius, a:	6,378.136 km
Polar radius, c:	6,356.753 km
Flattening factor (ellipticity), $f \equiv (a-c)/a$:	1/298.257 ≈ 0.003 352 81
Mean radius: $(a^2c)^{1/3}$:	6,371.000 km
Eccentricity, $e \equiv (a^2-c^2)/a = f(2-f)$:	0.081.818
Second eccentricity, $\varepsilon \equiv (a^2-c^2)/c$:	0.082.371

Of course, the oblate spheroid is also not a perfect model of the Earth's surface, but it is a remarkably good approximation. The difference between the polar radius and the equatorial radius is 21 km or about 0.3%. The next largest variation is the out-of-roundness of the Earth's equator, which is about 100 m or 0.002%. Differences in various Earth models are given in Table 9-3. Additional physical properties of the Earth are given in App. E.3.

TABLE 9-3. Comparison of Models of the Shape of the Earth. The variations listed may or may not result in measurement errors, depending on the application. The reference spheroid has an adopted equatorial radius of 6,378.136 km and flattening factor of 1/298.257.

Model	Deviation from Standard Reference
Sphere of radius 6,378.136 km	0 at the equator to +21.38 km at the pole
Reference spheroid	—
Ellipsoid with elliptical cross section on the equator	100 m max. variation on the equator (maxima at 160° and 340° E longitude)
Spheroid defined by 4th order spherical harmonic	0 at the equator and pole to –5 m at 45° latitude
Gravitational equipotential surface = *geoid = mean sea level*	+80 m near New Guinea to –100 m in Indian Ocean
Topological surface (i.e., the real surface)	+8.8 km (Mt. Everest) to –0.4 km (Dead Sea)
CO_2 layer in the atmosphere (sensed by horizon sensors)	~+40 km at equator to ~+30 km at pole in winter, depending on how sensed and weather conditions

Because of the Earth's oblateness, different coordinate systems are used for different applications. *Geocentric coordinates* are Earth centered spherical coordinates used for most space applications. They are used for all of the Earth-centered globe plots in this book and are easily transformed into rectangular Cartesian coordinates. The *geocentric latitude* of a point is just the angle between the Earth's equatorial plane and the vector from the center of the Earth to the point. For most mapping applications, the *geodetic* or *geographic latitude* is used. This is the angle between the equatorial plane and the tangent to the oblate reference ellipsoid. The difference between the two definitions of latitude is at most about 0.2 deg.* The maximum amount by which a line normal to the reference ellipsoid misses the center of the Earth is 21 km at a latitude of 45 deg. The transformation between geocentric and geodetic coordinates at satellite altitudes can add significant complexity to computations. This transformation is given in App. E.3.1, along with a discussion of *astronomical coordinates* which follow the Earth's equipotential surface.

Another characteristic of the oblate Earth is a change in the appearance of the Earth as seen from space. This is illustrated in Fig. 9-15 in which the out-of-roundness of the result has been increased by a factor of 100 to make the results visible. **The important point of the figure is that the apparent disk of the oblate Earth is not round and the center of the apparent disk is not in the direction to the center of the Earth.** This means that we must take the oblateness into account whenever we use the disk of the Earth to measure the attitude or position of the spacecraft or to identify locations with respect to the horizon. Using a spherical model can lead to errors on the order of 0.5 deg or larger, depending on the latitude, altitude, and algorithm.

The apparent shape of the oblate Earth is given by:

$$\rho = \cot^{-1}\left\{\left[\frac{\left(r^2 - S^2\right)}{R_E^2}\left(1 + \frac{(2-f)fS^2\cos^2(\lambda)}{(1-f)^2 R_E^2}\sin^2\Psi\right)\right]^{1/2} + \frac{(2-f)fS^2\sin^2(2\lambda)}{2(1-f)^2 R_E^2}\sin\Psi\right\} \tag{9-49}$$

where

$$S \equiv \frac{R_E - (1-f)}{\sqrt{1-(2-f)f\cos^2\lambda}} \tag{9-50}$$

Here ρ is the apparent angular radius of the Earth at azimuth ψ about the geocentric nadir measured from East. As shown in Fig. 9-16, R_E is the Earth's equatorial radius, r is the distance from the observer to the center of the Earth, f is the flattening factor, and λ is the geocentric latitude.

Unfortunately, Eq. (9-49) does not lend itself to easy incorporation in algorithms to process Earth observations. A convenient solution for avoiding this problem was developed by Collins [1992]. The solution is to transform the coordinate frame by expanding it in the polar (z) direction only such that in the expanded frame the Earth

---

* This does not mean that calculations done using geocentric coordinates are in error by 0.2 deg. We can define all of our variables, including locations on the surface of the Earth, in geocentric coordinates, such that the spherical geometry or equivalent Cartesian calculations are exact. However, we need to add another coordinate transformation if we wish to express the results precisely in geodetic coordinates as used, for example, in an atlas.

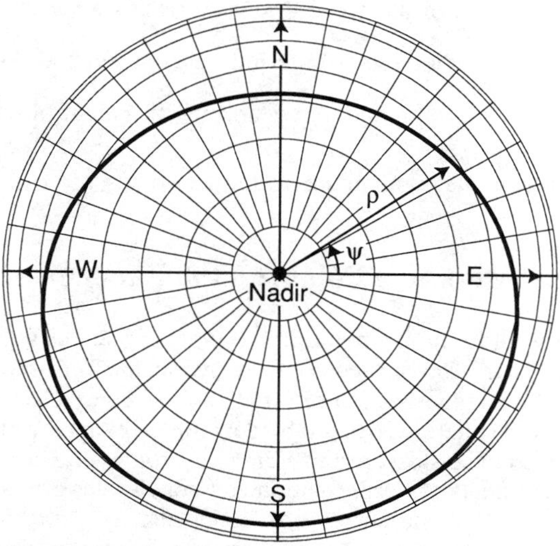

Fig. 9-16. The Shape of the Oblate Earth Seen from Space. The flattening factor used is 100 times the real value to make the effects visible. The shape shown is the disk of the Earth as seen from 200 km over the Earth's surface at 45 deg geocentric latitude.

is perfectly spherical. Horizon crossing vectors are then processed using simple spherical algorithms in the expanded frame. (Tangency is preserved by linear transformations. Thus, "horizon vectors" are still tangent to the surface in both frames.) Finally, the inverse transformation is applied to return to normal Cartesian coordinates for any remaining computations or distribution of results. The expansion transformation along an arbitrary polar axis, $\hat{\mathbf{P}}$, is given by.

$$\mathbf{h}' = \left[I - \left(\frac{f}{1-f} \right) \hat{\mathbf{P}} \otimes \hat{\mathbf{P}} \right] \mathbf{h} \qquad (9\text{-}51)$$

where $\mathbf{h}$ is an arbitrary vector in the original Cartesian space, $\mathbf{h}'$ is the vector in the expanded space, I is the 3 × 3 identify matrix, and ⊗ is the tensor or outer product defined by $\mathbf{u} \otimes \mathbf{v} = M_{ij} = [\mathbf{u}_i \mathbf{v}_j]$. Length is not preserved by the transformation, so $\mathbf{h}'$ is not a unit vector and must be normalized before it can be used. Note that the center of the spacecraft is chosen as the center of the expansion, so that the Earth has been both moved and stretched by the transformation. Consequently, the inverse transformation must be applied before the vector to the center of the Earth or other results can be used for computations. The complete algorithm for processing horizon measurements for an oblate Earth can be summarized as follows:

1. Compute horizon unit vectors in spacecraft body coordinates from sensor data and sensor mounting parameters
2. Determine the Earth polar axis in spacecraft body coordinates
3. Transform the horizon vectors into the stretched coordinate system and renormalize them

4. Compute an estimate of the geocentric vector using a spherical Earth model
5. Transform the geocenter vector back into unstretched coordinates
6. Compute geocentric roll, pitch, or distance to the center of the Earth as needed

For further details on the computation of the geocenter, see Collins [1992].

9.2 Apparent Motion of Points on the Earth Seen from Space

Frequently, we wish to track a point on the ground, such as a ground station, or a target being observed as the spacecraft flies overhead. This section describes the general pattern of the angular motion of points on the Earth as viewed on the spacecraft-centered celestial sphere. We begin by developing exact formulas for the motion of ground targets seen by a spacecraft in a circular orbit over a nonrotating Earth. We will then look at the effects of Earth rotation and noncircular orbits.

In general, targets enter the access area along the forward horizon, move most quickly and furthest from the apparent ground track when they are closest to nadir, and exit across the rearward horizon. As shown in Fig. 9-17, the general shape of the path is a shallow curve approximately parallel to the apparent ground track and bowed out somewhat about nadir. This shape is relatively insensitive to the altitude, although of course the numbers will change. As can be seen by the equal time tick marks along the path, the spacecraft will move slowly near the horizons and much more rapidly as it gets closer to nadir. (The asymmetry about the spacecraft velocity vector in Fig. 9-17B is due to the rotation of the Earth and will be discussed later.)

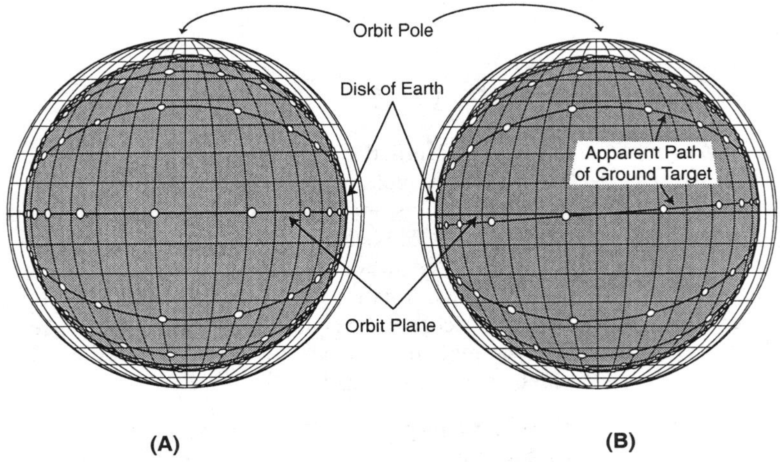

Fig. 9-17. Apparent Motion of Ground Targets as Seen on the Spacecraft-Centered Celestial Sphere. (A) Over a nonrotating Earth. (B) Effect of Earth rotation at the equator for a polar orbit. Tick marks are at 1 min intervals. Spacecraft is in a 700-km circular orbit. The shape of the path is relatively insensitive to the altitude. Ground targets are 5 deg apart on either side of the ground trace.

To calculate the apparent motion, we first look at the geometry of the motion on the surface of the Earth as shown in Fig. 9-18A. Here, β is the target *off ground track angle* which is the angular distance measured perpendicular to the ground track. All points with the same value of β will have the same general motion as seen by the spacecraft (except for the rotational velocity of the Earth, to be discussed shortly). λ_0 is the maximum Earth central angle from the subsatellite point at which the target comes into view. This can be either the true horizon or the effective horizon, depending on the problem being considered. Given β and λ_0, we then compute the other relevant parameters on the Earth for a satellite in a circular orbit as:

$$\sin \Phi_0 = \sin \beta / \sin \lambda_0 \tag{9-52}$$

$$\cos \psi_0 = \cos \lambda_0 / \cos \beta \tag{9-53}$$

$$T = (\psi_0 / 180)/P \tag{9-54}$$

where Φ_0 is the rotation angle about the subsatellite point from the ground track to the target, ψ_0 is the angle along the ground track at which the target first comes into view, P is the period, and T is the total time for which the target will be in view on this satellite pass. Note that in the last equation, ψ_0 is measured in degrees.

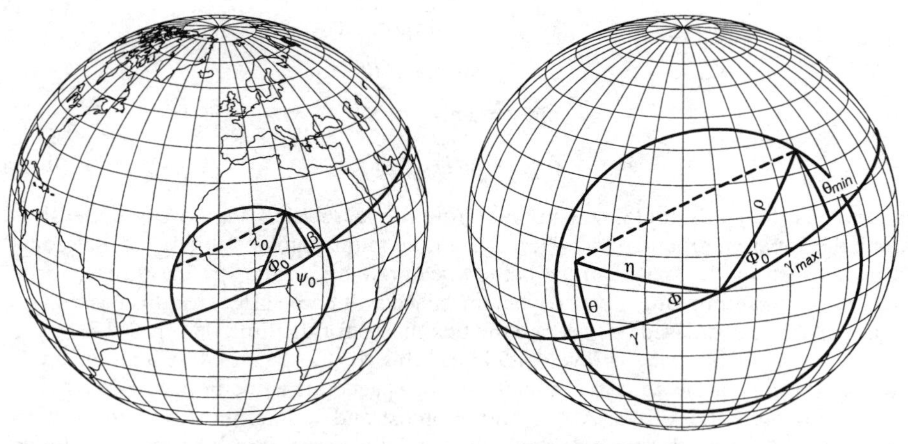

Fig. 9-18. Geometry for Apparent Motion of Targets on the Surface of the Earth. See text for relevant equations.

We then transform these parameters into the values seen on the spacecraft-centered celestial sphere, as shown in Fig. 9-18B, as follows:

$$\begin{aligned}\sin \theta_{min} &= \sin \rho \sin \Phi_0 \\ &= \sin \beta (\sin \rho / \sin \lambda_0)\end{aligned} \tag{9-55}$$

$$\tan \theta_{max} = \frac{\sin \rho \sin \beta}{1 - \sin \rho \cos \beta} \tag{9-56}$$

$$\cos \gamma_{max} = \cos \rho / \cos \theta_{min} \tag{9-57}$$

where θ_{min} and θ_{max} are the minimum and maximum values of the off-ground track angle, ρ is the angular radius of the Earth corresponding to the maximum Earth Central Angle above, and γ_{max} is the distance from nadir measured along the apparent ground track when the spacecraft crosses the horizon. As usual, Φ_0 is the same whether measured on the Earth or on the spacecraft.

We can use a similar process to calculate the entire path which the ground target follows. For the entire pass, the off-ground track angle, β, remains fixed. The motion is then parameterized in terms of ψ, the angle measured along the ground track as the satellite passes overhead. Again, we first compute the Earth Central Angle, λ, and azimuthal angle, Φ, as:

$$\cos \lambda = \cos \beta \cos \psi \tag{9-58}$$

$$\tan \Phi = \tan \beta \sin \psi \tag{9-59}$$

From these, we can then compute the parameters of apparent motion as seen from the spacecraft using the general notation of Fig. 9-18B as follows:

$$\Phi_{Earth} = \Phi_{spc} = \Phi \tag{9-60}$$

$$\tan \eta = \frac{\sin \rho \sin \lambda}{1 - \sin \rho \cos \lambda} \tag{9-61}$$

$$\sin \theta = \sin \eta \sin \Phi \tag{9-62}$$

$$\tan \gamma = \tan \eta \cos \Phi \tag{9-63}$$

$$\dot{\alpha}_{max} = V / D_{min} \tag{9-64}$$

where η is the nadir angle, θ is the off-ground track angle, γ is the angle measured along the apparent ground track, $\dot{\alpha}_{max}$ is the maximum angular velocity for the ground target as seen by the spacecraft, V is the linear velocity of the spacecraft in its orbit, and D_{min} is the minimum distance from the spacecraft to the target for this pass. These equations have been used to generate the tick marks for the time on Fig. 9-17.

In addition to the spacecraft velocity in its orbit, the Earth is rotating underneath the orbit at 450 m/s at the equator. In contrast, the spacecraft velocity in low-Earth orbit is approximately 7,500 m/s. At the northernmost and southernmost extremes of the spacecraft in motion, the ground track will be parallel to the Earth's rotational velocity. In this case, the shape of the curves will be nearly the same as for a nonrotating Earth, but the time in view will be approximately 6% longer because the Earth and spacecraft are moving in the same direction for a prograde orbit. For retrograde orbits, the time in view would be approximately 6% shorter. When the spacecraft is crossing the equator, the angular rotation of the Earth will not change the apparent velocity but will rotate the direction of motion such that the entire pattern of target paths is rotated by as much as 3.5 deg in low-altitude orbits.

As the altitude of the spacecraft increases, the area of the Earth that is seen increases and the spacecraft velocity slows such that the effect of the rotation of the Earth becomes substantially larger. A more detailed analytical discussion is provided in Sec. 9.4. By the time the spacecraft gets to geosynchronous altitudes, the apparent motion of objects on the Earth is dominated entirely by the rotation of the Earth. Here we can use the same formulas above with the motion of the spacecraft replaced by the rotational motion of the Earth.

The apparent motion of objects on the Earth will be substantially more complex for highly elliptical orbits. For orbits of low eccentricity, the effects are relatively minor. At apogee, the Earth's disk is smaller but the linear velocity is slower, such that the angular rates do not change greatly. On the other hand, the area on the ground is much larger than at perigee, so, consequently, the time in view is much longer. This is why satellites at apogee in elliptical orbits are potentially very good for communications as discussed in Secs. 2.5.4 and 12.4. The extrema for the apparent motion at apogee and perigee is very similar to that shown in Fig. 9-17, with the circular velocities replaced by the appropriate velocities for apogee and perigee in the ellipse. These curves are shown in Fig. 9-19 for an orbit with a perigee at 500 km and apogee at 5,000 km.

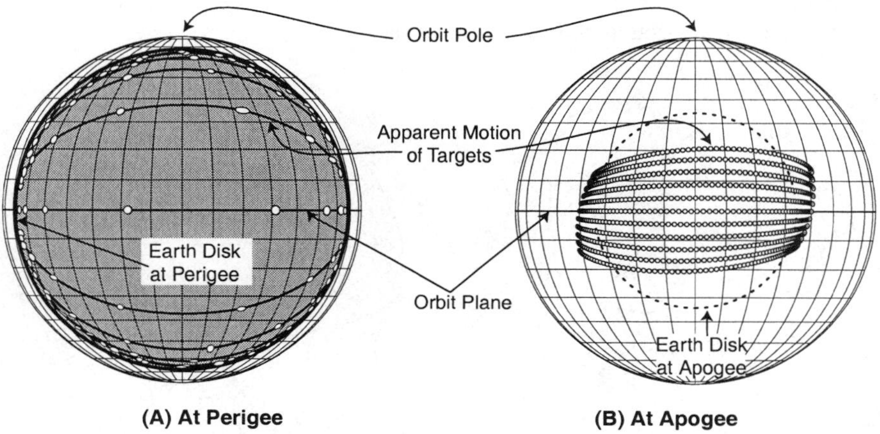

Fig. 9-19. Apparent Motion of Ground Targets as Seen on the Spacecraft-Centered Celestial Sphere for an Elliptical Orbit. (A) At perigee of 500 km, (B) at apogee of 5,000 km. The motion of the target goes beyond the apparent disk of the Earth at apogee because the satellite is no longer near apogee when the ground target crosses the horizon and, at that time, the Earth disk is larger.

9.3 The Satellite Ground Trace

As the spacecraft travels in its orbit, the path of the subsatellite point over the Earth's surface is called the *ground trace* or *ground track*. The *swath* is the area on the surface of the Earth around the ground trace that the satellite can observe as it passes overhead. The *swath width* is the angular width of this region measured from the center of the Earth perpendicular to the ground trace. For orbits which are approximately circular, the ground trace is very nearly the arc of a great circle over a small region. Because of the Earth's rotation, the spacecraft moves over the Earth's surface in a spiral pattern, with the displacement at successive equator crossings proportional to the orbit period. The ground trace and the swath determine the Earth coverage, and therefore are critical parameters in design of any orbit for which coverage is one of the important characteristics. This section examines the ground trace for satellites at various altitudes. The motion of the satellite as seen from the Earth is then covered in Sec. 9.4, and methods for evaluating Earth coverage are discussed in Sec. 9.5.

9.3.1 Circular LEO Orbits

Figure 9-20A shows the ground trace of a satellite in a circular orbit at 1,000 km. Figure 9-20B shows the swath width for the same orbit for elevation angles, ε , of 0 deg and 45 deg. (The swath for an elevation of ε = 90 deg is simply the ground trace of the satellite.) Note that the swath width and, therefore, the coverage is approximately 4 times as great at $\varepsilon = 0$ as at $\varepsilon = 45$ deg. This sensitivity is due to the strong foreshortening near the horizon and makes the minimum working elevation angle, ε, typically the single most important parameter in determining the coverage of a satellite or constellation. For satellites in a circular orbit, the ground trace and the edges of the swath are both dual-axis spirals, so that all of the formalism of Sec. 8.2 can be applied directly to ground traces and swaths. The geometry of the ground trace problem was defined in detail in Sec. 8.3.3. Consequently, this section simply presents the results in a format that can be used directly for ground trace analysis.

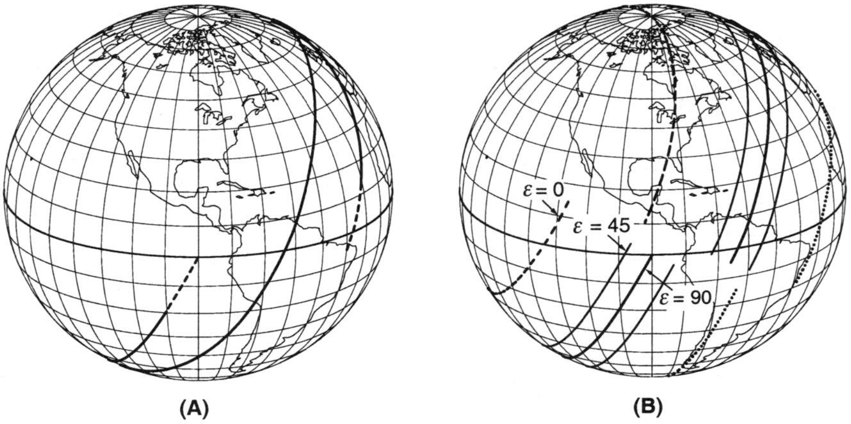

Fig. 9-20. Ground Trace of a Satellite in a Circular Low-Earth Orbit. (A) The ground trace is simply a dual-axis spiral. (B) The swath covers a wide area; however, most of this area will be at a very shallow elevation angle near the horizon. The edges of the swath are also dual-axis spirals.

In order to determine the ground trace, we first determine the angular rate of the satellite moving in its orbit, n, and the angular rate at which the Earth rotates with respect to the orbit plane, ω_R. These are:

$$n = 6 / P \tag{9-65}$$

$$\omega_R = -\omega_{day} - \omega_{J2}$$
$$\approx -0.004\ 178\ 075 - 2.396\ 288 \times 10^9\, a^{-7/2} \cos i \tag{9-66}$$

$$\text{at 1,000 km}\,\omega_{J2} = 0.000\ 069\ 46 \cos i \tag{9-67}$$

where ω_S is in deg/s, P is the orbit period in min, ω_{day} is the sidereal rotation rate of the Earth, and ω_{J2} is the rotation rate of the orbit plane in inertial space caused by the Earth's oblateness. In the approximation in Eq. (9-66), ω_R and ω_{day} are in deg/s, a is the semimajor axis of the orbit in km, and i is the inclination. The parameters for the approximation have been evaluated for a circular Earth orbit. In low-Earth orbit, n is approximately 0.06 deg/s, or $15 \times \omega_{day}$. At 1,000 km, ω_{J2} is less than 2% of the Earth's rotation rate for even low-inclination orbits. This term is often ignored because it is small, but is straightforward to include in most analyses and becomes more important as the altitude of the satellite increases.

From Eqs. (9-65), we determine immediately the expression for the angular distance along the ground track, ϕ_S, measured relative to north:

$$\phi_S = 270 \text{ deg} + \phi_{S_0} + nt \tag{9-68}$$

where ϕ_{S_0} is the angular distance along the ground track measured from the ascending node at time $t = 0$. For an orbit of low eccentricity, we can replace the last two terms in Eq. (9-68) with the sum of the argument of perigee, ω_0, and the true anomaly, ν. Thus, an alternative, more accurate, expression for ϕ_S is:

$$\phi_S = 270 \text{ deg} + \omega_0 + \nu(t) \tag{9-69}$$

Similarly, from Eq. (9-66), we have immediately:

$$\alpha_O = \alpha_{O_0} + \omega_R t \tag{9-70}$$

Here α_O is the longitude of the orbit pole at time, t, and α_{O_0} is the longitude at time $t = 0$. Note that α_O can take on any positive or negative value and is not restricted to the range 0 to 360 deg. The latitude of the orbit pole, δ_O, is fixed and is related to the inclination, i, by

$$\delta_O = 90 \text{ deg} - i \tag{9-71}$$

From the above equations, we can immediately apply the dual-axis spiral equations to determine α, the longitude of the satellite, and δ, the latitude of the satellite at any time. These are:

$$\alpha = (\alpha_O + \Delta\alpha)_{\text{mod } 360} \tag{9-72}$$

$$\delta = 90 \text{ deg} - \text{acos}(\sin i \cos \phi_S) \tag{9-73}$$

$$\Delta\alpha \equiv \text{acos2}\,[-\tan\delta / \tan i, -\text{H}(\phi_S)] \tag{9-74}$$

where again, i is the orbit inclination, and acos2 is the inverse cosine function defined by Eq. (8-1) in Sec. 8-1 (see also Table 8-5). acos2 is a function of two arguments and is conceptually equivalent to the FORTRAN atan2 function, which provides well defined inverse trig functions over the full range of 0 to 360 deg. Thus, α and $\Delta\alpha$ are defined over the range 0 to 360 deg and δ is defined over the range ±90 deg. Note that longitude is measured positive eastward, from 0 to 360 deg, in order to follow the right hand rule.

Figure 9-21 shows a number of successive orbits both at the ascending node and the descending node. The *longitude shift per orbit*, (= the *node spacing* between successive ascending or descending nodes), $\Delta\alpha_{orbit}$, is given by:

$$\Delta\alpha_{orbit} = \omega_R P \tag{9-75}$$

where ω_R is the angular rate at which the Earth rotates with respect to the orbit plane from Eq. (9-66) and P is again the orbit period. Notice from the figure that the spacing between successive orbits along the equator is larger than the spacing between them measured perpendicular to the ground trace because of the inclination of the orbit. If the swaths on two successive orbits overlap at the equator, then a single satellite will provide complete coverage of equatorial latitudes twice per day, once in the general vicinity of the ascending node, and once near the descending node. The minimum swath width, SW, to ensure complete double coverage is given by:

$$\sin(SW/2) = \left|\sin i \sin(\Delta\alpha_{orbit}/2)\right| \tag{9-76}$$

As expected, the minimum required swath width is less than the longitude shift per orbit.

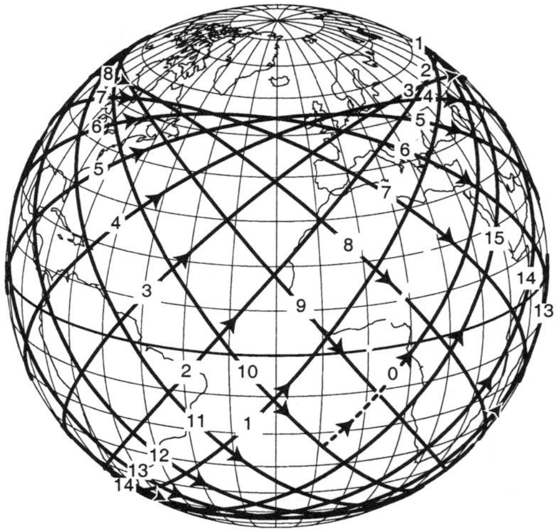

Fig. 9-21. Ground Trace of a Satellite in a Circular Low-Earth Orbit.

The longitude shift per orbit does not depend on what latitude we are at. Consequently, each orbit is continuously shifted from the succeeding orbit by a longitude shift of $\Delta\alpha_{orbit}$. The orbits begin to get closer together at the pole only because the longitude lines themselves get closer together. The spacing in $\Delta long$ remains fixed throughout the orbit.

Next we would like to determine the actual shape of the ground trace at any point and from that, the instantaneous velocity and direction of the ground trace. Recall that the ground trace is produced by having the satellite rotate about the orbit pole while at the same time the orbit pole is rotating about the celestial pole, or the Earth's polar axis. As discussed in Sec. 8.3.3, the combination of these two rotations will leave a single axis instantaneously at rest. This *instantaneous rotation axis*, or *Euler axis*, **E**, will be at the longitude of the orbit pole but a lower latitude. Because this axis is at rest, the satellite must be instantaneously rotating about **E**, as shown in Fig. 8-21 in Sec. 8.3.3. The latitude and longitude of the instantaneous rotation axis are:

$$\alpha_E = \alpha_O \tag{9-77}$$

$$\delta_E = \operatorname{atan}\left(\frac{\omega_R + n\cos i}{n\sin i}\right) \tag{9-78}$$

where all of the variables have been previously defined. The ground trace is swept out by the subsatellite point rotating about the instantaneous rotation axis at a uniform angular rate but at a range which varies with the latitude. Specifically:

$$\omega_E = n\,(\sin i / \cos \delta_E) \tag{9-79}$$

$$\rho_E = \operatorname{acos}(\sin\delta \sin\delta_E + \cos\delta \cos\delta_E \cos\Delta\alpha) \tag{9-80}$$

where ω_E is the angular rate of rotation about the instantaneous rotation axis and ρ_E is the rotation radius for the angle between **E** and the subsatellite point. The formulas for the ground trace for a circular orbit are summarized in Table 8-9 in Sec. 8.3.3.

The above results imply that over a short arc the best approximation to the ground trace will be a small circle of radius ρ_E centered on **E** with the satellite moving along this curve at an angular rate of ω_E. This approximation is illustrated in Fig. 8-21 in Sec. 8.3.3 for altitudes of 500 and 20,000 km, corresponding approximately to a LEO orbit and GPS. Table 8-10 in the same section provides values for the location of **E** and the rotation rate, ω_E, for these two examples. Another characteristic of this same phenomenon is the "apparent inclination" discussed in the boxed example in this section.

Finally, we can use the above equations and the dual-axis spiral logic to determine the angular velocity, n_G, measured along the ground track and the direction, ψ, of the instantaneous velocity measured at the subsatellite point relative to north. These are:

$$n_G = \omega_E \sin \rho_E \tag{9-81}$$

$$\psi = [\Delta\psi - 90\text{ deg}]_{\text{mod } 360} \tag{9-82}$$

$$\Delta\psi = \operatorname{acos2}\left[\frac{\sin\delta_E - \sin\delta\cos\rho_E}{\sin\rho_E\cos\delta},\ \mathrm{H}(\Delta\alpha)\right] \tag{9-83}$$

where again, ψ and $\Delta\psi$ are defined over the range 0 to 360 deg. From Eqs. (9-79) and (9-80), we see that when the satellite is crossing the equator, $\delta = 0$, $\rho_E = 90$ deg and the velocity along the ground trace is just equal to the rotation rate about the instantaneous rotation axis. The minimum ground track velocity occurs as one would expect when a satellite in prograde orbit is moving due East at its most northerly and most southerly altitudes. Thus the maximum and minimum velocities will be:

$$V_{max} = \omega_E \tag{9-84}$$

$$V_{min} = \omega_E \sin(90\text{ deg} + \delta_O - \delta_E) \tag{9-85}$$

Vector Formulation

In a vector formulation, the points along the path are very straightforward to compute. This is done by simply holding the target vector, **T**, fixed, stepping through the series of spacecraft position vectors, **S**, and calculating the sequence of observation vectors, **O**, from:

$$\mathbf{O} = \mathbf{T} - \mathbf{S} \tag{9-86}$$

Unfortunately, the various extrema are inconvenient to compute and are most easily found by simply numerically stepping through the sequence of spacecraft position vectors. Note that the spacecraft will cross the horizon when $\hat{\mathbf{T}} \cdot \hat{\mathbf{S}} < \cos\lambda_0$ and will be closest to nadir when $\mathbf{T} \cdot \mathbf{S}$ is a minimum

---

"Apparent Inclination" Viewed from a Rotating Reference Frame

Viewing an orbit in a frame of reference both inclined and rotating with respect to the orbit causes the apparent orbital inclination to oscillate. Consider a circular low-Earth orbit inclined at exactly 45 deg with respect to the Earth's equator in inertial space as shown in Fig. 9-22. (Assume there are no perturbations, such that the orbit is a perfect circle.) At 45 deg latitude the spacecraft will be going due east and the inclination with respect to the Earth will be 45 deg. However, when the satellite crosses the equator, it will be moving at an angle with respect to the Earth of $i' = \text{atan}\,(V_S \sin i \,/\, (-V_E + V_S \cos i))$, where i is the inertial inclination, V_S is the velocity of the satellite, and V_E is the velocity of the Earth at the equator (and at the altitude of the satellite) due to its rotation in inertial space.

This effect is even more apparent in a polar orbit as shown in Fig. 9-23. Here the orbit goes over the pole, but crosses the equator at an angle distinctly different than 90 deg. In this case, the oscillation in "apparent inclination" can be seen very clearly.

A satellite in a 45 deg inclined circular orbit at 500 km crosses the equator at an angle of 47.80 deg with respect to the Earth. At the same altitude, a satellite in a circular polar orbit (i = 90 deg) crosses the equator at an angle of 93.77 deg. Even the very slow rotation of the orbit due to oblateness (–5.4 deg/day = –0.0038 deg/min for i = 45 deg and 500 km altitude) causes an oscillation in apparent inclination of ±0.04 deg. These variations in angle (and velocity) with respect to the Earth are taken into account exactly by the dual-axis spiral equations (Table 8-8 in Sec. 8.2 or Table 8.9 in Sec. 8.3.3) and also by the Euler axis approximation in Sec. 9.3.1.

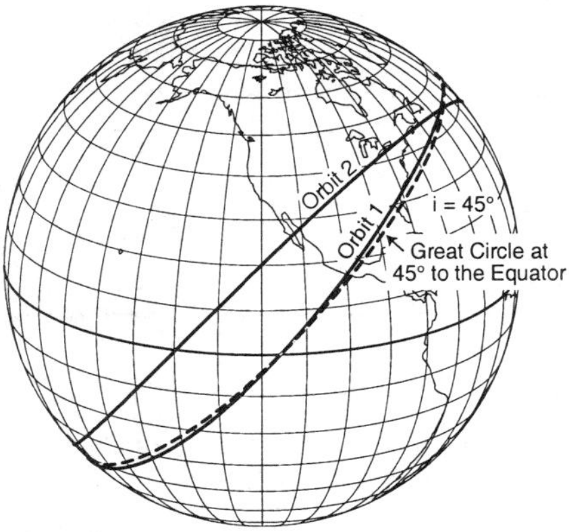

Fig. 9-22. Due to the Earth's Rotation, a Satellite in a 45 deg Inc. Orbit with No Perturbations Crosses the Equator at an Angle less than 45 deg with Respect to the Earth. In inertial space the equator crossings will be exactly 45 deg.

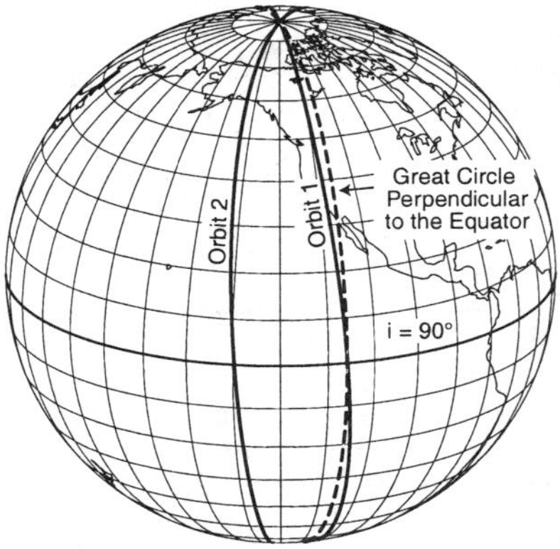

Fig. 9-23. A Polar Orbit at 500 km Crosses the Equator at an Angle of 93.77 deg with Respect to the Earth. Nonetheless, the orbit passes directly over the Pole.

As an example, we compute the parameters for the ground trace of a satellite in a circular orbit at an altitude of 1,000 km and inclination of 45 deg. We assume the satellite is crossing the ascending node at $t = 0$ and at a longitude of 110 deg east. Therefore, the orbit pole will be at 110 – 90 = 20 deg east longitude. We wish to find the position and velocity of the subsatellite point at time $t = 10$ min.

From Eq. (2-4) in Sec. 2.1 (or the tables on the inside rear cover) we determine the period to be 6,307 sec. From Eq. (9-65), we find the angular rate of the satellite in its orbit, $n = 0.0571$ deg/s. The rotation rate of the Earth relative to the orbit plane, from Eq. (9-66), is $\omega_R = -0.00425$ deg/s. From Eq. (9-68), the angular distance along the ground track at $t = 10$ min is 34.25 deg relative to the ascending node and, therefore, $\phi_S = 34.25 + 270 = 304.25$ deg relative to north. From Eqs. (9-70) and (9-71), the longitude of the orbit pole, α_O, is 17.45 deg east and the latitude of the orbit pole is 90 – 45 = 45 deg north. From Eq. (9-73), the satellite latitude at $t = 10$ min is 23.45 deg. The longitude difference from the orbit pole from Eq. (9-74) is $\Delta\alpha = 115.71$ deg. Therefore, from Eq. (9-72), the longitude of the subsatellite point is 17.45 + 115.71 = 133.15 deg East. In the 10 minute period, the satellite has moved 23.45 deg north and 23.15 deg east.

From Eq. (9-75), the longitude shift per orbit is 26.66 deg. This is the same at all latitudes. Eq. (9-76) then implies a swath width, measured perpendicular to the orbit, to insure complete twice per day coverage of 18.77 deg.

To evaluate the velocity and direction of the ground trace and provide good approximations for ground station coverage, we need to determine the parameters of the Euler axis or instantaneous rotation axis for the orbit. From Eq. (9-77), the longitude of the Euler axis is the same as that of the orbit pole, i.e., 17.45 deg east. From Eq. (9-78) the latitude of the Euler axis is 41.84 deg, or 3.16 deg below the orbit pole. The satellite rotates at a uniform rate of 0.0542 deg/s about the Euler axis, as given by Eq. (9-79). However, the radius of rotation, ρ_E, and, therefore, the velocity along the ground trace, vary as the satellite goes along the orbit. From Eqs. (9-80) and (9-81) the angular radius at the time in question is 91.78 deg which implies a rate along the ground track of 0.0604 deg/s, which is 5% slower than the inertial rate of 0.0571 deg/s above. Finally, from Eqs. (9-82) and (9-83), the change in heading is 42.19 deg and the heading, ψ, 42.19 – 90 = –47.81 deg = 312.19 deg relative to north, i.e., 42.19 deg north of east.

In addition, from Eqs. (9-84) and (9-85), we can compute the maximum and minimum ground track velocity as 0.0542 deg/s (the Euler rotation rate) and 0.0541 deg/s, respectively. Thus, while the ground track velocity is not constant, the range is quite small. Note that similar equations would be applicable to satellites in elliptical orbits (with the true anomaly, ν, replacing nt) and to points a fixed distance to the right or left of the ground track. For the later problem we need to return to the generic dual- axis spiral equations in Table 8-8 in Sec. 8.2.

9.3.2 Elliptical Orbits

Conceptually, elliptical orbits follow the same process as circular orbits above, except that the angular rate for the satellite in the orbit plane varies as the satellite moves. Consequently, the numerical details become more complex and most ground trace work is done by simply integrating the equations of motion in a simulator and plotting the results. Nonetheless, substantial analytical and numerical work on ground trace and coverage for satellites in elliptical orbits has been done, particularly by Draim [1991, 1992, 1995, 1998]. A general discussion of the properties and formulas for some of the extrema is given below. Figure 9-24 shows the characteristics for the ground trace of 2 highly elliptical orbits. The swath width corresponding to this ground trace is shown in Fig. 9-25. Recall from Chap. 2 that elliptical orbits used for orbit transfer will have a variety of inclinations, however, elliptical orbits used for planetary observations will nearly always be at the critical inclination of 63.4 deg so that apogee and perigee do not rotate.

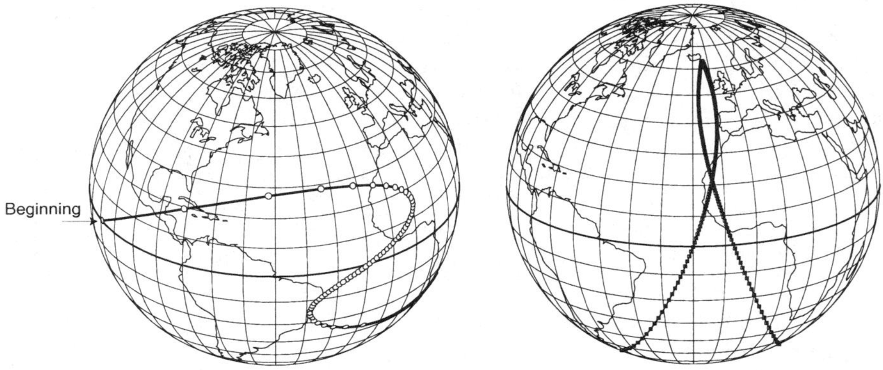

(A) Hohmann Transfer from LEO to GEO **(B) Molniya Communications Orbit**

Fig. 9-24. Ground Trace of an Elliptical Orbit. (A) A Hohmann transfer orbit from LEO to GEO. (B) A Molniya communications orbit.

For a satellite in an elliptical orbit, the motion is still nearly confined to a single plane in inertial space corresponding to a great circle on the celestial sphere. However, the rate of motion within the orbital plane changes substantially with the spacecraft moving most rapidly at perigee and most slowly at apogee. Consequently, the rotation of the Earth under the orbit plane will change along the orbit. If apogee extends all the way to geosynchronous orbit, then at apogee the satellite will be moving more slowly than a satellite in a circular orbit at GEO, and, consequently, more slowly than the rotational velocity of the Earth. In this case, the ground trace of the satellite will make a backward loop as can be seen in Fig. 9-24.

Computations for elliptical orbits are most conveniently done in terms of the *mean motion*, n, which as discussed in Chap. 2, is the average angular velocity of a satellite in its orbit. This is given by:

$$n = \sqrt{\mu / a^3} \approx 36{,}173{,}585\, a^{-3/2} \tag{9-87}$$

$$a = R_\oplus + (H_A + H_P)/2 \tag{9-88}$$

where $\mu \equiv GM$ is the gravitational constant, a is the orbit semimajor axis, $R_\oplus$ is the radius of the Earth, and H_A and H_P are the apogee and perigee heights. In the numerical approximation of Eq. (9-87), n is in deg/s and a is in km. By the conservation of angular momentum, the angular velocity will be inversely proportional to r, the instan-

(A) Hohmann Transfer Orbit.

(B) Molniya Communications Orbit (minimum elevation angle of 45 deg)

(C) Molniya Communications Orbit (minimum elevation angle of 5 deg)

Fig. 9-25. Swath Width for the Plots Shown in Fig. 9-24. (A) Hohmann transfer orbit from LEO to GEO. (B) Molniya communications orbit with minimum elevation angle of 45 deg. (C) Molniya communications orbit with minimum elevation angle of 5 deg. Because of the odd shape of the swath, (B) has been added as an intermediate figure to make (C) more understandable.

taneous distance from the center of the Earth. Thus:

$$\omega_{S,r} = n(a/r) \tag{9-89}$$

The maximum and minimum of the angular velocity will occur at perigee and apogee, respectively, such that:

$$\omega_{Smax} = na \,/\, (\mathrm{R}_{\oplus} + H_P) \tag{9-90}$$

$$\omega_{Smin} = na \,/\, (R_{\oplus} + H_A) \tag{9-91}$$

The angular velocity of the Earth relative to the orbital plane, ω_R, is nearly identical to the value for circular orbits except that we must now take into account the effect of eccentricity on the small oblateness correction, ω_O, thus:

$$\omega_R = \omega_{\oplus} + \omega_O$$

$$\approx -\,0.004\;178\;075 - 2.396\;288 \times 10^9 a^{-7/2}\,(1 - e^2)^{-2}\cos i \tag{9-92}$$

where, again, in the numerical approximation, ω_R and $\omega_{\oplus}$ are in deg/s, a is the semi-major axis in kilometers, e is the eccentricity, and i is the orbit inclination.

Although the angular rates are relatively easy to determine, they are no longer uniform and therefore Eqs. (9-68) through (9-74) of Sec. 9.3.1 no longer apply, and we do not have a simple closed form expression for the ground trace. However, starting at any point in the orbit, the satellite will return to the same latitude after one orbital period and consequently the longitude shift will be the same as for a circular orbit, that is:

$$\Delta\alpha_{orbit} = \omega_R P \tag{9-93}$$

where P is the orbit period. Consequently, each of the successive orbit loops will be nearly identical to the preceding loop, only shifted by a fixed longitude. In addition, if we have N satellites in a given orbit which are uniformly distributed in time (i.e., pass the ascending node at equal time intervals), then each of these satellites will provide a ground trace with the identical shape, shifted in longitude by:

$$\Delta\alpha_{sat} = \Delta\alpha_{orbit} / N \tag{9-94}$$

Note that in this arrangement, satellites will pass over every latitude at equal time intervals of P/N. However, because of the angular rates, the satellites will **not** be equally spaced along the orbit. Each satellite will spend more time at apogee than at perigee so that the density of satellites in a highly elliptical orbit will be much greater in the vicinity of apogee and much smaller in the vicinity of perigee.

The discussion of the instantaneous shape of the orbit in Sec. 9.3.1 remains applicable for elliptical orbits. Consequently, Eqs. (9-77) through (9-83) are still applicable for elliptical orbits with the instantaneous values of the various angular rates being used. Thus we can still model the coverage at any given point by looking at a small circle of radius ρ_S centered on the instantaneous rotation axis and rotating about this axis at an angular velocity of ω_E. Because the inclination remains fixed, the latitude of the orbit pole remains fixed and rotates at a uniform rate about the celestial pole. The instantaneous rotation axis remains on the great circle containing the orbit pole and the celestial pole but is no longer at a fixed latitude because of the variation in angular rates (see Eq. (9-78)). In most operational elliptical orbits, apogee and perigee are aligned at the most northerly and southerly portions of the orbit. In this case, the minimum ground track velocity will occur at apogee, and Eq. (9-85) will be applicable with ω_E evaluated at apogee. The maximum velocity will occur at perigee rather than at the node crossing and can be approximated by Eq. (9-85) with ω_E evaluated at perigee. The actual maximum will be slightly different, since this formula does not account for the varying contribution of the ground trace velocity produced by the Earth's rotation.

9.3.3 Geosynchronous Orbits

As previously described in Sec. 2.5.1, a geosynchronous orbit occurs at an altitude of 35,786 km when the period of the satellite becomes equal to the rotation period of the Earth relative to the fixed stars. This period is called the *sidereal day* and equals 23 hr 56 min 4.09186 sec, give or take a few microseconds. (For a discussion of sidereal time and the changing length of the day due to tidal friction and ice at the Earth's poles, see Sec. 4.1.4.)

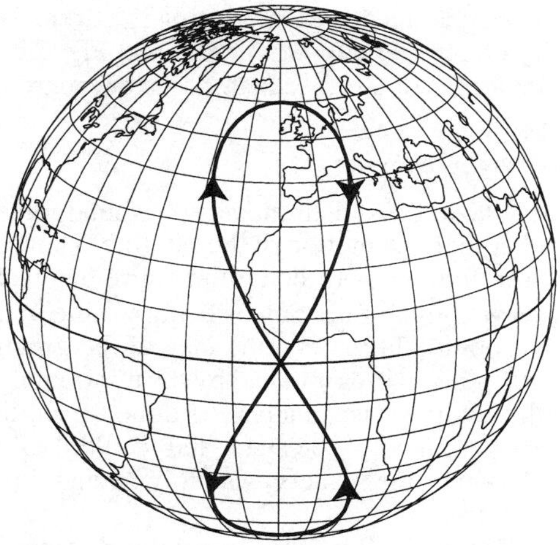

Fig. 9-26. Ground Trace of a Satellite in an Inclined Geosynchronous Orbit.

First, we consider the ground trace of a satellite in a circular inclined geosynchronous orbit, as shown in Fig. 9-26. As in the case of low-Earth orbits, the angular height of the ground trace will be equal to the inclination. However, the longitudinal motion has a very different appearance. Consider the satellite shown in Fig. 9-26, which is inclined at 60 deg, and initially crosses the equator going northward directly over the Greenwich Meridian at 0 deg longitude. Both the satellite and the point on the equator at the Greenwich Meridian are moving at the same angular velocity, however, the point on the equator is moving directly East while the satellite is moving northeast at a 60 deg angle. Consequently, the satellite will fall behind (i.e., westward of) the point on the equator. It will begin to catch up again as it moves northward and the satellite velocity becomes more easterly. At 90 deg from the ascending node, both the satellite and the point on the equator will have rotated 90 deg in inertial space and will again be over each other. However, at this point, the satellite is moving more rapidly in terms of longitude than the point on the equator, because degrees of longitude are shorter at higher latitudes. Consequently, the satellite will move ahead (eastward) of the point on the equator as it begins to move south. The path is symmetric with the northward trip such that the satellite again lies directly over the point on the equator at the descending node. The process then repeats itself in the Southern hemisphere. The net result is called an *analemma*, or figure 8. The mathematical properties of the analemma are described in more detail in the discussion of relative motion of satellites in Sec. 10.1.

Most geosynchronous satellite orbits have inclinations of less than 2 deg. In this case, the analemma of Fig. 9-26 becomes extremely narrow as discussed previously in Sec. 2.5.1. (See Fig. 2-23.) In addition, a non-zero eccentricity causes a once-per-orbit east-west oscillation, but no associated north-south oscillation. In general, the inclination and eccentricity motions will be superimposed on top of each other, resulting in two possible shapes for the geosynchronous satellite ground trace. If the nonzero inclination dominates, then the satellite will appear to move in a very narrow figure 8, as shown in Fig. 2-23A. If the eccentricity effect is larger than the inclination effect in the east-west direction, then the apparent motion will be an oval, as shown in Fig. 2-23B. Because the analemma due to inclination is extremely narrow at low inclinations, the eccentricity effect normally dominates and Fig. 2-23B is the more common shape for the ground trace of a near-equatorial geosynchronous satellite.

9.3.4 Orbits Above Geosynchronous

For orbits at altitudes above geosynchronous, the ground trace is dominated by the rotation of the Earth rather than the motion of the satellite. The region of the Earth that can be seen comes closer and closer to being the entire hemisphere centered on the subsatellite point, just as we think of the Sun as being visible in the entire hemisphere centered on the subsolar point. Ultimately, the idea of the ground trace of a satellite becomes no longer useful, since it is dominated by the rotation of the Earth, rather than the motion of the satellite. In this case, analysis is done by plotting the motion of the satellite relative to the background of the stars, and we think of the satellite much as we would think of the Moon or the planets as simply being objects that move among the background of fixed stars.

Even the language changes for satellites at a long distance from the Earth. For spacecraft in low-Earth orbit, we talk about ground station passes and targets coming into view. For the Moon or Venus or interplanetary spacecraft, we talk about rising and setting times each day, and how long the object will be *up*, i.e., high enough above the horizon to be conveniently visible. All of these parameters will be discussed in Sec. 9.4.4.

Figure 9-27 shows the ground trace of a satellite at twice the geosynchronous altitude and one at ten times the geosynchronous altitude. Here we can see that the ground trace plot is rapidly becoming of less utility and it is convenient to look at other alternatives for examining the motion of satellites.

9.4 Motion of a Satellite as Seen from Earth —Computing Parameters for Single Target or Ground Station Pass

The satellite ground trace represents the path of the subsatellite point across the surface of the Earth. In this section, we are interested in a related question—what is the motion of the satellite as seen from the point of view of an observer on the Earth?

We define a *target* is an object on or near the Earth's surface that we wish to observe or track. A *ground station* is an antenna fixed on the Earth with which we wish to communicate. However, for purposes of the relative geometry and motion there is essentially no distinction between them and we will use the two terms interchangeably throughout this section. Overall, it makes very little difference whether the target is stationary or moving over the surface of the Earth, such as airplanes flying in and out of a busy airport. The satellite velocity is far greater than any Earth targets, such that

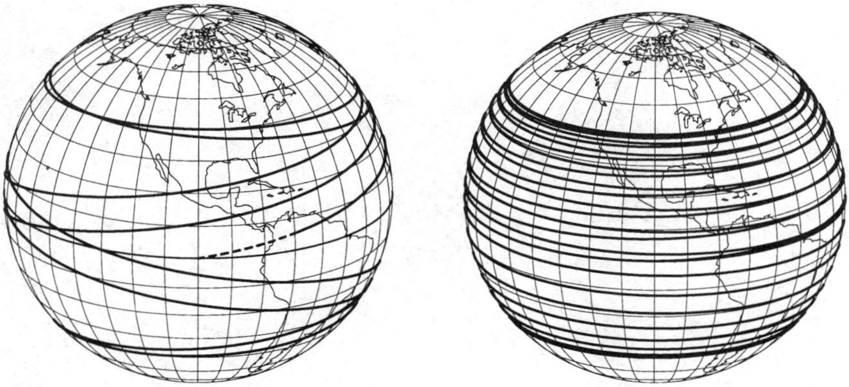

(A) At 2x GEO Altitude (B) At 10× GEO Altitude

Fig. 9-27. Ground Trace of a Satellite Above Geosynchronous Orbit. (A) At twice GEO. (B) At 10 times GEO. At high altitudes the ground trace plot rapidly becomes dominated by the rotation of the Earth, and therefore is no longer of much use. In addition, most satellites above GEO are in interplanetary orbits where the ground trace is essentially useless.

nearly all targets are essentially stationary in terms of coverage analysis as seen from spacecraft. (We can pick out moving targets using Doppler radar but they do not move very far in the time that the satellite is observing them.) The only realistic exception is rocket launches, which, of course, approach orbital velocities.

9.4.1 Circular LEO Orbits

This section looks at the characteristics of a ground station pass for a satellite in low-Earth orbit. We begin by looking at the qualitative characteristics of this pass and then compute the relevant parameters for the pass based on the assumption that the ground trace is a great circle arc. Finally, we compute the ground station parameters using the substantially more accurate approximation of the ground trace as a small circle centered on the instantaneous rotation axis.

Figure 9-28A shows the geometry of a ground station pass as seen on the surface of the Earth. Three representative orbit passes are drawn, one which passes directly overhead, one which passes within 5 deg of the ground station, and one which passes within 15 deg of the ground station. The appearance of these three orbits on the ground station-centered celestial sphere is shown in Fig. 9-28B. The general parameters for the shape of this orbit were defined in Sec. 6.3.4. The satellite which passes directly over the station will travel along a great circle arc which passes through the zenith. The others will have the appearance of an orbit viewed from nearby with the parameters as defined in Sec. 6.3.4. Although the satellite moves uniformly along the orbit path in Fig. 9-28A, it does not move uniformly across the sky as seen from the ground station (Fig. 9-28B). Generally, the spacecraft will appear to travel slowly when it is near the horizon due to both the greater distance and the substantial foreshortening. It will move most rapidly in apparent angular velocity as it passes the point nearest the ground station. It then repeats the process in a symmetric fashion and leaves slowly over the "forward horizon" (i.e., in the direction the satellite is moving).

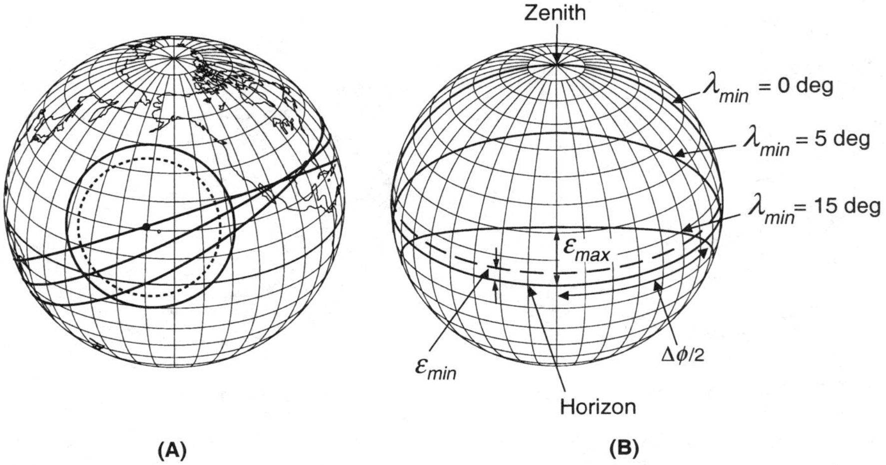

Fig. 9-28. Apparent Motion as Seen From the Earth of a Satellite in 1,000 km Circular Orbit. (A) Geometry on the Earth's surface. (B) Geometry on the ground station-centered celestial sphere.

Because the apparent satellite path is not a simple geometrical figure, it is best computed using a simulation program. A variety of commercial tools are available to do this. These programs also work with elliptical orbits so they are convenient, along with the appropriate formulas from this chapter, for evaluating specific orbit geometry. Unfortunately, a simulation does not provide the desired physical insight into the apparent motion of satellites, nor does it provide a rapid method for evaluating geometry in the general case, as is most appropriate when first designing a mission or trying to determine the most common parameters for a ground station pass. For these problems, we are interested in bounding or approximating the apparent motion rather than in computing the detailed path precisely.

Throughout this section, we will use the notation adopted in Sec. 9.1, and used in Fig. 9-29, which shows the geometry of a ground station pass where we have approximated the ground trace by a great circle centered on the orbit pole. (Later in this section, we will correct that approximation by shifting to a ground trace centered on the instantaneous rotation axis.) The small circle centered on the ground station represents the subsatellite points at which the spacecraft elevation, ε, seen by the ground station is greater than some minimum ε_{min}. The nature of the communication or observation will determine the value of ε_{min}. For ground station communications, the satellite typically must be more than 5 deg above the horizon, so ε_{min} = 5 deg. The size of this circle of accessibility strongly depends on the value of ε_{min}, as emphasized in the discussion of Fig. 9-6. In Fig. 9-29 we have assumed a satellite altitude of 1,000 km. The dashed circle surrounding the ground station is at ε = 0 deg (that is, the satellite's true outer horizon), and the solid circle represents ε_{min} = 5 deg. In practice we often select a specific value of ε_{min} and use that number for the entire analysis. However, you should remain aware that many of the computed parameters are extremely sensitive to this value.

Given a value of ε_{min}, we can define the *maximum Earth Central Angle*, λ_{max}, the *maximum nadir angle*, η_{max}, measured at the satellite from nadir to the ground station,

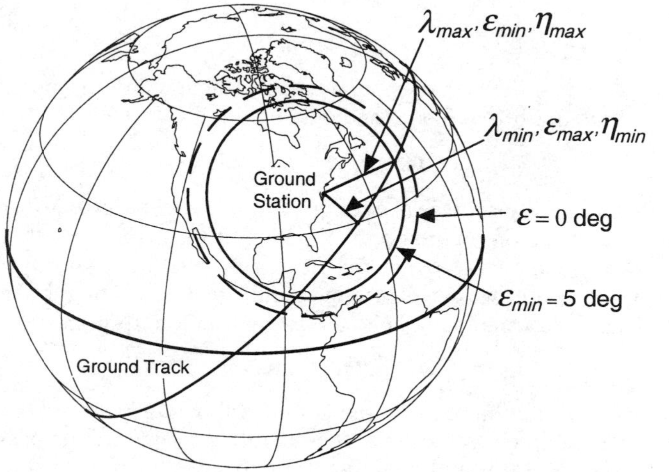

Fig. 9-29. Geometry of Satellite Ground Track Relative to an Observer on the Earth.

and the *maximum range*, D_{max}, at which the satellite will still be in view. These parameters, as determined by applying Eqs. (9-4) to (9-7), are given by:

$$\sin \eta_{max} = \sin \rho \cos \varepsilon_{min} \tag{9-95}$$

$$\lambda_{max} = 90 \text{ deg} - \varepsilon_{min} - \eta_{max} \tag{9-96}$$

$$D_{max} = R_{\oplus} \frac{\sin \lambda_{max}}{\sin \eta_{max}} \tag{9-97}$$

where ρ is the angular radius of the Earth as seen from the satellite; that is, $\sin \rho = R_{\oplus}/(R_{\oplus} + H)$. We will call the small circle of radius λ_{max} centered on the target the *effective horizon*, corresponding in our example to $\varepsilon_{min} = 5$ deg, to distinguish it from the *true* or *geometrical horizon* for which $\varepsilon = 0$ deg. Whenever the subsatellite point lies within the effective horizon around the target or ground station, then communications or observations will be possible. The duration, T, of this contact and the maximum elevation angle, ε_{max}, of the satellite will depend on how close the ground station is to the satellite's ground track on any given pass.

As described in Chap. 2, the plane of a spacecraft's orbit and, therefore, the ground track, is normally defined by the inclination, i, and either the right ascension, Ω, or longitude, L_{node}, of the ascending node. Except for orbit perturbations, Ω, which is defined relative to the stars, remains fixed in inertial space while the Earth rotates under the orbit. On the other hand, L_{node} is defined relative to the Earth's surface and, therefore, increases by 360 deg in 1,436 min, which is the rotation period of the Earth relative to the stars. (Recall that orbit perturbations affect the exact rotation rate of the node.) Because of this orbit rotation relative to the Earth, it is convenient to speak of the *instantaneous ascending node* which is L_{node} evaluated at the time of an observation or passage over a ground station. For purposes of geometry it is also often appropriate to work in terms of the *instantaneous orbit pole*, or the pole of the orbit plane at the time of the observation. The coordinates of this pole are:

$$lat_{pole} = 90 \text{ deg} - i \tag{9-98}$$

$$long_{pole} = L_{node} - 90 \text{ deg} \tag{9-99}$$

A satellite will pass directly over a target or ground station (represented by the subscript *gs*) on the Earth's surface if and only if:

$$\sin\,(long_{gs} - L_{node}) = \tan lat_{gs} \,/\, \tan i \tag{9-100}$$

There are two valid solutions to the above equation, corresponding to the satellite passing over the ground station on the northbound leg of the orbit or on the southbound leg. To determine when after crossing the equator the satellite passes over the ground station for a circular orbit, we can determine μ, the arc length along the instantaneous ground track from the ascending node to the ground station, from:

$$\sin\mu = \sin lat_{gs} / \sin i \tag{9-101}$$

Again, the two valid solutions correspond to the northbound and southbound passes.

Figure 9-29 defines the parameters of the satellite's ground station pass in terms of λ_{min}, the minimum Earth central angle between the satellite's ground track and the ground station. This will be 90 deg minus the angular distance measured at the center of the Earth from the ground station to the instantaneous orbit pole at the time of contact. If we know the latitude and longitude of the orbit pole and ground station (*gs*), then the value of λ_{min} will be given by:

$$\sin\lambda_{min} = \sin lat_{pole} \sin lat_{gs} + \cos lat_{pole} \cos lat_{gs} \cos\,(\Delta long) \tag{9-102}$$

where $\Delta long$ is the longitude difference between *gs* and the orbit pole. At the point of closest approach, we can compute the minimum nadir angle, η_{min}, maximum elevation angle, ε_{max}, and minimum range, D_{min} as:

$$\tan\eta_{min} = \frac{\sin\rho \sin\lambda_{min}}{1 - \sin\rho\cos\lambda_{min}} \tag{9-103}$$

$$\varepsilon_{max} = 90 \text{ deg} - \lambda_{min} - \eta_{min} \tag{9-104}$$

$$D_{min} = R_{\oplus}\left(\frac{\sin\lambda_{min}}{\sin\eta_{min}}\right) \tag{9-105}$$

At the point of closest approach, the satellite will be moving perpendicular to the line of sight to the ground station. Thus, the *maximum angular rate* of the satellite as seen from the ground station, $\dot{\theta}_{max}$, will be:

$$\dot{\theta}_{max} = \frac{V_{sat}}{D_{min}} = \frac{2\pi\left(R_{\oplus} + H\right)}{PD_{min}} \tag{9-106}$$

where V_{sat} is the orbital velocity of the satellite, and *P* is the orbit period.

Finally, it is convenient to compute the *total azimuth range*, $\Delta\phi$, which the satellite covers as seen by the ground station, the *total time in view*, *T*, and the azimuth, ϕ_{center}, at the center of the viewing arc where the elevation angle is a maximum:

$$\cos\frac{\Delta\phi}{2} = \frac{\tan\lambda_{min}}{\tan\lambda_{max}} \tag{9-107}$$

$$T = \left(\frac{P}{180\text{ deg}}\right) \operatorname{acos}\left(\frac{\cos \lambda_{max}}{\cos \lambda_{min}}\right) \tag{9-108}$$

where the arc cos is in degrees. ϕ_{center} is related to ϕ_{pole}, the azimuth to the direction of the projection of the orbit pole onto the ground, by

$$\phi_{center} = 180\text{ deg} - \phi_{pole} \tag{9-109}$$

$$\cos \phi_{pole} = (\sin lat_{pole} - \sin \lambda_{min} \sin lat_{gs}) / (\cos \lambda_{min} \cos lat_{gs}) \tag{9-110}$$

where $\phi_{pole} < 180$ deg if the orbit pole is east of the ground station and $\phi_{pole} > 180$ deg if the orbit pole is west of the ground station.

Table 9-4 summarizes the computations for ground station coverage and provides a worked example. As indicated above, T is particularly sensitive to ε_{min}. If we assume a mountain-top ground station with $\varepsilon_{min} = 2$ deg, then the time in view for the example increases by 15% to 14.27 min.

Thus far, we have ignored the impact of the rotation of the Earth on ground station coverage. While this is a reasonable simplification for some cases, the assumption becomes less valid as the altitude of the satellite becomes higher. In addition, the rotating Earth under the satellite changes not only the velocity of the satellite but also its direction of motion, as explained in detail in the boxed example at the end of Sec. 9.3.1. In addition, the dual-axis spiral formulation developed in Chap. 8 and further in Sec. 9.3.1 provides the mechanism to readily take this rotation into account. The geometry of doing so is shown in Fig. 9-30. Fundamentally, we want to replace the great circle centered on the orbit pole with a small circle of appropriate radius centered on the instantaneous rotation axis. This will correctly model the direction, the velocity and the curvature of the orbit as it passes the ground station.

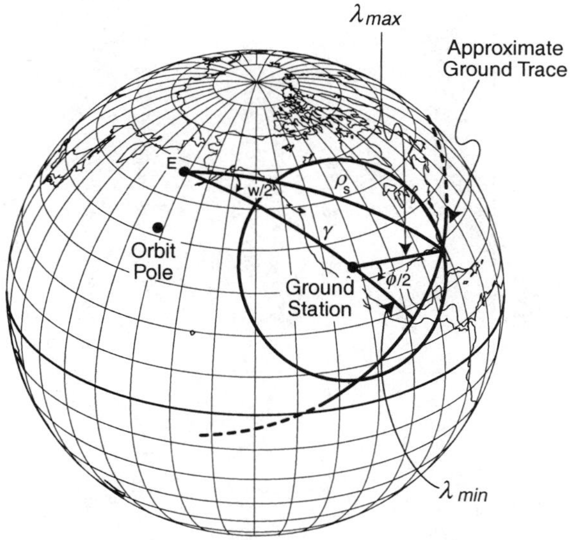

Fig. 9-30. Geometry for Using the Instantaneous Rotation Axis to Compute Ground Station Parameters.

TABLE 9-4. Summary of Computations for Ground Station Passes for LEO Circular Orbits. Example computations are based on the following: Circular orbit at H = 1,500 km, i = 50 deg, orbit pole at 40 deg N, 230 deg E, ground station in Phoenix at 33.5 deg N, 248 deg E, and minimum allowable elevation angle ε_{min} = 5 deg. "same" indicates that either the formula or value listed is the same for both approximations. See Fig. 9-21 in Sec. 9.3.1 for comparison of curves.

Parameter	"Nonrotating Earth"			"Rotating Earth"		
	Formula	Eq. No.	Example	Formula	Eq. No.	Example
Approximation	Great circle centered on instantaneous orbit pole			Small circle centered on instantaneous rotation axis		
Accuracy	Evaluation point only			Point plus 1st and 2nd derivatives of path and velocity		
Earth angular radius, ρ	$\sin\rho = R_\oplus / (R_\oplus + H)$	9-2	59.8 deg	same		same
Period, P	$P = 1.658\,669 \times 10^{-4} \times (6378.14 + H)^{3/2}$	2-4b	105 min	same		same
Max nadir angle, η_{max}	$\sin\eta_{max} = \sin\rho\cos\varepsilon_{min}$	9-5	59.4 deg	same		same
Max Earth central angle, λ_{max}	$\lambda_{max} = 90\text{ deg} - \varepsilon_{min} - \eta_{max}$	9-96	25.6 deg	same		same
Max distance, D_{max}	$D_{max} = R_\oplus(\sin\lambda_{max} / \sin\eta_{max})$	9-97	3,194 km	same		same
Min Earth central angle, λ_{min}	$\sin\lambda_{min} = \sin lat_{pole}\sin lat_{gs} + \cos lat_{pole}\cos lat_{gs}\cos(\Delta\text{long})$	9-102	15.4 deg	$\lambda_{min} = \lvert\rho_S - \gamma\rvert$	9-112	17.0 deg
Min nadir angle, η_{min}	$\tan\eta_{min} = (\sin\rho\sin\lambda_{min})/(1 - \sin\rho\cos\lambda_{min})$	9-103	54.1 deg	same		55.5 deg
Max elevation angle, ε_{max}	$\varepsilon_{max} = 90\text{ deg} - \lambda_{min} - \eta_{min}$	9-104	20.5 deg	same		17.5 deg
Min distance, D_{min}	$D_{min} = R_\oplus(\sin\lambda_{min} / \sin\eta_{min})$	9-105	2,095 km	same		2,258 km
Max angular rate, $\dot\theta_{max}$	$\dot\theta_{max} = [(360\text{ deg}(R_\oplus + H)] / (P\,D_{min})$	9-106	12.1 deg/min	$\dot\theta_{max} = [(2\pi\,(R_\oplus + H)] / (P\,D_{min})$		11.2 deg/min
Azimuth range, $\Delta\phi$	$\cos(\Delta\phi/2) = (\tan\lambda_{min} / \tan\lambda_{max})$	9-107	109.5 deg	$\cos(\Delta\phi/2) = \dfrac{\cos\gamma\cos\lambda_{max} - \cos\rho_s}{\sin\gamma\sin\lambda_{max}}$	9-113	100.7 deg
Azimuth of center of pass, ϕ_{center}	$\cos\phi_{center} = \dfrac{\sin\lambda_{min}\sin lat_{gs} - \sin lat_{pole}}{\cos\lambda_{min}\cos lat_{gs}}$	9-109	128.1 deg	same Eq. substituting $\sin lat_E$ for $\sin lat_{pole}$		130.8 deg
Time in view, T	$T = (P / 180\text{ deg})\,\text{acos}(\cos\lambda_{max} / \cos\lambda_{min})$	9-108	12.05 min	$T = W / (60 \cdot \omega_E)$ $\cos(W/2) = \dfrac{\cos\lambda_{max} - \cos\rho_s\cos\gamma}{\sin\rho_s\sin\gamma}$	9-112	10.09 min

We begin by noting that the instantaneous rotation axis or Euler axis lies on the great circle containing the orbit pole and the Earth's pole, with a latitude given by Eq. (9-78). There is a potential complication here in that the instantaneous rotation axis should be evaluated at the time when the satellite passes at the minimum distance from the ground station. Since we cannot compute this time precisely, we would in principle be left to an iterative process to determine the right time to evaluate both the orbit pole for the previous calculation and the instantaneous rotation axis for this calculation. However, the orbit pole and the instantaneous rotation axis are rotating about the Earth's pole at a rate of approximately 0.004 deg/s as defined by Eq. (9-66). Consequently, providing the correct time to evaluate the position of the rotation axes to within even a few minutes is sufficiently accurate for most analysis purposes.

Having determined the position of the pole, we now use Eqs. (9-79) and (9-80) to determine the angular rotation rate about the instantaneous rotation axis, E, and the arc length distance, ρ_S, from E to the subsatellite point, ρ_S. We then use the standard formula for arc lengths on the surface of the Earth to determine γ, the distance from the instantaneous rotation axis to the ground station:

$$\cos\gamma = \sin\delta_E \sin\delta_{gs} + \cos\delta_E \cos\delta_{gs} \cos(\alpha_E - \alpha_{gs}) \tag{9-111}$$

where as usual, α and δ are the longitude and latitude of the instantaneous rotation axis and the ground station. Having computed ρ_S and γ, the off ground track angle, or minimum Earth central angle, λ_{min}, is given by:

$$\lambda_{min} = |\rho_S - \gamma| \tag{9-112}$$

as can be seen from Fig. 9-30. Also from the figure, we can immediately determine both the azimuth range as seen from the ground station, $\Delta\phi$, and the arc through which the satellite moves, W, as measured about the instantaneous rotation axis. By the definition of the rotation rate about E, this lets us determine immediately the time in view, T. Specifically:

$$T = W/\omega_E \tag{9-113a}$$

where:

$$\cos(W/2) = \frac{\cos\lambda_{max} - \cos\rho_s \cos\gamma}{\sin\rho_s \sin\gamma} \tag{9-113b}$$

and

$$\cos(\Delta\phi/2) = \frac{\cos\lambda_{max} - \cos\gamma \cos\rho_s}{\sin\lambda_{max} \sin\gamma} \tag{9-114}$$

These equations allow us to obtain a substantially more precise yet still analytic estimate of the ground station pass parameters. The revised equations and an example of their application are provided in Table 9-4. The resulting patterns are shown in Fig. 9-21 in Sec. 9.3.1. It is important to recognize the basis for this revised formulation. Previously we represented the ground track by a great arc through the subsatellite point, but not quite tangent to the actual ground track. We are now representing it by a small circle which is both tangent to and has the same curvature as the real dual-axis spiral ground track.

9.4.2 Elliptical Orbits

The computation of viewing parameters for satellites in elliptical orbits are conceptually similar but computationally more complex than for circular orbits. At perigee, the access area is small, and the satellite is moving rapidly. At apogee, the access area is large, and the satellite moves more slowly. Consequently, substantially larger areas of the Earth will see the satellite at apogee for longer periods of time. Figure 9-31 shows the apparent motion as seen from the Earth for a spacecraft in a geosynchronous transfer orbit. The parameters for any specific ground station pass will be typically done by simulation because of the complexity of the analytic formulation. However, we can apply the elliptical orbit parameters defined in Sec. 9.3.2 and the coverage equations from Table 9-4 to compute the extrema at apogee and perigee and also representative parameters for other ground station passes for which the parameters are known. These computations using the previous equations are shown in Table 9-5 for a satellite in a Molniya communications orbit and ground station passes at apogee, at perigee, and when the satellite crosses the equator.

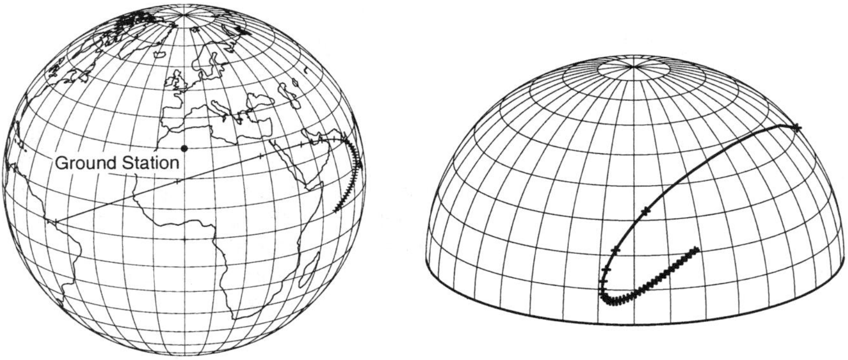

(A) On the Earth's Surface **(B) On the Ground Station Celestial Sphere**

Fig. 9-31. Apparent Motion of a Satellite in a 200 km × 26,000 km GEO Transfer Orbit.

9.4.3 Geosynchronous Orbits

Spacecraft in a near equatorial geosynchronous orbit remain approximately fixed with respect to an observer on the surface of the Earth. Consequently, our question of "motion as seen from the surface of the Earth" reduces simply to "Where are they in the sky?" The formulas for computing the appearance of any orbit as seen from nearby were given in Sec. 6.3.4, which allows us to determine the shape of the geostationary ring as seen from the surface of the Earth. In addition, Sec. 9.3.3 defined the relatively small motion of the satellite ground trace for a satellite at GEO due to both the inclination and eccentricity of the satellite's orbit. It remains to combine these to determine the shape and position of the orbit as seen by an observer on the Earth's surface.

In Sec. 6.3.4, it was determined that if the orbit is viewed from near the center, the shape of the apparent orbit can be approximated by a small circle of radius $(b_a + b_b)/2$ centered at the point $(b_b - b_a)/2$ below nadir on the great circle joining the orbit pole, nadir, and the point on the orbit nearest the observer. For example, consider the shape

TABLE 9-5. Summary of Computations for Ground Station Passes for Elliptical Orbits. "At Perigee" refers to a ground station pass centered on perigee and uses the subscript P. "At Apogee" refers to a ground station pass centered on apogee and uses the subscript A. Because of the large arc at apogee that can see the ground, the time in view computation there is valid only for small eccentricities. Sample calculations are based on a satellite in an elliptical orbit at 63.4 deg inclination, 500 km perigee, and 40,000 km apogee. The orbit pole is assumed to be at 26.6 deg N, 150.0 deg E. The ground station is at 33.5 deg N, 248.0 deg E. All formulas are based on the "non-rotating Earth" approximation of Table 9-4.

	At Perigee			At Apogee		
Parameter	**Formula**	**Eq.**	**Example**	**Formula**	**Eq.**	**Example**
Earth angular radius, ρ	$\sin\rho_{max} = R_\oplus/(R_\oplus + H_P)$	9-2	68.0 deg	$\sin\rho_{min} = R_\oplus/(R_\oplus + H_A)$	9-2	7.90 deg
Semimajor axis, a	$a = R_\oplus (H_A + H_P)/2$	2-10	26,628 km	same		same
Period, P	$P = 1.658\,669 \times 10^{-4}\ a^{3/2}$	2-4b	721 min	same		same
Mean motion, n	$n = (180/\pi)\sqrt{\mu/a^3}$	2-17	0.008 32 deg/s	same		same
Orbital angular velocity, ω	$\omega_{max} = na/(R_\oplus + H_P)$	9-89	0.032 2 deg/s	$\omega_{min} = na/(R_\oplus + H_A)$	9-90	0.004 78 deg/s
Max nadir angle, η_{max}	$\sin\eta_{maxP} = \sin\rho_{max}\cos\varepsilon_{min}$	9-5	67.5 deg	$\sin\eta_{maxA} = \sin\rho_{min}\cos\varepsilon_{min}$	9-5	7.87 deg
Max Earth central angle, λ_{max}	$\lambda_{maxP} = 90\text{ deg} - \varepsilon_{min} - \eta_{maxP}$	9-96	17.5 deg	$\lambda_{maxA} = 90\text{ deg} - \varepsilon_{min} - \eta_{maxA}$	9-95	77.1 deg
Max distance, D_{max}	$D_{maxP} = R_\oplus(\sin\lambda_{maxP}/\sin\eta_{maxP})$	9-97	2,078 km	$D_{maxA} = R_\oplus(\sin\lambda_{maxA}/\sin\eta_{maxA})$	9-96	45,385 km
Min Earth central angle, λ_{min}	$\sin\lambda_{min} = \sin lat_{pole}\sin lat_{gs} + \cos lat_{pole}\cos lat_{gs}\cos(\Delta\text{long})$	9-102	8.2 deg	same		same
Min nadir angle, η_{min}	$\tan\eta_{minP} = \dfrac{(\sin\rho_{max}\sin\lambda_{min})}{(1-\sin\rho_{max}\cos\lambda_{min})}$	9-103	58.2 deg	$\tan\eta_{minA} = \dfrac{(\sin\rho_{min}\sin\lambda_{min})}{(1-\sin\rho_{min}\cos\lambda_{min})}$	9-102	1.3 deg
Max elevation angle, ε_{max}	$\varepsilon_{maxP} = 90\text{ deg} - \lambda_{min} - \eta_{minP}$	9-104	23.5 deg	$\varepsilon_{maxA} = 90\text{ deg} - \lambda_{min} - \eta_{minA}$	9-103	80.5 deg
Min distance, D_{min}	$D_{minP} = R_\oplus(\sin\lambda_{min}/\sin\eta_{minP})$	9-105	1,075 km	$D_{minA} = R_\oplus(\sin\lambda_{min}/\sin\eta_{minA})$	9-104	40,076 km
Max angular rate, $\dot\theta_{max}$	$\dot\theta_{maxP} = \omega_{max}(H_P + R_\oplus)/D_{minP}$	9-105	0.206 deg/s	$\dot\theta_{maxA} = \omega_{min}(H_A + R_\oplus)/D_{minA}$	9-105	0.005 53 deg/s
Azimuth range, $\Delta\phi$	$\cos(D\phi_P/2) = (\tan\lambda_{min}/\tan\lambda_{maxP})$	9-106	125.4 deg	$\cos(\Delta\phi_A/2) = (\tan\lambda_{min}/\tan\lambda_{maxA})$	9-106	176.2 deg
Azimuth of center of pass, ϕ_{center}	$\cos\phi_{center} = \dfrac{\sin\lambda_{min}\sin lat_{gs} - \sin lat_{pole}}{\cos\lambda_{min}\cos lat_{gs}}$	9-108	116.5 deg	same	9-108	same
Time in view, T	$T_P = (1/\omega_{max})\,\text{acos}(\cos\lambda_{maxP}/\cos\lambda_{min})$	9-107	481 sec.	$T_A = (1/\omega_{min})\,\text{acos}(\cos\lambda_{maxA}/\cos\lambda_{min})$	9-107*	N/A*

* At apogee, the approximation given is valid only for low eccentricities.

of the geosynchronous orbit ring as viewed from a point on the surface of the Earth at 40 deg N latitude (i = 40 deg). Here D = 6,378 km and R = 6,378 + 35,786 = 42,164 km. From Eqs. (6-19) and (6-20), we find b_a = 35.02 deg and b_b = 133.72 deg. Consequently, the apparent orbit will be approximately a small circle with a radius of 84.37 deg centered at 49.35 deg below nadir. This puts the center of the apparent orbit (90 – 40 – 49.35) = 0.65 deg from the South celestial pole which is the orbit pole for geosynchronous orbit. This geometry is shown in Fig. 9-32.

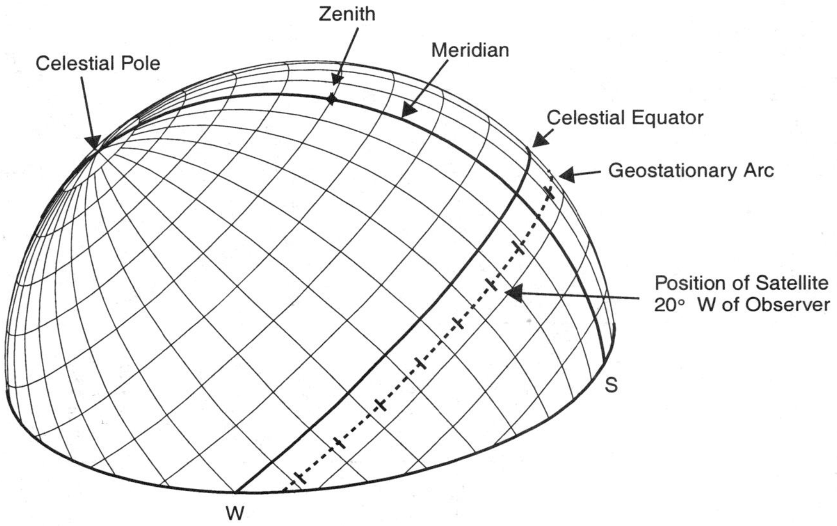

Fig. 9-32. Geosynchronous Orbit Viewed from 40 deg North Latitude. The shape is approximately a small circle of 84.37 deg radius centered 0.65 deg from the celestial pole. Tick marks represent steps of 10 deg in longitude difference between the observer and points along the orbit. (Note spacing between tick marks compared to 10 deg longitude lines in the grid pattern.)

Only the portion of the celestial sphere above the horizon is shown. The sphere itself is in celestial coordinates such that the poles are the celestial poles, and the equator on the plot is the celestial equator or the extension of the Earth's equator projected onto the sky. Consequently, the geostationary ring lies in the plane formed by the center of the Earth and this ring. Satellites will not appear to be on the celestial equator, because they are at a finite distance from us and we are looking from outside the equatorial plane. Because the observer is assumed to be above (north of) the Earth's equator, geostationary satellites will appear to be below, i.e., to the south, of the celestial equator. The marks are placed at azimuth angles of 10 deg along the geostationary ring. This corresponds to the difference in longitude between the observer and a geostationary satellite which is being viewed.

Figure 9-32 shows the apparent position of actual locations on the geostationary arc. The satellite, however, is moving in either a small ellipse or small analemma as described in Sec. 9.3.3. This figure will be centered on the satellite's location in GEO. Conceptually, these will be very small ellipses or analemmas about the various points on the geostationary arc. The details of the motion of any specific geostationary satellite are best done by simulation. In general, an observer on the surface of the Earth will be slightly closer to the orbit than the center of the Earth, and, therefore, the apparent shape of the orbit will be slightly magnified. At the extreme, an analemma or elliptical shape as seen from directly below on the equator on the Earth's surface will be larger by approximately 18%. This magnification will reduce as we go to higher latitudes and larger longitude differences.

9.4.4 Orbits Above Geosynchronous; Interplanetary Orbits

Beyond geosynchronous orbit, the motions of spacecraft and natural objects in the Solar System such as the Moon and planets are dominated by the rotation of the Earth. For example, Fig. 9-33 shows a photograph of the motion of the stars in the vicinity of the Earth's pole over a 4-hour period. The stars themselves form essentially a fixed reference frame such that the apparent motion is dominated entirely by the rotation of the Earth. Thus, the location of the celestial pole becomes apparent. While we are interested in the motion of the satellite in a frame of reference fixed relative to the Earth, we need to plot this motion relative to the background stars. We will determine the various viewing parameters for spacecraft in these orbits much as we would determine the viewing parameters for the Moon or planets. For example, Fig. 9-34 shows a plot of the motion of the Moon relative to the background stars over a 2-month period. A very similar plot would apply to the motion of a spacecraft near any of the Earth/Moon Lagrange points, since these points remain fixed in an Earth/Moon coordinate system, as discussed in Sec. 2.5.5.

Fig. 9-33. Photograph of the Apparent Motion of the Stars in the Vicinity of the Earth's Pole over a 4-Hour Period. The rotation of the Earth dominates the apparent motion of the Moon, planets, and distant spacecraft such that a plot of the motion of the spacecraft relative to a fixed observer on the Earth isn't typically useful. A plot of the motion relative to the background stars is used instead.

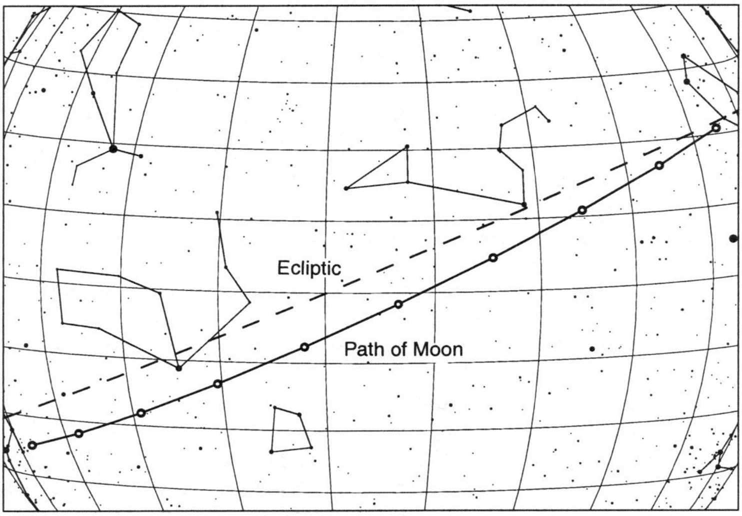

Fig. 9-34. Plot of the Motion of the Moon Relative to the Background Stars for 10 Days. Plot begins Jan. 1, 2010 with circles at 1 day intervals. A very similar plot would apply to the motion of a spacecraft near any of the Earth/Moon Lagrange points.

As we move further away from the Earth, the apparent motion becomes dominated more by the revolution of the Earth around the Sun than by the motion of the planet or the interplanetary spacecraft. For example, Fig. 9-35 shows a plot of the motion of Jupiter relative to the background stars over a period of 3 years. The various loops in the orbit are a result of the motion of the Earth in its orbit. Because the Earth is closer to the Sun, it is moving more rapidly than Jupiter. As the Earth catches up to Jupiter in any given year, it will be moving more rapidly than Jupiter, and Jupiter will appear to move backward across the sky. As the Earth swings past, this apparent motion will be reversed, and Jupiter will again appear to have a prograde motion with respect to the stars. Each of the outer planets demonstrates this general looping effect in apparent motion.

Determining the apparent position relative to the background stars is straightforward. Ordinarily an orbit propagator is used for the orbit of the spacecraft itself, although analytic approximations can also be used. A vector is then drawn from the observer to the spacecraft, and this gives the position relative to the background stars in either vector terms, or if transformed into celestial coordinates (i.e., right ascension and declination), in spherical geometry terms.

Once the position on the sky is known, the observation times for an observer on the Earth can be readily computed by techniques that are available in any observational astronomy book. The approach here ignores second order effects such as refraction and parallax but is adequate for determining approximate observing times because we will find the object relative to the background stars and will tend not to observe or communicate with it when it is just rising or setting. (For very precise methods, see for example Seidelmann [1992].)

The process for determining observing times is summarized in Table 9-6. The first step is to determine the local civil time at which the spacecraft will *transit,* or cross the

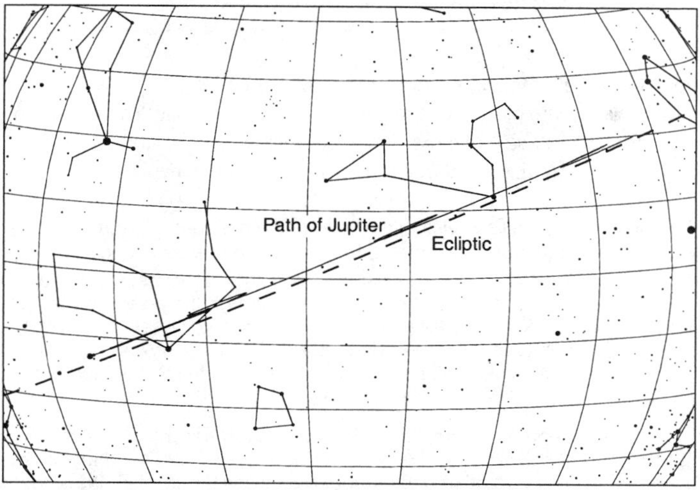

Fig. 9-35. Plot of the Motion of Jupiter Relative to the Background Stars for 40 Months. Plot begins in August, 2002 and ends in November, 2005. At these distances, planets and spacecraft move sufficiently slowly and the distances are large enough that the apparent motion is dominated by the revolution of the Earth around the Sun. Note the more open shape of the loop as Jupiter gets further from the ecliptic.

meridian. The meridian is the great circle going from south to north through the zenith. Transit is when the spacecraft will be highest in the sky for the observer and is the best time for either observations or communications. From Eqs. (4-7) and (4-9) in Sec. 4.1.3, we determined that at transit:

$$LST = RA^* = GST + EL/15 \tag{9-115}$$

where *LST* is the local sidereal time, *RA** is the right ascension of the target (star, spacecraft, or planet), *GST* is the *Greenwich sidereal time* (or sidereal time on the Greenwich meridian), and *EL* is the east longitude of the observer. All of the quantities in this expression are measured in degrees. We next use Eq. (4-14) in Sec. 4.1.3 to determine the Greenwich sidereal time in degrees for 0 hours *UT* (Universal time), on the date we wish to do the observing. The difference between this and the *GST* at transit gives us the UT time of transit for the spacecraft, which can be translated into hours using Eq. (4-6) in Sec. 4.1.3. Note that while Eq. (4-6) provides a precise transformation, for most practical purposes of determining broad time ranges, a conversion of 1 deg of angle = 4 min of time is adequate. Finally, we determine the local civil time of transit by determining the time zone is of the observer relative to the time zone of the Greenwich Meridian. These time zone differences for both standard time and daylight savings time are given in Table 4-1 in Sec. 4.1. This is when our target spacecraft will be highest in the sky, either due north or due south, and is the best time for observation or communications.

How we proceed depends on what we would like to determine. For a given observation time, we can determine how far the spacecraft will be above the local horizon. Alternately, if we have a defined limit on the angle above the horizon for which we wish to observe, we can translate this into a range of observability times when the

TABLE 9-6. Summary of Equations for Determining Observability Times.

Given:

ϕ = Observer Latitude, L = Observer East Longitude

JD = Julian Date of the observation at 0 hr UT (hence, it must end in ".5")

α = Right Ascension of the object to be observed, δ = its Declination

The object is *circumpolar* (always above or always below the horizon) if:

$$|\delta| > |90 \text{ deg} - |L||$$

Circumpolar objects will be always visible (i.e., above the horizon) if δ and L are the same sign and always invisible (i.e., below the horizon) if δ and L are opposite signs.

If the object is not circumpolar, then we can compute the times for rise, transit, and set. *Transit* is when the object is on the meridian (the great circle through the poles and the zenith), i.e., when it the highest in the sky that it will go and the best time for observation. First, we use Eq. (4-16) or (4-17) to compute the Greenwich Sidereal Time, *GST*, corresponding to 0 hr UT on the day the observation. The transit time of the object, T_T, in UT will then be:

$$T_T = \alpha + L - GST$$

where the units can be degrees, hours, or fractions of a day, but must, of course, be consistent. Translating from UT to local civil time is done with Eq. (4-1) or Table 4-1. Next we compute the hour angle, *HA*, which is the rotation angle about the celestial pole from the target to the observer's zenith. (See Fig. 9-35.)

$$\cos HA = \frac{\cos \zeta - \sin lat \, \sin \delta}{\cos lat \cos \delta}$$

where ζ is the zenith angle, or angle from straight overhead to the elevation angle at which the object is defined to rise or set. If we define rising and setting as being straight horizontal, then ζ = 90.5 deg where the additional 0.5 deg represents atmospheric refraction at the horizon. As a practical matter, most objects won't be observed when they are right on the horizon, so it is convenient to set ζ to 90 deg and, therefore, drop the cos ζ term in the above expression.

Finally, the rise time, T_R, and set time, T_S, are given by

$$T_R = T_T - HA$$

$$T_S = T_T + HA$$

where, again, any convenient, consistent units can be used and Table 4-1 can be used to convert UT to local civil time. More precise formulas can be found in Meeus [1991], pg. 97–100.

target spacecraft can be seen. The geometry for both circumstances is shown in Fig. 9-36. Here, ζ is the *zenith angle*, which is the angle between zenith and the target or 90 deg minus the elevation angle above the horizon. The *hour angle*, *HA*, is the rotation angle measured at the celestial pole between the target and zenith. When expressed in hours, this is just the time difference between transit and the time of the observation. The arc length from the celestial pole to zenith is just 90 deg minus the latitude, and the arc length from the celestial pole to the target is 90 deg minus the declination of the target. Consequently, if the hour angle is known, we can immediately determine the zenith angle from:

$$\cos \zeta = \sin lat \sin \delta + \cos lat \cos \delta \cos HA \tag{9-116}$$

or if the zenith angle is known, we can determine the hour angle from:

$$\cos HA = \frac{\cos \zeta - \sin lat \, \sin \delta}{\cos lat \cos \delta} \tag{9-117}$$

We can use these expressions to determine either the zenith angle at a particular observation time or a range of observation times centered on transit over which the spacecraft can be observed at a zenith angle less than a pre-defined limit.

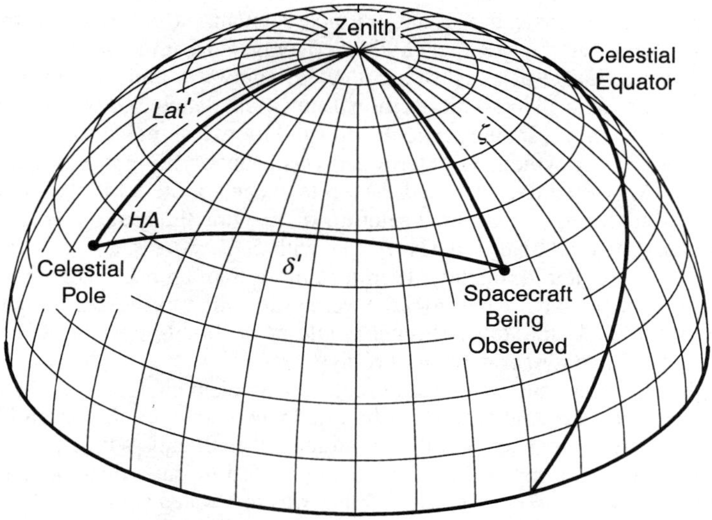

Fig. 9-36. Geometry for Determining Observability Times for Stars, Planets, or Interplanetary Spacecraft. See Sec. 11.5 for a discussion of the brightness of distant spacecraft.

For a spacecraft not at "infinity," there will be a parallax due to the angular difference between the position of the observer and the position of the center of the Earth. The range of motion due to parallax as the observer moves from one side of the Earth to the other will be equal to the angular diameter of the Earth as seen from the target. From the distance of the Moon, the Earth is 2 deg in diameter, therefore, the parallax of a spacecraft at the L_4 or L_5 Lagrange points will result in an apparent motion of the spacecraft of ±1 deg over a 12 hr period, as the spacecraft goes from one horizon to the other. At the closest distance of Mars to the Earth, the parallax due to the Earth's rotation will be approximately 0.005 deg.

9.5 Earth Coverage Analysis

For a large number of spacecraft, Earth coverage is the fundamental element of performance. The number of satellites we need or the utility of the data depends on coverage. Thus, coverage is often a key parameter in orbit and constellation design. Most typically, this is done by computer simulation and statistical analysis of the results. However, one of the most important coverage characteristics is that

> ***Earth coverage is not a Gaussian parameter and statistical data can give very misleading results.***

I would like to give a specific example of this problem. Several years ago, we were asked to do a constellation coverage analysis. Continuous coverage was not necessary, but the customer was concerned with minimizing the duration of the gaps in coverage, consistent with keeping down the number of satellites in the constellation, and therefore, the cost. Mindful of the fact that maxima are often a very poor measure of system performance, we chose instead to use as our most relevant measure of performance the *mean gap duration*, i.e., the average length of coverage gaps under a variety of circumstances and constellation designs. We collected, analyzed, and plotted a variety of mean gap statistics as well as some additional statistical data based on our simulations of coverage performance. In one particular constellation design, we had a mean gap of approximately 40 min, which we determined was probably longer than the customer would accept. Consequently, we added a satellite to each of the orbit planes in the constellation configuration, rephased the satellites to provide the best coverage possible, and re-ran our statistical analysis. The result, with 50% more satellites, was that the mean gap went from approximately 40 min to more than an hour. Budgets were not quite so tight in those days when rockets were still pulled by horses; nonetheless, it seemed highly unlikely that our customer would be willing to pay for 50% more satellites in order to have longer gaps in coverage.

Although our computations were correct, it was clear that something had gone terribly wrong with our analysis. What had happened was actually straightforward. Our original constellation had a number of large and small gaps with an average duration of 40 min. We had improved the coverage by adding satellites and had actually filled in quite a few of the smaller gaps. What was left was a small number of larger gaps such that the average gap duration was longer, even though the total of all of the gaps was significantly reduced.

When obvious errors such as the above occur, it becomes clear that something has gone wrong and the problem can be identified and corrected. Unfortunately, that rarely happens. We collect statistical data on constellation coverage not because it has any type of a Gaussian distribution, but because we always collect statistical data from simulations. Often, the results look "good" and do not have any manifest problems. Nonetheless, statistical analysis of coverage is based on an assumption which is simply not true, and, therefore, must be approached with substantial care.

I would not propose that you avoid statistical data in coverage analysis. In any case, that is almost impossible to do. What is important is to use several of the other coverage analysis tools described in this section to provide substantial physical insight into the nature of the coverage that is being provided. It is this insight into what is occurring that provides the checks and balances to be able to draw conclusions that are truly valid.

9.5.1 Earth Coverage for Low to Medium Altitude Circular Earth Orbits

Earth coverage refers to the part of the Earth that a spacecraft instrument* or antenna can see at one instant or over an extended period. As Fig. 9-37 shows, the *instantaneous field of view*, typically called the *FOV* or *footprint*, is the actual area the instrument or antenna can see at any moment. In contrast, the *access area* is the total area on the ground that could potentially be seen at that moment by turning the space-

*Throughout this section we will use *instrument* to refer to any spacecraft sensor or antenna for which we want to compute coverage.

craft or instrument. In the case of a truly omnidirectional antenna, these two would always be the same. For most operational instruments they are not.

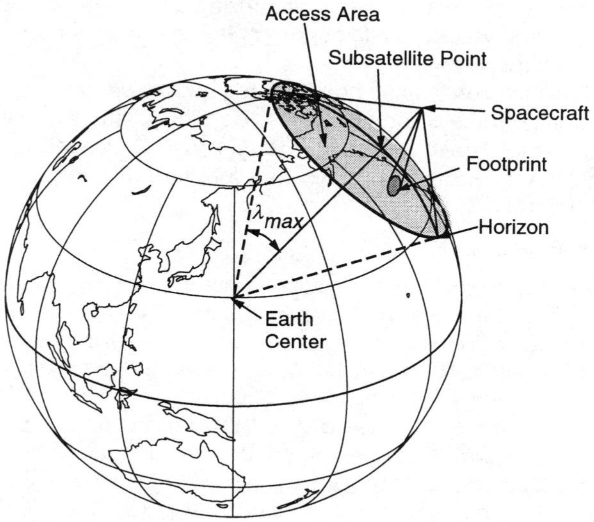

Fig. 9-37. Coverage of the Earth by a Satellite in Low-Earth Orbit. The instrument footprint (also called the field of view or FOV) is the instantaneous area of the ground being covered. The instantaneous access area is the total observable area at that time.

The second important distinction is between the area which can be seen at any one instant versus the rate at which new land comes into view as the spacecraft or instrument moves. Both are important, and either can be vital to mission success. In geosynchronous orbit, the instantaneous area is typically most important because the spacecraft is nearly stationary relative to the Earth's surface. In low-Earth orbit, satellites are moving rapidly over the surface, so the rate at which new land appears is often critical.

The two distinctions above lead to four parameters for Earth coverage:

- *Footprint Area* (*FA*, also *FOV area* or *instantaneous coverage area*) = area that a specific instrument or antenna can see at any instant.
- *Instantaneous Access Area* (*IAA*) = all the area that the instrument or antenna could potentially see at any instant if it were scanned through its normal range of orientations.
- *Area Coverage Rate* (*ACR*) = the rate at which the instrument or antenna is sensing or accessing new land.
- *Area Access Rate* (*AAR*) = the rate at which new land is coming into the spacecraft's access area.

For an instrument which covers all of the area available to it as the spacecraft moves along, the coverage rate and access rate will be the same. For instruments operating only part of the time or continuously selecting the region to be examined, the coverage rate and access rate may be dramatically different. Generally the access area and access rate depend only on the orbit and limiting geometry of the system, so we can easily compute them with only a minimal knowledge of the detailed system design. On the other hand, the actual area coverage rate during spacecraft operations may well depend on the spacecraft control system, power, and management systems, as well as the details of mission operations.

Coverage assessment conveniently divides into two areas: first, an analytic assessment to provide approximate formulas for coverage parameters as a function of mission variables as described in Secs. 9.5.1.1 to 9.5.1.3; second, numerical simulations to provide coverage Figures of Merit for more detailed studies. These are discussed in Sec. 9.5.1.4.

9.5.1.1 Analytic Approximations

In this section we present analytic approximations for various Earth coverage parameters. All of the formulas here take into account the spherical surface of the Earth, but do not account for oblateness, orbit eccentricity, or the rotation of the Earth underneath the orbit. These effects, in addition to those of coverage by multiple satellites, are ordinarily accounted for in numerical simulations as described in Sec. 9.5.1.4.

All of the formulas here are derived directly from the single-satellite geometry described in Sec. 5.2. In particular, we will use the notation developed there and summarized in Fig. 5-12 in Sec. 5.2. In this section we will parameterize coverage in terms of the Earth Central Angle, λ.* However, we can use Eqs. (5-23) to (5-27) to transform each of the formulas below into one for either the spacecraft-centered nadir angle, η, or spacecraft elevation angle, ε, seen from the ground.

As Fig. 9-37 shows, the instrument footprint is normally a beam projected onto the Earth's surface with a circular cross section substantially smaller than the access area. The nomenclature and computational geometry for the footprint are in Fig. 9-38. (For instruments which see very large portions of the Earth, we can use the access area formulas below. For those which have noncircular cross sections, the logic here along with the formulas of Secs. 5.2 and 9.1 allow us to develop mission-specific formulas for footprint size and area.)

The length (also called the height) of the footprint, L_F, is given by:

$$L_F = K_L\,(\lambda_{FO} - \lambda_{FI}) \tag{9-118a}$$

$$\approx D\,(\sin\theta / \sin\varepsilon) \tag{9-118b}$$

where the variables are defined in Fig. 9-38 and, for λ expressed in degrees,

$K_L = 1$	for length in deg
$K_L = 111.319\,543$	for length in km
$K_L = 60.107\,744\,7$	for length in nmi

Note: the linear approximation given in Eq. (9-118b) is computationally convenient but can be very inaccurate, particularly near the horizon where ε is small. (For a satellite at an altitude of 1,000 km with a 1 deg diameter beam, the error in Eq. (9-118b) is 400% at $\varepsilon = 1$ deg, 10% at $\varepsilon = 15$ deg, and 1% at $\varepsilon = 60$ deg.) However, the alternative computation of Eq. (9-118a) is much less convenient. To find the footprint length for

* λ may be thought of either as an angle at the Earth's center or as a distance measured along the Earth's surface and, therefore, may be expressed in either degrees or kilometers. We will use these two views interchangeably as convenient for the problem at hand.

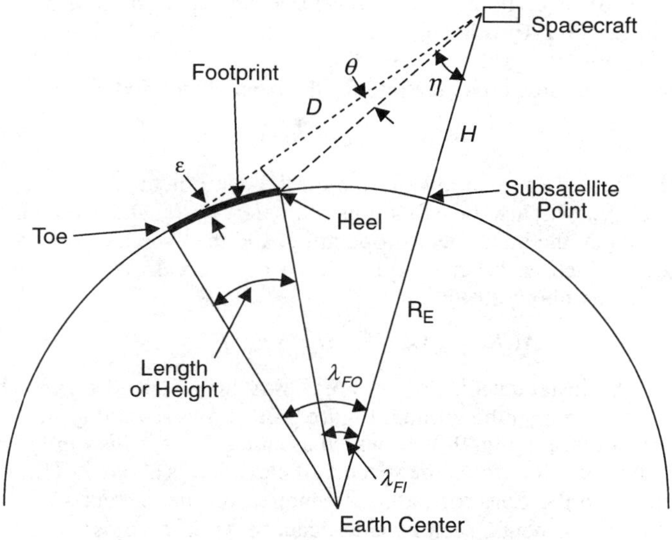

Fig. 9-38. Computational Geometry for Footprint Parameters. Note that ε is always measured at the toe because that is where performance is the worst.

a given spacecraft elevation angle at the toe of the beam, ε, we begin by computing η and λ at the toe, then subtract the beam width, θ, from η to determine η at the heel, compute λ at the heel, and finally subtract to get the footprint length from Eq. (9-118a). An alternative that improves the approximation somewhat is to use the center rather than the toe of the beam. Because the toe represents the worst-case link budget, it is most often used for performance computations and, therefore, is commonly used for geometry calculations as well.

The footprint width, W_F, is given by:

$$W_F = R_E \operatorname{asin}(D \sin\theta / \mathrm{R_E}) \tag{9-119a}$$

$$\approx D \sin\theta \tag{9-119b}$$

where $\mathrm{R_E} = 6{,}378.14$ km is the radius of the Earth, θ is the beam width, and D is the distance from the spacecraft to the toe of the footprint.* Here the error in the approximation in Eq. (9-119b) is proportional to $1 - (W_F / \sin W_F)^{\dagger}$ and is generally small relative to other errors. Thus, Eq. (9-119b) is adequate for most practical applications.

Finally, if we assume that the projection on the ground is an ellipse, then the footprint area, F_A, is given by:

$$F_A \approx (\pi/4) L_F W_F \tag{9-120}$$

---

* In the case of a noncircular beam, Eq. (9-99) can be used with the beam width, θ, perpendicular to the horizon and Eq. (9-100) can be used independently with the beam width parallel to the horizon.

† Here W_F should be in radians as seen from the center of the Earth.

Assuming that L_F was computed by Eq. (9-118a), the error in ignoring the curvature of the Earth in Eq. (9-120) is again proportional to $1 - (W_F / \sin W_F)$ and is negligible for most applications.

The instantaneous area coverage rate for the beam is defined by:

$$ACR_{instantaneous} \equiv F_A / T \tag{9-121}$$

where T is the exposure time or dwell time for the instrument. The *average area coverage rate*, ACR_{avg}, will also be a function of the *duty cycle*, *DC*, which is the fraction of the total time that the instrument is operating, and the average overlap between the footprint, O_{avg}, which is the amount by which two successive footprints cover the same area (typically about 20%):

$$ACR_{avg} = \text{DC}\,(1 - O_{avg})\, F_A / T \tag{9-122}$$

Computing the instantaneous access area, IAA, will depend on the shape of the potential coverage area on the ground. Figure 9-39 shows several typical shapes. The most common of these is Fig. 9-39A, which assumes that the instrument can work at any point on the Earth for which the spacecraft elevation is above ε. This corresponds to a small circle on the Earth of radius λ centered on the current subsatellite point. However, some instruments, such as radar, cannot work too close to the subsatellite point. As Fig. 9-39B shows, these instruments have both an outer horizon, λ_1, and an inner horizon, λ_2.

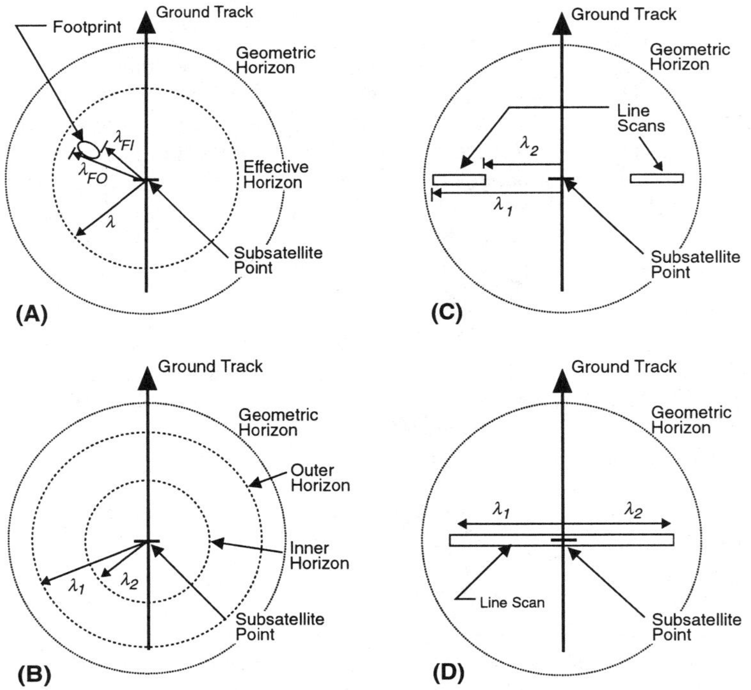

Fig. 9-39. Typical Access Areas for Spacecraft Instruments. See Table 9-7 for formulas. See Sec. 9.1.3 for sensor FOV analysis.

For instruments with an access pattern as shown in Fig. 9-39A, the instantaneous access area, *IAA*, will be just the area of the small circle, that is,

$$IAA = K_A(1 - \cos\lambda) \tag{9-123}$$

where

$K_A = 2\pi \approx 6.283\ 185\ 311$ for area in steradians
$K_A = 20{,}626.4806$ for area in deg^2
$K_A = 2.556\ 041\ 87 \times 10^8$ for area in km^2
$K_A = 7.452\ 225\ 69 \times 10^7$ for area in nmi^2

The instantaneous access areas or access lengths for the other patterns in Fig. 9-39 are given in Table 9-7, which also summarizes all of the coverage formulas for these patterns. These access area formulas take into account the curved surface of the Earth and are accurate for any access area size or satellite altitude to within very small corrections for the Earth's oblateness.

TABLE 9-7. Coverage Formulas for Patterns Shown in Fig. 9-39. See text for definition of variables. In pattern D, the minus sign applies if λ_2 is on the same side of the ground track as λ_1. The approximation for footprint area is invalid when $\varepsilon \approx 0$. The ACR formulas for patterns C and D assume that the instrument is side-looking. *P* is the orbit period.

Pattern	Typical Application	Footprint Area (*FA*)	Instantaneous Access Area (*IAA*) or Length (*IAL*)	Area Coverage Rate (*ACR*)	Area Access Rate (*AAR*)
A	Omni-antenna, Ground station coverage, General sensing	$(\pi D K_L/4) \sin\theta \times (\lambda_{FO} - \lambda_{FI}) \approx (\pi D^2/4) \times \sin^2\theta / \sin\varepsilon$	$IAA = K_A(1 - \cos\lambda)$	$\dfrac{F_A(1-O_{avg})DC}{T}$	$\dfrac{2K_A \sin\lambda}{P}$
B	Doppler Radar	As above	$IAA = K_A(\cos\lambda_2 - \cos\lambda_1)$	As above	$\dfrac{2K_A \sin\lambda}{P}$
C	Synthetic Aperture Radar	As above	$IAL = 2K_L(\lambda_1 - \lambda_2) \approx 2K_L D \dfrac{\sin\theta}{\sin\varepsilon}$	$\dfrac{2K_A(\sin\lambda_1 - \sin\lambda_2)}{P}$	$\dfrac{2K_A(\sin\lambda_1 - \sin\lambda_2)}{P}$
D	Scanning Sensor	As above	$IAL = K_L(\lambda_1 \pm \lambda_2)$	$\dfrac{K_A(\sin\lambda_1 \pm \sin\lambda_2)}{P}$	$\dfrac{K_A(\sin\lambda_1 \pm \sin\lambda_2)}{P}$

We now wish to determine the length of time a particular point on the Earth is within the satellite access area and the access area rate at which land enters or leaves the access area. Consider a satellite in a circular orbit at altitude *H*. The orbit period, *P*, in minutes is given by:

$$P = 1.658\,669 \times 10^{-4} \times (6{,}378.14 + H)^{3/2} \qquad H \text{ in km} \qquad (9\text{-}124)$$

$$P = 4.180\,432 \times 10^{-4} \times (3{,}443.9 + H)^{3/2} \qquad H \text{ in nmi} \qquad (9\text{-}125)$$

We define the *maximum Earth Central Angle*, λ_{max}, as the radius of the access area for the observation in question. Twice λ_{max} is called the *swath width* and is the width of the coverage path across the Earth. As shown in Fig. 9-40, the coverage for any point **P** on the surface of the Earth will be a function of λ_{max} and of the off ground-track angle, λ, which is the perpendicular distance from **P** to the satellite ground track for the orbit pass being evaluated. The fraction of the orbit, F_{view}, over which the point **P** is in view is:

$$F_{view} = \Delta\nu / 180 \text{ deg} \qquad (9\text{-}126)$$

where:

$$\cos \Delta\nu = \cos \lambda_{max} / \cos \lambda \qquad (9\text{-}127)$$

Therefore the time in view, T, for the point **P** will be

$$T = PF_{view} = \left(\frac{P}{180 \text{ deg}}\right) \operatorname{acos}\left(\frac{\cos\lambda_{max}}{\cos\lambda}\right) \qquad (9\text{-}128)$$

which is equivalent to Eq. (9-108). Note that here we use λ rather than λ_{min} for the off ground-track angle and that $\Delta\nu$ is one half of the true anomaly range (i.e., angle along the ground track) over which the point **P** is in view by the satellite. See Fig. 9-29 in Sec. 9.4.1 for the geometry of this computation.

Fig. 9-40. Earth Coverage Geometry. λ is the *off ground-track angle* and 2 λ_{max} is the *swath width*. **P** is the target or ground station.

Finally, the area access rate as the satellite sweeps over the ground for the access area of Fig. 9-39A is:

$$AAR = (2\, K_A \sin \lambda) / P \qquad \text{(Pattern A)} \qquad (9\text{-}129)$$

Formulas for other patterns are in Table 9-7. Again note that because of the curvature of the Earth's surface, this area access rate is **not** equal to the diameter of the access area times the subsatellite velocity.

As an example of the above computations, consider a spacecraft at 2,000 km altitude with a 1 deg diameter beam staring perpendicular to the ground track at an elevation angle of 10 deg as seen from the ground. Our linear estimate of the footprint height is 446 km from Eq. (9-118ab).* However, from Table 9-7 we see that the true height is 355 km and therefore need to use the somewhat more complex Eq. (9-118a). From Eqs. (9-2), (9-5) and (9-6) we determine $\lambda_{FO} = 31.43$ deg and $\lambda_{FI} = 28.24$ deg. The footprint width from Eq. (9-119a) is 77 km. From Eq. (9-120) the footprint area is 21,470 km^2. The accuracy of the area is proportional to $1 - (77/6{,}378)/\sin(77/6{,}378) = 0.002\%$. The ground track velocity is the circumference of the Earth divided by the orbit period [from Eq. (9-124)] = 40,075 km/127 min = 315.6 km/min = 5.26 km/s. Multiplying this by the footprint height of 355 km gives a crude estimate of the area coverage rate of 1,867 km^2/s. Using the more accurate formula in Table 9-7 (Pattern D) and the values of λ above, we obtain a more accurate value of $ACR = 2.556 \times 10^8 \times (\sin 31.43 \text{ deg} - \sin 28.24 \text{ deg})/(127 \times 60) = 1{,}620$ km^2/s which implies an error of 15% in the less accurate approximation.

9.5.1.2 Identifying Coverage Patterns

As previously indicated, Earth coverage is not a statistically distributed parameter. Coverage tends to come in "chunks." Thus, at any given time, whether there is Earth coverage at some point on the Earth's surface is very strongly correlated with whether there was coverage at the last time step. Consequently, we need not only statistical data generated from simulations but also other types of analyses that can begin to identify coverage patterns and how coverage works in both a qualitative sense and analytical approximations.

One of the most useful approaches for analyzing coverage patterns is simply the ground track plot described in some detail in Sec. 9.3. A typical of ground track plot is shown in Fig. 9-41 for a satellite in an orbit at an altitude of 1,000 km and inclination of 60 deg. In previous plots, we have drawn the access area on the surface of the Earth corresponding to the area that is visible for a specific satellite. In this figure, we draw a circle of the same size centered not on the position of the satellite but on a specific target or ground station, in this case, Miami. For a satellite at 1,000 km and minimum elevation angle of 5 deg, the maximum Earth Central Angle is 25 deg, i.e., any point on the ground within 25 deg of the subsatellite point is within view. Conversely, whenever the subsatellite point for a spacecraft is within 25 deg of a specific target or ground station, then that target can be seen by the spacecraft. Therefore, the small circle of 25 deg radius centered on Miami encloses all possible subsatellite points for which a satellite at 1,000 km altitude can see Miami with a minimum elevation angle at the target greater than 5 deg.†

---

*As indicated previously, this estimate would be substantially improved if the 10 deg elevation angle was at the center of the beam. However, we would then need to keep track of beam-center parameters for the geometry and beam-edge parameters for performance estimates.

†Another way to think of the construction of this plot is to consider a cone of 85 deg radius centered on Miami, with its axis toward the zenith. The intersection of this cone with a sphere 1,000 km above the Earth produces the small circle shown in the figure. In this equivalent representation, the small circle represents all possible locations of the satellite which can see Miami with the appropriate conditions.

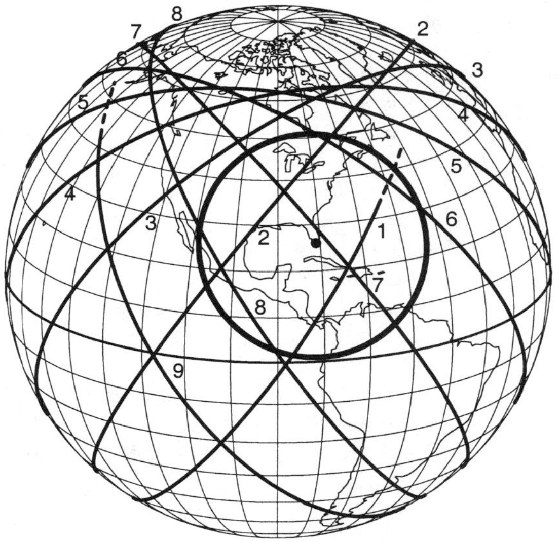

Fig. 9-41. Ground Track for 8 Successive Orbits (Out of 14 per Day) for a Satellite in a 1,000 km Circular Orbit. The heavy circle covers subsatellite points for which the satellite will be at an elevation angle, ε, of 5 deg or higher.

By simply looking at the plot, it is clear what the nature of the coverage will be. Notice that the orbits on the plot are numbered consecutively and that coverage of Miami is provided on orbits 1 and 2 and is then not available on orbits 3, 4, and 5 but is available again on orbits 6, 7, and 8. For this example, there will be 2 or 3 orbits of coverage followed by 3 or 4 orbits with no coverage and then another 2 or 3 orbits of coverage after which the process repeats. The specific coverage will depend on how the orbit lies with respect to the particular target. The orbit period at this altitude is approximately 105 min. A pass that goes directly over Miami will provide coverage for approximately $(50/360) \times 105$, or a bit less than 15 min. Thus, an "orbit of coverage" will consist of somewhat less than 15 min of coverage followed by a bit more than 90 min of no coverage.

What happens if we move our ground station either north or south? As the ground station moves toward the equator, the coverage patterns become more symmetric, with coverage occurring twice per day at times centered 12 hr apart. As we move toward the pole, coverage becomes more "one-sided" in terms of its daily distribution. There will be a larger number of orbits in a row which provide coverage, and then a longer gap with no coverage, with the process repeating on a daily basis. If we get close enough to the pole, there will be either no coverage if the radius of the coverage region is less than 90 deg minus the inclination, or a short region of coverage on every orbit.

We can learn a great deal about the nature of coverage and how it is distributed by simply looking carefully at a ground track plot for the orbit. One way to demonstrate this coverage as a function of latitude is a *coverage histogram* or *tombstone plot* as shown in Fig. 9-42. The horizontal axis is time and the various lines which look like a strip chart recorder are the coverage for points at the longitude of Miami and at 10 deg steps in latitude. When the line is up, there is coverage; when it is down, there is no coverage. Here you can see clearly the general characteristic of what we have discussed, including the symmetry of coverage which occurs near the equator and the asymmetry which occurs as we approach the poles.

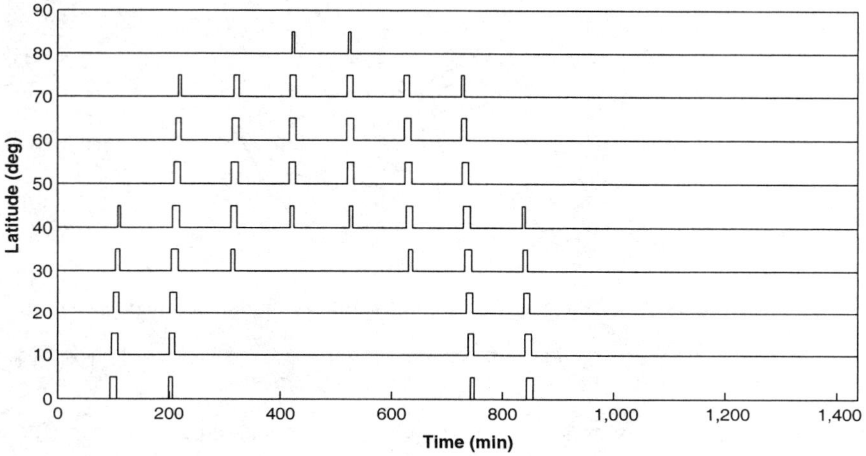

Fig. 9-42. Histograms of Coverage Over a Day for Ground Stations at the Same Longitude Shown in Fig. 9-41, but Varying Latitudes. Note the asymmetry as the ground station moves toward the pole. See text for discussion.

We can also use the information from Fig. 9-41 to immediately calculate one statistical parameter. The access area represents just less than 5% of the surface area of the world. Consequently, in general the mean coverage for any single point on the surface of the Earth will be 5%. Five percent of the Earth is covered at any one time, and over the course of time a random point will be covered approximately 5% of the time. While this is true, it does remarkably little to reflect the reality of the curves in Fig. 9-42 or the understanding we can gain by looking at Fig. 9-41.

9.5.1.3 Analytic Coverage Computations

Figure 9-40 in Sec. 9.5.1.1 shows the geometry for a single ground station or target pass. Note that this is the same computational geometry that was done in detail in Sec. 9.4.1. Consequently, all of the tables and computations in that section are applicable to Earth coverage for a single point. These computations were summarized in Table 9-2 in Sec. 9.4.1.

It is also of interest to compute the coverage as a function of latitude, *L*. Conceptually, this is most conveniently done by thinking of the orbit and coverage pattern as fixed and the Earth as rotating underneath as shown in Fig. 9-43. The large dots show the position of a ground station or target on successive orbits. Here we can see both the discrete nature of coverage and the derivation of the continuous analytic formulas. If the ground swath is thinner then the spacing between successive dots, then we may or may not get coverage on a given ascending or descending pass. If it is wider than one space but less then two spaces, then we will get coverage on either 1 or 2 passes at each ascending and descending node. Thus, we could divide the world into latitude

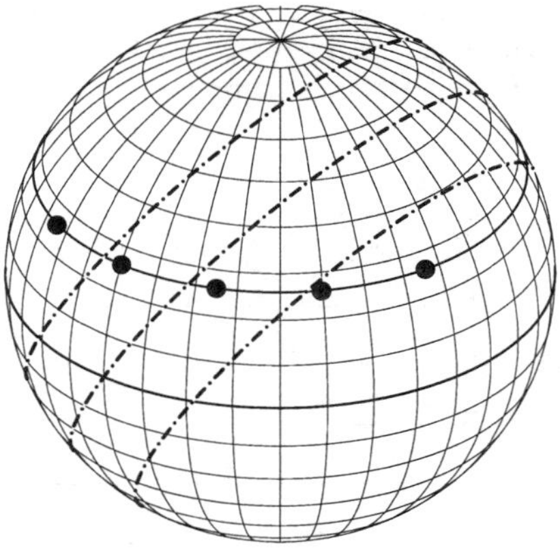

Fig. 9-43. Alternative View of a Rotating Ground Track. For some computations it is convenient to think of the orbit coverage pattern as fixed in inertial space and the Earth rotating under it. The large dots represent locations of a ground target on successive passes.

bands with each band having a discrete set of possible coverage patterns, corresponding approximately to the histogram of Fig 9-42.

To obtain a continuous analytic approximation, we note that the arc length along the small circle connecting the dots is directly proportional to the percent coverage at that latitude.* Specifically, we assume that there is a satellite in a circular orbit at inclination i and that observations can be made at any off ground track angle less then or equal to λ_{max} on either side of the ground track. We also assume that L is positive, i.e., in the northern hemisphere. (The extensions are straightforward for the southern hemisphere or nonsymmetric observations.) As shown in Fig 9-44 there will be either no coverage, a single long region of coverage, or two shorter regions of coverage depending on the latitude and inclination as follows:

LATITUDE RANGE	NUMBER OF COVERAGE REGIONS	PERCENT COVERAGE	
$L > \lambda_{max} + i$	0	0	(9-130a)
$i + \lambda_{max} > L > i - \lambda_{max}$	1	$\phi_1/180$	(9-130b)
$i - \lambda_{max} > L > 0$	2	$(\phi_1 - \phi_2)/180$	(9-130c)

where:

$$\cos\phi_{1 \text{ or } 2} = \frac{\pm\sin\lambda_{\text{max}} + \cos i \sin L}{\sin i \cos L} \tag{9-131}$$

---

* We need to emphasize once again that coverage is not a statistical variable. If the orbit is a 1-day repeating ground track, then the targets will appear in the same locations with respect to the orbit every day. In this case, coverage will be a function of both latitude and longitude and each Earth location will have its own fixed coverage pattern. If the orbit is not a repeating ground track, then the "percentage coverage" rules are applicable.

where the minus sign applies for ϕ_1 and the plus sign for ϕ_2. Here ϕ is one-half the longitude range over which coverage occurs. The formula in the third column above represents the fraction of all points at a given latitude in view of the satellite during one orbit. This is approximately equal to the fraction of orbits that will cover a given point at that latitude.

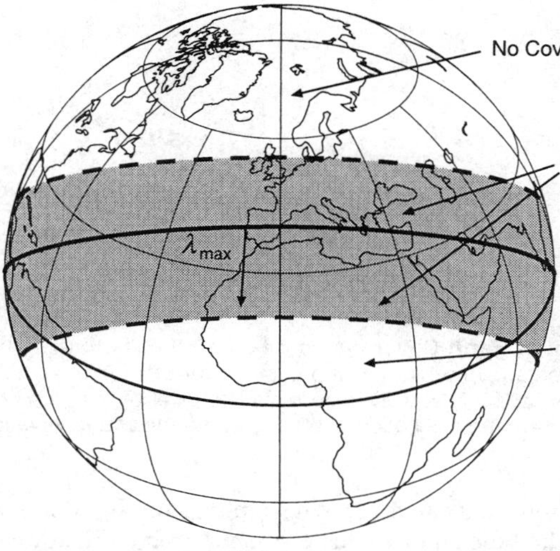

Fig. 9-44. Single Orbit Coverage is a Function of Latitude, Orbit Inclination, and Swath Width. See text for formulas.

As an example of the above formula, consider a satellite in a 62.5 deg inclined orbit which can see to an off-ground-track angle, λ_{max} = 20 deg. At a ground station latitude of 50 deg, the percent coverage will be 49.3%. On any orbit, 49% of the points at a latitude of 50 deg will be within view of the satellite at some time. Conversely, a given point at 50-deg latitude will be covered at some time on approximately 49% of the satellite orbits. Because there is only one coverage region, the covered orbits will occur successively during the day. If the satellite orbit period is 2 hours, then our hypothetical ground station at 50 deg latitude will typically see the satellite on six successive orbits followed by six orbits of no coverage. The number and duration of coverage passes on a given day will depend on where the ground station is located with respect to the orbit node.

Figure 9-45 shows a representative plot of Earth coverage as a function of latitude, based on the above equations. For latitudes below $i - \lambda$, there will be two distinct coverage regions. In this area, the coverage increases somewhat as we go further from the equator, because the orbit is tilting more and therefore covering more of a given latitude line. At a latitude of $i - \lambda$, we transition from two coverage regions to a single coverage region which is extremely long. This can be seen in Fig. 9-44, and occurs where the underlying latitude line is just tangent to the southernmost edge of the coverage band. This is the latitude with the highest coverage and is frequently missed in histograms such as those described above. As we proceed further north, coverage drops as the single coverage region gets smaller until coverage disappears entirely at a latitude of $i + \lambda$.

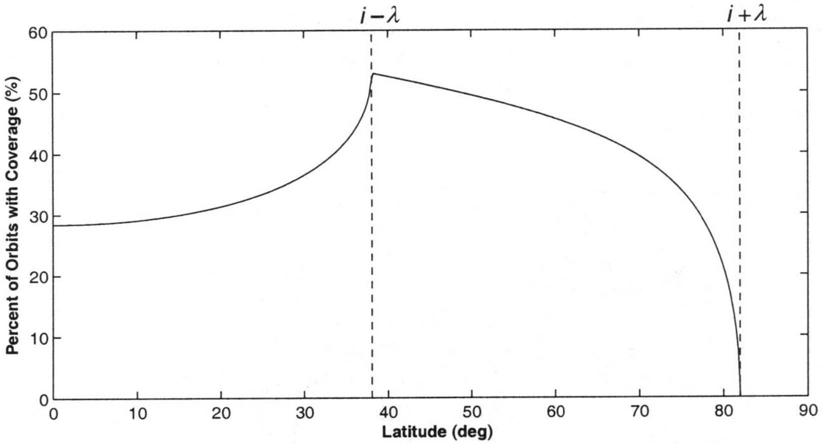

Fig. 9-45. Representative Plot of Earth Coverage as a Function of Latitude. Note that the chart gives the percentage of orbits which provide coverage, but does not reflect the coverage distribution, which is equally important. The satellite is assumed to be in a circular orbit at 1,000 km, an inclination of 60 deg and a minimum elevation angle of 5 deg.

There are several conclusions that can be drawn from this curve. First of all, coverage varies significantly with latitude and we can design our orbit inclination to provide the greatest coverage where it is most needed. For example, a communications constellation might choose to use an inclination such that the coverage is maximized over the mid northern latitudes, where the principal population densities occur. Our second conclusion is that the coverage curve from Fig. 9-45 is interesting and informative but does not tell the whole story. It does not provide the information on the distribution of coverage that we get from either the ground track plot or the coverage histogram. While useful, it needs to be combined with other types of information in order to provide a clear understanding of coverage patterns.

9.5.1.4 Numerical Simulations

The analytic formulas presented above provide an easy and rapid way to evaluate Earth coverage and provide good physical insight into the nature of that coverage. However, to provide additional numerical details, simulations are nearly always required. The numerical simulations themselves are relatively straightforward. Simply set up representative points you are interested in or a grid of points covering the Earth, "fly" the spacecraft over the grid for one or more days, and collect the results. The difficult part is interpreting the meaning of the results and avoiding both computational problems and interpretations which misrepresent the real coverage.

There are four principal numerical interpretation problems that the user should be aware of in developing and using point coverage simulations. These are:

Spacing of Grid Points:

If we use a grid of points in our numerical simulation, we frequently want to compare coverage performance at different latitudes. To do this, we need to have grid points covering approximately equal areas over the surface of the globe. If the gridpoints are at equal intervals of latitude and longitude (every 10 deg, for example) then the number of points per unit area will be much greater near the poles, thus incorrectly weighting polar data in the overall global statistics. This problem is easily resolved by either using grid points at a constant latitude spacing with the number of points at each latitude proportional to the cosine of the latitude, or by adjusting the weighting of the points in creating the global statistics.

Gaps at the Beginning and End of the Simulation:

If the system being simulated is not intended for continuous global coverage, then there will be gaps in coverage for which the statistics are usually important. However, these statistics can be biased by gaps which occur at the beginning and end of the simulation run. For example, if the simulation covers exactly 24 hr and there is a 4-hr gap in coverage during the period when the simulation begins, then this may be misinterpreted as two 2-hr gaps. The easiest solution to this problem is to run the simulation long enough that start and end data have minimal impact on the overall statistics.

Incorrect Step Size:

In a time stepped simulation, the simulation itself does not see a continuous coverage distribution but rather a series of steps. If the steps are far apart in order to make the simulation easy to run it is possible to step "over" some of the grid points such that coverage which actually exists is missed. The principal requirement to avoid this happening too much is to keep the simulation step small relative to the dimensions of the coverage regions.

Incorrect Interpretation of Results:

As we have discussed previously, Earth coverage is not a statistically distributed phenomenon. Consequently, statistical figures of merit can prove extremely misleading. The principal solution to this problem is twofold. First, we should use more than one figure of merit for evaluating coverage so that multiple pieces of information are available and can be compared. The second approach is to use any of the more analytic approaches to understand the coverage such that we can be sure that the statistical data reflects a true assessment of the nature of the coverage.

Our most important step in creating a coverage simulation is to find the appropriate way to accumulate coverage statistics and to evaluate the quality of coverage. This is done by way of coverage figures of merit which are the numerical mechanisms for comparing the coverage of satellites and constellations. We would like to find a figure of merit which is physically meaningful, easy to compute in a numerical simulation, and fair in comparing alternative orbits and constellations. In the end, no one coverage figure of merit will prove successful by itself and a combination of techniques is most appropriate. The most common coverage figures of merit are:

Percent Coverage:

The *percent coverage* for any point on the grid is simply the number of times that point was covered by one or more satellites divided by the total number of simulation time steps. It is numerically equal to the analytically computed percent coverage in Eq. (9-129). The advantage of percent coverage is that it shows directly how much of the time a given point or region on the ground is covered. However, it does not provide any information about the distribution of gaps in that coverage.

Maximum Coverage Gap (= Maximum Response Time):

The *maximum coverage gap* is simply the longest coverage gap encountered for an individual point. When looking at statistics over more than one point, we can either average the maximum gaps or take their maximum value. Thus the worldwide *mean maximum gap* would be the average value of the maximum gap for all the individual points, and the worldwide *maximum gap* would be the largest of any of the individual gaps. This statistic conveys some worst-case information, but it incorrectly ranks constellations because a single point or a small number of points determine the results. Thus, the maximum coverage gap, or maximum response time, is a poor figure of merit.

Mean Coverage Gap:

The *mean coverage gap* is the average length of breaks in coverage for a given point on the simulation grid. To compute mean gap statistics, we must have three counters for each point on the simulation grid. One counter tracks the number of gaps. A second tracks total gap duration. The third tracks the duration of the current gap and is reset as needed. During the simulation, if no satellite covers a given point on the grid, we increment the gap length counter (3) by one time step. If the point is covered but was not covered the previous time (indicated by a value of the gap length counter greater than 0), then we have reached the end of an individual gap. We increment the counter for the number of gaps (1) by one and add the gap duration to the total gap counter (2) or incorporate it in other statistics we want to collect. The final mean coverage gap is computed by dividing the total gap length by the number of gaps. As noted above, what happens at the beginning and end of the simulation influences all statistics relating to gap distribution.

Time Average Gap:

The *time average gap* is the mean gap duration averaged over time. Alternatively, it is the average length of the gap we would find if we randomly sampled the system. To compute the time average gap, two counters are required—one for the current gap length and one for the sum of the squares of gap lengths. During the simulation, if no satellite covers a given point on the grid, add one to the current gap length counter. If the point is covered, square the current gap length, add the results to the sum of the squares counter, and reset the current gap length counter to zero. (If the current gap length counter was previously zero, then no change will occur in either counter.) The time average gap is computed at the end of the simulation by dividing the sum of the squares of the gaps by the duration of the simulation.

Mean Response Time:

The *mean response time* is the average time from when we receive a random request to observe a point until we can observe it. If a satellite is within view of the point at a given time step, the response time at that step will be 0.* If the point in question is in a coverage gap, then the response time would be the time until the end of the coverage gap. In principle, response time should be computed from a given time step to the end of a gap. But by symmetry we could also count the time from the beginning of the gap—a computationally convenient method with the same results. Thus, the response time counter will be set to 0 if a point is covered at the current time step. We advance the response time counter by one time step if the point is not now covered. The mean response time will then be the average value of all response times for all time steps. This figure of merit takes into account both coverage and gap statistics in trying to determine the whole system's responsiveness. As shown below, the mean response time is most often the best coverage figure of merit for evaluating overall responsiveness.

To illustrate the meaning and relative advantages of these figures of merit, Fig. 9-46 diagrams a simplified coverage simulation for 3 satellite systems: A, B, and C. These could, for example, be 3 sample fire detection constellations. Our goal is to see events as quickly as possible, and therefore, minimize gaps. Constellation B is identical to A except for one added gap, which makes B clearly a worse solution than A. C has the same overall percent coverage as A, but the gaps are redistributed to create a rather long gap, making C the worst constellation for regular coverage.

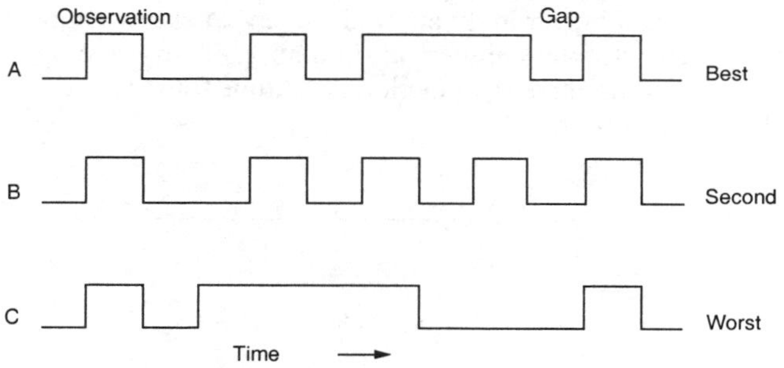

	Percent Coverage	Maximum Gap	Mean Gap	Time Average Gap	Mean Response Time
A	60	2	1.33	0.6	0.5
B	50	2	1.25	0.7	0.6
C	60	3	2.00	1.0	0.7

Fig. 9-46. Simulation of Coverage Figures of Merit. See text for explanation.

The table at the bottom of Fig. 9-46 shows the numerical values of the figures of merit defined above. The percent coverage correctly ranks constellation A better than

* One advantage of response time as a figure of merit is that delays in processing or communications (for both data requests and responses) can be directly added to the coverage response time. This results in a *total response time,* which measures the total time from when users request data until they receive it. We can also evaluate minimum, mean, and maximum total response times which have much more operational meaning than simple gap statistics and are still easy to compute.

B, but because it does not take gap statistics into account, it cannot distinguish between A and C. Similarly, the maximum gap cannot distinguish between A and B, even though B is clearly worse by having an additional gap. In this case the maximum gap tells us which constellation is worst but cannot distinguish between two constellations which are clearly different.

The mean gap statistic is even more misleading. By adding a short gap to constellation B, the average length of the gaps has been decreased, and consequently, this figure of merit ranks constellation B **above** constellation A. (As discussed in the introduction to Sec. 9.5, this can happen in real constellation statistics. By adding satellites we may eliminate some of the very small gaps, thus **increasing** the average gap length, even though more satellites provide more and better coverage.)

Finally, the time average gap and mean response time in the fourth and fifth columns correctly rank the three constellations in order of preference by taking into account both the percent coverage and gap statistics. Consequently, both of these are better figures of merit than the other three. I believe the mean response time is the stronger figure of merit because it provides a more useful measure of the end performance of the system and because it can be easily extended to include delays due to processing, communications, decision making, or the initiation of action. However, because each figure of merit represents different characteristics we should evaluate more than one. Specifically, I recommend evaluating mean response time, percent coverage, and maximum gap, and qualitatively (not quantitatively) weighting the results in that order, keeping strongly in mind the caveat at the beginning of Sec. 9.5.

Figures 9-47 and 9-48 show a numerical simulation of coverage figures of merit for several individual locations and as a function of latitude for the same orbit used to create Figs. 9-41, 9-42, and 9-46.

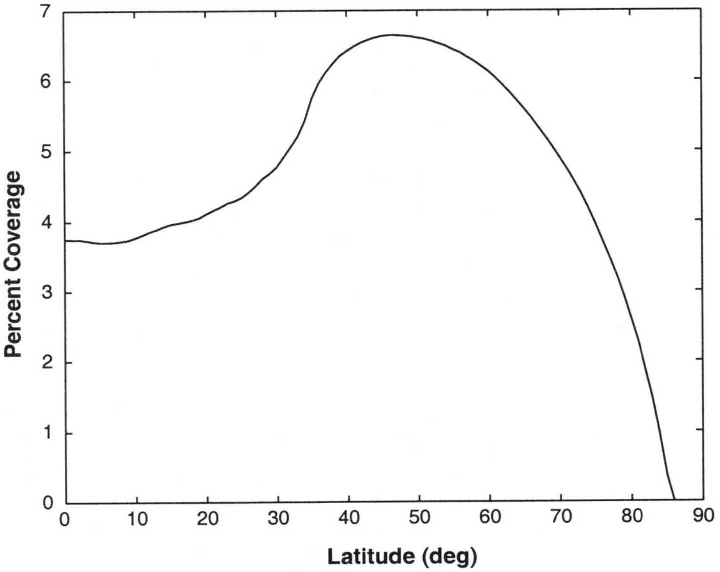

Fig. 9-47. Earth Coverage as a Function of Latitude. Orbit is the same as that used for Figs. 9-42, 9-43, and 9-46.

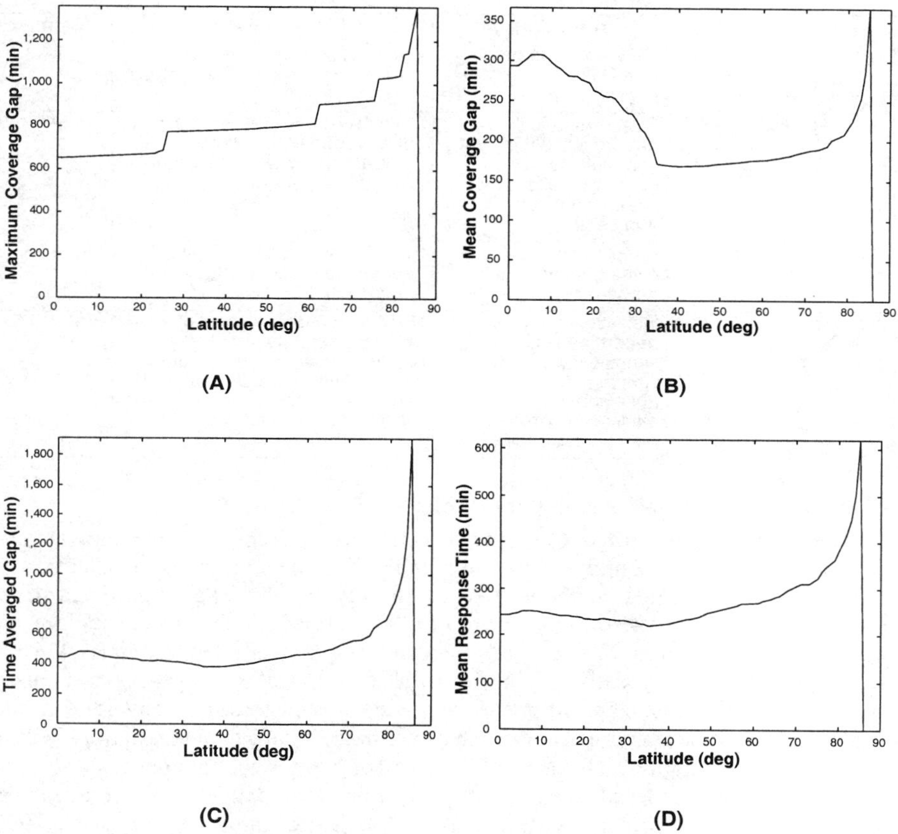

Fig. 9-48. Simulation of Representative Coverage Figures of Merit. Coverage FOMs globally, for individual locations, and as a function of latitude for the same orbit as Figs. 9-41, 9-42, and 9-45.

We have seen that there are four broad techniques available for evaluating Earth coverage:

- Ground track plots
- Coverage histograms
- Analytic coverage assessment (single location or vs. latitude)
- Numerical figures of merit

Table 9-8 summarizes some of the relative advantages and disadvantages of each of these approaches. In the end, there is no substitute for developing physical insight into the nature of the coverage and finding the most effective way to express that for each individual problem.

TABLE 9-8. Advantages and Disadvantages of Different Approaches to Evaluating Coverage. See text for discussion of each.

Approach	Advantages	Disadvantages	Example
Ground Trace Plot	Very simple to do; provides excellent physical insight	Does not provide quantitative results; hard to compare systems	Fig. 9-41
Coverage Histogram	Simple to calculate; gives excellent insight into multiple coverage characteristics; best overall evaluation approach	Difficult to compare systems; can not be reduced to a single number; may miss key features at locations not evaluated	Fig. 9-42
Analytic Coverage Functions	Simple to calculate; gives good insight into percent coverage	Provides no information about gaps or coverage distribution	Fig. 9-45
Numerical Simulations and Coverage Figures of Merit	Relatively easy to determine via simulation; provides simple numerical answers that can be easily compared (but may be misleading)	Requires coverage simulation; many parameters to select; provides statistical information on inherently nonstatistical data; can lead to *very* misleading results and conclusions	Figs. 9-46, 9-48

9.5.2 Earth Coverage for Elliptical Orbits

Generally, Earth coverage for elliptical orbits is more complex to evaluate than for circular orbits. Consequently, we are more likely to need simulations to provide good estimates. All the same methods and constraints for coverage figures of merit described in Sec. 9.5.1.4 are relevant to elliptical orbits as well. Consequently, the same simulation process for circular orbits can be equally applied to elliptical orbits. Note however, that the greatly varying velocities in elliptical orbits poses problems for simulations. If the time steps are made long, then it is easy to miss coverage around perigee. On the other hand, if the time steps are made small, then simulations will be very time consuming to run because of the very long time spent at apogee.

John Draim has undertaken extensive analyses over an extended period of the use of elliptical orbits to provide Earth coverage. (See for example Draim [1991, 1992, 1995, 1998].) His fundamental conclusion is that using elliptical rather than circular orbits provides an additional set of free parameters that can be adjusted as needed to optimize coverage. By choosing the orbit parameters correctly, we may provide improved coverage over regions of high traffic density at appropriate times of day. The logic of most circular orbit designs is to provide approximately uniform coverage over the world. However, for most types of activity this provides excess coverage over the world's poles and oceans in order to satisfy a philosophical need for symmetry. Using elliptical orbits allows us to more nearly match the coverage to the needs of the mission, and thereby reduce the number of satellites.

The penalty paid for using elliptical orbits is the varying altitudes and, therefore, the need for fundamentally more complex spacecraft. We need to accommodate a wider range of altitudes in our attitude sensors, a range of Earth sizes for coverage, and a range of slew rates for the spacecraft to maintain either nadir pointing or pointing toward particular targets. Consequently, although we may have a smaller number of spacecraft, this will be compensated in part by requiring more complex spacecraft and more complex operational procedures. In addition, we are likely to spend greater amounts of time in the Van Allen belts, and, therefore, require more shielding than would be the case in low-Earth orbits.

As in the case of circular orbits, substantial insight can be obtained by using ground trace plots to evaluate coverage. For example, Fig. 9-49 shows the ground swath for a satellite in a highly elliptical orbit, inclined at the critical inclination of 63.4 deg. Note that the use of the ground track plots becomes more complex both because the size of the coverage region varies and because the velocity of the spacecraft along the ground track also varies strongly. Because of this, coverage histograms such as those in Fig. 9-50 provide additional insight into the performance.

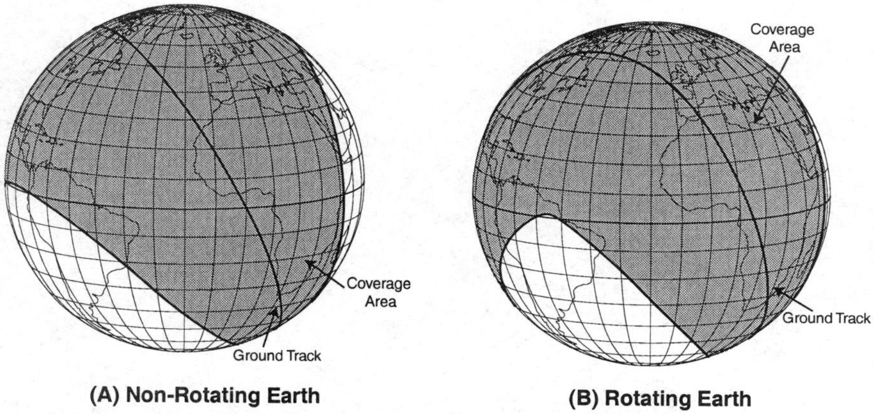

Fig. 9-49. Ground Swath Plot for a Satellite in a 200 km × 10,000 km Elliptical Orbit at 63.4 deg Inclination. The heavy line is the ground track for one orbit. The shaded area is the swath. At any given position the instantaneous coverage is a circle centered on the ground track and tangent to the ground swath limit. (A) shows the swath over a non-rotating Earth. (B) shows the real coverage over the rotating Earth.

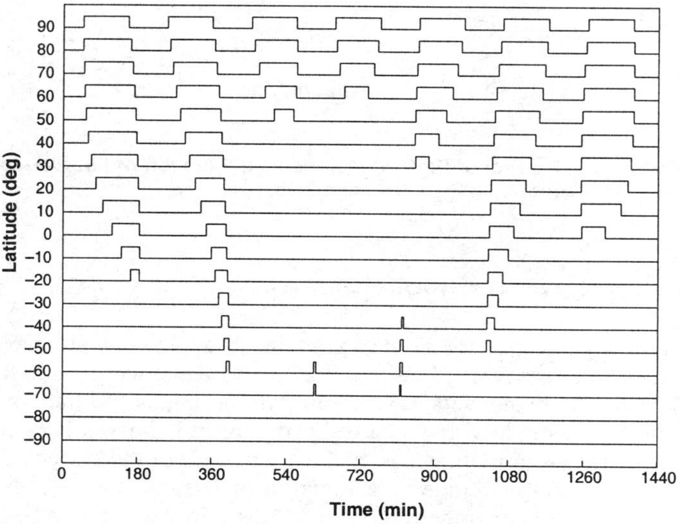

Fig. 9-50. Histograms of Coverage Over a Day for Ground Stations at the Same Longitude, but Varying Latitudes. The elliptical orbit is the same as that illustrated in Fig. 9-49.

Figure 9-51 shows a representative plot of coverage as a function of latitude for the same orbit, and finally, Fig. 9-52 shows representative coverage figures of merit for the same orbit conditions. In the case of the elliptical orbit, coverage figures of merit are probably the best approach for numerically evaluating coverage, since they take into account the different times spent in various segments of the orbit. Nonetheless, as always, coverage figures of merit must be evaluated with care and must include some physical insight into the nature of the coverage process.

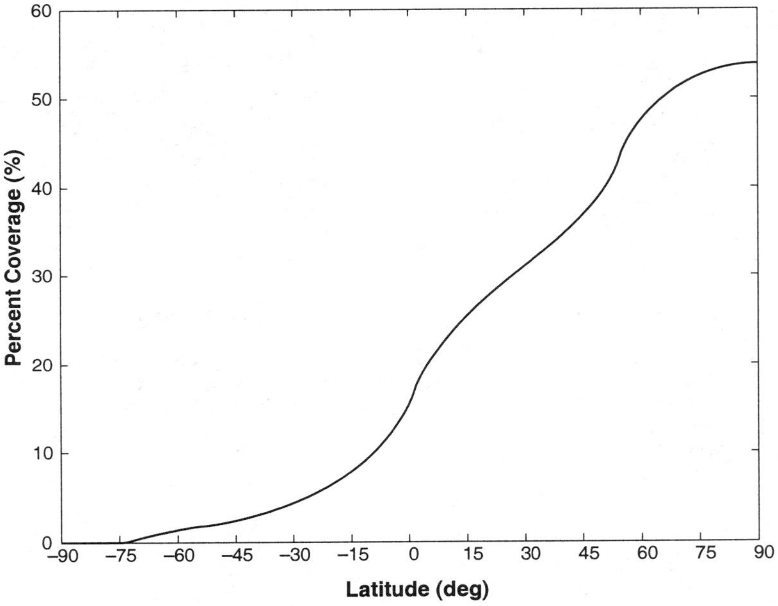

Fig. 9-51. Representative Plot of Earth Coverage as a Function of Latitude for the Same Satellite Illustrated in Figs. 9-49 and 9-50.

9.5.3 Earth Coverage for Geosynchronous Orbits

By definition, geostationary orbits maintain an approximately fixed location over the Earth. Small amounts of motion due to a low inclination, small eccentricity, or stationkeeping maneuvers have essentially no impact on the coverage area of the satellite. Consequently, the area of Earth covered is essentially fixed and is a function only of the minimum working elevation angle of the system. Figure 9-53 is a plot of the percent coverage as a function of latitude for various minimum elevation angles. These coverage regions are drawn on the Earth in Fig. 9-54. For inclined geosynchronous orbits, all of the mechanisms of the low-Earth orbit analysis are applicable.

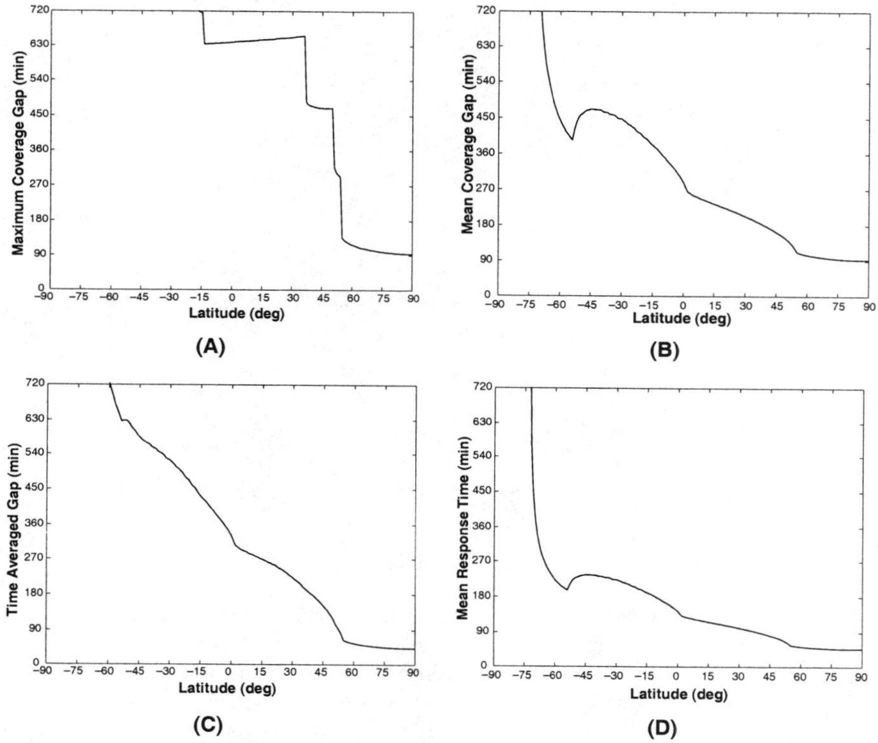

Fig. 9-52. Representative Coverage Figures of Merit for the Same Orbit as Previous Plots. Coverage FOMs are probably the best approach for numerically evaluating coverage for elliptical orbits since they can take into account the different time spent in various segments of the orbit.

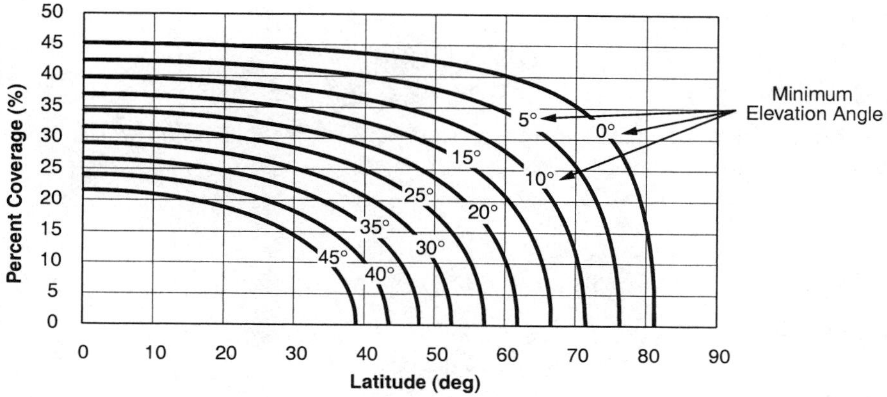

Fig. 9-53. Coverage from Geostationary Orbit as a Function of Minimum Elevation Angle.

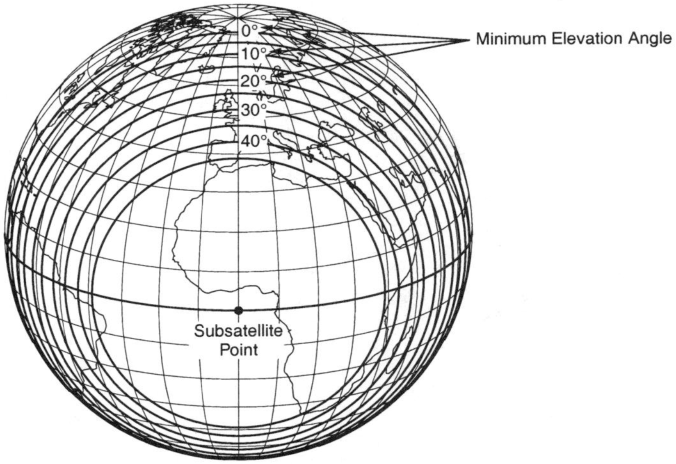

Fig. 9-54. Coverage from Geostationary Orbit Projected onto the Earth.

9.6 Coverage Analysis Example

The purpose of this section is to provide a detailed example of how we might go about analyzing a particular coverage problem. Our example problem is to provide observations of the island of Haiti in the Caribbean at an elevation angle of greater than 25 deg, while simultaneously being in contact with a groundstation located on Wallops Island, VA, at an elevation angle greater than 5 deg. We would like to do this with a satellite at an altitude of 850 km and an inclination of 65 deg. The general objectives for the problem are shown in Fig. 9-55. What we would like to find out is not only whether or not the problem can be done but how much coverage we will have, how sensitive that coverage is to the various orbit parameters, and how we might be able to redesign either the problem or the orbit in order to provide better coverage.

We begin by computing the angular radius of the Earth and maximum Earth central angle from Eq. (9-2), as:

$$\rho = 61.93 \text{ deg} \tag{9-132}$$

$$\lambda_0 = 28.07 \text{ deg} \tag{9-133}$$

We then compute fundamental coverage parameters for Wallops Island (W) using Eqs. (9-4-b) and (9-6), as:

$$\varepsilon_{min,W} = 5 \text{ deg} \tag{9-134}$$

$$\lambda_{max,W} = 24 \text{ deg} \tag{9-135}$$

$$\eta_{max,W} = 61.62 \text{ deg} \tag{9-136}$$

and for Haiti (H), the same set of equations yield:

$$\varepsilon_{min,H} = 25 \text{ deg} \tag{9-137}$$

$$\lambda_{max,H} = 12 \text{ deg} \tag{9-138}$$

$$\eta_{max,H} = 53.27 \text{ deg} \tag{9-139}$$

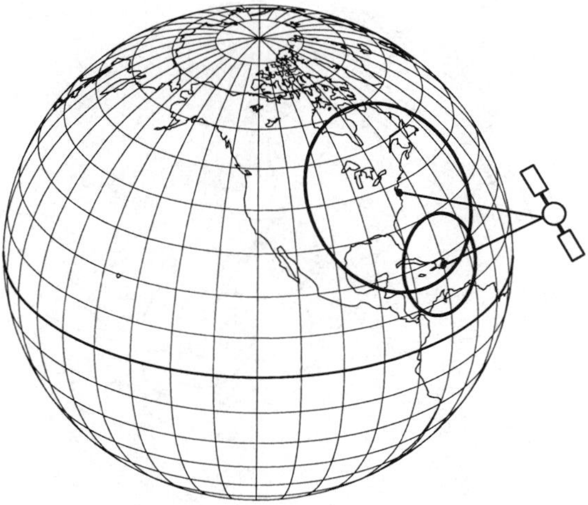

Fig. 9-55. The Wallops/Haiti Coverage Example. We would like to determine how difficult it would be to photograph Haiti at an elevation angle greater than 25 deg while simultaneously communicating with Wallops Island at an elevation angle greater than 5 deg. See text for discussion.

We use the above data to construct Fig. 9-56, which shows a representative coverage pass near the descending node, which sees both Wallops Island and Haiti. For several positions along the ground track we have drawn the coverage circles for both locations. The dashed outer circle is the maximum coverage area for communicating with Wallops, and the solid inner circle is the limit for observations of Haiti. Note that at the upper time step we have begun to communicate with Wallops Island, but are still well away from Haiti. At the middle time step, Haiti is beginning to come into view within the observation limit, and we can still communicate with Wallops, although it is behind us. In the third step, Haiti is leaving the observation region, though we lost contact with Wallops Island some time ago.

Figure 9-57 shows the mission geometry as seen from the spacecraft for the central time step in the previous figure. The spacecraft is now approximately midway between Florida and Cuba. The outer circle represents the angular radius of the Earth at 61.93 deg. Just inside of that is a circle almost touching it which shows the limit at which we can communicate with Wallops. Clearly observations at that distance where foreshortening is so dramatic would not be possible, but communications are acceptable. The inner circle is the 25 deg elevation angle curve at which we can begin observations. In this particular plot, Haiti is just coming into view within the observation limit. We could no longer observe Wallops but it is still well within our communications band for at least a brief period.

Figure 9-58 shows the geometry at the same time as viewed from the Wallops Island ground station. Here the path of the satellite is plotted against the background of the stars in the Milky Way. Notice that the satellite has long since passed its peak elevation and is heading toward the horizon, although we're still well above the 5 deg elevation angle limit for communications. Figure 9-59 shows the same information as viewed by an observer on Haiti. Here the satellite is just passing the 25 deg elevation

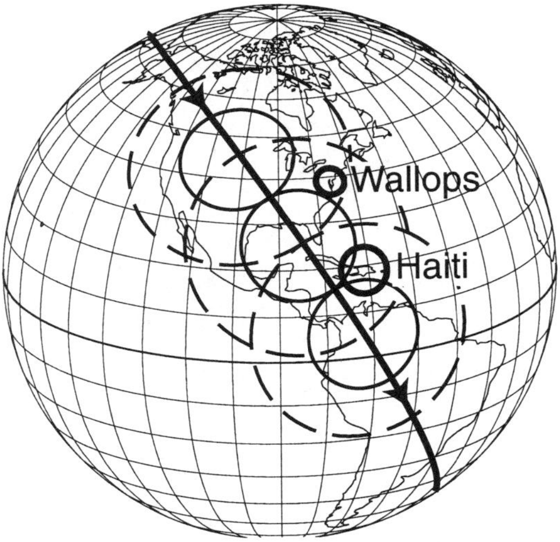

Fig. 9-56. Motion of the Spacecraft Along the Orbit Showing Visibility Regions for Both Haiti (Solid Circle) and Wallops Island (Dashed Circle).

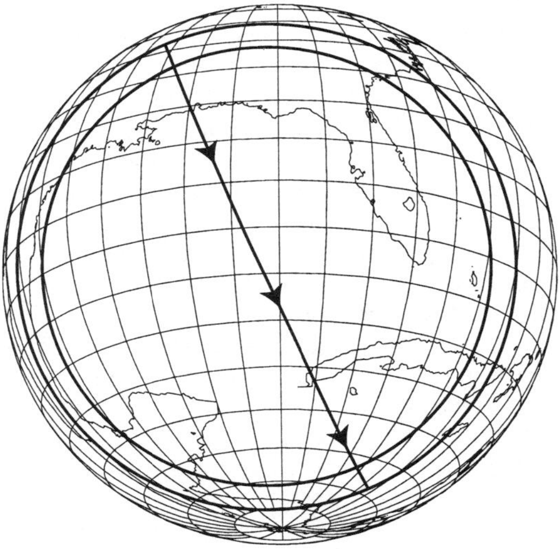

Fig. 9-57. View from the Spacecraft at the Time of the Center Plot in Fig. 9-56. Haiti is just coming into view on the forward horizon and Wallops is near the horizon, but still within communications range near the rearward horizon.

angle limit for observations and will be above this limit for some time to come. We can make use of these plots to understand the observation and communications geometry as seen on the surface of the Earth, as seen from the perspective of the satellite, and as seen from the perspective of the communications station at Wallops Island and the observation area in Haiti.

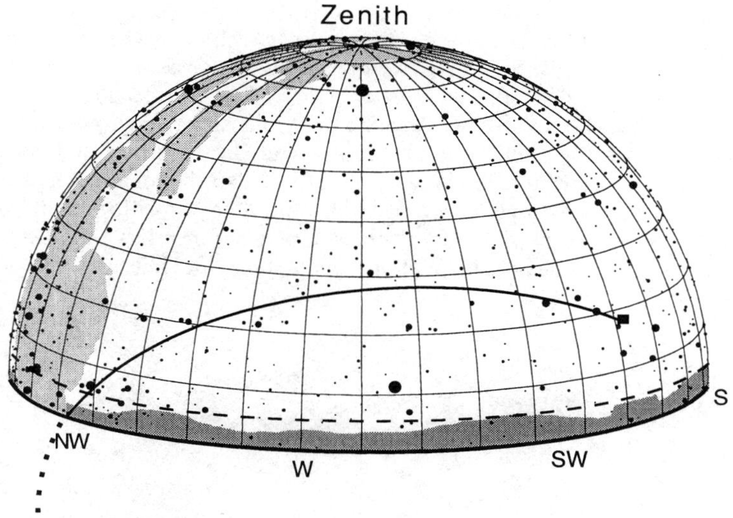

Fig. 9-58. View from Wallops Island at the Time of Fig. 9-57. The satellite has passed its highest point and is on the way down as it begins to see Haiti.

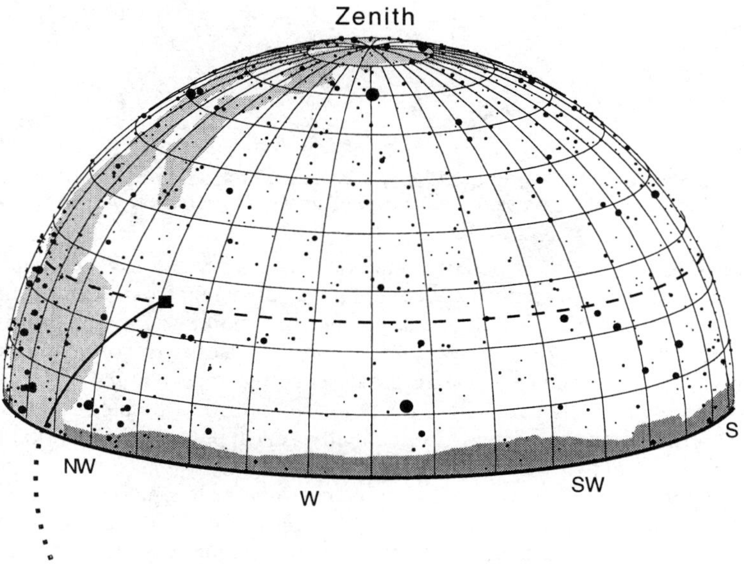

Fig. 9-59. View from Haiti at the Time of Fig. 9-57. Here the satellite is just rising over the 25 deg effective horizon. By the time the satellite reaches its highest point, Wallops Island will no longer be visible to the satellite.

Figure 9-60 provides a method of analyzing the orbit geometry and coverage characteristics for this problem. We have drawn a circle of 24 deg radius around Wallops Island representing all possible subsatellite points where we're in potential communication with Wallops. Similarly, we have drawn a circle of 12 deg radius about Haiti indicating the subsatellite points for which Haiti can be observed within the observation limits. The overlap between the two is the shaded region in which we can simultaneously observe Haiti at an elevation angle above 25 deg and communicate with Wallops at an elevation above 5 deg. We have also shown a representative orbit pass near the descending node for our satellite. At point A, Wallops comes into view for communications. At point B, Haiti comes into view for observation. At C, we lose the capacity to communicate with Wallops, and at point D, Haiti goes out of observation range.

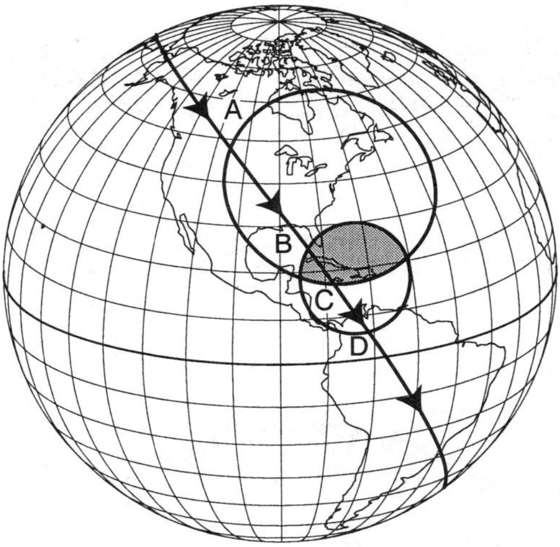

Fig. 9-60. Coverage Analysis of the Wallops Island/Haiti Problem. See text for discussion. Plots of this type provide a very powerful analysis tool and are very easy to generate.

Simulations can provide a detailed numerical assessment of how well our problem works. However, we can gain a high level of physical insight by simply examining the ground track plot in Fig. 9-60. For the geometric conditions shown, approximately 60% of the time that Haiti can be observed, we can also be in communication with Wallops Island. Irrespective of where the descending or ascending nodes occur, we will have somewhat more than half of the observation time available to us on any orbit for which observations can occur. Consequently, this appears to be a workable geometry for the problem that we have defined.

By examining Fig. 9-60, we can determine not only the extent to which the problem can be done, but the impact of changing virtually any of the parameters. For example, if we increase the minimum elevation angle for observation, we will reduce the coverage circle centered around Haiti and will have less total observation time available. Nonetheless, we will continue to have the same or more percentage contact time with Wallops. As another example, if we move the ground station from Wallops Island to Chicago, we will significantly reduce the amount of overlap but we will still have some on most orbits. However, for some orbits in the vicinity of the ascending node it would be able to slip past such that observations could be made but communications were not possible. If we move the ground station from Wallops to Los Angeles, then the two regions will not overlap and irrespective of the orbit there will be no position of the spacecraft, for which we are able to both observe Haiti and communicate with Los Angeles simultaneously. By closely examining Fig. 9-60, we can determine the impact of varying essentially any of the defining parameters of the problem. We can understand what makes the problem work and not work, and how to go about adjusting the parameters so as to provide better coverage or to cover other scenarios as well. This is indicative of the substantial power available from relatively straightforward analytic and plotting techniques.

Finally, Fig. 9-61 shows the results of a coverage simulation run for our example. The two tombstone plots represent observations of Haiti and communication with Wallops, and, of course, the overlap region between them is where both are possible simultaneously. This provides a good assessment of the timelines, and allows us to evaluate time intervals between coverage periods. It shows us how many observations we will have in the course of a day, and approximately how they will be distributed. It does not, however, provide the same level of insight as Fig. 9-60, as to the impact of changing the defining parameters or varying any of the conditions of observation. Each type of analysis is useful, and together they can provide strong mechanisms for evaluating satellite coverage.

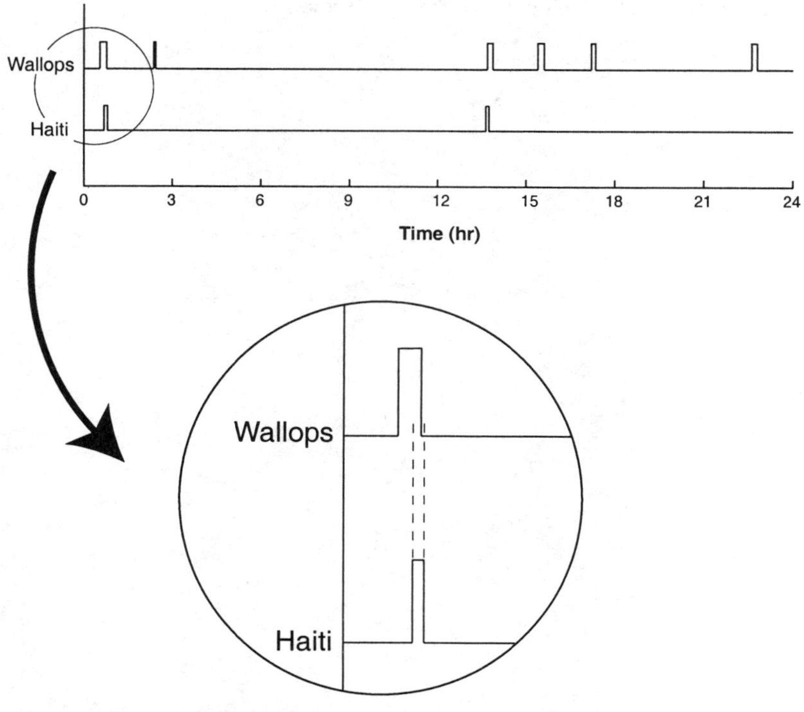

Fig. 9-61. Results of a Coverage Simulation Run for the Example Problem.

References

Collins, Steve. 1992. "Geocentric Nadir and Range from Horizon Sensor Observations of the Oblate Earth." Paper No. AAS 92-176, presented at the AAS/AIAA Spaceflight Mechanics Meeting, Colorado Springs, CO, 24–26 February.

Draim, John. 1991. "Continuous Global N-Tuple Coverage with $(2N + 2)$ Satellites." *Journal of Guidance, Control, and Dynamics*. 14(1): 17–23.

________. 1992. "Lightsat Constellation Designs." Paper No. AIAA-92-1988, presented at the 14th AIAA International Communication Satellite Systems Conference & Exhibit, Washington, DC, 22–26 March.

.________. 1995. "Elliptical-Orbit MEO Constellations: A Cost-Effective Approach for Multi-Satellite Systems." Paper No. IAF-95-M.4.05, presented at the 46th International Astronautical Congress, Oslo, Norway, 2–6 October.

________. 1998. "Design Philosophy for the ELLIPSO™ Satellite System." Presented at the 17th AIAA International Communications Satellite Systems Conference and Exhibit, Yokohama, Japan, 23–27 February.

Meeus, J. 1991. *Astronomical Algorithms.* Richmond, VA: Willmann-Bell.

Seidelmann, P. Kenneth, ed. 1992. *Explanatory Supplement to the Astronomical Almanac*. Mill Valley: University Science Books.

Chapter 10

Satellite Relative Motion

Thus far, we have been concerned primarily with the motion of satellites relative to the surface of the Earth, or the apparent motion as seen from Earth. However, as illustrated in Fig. 10-1, the motion of satellites relative to each other is also of interest. This

Fig. 10-1. INTELSAT Communications Satellite Seen from the Space Shuttle Orbiter. Because the satellite is about to be captured, the orbits have been nearly perfectly matched and the two vehicles are moving very slowly with respect to each other. In most cases, satellites cross paths moving at relative velocities on the order of 7 km/sec or 30 times the speed of normal commercial jet airliners. (Photo courtesy of Johnson Space Center.)

is important for constellation analysis and design, operations planning and analysis, and intersatellite communications, such as data transfer between the Space Shuttle and TDRS, the use of GPS by other satellites for navigation, or low-Earth orbit communications constellations.

What does the motion of one spacecraft look like as seen from another? In some sense, the answer is easy. We integrate the equations of motion for both the target and the observer, difference the two, plot the results against the background of fixed stars, and the computer will have done all the work for us. This is the traditional approach. It works well for detailed analysis in an operations environment but is entirely unsuccessful at providing the physical insight and broad overview critical for conceptual mission design, constellation design and analysis, mission and operations planning, or the analysis of alternative approaches. This chapter provides this broad picture, while Vol. III provides the numerical basis for the equations of motion approach. Consequently, we are interested here not in a precise numerical answer but in broad characteristics and general limits on the motion, so that we can understand how to design, plan, and analyze the process of spacecraft interacting with each other.

Because the relative motion of spacecraft, particularly on a large scale, is normally done by computer simulation, there have been very few analytical studies of the characteristics of this motion. The one exception to this is the case of two spacecraft orbiting very near each other. Here the equations of motion can be considerably simplified and are reduced to what are frequently called Hill's equations or the Clohessy-Wiltshire equations. These are summarized in Sec. 10.2.3. While there are few external references, the large-scale relative motion of satellites is another example of the dual-axis spiral introduced in Chap. 8. Consequently, all of the concepts and formulas provided there can be applied to the problem of relative motion. Applications of this relative motion analysis are, in turn, used in Chap. 13 for constellation design. Nearly all of the material in this chapter is new and has not previously been published.

The chapter begins with the relative motion of satellites in circular orbits at the same altitude. While this is a special case, it is both the easiest to understand and the most common in practice, since much of the relative motion analysis is applied to constellations in circular orbits at the same altitude. Sec. 10.2 then looks at relative motion in a formation in which the satellites are close together but may have small differences in altitude. Finally, Sec. 10.3 then looks at the relative motion of satellites at different altitudes—looking at lower satellites from above, higher satellites from below, and satellites in an elliptical transfer orbit seen from both the origin and the destination.

10.1 Satellite Relative Motion of Co-Altitude Constellations

The relative motion of satellites naturally breaks down into three broad areas. First, there is the large-scale relative motion due to individual satellites not being in the same orbit. This creates the gross motion of one satellite relative to another that is needed for constellation design, coverage computations, or how to fill in holes in coverage. Superimposed on this is the small-scale relative motion due to varying orbit perturbations on each satellite and individual satellites not being in precisely the intended orbit. This produces almost a "Brownian motion" within the constellation that causes each satellite to move around relative to its ideal location. This small-scale motion impacts the size of the stationkeeping box that we can create in a constellation and, therefore, impacts coverage and crosslink communications. Finally, in addition to how satellites actually move, we are interested in how they appear to move as seen from an observer satellite. This is important for understanding how to design and point antennas, lasers, or cameras for communications or observations.

Because we are interested in the overall characteristics of the motion for analysis, planning, and design, it is insufficient to rely exclusively on computer simulations and integration of the equations of motion. We need a broadly applicable analytic approach to assess coverage, closest approach for collision avoidance, and satellite-to-satellite visibility. This general analytic approach can also provide broad rules for pointing to any other satellite in the constellation, can be used for pointing-related analysis (attitude error budgets, attitude rates, or interference assessment), and can be used for evaluating blockage and Sun interference as satellites become obstructed behind the Earth or appear in a line of sight to the Sun.

10.1.1 Large-Scale Relative Motion

We begin by looking at the large-scale relative motion of co-altitude satellites in circular orbits. This is a special case of the dual-axis spiral with particularly simple results because the angular frequency of the two rotations are the same and, as we shall see shortly, the secondary angular radius is 90 deg. As illustrated in Fig. 10-2, there are two key parameters in satellite relative motion. The *relative inclination*, i_R, is the angle at which the orbits of the two satellites intersect. This is **not** the same as the difference between the inclinations of the two orbits since orbits at the same inclination but different nodes will intersect at a non-zero angle. (See, for example, Fig. 13-3 in Sec. 13.1.) The second parameter is the *relative phase*, ϕ_R, which is the angular separation between the two satellites at the time they pass through one another's orbit plane. As can be seen from Fig. 10-2, this will occur four times per orbit—once when satellite 1 crosses the plane of satellite 2 and later when satellite 2 crosses the plane of satellite 1. It then occurs twice more at the other intersection of the orbits, 180 deg away.

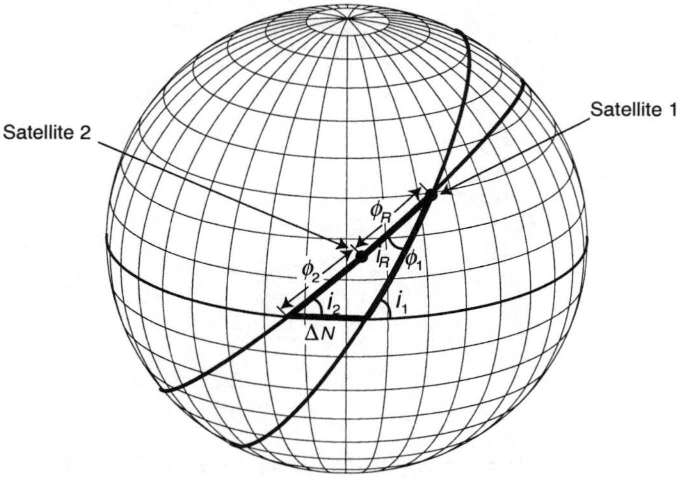

Fig. 10-2. The Relative Motion of Co-Altitude Satellites in Circular Orbits Depends on Only Two Parameters—the Relative Inclination, i_R, and the Relative Phase, ϕ_R.

The relative phase and relative inclination fully define the relative motion between the satellites. This is perhaps the most important message of this section:

The relative motion of co-altitude satellites in circular orbits depends only on the relative phase and relative inclination.

It does not depend on the specific inclination or on the satellite's being at a common inclination. Once we have calculated i_R and ϕ_R, we can ignore the actual inclinations and use these parameters to calculate all of the characteristics of the relative motion of the satellites.

In most constellations, the actual inclination of any two satellites is the same, i.e. $i_1 = i_2 = i$. (See Fig. 10-3.) In this case, there are particularly simple expressions for i_R and ϕ_R:

$$\cos i_R = \cos^2 i + \sin^2 i \cos \Delta N \tag{10-1a}$$

$$\phi_R = (T_2 - T_1)n + \Delta\phi \tag{10-1b}$$

where

$$\Delta\phi = 180 \text{ deg} - 2\phi \tag{10-1c}$$

$$\tan\phi = \frac{\tan(90 \text{ deg} - \Delta N / 2)}{\cos i} \tag{10-1d}$$

ΔN is the angular separation along the equator between the two ascending nodes, $T_2 - T_1$ is the time between satellites 1 and 2 crossing their respective ascending nodes, n is the mean motion or angular frequency of both satellites, ϕ is defined on Fig. 10-3, and $\Delta\phi$ is an intermediate variable that represents the difference in arc length from the point where the two orbits intersect to their respective ascending nodes.

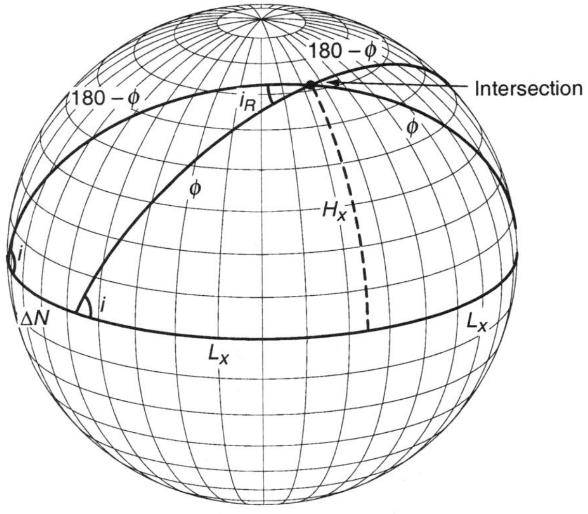

Fig. 10-3. Intersection of Two Orbits with the Same Inclination. The intersection point will be midway between the pairs of ascending and descending nodes. For one satellite the arc length, ϕ, from the ascending node to the intersection point will be less than 90 deg. For the other it will be 180 deg – ϕ. See also Fig. 13-3 in Sec. 13.1.

In terms of classical orbit elements, Eq. (10-1b) can be replaced by:

$$\phi_R = L_{0_2} - L_{0_1} + \Delta\phi \qquad (10\text{-}2a)$$

where the *spacecraft longitude*, L_{0_1} is defined by:

$$L_{0_i} \equiv M_{0_i} + \omega_i \qquad (10\text{-}2b)$$

where ω_i is the argument of perigee and M_{0_i} is the anomaly at a common epoch for the two orbits. For nearly circular orbits ω_i and M_{0_i} will not be well-defined but L_{0_i} will be.*

In the more general case in which the inclinations of the two satellites are different ($i_1 \neq i_2$), the relative inclination and relative phase are somewhat more complex:

$$\cos i_R = \cos i_1 \cos i_2 + \sin i_1 \sin i_2 \cos\Delta N \qquad (10\text{-}3a)$$

$$\phi_R = (T_2 - T_1)n + \Delta\phi \qquad (10\text{-}3b)$$

where

$$\Delta\phi = \phi_2 + \phi_R - \phi_1 \qquad (10\text{-}3c)$$

$$\cos\phi_1 = \left[\frac{\cos i_2 - \cos i_R \cos i_1}{\sin i_R \sin i_1}\right] \qquad (10\text{-}3d)$$

$$\cos\phi_2 + \cos\phi_R = -\left[\frac{\cos i_1 + \cos i_R \cos i_2}{\sin i_R \sin i_2}\right] \qquad (10\text{-}3e)$$

Here ϕ_1 is the arc length from the ascending node of satellite 1 to the intersection of the orbits and ϕ_2. ϕ_2 is the arc length from the ascending node of satellite 2 to where satellite 2 will be when satellite 1 is at the intersection of the orbits.

We can use the above equations to determine the motion of a satellite relative to any arbitrarily defined *base satellite*. Any satellite in a constellation may be chosen as the base satellite. If the constellation is highly symmetric, it will not matter which satellite is chosen as the base.

To simplify the analysis, we use the *relative motion reference frame* defined in Fig. 10-4. This is an Earth centered frame of reference, co-rotating with the base satellite, with the equator of the frame aligned with the orbit plane and the coordinate pole at the orbit pole. In comparing the motion of two satellites, it doesn't matter which is the base satellite. Changing the base satellite simply flops the relative motion pattern to the other side and reverses the sequence of motion, leaving the pattern unchanged. The purpose of using the relative motion reference frame is to remove the rotation of the base satellite relative to the Earth and concentrate on the motion relative to the satellites themselves. (For most constellation designs we want complete coverage of the Earth so our location with respect to the surface doesn't matter. However, we can easily go back to motion over the surface of the Earth if this becomes important.) Depending on what is convenient, we can think of the surface of the Earth-centered sphere containing the base satellite as representing either the direction as seen from the center of the Earth or the sphere with radius equal to the common altitude, i.e. the sphere which contains the actual motion of the satellites.

---

* If the orbit is circular, we simply use the spacecraft longitude, L_{0_i}, with respect to node as the defining element.

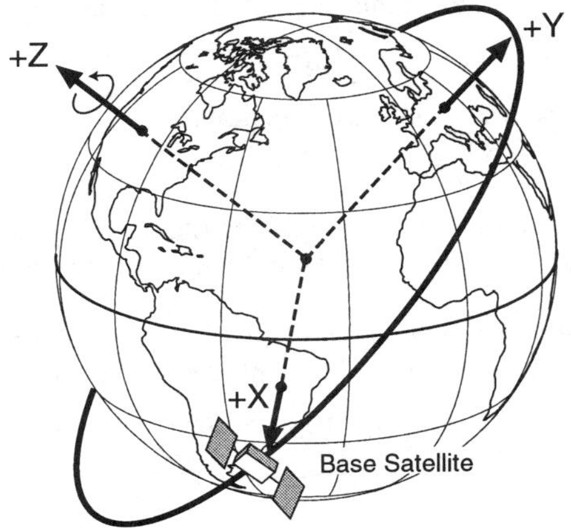

Fig. 10-4. Coordinate Frame Used for Relative Motion Analysis.

For circular co-altitude orbits, the relative motion of any satellite with respect to the other is an *analemma* or figure eight in the relative motion frame. This shape is the same as the motion of the field-of-view of a rotating sensor on a spinning spacecraft as defined in Sec. 8.3.1. Its astronomical origins are given in the boxed example. As shown in Fig. 10-5 the half height of the analemma equals the relative inclination and the distance along the equator from the base satellite equals the relative phase. Thus, if the orbit planes remain the same but the satellites change position within the orbit, then the relative motion analemma will remain unchanged, but will be located at a different distance, ϕ_R. The equations of motion for the analemma are given most easily in parametric form:

$$\sin \delta = \sin i_R \sin nt \tag{10-4}$$

$$\alpha = nt - \text{atan}(\cos i_R \tan nt) \tag{10-5}$$

where t is the time, n is the angular frequency of both satellites, δ is the elevation component in the relative motion frame, and α is the azimuthal component, relative to the point where the analemma crosses the equator (i.e. α and δ are the azimuth and elevation coordinators in Fig. 10-5). At the orbit plane, the left and right sides of the analemma cross at an angle equal to the relative inclination. Consequently, the angle that each curve makes with respect to the base orbit plane as it crosses this plane is 90 deg $- i_R/2$. The minimum angular separation, λ_{min}, from the base satellite will be the radius of a small circle centered on the base satellite and tangent to the inside to the analemma. This is given by:

$$\sin(\lambda_{min}/2) = \sin(\phi_R/2)\cos(i_R/2) \tag{10-6}$$

Similarly the maximum distance, λ_{max}, is the radius of the larger small circle tangent to the outside of the analemma given by:

$$\cos(\lambda_{max}/2) = \cos(\phi_R/2)\cos(i_R/2) \tag{10-7}$$

The shape of the relative motion analemma is a one parameter family of curves depending only on the relative inclination between the two orbits. A few representative

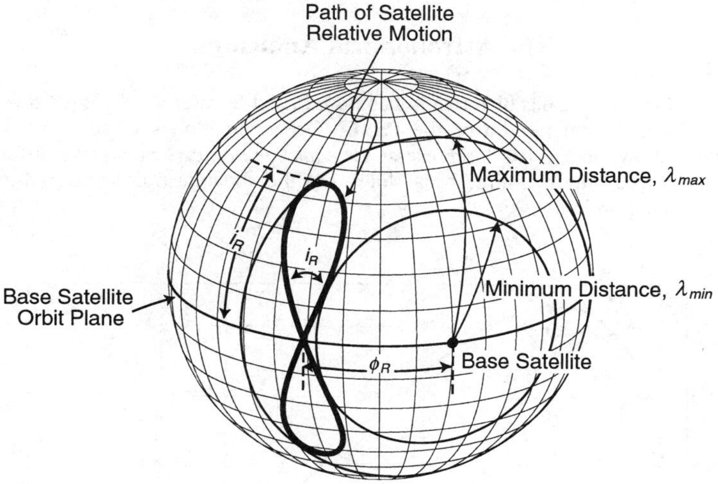

Fig. 10-5. The Relative Motion of Two Co-Altitude Satellites in Circular Orbits as Seen in the Relative Motion Frame. Here the motion is simply an analemma offset from the base satellite by the relative phase and with height equal to the relative inclination.

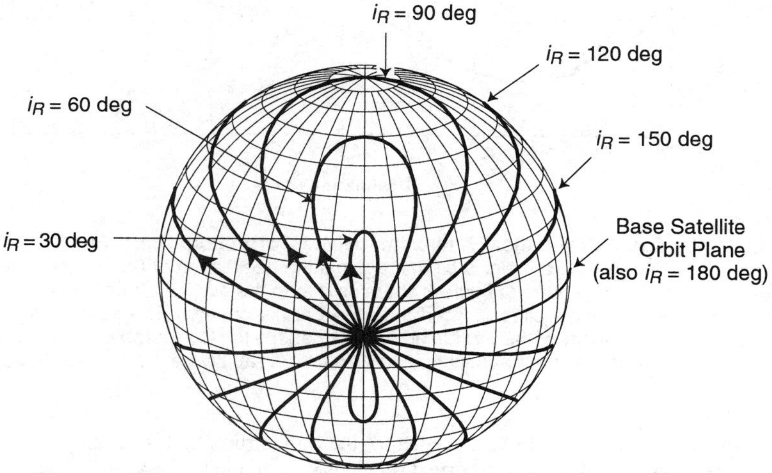

Fig. 10-6. Representative Relative Motion Analemma for Co-altitude Satellites. The shape of the relative motion analemma for co-altitude satellites depends only on the relative inclination, i_R, which is listed on each curve. i = 180 deg is a satellite in the same orbit as the base satellite, but moving in the opposite direction.

analemmas are shown in Fig. 10-6. Recall that the height of the analemma equals the relative inclination. If the two satellites are in the same orbit plane, the height will be 0 and the analemma reduces to a point offset from the base satellite by an amount equal

The Astronomical Analemma

The word *analemma* has historically been used most to refer to the figure 8 pattern usually placed in the middle of the Pacific Ocean on globes of the Earth. This analemma, shown in Fig. 10-7, represents the *equation of time* which is the difference between the true time measured by a clock, and the apparent time measured by the position of the Sun in the sky.

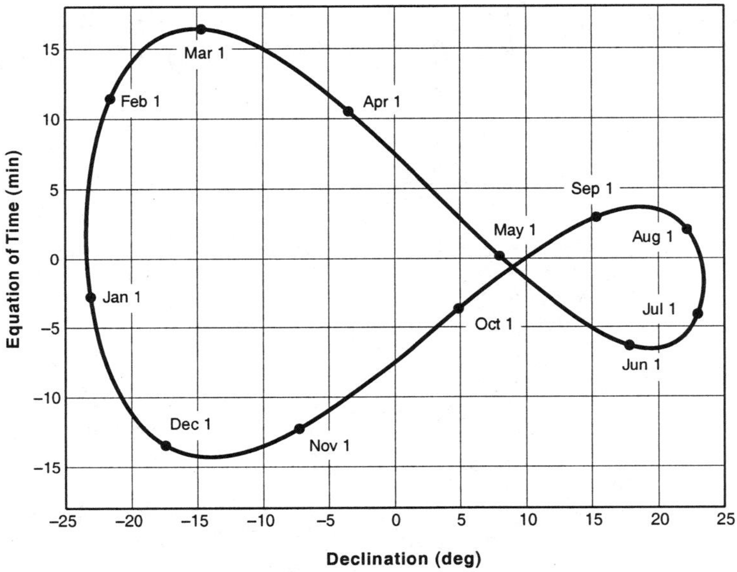

Fig. 10-7. The Astronomical Analemma Gives Corrections for a Sundial. The "time late" for the sundial is plotted against the declination of Sun for each day of the year. The general figure 8 shape is due to the ecliptic, or path of the Sun in the sky, being inclined 23.5 deg to the Earth's equator. The asymmetry is due to eccentricity of the Earth's orbit which causes the Sun to move more slowly along the ecliptic near aphelion in July and more rapidly near perihelion in January.

The equation of time indicates whether the Sun is running fast or slow relative to its average position and is used to correct readings on a sundial. The analemma comes about because the *mean Sun,* or average position of the Sun if it were moving at a constant rate, moves uniformly along the celestial equator whereas the true Sun moves non-uniformly along the ecliptic at an angle of 23.5 deg to the equator. By definition, they both move at the same average frequency, such that the analemma is a closed curve over a year. One side of the analemma is larger than the other because the motion of the true Sun in the sky is the result of the Earth's orbital motion, which is non-uniform due to the orbit eccentricity. Thus, one way to measure both the inclination and shape of the Earth's orbit about the Sun is to plot the position of the Sun in the sky at exactly noon throughout the year.

to the spacing between the two satellites. For very small values of the relative inclination, the analemma is nearly a vertical line with very little sideways motion, as discussed in Sec. 10.2.1. As the analemma gets larger, it also gets "fatter" and covers a larger azimuth range. If the two orbits are at right angles to each other, the analemma crosses the equator at 45 deg and just reaches the pole of the coordinate system. When the relative inclination is larger than 90 deg, the two satellites are traveling in opposite directions and the analemma sweeps through all azimuth angles. Finally, when the relative inclination becomes 180 deg, the analemma reduces to a great circle along the coordinate equator, with the two satellites moving in the same plane but in opposite directions, such that they pass each other twice per orbit.

We can use the relative motion analemma to determine when 2 satellites can see each other. Ignoring atmospheric refraction and absorption, satellites will be able to just see each other when the line joining them is tangent to the surface of the Earth. As shown in Fig. 10-8, this will occur at twice the maximum Earth central angle seen by a single satellite. This is another way of saying that whenever two satellites can see the same point on the surface of the Earth, they must be able to see each other. Thus, on our relative motion reference frame we can draw a circle centered on the base satellite with a radius equal to twice the Earth central angle corresponding to the true horizon. Whenever the second satellite is within this circle, it will be above the horizon and visible to the base satellite. Whenever it is outside this circle, it will be below the horizon and the satellites cannot see each other. (See Fig. 10-10A later in the section.)

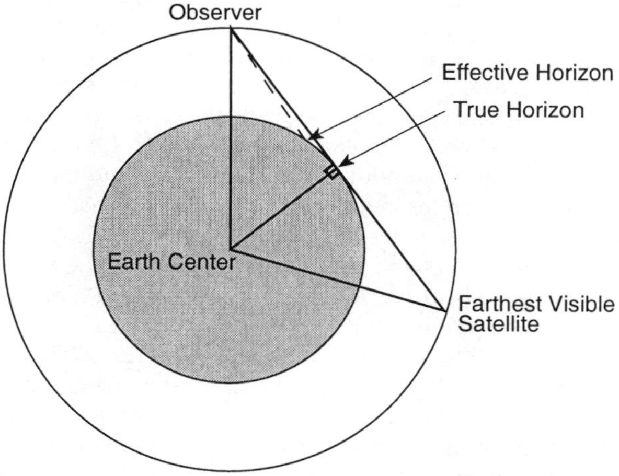

Fig. 10-8. Determining Regions of Intersatellite Visibility. Whenever two satellites are within twice the maximum Earth central angle (true horizon), they will be able to see each other.

As shown in Fig. 10-9, we can extend this concept to determine the nadir angle, η, as seen from either satellite to the other. For any co-altitude satellite at Earth central angle, λ, the nadir angle from each satellite to the other is given by:

$$\eta = 90 \text{ deg} - \lambda / 2 \tag{10-8}$$

As must be the case, all co-altitude satellites will be seen within 90 deg of nadir.

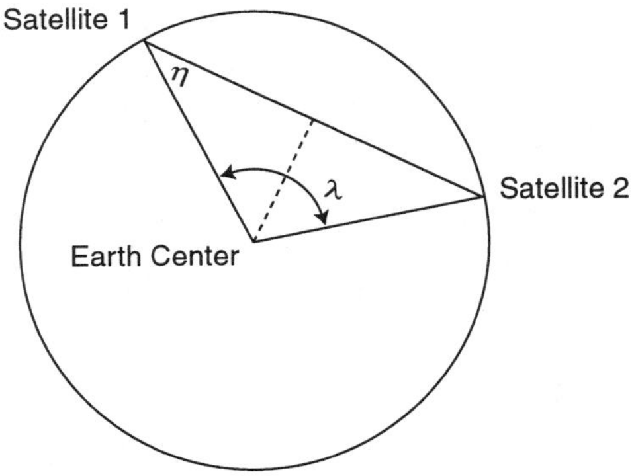

Fig. 10-9. Relationship Between Geometry as Seen from the Satellite and as Seen from the Earth's Center.

In addition to the relative motion of the two satellites, we are also interested in the apparent motion, that is, how does one satellite move in the spacecraft-centered celestial sphere of the other satellite. This problem is similar in many respects to transforming between geometry on the surface of the Earth and geometry as seen by the satellite, with similar results. Like the Earth projection problem, azimuths measured relative to the base satellite don't change. They are the same in Earth-centered and spacecraft-centered coordinates. However, the Earth central angle, measured in the relative motion frame, is transformed into the nadir angle measured in the spacecraft frame according to Eq. (10-8). This allows us to transform any of the relative motion analemmas into the apparent motion, as seen from the base satellite.

Fig. 10-10 shows this relative motion and apparent motion for a series of satellites in a plane at a relative inclination of 25 deg with respect to the base satellite's orbit plane. We have put 11 satellites in the inclined plane such that they are 32.7 deg apart and have spaced them so that the relative phase of the closest one is as large as possible, i.e. 16.4 deg. The relative motion analemmas are shown is Fig. 10-10A. All of the analemmas are the same and are simply spaced out along the equator of the coordinate frame. The visibility limit is also shown. Fig. 10-10B shows the same analemmas transformed into the spacecraft-centered celestial sphere, centered on the base satellite. The general effect is to bend each analemma about the nadir direction and elongate the analemma for those which are nearest to the base satellite.

To get a better feel for the relative motion, we can think of the background sphere in Fig. 10-10A as the sphere containing the constellation of circular orbits and rotating such that the "base satellite" remains fixed on the x axis. The orbit plane of the base satellite is the equator of the plot and the orbit pole is the pole of the plot. The 10 other satellites in the orbit plane of the base satellite are the dots, a through i, spread out along the equator. The next plane over in our constellation is at a relative inclination, i_R, of 25 deg and contains 11 satellites. The paths of these 11 satellites in this coordinate frame are the 11 analemmas, A through K. The nearest plane on the other side would have a similar series of 11 analemmas, although the phase of the satellites within each analemma would be different. Planes that are further away would have a larger relative inclination and, therefore, larger analemmas. Nonetheless, all of the relative motion analemmas for all of the other satellites will be centered on the equator

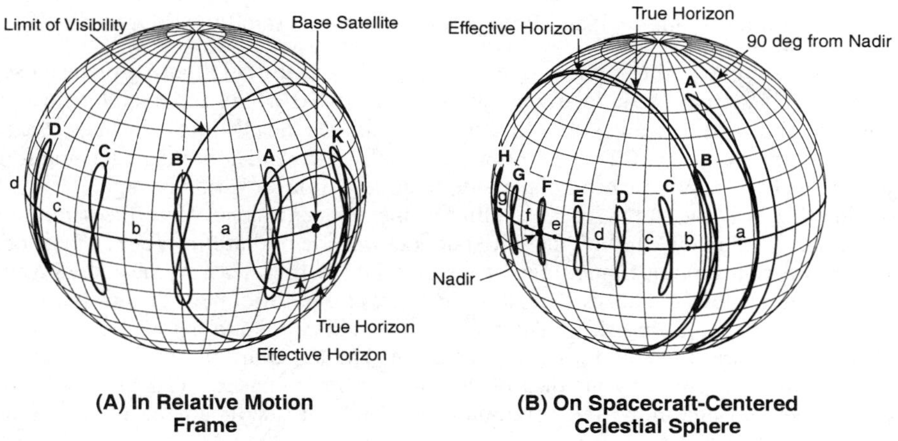

Fig. 10-10. Relative Motion vs. Apparent Motion. Satellites A to K are assumed to be in a common plane at $i_R = 25$ deg with respect to the base satellite orbit plane. See text for discussion.

in the plot. While the figure would get "busy" if we tried to plot them all, this process gives us a good way to understand the relative motion of all of the other satellites in the constellation.

In Fig. 10-10B, we are looking at the motion as seen by an observer sitting on the base satellite. The other satellites in the same plane are simply at fixed locations in front or behind. The closest satellites (a and l) are always visible and the rest are always invisible. The closest satellite in the neighboring plane (A or K), oscillates back and forth across the base orbit plane moving mostly parallel to the horizon. The furthest satellite in this adjacent plane (F), moves in a very small apparent analemma but is never visible because it is always behind the Earth's disk, as are the 3 satellites on either side of it. Thus, of the 11 satellites in the adjacent plane, 2 are always visible, 7 are always invisible, and 2 are invisible part of the time and visible, but very near the horizon, most of the time.

From the plot, we can determine a number of **general characteristics of the apparent motion of satellites:**

- All co-altitude satellites are within the hemisphere centered on nadir (i.e., below the *horizontal plane* which is the great circle perpendicular to nadir and is the limit of apparent satellite positions when they are very close to the base satellite).

- Satellites near the base satellite will appear near the horizontal plane; those far from the base satellite will appear near nadir and will be obscured by the Earth disk.

- The visible motion is confined to an annulus or band between the horizontal plane and the Earth's horizon. Any satellite which is over a location on the Earth less than twice as far away as the true geometric horizon will be visible and in this band.

- Generally, the motion is back and forth, approximately parallel to the horizon; the center of this back and forth motion is the base satellite orbit plane.

As an example of this motion, satellite A is the one in the neighboring plane closest to the base satellite. In the relative motion frame (10-10A), the analemma is near the base satellite and is well within the limit of visibility at all times. In the apparent motion frame (Fig. 10-10B), the motion is basically horizontal, moving back and forth across the base satellite's orbit plane with relatively little elevation change.

Satellite B is the next closest satellite in the adjacent plane. Here the satellite is principally within the limit of visibility but goes outside of that limit for brief periods. In the apparent motion frame, this means that the satellite lies very near the Earth's horizon. It is above the horizon most of the time, and for brief periods dips below the horizon and becomes invisible. The remaining satellites remain below the horizon at all times and are invisible to the base satellite. The apparent motion is still an analemma but is obscured by the disk of the Earth. Combining Eqs. (10-6), (10-7), and (10-8), we can determine the maximum and minimum nadir angles for any other satellite as follows:

$$\sin \eta_{min} = \cos(\lambda_{max} / 2) = \cos(\phi_R / 2) \cos (i_R / 2) \tag{10-9}$$

$$\cos \eta_{max} = \sin(\lambda_{min} / 2) = \sin(\phi_R / 2) \cos (i_R / 2) \tag{10-10}$$

In addition, we can determine the following expression for the maximum azimuth angle, α_{max}, as seen from the base satellite as:

$$\tan \eta_{max} = \tan (i_R / \sin \phi_R) \tag{10-11}$$

Finally, Table 10-1 summarizes the results of our assessment of the large scale relative motion for co-altitude satellites.

TABLE 10-1. Results of Large-Scale Relative Motion for Co-altitude Satellites.

- For co-altitude satellites in circular orbits, the large-scale relative motion depends only on the relative inclination and relative phase of the satellites
- The general motion is an analemma centered on the base satellite orbit plane
  - Height is equal to relative inclination
  - Position of central point is equal to the relative phase
- The apparent motion as seen from one of the satellites "bends" the analemma about the nadir direction
  - Visible motion is confined to a band between the Earth's horizon and the horizontal plane perpendicular to nadir
  - Generally, the motion is back-and-forth, approximately parallel to the horizon, and centered on the orbit plane
  - Any satellite will be visible when it is over a location on the Earth less than twice as far as the true (geometric) horizon

10.1.2 Small-Scale Relative Motion

Superimposed on the large-scale relative motion is a small-scale relative motion that resembles Brownian motion or vibration within the constellation structure. This is due to both variations in the orbital elements and variations in the perturbations for different satellites. The net result serves to define the minimum "stationkeeping box" that can contain the satellite motion.

As listed in Table 10-2, the causes of the small-scale motion are well known. The magnitude of this motion depends both on how the satellites are controlled and, equally important, how the relative motion is defined. We can define the small-scale relative motion with respect to another nearby satellite, a more distant satellite, the analytic approximations of a Keplerian orbit, or a perfect circle. Each approach is useful for various applications. For example, consider a group of nearly identical satellites flying a few kilometers apart. Perturbations will move all of the satellites nearly the same way. Consequently, for this grouping, we are interested only in the differences of the orbital elements and the relative motion among the satellites can be made very small.

TABLE 10-2. Causes of Small-Scale Relative Motion. In a close formation, a stationkeeping box may be only hundreds of meters long. For a global constellation defined relative to perfectly circular orbit, the box must be 10 km to 50 km long.

Cause	Comment
Measurement Error	Error depends on whether absolute or relative measurements are required.
Small Differences in Orbit Elements	Results in long-term drift with both cyclic and secular component; dominant variation for close formations.
Orbit Perturbations	Causes both non-uniform motion and long-term differential drift from small differences in orbital elements.
Variations in Orbit Perturbations	Due to variations in attitude, cross section, and inertial orientation (and thus variations in drag); makes long-term formation flying difficult with different satellite configurations.
Non-uniform Motion Along the Orbit	Unimportant in close formations; dominant variation across a full constellation.

In a global constellation, we might be more interested in how the satellites move relative to other satellites in the constellation or relative to a perfectly circular, idealized baseline orbit. This tells us how much coverage overlap we need to ensure full coverage at all times. Alternatively, we might be interested only in the magnitude of the motion relative to the next nearest neighbors, so that we can minimize any unnecessary overlap. All of these are useful definitions, but will result in different estimates of the magnitude of the small-scale motion. We will show the magnitude of the variations as a function of the angular separation between satellites and give formulas for the impact of variations in each of the orbital elements.

As discussed in Sec. 2.4.1, the most basic effect of perturbations, due primarily to the J_2 Earth oblateness term, is to distort a "perfectly circular" orbit into a shape somewhat resembling a potato chip. During constellation design, we frequently think of satellites being in perfectly circular orbits and as being equally spaced around the orbit. In fact, neither of these will be true. In low-Earth orbit, the minimum variations from perfectly circular motion is on the order of 3 km. This is small relative to the size of the orbit itself and would be invisible in a large drawing of the orbit. Nonetheless, it does mean that satellites covering the entire Earth can not hold a formation more accurately than about 3 km. As a practical matter, no realistic amount of propellant can overcome these large perturbations due primarily to the Earth's non-spherical shape.

In order to provide numerical examples of the effect of the principal perturbations and variations in the orbit parameters, we define a representative baseline orbit at an altitude of 700 km, inclination of 45 deg, and 0 eccentricity. Tables 10-3 through 10-5 show the effect of perturbations and variations in the orbital elements on this orbit. In each case, we assume that the variations due to all of the other effects are zero. The real motion is, of course, a composite of all the effects. However, this becomes too complex to easily understand. Consequently, it is more convenient to assess the effects independently. Also, because they are individually small, the effects will generally be additive.

Table 10-3 shows the representative differential motion due to variations in the Keplerian orbital elements. Some of these, such as variations in the eccentricity and ascending node, are basically cyclic such that the satellite returns to its same position orbit after orbit. Others, such as variations in the semimajor axis, produce a cumulative drift or secular variation in the remaining elements.

TABLE 10-3. Representative Differential Motion Due to Variations in Orbit Elements. Effects listed here and in the following two tables are characteristic of most low-Earth orbit constellations. (Baseline = 700 km, $e = 0$, $i = 45$ deg)

Element	Deviation	Impact
Semimajor axis, a	100 m	100 m radial; 0.0021 min = 0.13 sec in period = 942 m per orbit
Eccentricity, e	0.001	7.1 km radial; 14.3 km in-track
Inclination, i	0.01 deg	1.3 km cross-track; 0.0012 deg/day = 0.43 deg/yr in differential node rotation
Argument of perigee, ω	0.01 deg	no impact (1.3 km fixed offset)
Right ascension of the ascending node, Ω	0.01 deg	1.3 km cross-track
$M + \omega$ or $\omega + v$	0.01 deg	1.3 km in-track
Period, T	1 sec	770 m radial (semimajor axis) 7.4 km in-track per orbit

Table 10-4 shows the results of variations in the position and velocity at any one time such as orbit injection. Here the variations are expressed in terms of in-track, cross-track, and radial components corresponding to variations in the direction of motion, perpendicular to the direction of motion (and to the center of the Earth), and in the direction toward the center of the Earth. Finally Table 10-5 summarizes the major perturbations applicable to low-Earth orbit satellites and gives the approximate impact of these variations.

Nearly all of the variations in orbit elements and orbit perturbations have very similar effects for different satellites with the exception of atmospheric drag. As discussed in detail in Chap. 2, atmospheric drag depends on both the density of the atmosphere and on the ballistic coefficient of the satellite which is itself a function of mass, cross-sectional area, and drag coefficient. The basic equations for drag variation from Chap. 2 are:

$$\Delta V = \pi \frac{C_d}{m} \rho a V \tag{10-12a}$$

$$\Delta a = -2\pi \frac{C_d A}{m} \rho a^2 \tag{10-12b}$$

TABLE 10-4. Motion Resulting from Initial Variations in Position, *x*, and Velocity, *v*. Each variation is based on assuming that all other variations from the baseline are 0. The baseline orbit is the same as Table 10-3.

Element**	Deviation	Impact	Maximum Δx *(km)*	Minimum Δx *(km)*
x_I	1 km	Advances phase by 0.008 deg	1	0
x_C	1 km	Rotates orbit plane 0.008 deg about a line perpendicular to the radius vector	1	1
x_R	1 km	Increases *a* by 2 km and *e* by 0.000 14	19*	2.3
v_I	1 m/s	Increases *a* by 1.9 km and *e* by 0.000 27	18*	3.6
v_C	1 m/s	Rotates orbit plane 0.008 deg about the radius vector	1	1
v_R	1 m/s	Increases *e* by 0.000 13	4	1.4

* Accumulates from orbit to orbit **I = In-track; C = Cross-track; R = Radial

TABLE 10-5. Summary of the Effect of Perturbations on Small-scale Relative Motion. Each perturbation is based on assuming that all other perturbations have no effect. The baseline orbit is the same as Table 10-3.

Perturbation	Impact
Atmospheric Drag	Secular decay of < 1 m/day*
J_2 (oblateness)	• Secular node rotation of –6 cos *i* deg/day • Secular phase rotation of 6.4 deg/day • Changes shape of orbit—up to 3 km variation between satellites in the same orbit
Higher Order Harmonics (zonal)	Eccentricity oscillation of 0.001 about a mean value of 0.0013
Solar/Lunar	• General effect is to rotate orbit pole about the ecliptic pole and the pole of the Moon's orbit. Results in: – Secular drift in inclination and node of up to 3.5×10^{-5} deg/day – Low amplitude oscillations in inclination and node
Solar Radiation Pressure	Small

* Secondary secular drift in node, due to coupling with J_2, of up to 0.008 deg/day

$$\Delta T = -6\pi^2 \frac{C_d A}{m} \rho \frac{a^2}{V} \tag{10-12c}$$

Because atmospheric density at satellite altitudes can vary by 2 orders of magnitude and the cross-sectional area can vary by 1 order of magnitude (depending principally on the orientation of the solar arrays), atmospheric drag can change dramatically, not only between orbits but even for a single satellite. Thus, while almost all of the other perturbations can be taken as approximately fixed for any given orbit configuration, the variations in atmospheric drag must be taken into account for determining both the impact of drag and the propellant required to counterbalance it.

The next several figures provide plots of the displacement of the baseline trajectory due to the Earth's oblateness (i.e., the J_2 term in the geopotential expansion). Figure 10-11 shows the in-track displacement due to oblateness. This is shown in Fig. 10-11A relative to motion in a perfect circle and in Fig. 10-11B relative to two satellites which are 45 deg apart in phase. For satellites which are very close together, the in-track dis-

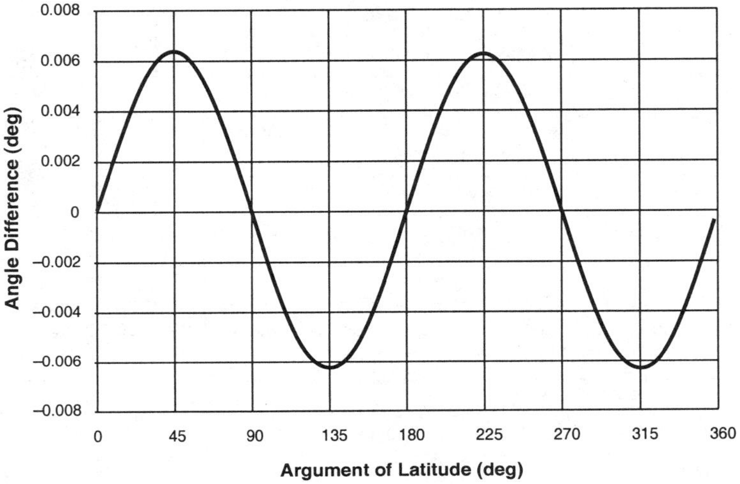

(A) Relative to Perfect Circular Motion

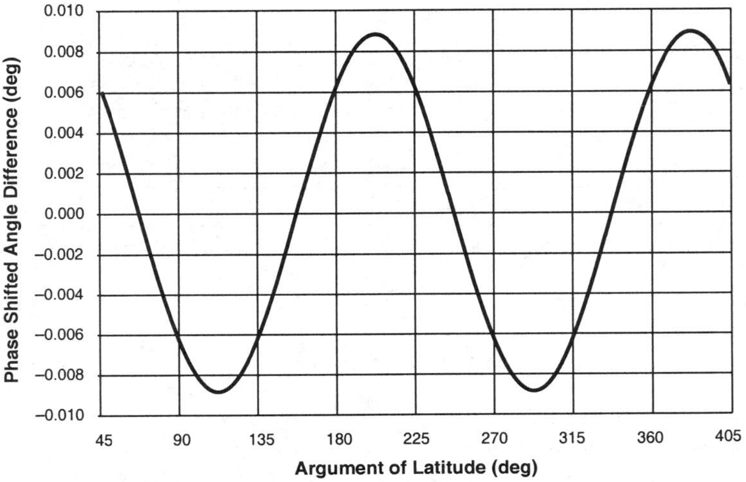

(B) Between 2 Satellites 45 deg Apart In Phase

Fig. 10-11. Representative In-Track Displacement Due to J_2. The baseline orbit is the same as Table 10-3, except that inclination is 90 deg.

placement due to the perturbations will be negligible. Figure 10-12 shows the impact of the same perturbation on the altitude displacement. In (A), the altitude displacement is measured relative to a constant radius from the center of the Earth. In (B), it is measured relative to the Earth's surface, assumed to be an oblate spheroid. In (C), the vertical displacement is shown for two satellites 45 deg apart in phase. Curve (D) then shows the difference of these two, i.e. the vertical displacement of one satellite with respect to a second satellite 45 deg in front of it. And finally, in curve (E), we express this same motion as a vertical angular displacement of one satellite relative to the other. Thus, even for two satellites which are in the identical orbit, if they are 45 deg apart, there will be a vertical motion of one relative to the other of ±0.02 deg. Finally, Fig. 10-13 shows the displacement of the cross-track component for the same perturbations. Again, relative to a perfect circle and to a satellite 45 deg ahead or behind.

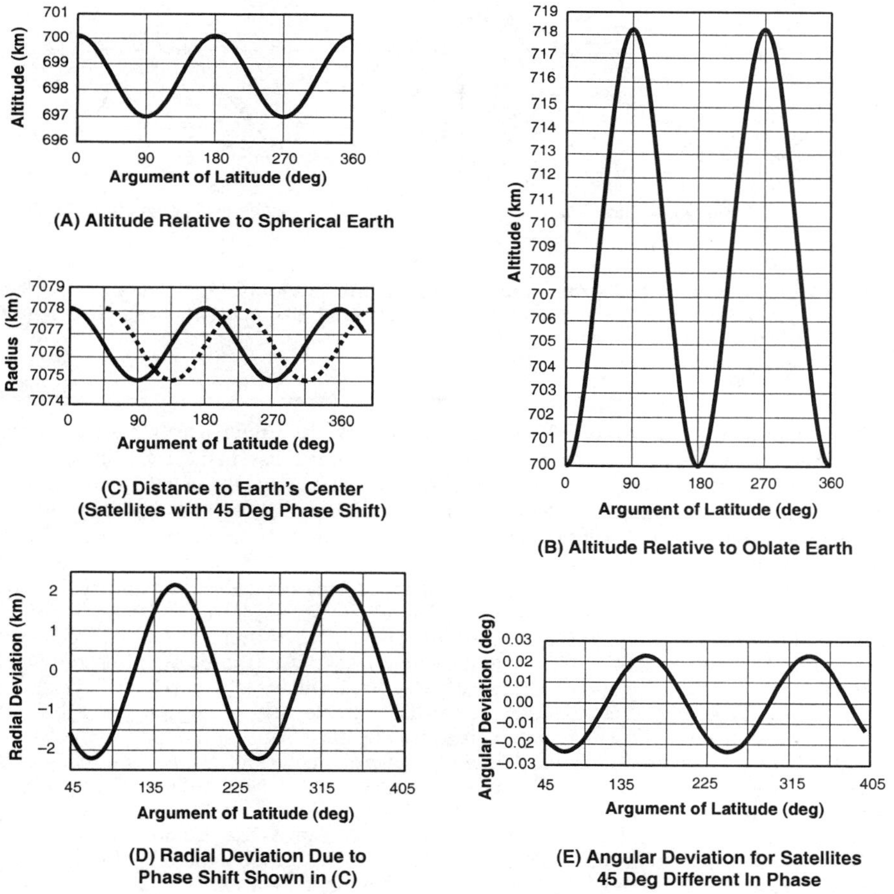

Fig. 10-12. Representative Radial Displacement Due to J_2. The baseline orbit is the same as Fig. 10-11. See text for discussion.

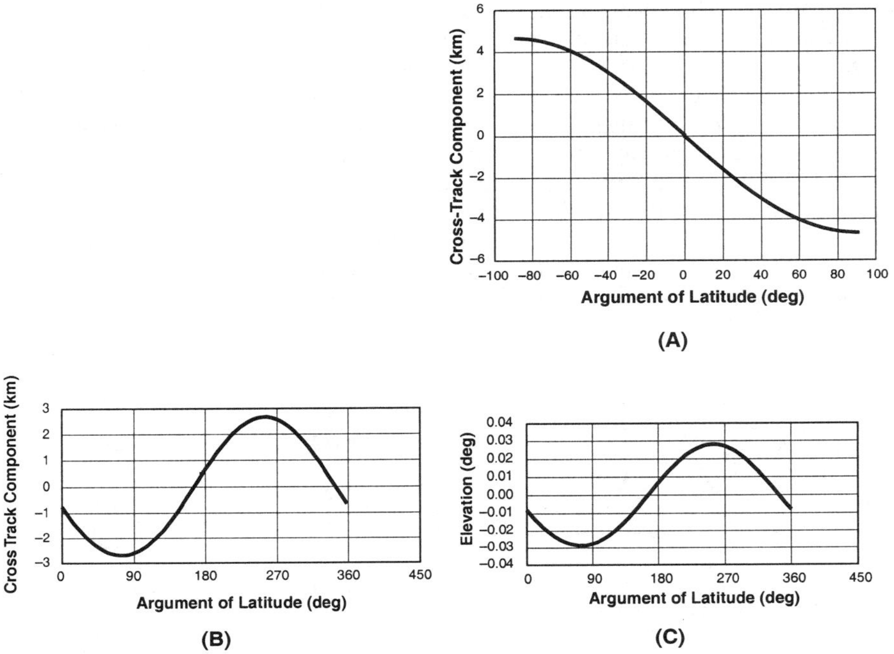

Fig. 10-13. Representative Cross-track Displacement Due to J_2. (A) Relative to a perfectly circular orbit. (B) and (C) Between satellites 45 deg apart in phase. The baseline orbit is the same as Table 10-3.

Fig. 10-13 shows the cross-track displacement relative to a reference frame rotating at a uniform rate equal to the node rotation rate caused by the oblateness. In this frame it appears that the effect of oblateness is to change the inclination by a nearly fixed amount around the orbit. However, in an inertial frame, the inclination oscillates sinusoidally by approximately this same amount. This comes about because of the effect of a rotating frame on the apparent inclination. (See the boxed example at the end of Sec. 9.3.1.)

Specifically, viewing an orbit in a frame of reference both inclined and rotating with respect to the orbit causes the apparent orbital inclination to oscillate. Consider a circular low-Earth orbit inclined at exactly 45 deg with respect to the Earth's equator in inertial space. (Assume there are no perturbations, such that the orbit is a perfect circle.) At 45 deg latitude the spacecraft will be going due east and the inclination with respect to the Earth will be 45 deg. However, because of the Earth's rotation it will cross the equator at an angle greater than 45 deg relative to the Earth. When the satellite crosses the equator, it will be moving at an angle with respect to the Earth of $i' = \text{atan}\ ((V_E + V_S \sin i) / V_S \cos i)$, where i is the inertial inclination, V_S is the velocity of the satellite, and V_E is the velocity of the Earth at the equator (and at the altitude of the satellite) due to its rotation in inertial space.

A satellite in a 45 deg inclined circular orbit at 500 km crosses equator at an angle of 47.55 deg with respect to the Earth. (See Fig. 9-22 in Sec. 9.3.1.) Even the very slow rotation of the orbit due to oblateness (–5.4 deg/day = –0.0038 deg/min for our example) causes an oscillation in apparent inclination of ±0.04 deg. These variations in angle (and velocity) with respect to the Earth are taken into account exactly by the dual-axis spiral equations (Table 8-8 in Sec. 8.2 or Table 8-9 in Sec. 8.3.3) and also by the Euler axis approximation in Sec. 9.3.

Figures 10-14 through 10-16 show the long-term variation in orbit elements due primarily to solar and lunar perturbations. Here we can see clearly the variations with an approximate 6 month period due to the orientation of the Sun relative to the orbit plane, and with a 2 week period due to the motion of the Moon relative to the orbit plane. Figure 10-16 shows the oscillation in eccentricity dominated by the Earth's zonal harmonics. It is this general oscillation in eccentricity that leads to the concept of a frozen orbit in which the eccentricity is maintained at its mid-value of approximately 0.002.

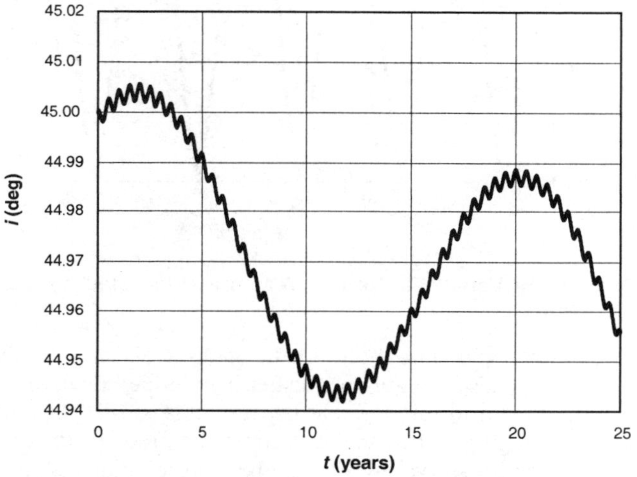

Fig. 10-14. Long-term Inclination Drift Due Primarily to Solar/Lunar Perturbations.

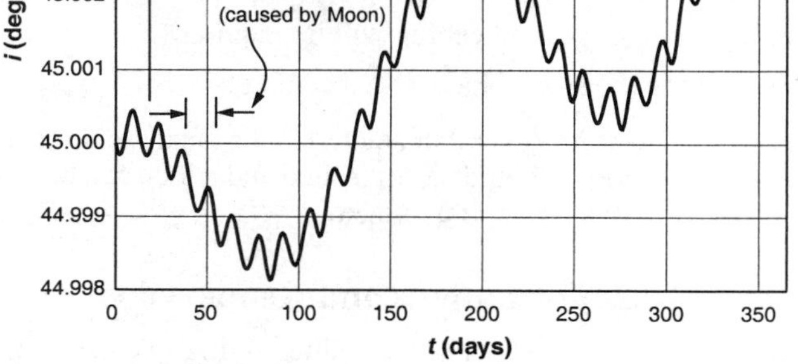

Fig. 10-15. Closeup of Inclination Variations Showing Short Period Variations Due to Perturbations.

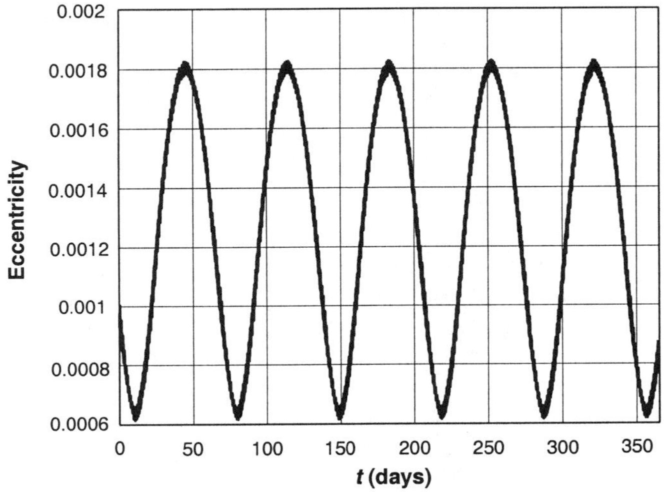

Fig. 10-16. Eccentricity Variations Over a Year are Dominated by Odd-Order Zonal Harmonics.

The general results of perturbations in the motion of satellites imply that the stationkeeping box depends strongly on whether it is defined relative to nearby satellites, distant satellites, or an absolute Keplerian or circular orbit. This, in turn, depends on whether we are trying to control an entire constellation or a formation of satellites flying near each other. In most low-Earth orbit constellations, it is clear that the inclination will need to be controlled in order to counter the strong differential node rotation due to the Earth's oblateness. In addition, differential inclination growth among the various orbit planes due to solar and lunar perturbations may require that the node and inclination be controlled over a long period of time. The short period differential motion due to the Earth's oblateness (i.e., the potato chip shape of low-Earth orbits) is a major factor in setting the size of a constellation stationkeeping box. This is a perturbation that cannot be effectively controlled because it would require far too much propellant to make continuous adjustments.

The key implications here for the small-scale relative motion assessment are:

- Determining propellant budget sizing based on the perturbations to be controlled
- Determining whether stationkeeping will be required
- If so, determining the size of the stationkeeping box

In addition, we will use the general character of the small-scale relative motion to determine which perturbations should be controlled and which can be left uncontrolled and accounted for in the stationkeeping budget.

10.2 Formations and Rendezvous

A *formation* is a group of one or more satellites flying in close proximity that are interacting or working together for a common purpose. Examples would include the Space Shuttle when it is docking with the International Space Station or two satellites flying together as an interferometer. "Close proximity" means that the satellites are close enough to see each other, communicate, and feel approximately the same orbit perturbations. We will first look at the kinematics of this motion in the absence of external forces and perturbations and then look at formation dynamics in the presence of discrete and continuous thrusting.

10.2.1 Relative Motion of Satellites in a Co-Altitude Formation

The traditional approach to this problem is to assume that the satellites are close to each other and linearize the general equations of motion to obtain what are known as *Hill's equations* or the *Clohessy-Wiltshire equations*. This approach, which is valid only for short periods for nearby satellites in near-circular orbits, is described in Sec. 10.2.3 and in most standard references on astrodynamics. (See, for example, Vallado [2001] or Chobotov [1996].) These equations are excellent for working with thrusting spacecraft such as docking of the Space Shuttle or the Manned Maneuvering Unit. However, they do not provide as much insight as we would like into the general character of the motion of satellites in a formation which are either nonthrusting or do so only occasionally for stationkeeping purposes.

An alternative approach is to provide closed form solutions for the relative motion in terms of the Keplerian elements of the satellites. The simplest case is two satellites in the same circular orbit with a phase offset. Here, the satellites maintain the same relative position throughout and simply trail or lead one another by a constant distance throughout the entire orbit.

Nearly as straightforward is the case of two satellites in co-altitude circular orbits, which intersect at a small angle. This can mean satellites with the same inclination but different node crossings or different inclinations. In each of these cases, the relative motion between the satellites is a just a special case of the relative motion analemma shown previously in Fig. 10-5, with the equations of motion given in Eqs. (10-1) and (10-2). As the relative inclination becomes small, the motion of one satellite relative to the other (called the *base satellite*) reduces to simply a sinusoidal oscillation along a line perpendicular to the base satellite orbit plane, as shown in Fig. 10-17. The equation of motion is given by:

$$z = i_R \sin(nt + \phi_R) \tag{10-13}$$

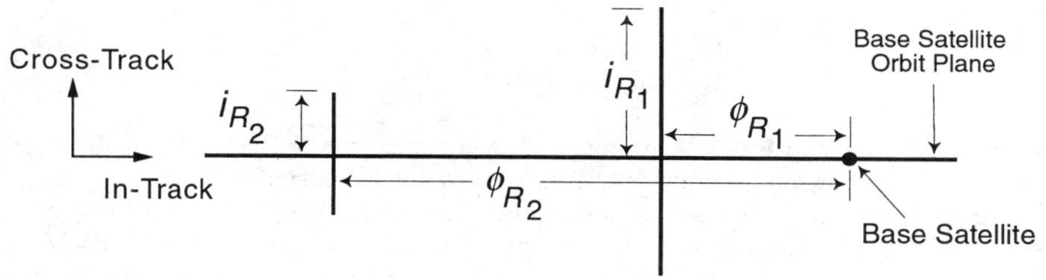

Fig. 10-17. Relative Motion of Co-Altitude Satellites in Circular Orbits for which the Relative Inclination, i_R, is Small. Each satellite moves in a back-and-forth sinusoidal oscillation about the orbit plane of any of the others. The parameters of the motion are determined entirely by the relative inclination, i_R and relative phase, ϕ_R. The motion of two satellites, *i* and *j*, relative to a base satellite is shown.

where again z is the cross-track motion (measured in angular units of Earth central angle), i_R is the relative inclination, ϕ_R is the relative phase, n is the orbit frequency or mean motion and t is the time. The base satellite can, of course, be either an actual satellite in a circular orbit, or simply a reference point in space. The back-and-forth motion is determined entirely by the relative inclination. Adjusting the relative phase simply moves the position of the perpendicular line relative to the base satellite. Note that this represents the only possible motion in the cross-track direction. Table 10-6 shows the degree to which the linear approximation of Eq. (10-13) is valid. It becomes exceptionally good for small displacements. Thus, for cross-track motion of ±10 km, the in-track motion is only ±3 m, and if the cross-track motion is reduced to ±1 km, the in-track motion is reduced to about 3 cm. Thus, if the satellites are in perfectly circular orbits, there will be essentially no in-track relative motion.

TABLE 10-6. Height and Width of the Relative Motion "Analemma" for Two Co-Altitude Satellites in Circular Orbits. The satellites are assumed to be at an altitude of 1,000 km.

Relative Inclination (deg)	Cross-Track Motion (± deg)	Cross-Track Motion (± km)	Along-Track Motion (± km)
77.66	77.66	10,000	5,110
7.766	7.766	1,000	33.5
0.7766	0.7766	100	0.334
0.077 66	0.077 66	10	0.0033
0.007 77	0.007 77	1	0.000 033

In order to provide in-track motion in a co-altitude formation, we need to put one or more of the satellites in slightly eccentric orbits. For simplicity, consider first the relative motion of a satellite in an orbit of small eccentricity relative to a satellite or reference point in a perfectly circular orbit with the same semimajor axis and period. Using Eqs. (2-12) and (2-13), we can expand the in-track and radial motion for the satellite in a power series in the eccentricity and keep only the first term:

$$M(t) = M_0 + nt \qquad (10\text{-}14)$$

$$\nu(t) \approx M_0 + nt + 2e\sin(M_0 + nt) \qquad (10\text{-}15)$$

$$r(t) \approx a\,(1 - e\cos(M_0 + nt)) \qquad (10\text{-}16)$$

$$\text{offset} \equiv M_0 \qquad (10\text{-}17)$$

where M is the mean anomaly at time t, M_0 is the mean anomaly at time $t = 0$, ν and r are the true anomaly and radial distance, and e is the eccentricity.

Since eccentricities for near-circular orbits are typically in the range of 0.002, this power series expansion is an excellent approximation. As shown in Fig. 10-18, the relative motion here is extremely simple. It is an ellipse in the orbit plane with the major axis in the in-track direction and minor axis in the radial direction. The length of the semimajor axis of the ellipse is $2ae$, and the height of the semiminor axis is ae, or half the semimajor axis. The center of the ellipse is offset from the reference point by the mean anomaly at time $t = 0$. As one would expect, the maximum height relative to the reference point will occur when the satellite is at apogee, and the minimum height below the reference point when the satellite is at perigee. The maximum displacement in front and behind the reference satellite will be 90 deg ahead of and behind the apogee and perigee points. The key point here is that in-track motion is always coupled with radial motion in a 2:1 ellipse. **We cannot get in-track motion without radial motion, and visa versa.**

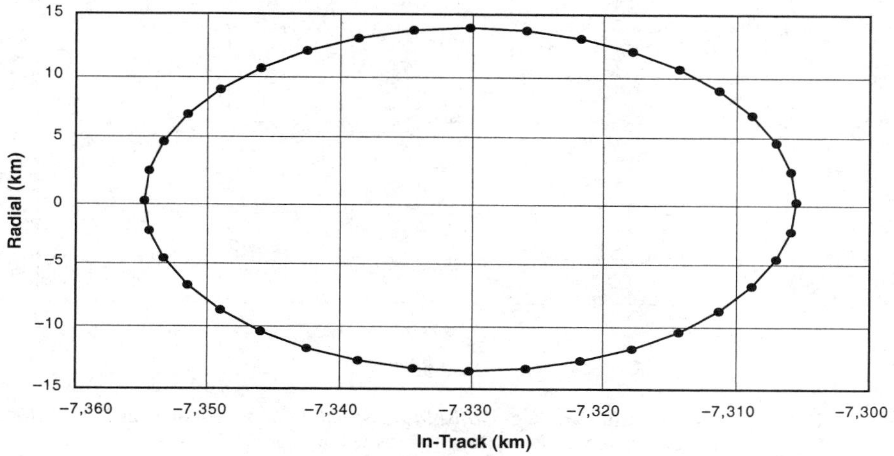

Fig. 10-18. In-Plane Motion of a Satellite in a Low-Eccentricity Orbit Relative to a Reference Point in a Circular Orbit at the Same Mean Altitude. The relative motion is an ellipse with the major axis in the in-track direction and the minor axis in the radial direction. The ellipse will always be twice as long as it is high.

In general, the in-plane relative motion of two satellites with small but different eccentricities can be found by simply differencing the motion described above. Although the arithmetic is now somewhat more complex, the relative motion is equally simple, as shown in Fig. 10-19. Irrespective of the values of the eccentricity, argument of perigee, and mean anomaly, the relative motion between the two satellites is always a 2:1 ellipse, with the major axis in the in-track direction and the minor axis in the radial direction. The largest possible half-height for this relative motion ellipse is simply $ae_1 + ae_2$, and occurs when one satellite is at perigee at the same time the other is at apogee. Similarly, the smallest relative motion ellipse will have a half height of $|ae_1 - ae_2|$, and will occur when the satellites are at apogee and perigee simultaneously.

The biggest problem in determining the actual relative motion ellipse is simply keeping track of the variables. For convenience, these are summarized in Table 10-7. The maximum radial separation will occur at a time $t_{\Delta rmax}$ given by:

$$\tan n\, t_{\Delta\, rmax} = \frac{e_1 \sin M_{0_1} - e_2 \sin M_{0_2}}{e_2 \cos M_{0_2} - e_1 \cos M_{0_1}} \qquad (10\text{-}18)$$

The maximum in-track separation will occur 90 deg in front of and behind this point, at a time $t_{\Delta\phi max}$ given by:

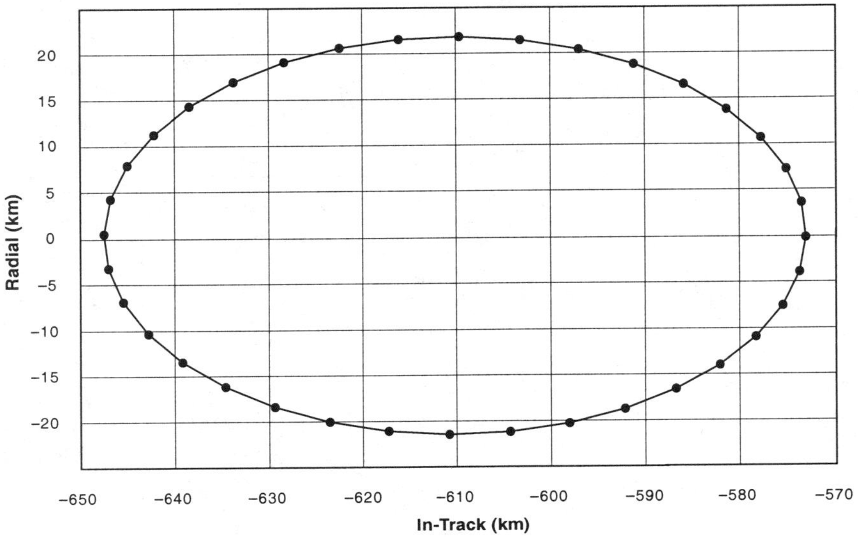

Fig. 10-19. Relative In-Plane Motion of Co-Altitude Satellites in Near-Circular Orbits. As in the case of single satellite motion, the relative motion of the satellites is an ellipse with the major axis in the in-track direction and minor axis in the radial direction. The ellipse will always be twice as long as it is high. (Compare with Fig. 10-18.)

TABLE 10-7. Definition of Variables for Relative Motion in Terms of Keplerian Elements.

Element	Satellite 1	Satellite 2	Sat. 1 – Sat. 2
Semimajor axis, a	a	a	$\Delta a = 0$
Period, P	P	P	$\Delta P = 0$
Mean orbit frequency, n	$n = 2\pi / P$	$n = 2\pi / P$	$\Delta n = 0$
Inclination, i	i_1	i_2	$\Delta i = i_1 - i_2$
Eccentricity, e	e_1	e_2	$\Delta e = e_1 - e_2$
Ascending Node, N	N_1	N_2	$\Delta N = N_1 - N_2$
Argument of Perigee, ω	ω_1	ω_2	$\Delta \omega = \omega_1 - \omega_2$
Mean Anomaly, M_0	M_{0_1}	M_{0_2}	$\Delta M_0 = M_{0_1} - M_{0_2}$
Initial Longitude, L_0	$L_{0_1} = M_{0_1} + \omega_1$	$L_{0_2} = M_{0_2} + \omega_2$	$\Delta L_0 = L_{0_1} - L_{0_2}$
Relative Inclination, i_R			Eqs. (10-1) or (10-2)
Node to intersection of orbits, λ	λ_1 from Eqs. (10-1) or (10-2)	λ_2 from Eqs. (10-1) or (10-2)	$\Delta \lambda = \lambda_1 - \lambda_2$
Offset = Relative Phase, ϕ_R			$\phi_R = \Delta \lambda - \Delta L_o$

$$\tan n\, t_{\Delta\phi max} = \frac{e_2 \cos M_{0_2} - e_1 \cos M_{0_1}}{e_2 \sin M_{0_2} - e_1 \sin M_{0_1}} \tag{10-19}$$

where the variables are defined in Table 10-7. Finally, the offset between the base satellite and the center of the relative motion ellipse is simply the relative phase between the two satellites:

$$\text{offset} = \phi_R \tag{10-20}$$

As in the case of cross-track motion, the two satellites do not need to be near each other. The relative motion ellipse can be displaced any distance in front of or behind the base satellite and can be as much as 180 deg out of phase. In the case of large offsets, the distance from the base satellite to the center of the ellipse is defined along the curved orbit path and the in-track and radial directions are defined at the center of the relative motion ellipse. Thus, at large distances, this relative motion ellipse would be inclined to the line of sight to the base satellite, and the two satellites may be entirely out of sight of each other.

The combined motion in three dimensions will be simply the linear sum of the cross-tack motion from Fig. 10-17 and the in-plane motion from Fig. 10-19 The general rules for this relative orbital motion are summarized in Table 10-8. Examples of the motion are shown in Figs. 10-20, 10-21, and 10-22.

TABLE 10-8. General Rules for Relative Orbital Motion. The assumptions are that the satellites have the same semimajor axis, the relative inclination is small, and the eccentricities are small. The satellites need not be close together.

Cross-Track Motion

The out-of-plane motion is a sinusoidal oscillation along a line perpendicular to the base orbit plane. The distance of the line from the base satellite is the relative phase and the magnitude of the oscillation is the relative inclination, i.e., the angle at which the two orbit planes intersect. See Fig. 10-17.

In-Plane Motion

The in-plane relative motion of any two satellites (or between a satellite and an orbiting reference point) is an ellipse with its major axis in the in-track direction and its minor axis in the radial direction. The major axis (in-track) is always twice the minor axis (radial). See Fig. 10-18. Using the notation of Table 10-7, the properties of the relative motion ellipse are:

1. The maximum length of the minor axis of the relative motion ellipse is $a_{e1} + a_{e2}$ and the minimum length of this axis is $|a_{e1} - a_{e2}|$.
2. The mean offset between the two satellites is the relative phase, ϕ_R.
3. The maximum radial separation occurs as given in Eq. (10-9).
4. The value of this maximum is obtained by evaluating Eq. (10-7) for both orbits.
5. The maximum in-track separation will occur 90 deg later and will be twice the maximum radial separation + the mean offset.

Total Motion

The total motion is the sum of the 2:1 in-plane ellipse and the sinusoidal side-to-side oscillation. The phase between the in-plane and cross-plane motions is adjustable (i.e., a free parameter in the design). Representative examples are shown in Figs. 10-20 to 10-22.

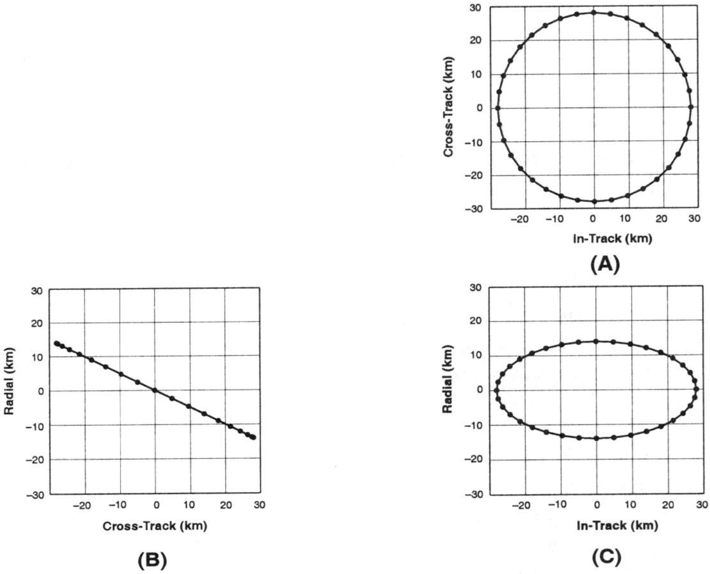

Fig. 10-20. Relative Motion with a Circular Projection in the Horizontal Plane. This will occur when the cross-track motion is twice the in-track motion and L_0 is the same (or 180 deg out of phase) for both satellites. The true relative motion is an ellipse inclined 30 deg to the horizontal.

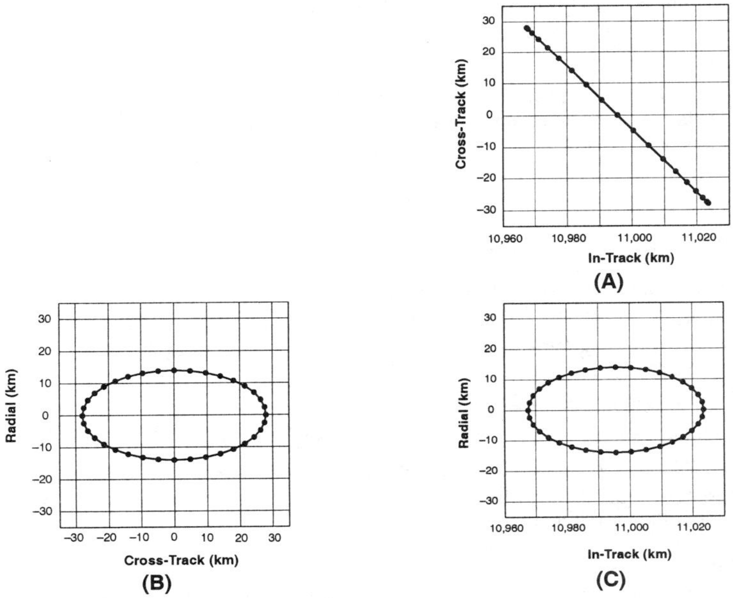

Fig. 10-21. Relative Motion with a Linear Projection in the Horizontal Plane. This will occur when L_0 is 90 deg out of phase for both satellites. The true relative motion is an ellipse in a vertical plane tilted 45 deg to the velocity vector.

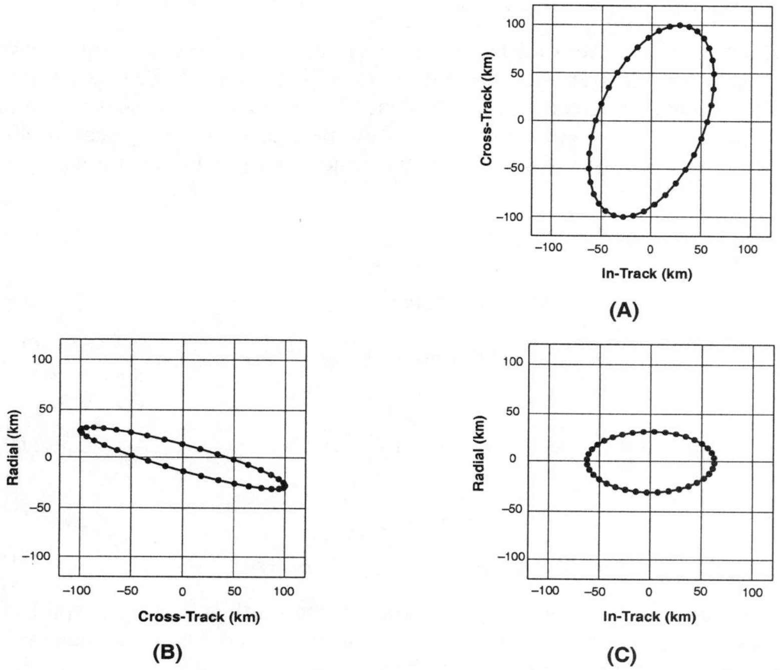

Fig. 10-22. General Shape of Relative Motion Ellipse for Satellites in Low-Eccentricity Orbits with a Small Relative Inclination. The satellites do not need to be near each other for these curves to apply.

Any specific set of satellites may or may not include cross-track motion or in-track motion; however, in-track motion is always coupled with radial motion. For example, we cannot move one satellite in a horizontal circle about another satellite because the back-and-forth in-track motion will require a corresponding radial component. However, as shown in Fig. 10-20, we can produce the projection of a circle in the horizontal plane by projecting an ellipse which is inclined at 30 deg to the horizontal. This will produce an apparent linear oscillation at 30 deg to the horizontal, as seen from directly in front of or behind the satellite. Similarly, as shown in Fig. 10-21, we can have an apparently linear oscillation as seen looking down on the satellite from above; although again, this will be elliptical motion in a vertical plane.

The general motion is shown in Fig. 10-22, in which the projected motions along all three principal axes are ellipses. As in the case of the component motion, the only approximations here are that the satellite orbits intersect at a small angle, and that the eccentricities of both orbits are small. The satellites do not need to be close to each other at all. Indeed, even these approximations can be easily overcome by using the general motion analemma in Fig. 10-2, or in the case of eccentric orbits, including additional terms in the power series expansion. (This is different from Hill's equations which break down for non-near-circular orbits.) However, in practice, it is probably easier to use the general orbital motion equations when the relative inclination or the eccentricities are large.

10.2.2 Nearly Co-Altitude Satellites

All of the discussion thus far has been for satellites that have the same semimajor axis. Unless the satellites are very accurately controlled, there will be small differences in this component as there are in all the others. These small differences in semimajor axis, Δa, will result in small differences in the period, P, and the mean motion, n. Again using the power series expansion, this time in terms of the semimajor axis, a, we have:

$$\Delta n = -1.5(\Delta a / a)n \tag{10-21a}$$

$$= -1.5\mu^{1/2}a^{-5/2}\Delta a \tag{10-21b}$$

$$\approx -2.994\ 747\ 050 \times 10^7\ a^{-5/2}\Delta a\ (\text{rad / sec}) \tag{10-21c}$$

and

$$\Delta P = -3\pi(\Delta a / a)(1/n) \tag{10-22a}$$

$$= -3\pi\mu^{-1/2}a^{1/2}\Delta a \tag{10-22b}$$

$$\approx -4.720\ 654\ 7 \times 10^{-7} a^{1/2}\Delta a\ (\text{sec}) \tag{10-22c}$$

where, as usual, μ is the gravitational constant of the Earth and in the (c) part of both equations, a and Δa are in m, n and Δn are in rad/sec, and ΔP is in seconds. The shift in in-track position per orbit, Δv, will be just

$$\Delta v = an\Delta P \tag{10-23a}$$

$$= \mu^{1/2}a^{-1/2}\Delta P \tag{10-23b}$$

$$\approx 1.996\ 498\ 039 \times 10^7\ a^{-1/2}\Delta P\ (\text{m}) \tag{10-23c}$$

where, in the last equation, a and Δv are in m and ΔP is in seconds. Consider for example, a reference satellite at an altitude of 700 km. A second satellite 100 m higher or lower will have a shift in mean motion of 2.25×10^{-8} rad/sec, a shift in period of 0.13 sec, and an in-track shift of 940 m per orbit. The cross track motion for satellites at slightly different altitudes is shown in Fig. 10-23 and the in-track and radial motion are shown in Fig. 10-24.

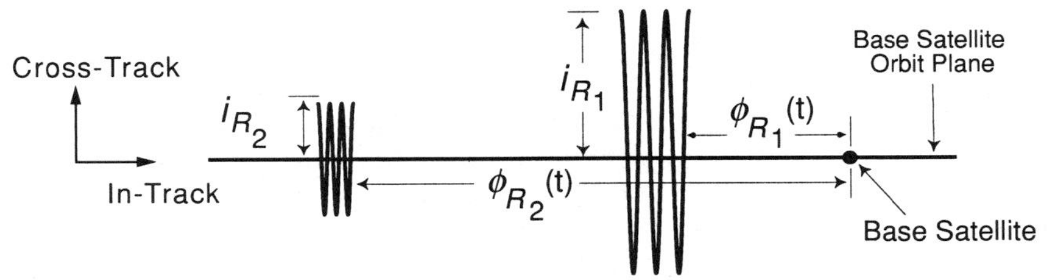

Fig. 10-23. Cross-Track Motion Combined with a Small Variation in Mean Altitude.

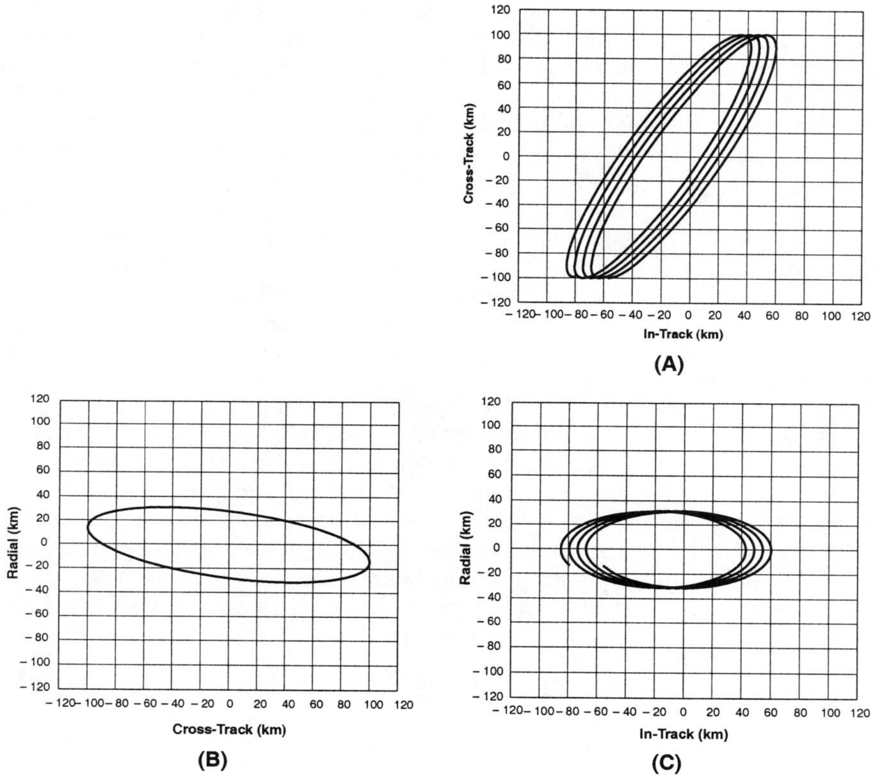

Fig. 10-24. In-Track and Radial Motion Combined with a Small Variation in Mean Altitude.

10.2.3 Hill's Equations and Rendezvous*

Sections 10.2.1 and 10.2.2 dealt with formation kinematics, i.e., the relative motion of spacecraft with no external forces other than the central gravitational force. The remaining two subsections deal with the response to discrete or continuous forces. In both the kinematics and dynamics approach, a precise answer comes from integrating the equations of motion in a high accuracy orbit propagator, taking into account both natural and applied forces. Nonetheless, a great deal of insight can be obtained in kinematics by making use of the dual axis spiral and Euler axis or by expanding the equations of motion in a power series. Similarly, we can gain substantial insight into the dynamics of nearby objects by linearizing the equations of motion and ignoring the long-term effects of the natural perturbations. (Of course, these perturbations will be important for long term motion and stability.) This was first done by George Hill [1878] in the nineteenth century and was rediscovered at the beginning of the space program by W. R. Clohessy and R. S. Wiltshire [1960] while looking at the problem

* The discussion of Hill's equations is due to Simon Dawson and Herb Reynolds. The discussion of proximity operations is from Hans Meissinger.

of terminal guidance for satellite rendezvous. *Hill's equations* or the *Clohessy-Wiltshire equations* use a uniformly rotating coordinate frame corresponding to a reference satellite (or reference point in space) in a circular orbit. An alternative approach, developed by Battin [1964, 1987], makes use of universal variables which allows it to be used for elliptical and hyperbolic orbits. This approach was later substantially simplified and generalized by Der and Danchick [1997]. In all cases, the results are based on linearized equations of motion and, therefore, apply only for control applications or when the spacecraft involved are close together. (Recall that the relative motion in the absence of applied forces in Sec. 10.2.1 and 10.2.2 required that the orbit elements be similar, but not that the satellites be close together, i.e., the satellites could be in the same orbit, but on opposite sides of the Earth.) For a discussion of formation control see, for example, Folta, et al. [1996, 1997, 1998].

We begin by defining a reference frame centered on a *target* or *reference satellite* moving in a perfectly circular reference orbit about a point mass. The target could be either a real satellite, such as docking maneuvers relative to the ISS, or an empty point in space, such as maneuvers relative to the defined center of a formation or station-keeping box. The *chaser*, or sometimes just the "spacecraft," is the potentially maneuvering satellite that is moving relative to the target. Thus, all of the equations and plots will be in terms of the motion of the chaser relative to the target, which is assumed to be at the origin of the coordinate system. The variables nearly always used for this problem are the radial direction, r, the in-track direction (of the reference point), ϕ, and the cross-track direction, z, perpendicular to the reference orbit plane. Note that in the linearization here, ϕ is a linear dimension, not an angle. In this coordinate frame, Hill's differential equations for the relative motion are:

$$F_r = \ddot{r} - 2n\dot{\phi} - 3n^2 r \tag{10-24}$$

$$F_\phi = \ddot{\phi} + 2n\dot{r} \tag{10-25}$$

$$F_z = \ddot{z} + n^2 z \tag{10-26}$$

where $n = (u/a^3)^{1/2}$ is the mean motion of the reference point, $u = GM$ is the gravitational constant, a is the semimajor axis, and F_r, F_ϕ, and F_z are the components of the perturbing force acting on the chaser. The perturbing forces can be either the natural perturbations, discussed in Sec. 2.4, or the result of discrete or continuous thrusting.

The general solution of the associated homogenous equations is

$$r_h = \left(\frac{\dot{r}_0}{n}\right)\sin nt - \left(\frac{2\dot{\phi}_0}{n} + 3r_0\right)\cos nt + 2\left(\frac{\dot{\phi}_0}{n} + 2r_0\right) \tag{10-27}$$

$$\phi_h = 2\left(\frac{2\dot{\phi}_0}{n} + 3r_0\right)\sin nt + 2\left(\frac{\dot{r}_0}{n}\right)\cos nt + \left(\phi_0 - \frac{2\dot{r}_0}{n}\right) - 3\left(\dot{\phi}_0 + 2nr_0\right)t \tag{10-28}$$

$$z_h = \frac{\dot{z}_0}{n}\sin nt + z_0 \cos nt \tag{10-29}$$

where r_0, ϕ_0, z_0 and $\dot{r}_0$, $\dot{\phi}_0$, $\dot{z}_0$ are the initial relative position and velocity components of the chaser relative to the reference spacecraft. From simple harmonic oscillator theory, these equations may be written

$$r_h = -A\cos(nt+\alpha) + 2(\dot{\phi}_0 / n + 2r_0) \tag{10-30}$$

$$\phi_h = 2A\sin(nt+\alpha) + (\dot{\phi}_0 - 2\dot{r}_0 / n) - 3(\dot{\phi}_0 + 2nr_0)t \tag{10-31}$$

$$z_h = A_z \sin(nt+\alpha_z) \tag{10-32}$$

where the amplitude and phase angle of the radial and in-track oscillation are, respectively,

$$A = \sqrt{\left(\frac{\dot{r}_0}{n}\right)^2 + \left(\frac{2\dot{\phi}_0}{n} + 3r_0\right)^2}. \tag{10-33a}$$

$$\alpha = \operatorname{atan}\left(\frac{\dot{r}_0}{2\dot{\phi}_0 + 3r_0 n}\right) \tag{10-33b}$$

Similarly, for the cross-track oscillation

$$A_z = \sqrt{z_0^2 + \left(\frac{\dot{z}_0}{n}\right)^2} \tag{10-34a}$$

$$\alpha_z = \operatorname{atan}\left(\frac{nz_0}{\dot{z}_0}\right) \tag{10-34b}$$

The cross-track and radial motion are simple harmonic oscillation, and the in-track motion has a linear drift term. As discussed in Sec. 10.2.1, the amplitude of the in-track motion has twice the amplitude of the radial motion, and their oscillations are 90 deg out of phase. That is, the in-track oscillation is a quarter of a period ahead of the radial oscillation.

The motion in the orbit plane can be expressed in terms of orbital elements. To first order in the eccentricity, e, the radius vector, r, and true anomaly, v, of an orbiting object are:

$$r \approx a(1 - e\cos M) \tag{10-35}$$

$$v \approx M + 2e\sin M \tag{10-36}$$

where a is the semimajor axis and M is the mean anomaly. Let ω be the argument of perigee and let $\theta = v + \omega$. Since $M = n(t - t_p)$, where n is the mean motion and t_p is the time past perigee, we have

$$r = a\left[1 - e\cos n(t - t_p)\right] \tag{10-37}$$

$$\theta = \theta_0 + nt + 2e\sin n(t - t_p) \tag{10-38}$$

where $\theta_0 = \omega - nt_p$. Now, by differentiation, we can compare two orbits of small e and almost the same a. Neglecting terms of order $e\delta a$ we have,

$$r_h = \delta r = -a\delta e \cos n\left(t - t_p\right) + \delta a \tag{10-39}$$

$$\phi_h = a\delta\theta = +2a\delta e \sin n\left(t - t_p\right) + a\delta\theta_0 - \frac{3}{2}(n\delta a)t \tag{10-40}$$

It follows by comparison with the solution to Hill's equations that

$$A = a\delta e \tag{10-41}$$

$$\alpha = nt_p \tag{10-42}$$

$$\delta a = 2\left(\dot{\phi}_0 / n + 2r_0\right) \tag{10-43}$$

$$a\delta\theta_0 = \phi_0 - 2\dot{r}_0 / n \tag{10-44}$$

If the two spacecraft have the same altitude, $\delta a = 0$, the motion in the orbit plane is elliptical, and the out of plane motion is harmonic, as discussed in Sec. 10.2.1.

The complete solution to the non-homogenous equations is obtained by adding the particular solution, so that

$$r = rh + \frac{1}{n}\int_{t_0}^{t} F_r(\tau)\sin n(t-\tau)d\tau + \frac{2}{n}\int_{t_0}^{t} F_\phi(\tau)\left[1 - \cos n(t-\tau)\right]d\tau \tag{10-45}$$

$$\phi = \phi_h - \frac{2}{n}\int_{t_0}^{t} F_r(\tau)\left[1 - \cos n(t-\tau)\right]d\tau + \frac{1}{n}\int_{t_0}^{t} F_\phi(\tau)\left[4\sin n(t-\tau) - 3n(t-\tau)\right]d\tau \tag{10-46}$$

$$z = z_h + \frac{1}{n}\int_{t_0}^{t} F_z(\tau)\sin n(t-\tau)d\tau \tag{10-47}$$

If the perturbing force is simple, such as, constant drag or thrust, the integrals can easily be integrated analytically. Suppose, for example, that the drag, d, is constant. Then $f_x = f_z = 0$, and $f_y = d$ = constant so that

$$r = r_h + \frac{2\Delta d}{n}\left[\left(t - t_0\right) - \frac{1}{n}\sin n\left(t - t_0\right)\right] \tag{10-48}$$

$$\phi = \phi_h + \frac{2\Delta d}{n}\left\{-\frac{3}{4}n\left(t - t_0\right)^2 + \frac{2}{n}\left[1 - \cos n\left(t - t_0\right)\right]\right\} \tag{10-49}$$

$$z = z_h \tag{10-50}$$

We could also replace a with Δd, the difference in drag on the two spacecraft. If it is negative, the relative radial component exhibits a secular decay and the in-track component a quadratic advance.

Finally, we can draw some basic rules for interpretation of the above equations under varying initial conditions. These rules are illustrated in Fig. 10-25 to Fig. 10-28.

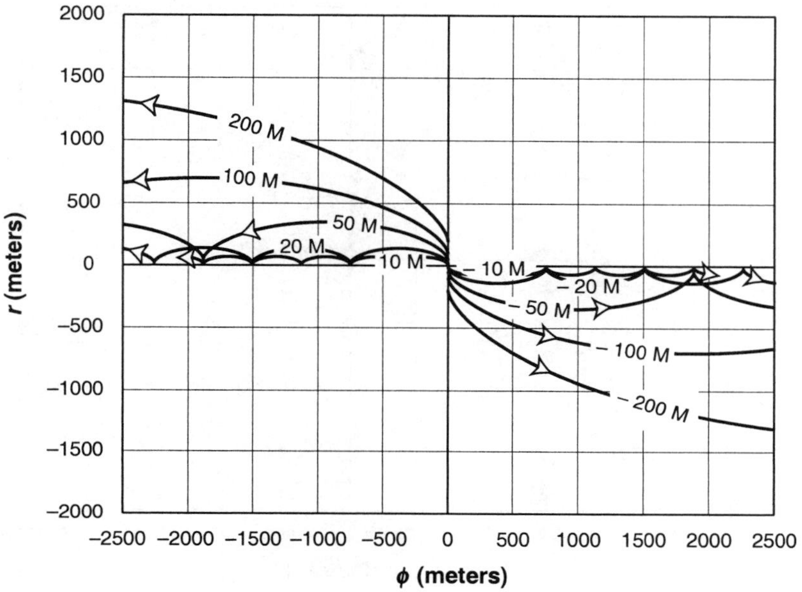

Fig. 10-25. Effects of Variations in r_0.

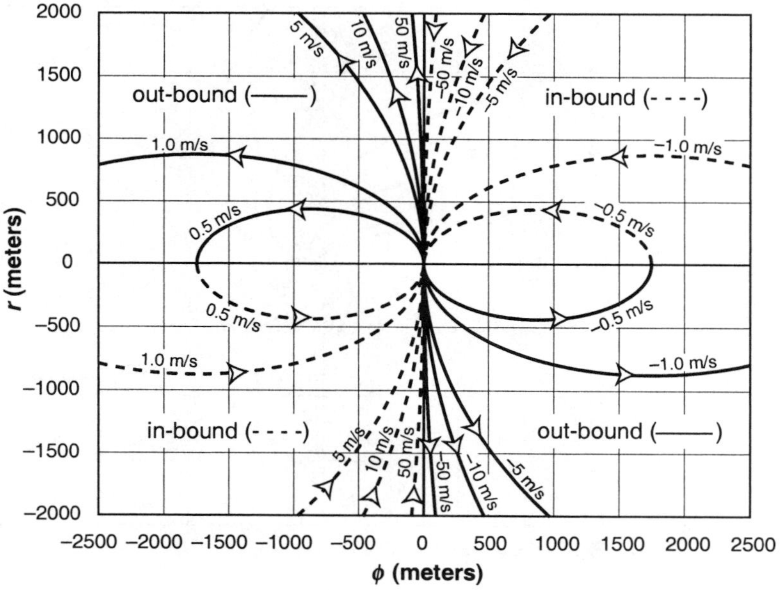

Fig. 10-26. Effects of Variations in $\dot{r}_0$.

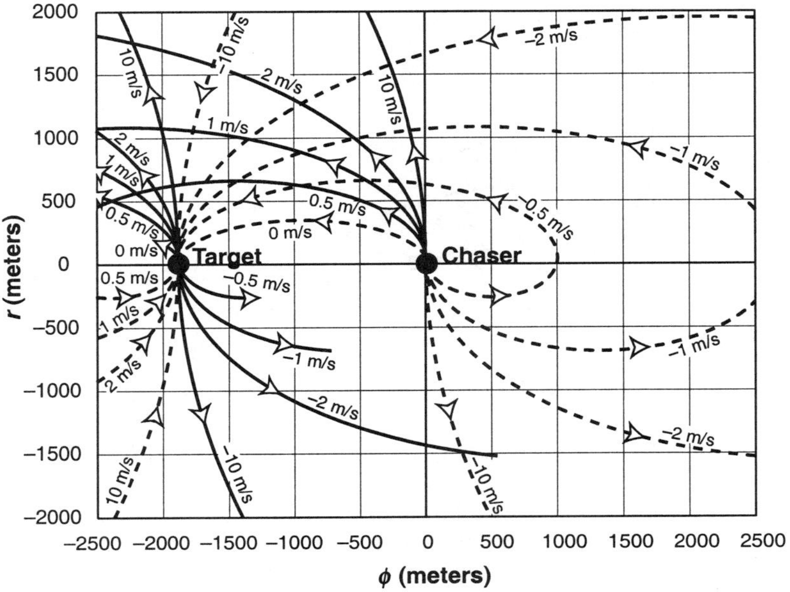

Fig. 10-27. Effects of Variations in $\dot{r}_0$ Combined with a Fixed r_0 Offset of +50 meters.

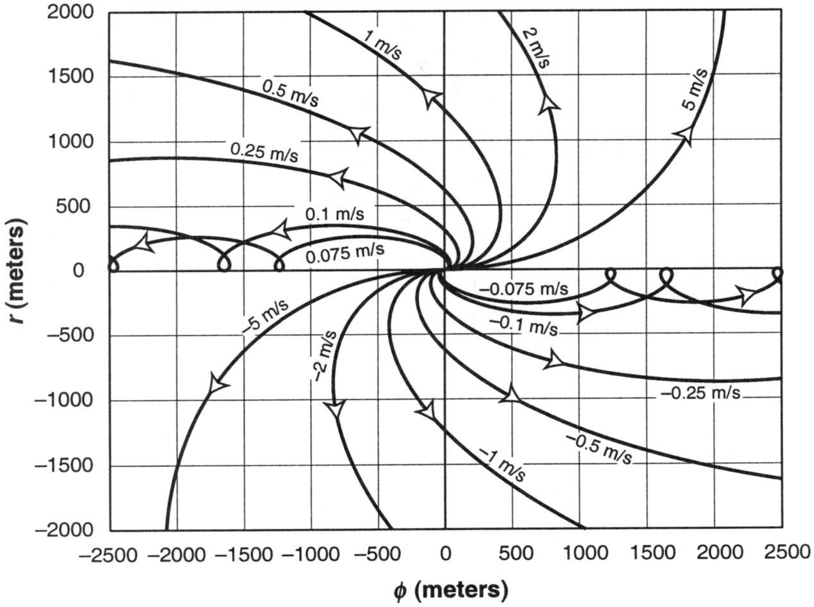

Fig. 10-28. Effects of Variations in $\dot{\phi}_0$.

1. If the chaser is below the target ($r_0 < 0$) then it will tend to drift in the positive in-track direction ($\phi > 0$). Conversely, if the chaser is above the target ($r_0 > 0$) then it will tend to drift in the negative in-track direction ($f < 0$) (Fig. 10-25).

2. The greater the offset from the target in r_0 then the greater the magnitude of the relative motion (Fig. 10-25).

3. A non-zero value of $\dot{r}_0$ **alone** will result in elliptical motion, specifically an *osculating ellipse*. It is an osculating ellipse since it 'kisses' the target orbit once every period. Example plots are shown in Fig. 10-27.

4. A special case exists at $\dot{\phi}_0 = -2nr_0$. Adjusting the ϕ-velocity to this value stops any drift in the ellipse. For ϕ-velocities larger than this value a negative in-track drift rate results, whereas ϕ-velocities smaller than this value result in positive in-track drifts. (Figs. 10-26, 10-27, and 10-28).

5. Additional changes in ϕ do not affect the shape or size of the motion since the motion is merely translated along the in-track axis. In essence, the semimajor axis and the orbital eccentricity of the underlying orbits are unchanged by an in-track-only shift. Moreover, a relative motion that can be described by a change in ϕ alone does not result in a plot tracing out any motion—the chaser is stationary with respect to the target and, hence, a plot of its motion is a dot located on the ϕ-axis.

6. A non-zero z, or $\dot{z}$, value results in an uncoupled oscillatory motion in the z-direction that is superimposed on the coupled motions in r and ϕ.

7. A final special case allows a chaser that is displaced in r to have no oscillatory motion at all when $\dot{\phi}_0 = -3/2r_0 n$. This produces linear motion parallel to the ϕ-axis at an 'altitude' of $r_0 = 2\dot{\phi}_0 / 3n$.

Thrust-Free Departure and Rendezvous

Hill's equations and various special cases of them have been used to develop a variety of rendezvous and docking strategies. (See, for example, Meissinger [1983, 1998].) A particularly interesting strategy is to make use of the very small gravity gradient forces to create thrust-free departure or rendezvous trajectories. Not having to fire thrusters at the end of the rendezvous process is particularly valuable in that it is a fail-safe approach in which the relative velocities will go to 0, even in the absence of any terminal thrusting. In addition, it prevents the chaser vehicle from having to fire thrusters toward the target and, therefore, avoids the problem of plume impingement. Unfortunately for rendezvous, most spacecraft have large solar arrays away from the body. These have both a large area and long moment arm with respect to the center of mass. Consequently, any plume impingement on the arrays, or other large deployables, can result in very large torques being applied to the target vehicle at a time when we would much prefer to have the target stable and quiescent.

We can obtain the thrust free departure conditions by reducing Hill's equations to the case where we are holding a spacecraft, for example, on the robot arm of the Shuttle or Space Station, a fixed distance r_0 above or below the reference vehicle. Thus, $\phi_0 = z_0 = \phi_0 = z_0 = r_0$. Releasing the spacecraft results in the following equations of motion as a function of time:

$$\phi = 6r_0(nt - \sin nt) \tag{10-51}$$

$$r = r_0(4 - 3\cos nt) \tag{10-52}$$

where, as usual, ϕ is the in-track distance, r is the radial distance, and n is the mean motion. Fig. 10-29 shows a family of zero-thrust departure trajectories with the initial offset distance, r_0, as the free parameter for the series of curves. For example, with a 90 minute orbit period in low Earth orbit and an initial offset of 25 m either above or below the reference vehicle, the chaser will reach a separation of 157 m in 25 min and 588 m in 50 min. While the separation process is slow, it has the substantial merit of requiring no thruster firings at all when the spacecraft are close together. The process is fully reversible, such that the left-hand side of Fig. 10-29 shows the comparable zero-thrust arrival trajectories. This process is often referred to as an *R-Bar approach* or departure and has been used for docking the Space Shuttle Orbiter with both the Russian Mir space station and the ISS. As seen from the Station, the Orbiter approaches straight up from the Earth using the small gravity gradient forces to slow and stop its ascent.

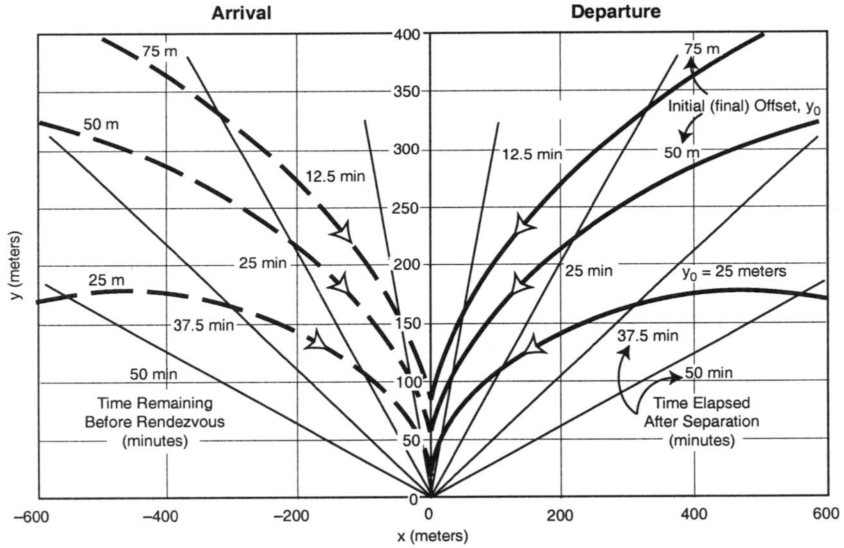

Fig. 10-29. Trajectories of Zero-Thrust Approach and Departure. See text for discussion. [Meissinger, 1983].

10.2.4 Continuous Thrust Formations

As described in Sec. 10.2.1, the force-free motion of satellites in a formation is very constrained. The only possible motion within the orbit plane is an ellipse twice as long as it is high. The only cross-track motion is a sinusoidal oscillation back and forth across the reference orbit plane. (See, for example, Figs. 10-17 and 10-19 in Sec. 10.2.1.) However, by applying low levels of continuous thrust these substantial constraints can be overcome such that any desired formation shape can be created.

These are called *continuous thrust* or *non-inertial formations* because they do not occur naturally and the formation will rapidly decay if the thrust ceases to be applied. (See, for example, Helvajian [1999].)

Initially, consider the force required to hold a spacecraft at a fixed position relative to another spacecraft traveling in a circular, Keplerian orbit. We can, of course, orbit an arbitrary fixed distance in front or behind the reference satellite with no thrust. However, a fixed radial or cross-track displacement requires a continuous application of force. Conceptually, we can think of these non-inertial orbits in several ways. For example, we can compare a vertical displacement to a Lagrange Point orbit (Sec. 2.5.5) in which the gravitational force of the secondary is replaced by the thruster force from the satellite.

An alternative is to regard the small forces required as balancing the *micro-gravity* or *gravity-gradient* forces acting within an extended structure in space. (See, for example, Wertz [1999], Sec. 8.1.2.) Very small forces pull on objects within a large space structure and cause unrestrained objects to drift. To maintain the structure, these forces are compensated by the structure itself, or, in the case of a formation of satellites, by small continuous thruster firings. In the cross-track direction, the gravity-gradient force pulls objects toward the center, such that a continuous outward thrust is required to negate it. In the radial direction, gravity-gradient force pulls objects away from the center of mass. Consequently, maintaining a satellite continuously above or below a reference or target satellite requires continuous thrusting toward the target. This is particularly convenient since the plume will then be directed away from the target and the satellite can be maintained in its non-inertial orbit without disturbing the target as discussed at the end of Sec. 10.2.3.

Using the notation of the previous section, we can use Hill's equations (Eq. 10-24) to write down the acceleration required for a continuous offset, z_0, in the cross-track direction:

$$\ddot{z} = n^2 z_0 \tag{10-53a}$$

where n is the mean motion. Using Eq. (2-16) for n, we have

$$\ddot{z} = \left(\mu / a^3\right) z_0 \tag{10-53b}$$

$$= 3.986\ 004\ 41 \times 10^{14} \left(a^{-3}\right) z_0 \qquad (\text{m/s}^2) \tag{10-53c}$$

where $\mu = GM$ is the gravitational constant for the Earth, and a is the orbit semimajor axis, expressed in m in the last equation. For example, consider a satellite in a circular orbit at 700 km. Then $z = 1.12 \times 10^{-6}\ z_0$. Thus, a fixed horizontal offset of 100 m requires a continuous acceleration of 1.12×10^{-4} m/s^2 = 0.011 m-g's. While a continuous force is required, the level of the force is very small.

Using the same process, the acceleration required for a continuous offset, r_0, in the radial direction is:

$$\ddot{r} = -3n^2 r_o \tag{10-54a}$$

$$= -3(\mu/a^3) r_0 \tag{10-54b}$$

$$= -1.195\ 801\ 325 \times 10^{15}\ (1/a3) r_0 \qquad (\text{m/s}^2) \tag{10-54c}$$

Thus, maintaining a fixed offset in the radial direction is 3 times as expensive in terms of propellant usage as a similar offset in the cross-track direction. For the example above, it would require a continuous acceleration of 3.36×10^{-4} m/s^2 = 0.033 m-g's to maintain a satellite 100 m above or below the reference satellite. This corresponds to 29 m/s per day or 10.6 km/s per year. Thus, while the forces required are small, the integrated ΔV can be very large if we wish to maintain the formation over an extended period.

Finally, we can combine the offset in all 3 axes to maintain a satellite continuously at any location we would like relative to a reference satellite. Similarly, we could circumnavigate the reference satellite in whatever "orbit" about it that we choose. The principal issue is the period of time required, since continuous or near-continuous, low-level thrusting will be an integral part of the process.

10.3 Relative Motion of Satellites at Different Altitudes

As indicated at the beginning of this chapter, we can always work the relative motion problem by simply numerically computing the two orbits to determine the positions of the satellites and then plot the results in inertial space or relative to the direction of the Earth. For very precise analysis or dealing with orbits which are very complex, this is indeed the appropriate approach. However, we can still gain insight into the problem by looking at the general rules of motion in determining both the characteristics and limits of that motion.

We first look at the general rules for the relative and apparent motion of satellites at different altitudes and then at specific cases of practical interests—low-Earth orbits and geosynchronous satellites looking at each other, the motion of a satellite in a transfer orbit relative to the target circular orbit, and the case of "nearby" satellites which are at different altitudes.

10.3.1 General Characteristics of Motion

The relative motion and limits of satellite visibility do not depend on which satellite is the base satellite. However, the transformation from a separation in Earth central angle between the two satellites to the nadir angle as viewed from a specific satellite will be different for each and gives rise to the different apparent motion depending on whether we are on the higher satellite looking down or the lower one looking up.

Over a short period of time, the orbit planes of the two satellites will be fixed in inertial space and remain at a fixed relative inclination. This is true indefinitely for purely Keplerian orbits. However, in practice, differential node rotation due to the Earth's oblateness implies that in reality there will be a slow drift between the orbit planes of satellites not at the same altitude. Ignoring this slow node rotation, the geometry of Fig. 10-5 applies to satellites of different altitudes with one major change. The satellites are now rotating at different rates such that relative phase is no longer constant but is continuously changing with time. Consequently, the simple analemma of Fig. 10-5 will become a more general dual axis spiral. For satellites at nearly the same altitude, the analemma will simply drift slowly with time, as shown in Fig. 10-30. This is the most general case of the relative motion of nearby satellites shown in Figs. 10-23 and Fig. 10-24. The drift rate of the analemma will be directly proportional to the ratio of the angular frequencies of the two satellites. Thus if the period of the lower satellite is 1% less, the angular frequency will be 1% higher and the analemmas will drift by 1% per orbit, which is 3.6 deg along the equator of the coordinate system. As discussed is Sec. 10.3.2 and 10.3.3, the relative motion will begin to look quite different for satellites that are at widely varying altitudes.

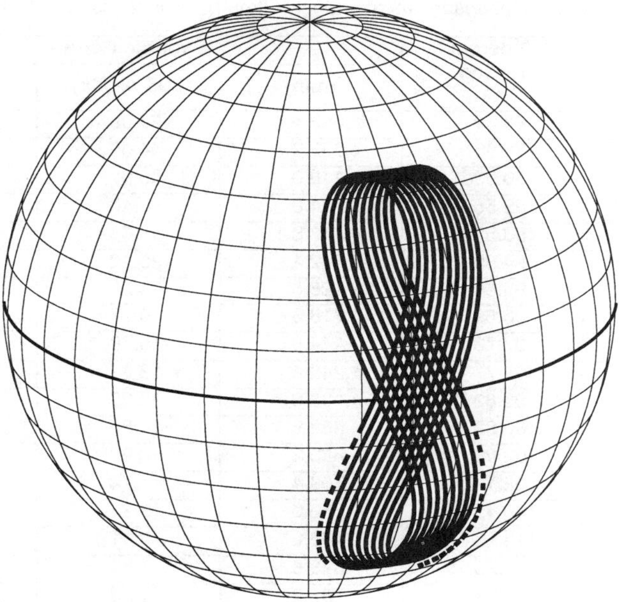

Fig. 10-30. Relative Motion for Satellites in Circular Orbits at Nearly the Same Altitude. Compare with Fig. 10-5. The drift rate of the analemma will be proportional to the ratio of the orbit periods.

In applying the logic of Chap. 8 to the relative motion at different altitudes, one additional concept is useful. In intersatellite or interplanetary viewing, we are typically given the inertial rates of the two objects but not the rates relative to each other. In the dual axis spiral analysis, what we have labeled the secondary rotation rate, ω_2, is more commonly known in astronomy as the *synodic rate* as shown in Fig. 2-11 in Sec. 2.2. It is more commonly expressed as the *synodic period* or period of one planet or satellite with respect to another. From Eq. (2-18), the synodic period, S, of one planet or satellite relative to another is given by:

$$\frac{1}{S} = \frac{1}{P_1} - \frac{1}{P_2} \tag{10-55}$$

where P_1 and P_2 are the periods of the individual satellites. The synodic periods for various planets are listed in Table 2-5.

This concept can also be extended to satellites. In this case, the synodic period represents the time in which they will return to the same relative orientation in phase or in-track position. (Note that if they are at significantly different inclinations, then this can still result in very different relative geometries.) The synodic period of various circular orbits relative to the Space Station at 350 km is shown in Table 10-9.

TABLE 10-9. Synodic Period of Earth Satellites (ES) Relative to the International Space Station (ISS) at 350 km (91.54 min period). After this period the relative position of the satellites will be approximately the same and the motion will repeat. Not applicable for spacecraft at strongly different inclinations. See text for discussion.

Spacecraft Altitude (km)	Sidereal Period (min)	Synodic Period		
		(min)	(ISS orbits)	(ES orbits)
200	88.49	2,662.4	29.09	30.09
250	89.50	4,032.7	44.05	45.06
300	90.52	8,148.0	89.01	90.01
400	92.56	8,274.8	90.40	89.40
450	93.59	4,178.8	45.65	44.65
500	94.62	2,812.1	30.72	29.72
550	95.65	2,128.5	23.25	22.25
600	96.69	1,718.3	18.77	17.77
650	97.73	1,444.8	15.78	14.78
700	98.77	1,249.4	13.65	12.65
750	99.82	1,102.9	12.05	11.05
800	100.87	988.9	10.80	9.80
900	102.99	823.2	8.99	7.99
1,000	105.12	708.4	7.74	6.74
1,200	109.42	560.0	6.12	5.12
1,400	113.78	468.2	5.11	4.11
2,000	127.20	326.5	3.57	2.57
5,000	201.31	167.9	1.83	0.83
10,000	347.66	124.2	1.36	0.36
20,000	710.60	105.1	1.15	0.15
35,876	1,440.67	97.7	1.07	0.07

It is the synodic period that is relevant for calculating when we can transfer from one satellite to another or fill in a hole in a constellation pattern. Thus, the synodic period of 2 years between the Earth and Mars implies that missions to Mars will appear at 2 year intervals. For planets or satellites at widely differing altitudes, the synodic period is approximately equal to the period of the lower object. Thus, we can launch a mission to Jupiter once per year or transfer from low-Earth orbit to geosynchronous at one opportunity for every revolution of a low-Earth orbit satellite. As the two objects get closer together in altitude, the synodic period gets longer. Thus, opportunities for missions to Mars or Venus occur less frequently than those for missions to Mercury or Jupiter. This is because when the objects are closer together they are moving at nearly the same rate and it takes longer for them to return to the same position relative to each other. Two satellites that are very nearly at the same altitude in low-Earth orbit will "slide" relative to each other at a very slow rate and many orbits will be required for them to return to same relative position at which they started. For example, from Table 10-9 we see that a satellite at 300 km will have a synodic period of 8,148 min, or more than 5 days, relative to the Space Station at 350 km. In this time the Space Station will have gone 89.01 orbits and the satellite will have "lapped" it one time by going 90.01 orbits.

The synodic period can be computed for any two orbits. However, it is a useful concept primarily for near-circular orbits which are at relative inclinations that are not too large. The purpose of the synodic period is to determine when objects will return to their same relative location. In orbits which are very eccentric or ones which are nearly at right angles to each other but at different frequencies then after a synodic period, they will be at different locations within their individual orbit and the relative geometry between them will no longer be similar. For example, the synodic period of a comet is not as important in determining how bright the comet will be as is the closeness of the comet to the Earth when it returns.

As was the case for co-altitude satellites, the equations of motion of one satellite in a circular orbit with respect to another in a circular orbit at a different altitude and inclination can be taken directly from the dual-axis spiral equations summarized in Table 8-8. In this case, **P** will be the position (α, δ) of Satellite 2 in the relative motion reference frame of Satellite 1 (the base satellite) as defined in Fig. 10-4. The primary axis, $\mathbf{OP}_1$, is the orbit pole of Satellite 1 and the secondary axis, $\mathbf{OP}_2$, is the orbit pole of Satellite 2. Physically, rotating about $\mathbf{OP}_1$ with an angular velocity equal to the mean angular motion, n_1, of Satellite 1 simply negates the orbital rotation and brings us back to an inertial frame. In this frame, Satellite 2 then rotates with velocity n_2 about $\mathbf{OP}_2$. The angular distance, ρ_2, from $\mathbf{OP}_2$ to Satellite 2 is just 90 deg and the angular distance, ρ_1, between the two rotation axes is just the relative inclination, i_R, which is equal to the angle between the two orbit poles $\mathbf{OP}_1$ and $\mathbf{OP}_2$. With these definitions, the equations in Table 8-8 can be transformed directly to yield the relative motion equations in Table 10-10.

As illustrated in Fig. 10-31, the rules for intersatellite viewing for non-coaltitude satellites are very similar to those for satellites at the same altitude. Any two satellites that can view the same point on the ground simultaneously can see each other. Thus, the condition for intersatellite visibility is just that the satellite separation in Earth central angle be less than the sum of the maximum Earth central angle for the two satellites individually.

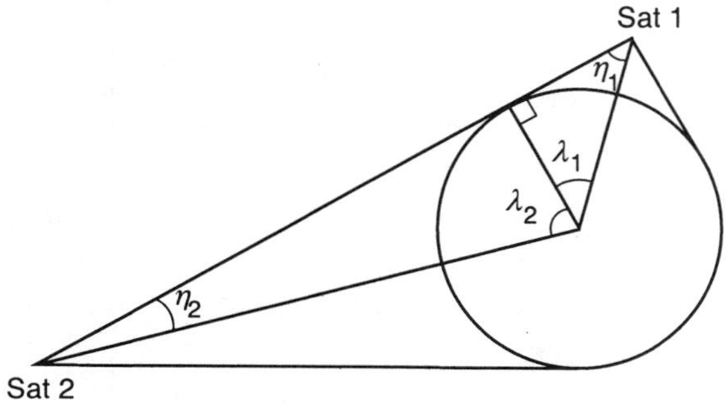

Fig. 10-31. The Condition for Intersatellite Visibility is Comparable to that for Co-Altitude Satellites. Compare with Fig. 10-7.

Determining the equations for transforming the Earth central angle into viewing angles from each of the two satellites is comparable to the problem of transforming between nadir angles and elevation angles as seen from the Earth. Thus, we first compute ρ_1 = the angular radius of the orbit of satellite 2 (lower) as seen from satellite 1 (higher):

$$\sin\rho_1 \equiv \frac{R_2}{R_1} \tag{10-56}$$

then:

$$\tan\eta_1 = \frac{\sin\rho_1 \sin\lambda}{1-\sin\rho_1 \cos\lambda} \tag{10-57a}$$

$$\eta_2 = 180 \text{ deg} - \eta_1 - \lambda h \tag{10-57b}$$

$$D = R_1\left(\frac{\sin\lambda}{\sin\eta_1}\right) \tag{10-57c}$$

where η_1 is the angle at the higher satellite from the center of the Earth to satellite 2, η_2 is the angle at the lower satellite from the center of the Earth to satellite 1, λ is the separation between the two in Earth central angle, and D is the distance between the satellites. We can use these equations to plot the nadir angle versus Earth central angle for satellites in low-Earth and geosynchronous orbits which are viewing each other as shown in Fig. 10-32. From the higher satellite, the lower satellite always remains in the general vicinity of the Earth and the nadir angle has a maximum value equal to the angular radius of the low orbit as seen from the higher one. On the other hand, as seen from the low orbit, the satellite in the higher orbit can have any angle from nadir ranging from 0 to 180 deg. Thus, the lower satellite has a much wider range of gimbal angles that must be accommodated.

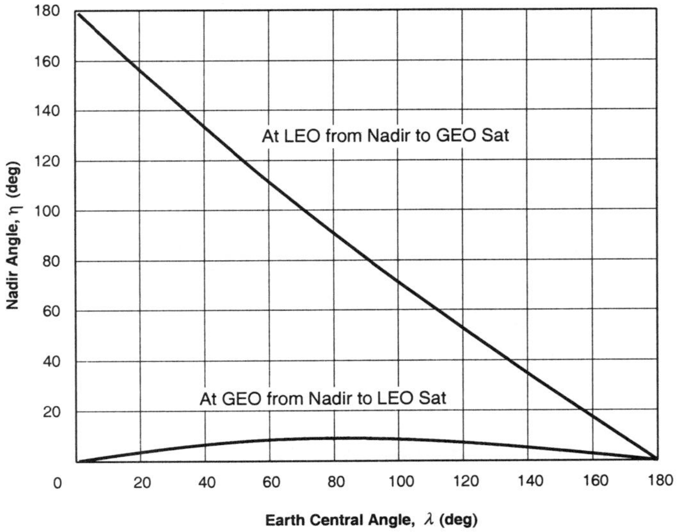

Fig. 10-32. Plot of Nadir Angle vs. Earth Central Angle for Satellites in LEO (300 km) and GEO.

TABLE 10-10. Summary of Equations for the Relative Motion of Two Satellites. Both orbits are assumed to be circular, but not necessarily at the same altitude.

	Variable	Equations or Definitions	Conditions	Where Discussed
Definitions	*Defining Parameters*	Satellite 2, with position **P** = (α, δ) with respect to Satellite 1, rotates with mean angular velocity n_2 about its orbit pole **OP**$_2$, which in turn is rotating with mean angular velocity n_1 about **OP**$_1$, the orbit pole for Satellite 1. **P** is always 90 deg from **OP**$_2$. The angle between **OP**$_1$ and **OP**$_2$ is i_R.	$0 \le i_R \le 180$ deg **OP**$_1$ at (0°, 90°) **P**, **OP**$_2$ anywhere n_1, n_2 arbitrary	See Text
Intermediate Variables	ϕ_1 = *Azimuth of* **OP**$_2$ *about* **OP**$_1$ relative to $\alpha = 0$	$\phi_1 = \phi_{1_0} + n_1 t$	no constraints	Eq. (8-27)
	ϕ_2 = *Azimuth of* **P** *about* **OP**$_2$ relative to **OP**$_1$	$\phi_2 = \phi_{2_0} + n_2 t$	no constraints	Eq. (8-27)
	$\Delta\alpha$ = *Change in Azimuth of* **P** *about* **OP**$_1$	$\Delta\alpha = \text{acos2}\left[\dfrac{\tan\delta}{\tan i_R}, \quad -H(\phi_2)\right]$	$0 \le \Delta\alpha < 360°$	Eq. (8-28a)
	ρ_E = *Angle from* **P** *to Euler Axis* **E**	$\rho_E = \text{acos}\left(\cos\delta'_E \sin\delta + \sin\delta'_E \cos\delta \cos\Delta\alpha\right)$	$0 \le \rho_E \le 180°$	Eq. (8-24)
	ω_E = *Rate of Rotation about* **E**	$\omega_E = \dfrac{n_2 \sin i_R}{\sin\delta'_E}$ $= \sqrt{n_1^2 + n_2^2 + 2n_1 n_2 \cos i_R}$	$\omega_E \ge 0$	Eq. (8-23b) Eq. (8-23c)
	δ'_E = *Angle from* **OP** *to* **E**	$\delta'_E = \text{atan}\left[\dfrac{n_2 \sin i_R}{(n_1 + n_2 \cos i_R)}\right]$	$0 \le \delta'_E \le 180°$*	Eq. (8-23a)
	$\Delta\psi$ = *Change in Direction of Motion of* **P**$_1$	$\Delta\psi = \text{acos2}\left[\dfrac{\cos\delta'_E - \cos\rho_E \sin\delta}{\sin\rho_E \cos\delta}, \quad H(\Delta\alpha)\right]$	$0 \le \Delta\psi < 360°$	Eq. (8-25a)
Results	α = *Azimuth of* **P** *about* **OP**$_1$	$\alpha = [\phi_1 + \Delta\alpha]\text{mod}_{360}$	$0 \le \alpha < 360°$	Eq. (8-28b)
	δ = *Elevation of* **P** *relative to* **OP**$_1$	$\delta = 90° - \text{acos}(\sin i_R \cos\phi_2)$	$-90° \le \delta \le 90°$	Eq. (8-28c)
	v = *Velocity of* **P**	$v = \omega_E \sin\rho_E$	$0 \le v \le \omega_E$	Eq. (8-26)
	ψ = *Direction of Motion of* **P**	$\psi = [\Delta\psi - 90°]\text{mod}_{360}$	$0 \le \psi < 360°$	Eq. (8-25b)

* The output of the atan function should be converted to the range 0 to 180 deg.

10.3.2 LEO Satellites as Seen from High Altitudes

We can apply all of the general formulas above to the motion of a low-Earth orbit satellite as seen from a higher satellite. For specificity, we will look at the motion of satellites in LEO as seen from geosynchronous orbit. Recall that low-Earth orbit is a region of space within approximately 20% of the surface of the Earth. Consequently, LEO satellites will be constrained to move within a region only approximately 20% larger than the size of the disk of the Earth as seen from GEO. From Eq. 10-10, the synodic period seen from GEO will be approximately 6.5% longer than the inertial period of the LEO satellite itself. Consequently, the general motion for a LEO satellite seen from GEO is for the satellite to move in an approximately elliptical shape that is 10% to 20% longer than the diameter of the Earth's disk and at a rate corresponding to a period approximately 6.5% longer than the period of the satellite. This motion is shown in Fig. 10-33, both in the relatively motion frame and also as the apparent motion with respect to the surface of the Earth. The motion from GEO of a satellite in a near equatorial orbit is shown in Fig. 10-34A, and for one at approximately polar or Sun-synchronous orbit in Fig. 10-34B. When the LEO satellite is in a polar orbit, the appearance of the orbit from GEO will change from being seen nearly edge-on to being seen from the pole as the geosynchronous satellite goes through its orbit once per day and the low-Earth orbit satellite remains nearly fixed in inertial space.

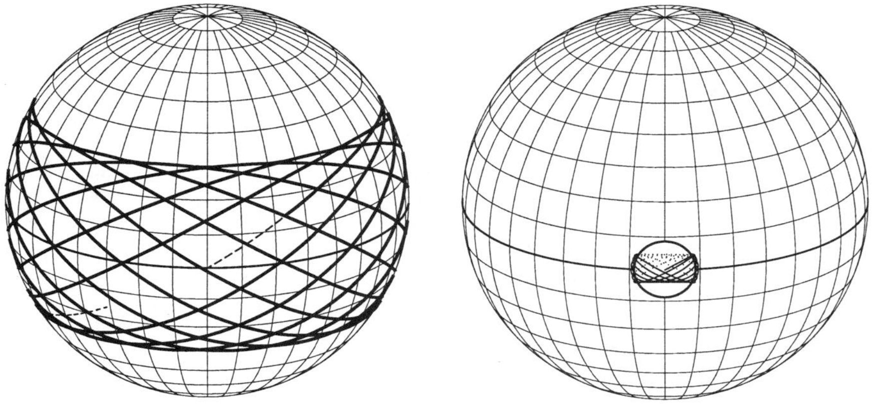

(A) (B)

Fig. 10-33. Relative Motion of LEO Satellite Seen from GEO. (A) in relative motion frame. (B) apparent motion with respect to the Earth as seen from GEO satellite.

The apparent motion of the LEO satellite in inertial space is simply the motion shown in Figs. 10-33 and 10-34 spread out across the sky as the Earth moves with respect to the background stars. A representative sample of this motion is shown in Fig. 10-35 for the same conditions as Fig. 10-33B. The semimajor axis of the apparent ellipse of the motion of the LEO satellite on the sky, ρ_{LEO}, is given by:

$$\sin(\rho_{LEO}/2) = a_{LEO}/a_{GEO} \tag{10-58}$$

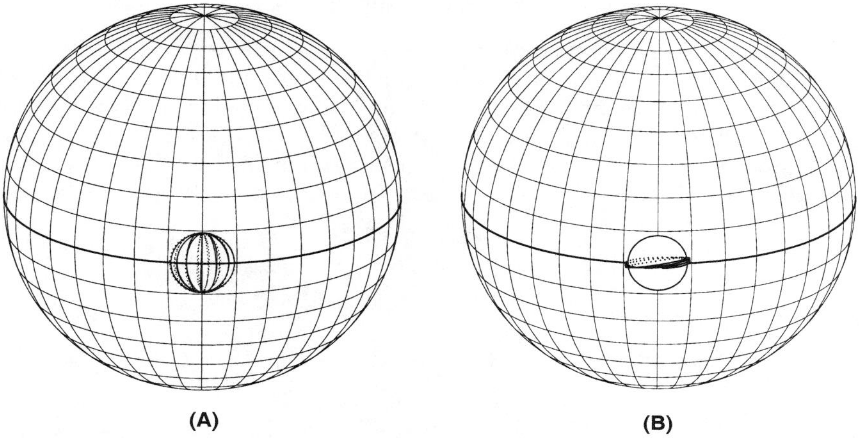

Fig. 10-34. Apparent Relative Motion for LEO Satellites at Differing Inclination. (A) satellite in polar orbit. (B) satellite in nearly equatorial orbit.

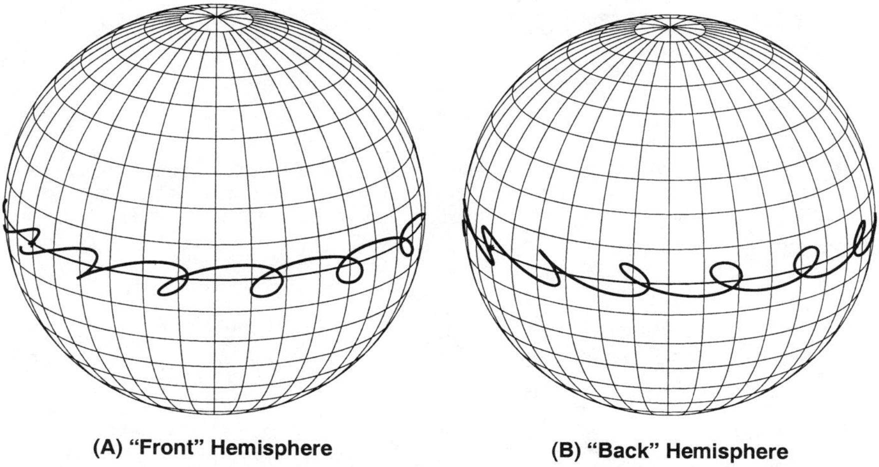

Fig. 10-35. Apparent Motion with Respect to the Background Stars of a LEO Satellite as Seen from GEO.

where a_{LEO} is the semimajor axis of the approximately circular LEO orbit and a_{GEO} is the semimajor axis for satellites in GEO. The apparent looping motion of the LEO satellite across the sky will be contained within a band of width w given by:

$$\sin(w/2) = \sin i_R \sin(\rho_{LEO}/2) \qquad (10\text{-}59)$$

where i_R is the relative inclination between the two orbits, which will be approximately equal to the inclination of the low orbiting satellite when the higher satellite is in an equatorial orbit.

10.3.3 High Altitude Satellites Seen From Lower Orbits

The motion of spacecraft in geosynchronous orbit is the inverse problem of that in the previous section. Consequently, we can either redo the initial formulas, or simply invert the charts from the previous section, taking into account the differences in nadir angle corresponding to low altitude and high altitude satellites. Fig. 10-36, corresponding to Fig. 10-33, shows the relative motion of the GEO satellite as seen from LEO and Fig. 10-37 shows the same motion for LEO satellites at differing inclinations.

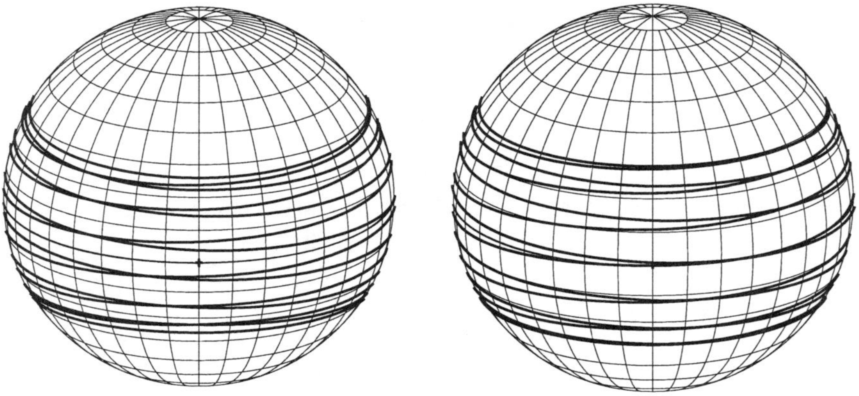

(A) (B)

Fig. 10-36. Relative Motion of GEO Satellite Seen from LEO. (A) in relative motion frame. (B) apparent motion with respect to the Earth as seen from the LEO satellite. See Fig. 10-33 for comparison with motion seen from the perspective of the GEO satellite.

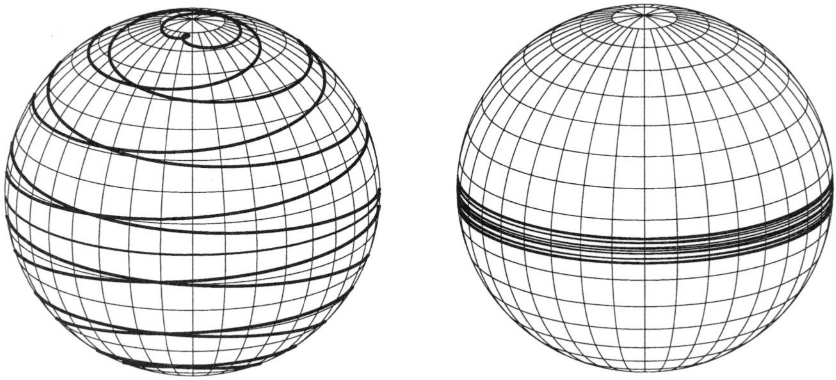

(A) (B)

Fig. 10-37. Relative Motion for Satellites at Differing Inclination. (A) observing satellite in polar orbit. (B) observing satellite in nearly equatorial orbit. Compare with Fig. 10-34.

The apparent motion of a satellite in GEO as seen from low-Earth orbit has a much broader angular range covering virtually the entire celestial sphere. In addition, the angular rates can be substantially larger. From a numerical perspective, this can be seen in Fig. 10-32 in Sec. 10.3.1, which showed the range of nadir angles for the low and high altitude satellites. From a physical perspective, the geostationary satellite remains approximately fixed in inertial space over the period of one low-Earth orbit. Consequently, it will go through 360 deg as the satellite in LEO goes through a complete orbit. For a satellite in a highly inclined low-Earth orbit, the geosynchronous satellite can appear essentially anywhere in the spacecraft's sky, from zenith to being hidden behind the disk of the Earth. Consequently, an antenna on a low-Earth orbit spacecraft will need to cover nearly the full zenith hemisphere in order to follow the general motion of satellites in GEO. This makes the gimbal and tracking problem significantly more complex for the LEO satellite than it is for the geosynchronous satellite.

As seen in Fig. 10-38, the motion of the geosynchronous satellite with respect to the background stars will be essentially identical to that of the LEO satellite seen from GEO. Here we are simply tracking the motion of the satellites with respect to the background stars and in this frame the two satellites will be 180 deg away from each other at all times.

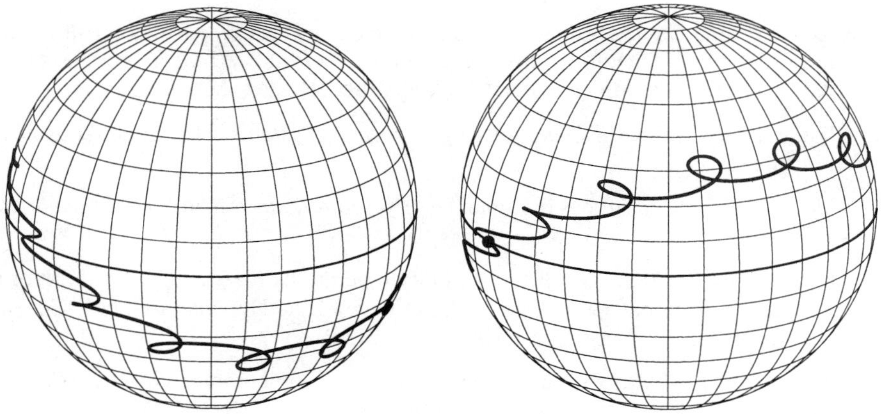

(A) "Front" Hemisphere (B) "Back" Hemisphere

Fig. 10-38. Apparent Motion with Respect to the Background Stars of a GEO Satellite as Seen from LEO. Compare with Fig. 10-35 for the motion as seen from GEO.

Just as for the Sun or other objects approximately fixed in inertial space, there may satellite orbit pole in which the GEO satellite will never appear. Specifically, a satellite in a circular, equatorial, geosynchronous orbit at distance $R_G = 42{,}164$ km can not be closer than E to the orbit pole of a LEO satellite in a circular orbit of inclination i and radius, R_S, where:

$$\tan E = (R_G \cos i - R_S) / (R_G \sin i) \tag{10-60}$$

References

Battin, Richard. 1964. *Astronautical Guidance*. New York: McGraw-Hill.

Battin, Richard. 1987. *An Introduction to the Mathematics and Methods of Astrodynamics*. New York: AIAA Education Series.

Chobotov, Vladimir A., ed. 1996. *Orbital Mechanics,* 2nd ed. Washington, DC: American Institute of Aeronautics and Astronautics.

Clohessy, W.H. and R.S. Wiltshire. 1960. "Terminal Guidance System for Satellite Rendezvous." *Journal of the Aerospace Sciences*, Vol. 27, No. 9. pp. 653–674.

Der, Gim J., and Roy Danchick. 1997. "An Analytic Approach to Optimal Rendezvous Using the Der-Danchick Equations." AIAA Paper 97-647, AAS/AIAA Astrodynamics Specialist Conference, Sun Valley, Idaho, Aug. 4–7.

Folta, David C. 1996. "Foundations of Formation Flying for Mission to Planet Earth and New Millennium," AAS Paper 96-3465, Astrodynamics Specialist Conference, San Diego, CA. July 29–31.

Folta, David C. and David Quinn. 1997. "Enhanced Formation Flying for the Earth Observing-1: (Eo-1) New Millennium Mission." Flight Mechanics Symposium, NASA GSFC. May 19–21.

Folta, David C. and David Quinn. 1998. "A Universal 3-D Method for Controlling the Relative Motion of Multiple Spacecraft in Any Orbit." AIAA Paper 98-4193, AIAA/AAS Astrodynamics Specialist Conference, Boston, MA, August.

Helvajian, H. (ed.) 1999. *Microengineering Aerospace Systems*. El Segundo, CA: The Aerospace Press.

Hill, George. 1878. "Researches in Lunar Theory." *American Journal of Mathematics*. Vol. 1: 5–26.

Meissinger, Hans F. 1983. "Satellite Proximity Operations Near a Space Shuttle or a Future Space Station," 1983 Annual Conference of the Herrmann-Oberth-Gesellschaft, Koblenz, Germany, Sept., 1983.

Meissinger, Hans F. 1998. "Proximity Operations," in supplement to *On-Orbit Servicing of Space Systems*, by Donald M. Waltz. Malabar, FL: Krieger Publishing Co.

Vallado, David A. 2001. *Fundamentals of Astrodynamics and Applications,* 2nd ed. El Segundo, CA and Dordrecht, The Netherlands: Microcosm Press and Kluwer Academic Publishers.

Wertz, James R., and Wiley J. Larson. 1999. *Space Mission Analysis and Design (third edition)*. Torrance, CA and Dordrecht, The Netherlands: Microcosm, Inc., and Kluwer Academic.

Chapter 11

Viewing and Lighting Conditions

Prior chapters have dealt with the geometry of spacecraft motion and observations. In addition, for many observations lighting conditions are also critical. What is the level of illumination on the target or the background? Are the shadows long or short, and in what direction are they? Is target viewing blocked by glare from the Sun? This chapter deals with the fundamental issues of the lighting conditions on the spacecraft itself and on the target body, either a planet or another spacecraft.

For any object on the surface of the planet or in space there are three fundamental sources of potential illumination:

- Internal illumination, such as a fire, city lights, or the surface of the Sun
- Reflected illumination from an external source
  —Direct sunlight
  —Reflected light from a nearby object or planet
- Radar, laser, or other illumination associated with the sensor

Each of these sources of illumination behaves somewhat differently. All objects radiate electromagnetic energy at a wavelength and intensity corresponding to their absolute temperature and, therefore, create internal illumination characteristic of their temperature.* This radiation may propagate approximately uniformly in all directions

* This *blackbody radiation* or *thermal radiation* is described in more detail by Wertz and Larson [1999] or Gilmore and Bello [1994].

(i.e., *isotropic*) or may have a preferential direction, such as a flashlight or directional antenna. In either case, the intensity of the radiation falls off as $1/r^2$ with the distance from the object to the observer.

Objects which shine by reflected light such as the planets or most spacecraft also have their brightness drop off as $1/r^2$ with respect to the distance to the observer. However, their brightness also decreases as $1/r^2$ with the distance between the illumination source (typically the Sun) and the object being illuminated. In addition, the amount of illumination depends strongly on the *phase angle*, which is the angle at the target between the Sun and the observer. For example, a first or last quarter Moon is one in which the *terminator*, or the line separating light and dark, is directly through the middle of the Moon as seen by the observer, and the Sun and the observer are at right angles as seen from the Moon. Thus, approximately half of the visible surface of the Moon is illuminated. However, the intensity of the first and last quarter Moon is only about 10% of the intensity of the full Moon, both because of very much lower levels of illumination near the terminator and because much of the light is reflected back in the general direction of the source. In contrast, highly reflective flat surfaces can create a specular reflection in which the light is reflected directly toward the observer. This occurs, for example, with the Iridium spacecraft phased array downlink antenna, which provides an extremely bright "Iridium flash" that can, at times, be brighter than anything in the sky other than the Sun or the Moon.

Finally, with radar or laser illumination, the source of the illumination is associated with the observer. Consequently, the level of illumination falls off as $1/r^2$ and the brightness of the object for a given illumination also falls off as $1/r^2$, such that the radar intensity drops off as $1/r^4$. Consequently, space-based radars are generally very high power devices and will normally be effective only in relatively low-Earth orbit, since the power requirement for a radar in geosynchronous orbit would be dramatically higher. A detailed analysis of the illumination of any object in space requires models of the source, the target, and the spacecraft, and substantial numerical computation. The purpose of this chapter is to provide an overview of the lighting and illumination problem, and a first-order computational capability to give a broad understanding of what levels of illumination can be expected.

Another concept which is important in discussing illumination is the *surface brightness* of an object or the brightness per square degree as we look at it. The most important characteristic is that the surface brightness does **not** depend on distance. The brightness of an object drops off as $1/r^2$ as we get further from it, however, the angular area which it subtends also drops off as $1/r^2$. Consequently, the surface brightness, or brightness per unit angular area, remains constant. For photographers, the required exposure time in daylight remains approximately the same, whether I am photographing a flower very close, a scene across the street, or a view of the distant mountains. It is the intensity per square degree that is ultimately recorded on film, and which is largely independent of distance. In contrast, a flash photograph at night is similar to radar. A flash photograph of a person in a large room will show the person well and the distant walls will be very dark. The fact that surface brightness is independent of distance leads to an interesting astronomical phenomenon known as *Olbers' Paradox*, described in the boxed example.

Why is the Sky Dark at Night?

We all understand that on a very dark and cloudless night away from the bright lights of the city, the sky is far darker than when we are looking directly at the Sun. But why is this so? The question was first raised by a German physician and astronomer, Heinrich Olbers, in 1826. *Olbers' Paradox* had a profound effect on early cosmology, and led astronomers to question the structure of the Universe as we know it.

Olbers' reasoning was as follows: If the Universe is infinitely large, then in any direction that we look, we should ultimately run into the surface of a star. (See Fig. 11-1.) However, since surface brightness does not depend on distance, the surface brightness of the distant star should be the same as the surface brightness of the Sun. Consequently, the entire sky should be as bright as the surface of the Sun.

Fig. 11-1. Olbers' Paradox: If the Universe is Infinitely Large, Then in any Direction We Go, Sooner or Later We Should Run into the Surface of a Star.

Even if the Universe is filled with gas and dust, this does not help our problem. Our interstellar cloud will either reflect the light from the distant stars, or absorb it and reradiate it. The temperature of the gas and dust will rise until it radiates as much energy as it takes in, and therefore, be just as bright as the surface of the stars which are illuminating it.

The simple observation that the sky is dark at night appears to say something very important about the nature of the Universe as a whole. The solution to Olbers' Paradox is in the footnote on the next page.*

11.1 Introduction to Spacecraft Lighting

The general lighting conditions for a spacecraft orbiting any of the planets or moons in the solar system is shown in Fig. 11-2. The *umbra*, or *shadow cone*, is the conical shaped region opposite the direction of the Sun in which the entire disk of the Sun is hidden by the planet. An *eclipse* occurs when the spacecraft enters the umbra. How dark it becomes during the eclipse depends upon the conditions at the perimeter of the surface of the planet, as seen by the spacecraft. For central bodies with no atmosphere such as the Moon, the region within the umbra will be extremely dark with very low levels of illumination produced by some scattering around the perimeter and a small amount of light from other celestial objects. For central bodies such as the Earth, the level of illumination within the umbra will depend on atmospheric conditions at the time of the eclipse. During a *lunar eclipse* or *eclipse of the Moon*, when the Moon enters the umbra, it is possible to determine the approximate weather conditions around the edge of the Earth by looking at the illumination of the Moon's disk. If it is clear weather, there will be substantial refraction and scattering of sunlight through the atmosphere into the shadow cone, and the Moon will take on a dull reddish color. If it is cloudy weather around much of the world, the Moon will be much darker and the illumination level within the shadow cone will be much lower.

Unlike the drawing in Fig. 11-2, the actual spacing between the Earth and the Sun is far larger than the diameter of either. Consequently, real shadow cones for the planets are extremely long and extends some distance into space. The shadow cone of the Earth extends to approximately 4 times the distance to the Moon. The angular diameter of the shadow cone will be equal to the angular diameter to the Sun as seen from the distance of the planet, or 0.5 deg in the case of the Earth's shadow cone.

Just outside of the umbra is a region called the *penumbra*, in which the disk of the Sun is partially, but not wholly, obstructed by the disk of the central body. Consequently, this is a region of partial illumination. As a practical matter, even a very small fraction of the disk of the Sun provides a relatively high level of illumination, such that it is difficult to tell when the Moon, for example, enters the penumbra of the Earth's

---

* Modern cosmology has resolved Olbers' Paradox by finding $2^1/_2$ reasons why the surface of the sky is not as bright as the surface of the Sun. The first reason is that the Universe is expanding. As we look out to distant galaxies, they are receding from the Earth at a rate proportional to their distance; that is, the further the galaxy, the faster it is moving away from us. This expansion of the Universe causes a red shift which in turn shifts all of the energy toward the red end of the spectrum. As galaxies get further away, the light which is now in the visible portion of the spectrum will eventually be shifted into the infrared and will not be visible to us.

The second explanation is that the Universe has a finite age of approximately 15 billion years. As we look out on the Universe, we are also looking backward in time. For an object which is a *light-year* away (i.e., the distance that light travels in a year), we are also looking a year back in time. At more than 15 billion light-years, the light which we would see would have to have started before the creation of the Universe, and, therefore, has not yet reached us.

Finally, our "half" answer, is that the sky **is** uniformly bright at night. The very bright light from near the time of the creation of the Universe has expanded dramatically and been red-shifted into the microwave region of the spectrum. This *microwave background*, now corresponding to a thermal temperature of only 3 K, provides a very nearly isotropic background that fills the entire sky. If we simply look in the right wavelength, we can look in any direction and see the creation of the Universe.

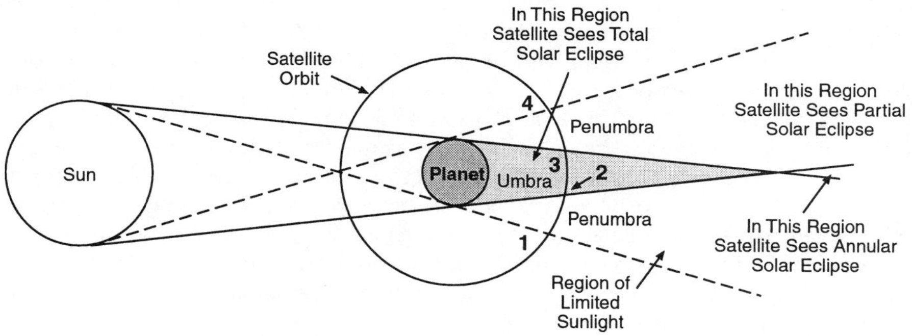

Fig. 11-2. Definition of the Lighting Conditions for a Satellite. The geometry has been substantially exaggerated to show the phenomenon. In reality, the Earth's total eclipse shadow cone extends to approximately 4 times the distance of the Moon.

shadow. It is the entrance into the umbra that provides a very distinct transition and can be easily seen as the shadow of the Earth on the surface of the Moon as the Moon enters eclipse. The diameter of the penumbral cone will also be equal to the angular diameter to the Sun, but will have its point toward the Sun in the illuminated portion of the orbit. Outside of the penumbra, the spacecraft will be in full illumination, although portions of the Earth's disk beneath the spacecraft may still be in darkness.

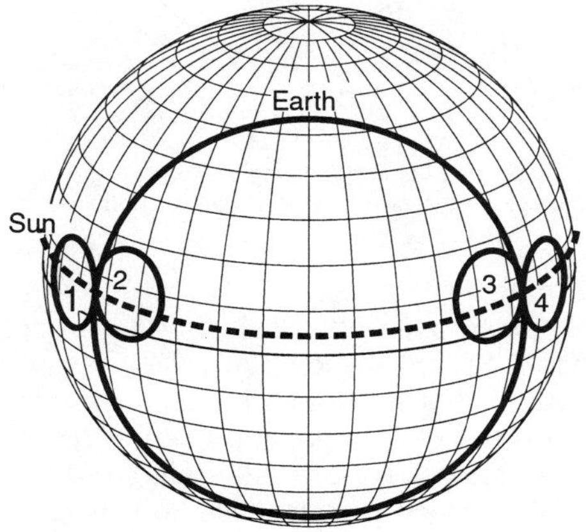

Fig. 11-3. Same Geometry as Fig. 11-2, Viewed on the Spacecraft-Centered Celestial Sphere. See text for discussion. The size of the Sun has been greatly exaggerated. At the distance of the Earth, the Sun's angular diameter is only 0.5 deg.

The same geometry in Fig. 11-2 is shown in Fig. 11-3 on the spacecraft-centered celestial sphere. Here we have used a coordinate system in which the Earth remains fixed such that the Sun appears to move once per orbit on a small circle centered on the orbit pole, as described in Sec. 6.1.1. To illustrate the effects, we have significantly exaggerated the size of the disk of the Sun. In practice, the Earth's disk in low-Earth orbit has an angular diameter of approximately 120 deg and the Sun's angular diameter is approximately 0.5 deg. When the spacecraft reaches point 1, it will enter the penumbra, a portion of the Sun's disk will be obstructed by the central body, and a partial eclipse will begin. This becomes a total eclipse at point 2, where the disk of the Sun is completely hidden behind the disk of the central body. (Atmospheric refraction can bend the light grazing the disk of the Earth by as much as half a degree, and therefore extend the penumbral region into the geometrical region of the umbra.) When the spacecraft reaches 3, the total eclipse is over, and at 4, it again enters full illumination with the end of the second partial eclipse. Note that the Sun may or may not be in the orbit plane. Eclipses will be longest when the Sun lies in the orbit plane and will be shorter as it gets further from the orbit plane until the eclipse does not occur at all when the Sun is further from the orbit plane than the angular radius of the Earth.

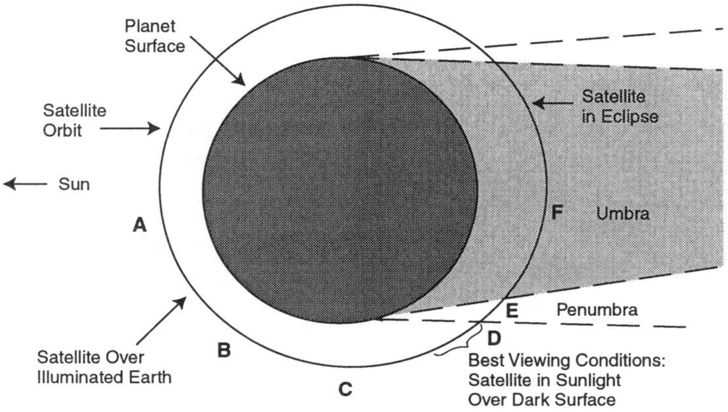

Fig. 11-4. Enlarged View of Fig. 11-2. The viewing conditions depend on the lighting on the observer, the lighting on the target, and angles of both with respect to the Sun. See text for discussion.

In order to get a better understanding of the lighting conditions on the satellite and on the surface of the Earth, Fig. 11-4 shows an enlarged view of the geometry of Fig. 11-2. The viewing and lighting conditions for the points marked in Fig. 11-4 are described in Table 11-1, and two of them are illustrated in Fig. 11-5. At point A, both the spacecraft and the Earth beneath it are in full sunlight. Although the Sun is at our back if we are sitting in the spacecraft viewing the Earth, there are very few shadows. The Earth below will be extremely bright but there will be very poor contrast with limited detail. As the spacecraft moves into region B, there will be excellent conditions for viewing the Earth below. The sky will be bright and the Earth will be in full daylight; however, there will be a more moderate level of illumination with long shadows. These are the best conditions for visible light observations. Details will stand out clearly. It will be early morning or late afternoon for the subsatellite region, which is a time when photographers get the best detail in distant scenes.

At region C, the *terminator,* or line between light and dark on the surface of the Earth, will be visible. Light levels will be extremely low with long shadows. There will be good contrast, but low light levels will make it difficult to see detail, unless the

TABLE 11-1. Viewing and Lighting Conditions for the Points Marked in Fig. 11-4. See Fig. 11-5 for illustrations.

Pt	Satellite Lighting	Satellite Visibility from Earth	Earth Lighting	Earth Features Viewed from the Satellite
A	Sun near zenith, dark side facing Earth	Very bad; Looking into Sun, dark side facing the observer	High Sun angles, very short shadows	Poor—excellent brightness, but short shadows give very poor contrast, limited detail
B	Sun away from overhead, but still on the zenith side of the spacecraft	Poor; bright sky, satellite illumination moderate to good	Moderate Sun angles, illumination, and shadows; Terminator not visible or near edge of Earth disk	Excellent—moderate illumination level and long shadows; best conditions for visible light observations
C	Sun approximately perpendicular to nadir	Poor to moderate; gets better as sky gets darker; half of satellite illuminated by the Sun	Terminator visible with most of the Earth lit; light levels low with very long shadows	Good to fair—long shadows and good contrast; depends strongly on local cloud conditions
D	Sun shining on nadir face; brightest time as seen from Earth	Excellent—bright satellite against dark sky; most LEO satellites easily visible to naked eye	Terminator visible with most of the Earth dark; light levels very low	Poor due to low light levels and Sun shining on nadir face; however, shadows are long and contrast excellent if local weather is clear
E	Satellite in partial darkness—light fades as Sun goes behind the disk of the Earth	Poor—illumination of the satellite fades rapidly	Earth is dark—bright limb and atmospheric glow on the horizon toward the Sun	Not visible, except under unusual circumstances
F	Satellite in complete darkness	No—satellite not illuminated	Earth disk is fully dark	Not visible, except for fires, city lights, etc.

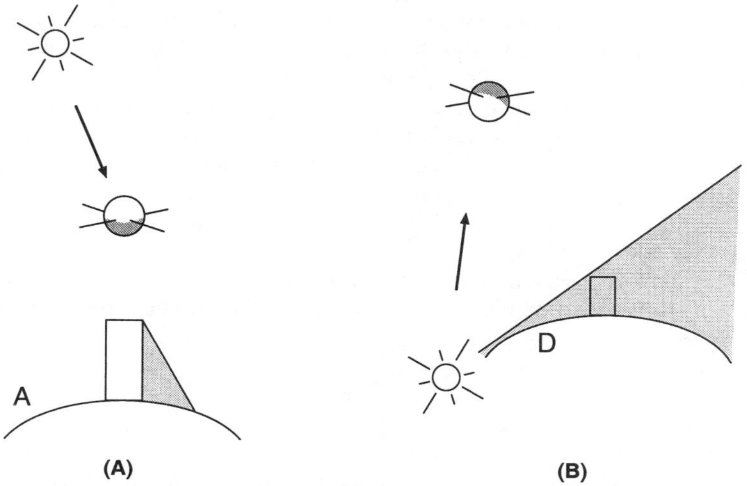

Fig. 11-5. Illumination for Conditions A and D Shown in Fig. 11-4 and Table 11-1. See text for discussion.

weather is very clear. At D, the spacecraft will still be in sunlight, but the Earth below will be in darkness, and therefore, there will be extremely poor visibility in trying to look from bright sunlight onto a dark Earth (Fig. 11-5B). On the other hand, the view from the Earth looking upward will be quite good, since the Earth will be in darkness and the satellite will be in bright sunlight. This is the geometry when spacecraft are seen passing overhead shortly after sunset or before sunrise. The nadir face of the spacecraft is nearly fully illuminated, and the spacecraft is seen against a dark background sky for the observer on the Earth. Consequently, it frequently appears quite bright and occasional glints off solar arrays or other spacecraft panels can make the spacecraft the brightest object in the sky for a brief period. For example, the Iridium spacecraft have a well documented and easily computed Iridium flare that occurs where a specular reflection from the Sun off of the phased array antenna falls on an observer on the Earth's surface after dark. In this case, the Iridium spacecraft can reach visual magnitudes of –7, brighter than any of the planets.

As the spacecraft enters the penumbra in E, its brightness fades rapidly, until it enters the umbra in F, where neither the spacecraft nor the Earth below are illuminated. In this case, both the satellite and the Earth's features are not visible unless they are illuminated by some external means such as city lights, forest fires, or lights on the spacecraft. Since the spacecraft is moving in its orbit at about 4 deg per minute, it typically will take less than 10 sec to cross the penumbra from full illumination into total eclipse. The eclipse itself can last up to 30 min when the disk of the Earth is 120 deg in diameter.

11.2 Computing Illumination and Thermal Input on an Arbitrary Spacecraft Face

Section 6.3.3 discussed the geometry and derived the basic summary formulas for computing the Sun angle on an arbitrary spacecraft face. We summarize the results here and extend them to include the solar radiation intensity averaged over the orbit on any spacecraft face. The notation here is the same as that introduced in Sec. 6.3.3.

The general approach is straightforward. As shown in Fig. 11-7, we represent an arbitrary face by the unit vector $\hat{\mathbf{N}}$ normal to the face. We then examine the Sun angle, β, between $\hat{\mathbf{N}}$ and the direction to the Sun, $\hat{\mathbf{S}}$, in order to determine the solar radiation intensity. Specifically, if I is the incident energy on the face, F, of area A, then at any given moment when the Sun is shining on the face (i.e., the spacecraft is not in eclipse and $\beta < 90$ deg), then

$$I = AK \cos \beta \tag{11-1}$$

where K is the solar constant in the vicinity of the Earth (= 1,367 W/m^2). For an inertially fixed spacecraft, β will be constant as the spacecraft goes around the Earth and will be given by

$$\beta = \operatorname{acos}(\hat{\mathbf{N}} \cdot \hat{\mathbf{S}}) \tag{11-2}$$

For either a spinning spacecraft or a spacecraft keeping one face continuously toward the Earth (i.e., spinning once per orbit about the orbit normal), β is given by:

$$\cos \beta = \cos \gamma \cos \beta_s' + \sin \gamma \sin \beta_s' \cos(\Delta Az) \tag{11-3}$$

The Effect of Lighting Conditions: Seeing a 2.5 mm Diameter Line from 500 km

A significant number of tethers have been deployed in space at various times. One well known example is the Shuttle Tether Experiment, which occurred in October 1996 in which a tether approximately 2.5 mm in diameter was deployed for a length of 7 km. Unfortunately, the tether broke when nearly fully deployed and proceeded to float freely in space until it decayed due to atmospheric drag. The tether remained loosely extended while it drifted in orbit. When seen at a low angle from the Earth, it would be at a distance on the order of 500 km. At this range, the tether has an angular diameter of approximately 0.001 arc sec, far below the normal angular resolution of the human eye. Nonetheless, at about magnitude +3, the tether was easily visible to the naked eye even in suburban Los Angeles, and was seen by quite a few amateur astronomers. A photograph of the tether is shown in Fig. 11-6. In terms of angular diameter, this is equivalent to standing in Los Angeles and seeing or photographing a clothesline at the distance of San Francisco. Viewing and lighting conditions really do make an enormous difference in our capacity to see objects in space.

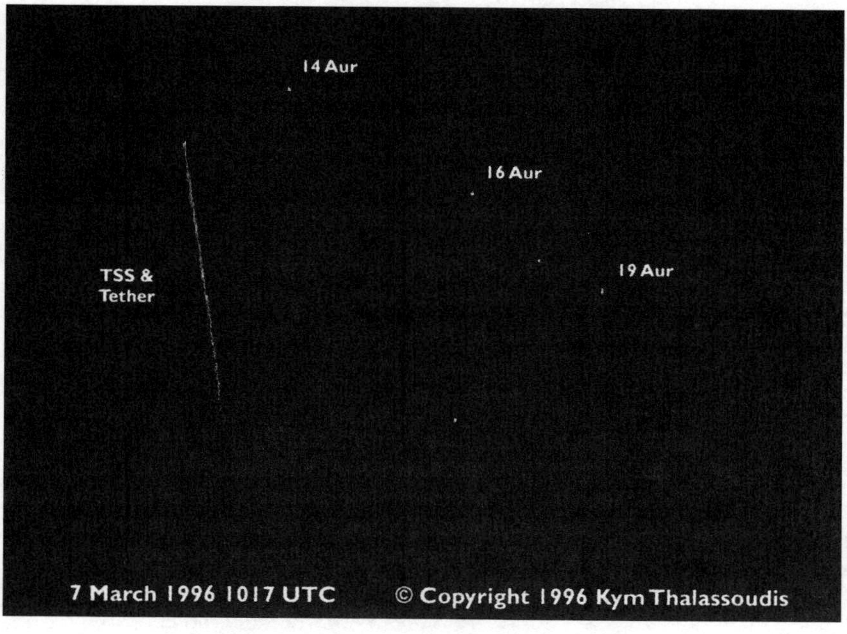

Fig. 11-6. A Broken Satellite Tether as Seen from the Surface of the Earth. The tether was 7 km long and 2.5 mm in diameter. (Photo courtesy of Kym Thalassoudis.)

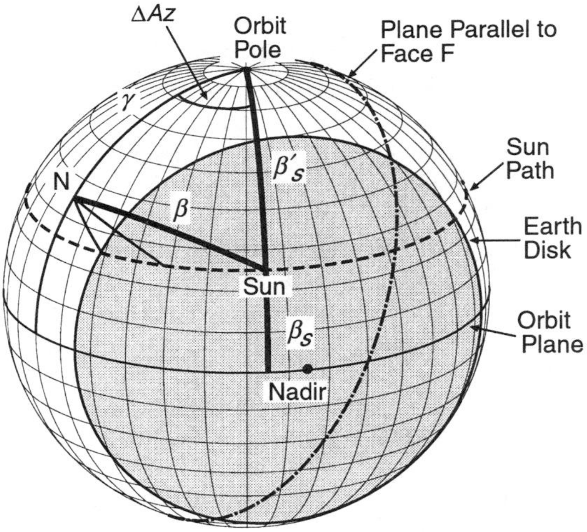

Fig. 11-7. Geometry for Computation of Sun Angle on an Arbitrary Spacecraft Face. $\hat{\mathbf{N}}$ is the unit vector normal to the face. As the spacecraft moves in its orbit, the apparent position of the Sun moves along the dashed line and the arc length, β, between the Sun and $\hat{\mathbf{N}}$ undergoes a sinusoidal oscillation.

where γ is the angle between $\hat{\mathbf{N}}$ and the orbit pole or spin axis, $\beta_S' \equiv 90\,\text{deg} - \beta_S$ is the angle between the orbit pole and the Sun, and ΔAz is the difference in azimuth measured about the orbit pole between the direction to the Sun and the direction to $\hat{\mathbf{N}}$. By inspection, the maximum and minimum angles between the Sun and $\hat{\mathbf{N}}$ are:

$$\beta_{max} = \beta_S' + \gamma \quad \text{and} \quad \beta_{min} = |\beta_S' - \gamma| \tag{11-4}$$

See Fig. 11-7 or Fig. 6-22 in Sec. 6.3.3 for the geometry used to compute these parameters.

Solar Radiation Intensity

We can continue to extend the example in Sec. 6.3.3 to look at the average solar radiation input, I_{avg}, on any spacecraft face over an orbit. This is given by:

$$I_{avg} = AKF \tag{11-5}$$

where, as before, A is the area of the face and K = 1,367 W/m^2 is the solar constant in the vicinity of the Earth. F is the time average fraction of the surface area projected in the direction of the Sun and must lie between 0 and 1. If the attitude of the spacecraft is inertially fixed, then the angle, β, between the unit vector, $\hat{\mathbf{S}}$, in the direction of the Sun and the unit vector, $\hat{\mathbf{N}}$, normal to the face remains constant over an orbit. If there is no eclipse during a given orbit, then:

$$F = \hat{\mathbf{N}} \cdot \hat{\mathbf{S}} = \cos\beta F = \hat{\mathbf{N}} \cdot \hat{\mathbf{S}} = \cos\beta \qquad \text{(inertially fixed, no eclipse)} \tag{11-6}$$

which gives the same result as using Eq. (11-1) directly.

For a three-axis-stabilized, nadir-oriented spacecraft in a circular orbit, the angle β will oscillate sinusoidally as can be see from Fig. 11-7. The amount of sunlight on the face will depend on both γ, the angle from the orbit normal to $\hat{\mathbf{N}}$, and on β_s', the angle from the orbit normal to the Sun. If $(\gamma + \beta_s') \leq 90$ deg, then the face will always be in sunlight and, assuming no eclipse:

$$F = \cos\gamma \cos\beta_s' \qquad \text{(nadir fixed, full sunlight, no eclipse)} \qquad (11\text{-}7a)$$

If $|\gamma - \beta_s'| \geq 90$ deg, then the surface will always be shaded and, of course:

$$F = 0 \qquad \text{(nadir fixed, continuous shade)} \qquad (11\text{-}7b)$$

If neither of the above conditions hold, then the face will be shaded part of the time and in sunlight part of the time. In this case, we integrate the instantaneous fraction of the surface area projected in the direction of the Sun over ΔAz, starting and ending when β, the Sun angle, is 90 deg. Dividing by 2π gives the average F over one orbit:

$$F = \frac{1}{2\pi}\int_{-\phi_{90}}^{\phi_{90}} \cos\beta \, d(\Delta Az) = \frac{1}{2\pi}\int_{-\phi_{90}}^{\phi_{90}} \left[\cos\gamma\cos\beta_s' + \sin\gamma\sin\beta_s'\cos(\Delta Az)\right] d(\Delta Az)$$

$$= (\phi_{90}\cos\gamma\cos\beta_s' + \sin\phi_{90}\sin\gamma\sin\beta_s')/\pi$$

$$\text{(nadir fixed, partial shade, no eclipse)} \qquad (11\text{-}7c)$$

where ϕ_{90} is expressed in radians and

$$\cos\phi_{90} = -1/(\tan\gamma \ \tan\beta_s') \qquad (11\text{-}8)$$

The quantity ϕ_{90} is the value of ΔAz at which $\beta = 90$ deg, i.e., when the transition occurs between shade and sunlight.

Consider our previous example from Sec. 6.3.3 for which $\beta_s' = 65$ deg and $\gamma = 55$ deg. In this case, Eq. (11-7c) is applicable and, from Eq. (11-8), $\Phi_{90} = 109.1$ deg. This means that the Sun will shine on the face in question whenever the azimuth of the Sun is within 109.1 deg of the azimuth of $\hat{\mathbf{N}}$. If the face in question has a surface area of 0.5 m^2, then the average solar input over an orbit with full sunlight is (0.5)(1,358)(0.370) = 251 W.

The nadir-oriented satellite above is spinning at one rotation per orbit in inertial space. Thus, all of the above formulas can be applied to spinning spacecraft with the interpretation that I_{avg} is the average solar radiation input over one spin period, γ is the angle from the spin axis to the face in question, and β_s' is the angle from the spin axis to the Sun.

In practice, there are two principal corrections to the above formulas:

- F is reduced by eclipses
- The effective F is increased by reflected or emitted radiation from the Earth

For either an inertially fixed spacecraft or a spinning spacecraft, the effect of eclipses is simply to reduce F by the fraction of the orbit over which the spacecraft is in eclipse:

$$F = F_0\,(\Phi / 360 \text{ deg}) \qquad (11\text{-}9)$$

where F_0 is the non-eclipse value of F determined from Eqs. (11-6) or (11-7) and Φ is the eclipse fraction from Eq. (6-9).

For Earth-oriented spacecraft the situation is more complex, because the solar input depends on the orientation of the Sun relative to both the Earth and spacecraft face being evaluated. Let η be the angular distance from $\hat{\mathbf{N}}$ to nadir and ρ be the angular radius of the Earth. If the face in question is sufficiently near zenith (opposite the direction to the center of the Earth) that $\eta - \rho = \geq 90$ deg, then $F = F_0$ and F will not be reduced by eclipses. For this condition, any eclipses which occur will happen when the face is shaded. Alternatively, consider what happens when $|\gamma + \beta_s'| < 90$ deg. In this case, there is only a small portion of the orbit when the Sun shines on the face. Let ϕ be the eclipse fraction from Eq. (6-9) and ϕ_{90} the azimuth defined above at which the transition occurs from sunlight to shade. If $\phi \geq \phi_{90}$, then the spacecraft will be in eclipse when the Sun is in a position to shine on the face. In this case F will be reduced to 0. For conditions in between these two extremes, F will be between 0 and its non-eclipse value. Specific values will need to be evaluated numerically using Eqs. (11-7c) and (11-8).

The heat input from both reflected and emitted radiation from the Earth increases the effective value of F. It is significantly more complex to compute than the effect of eclipses because of the extended size of the disk of the Earth and the variability in the intensity of reflected radiation. However, reasonable upper limits for radiation from the Earth are:

- 475 W/m^2 for reflected solar radiation (*albedo*)
- 230 W/m^2 for emitted IR radiation (thermal radiation)

The radiation balance for the Earth at different times of the year is given in Table 11-2 in Sec. 11.5. For further details, see for example, Gilmore and Bello [1994].

11.3 Transits and Occultations

Transit and *occultation* refer to the relative orientations of a planet, a satellite, and an observer, as illustrated in Fig. 11-8. *Transit* occurs when a satellite passes in front of the disk of a planet as seen by the observer. *Occultation* occurs when the satellite passes behind the disk of the planet, and is *occulted*, or blocked, from the observer's view. Whether transits or occultations occur is only a function of the angular separation between the bodies involved, so that all of the results of the relative motion discussion in Chap. 10 can be applied directly.

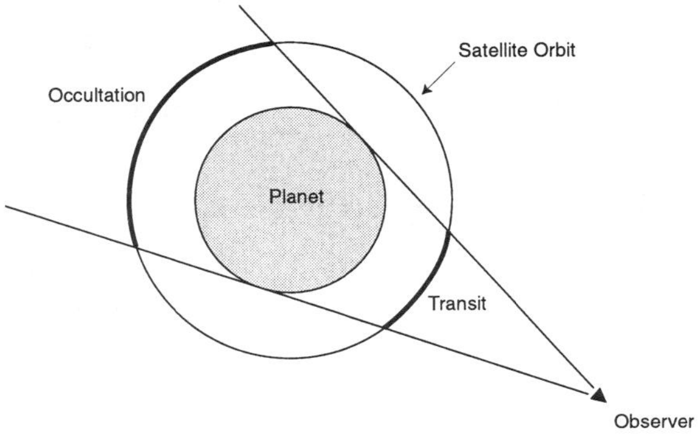

Fig. 11-8. Transits and Occultations. Transit occurs when the target moves in front of an extended object such as the Earth or Sun and occultation occurs when it moves behind it.

Occultation, when applied to satellites, is simply a formal terminology for the fact that the satellites are not visible to each other. This is a topic which has already been fully discussed in Chap. 10. Whenever the angular separation between a central body and another satellite, as seen by either satellite, becomes less than the angular diameter of the central body, and they are on opposite sides of the central body, an occultation will occur and the two satellites will be invisible to each other. The satellites will be able to see each other if and only if they can both see at least one point in common on the surface of the central body. If this does not occur, i.e., the two horizon circles of the two spacecraft do not overlap, then each will be occulted with respect to the other.

Transit means that the lower satellite will be in front of the disk of the central body as seen by the observer. Depending on the conditions under which observations are being made, this may make the satellite more or less visible. Figure 11-9 shows a transit of one of the moons of Jupiter as seen from the Earth, as well as the shadow cone of the moon falling on Jupiter's cloud tops.

Fig. 11-9. Transit of one of Jupiter's Moons as Seen from Earth. Note the shadow of the moon on Jupiter's surface. For an observer on Jupiter under the shadow, this would be a total eclipse of the Sun. (Photo courtesy of JPL.)

Of course, transit cannot occur for co-altitude satellites. For non-co-altitude satellites, transit, or occultation will occur whenever the angular separation between the lower satellite and the center of the Earth is less than the angular radius of the Earth. We can easily compute the conditions for transit and occultation in terms of the geometry as seen from either the higher satellite, the lower satellite, or the center of the Earth. Specifically, we define ρ_h as the angular radius of the Earth as seen from the higher satellite and ρ_l as the angular radius of the Earth as seen from the lower satellite. We then define λ_t, the Earth central angle for transits, as:

$$\lambda_t \equiv \rho_l - \rho_h \tag{11-10}$$

and λ_o, the Earth central angle for occultations, as:

$$\lambda_o \equiv 180 \text{ deg} - \rho_l - \rho_h \tag{11-11}$$

The necessary and sufficient conditions for transit to occur can then be written in any of three ways:

$\eta_h < \rho_h$	(as seen from higher spacecraft)	(11-12a)
$\eta_l > 180 \text{ deg} - \rho_l$	(as seen from the lower spacecraft)	(11-12b)
$\lambda < \lambda_t$	(as seen from Earth center)	(11-12c)

Here η_h is the angle from nadir to the lower satellite as seen from the higher satellite, and η_l is the angle from nadir to the higher satellite as seen from the lower satellite. Similarly, the necessary and sufficient conditions for occultation can be written from the same points of view as:

$\eta_h < \rho_h$ and $D > D_o$	(as seen from higher spacecraft)	(11-13a)
$\eta_l < \rho_l$	(as seen from the lower spacecraft)	(11-13b)
$\lambda > \lambda_o$	(as seen from Earth center)	(11-13c)

where D_o is the distance from the higher satellite to the horizon, $= H \cos \rho_h$, where H is the distance from the higher spacecraft to the center of the Earth. If neither the transit nor occultation condition is satisfied, then the two spacecraft can see each other against the background of space.

These results are illustrated for two satellites at altitudes of 1,000 km and 5,000 km in Fig. 11-10. The same geometry is shown on the Earth-centered celestial sphere in Fig. 11-11 and on the spacecraft-centered celestial spheres for both the low orbiting satellite and the high orbiting satellite in Figure 11-12. Note that for the lower satellite, the higher one can appear anywhere in the spacecraft sky. From the higher satellite, the lower satellite is confined by a region about nadir of radius ρ_{l0} as given by

$$\sin \rho_{l0} = R_l / R_h \tag{11-14}$$

where R_l is the radius of the lower orbit and R_h is the radius of the upper orbit.

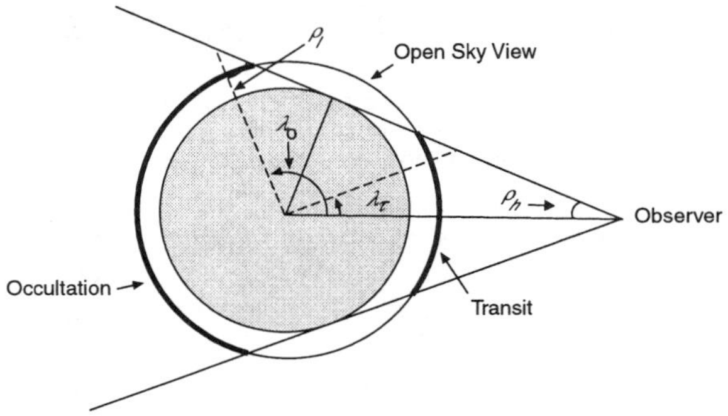

Fig. 11-10. Transit and Occultation Conditions. For drawing convenience, the observer is assumed to be in the orbit plane, but this is not necessary for the computations.

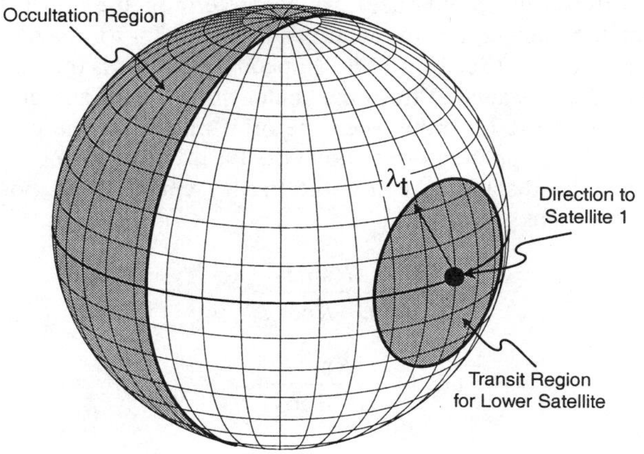

Fig. 11-11. Conditions for Transit and Occultation as Viewed on the Earth-centered Celestial Sphere. The two orbits need not be coplanar.

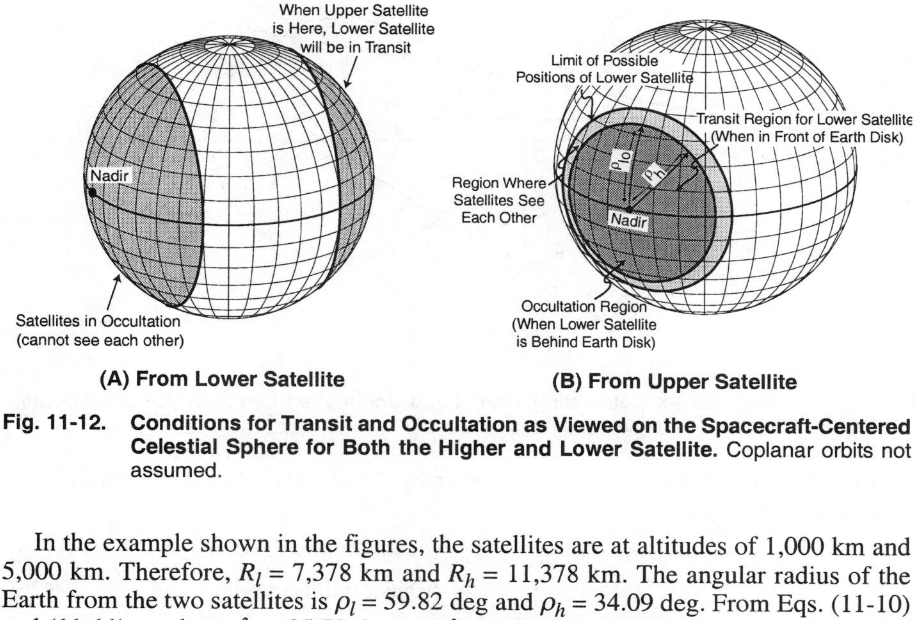

Fig. 11-12. Conditions for Transit and Occultation as Viewed on the Spacecraft-Centered Celestial Sphere for Both the Higher and Lower Satellite. Coplanar orbits not assumed.

In the example shown in the figures, the satellites are at altitudes of 1,000 km and 5,000 km. Therefore, R_l = 7,378 km and R_h = 11,378 km. The angular radius of the Earth from the two satellites is ρ_l = 59.82 deg and ρ_h = 34.09 deg. From Eqs. (11-10) and (11-11), we have λ_t = 25.73 deg and λ_0 = 86.09 deg. Wherever the Earth central angle between the two satellites is less than 25.73 deg, then the angle at the higher satellite from nadir to the lower satellite will be less than 34.09 deg, the angle at the lower satellite from nadir to the higher satellite will be greater than 180 – 59.82 = 120.18 deg, and there will be a transit of the lower satellite as seen from the higher one. Irrespective of their relative inclinations or orbit positions, the lower satellite will always be within ρ_{l0} = 40.42 deg of nadir as seen from the higher satellite.

For circular orbits viewed obliquely, we can determine the transit and occultation conditions by making use of the computations in Sec. 6.3.4 for the shape of a circular orbit viewed from nearby. (See Fig. 11-13.) Specifically, if R is the radius of a circular orbit being viewed at distance D from the center of the Earth and at an angle I measured at the center of the Earth between the orbit plane and the observer, then the angular height α of the apparent orbit above the Earth's center (on the far side of the orbit) and the angular distance β below the Earth's center (for a point on the orbit nearest the observer) are given by:

$$\tan \alpha = \frac{R \sin I}{D + R \cos I} \tag{11-15}$$

$$\tan \beta = \frac{R \sin I}{D - R \cos I} \tag{11-16}$$

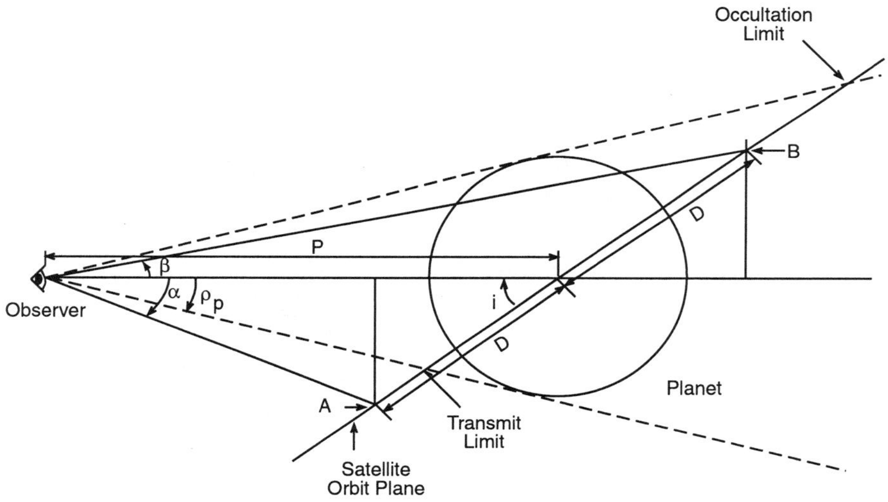

Fig. 11-13. Geometry for Calculating Transit and Occultation Limits for Elliptical Orbits. See text for discussion and formulas.

If ρ is the angular radius of the Earth seen by the observer then the conditions for eclipse and occultation are

$$\rho > \tan a \quad \text{(occultation will occur)} \tag{11-17a}$$

$$\rho > \tan b \quad \text{(transit will occur)} \tag{11-17b}$$

Since the orbit has a larger angular extent on the near side, as illustrated in Fig. 6-23 in Sec. 6.3.4, if transit occurs during the orbit, then occultation must occur. However, occultations can occur without transit occurring on the near side, as illustrated in the figure.

As we would expect, the situation is more complex for elliptical orbits. In this case, either transit or occultation can occur without the other. Nonetheless, we can put at least some broad limits on viewing conditions by applying the rules above to apogee.

Thus, if R in Eqs. (11-15) and (11-16) is replaced by the radius of apogee, R_a, then the conditions in Eq. (11-17) will continue to hold, but will be less constraining. In general, we can always return to the conditions of Figs. 11-10 and 11-11 to determine whether transit or occultation occur at any specific time or in any specific orbit.

11.4 Spacecraft Eclipses

Eclipses are the phenomena of transits and occultations relative to the Sun. An *eclipse of the Sun* is a transit of an object in front of the sun, blocking all or a significant part of the Sun's light from the observer. An eclipse of any other object (e.g., an eclipse of the Moon) is an occultation of that object by another object relative to the Sun. Because the Sun is the largest object in the solar system, the shadows of all the planets and natural satellites are shaped as shown in Fig. 11-14. As discussed in Sec. 11.1, the *umbra*, or *shadow cone*, is the conical region opposite the direction of the Sun in which the disk of the Sun is completely blocked from view by the disk of the planet. Outside the umbra is the *penumbra*, where a portion of the disk of the Sun is blocked form view and, therefore, where the illumination on objects is reduced.

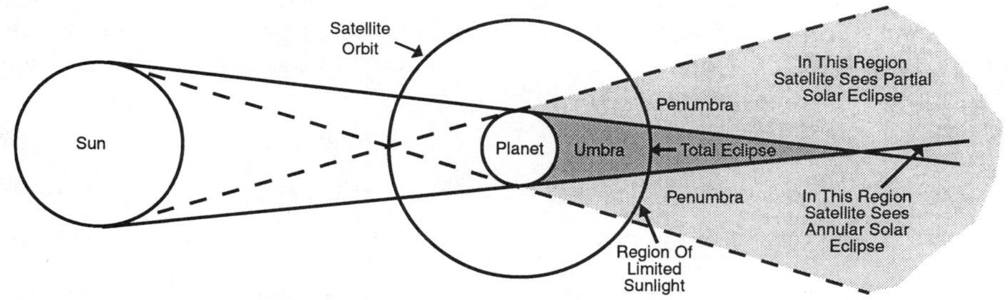

Fig. 11-14. Definition of Satellite Eclipse Conditions. Sun, planet, and orbit are all in the plane of the paper.

Unfortunately, the terminology of eclipses depends on whether the observer is thought of as being on the object which is entering the shadow or viewing the event from elsewhere. If the observer enters the shadow, the Sun is partially or wholly blocked from view and the event is referred to as an *eclipse of the Sun* or *solar eclipse* as shown in Fig. 11-15. A *total solar eclipse*, which is frequently shortened to just *eclipse* in spaceflight applications, occurs when the observer enters the umbra. If the observer is farther from the planet than the length of the shadow cone and enters the cone formed by the extension of the shadow cone through its apex, the observer will see an *annular eclipse* in which an annulus or ring of the bright solar disk is visible surrounding the disk of the planet. If the observer is within the penumbra, but outside the umbra, the observer will see a portion of the Sun's disk blocked by the planet and a *partial eclipse of the Sun* occurs.

If the observer is viewing the event from somewhere other than on the satellite being eclipsed, the event is called an *eclipse of the satellite*. A *total eclipse* of the satellite occurs when the entire satellite enters the umbra and a partial eclipse occurs when part of an extended satellite (such as the Moon) enters the umbra. If the satellite

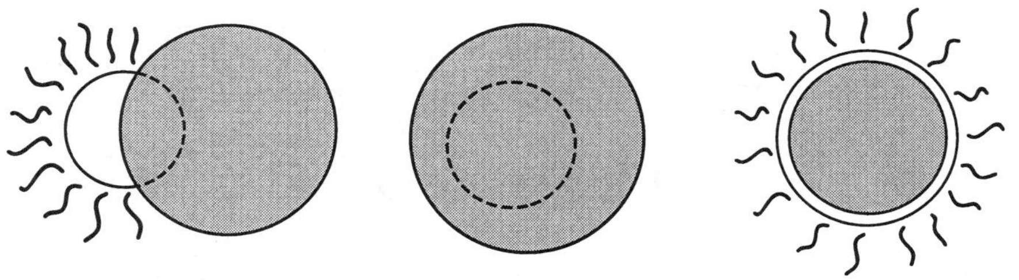

(A) Partial Solar Eclipse (B) Total Solar Eclipse (C) Annular Solar Eclipse

Fig. 11-15. Solar Eclipse Geometry. Shaded circle is the planet. Unshaded circle is the Sun.

enters the penumbra only, the event is called a *penumbral eclipse*. Thus, a total eclipse of the Moon to an observer on the Earth is a total solar eclipse to a lunar observer and a penumbral eclipse of a satellite to an observer on the Earth is a partial eclipse of the Sun to an observer on the satellite.

To determine conditions under which eclipses occur, we can apply all of the geometry of the previous section. From the point of view of the spacecraft, an eclipse occurs whenever all or part of the disk of the Sun is occulted by the central body. If η is the angle from the center of the planet to the center of the Sun, ρ_p is the angular radius of the planet, and ρ_S is the angular radius of the Sun (= 0.25 deg at the distance of the Earth), thus the following conditions hold:

$$\eta > \rho_p + \rho_S \qquad \text{(Full sunlight)} \tag{11-18}$$

$$\rho_p + \rho_S > \eta > |\rho_p - \rho_S| \qquad \text{(Partial eclipse)} \tag{11-19}$$

$$|\rho_p - \rho_S| > \eta \text{ and } \rho_p > \rho_S \qquad \text{(Total eclipse)} \tag{11-20}$$

$$|\rho_p - \rho_S| > \eta \text{ and } \rho_S > \rho_p \qquad \text{(Angular eclipse)} \tag{11-21}$$

Here all of the angles are measured from the spacecraft, i.e., on the spacecraft-centered celestial sphere.

Alternatively, we can determine the three-dimensional conditions under which eclipses will occur by determining the size of the shadow cone being produced by the planet. We first determine the length, C, and angular radius, ρ_C, of the shadow cone for any of the planets or natural satellites (see Fig. 11-16). Let S be the distance from the planet to the Sun, R_p be the radius of the planet, R_s be the radius of the photosphere (i.e., the visible surface) of the Sun, and C be measured from the center of the planet to the apex of the shadow cone. Then,

$$C = \frac{R_p S}{(R_s - R_p)} \tag{11-22}$$

and

$$\rho_c = \arcsin\left(\frac{R_s - R_p}{S}\right)$$

$$\approx \arcsin\left(\frac{R_s}{S}\right) \tag{11-23}$$

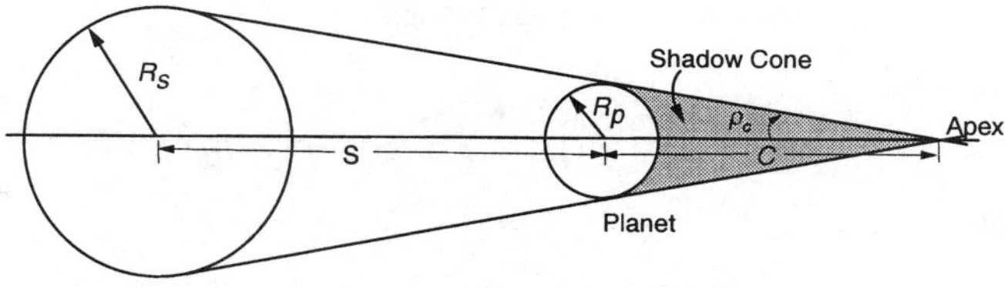

Fig. 11-16. Shadow Cone Geometry.

For the Earth, the size of the shadow cone for its mean distance from the Sun is $C = 1.385 \times 10^6$ km and $\rho_C = 0.264$ deg. For the Moon, the mean size is $C = 3.75 \times 10^5$ km and $p_c = 0.266$ deg. The length of the shadow cone for the Moon is just less than the semimajor axis of the Moon's orbit of 3.84×10^5 km. Therefore, eclipses of the Sun seen on the Earth are frequently annular eclipses, and when they are total eclipses they are seen over a very narrow band on the Earth because the maximum radius of the Moon's shadow cone at the distance of the Earth's surface is 135 km.

The presence of an atmosphere on some planets and the non-negligible radius of the natural satellites may be taken into account by adjusting the radius of the planet, as will be discussed later. Initially, we will assume that there are no atmospheric effects and that we are concerned with eclipses seen by objects of negligible size, such a spacecraft. The conditions for the satellite to see a total eclipse of the Sun are exactly those for a transit of the satellite as viewed from the apex of the shadow cone. Similarly, the conditions for spacecraft to see a partial eclipse are nearly the same as those for occultation of the spacecraft viewed from a point in the direction of the Sun equidistant from the planet as the apex of the shadow cone.

To develop specific eclipse conditions, let $\mathbf{D}_s$ be the vector from the spacecraft to the Sun and let $\mathbf{D}_p$ be the vector from the spacecraft to the center of the planet. Three quantities of interest are the angular radius of the Sun, ρ_S, the angular radius of the planet, ρ_p, and the angular separation, η, between the Sun and planet as viewed by the spacecraft, as shown in Fig. 11-17. These are given by:

$$\rho_s = \arcsin\,(R_s/D_s) \tag{11-24}$$

$$\rho_p = \arcsin\,(R_p/D_p) \tag{11-25}$$

$$\eta = \arccos(\hat{\mathbf{D}}_\mathbf{s} \cdot \hat{\mathbf{D}}_p) \tag{11-26}$$

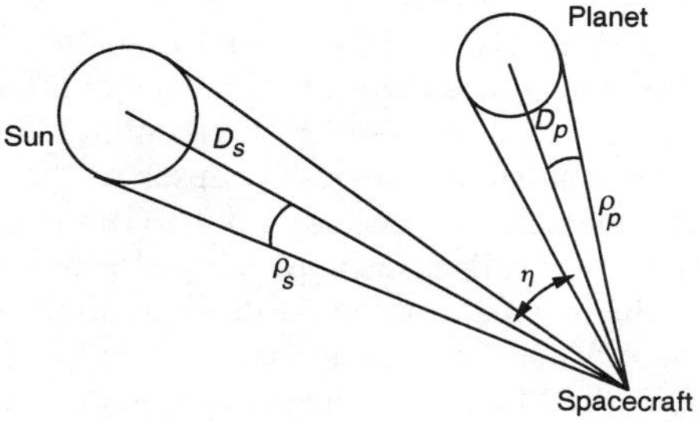

Fig. 11-17. Variables for Eclipse Geometry.

The necessary and sufficient eclipse conditions are

1. Partial Eclipse:

$$D_s > S \quad \text{and} \quad \rho_P + \rho_S > \eta > |\rho_P - \rho_S| \tag{11-27}$$

2. Total Eclipse:

$$S < D_s < S + C \quad \text{and} \quad \rho_P - \rho_S > \eta \tag{11-28}$$

3. Annular Eclipse:

$$S + C < D_s \quad \text{and} \quad \rho_P - \rho_S > \eta \tag{11-29}$$

These eclipses are illustrated in Fig. 11-15.

The surface brightness of the Sun is nearly uniform over the surface of the disk. Therefore, the intensity, I, of the illumination on the spacecraft during a partial or annular eclipse is directly proportional to the area of the solar disk which can be seen by the spacecraft. These relations may be obtained directly from App. A as:

1. Partial Eclipse

$$I_0 - I = \frac{I_0}{\pi(1 - \cos\rho_S)}\left[\pi - \cos\rho_S \arccos\left(\frac{\cos\rho_P - \cos\rho_S\cos\eta}{\sin\rho_S\sin\eta}\right)\right.$$
$$\left. - \cos\rho_S \arccos\left(\frac{\cos\rho_S - \cos\rho_P\cos\eta}{\sin\rho_P\sin\eta}\right)\right]$$
$$- \arccos\left(\frac{\cos\eta - \cos\rho_S\cos\rho_P}{\sin\rho_S\sin\rho_P}\right) \tag{11-30}$$

2. Annular Eclipse

$$I_0 - I = I_0\left(\frac{1 - \cos\rho_P}{1 - \cos\rho_S}\right) \tag{11-31}$$

where I_0 is the fully illuminated intensity, and the inverse trigonometric functions in Eq. (11-30) are expressed in radians.

The effect of a planetary atmosphere is difficult to compute analytically because the atmosphere absorbs light, scatters it in all directions, and refracts it into the shadow cone. Close to the surface of the Earth, only a small fraction of the incident light is transmitted entirely through the atmosphere. Thus, the major effects are an increase in the size of the shadow and a general lightening of the entire umbra due to scattering. The scattering becomes very apparent in some eclipses of the Moon, as seen from Earth when the Moon takes on a dull copper color due to refracted and scattered light. The darkness of individual lunar eclipses is noticeably affected by cloud patterns and weather conditions along the boundary of the Earth where light is being scattered into the umbra. The atmosphere of the Earth increases the size of the Earth's shadow by about 2% at the distance of the Moon over the size the shadow would be expected to have from purely geometrical considerations. (See Seidelmann [1992].) Some ambiguity exists in such measurements because the boundary of the umbra is diffuse rather than sharp. If the entire 2% at the Moon's distance is attributed to an increase in the effective linear radius of the Earth, this increase corresponds to about 90 km.

In considering the general appearance of the solar system as seen by a spacecraft we may be interested in eclipses of the natural satellites as well as eclipses of spacecraft. In the case of natural satellites, the large diameter of the satellite will have a considerable effect on the occurrence of eclipses. This may be taken into account easily by changing the effective linear diameter of the planet. Let R_p be the radius of the planet, R_m be the radius of the natural satellite, and define the effective planetary radii $R_{e1} \equiv R_p + R_m$ and $R_{e2} \equiv R_p - R_m$. Then, when the center of the satellite is within the shadow formed by an object of radius R_{e1}, at least part of the real satellite is within the real shadow cone. Similarly, when the center of the satellite is within the shadow cone defined by an object of radius R_{e2}, then all of the real satellite is within the shadow cone; this is referred to as a total eclipse of the satellite when seen form another location. This procedure of using effective radii ignores a correction term comparable to the angular radius of the satellite at the distance of the Sun.

We may use Eqs. (11-24) through (11-28) to determine the conditions on a satellite orbit such that eclipses will always occur or never occur. Let D_p be the perifocal distance, D_A be the apofocal distance, i be the angle between the vector to the Sun and the satellite orbit plane, and C and ρ_c be defined by Eqs. (11-22) and (11-23). We define γ and δ by:

$$\tan\gamma = \left(\frac{D_p}{C - D_p \cos i}\right)\sin i \tag{11-32}$$

$$\tan\delta = \left(\frac{D_A}{C - D_A \cos i}\right)\sin i \tag{11-33}$$

An eclipse will not occur in any orbit for which $\gamma > \rho_c$. An eclipse will always occur in an orbit for which $\delta < \rho_c$.

11.5 Lighting Conditions Looking at Earth from Space

A key issue for many space missions is not only eclipses and lighting on the spacecraft, but also the lighting on the Earth or other central body that the spacecraft is looking at. This determines both viewing and thermal conditions since the radiation reflected from the Earth is a major source of thermal input for the spacecraft. Viewing conditions are important principally for observation satellites, but can also be used for both orbit and attitude sensing as described in Chaps. 2 and 3.

The surface of the Earth is in thermodynamic equilibrium with its surroundings in that the total energy received from the Sun approximately equals the total energy which the Earth radiates into space.* If this were not the case, the Earth would either

---

* They are not exactly equal because some energy goes into chemical bonds and some additional energy is supplied by radioactivity and by thermal cooling of the Earth's interior. For the Earth, the heat flow from the interior is approximately 0.004% of the energy received from the Sun.

heat up or cool down until the radiated energy balanced the energy input. Table 11-2 shows the global average radiation for the Earth. For further discussion, see for example, Gilmore and Bello [1994].

TABLE 11-2. Radiation Balance of the Earth-Atmosphere System. Data from Lyle, et al., [1971].

Radiation	Global Average				
	Dec.–Feb.	Mar.–May	June–Aug.	Sep.–Nov.	Annual Average
Incident Solar Radiation (W/m^2)	356	349	342	349	349
Absorbed Solar Radiation (W/m^2)	244	244	258	251	249
Reflected Solar Radiation (W/m^2)	112	105	84	98	100
Planetary Albedo	0.31	0.30	0.25	0.28	0.29
Emitted Infrared Radiation (W/m^2)	223	230	230	237	230

The *albedo* of an object is the fraction of the incident energy that is reflected back into space. (The word is also used for the reflected radiation itself.) The Earth's albedo is approximately 0.30, although it fluctuates considerably because clouds and ice reflect more light than the land or water surface. The spectral characteristics of the reflected radiation are approximately the same as the incident radiation. Thus, the Earth's albedo is most intense in the visual region of the spectrum, i.e., the region to which the human eye is sensitive, from about 0.4 to 0.7 μm wavelength.

Sensors operating in the visible region are called *albedo sensors*, or *visible light sensors*. The principal advantage of this spectral region is that the intensity is greatest here. For attitude sensing, however, a significant disadvantage is the strong variation in albedo—from 0.05 for some soil- and vegetation-covered surfaces to over 0.80 for some types of snow and ice or clouds [Lyle, et al., 1971].

The incident energy which is not reflected from the Earth is transformed into heat and reradiated back into space with a blackbody spectrum characteristic of the temperature. The Earth's mean surface temperature of approximately 290 K corresponds to a peak intensity of emitted radiation of about 10 μm in the infrared region of the spectrum. This *emitted*, or *thermal*, radiation is typically used for attitude sensing because the intensity is much more uniformly distributed over the disk of the Earth than for visible light.

Fig. 11-18 shows a photo of the Earth in the visible region of the spectrum. The *lit horizon* is the illuminated edge of the disk of the Earth. The fuzzy boundary where the edge fades away to darkness, corresponding to sunrise or sunset on the Earth, is called the *terminator*. The center of the picture is, of course, nadir and the intersection of a vector in the *nadir* direction with the surface of the Earth is called the *subsatellite point, SSP*. As we might expect, the most important element in determining lighting conditions on the surface of the Earth is direction to the Sun. This is most easily evaluated with respect to the *subsolar point*, which is location on the surface of the Earth for which the Sun is straight overhead. This can be determined at any time from the Earth's ephemeris or, except during eclipse, by observing the position of the Sun from the spacecraft. In Earth orbit, the position of the Sun in the spacecraft sky is the same as its position as seen from the subsatellite point or as seen from the center of the Earth to within less than 0.01 deg. Thus, the *Sun angle*, β, between zenith and the Sun is the same for calculating lighting conditions whether measured from the subsatellite point on the Earth or from the spacecraft.

Fig. 11-18. Photograph of the Nearly-Full Earth as Seen from Apollo 8. The Baja Peninsula in Mexico and most of Florida are visible. Note the bright spot in the ocean that is the specular reflection of the Sun on the ocean surface. (Photo courtesy of NASA.)

Fig. 11-18 illustrates 3 key features of the Earth as seen from space in the visible region of the spectrum:

- The terminator is a very poorly defined boundary, with its apparent location often depending on the amount of cloud cover in the region. (Terminator modeling is discussed in Sec. 11.5.2)
- Near the center of the photo is bright spot about 1 cm in diameter. This is the location on the Earth midway between the subsatellite point and the subsolar point. Here *specular reflection* will occur off the surface of the ocean with the angle of incidence equal to the angle of reflection. (The Sun angle at various locations on the Earth is discussed in Sec. 11.5.1)
- The overall brightness of locations on the Earth varies dramatically, depending primarily on whether there's cloud cover. The albedo can vary from about 0.05 for some types of soil and vegetation to over 0.80 for snow, ice, and clouds.

As the spacecraft goes around the Earth, the Earth goes through a series of phases similar to the Moon's phases. A schematic diagram of how these come about is shown in Fig. 11-19 and the shape of the illuminated Earth in each of the marked locations is shown in Fig. 11-20. The effect of the lighting conditions on viewing at each location is described in Table 11-1 at the front of the chapter. As an example, a photo of the crescent Earth is shown in Fig. 11-21. As on the gibbous Earth seen in Fig. 11-18, the terminator is poorly defined as the light from the Sun fades out at sunrise and sunset. The *cusps* of the illuminated disk are the points where the terminator meets the lit horizon. The perpendicular bisector of a line joining the *cusps* will point toward the Sun with the Sun being in the direction of the illuminated Earth. While the light level is low near the terminator, the shadows are long and the contrast is high. Consequently, more detail is typically visible along the terminator than when the Sun is at the zenith and the shadows have disappeared.

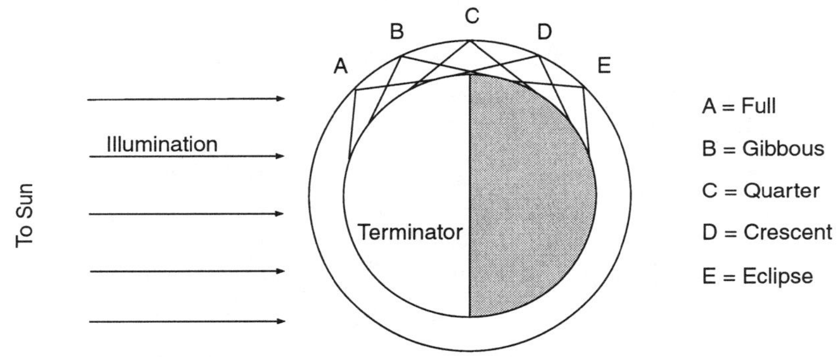

Fig. 11-19. As the Spacecraft Goes Around the Orbit, the Lighting on the Earth Changes Depending on the Relationship to the Sun.

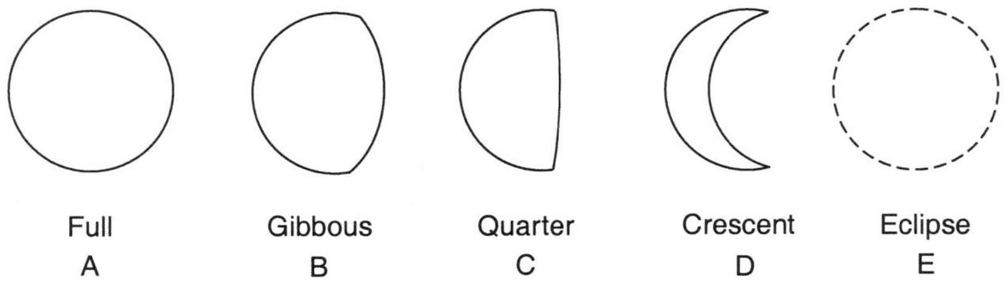

Fig. 11-20. Approximate Appearance of the Earth at Each of the Locations Marked Fig. 11-19.

The sequence of events on any given orbit can most easily be seen in Fig. 11-25. Because both the terminator and the orbit ground trace are approximately great circles, they will intersect in 2 locations, except when the ground trace lies along the terminator. If the orbit gets close enough to the subsolar point, the Sun will be high in the spacecraft sky and the Earth beneath will be fully illuminated. At some point the terminator will just become visible along the edge of the disk of the Earth and the Earth

Fig. 11-21. Photograph of a Crescent Earth as Seen from Apollo 11. Note that the terminator itself is poorly defined. However, near the terminator objects stand out on the surface because of the long shadows. A portion of East Africa is visible near the terminator. (Photo courtesy of NASA.)

will take on a gibbous phase. The Earth will become continuously less illuminated until the spacecraft crosses the terminator which will bisect the visible disk at the quarter Earth.* (The width of the band on the Earth representing the gibbous or crescent phases is just the maximum Earth central angle, λ.) The Earth now enters the crescent phase and continues to become less illuminated. At the same time, the Sun gets closer to the horizon until the spacecraft just enters eclipse with the Sun on the horizon and a very slim crescent Earth visible as sunlight is refracted through the atmosphere. Both the spacecraft and the Earth below will then be in darkness until the process repeats in reverse order on the other side of the orbit.

The spacecraft orbit remains approximately fixed in inertial space as the Earth rotates underneath it. Thus, each successive low Earth orbit crosses a new region of the Earth. However, the Sun also remains approximately fixed in inertial space and the illumination cycle remains very nearly the same on successive orbits. Fig. 11-22 is best thought of as being in Earth-centered inertial coordinates such that the ground trace and illumination regions are fixed on the figure as the Earth rotates underneath. Thus, successive "first quarter" terminator crossings will occur with the same geometry at the same point in the orbit, but the land underneath will have changed.

---

* By analogy with the Moon's phases, the *first quarter Earth* occurs when the spacecraft crosses the terminator from the dark side toward the bright side and the *third quarter* or *last quarter Earth* occurs when the spacecraft is going from the bright side toward the dark side.

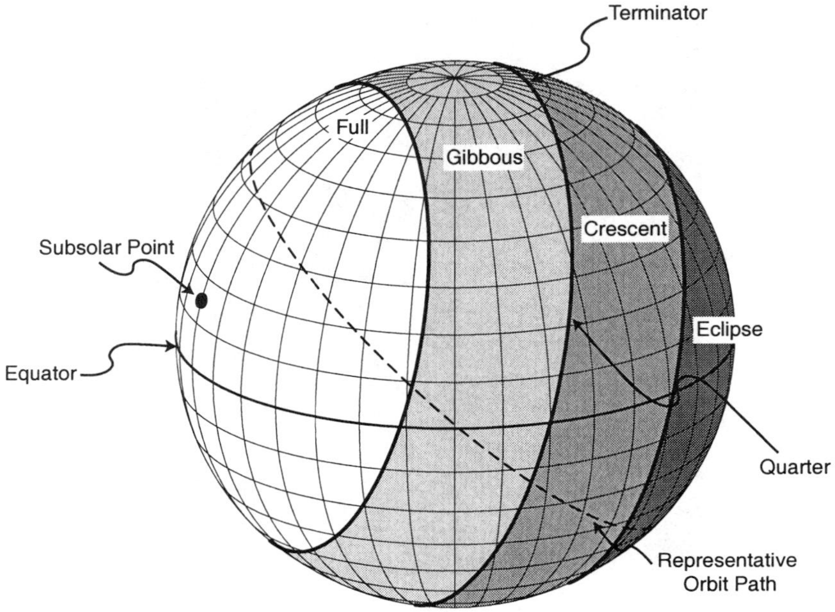

Fig. 11-22. Visibility of the Terminator from Space. See also Fig. 11-19 and Table 11-3.

11.5.1 Sun Angles on the Earth as Seen from Space

The *Sun angle*, β, is the angle between zenith and the Sun. As discussed above, the Sun angle will be nearly the same at the subsatellite point as it is at the spacecraft. Thus, a very accurate measurement of the Sun angle directly beneath the spacecraft can be made by simply measuring the angle from the Sun to nadir and subtracting from 180 deg. Similarly, it can be done analytically from the ephemerides of the spacecraft and the Sun (which is also the Earth's ephemeris) and taking the arc cosine of the dot product between the unit vectors to the spacecraft and to the Sun.

From low-Earth orbit, the area on the Earth that can be seen is typically between 20 and 30 deg in radius. Observations are typically done near the subsatellite point due to foreshortening and absorption near the edge of the disk. Consequently, in most cases the Sun angle at the subsatellite point is a reasonable estimate of the Sun angle throughout the scene. The direction of the shadows on the surface of the Earth will be just 180 deg away from the direction to the subsolar point. As discussed in Sec. 9.1, azimuth angles about nadir are the same on the spacecraft-centered celestial sphere as they are projected onto the Earth's surface. Consequently, this measurement can be made either on the surface of the Earth or as seen from the spacecraft, depending on which is more convenient for the problem at hand.

A more accurate computation of the Sun angle and shadow direction can be done either on the surface of the Earth, as shown in Fig. 11-23A or on the spacecraft-centered celestial sphere as shown in Fig. 11-23B. On the Earth, the assumed known quantities are the locations of the subsatellite point, **SSP**, the subsolar point, **S**, and the

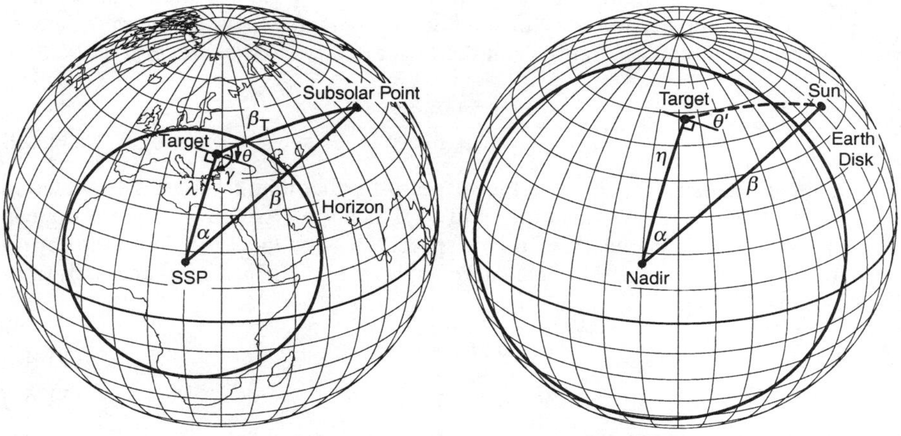

(A) On the Earth **(B) On the Spacecraft-Centered Celestial Sphere**

Fig. 11-23. Geometry for Determining the Sun Angle, β_T, and Shadow Angle, θ'. See text for equations.

target, **T**, at which the Sun angle and shadow direction are to be determined. Given the coordinates of these points on the Earth, we can immediately determine the arc lengths between. (See App. A.) Thus, the known quantities become the Sun angle, β, the angle from **S** to **T**, β_T, and the Earth central angle from **SSP** to **T**, λ. From the previous discussion, β_T is equal to the Sun angle at the target. From these quantities, we determine the angle, γ, at the target between **S** and **SSP**:

$$\cos\gamma = \frac{\cos\beta + \cos\lambda\cos\beta_T}{\sin\lambda\sin\beta_T} \tag{11-34}$$

The shadow direction on the Earth, θ, relative to the normal to the line to the subsatellite point is then given by

$$\theta = |\,90\,\text{deg} - \gamma\,| \tag{11-35}$$

This can be transformed into the shadow direction relative to horizontal as seen on the spacecraft-centered celestial sphere, θ, by using Eq. (9-25) in Sec. 9.1.3. (See Fig. 9-7.) Thus,

$$\tan\theta' = \tan\theta\sin\varepsilon \tag{11-36}$$

Here the elevation angle, ε, of the spacecraft as seen from the target and the nadir angle, η, at the spacecraft from nadir to the target are given by Eqs. (9-3) and (9-4) as

$$\tan\eta = \frac{\sin\rho\sin\lambda}{1 - \sin\rho\cos\lambda} \tag{11-37}$$

$$\varepsilon = 90\,\text{deg} - \lambda - \eta \tag{11-38}$$

where ρ is the angular radius of the Earth as seen from the spacecraft as given in Eq. (9-2). While not needed for the shadow computation, it is also convenient to compute the azimuth on the Earth, α, of the target relative to the direction to the Sun:

$$\cos\alpha = \frac{\cos\beta_T + \cos\lambda\,\cos\beta}{\sin\lambda\,\sin\beta} \tag{11-39}$$

If the measurements are done on the spacecraft rather than the Earth, as shown in Fig. 11-23B, then the known quantities will be β, α, and η. As above, the Sun angle at nadir, β, will be the same measured on the spacecraft or on the Earth. With the definitions above, we first compute the elevation angle, ε, and Earth central angle, λ, from Eqs. (9-4) and (9-6) as:

$$\cos\varepsilon = \sin\eta\,/\sin\rho \tag{11-40}$$

$$\lambda = 90\text{ deg} - \eta - \varepsilon \tag{11-41}$$

Next, the Sun angle at the target, β_T, and angle at the target, γ, from **T** to **SSP**, are computed by:

$$\cos\beta_T = \cos\lambda\,\cos\beta + \sin\lambda\,\sin\beta\,\cos\alpha \tag{11-42}$$

$$\cos\lambda = \frac{\cos\beta + \cos\lambda + \cos\beta_T}{\sin\lambda\,\sin\beta_T} \tag{11-43}$$

Finally, as above, the shadow direction on the Earth, θ, and as seen by the spacecraft, θ', are:

$$\theta = |\,90\,\text{deg} - \gamma\,| \tag{11-44}$$

$$\tan\theta' = \tan\theta\sin\varepsilon \tag{11-45}$$

It is important to understand the meaning of the *shadow direction* in this context. Specifically, θ', is the angle measured from the spacecraft between the horizontal and the target's shadow. Thus, if we photograph the target from the spacecraft and draw a line through the target parallel to the horizon (or perpendicular to the direction to nadir), then θ' will the angle on the photograph between the shadow and the horizontal line.

11.5.2 The Terminator

As we have seen in Figs. 11-18 and 11-21, the terminator between the lit and dark parts of the Earth is very poorly defined. This is due to the three effects: (1) the gradual decrease in overall illumination with increasing Sun angle, (2) the extreme albedo variations between clouds and the planetary surface, and (3) the finite angular diameter of the Sun. We define the *dark angle*, ξ, as the angle at the center of a planet from the antisolar point to the point at which a ray from the upper limb of the Sun is tangent to the surface of the planet, as shown in Fig. 11-24. The dark angle, ξ, differs from 90 deg by three small correction terms:

$$\xi = 90\,\text{deg} + \rho_E - \rho_S - \sigma \tag{11-46}$$

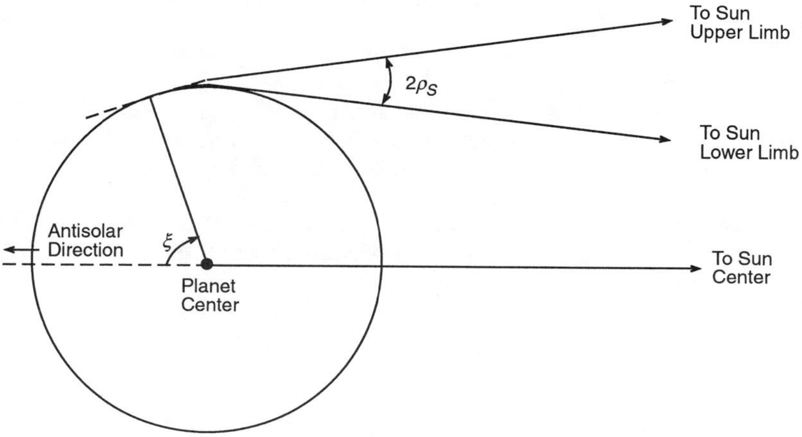

Fig. 11-24. Dark Angle of a Planet, ξ, Showing the Effects of Atmospheric Refraction and Finite Size of the Disk of the Sun.

where ρ_E is the angular radius of the planet as seen from the Sun (i.e., the displacement of the center of the Sun as seen by an observer at the terminator, relative to an observer at the center of the planet), ρ_S is the angular radius of the Sun as seen from the planet, and s is the atmospheric refraction for an apparent zenith angle of 90 deg. ρ_E is only 0.002 deg for the Earth and ρ_S is 0.267 deg at the Earth's mean distance of 1.0 AU. Atmospheric refraction is a strong function of zenith angle near the horizon. (For example, at sunset, the lower of the Sun is refracted upward more than the upper limb, producing the appearance of an oblate Sun.) For the Earth, this function is well known. (See for example, Cox [2000].) At an apparent zenith angle of 90 deg $\sigma = 0.524$ deg. Thus for Earth,

$$\begin{aligned} \xi &\approx 90\,\text{deg} + 0.002\,\text{deg} - 0.267\,\text{deg} - 0.524\,\text{deg} \\ &\approx 89.21\,\text{deg} \end{aligned} \tag{11-47}$$

For the Moon, ρ_M is negligible, ρ_S has the same average value as for the Earth, and s = 0. Therefore,

$$\xi_M \approx 90\,\text{deg} - 0.267\,\text{deg} \approx 89.67\,\text{deg} \tag{11-48}$$

The fraction, f_S, of the area of a planet from which at least some portion of the Sun can be seen is given by:

$$\begin{aligned} f_S &= 0.5\left(1 + \cos\xi\right) \\ &= 0.507 \qquad \text{for the Earth} \\ &= 0.503 \qquad \text{for the Moon} \end{aligned} \tag{11-49}$$

At best, the expressions for ξ are average values. The correction terms are normally dominated by local effects such as terrain (e.g., valleys where sunset is early and mountains where it is late) and albedo variations depending on both the nature of the surface and the local weather.

Fig. 11-25 shows the geometry for computing terminator visibility, taking into account the dark angle, ξ, as discussed above. As usual, β is the Sun angle measured from zenith to the Sun and will be the same at the satellite, the subsatellite point, and the center of the Earth. ρ is the angular radius of the Earth as seen from the satellite and λ_0 is the maximum Earth central angle. For convenience, we define the angle at the spacecraft from the Sun to nadir, $\beta'' = 180$ deg $- \beta$ and the angle at the center of the Earth from the Sun to the terminator, $\xi'' = 180$ deg $- \xi$. The resulting conditions for the various Earth phases as seen from the spacecraft, the surface of the Earth, and the center of the Earth are given in Table 11-3.

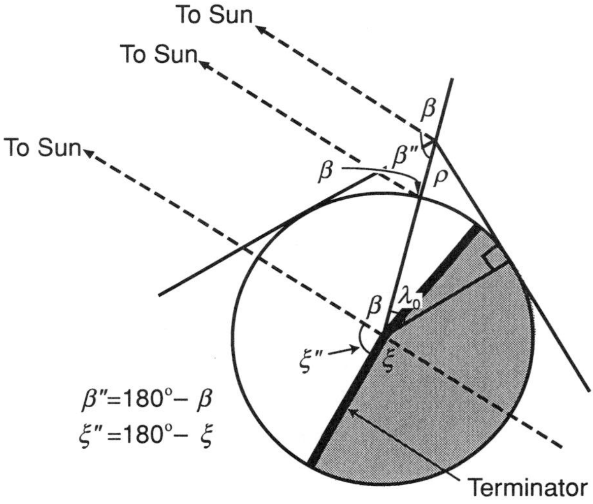

Fig. 11-25. Geometry for Computing Terminator Visibility.

TABLE 11-3. Conditions of Terminator Visibility. Formulas ignore a term equal to the parallax of the orbit as seen from the Sun of approximately 0.005 deg.

Phase	% Illumination	Terminator	Condition (from Spacecraft)	Condition (from surface)	Condition (from Earth Center)
Full	100	Not Visible	$\beta'' > 90° + \xi - \rho$	$\beta < 90° - \xi'' + \rho$	$\beta < 180° - \xi'' - \lambda_0$
Gibbous	>50	Visible	$90° + \xi - \rho > \beta'' > \xi$	$\xi'' > \beta > 90° - \xi'' + \rho$	$\xi'' > \beta > 180° - \xi'' - \lambda_0$
Quarter	50	Through Sub-Satellite Point	$\beta'' = \xi$	$\beta = \xi''$	$\beta = \xi''$
Crescent	<50	Visible	$\xi > \beta'' > 90° - \xi + \rho$	$90° + \xi'' - \rho > \beta > \xi''$	$\xi'' + \lambda_0 > \beta > 90°$
Eclipse	0	Not Visible	$\beta'' < 90° - \xi + \rho$	$\beta > 90° + \xi'' - \rho$	$\beta > \xi'' + \lambda_0$

If the terminator is visible, then the great circle going through the Sun and nadir will be the perpendicular bisector of the terminator. The angular width on the Earth, W_{bright}, of the illuminated portion of the area visible to the satellite can be calculated directly as shown in Fig. 11-26:

$$W_{bright} = \lambda_0 + \xi'' - \beta \tag{11-50}$$

The angular width of the dark portion, W_{dark}, will be

$$W_{dark} = 2\lambda_0 - W_{bright} \tag{11-51}$$

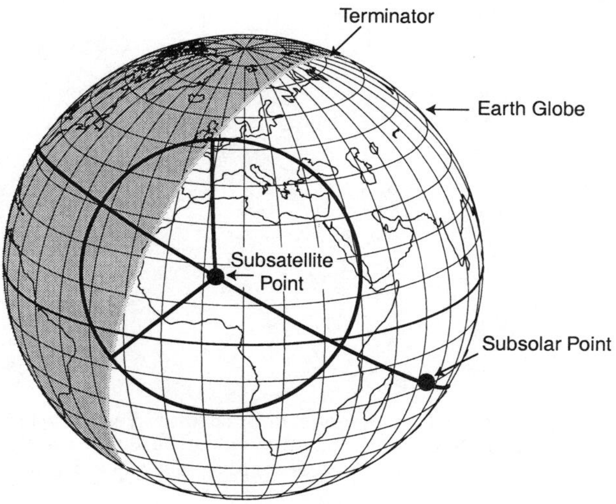

Fig. 11-26. Measuring the Angular Width and Azimuth Range of the Illuminated and Dark Portions of the Earth seen by the Spacecraft.

We can then transform these into the same parameters as seen from the spacecraft as:

$$W_{bright}' = \rho + a\tan\left[\frac{\sin\rho\sin(\xi'' - \beta)}{1 - \sin\rho\cos(\xi'' - \beta)}\right] \tag{11-52}$$

and

$$W_{dark}' = 2\rho - W_{bright}' \tag{11-53}$$

Finally, let ϕ be the azimuthal range of the terminator measured about the subsatellite point, i.e., the angle measured at the subsatellite point between the two cusps. Ignoring the small deviation of the terminator from being a great circle, we have

$$\cos(\phi/2) = \tan(\xi'' - \beta) / \tan\lambda_0 \tag{11-54}$$

Because azimuth angles do not change in going from the surface of the Earth to the spacecraft-centered celestial sphere, ϕ will also be the angle between the cusps measured about nadir as seen from the spacecraft.

11.6 Brightness of Distant Spacecraft and Planets

We would like to determine general expressions for the brightness of planets or spacecraft as seen from any location in the solar system and at an arbitrary distance. However, the brightness depends not only on the relevant distances and angles, as shown in Fig. 11-27, but also on the surface characteristics and attitude of the object we are looking at. A flat, reflective surface that catches the sunlight can be many times brighter than the rest of the spacecraft. Thus, tumbling spacecraft will often appear to twinkle or vary in brightness as different surfaces are presented to the observer.

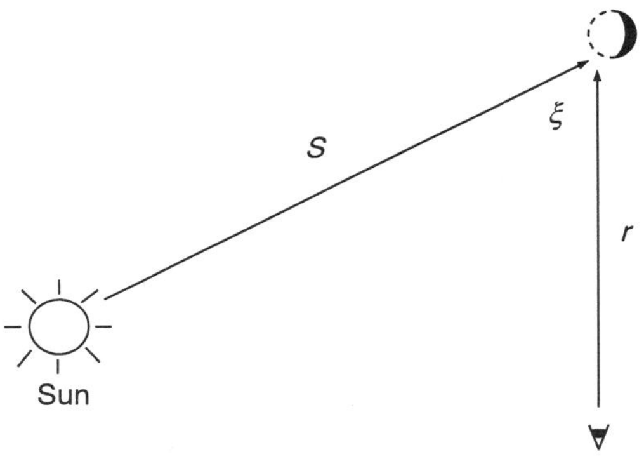

Fig. 11-27. The Magnitude of a Distant Planet or Spacecraft. The magnitude depends on the distances to the Sun and the observer and the angle between them (known as the *Phase Angle*), as well as on the surface properties of the object being viewed.

While exact calculations are difficult, some approximate limits and relative relationships are available. Astronomers measure the brightness of any observed object in terms of *magnitude*, m, which is a logarithmic measure of its brightness or *flux density*, F, defined by $m \equiv m_0 - 2.5 \log F$, where m_0 is a scale constant.* Two objects of magnitude difference Δm differ in intensity by a factor of $(\sqrt[5]{100})^{\Delta m} \approx 2.51^{\Delta m}$ with smaller numbers corresponding to brighter objects; e.g., a star of magnitude −1 is 100 times brighter than a star of magnitude +4. The magnitude of an object depends on the spectral region over which the intensity is measured. In this section, we are concerned only with *visual magnitude*, V, which has its peak sensitivity at about 0.55 μm. On a very dark night, the stars visible to the naked eye from the surface of the Earth have visual magnitudes ranging from approximately 0 to +6.

In addition to measuring brightness and magnitudes, it is frequently convenient to measure distances in *astronomical units*, *AU*, where 1 AU = 1.496×10^8 km is the mean distance of the Earth from the Sun. Consequently, for spacecraft observers in the

* Like many astronomical inventions, the magnitude scale came about before precise measurements of star magnitudes were possible. Thus, a difference of 1 magnitude represented approximately the difference that could be distinguished by an observer. This was later made more precise by defining 5 magnitudes as exactly 100 times brighter or fainter and, therefore, 1 magnitude as $100^{0.2} \approx 2.51$.

general vicinity of the Earth or the Moon, the spacecraft can be thought of as 1 AU from the Sun, which makes logarithmic computations particularly easy. Since the computations are done primarily with logarithms, note that:

$$\begin{aligned}\log D\,(\text{AU}) &= \log D\,(\text{km}) - 8.17 \\ &= \log D\,(\text{m}) - 11.17\end{aligned} \tag{11-55}$$

To compute the visual magnitude of an object, let S be the distance of the object from the Sun in AU, r be the distance of the object from the observer in AU, ξ be the phase angle at the object between the Sun and the observer, and $P(\xi)$ be the ratio of the brightness of the object at *phase angle* ξ to its brightness at zero phase (i.e., fully illuminated). Because the brightness falls off as S^{-2} and r^{-2}, the visual magnitude as a function of ξ, r, and S is given by:

$$\begin{aligned}V(rS,\xi) &= V(1,0) + 5\log(rS) - 2.5\log P(\xi) \\ &= V(1,0) + 5\log r + 5\log S - 2.5\log P(\xi)\end{aligned} \tag{11-56}$$

where $V(1,0)$ is the visual magnitude at opposition relative to the observer* (i.e., $\xi = 0$) and at a distance such that $rS = 1$. If we continue to express S in AU but express r in kilometers, Eq. (11-56) becomes:

$$V(r,S,\xi) = V(1,0) + 5\log r + 5\log S - 2.5\log P(\xi) - 40.85 \tag{11-57}$$

Note that $P(\xi)$ is independent of distance only as long as the observer is sufficiently far from the object that he is seeing nearly half of the object at any one time; for example, for a low-Earth orbit satellite, the illuminated fraction of the Earth seen by the satellite depends on both the phase and the satellite altitude as discussed previously in Sec. 11.5.

If the mean visual magnitude, V_0, at opposition† to the Earth is the known quantity, then:

$$V(1,0) = V_0 - 5\log[D(D-1)] \tag{11-58}$$

where D is the mean distance of the object from the Sun in AU. Values of V_0 and $V(1,0)$ for the Moon and the planets are tabulated in Table 11-4.

For planets or other objects for which V_0 or $V(1,0)$ is known, the major difficulty in determining the magnitude is determining the *phase law*, $P(\xi)$. Unfortunately, there is no theoretical model available to predict $P(\xi)$ accurately for various phases of the planets, or, even more difficult, spacecraft. Thus, the best phase law information is empirically determined and for planets outside the Earth's orbit only a limited range of phases $\xi = 0$ are observed from the Earth. Basically, it is very difficult to determine what the phase law would be for a "first quarter Jupiter" since we have never seen Jupiter from that angle. Although no method is completely satisfactory, the three most convenient methods for estimating the phase law for an object are: (1) assume that the intensity is proportional to the observed illuminated area, that is, $P(\xi) = 0.5(1 + \cos\xi)$; (2) for objects similar in structure to the Moon, assume that the Moon's phase law, which is tabulated numerically in Table 11-5, holds; or (3) for the planets, assume that

---

* Equation (11-56) holds only for objects which shine by reflected sunlight. Additional terms are needed if lighting is generated internally or by planetary reflections.

† An object is said to be in *opposition* to an observer if it is opposite the direction to the Sun, i.e., as seen from the object, the Sun and the observer are in the same direction.

TABLE 11-4. Values of the Apparent Visual Magnitude for the Moon and Planets at Opposition to the Earth. See text for definitions. Data from Seidelmann [1992].

Planet	Visual Magnitude		Small Angle Phase Coefficient, a_1
	V (1,0)	V_0	
Moon	+0.21	−12.74	—
Mercury	−0.42	—	0.038
Venus	−4.40	—	0.009
Earth	−3.86	—	—
Mars	−1.52	−2.01	0.016
Jupiter	−9.40	−2.70	0.005
Saturn	−8.88	+0.67	—
Uranus	−7.19	+5.52	0.0028
Neptune	−6.87	+7.84	—
Pluto	−0.81	+15.12	0.37

the phase dependence on the magnitude for small ξ is of the form $V = V_0 + a_1\xi$, where the empirical coefficients a_1 are given in Table 11-3. For Saturn, the visual magnitude depends strongly on the orientation of the observer relative to the ring system. Because the ring system is inclined to the ecliptic, the orientation of the rings relative to the Earth changes cyclically with a period equal to the period of revolution of Saturn, or about 30 years. Additional information on visual magnitudes of planets are given by Cox [2000].

TABLE 11-5. Phase Law for the Moon. Note the strongly non-linear character. When the Moon is half illuminated (first or last quarter, ξ= 90 deg), the intensity is only 10% of that of the full Moon.

ξ (deg)	P(ξ)	$V(r,\xi) - V(r,0)$	ξ (deg)	P(ξ)	$V(r,\xi) - V(r,0)$
0	1.000	0.00	80	0.1155	2.34
5	0.929	0.08	90	0.0802	2.74
10	0.773	0.28	100	0.05705	3.11
20	0.5945	0.56	110	0.0391	3.52
30	0.4595	0.84	120	0.0255	3.98
40	0.353	1.13	130	0.01545	4.53
50	0.274	1.41	140	0.0093	5.08
60	0.211	1.69	150	0.0046	5.88
70	0.1585	2.00	160	0.001	7.50

The phase law of the Moon given in Table 11-5 above illustrates the fundamental difficulty with estimating the brightness of an object as a function of phase. A *first quarter Moon* will have a phase angle of 90 deg and half of the Moon will appear to be illuminated, i.e., the terminator will approximately bisect the disk of the Moon. Although the Moon is half illuminated, the intensity of the Moon is only 10% that of the intensity of the full Moon. This is due principally to two effects. First, most of the illuminated area that we are looking at in the first quarter Moon is near the terminator, and therefore, near sunrise on the Moon. Here, the illumination angle is extremely low and sunlight is spread out over a much larger area due to the shallow elevation angle of the Sun. In addition, light tends to be scattered more strongly in a direction back toward the source of illumination, thus, further increasing the brightness of the full Moon relative to what one would expect if it were a purely diffuse sphere.

For objects for which no a priori magnitude is known but which shine by reflected sunlight, we may estimate $V(1,0)$ from the relation:

$$V(1,0) = V_S - 5 \log R_p - 2.5 \log g \qquad (11\text{-}59a)$$

$$= -26.74 - 5 \log R_p - 2.5 \log g \qquad (R_p \text{ in AU}) \qquad (11\text{-}59b)$$

$$= 29.14 - 5 \log R_p - 2.5 \log g \qquad (R_p \text{ in m}) \qquad (11\text{-}59c)$$

where V_S is the visual magnitude of the Sun at 1 AU, R_p is the radius of the object in AU, and g is the *geometric albedo* or the ratio of the brightness of the object to that of a perfectly diffusing disk of the same apparent size at $\xi = 0$. For the planets, g ranges from 0.10 for Mercury to 0.57 for Uranus, and is about 0.37 for the Earth, although it is a function of both weather and season. Table 11-4 lists the *Bond albedo*, A, of the planets, which is the ratio of the total light reflected from an object to the total light incident on it. The Bond and geometric albedos are related by:

$$A = gq \qquad (11\text{-}60)$$

where

$$q \equiv \int_0^{\pi} P(\xi) \sin \xi \, d\xi \qquad (11\text{-}61)$$

where $P(\xi)$ is the phase law. The quantity q represents the reflection of the object at different phase angles and has the following values for simple objects:

- $q = 1.00$ for a perfectly diffusing disk
- $q = 1.50$ for a perfectly diffusing (Lambert) sphere
- $q = 2.00$ for an object for which the magnitude is proportional to the illuminated area
- $q = 4.00$ for a metallic reflecting sphere.

For the planets, q ranges from 0.58 for Mercury to about 1.6 for Jupiter, Saturn, Uranus, and Neptune.

Consider as an example, Fig. 11-28 which shows the Cassini spacecraft en route to its fly-by of Venus. We assume the spacecraft is about 6 m in diameter, so $R_p = 3$ m. The geometric albedo is unknown so we will pick an intermediate value of 0.5. Then, from Eq. (11-59c), we have $V(1,0) = 29.14 - 5 \log (3) - 2.5 \log (0.5) = 27.51$. We also assume an intermediate phase angle of 45 deg and a phase law proportional to the illuminated area, such that $P(\xi) = 0.5\ (1 + \cos \xi) = 0.85$. Finally, the distance to the spacecraft, r, is 26,000 km and the distance to the Sun, S, is 1 AU. Consequently, from

Eq. (11-57), we have an estimate of the visual magnitude $V = 27.51 + 5\log(26{,}000) + 5\log(1) - 2.5\log(0.85) - 40.85 = 8.91$. This is in reasonable agreement with the stars in the photo. Note that the star images build up over the 17 sec exposure, while the images of the spacecraft and upper stage are spread out over a trail. In addition, the brightness of the spacecraft fluctuates considerably as sides that are more or less reflective turn toward the observer.

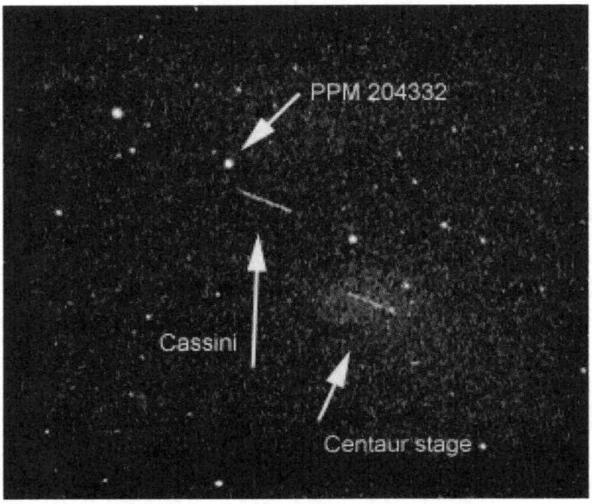

Fig. 11-28. Cassini Spacecraft and Centaur Upper Stage at a Range of Approximately 26,000 km. A cloud of propellant vented after separation surrounds the Centaur stage. The star PPM 204332 is of visual magnitude 8.8. The 17 sec exposure had a limiting stellar magnitude of about 15.0. (Photo by Gorden Garradd from New South Wales, Australia.)

11.7 Radar and Laser Illumination of Surfaces

Space-based radar and space-based lasers are generally very high-power devices because of the large distances involved in space missions. Nonetheless, they have been used throughout the space program to serve a variety of purposes. There are a number of advantages to the use of both radar and lasers in space. First, we can control both the amount of illumination and the spectral characteristics in order to get as much information as possible. In addition, we can adjust the wavelength to provide cloud penetration as in the case of using radar to map the surface of Venus, as illustrated in Fig. 11-29. The largest detriment to this approach is that we must carry our own source of radar or laser illumination, which typically requires very high levels of power.

It is important to recognize that the dependence of radar power on distance depends on how the radar is used, as shown in Table 11-6. Space-based radar works in a series of *dwells*, or looks, in which a burst of energy is sent out by the radar antenna and typically received by the same antenna after bouncing off the target. Since the same antenna is used for both transmit and receive, the beam size or angular diameter of the field of view of the radar, will be the same for both transmit and receive. The beam size is inversely proportional to the size of the antenna, thus large antennas correspond to narrow beams and small antennas correspond to large beams, just as it is for parabolic radio antennas.

Fig. 11-29. Radar Map of the Surface of Venus. Taken by Magellan spacecraft. (Photo courtesy of NASA.)

Ordinarily, we think of the beam size as being much larger than the target we are looking at. For example, in using radar to search for spacecraft, we will use a large beam to search for spacecraft with small angular diameter (row 1 in Table 11-6). Assuming that we hit the target with the radar beam, a single dwell or look is sufficient to see the target. However, the required power per dwell increases as r^4, where r is the distance between the radar and the target. As the target gets farther away, the area covered by the radar beam increases as r^2, which means we must increase the power as r^2 to provide a given level of illumination at the target. With a given level of illumination, the surface brightness of the target in terms of the reflected radar energy will be independent of distance, as described in Sec. 11.0. However, the angular diameter of the target as seen from the radar antenna will fall off as $1/r^2$ such that the total intensity will fall off as $1/r^2$. This implies a need to further increase the power by r^2 to account for the smaller angular size. The net effect is that the power required with a large radar beam and a small target increases as r^4. Because the distances involved for a space-based radar are typically very large, they are ordinarily very high-power devices.

TABLE 11-6. Power Requirements as a Function of Range for Differing Beam and Target Sizes. See text for discussion.

Beam Size	Target Size	# of Dwells Required	Power per Dwell	Power for Whole Target
Large	Small	1	r^4	r^4
Small	Large	$1/r^2$	r^2	Independent of r
= Target	= Beam	1	Independent of r	Independent of r

Next, consider what happens if the target is much larger than the beam size (row 2 in Table 11-6). This would occur, for example, if we want to make a radar map of the state of Texas. As we increase the distance between the target and the radar, the area covered on the ground becomes larger by r^2. In order to maintain a fixed level of illumination per square meter, we must increase the power per dwell proportional to r^2. However, we do not have the same problem in the receive antenna. The size of the receive beam is the same as the size of the area being illuminated. The surface brightness is constant, therefore, the energy return will also be constant. From the point of view of the radar, it is very much like looking at the surface of the Earth illuminated by the Sun. There is a constant illumination level irrespective of distance (due to the increased transmitter power in proportion to r^2); therefore, the surface brightness remains the same and the exposure time or received energy also remains the same. Consequently, the total power required per dwell increases only as r^2 rather than as r^4. What's more, the area covered by each dwell also increases as r^2 and, therefore, the number of dwells required to cover the state of Texas is reduced by $1/r^2$. Consequently, the total power required to make a radar map from space of the state of Texas is independent of the distance so long as the radar beam remains smaller than the size of the state.*

Finally, consider the case in which the target and the beam are the same size (row 3 in Table 11-6). Note that for a target of fixed size, this means that the antenna must get bigger as I get farther away in order to make the beam smaller so that it remains the same angular size as the target. In this case, the power per dwell required to provide a given level of illumination is independent of distance. All of the energy transmitted by the beam is falling on the target and none is being wasted. Consequently, the energy per square meter at the target is independent of distance (it is simply the energy in the beam divided by cross-sectional area of the target in m^2). As in the case above, I'm looking at a uniformly illuminated target, so once again, the required power per dwell will be independent of distance. Because the target and the beam are the same size, I require only a single look to see it and, consequently, the power required to view the entire target is independent of distance. Of course the practical limitation here is that as I get farther and farther away, I must use larger and larger diameter antennas in order to make the beam as small as the size of the target. If I do this, however, I can create a radar for which the power requirement is independent of distance.

The above results seem strange at first glance. The physical reason that the power required is independent of distance is that I am being efficient in using all of the energy that I am transmitting. None of it is wasted by spilling out into space. This is illustrated conceptually in Fig. 11-30. The same logic applies to laser illumination or the use of a flashlight and a pair of binoculars on the surface of the Earth.

For much more extensive discussions of space-based radar and space-based lasers and their application for both military purposes and observation, see, for example Cantafio [1989], Jenn [1995], or Skolnik [1990].

---

* Another way to think of this is as follows. I need to illuminate the whole state with so many W/m^2 and, therefore, so many watts. (There is a reasonably well-defined number of m^2 in Texas, even though that number is large.) I am being efficient in only taking a "picture" of those m^2 which are currently being illuminated. Therefore, I only need the prescribed total number of watts, irrespective of how far away the "camera" and the "light source" are.

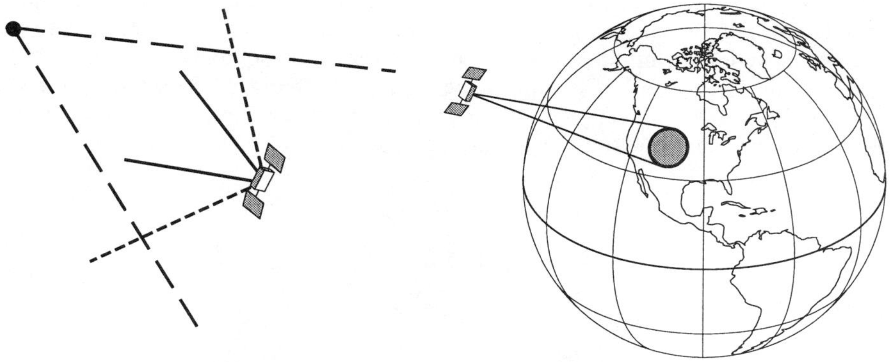

Fig. 11-30. Power Requirements for Radar or Laser Illumination of Surfaces. (A) A broad illuminator and a small target. (B) A narrow illuminator and a large target. See text for discussion.

11.8 Jamming and RF Interference

Jamming is the process of making an observation useless by overwhelming the signal with noise. It is usually associated with radar or radio signals, but can be done with optical images as well. Typically jamming is intentional to prevent someone else from making an observation or getting a message, such as jamming a radar signal or a radio broadcast.* In contrast RF interference is the unintentional overlap of signals that causes noise, static, or double signals in everything from radio and television reception to cellular telephones and radio telescopes. Interference can be natural, such as when we try to communicate with a satellite too near the Sun. However, as man-made RF signals proliferate, unintentional interference from other broadcasting sources becomes an ever-increasing problem. For example, LEO communications constellations are concerned with RF interference from GEO satellites and may have areas of the world they can not cover because of this.

For space applications, signal strength and processing issues associated with jamming and interference are covered in detail by most references on radar [Cantafio, 1989] and satellite communications (for example, Elbert [1997, 1999]). In this section, we are concerned with geometrical and orbit issues associated with when jamming and RF interference will occur and how they can be avoided.

Jamming typically occurs when a *jammer* (i.e., a large RF source operating in the same frequency band as the observation or communications system) is located near a target. Here "target" refers to the object we are trying to see or communicate with, such as a ground station or radar target. As discussed in detail in Sec. 9.1, the ability to see a target depends on both the satellite altitude and the minimum elevation angle. As shown in Fig. 11-31, these parameters define a coverage small circle, called the *effective horizon*, centered on the target with a radius equal to the maximum Earth central angle. (See Secs. 9.1.1 and 9.5.1.1 for the relevant coverage formulas.) Similarly,

---

* An example of "unintentional jamming" is glare when a star camera looks too close to the Sun.

there is small circle centered on the jammer which represents all of the subsatellites points at which the jammer can see the satellite above the jammer minimum working elevation angle. The minimum elevation angle for the sensor and the jammer need not be the same, but are typically similar. The shaded area in Fig. 11-31 is the region where the satellite can see the target but the jammer can not see the satellite, i.e., the region where observations or communications are possible.

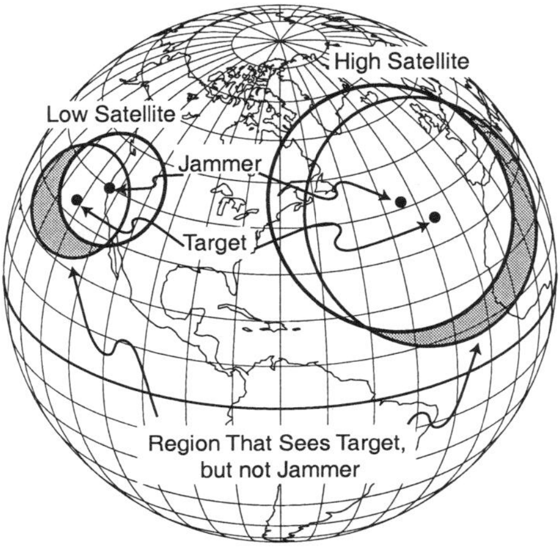

Fig. 11-31. Jamming Susceptibility. Flying at a low altitude does not reduce jamming susceptibility. At lower altitudes, both jamming and nominal operations occur closer to the target.

Fig. 11-31 also illustrates a common misconception about space-based radar and jamming systems. It is often assumed that, similar to terrestrial aircraft, there is an advantage to flying low, i.e., to coming in under the field of view of the jammer. This is not the case. The figure illustrates two systems in which the target and the jammer are the same distance apart. The one on the left is for a satellite at a low altitude and the one on right is for a higher altitude. As can be seen, there is no advantage to the lower altitude system and, to the contrary, the higher system has a considerably larger area and range of both latitudes and longitudes from which to work. Of course, the higher altitude system must be designed to work from further away, but that is the case irrespective of jamming considerations. Lower altitude systems will generally require less power (within the constraints discussed in Sec. 11.7), but have no advantage and some disadvantages from a jamming perspective.

In contrast to jammers, RF interference usually covers only a segment of the operational area of a system. As illustrated in Fig. 11-32, interference between two satellites will typically occur when the line of sight to the two satellites as seen from the target or ground station are within a given keep-out angular radius, q, of each other. For example, we may be able to work with a LEO communications satellite when it is above a minimum elevation angle of 10 deg and further than 20 deg from the line of sight to a GEO satellite operating in the same or very nearby frequency band. In this case, the RF interference region will be a cone of radius θ centered on the direction to the GEO satellite.

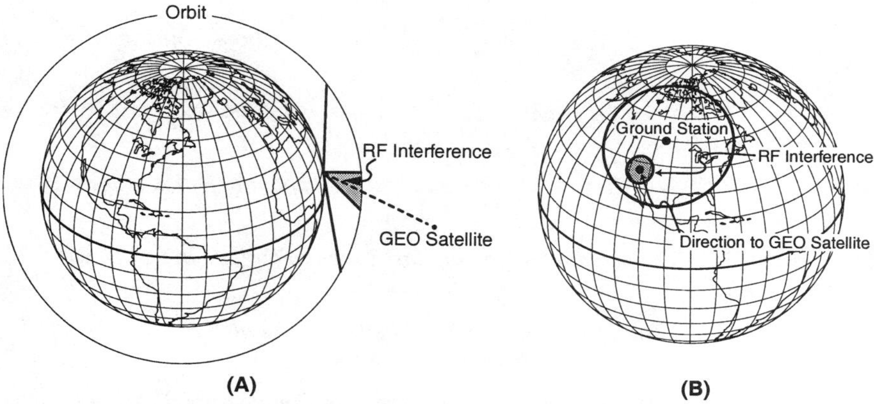

Fig. 11-32. RF Interference Geometry. RF communications can occur when the communications satellite is above a minimum working elevation angle and outside a keep-out angular radius of the interference source.

As shown in Fig. 11-33, the percentage of the coverage region that is blocked depends on both the keep out-radius and whether the interference source is near the horizon. However, as can best be seen in Fig. 11-32A, the percentage blocked does not depend on the altitude. The relative angular area between the coverage cone and the interference cone depends only on the two angular radii and not on how far the cones extend into space. Similarly, if the blockage cone is entirely within the communications cone, then the percentage blocked will not depend on where within the communications cone the interference source lies. In the case of an interference source along the horizon, the percentage is reduced simply because a part of the blockage cone lies outside the effective horizon.

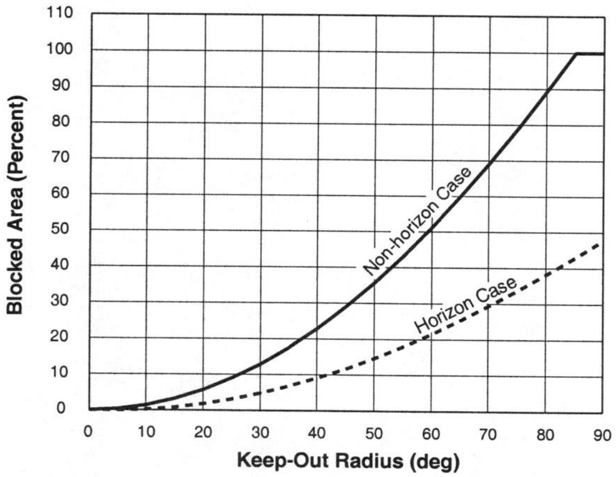

Fig. 11-33. RF Interference as a Function of the Angular Keep-Out Radius. The percentage blocked is independent of the altitudes of the satellites. It is also independent of the direction to the interference source so long as all of the interference cone lies inside the communications effective horizon.

References

Cantafio, Leopold J., ed. 1989. *Space-Based Radar Handbook.* Boston MA: Artech House.

Cox, Arthur N, ed. 2000. *Allen's Astrophysical Quantities,* 4th ed. New York: Springer-Verlag.

Elbert, Bruce E. 1997. *The Satellite Communication Applications Handbook.* Boston, MA: Artech House.

Elbert, Bruce E. 1999. *Introduction to Satellite Communication,* 2nd ed. Boston, MA: Artech House.

Gilmore, David G., and Mel Bello. 1994. *Satellite Thermal Control Handbook.* El Segundo, California: The Aerospace Corporation.

Jenn, David C. 1995. *Radar and Laser Cross Section Engineering*. Washington D.C.: AIAA

Lyle, Robert, James Leach, and Lester Shubin. 1971. *Earth Albedo and Emitted Radiation.* NASA SP-8067, July.)

Seidelmann, P. Kenneth. 1992. *Explanatory Supplement to the Astronomical Almanac.* Mill Valley, CA: University Science Books.

Skolnik, Merrill. 1990. *Radar Handbook,* 2nd ed. New York: McGraw Hill.

Wertz, James R. and Wiley J. Larson. 1999. *Space Mission Analysis and Design (3rd edition).* Torrance, CA and Dordrecht, The Netherlands: Microcosm, Inc. and Kluwer Academic Publishers.

PART III

ORBIT AND CONSTELLATION DESIGN

Part III is a practical guide to the process of selecting, designing, and maintaining orbits, including those for single spacecraft (in Earth orbit and beyond), formations, and constellations.

Chapter 12

Orbit Selection and Design

Chapters 2, 9, and 10 introduced the geometry and physics of spacecraft orbits as well as formulas for computing orbit parameters. Those chapters are fundamentally computational in that there is a well defined answer to how the satellite will move in response to a given set of forces or what portion of the Earth I can see with a camera oriented in a specific direction. In contrast, orbit selection and design is a much fuzzier process. The question that we are trying to deal with is not how the spacecraft will move but what orbit should we put it in. This is, of course, a mix of mission objectives, cost, available launch vehicles, and operational requirements to support the mission. There is no precise answer or correct solution.

In most cases, orbit design consists of choosing among relatively similar, simple orbit shapes. However, as illustrated in Fig. 12-1, some orbit design problems can become very complex, particularly when there are multiple mission phases to be satisfied. In addition, the orbit selection process itself is typically complex, involving trades between many parameters. The orbit normally defines the space mission lifetime, cost, environment, viewing geometry, and frequently, the payload performance. Nonetheless, the single most common trade is between the velocity required to achieve an orbit as a measure of cost vs. the coverage to be achieved as a measure of performance.

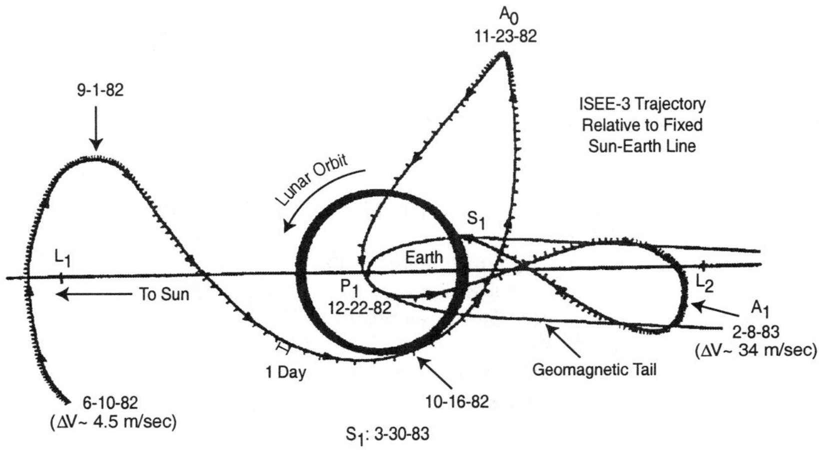

Fig. 12-1. Orbit Design for the ISEE-C Spacecraft. Most orbit design consists of choosing among similar, simple orbit shapes and sizes. A few, such as ISEE-C shown here, involve complex trajectories in order to meet multiple mission objectives. [Farquhar, 2001].

The orbit selection and design discussion is divided into three chapters:

- Chapter 12 introduces the broad topic and lets us choose between high level options, i.e., geosynchronous vs. low-Earth orbit, or Sun-synchronous vs. low inclination.
- Chapter 13 addresses specific issues in designing a constellation.
- Chapter 14 addresses the details of, having chosen a particular orbit or constellation, how we select the specific parameters or range of parameters, including all of the orbit elements, launch windows, and intermediate orbit parameters, to get us where we want to go.

12.1 The Orbit Design Process

Orbit and constellation selection and design is a process rather than a set of specific computations. Throughout the next three chapters, we will use a series of process tables to summarize the fundamental steps and how to undertake them. These should be treated as guides to the issues involved rather than complete and definitive recipes. There is a wide variety of mission types, each of which will be unique in the orbit selection process. Nonetheless, the tables here should be used as a starting point to create a process appropriate for your particular mission.

Table 12-1 summarizes the steps in the overall orbit selection and design process. Each step is discussed below and in greater detail in the sections listed in the table. Effective orbit design requires clearly identifying the reasons for orbit selection, reviewing these reasons regularly as mission requirements change, or mission definition improves, and continuing to remain open to alternatives. Several different designs may be credible. Thus, communication systems may work effectively through a single large satellite in geosynchronous orbit, or a constellation of small satellites in low-Earth orbit. We may need to keep both options for some time before selecting one for a particular mission.

TABLE 12-1. The Orbit Design Process. See text for discussion of each step. This should be treated as a general guide, rather than a definitive process.

Step	Where Discussed
1. Establish orbit types	Table 12-2
2. Determine orbit-related mission requirements	Chaps. 1, 5
3. Assess applicability of specialized orbits	Secs. 2.5, 12.4, 12.5
4. Evaluate whether a single satellite or a constellation is needed	Chap. 13
5. Do mission orbit design trades	
Assume circular orbit (if applicable)	
Conduct altitude/inclination trades	Sec. 12.4, 12.5
Evaluate use of eccentric orbits	Sec. 12.4, 12.5
6. Evaluate constellation growth and replenishment (if applicable), or single satellite replacement strategy	Sec. 13.6
7. Assess retrieval or disposal options	Sec. 13.6
8. Create ΔV budget	Sec. 12.2
9. Determine launch options and cost	
Identify launch vehicle options and cost	Sec. 12.3
Identify low cost options (if applicable)	Sec. 12.3
Compute the Orbit Cost Function	Sec. 12.3.1
Estimate launch cost vs. available on-orbit mass	Sec. 12.3.2
10. Document selection criteria, key orbit trades, selected orbit parameters, and allowed ranges	Chap. 14
11. Iterate as needed	

Step 1. Establish Orbit Types

To design orbits we first divide the space mission into segments and classify each segment by its overall function. In terms of orbit requirements, each segment falls into one of four basic orbit types, listed in Table 12-2. The first two entries are operational orbits in which the spacecraft is intended to spend a large fraction of its operational life, and to do most of the useful work of the mission. In contrast, the bottom two entries are simply means of getting the spacecraft where we want it, when we want it there. Typically, the requirements for the latter two are much less stringent, with the exception that it may be necessary to get the spacecraft where we want it with very precise timing, such as the requirement to attempt to land a probe at a particular location on Mars.

TABLE 12-2. Principal Orbit Types. For orbit design it is convenient to divide the mission into a series of orbit types based on the varying requirements as the mission progresses.

Type	Definition	Examples	Where Discussed
Earth-Referenced Orbit	An operational orbit which provides the necessary coverage of the surface of the Earth or near-Earth space (also applicable to the Moon and planets)	Geosynchronous orbit, low-Earth communications or observation constellations	Sec. 12.4.2, Chap. 13
Space-Referenced Orbit	An operational orbit whose principal characteristic is being or pointing somewhere in space, such that specific orbit parameters may not be critical	Hubble Space Telescope orbit, space manufacturing orbit	Secs. 12.4, 12.5
Transfer Orbit	An orbit used for getting from place to place	Geosynchronous transfer, interplanetary transfer to Mars	Secs. 12.5, 12.6
Parking Orbit	A temporary orbit providing a convenient location for satellite check-out, storage between activity or at end-of-life, or used to match conditions between phases	After launch, while awaiting proper conditions for orbit transfer; end-of-life 500 km above geosynchronous	Chap. 14

An example of the changing orbit types throughout the mission would be a geosynchronous communication satellite initially launched along with a transfer stage into a low-Earth orbit. Once ejected from the launch vehicle, the spacecraft stays briefly in a parking orbit to provide test and checkout of the spacecraft and transfer vehicle subsystems. The next mission segment is a transfer orbit which moves the spacecraft from the parking orbit to a geosynchronous equatorial orbit. Frequently, to preserve propellant, the spacecraft is initially put into a drift orbit near GEO such that any errors in the transfer process can be taken out by small adjustments associated with achieving the desired geosynchronous station location. The spacecraft then enters its operational orbit in the geostationary ring where it will spend the rest of its active life. While the spacecraft itself is still functional and before its stationkeeping propellant runs out, we must move it out of the geostationary ring to avoid possible collisions with other satellites and to free the orbital slot for a replacement, as illustrated in Fig. 12-2. Putting the nearly dead spacecraft into a final disposal orbit a few hundred kilometers above the geostationary ring requires a relatively small transfer orbit. Going above the geostationary ring rather than below avoids the potential for collisions with other satellites during subsequent geosynchronous transfers.

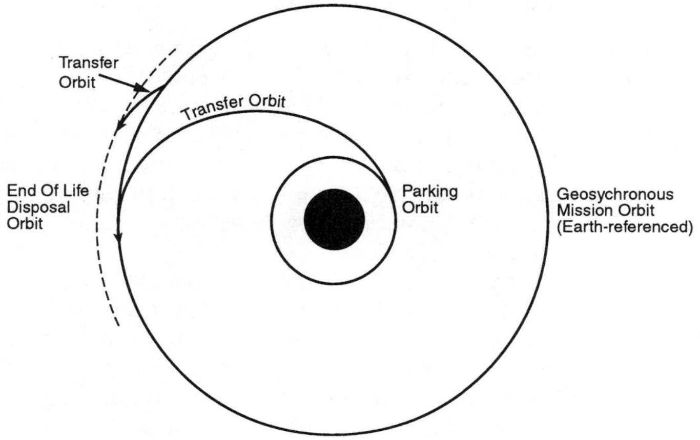

Fig. 12-2. Typical Orbit Phases. At end-of-life, the spacecraft should be either de-orbited or moved into a higher orbit where it will not interfere with other spacecraft.

Step 2. Establish Orbit-Related Mission Requirements

For each mission segment defined in Step 1, we define the orbit-related requirements. They may include orbital limits, individual requirements such as the altitude needed for specific observations, or a range of values constraining any of the orbit parameters. Sections 12.4 and 12.5 discuss in detail the requirements for designing operational orbits. Ordinarily, these multiple requirements drive the orbit in different directions. For example, resolution or required aperture tend to drive the orbit to low altitudes, but coverage, lifetime, and survivability drive the spacecraft to higher altitudes. Consequently, the operational orbit trades are typically complex, involving the evaluation of multiple parameters in selecting a reasonable compromise that meets mission objectives at minimum cost and risk.

Selecting parking, transfer, and space-referenced orbits is normally conceptually much simpler, although it may be mathematically complex. Here the normal trade is meeting the desired constraints on a mission, such as lifetime, thermal, or radiation environments, at the lowest possible propellant cost. Sections 12.5 through 12.7 discuss these types of orbits in more detail.

Step 3. Assess Specialized Orbits

In selecting the orbit for any mission phase, we must first determine if a specialized orbit applies. *Specialized orbits* are those with unique characteristics, which set them apart from the broad continuum of orbit parameters. (See Table 2-10 in Sec. 2.5 and Table 12-10 in Sec. 12.4.2.) Geosynchronous orbits, Sun-synchronous orbits, Molniya orbits, and Lagrange point orbits are typical examples. We examine each of these specialized orbits to see if its unique characteristics are worth its cost. This examination precedes the more detailed trades, because specialized orbits constrain parameters such as altitude or inclination, and, therefore, often lead to very different solutions for a given mission problem. Consequently, we may need to carry more than one orbit into more detailed design trades, such as keeping open a geosynchronous option and a low-Earth orbit option as possibilities for further trade studies.

Step 4. Select Single Satellite or Constellation

The principal advantage of a single satellite is that it reduces cost by minimizing the mission overhead. One satellite will have one power system, one attitude control system, one telemetry system, and require only a single launch vehicle. A constellation or multiple spacecraft, on the other hand, may provide better coverage, higher reliability if a satellite is lost, and more survivability. We may also need a constellation to provide the multiple conditions to carry out a mission, such as varying lighting conditions for observations, varying geometries for navigation, or continuous coverage of all or part of the Earth for communications.

To meet budget limits, we often trade a single large satellite with larger and more complex instruments against a constellation of smaller, simpler satellites. This decision may depend on the technology available at the time of system design. As discussed in detail by Wertz and Larson [1996, 1999] small satellites have become more capable through miniaturized electronics and onboard processing. Consequently, we may be able to construct constellations of small, low-cost satellites, frequently called *LightSats*, that were not previously economically feasible. Another issue for large constellations is the operational problem of providing continuous navigation and orbit control. The introduction of low-cost navigation and autonomous orbit control described in Chap. 4 can resolve many of these problems and promote larger constellations of small satellites in the future.

Step 5. Do Mission Orbit Design Trades

The next step is to select the mission orbit by evaluating how orbit parameters affect each of the mission requirements defined in Chap. 5 and Sec. 12.4.1. As shown in Table 12-9 in Sec. 12.4.1, orbit design in Earth orbit depends principally on altitude. The easiest way to begin is by assuming a circular orbit and then conducting altitude and inclination trades. This process establishes a range of potential altitudes and inclinations, from which we can select one or more alternatives. Documenting the results of this key trade is particularly important, so we can revisit the trade from time to time as mission requirements and conditions change. We then evaluate the use of eccentric orbits as discussed in Sec. 12.4.3. If a satellite constellation is one of the alternatives, then re-phasing the satellites within that constellation is a key characteristic, as described in Chap. 13.

Note that constellations of satellites are normally at a common altitude and inclination because the orbit's drift characteristics depend largely on these parameters. Satellites at different altitudes or inclinations will drift apart so that their relative orientation will change with time. Thus, satellites at different altitudes or inclinations typically cannot work well together as a constellation for extended times.

Step 6. Evaluate Constellation Growth and Replenishment or Single-Satellite Replacement Strategy

An important characteristic of any satellite constellation is growth, replenishment, and graceful degradation. A constellation that becomes operational only after many satellites are in place causes many economic, planning, and checkout problems. Constellations should be at least partly serviceable with a small number of satellites. *Graceful degradation* means that if one satellite fails, the remaining satellites provide needed services at a reduced level rather than a total loss of service. Section 13.6

discusses further the critical question of how we build up a constellation and how to plan for graceful degradation. Constellations are often launched with multiple small satellites on a single large launcher. If this is the case, a key logistics question is how we launch replacement satellites when spacecraft die in orbit.

Step 7. Assess Retrieval or Disposal Options

Although given little consideration in many past missions, retrieval and disposal of spacecraft have become critical to mission design. These represent potentially major legal, political, and economic issues. Spacecraft disposal options are discussed in detail in Sec. 2.6.4. Spacecraft that will reenter the atmosphere must either do controlled reentry over the ocean or break up into pieces harmless to the Earth's surface.

If the spacecraft will not reenter the atmosphere in a reasonable time, we must still dispose of it at the end of its useful life so it is not hazardous to other spacecraft. This problem is particularly acute in geosynchronous orbit where missions compete strongly for orbit slots. (See Cefola [1987] for an excellent analysis of the requirements for removing satellites from geosynchronous orbit.) As pointed out in Sec. 13.5, a collision between two spacecraft not only destroys them but also causes a debris cloud dangerous to their entire orbital area. Consequently, this is a major concern for satellite constellations.

A third option is satellite retrieval, done either to refurbish and reuse the satellite, or to recover material (such as radioactive products) which would be dangerous if they entered the atmosphere uncontrolled. Currently, the Space Shuttle can retrieve spacecraft only from low-Earth orbit. In the future, it is likely that we will be able to retrieve satellites as far away as geosynchronous orbit and return them to either the Orbiter or Space Station for refurbishment, repair, disposal, or reuse. Spacecraft beyond geosynchronous orbit are ordinarily allowed to continue to drift in interplanetary space at the end of their useful life. If a spacecraft is not specifically designed to encounter a planetary surface, then normal practice calls for preventing collisions with planets or moons in order to avoid the potential of biological contamination. At the end of their normal mission, Pioneers 10 and 11 became the first spacecraft to begin the exploration of interstellar space and continued to send back signals for an extended time on the environment which they encountered.

Step 8. Create a ΔV Budget

To numerically evaluate the cost of an orbit, we first create a ΔV budget for the orbit, as described in Sec. 12.2. This then becomes the major component of the propellant budget and the Orbit Cost Function as described in Step 9.

Step 9. Assess Launch and Orbit Transfer Cost

Section 12.3.1 discusses current satellite launch options, including the options for small systems which cannot afford the cost of a dedicated launch vehicle. The selection of specific launch vehicles is discussed by Wertz and Larson [1999], Chap. 18; Isakowitz [1999] provides detailed numerical summaries of currently available launch vehicles worldwide. The launch vehicle contributes strongly to mission cost, and ultimately limits the amount of mass that can be placed in any given orbit. During early mission definition, we must provide enough launch margin to allow for later changes in launch vehicles or spacecraft mass. New designs require more margin than existing ones, with 20% being typical for new missions.

Section discusses the *orbit cost function* which is a mechanism for defining the approximate cost of orbit transfer in terms of the mass that must be put in low-Earth orbit to achieve the end mission orbit. Consequently, it provides a cost multiplier to be used in conjunction with launch vehicle cost estimates from other sources.

Steps 10 and 11. Document and Iterate

A key component of orbit or constellation design is documenting the mission requirements used to define the orbit, the reasons for selecting the orbit, and the numerical values of the selected orbit parameters. With this documentation, the baseline selection can be reevaluated from time to time as mission conditions change. Because mission design nearly always requires many iterations, we must make the iteration process as straightforward as possible and readdress orbit parameters throughout the mission design to ensure that they continue to meet all of the mission objectives and requirements at minimum cost and risk.

12.2 The ΔV Budget

As discussed above, a space mission is a series of different orbits. For example, a satellite may be released in a low-Earth parking orbit, transferred to some mission orbit, go through a series of rephasings or alternative mission orbits, and then move to some final orbit at the end of its useful life. Each of these orbit changes requires energy. The *ΔV budget* is traditionally used to account for this energy. It is the sum of the velocity changes, or ΔVs, which must be imparted to the spacecraft throughout mission life. In a broad sense the ΔV budget represents the cost for each mission orbit scenario. In designing orbits and constellations, we must balance this cost against the utility achieved.

We use the ΔV budget to create a propellant budget and estimate the propellant mass, m_p, weight required for the space mission. (See for example Wertz and Larson [1999] or Humble et al. [1995].) For preliminary design, we estimate the propellant mass, m_p, needed for a space mission by using the *rocket equation* to determine the total required spacecraft plus propellant mass, $m_i \equiv m_0 + m_p$, in terms of the dry mass of the spacecraft, m_0, the total required ΔV, and the propellant exhaust velocity, V_0:

$$m_i = m_0 e^{(\Delta V / V_0)} \equiv m_0 e^{(\Delta V / I_{sp} g)} \tag{12-1}$$

where the *specific impulse*, $I_{sp} \equiv V_0 / g$, and g is the acceleration of gravity at the Earth's surface.* Typical exhaust velocities for chemical propellants are in the range of 2 to 4 km/s and up to 30 km/s for electric propulsion systems. We can see from Eq. (12-1) that a total ΔV much smaller than the exhaust velocity (i.e., a few hundred meters per second) will require a propellant mass which is a small fraction of the total mass. If the total ΔV required is equal to the exhaust velocity, then we will need a total propellant mass equal to $e - 1 \approx 1.7$ times the mass of the spacecraft. Propulsion systems require additional structure such as tanks, so a ΔV much greater than the exhaust velocity is

* Note that g in the definition of I_{sp} is best thought of as a units conversion factor. It does **not** depend on the actual acceleration of gravity where the rocket happens to be operating.

difficult to achieve. It may make the mission effectively impossible, or require some alternative, such as staging or refueling. The fractional mass of the spacecraft that must be devoted to propellant depends directly on the ΔV that must be supplied during the life of the mission (we will return to this in Sec. 12.3.3). Consequently, calculating ΔVs is a basic step in assessing the cost of a particular orbit.

The process for constructing a ΔV budget is summarized in Table 12-3. We begin by writing down the basic data needed to compute ΔVs: the launch vehicle's initial conditions, the mission orbit or orbits, the mission duration, required orbit maneuvers or maintenance, and the mechanism for spacecraft disposal. We then transform each item into an equivalent ΔV requirement using the formulas given in Chap. 2 and listed Table 12-3. Each of these formulas is discussed in more detail in the location referenced.

TABLE 12-3. Creating a ΔV Budget. Formulas for the ΔV required for specific maneuvers are summarized in Chap. 2. The right column gives representative values for a 5-year mission in circular orbit at 1000km and 55 deg inclination.

Item	Where Discussed	Representative Example
Basic Data		
Initial Conditions	Sec. 12.3.1	150 km, 45 deg
Mission Orbit(s)	Secs. 12.4, 12.5	1,000 km, 55 deg
Mission Duration (Each Phase)	Sec. 12.1	5 yr
Orbit Maintenance Requirements	Sec. 2.7.2	Altitude maintenance
Drag Parameters	Sec. 2.4.4	$m/C_d A = 25$ kg/m^2 $\rho = 3 \times 10^{-15}$ kg/m^3
Orbit Maneuver Requirements		None
End-of-life Conditions	Secs. 2.6.4, 14.3	Positive reentry
ΔV Budget (m/s)		
Orbit Transfer		
1st Burn	Eqs. (2-68), (2-71)*	731 m/s**
2nd Burn	Eqs. (2-69), (2-71)*	671 m/s**
Altitude Maintenance (LEO)	Eq. (2-36)	<1 m/s (for 5 years)
North/South Stationkeeping (GEO)	Eqs. (2-46), (2-47)	N/A†
East/West Stationkeeping (GEO)	Eq. (2-48)	N/A†
Orbit Maneuvers		
Rephasing, Rendezvous	Eq. (2-79)	None
Node or Plane Change	Eq. (2-76)	None
Spacecraft Disposal	Eq. (2-84)	272 m/s
Total ΔV	Sum of above	1674 m/s
Other Considerations		
ΔV Savings	Table 2-17, Sec. 12.2	N/A
Margin	Sec. 12.2	Contained in propellant budget

* Sec. 2.6.2 (Eq. [2-76]) if plane change also required.
** Including 5 deg plane change in both first and second burns.
† For GEO missions N/S stationkeeping represents about 50 (m/s)/yr and E/W stationkeeping is about 10% of the N/S amount.

What is the ΔV cost of putting a satellite into orbit at varying altitudes? Figure 12-3 shows representative orbit acquisition and de-orbit ΔV requirements for a satellite dropped off at 185 km altitude. As can be seen from the figure, a plane change as large as 30 deg tends to dominate all of the other characteristics. Figure 12-4 shows the altitude maintenance ΔV for spacecraft at varying altitudes and with a ballistic coefficient of 100 kg/m^2. Recall from Eq. (2-34) that the ΔV requirement is inversely proportional to the ballistic coefficient such that ΔVs required for spacecraft with different ballistic coefficients can be easily estimated from the figure.

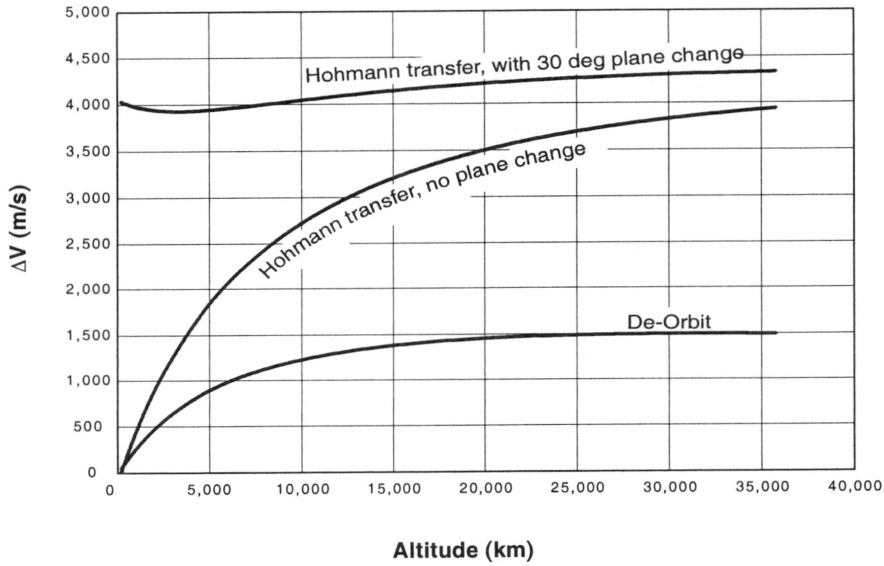

Fig. 12-3. Representative Orbit Transfer and De-Orbit ΔV Requirements. Assumes satellite is dropped off at 185 km altitude and raised via a 2-burn Hohmann transfer. De-orbited is assumed to be an elliptical orbit with a perigee altitude of 50 km.

The higher the mission orbit, the more propellant it takes for both orbit acquisition and de-orbit, but the less it takes for orbit maintenance. This represents the ΔV cost which must be compared to the overall utility of the orbit to make an intelligent selection decision. Figure 12-5 shows the total ΔV for boost, maintenance, and de-orbit as a function of altitude for orbits with no plane change and a 30-deg plane change, respectively. Depending on the desired lifetime of the mission and the phase during the solar cycle, there exists an optimal altitude that balances the orbit acquisition process and orbit maintenance. However, this may or may not be useful for orbit design because of the dramatically high variability in the atmospheric density, depending on the phase in the solar cycle, as discussed in Sec. 2.4.4 and shown in Fig. 12-4. Beyond plane change requirements, the principal factors which will increase the ΔV cost in low-Earth orbit are a low altitude and long mission lifetime. The atmosphere increases in density exponentially as the altitude decreases, thus

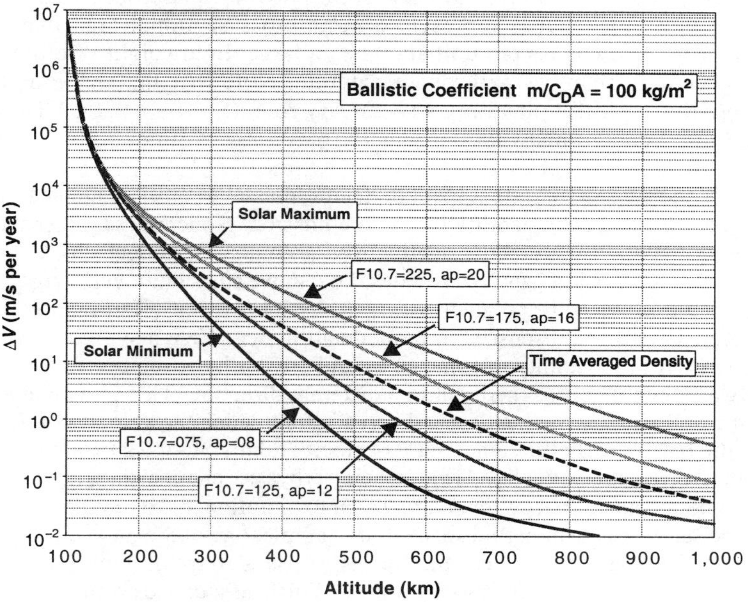

Fig. 12-4. Altitude Maintenance ΔV for a Ballistic Coefficient of 100 kg/m^2. The required ΔV will be inversely proportional to the ballistic coefficient. See Sec. 2.4.4 for a discussion of ballistic coefficients, solar activity, and atmospheric density.

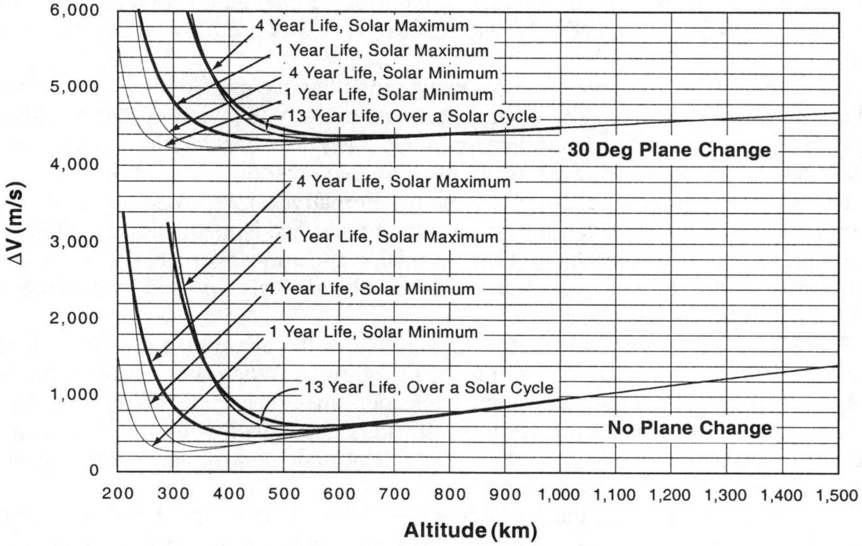

Fig. 12-5. Boost, Maintenance, and De-Orbit ΔV as a Function of Altitude for Low-Earth Orbits with No Plane Change Required.

dramatically increasing drag as altitude comes down. In addition, very large solar arrays or other appendages represent a large cross sectional area that will also increase drag. A low mass per unit area, i.e., a large, lightweight satellite will also have higher drag than a small, dense satellite. Note that the shape and surface characteristics typically play only a secondary role. (See Sec. 2.4.4.) They impact the drag coefficient somewhat but usually play only a minor role in overall ΔV requirements.

The ΔV budget has a strong impact on the propulsion requirements and, therefore, on the final cost and achievability of a space mission. Nonetheless, other factors can vary the propellant requirements relative to a nominal ΔV budget. For example, although rocket propulsion usually provides the ΔV, we can obtain very large ΔVs from a flyby of the Moon, other planets, or even the Earth itself [Kaufman et al., 1966; Meissinger, 1970)]. As discussed in more detail in Sec. 12.5, a spacecraft in a planetary flyby leaves the vicinity of some celestial body with the same velocity relative to the body as when it approached, but in a different direction. This phenomenon is like the elastic collision between a baseball and a bat, in which the velocity of the ball relative to the bat is nearly the same, but its velocity relative to the surrounding baseball park can change dramatically. We can use flybys to change direction, to provide increased heliocentric energy for solar system exploration, or to reduce the amount of energy the satellite has in inertial space. For example, one of the most energy-efficient ways to send a space probe near the Sun is to use a flyby of Jupiter to reduce the intrinsic heliocentric orbital velocity of the Earth associated with any spacecraft launched from here.

A second way to produce a large ΔV without burning propellant is to use the atmosphere of the Earth or other planets to change the spacecraft's direction or reduce its energy relative to the planet. The manned flight program has used this method from the beginning to dissipate spacecraft energy for return to the Earth's surface. It can also be used to produce a major plane change through an *aeroassist trajectory* [Austin et al., 1982; Mease, 1988]. This was used, for example, on the Mars orbiter mission.

The *solar sail* is a third way to avoid using propellant. A large, lightweight sail uses solar radiation pressure to slowly push a satellite the way the wind pushes a sailboat. Of course, the low-pressure sunlight produces **very** low acceleration. Hence, very large solar sail areas are required as discussed in Sec. 12.7.6.

The aerospace literature discusses many alternatives for providing spaceflight energy because of its importance for a variety of missions. Nonetheless, experimental techniques (i.e., those other than rocket propulsion and atmospheric braking) are risky and costly, so that normal rocket propulsion will ordinarily be used to develop the needed ΔV, if this is at all feasible.

The ΔV budget described in Table 12-3 measures the energy we must give to the spacecraft's center of mass to meet mission conditions. When we transform this ΔV budget into a propellant budget, we must consider other characteristics as well. These include, for example, inefficiencies from thrusters misaligned with the ΔV direction, and any propulsion diverted from ΔV to provide attitude control during orbit maneuvers or desaturation of momentum wheels.

For most circumstances, the ΔV budget does not include margin because it results from astrodynamic equations with very little error relative to most other errors in system design. Instead, we maintain the margin in the propellant budget itself, where we can reflect specific elements such as residual propellant. An exception is the use of

ΔV to overcome atmospheric drag. Here the ΔV depends upon the density of the atmosphere, which is both highly variable and difficult to predict. Consequently, we must either conservatively estimate atmospheric density or incorporate a ΔV margin for low-Earth satellites to compensate for atmospheric variability.

12.3 Estimating Launch Cost and Available On-Orbit Mass

The key characteristic of any orbit is performance vs. cost. What is the performance we can obtain vs. the cost required to put the payload into that orbit? In these terms, GEO is an "expensive" orbit in that approximately 5 kg must be launched into low-Earth orbit for every kilogram that ultimately arrives in geosynchronous orbit. The purpose of this section is to look at alternative launch options and quantify the assessment of cost as much as possible.

12.3.1 Launch Options

A detailed discussion of specific launch vehicles is beyond the scope of this book. Excellent general discussions are provided by Hujsak [1994] and London [1994, 1996]. Isakowitz [1999] has become the standard reference for detailed launch system cost and performance data. This information must, of course, be updated as specific launch vehicles change.

The basic goal of the launch vehicle is to expel hot gases at velocities on the order of 2 to 3 km/s in order to achieve a final vehicle velocity of 8 km/s or more, even for low-Earth orbit. This means that the mass of any launch vehicle will be dominated by propellant and that the vehicle itself will need to be designed for minimum excess weight. This in turn implies that launch will be dramatically expensive and will always entail significant risk since each launch vehicle sitting on the pad is more than 95% explosive propellant and virtually nothing to contain the resulting explosion should some error occur. Table 12-4 lists the maximum payload available in low-Earth orbit, the launch cost, and the *specific launch cost* or cost per kilogram for a representative sample of current launch vehicles. Note that the Saturn V used for the Apollo program was the most efficient launch vehicle ever created by the United States at a bit more than $5,000 per kg. Current vehicles, in part because they are significantly smaller, fall more typically in the range of $10,000 to $20,000 per kg. It is this dramatically high cost per kg that is largely responsible for the very specialized and optimized design of most spacecraft launched today. Because launching spacecraft to geosynchronous orbit costs more than $50,000 per kg, it is worth $40,000 for the spacecraft manufacturer to eliminate a kg of spacecraft in order to provide, for example, more power for additional transponders.

The specific launch cost is a valuable figure for comparing launch costs for various launchers and spacecraft. However, it can also be misleading. Launches are almost never sold "by the kilogram" but simply for the entire launch. Thus, once a launch vehicle has been selected, there is no added cost for "filling it up," unless doing so moves one into the next larger vehicle, in which case the cost is extremely high.

A large number of low-Earth orbit constellations are being developed and deployed. This has the potential for reducing cost due to economies of scale, or increasing them due to limitations in the supply of existing launch vehicles. Unfortunately, as shown in Fig. 12-6, the cost per kilogram to low-Earth orbit has remained

TABLE 12-4. Launch Vehicle Costs in FY00$M. The data assumes launch from the country's main site. Except where noted, LEO altitude is 185 km (circular orbit) and inclination is 28.5 deg (5.2 deg for Ariane). Data from Isakowitz [1999]. See Fig. 12-9 for capability for interplanetary missions.

Launch Vehicles	Maximum Payload-to-Orbit (kg)			Unit Cost (FY00$M)	Cost per kg to LEO (FY00$K/kg)
	LEO	GTO	GEO		
USA					
Atlas IIIB	10,600	4,510	—	75*	7.1
Atlas V 551	17,420	8,570	3,890	90*	5.2
Athena 1	820	—	—	16.5–17.5	20.7
Athena 2	2,065	590 (Centaur)	—	22.7–26.8	12.0
Athena 3	3,650			31	8.5
Delta II (7920, 7925)	5,140	1,870	—	52–62	11.0
Delta III 3940-11	8,290	3,810	1,320	78*	9.4
Delta IV 4450-14		6,337	1,940	80*	
Delta IV 4050H-19		12,850	5,960	120*	
Pegasus XL	443	—	—	12.4–15.5	31.4
Saturn V	127,000	—	—	820	6.5
Shuttle† (IUS or TOS)	24,400	5,900	2,360	400	16.4
Titan II	1,900	—	—	31–41	19.0
Titan IV	21,680	—	5,760 (Centaur)	361–464	19.0
Taurus	1,380	448	—	18.6–20.6	14.2
ESA					
Ariane 4 (AR40)	5,000	2,175	—	67–88	15.5
Ariane 4 (AR42P)	6,600	2,890	—	72–93	12.5
Ariane 4 (AR44L)	10,200	4,790	—	103–129	11.4
Ariane 5 (550 km)	18,000	6,800	—	155–186	9.5
CHINA					
Long March (LM-3B)	11,200	5,100	—	51.5–72	5.5
RUSSIA					
Proton (SL-13)	19,760	4,910	1,880	93–101	4.9
Kosmos (C-1)	1,500	—	—	12.4	8.2
Soyuz	7,000	1,350 (Soyuz/ Fregat)	—	31–52	5.9
Tsiklon	4,100	—	—	20.6–25.8	5.7
Zenit 2	13,500	—	—	36–52	3.3
JAPAN					
H-2	10,060	3,930	—	170–175	17.2
J-1	850	—	—	44–46	53.3
GTO = Geosynchronous Transfer Orbit; GEO = Geostationary Orbit; LEO = Low-Earth Orbit					

* Estimated

† There is no official price for a Space Shuttle launch. Following the Challenger loss, only government payloads have been allowed. The GAO has assigned a price of $400 million per flight, but the actual cost depends strongly on the flight rate.

approximately constant for 30 years. While many new programs are being initiated to dramatically reduce launch costs, none of these as yet has been strongly successful. An excellent summary of the problem and alternative solutions is given by London [1994, 1996].

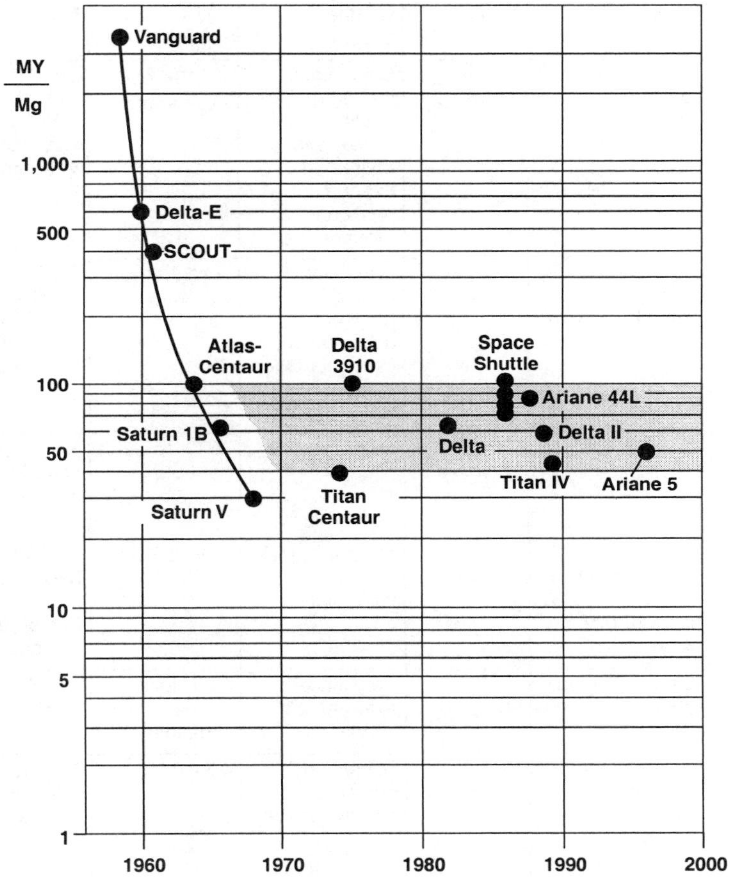

Fig. 12-6. Historical Specific Launch Cost (= Cost per Kilogram) to Low-Earth Orbit. (Data from Koelle [2000].) Costs are in man-years (MY) per megagram (Mg). See Fig. 12-11 for current values.

Large spacecraft have little choice but to go with one of the dedicated launchers from Table 12-4, unless the program is sufficiently large to justify the nonrecurring development cost of a new vehicle. However, small spacecraft have a number of much lower cost alternatives, as shown in Table 12-5. In particular, small spacecraft should consider non-orbital alternatives, even if it requires multiple flights to achieve mission objectives. Within orbital flights, sharing launch vehicles or being launched as a secondary payload on any of the major launchers can dramatically reduce the launch cost for small payloads.

TABLE 12-5. Low-Cost Alternatives to Dedicated Launches. For a more extensive discussion, see London [1996], from which this table is adapted.

Option	Characteristics	Weight Limits	Principal Constraints	Approximate Cost	Sources
Balloon Flights	Hours to days at ≈ 30 km altitude	Up to 70 kg for low-cost flights	Not in space, not 0-g, weather concerns	\$5K to \$15K	U. of Wyoming, USAFA, NSBF
Drop Towers	1 to 10 sec of 0-g with immediate payload recovery	Up to 1,000 kg	Brief "flight," 5 to 50 g landing acceleration, entire experiment package dropped	≈ \$10K per experiment	ZARM, JAMIC, NASA LeRC and MSFC, Vanderbilt U.
Drop Tubes	1 to 5 sec of 0-g with immediate sample retrieval	<0.01 kg	Brief "flight," 20 to 50 g landing acceleration, instrumentation not dropped with sample	≈ \$0.02K per experiment	ZARM, JAMIC, NASA LeRC and MSFC, Vanderbilt U.
Aircraft Parabolic Flights	Fair 0-g environment, repeated 0-g cycles	Effectively unlimited	Low gravity is only 10^{-2} g	\$6.5K to \$9K per hour	NASA LeRC and JSC, Novespace
Sounding Rockets	Good 0-g environment, altitude to 1,200 km, duration of 4 to 12 min	Up to 600 kg	Much less than orbital velocities	\$1M to \$2M	NASA GSFC, NRL, ESA, OSC, EER, Bristol Aerosp., Microcosm
GAS Containers	Days of 0-g on board the Shuttle	Up to 90 kg	Very limited external interfaces	\$27K for largest container	NASA GSFC
Secondary Payloads	Capacity that is available in excess of primary's requirements	Up to ≈1,000 kg	Subject to primary's mission profile	< \$10M	Ariane, OSC, MDA, Russia
Shared Launches	Flights with other payloads having similar orbital requirements	Up to ≈ 5,000 kg	Integration challenges	Up to ≈ \$60M	Ariane, OSC, Russia

Factors other than cost, such as availability, launch site, reliability, and national interests can also have a major impact on launch vehicle selection. Most national programs require that spacecraft be launched on vehicles from that country if there is a national launch vehicle program. The builders of the large commercial communications constellations have typically decided that the conservative approach to obtaining launch is to buy launch services from multiple vendors. The principal reason for this is to ensure that launch is available in case of problems with any single launch vehicle (A launch vehicle failure normally results in a 4–10 month slip in subsequent launches of that vehicle in order to allow a thorough evaluation and correction of whatever problems have occurred). These factors and others which impact the practical selection of launch vehicle options are discussed in Chap. 18 of Wertz and Larson [1999].

12.3.2 The Orbit Cost Function

Given that we can estimate the total launch cost or specific launch cost for putting mass into low-Earth orbit, how can we translate this into the mass available in a mission orbit. Equivalently, what is the ultimate cost per kilogram to get where we want to go and achieve our mission objectives? To address this, we define the *Orbit Cost Function*, *OCF*, as the ratio of the mass available in a 185-km circular orbit due East from the launch site to that available in the mission orbit, or at the end of mission life. This can be thought of either as a multiplier on the cost of putting a spacecraft into its mission orbit, or, for a given launch vehicle, an inverse multiplier for the amount of payload that can be put into that mission orbit. Section 12.3.3 will look at the practical applications of using the *OCF* as a means of estimating launch costs and available mass.

The *OCF* depends on how the spacecraft is launched. For example, direct injection into Jupiter transfer orbit has a total *OCF* on the order of 10. Using a Venus swingby followed by an Earth swingby can reduce this to approximately 6. In this case, we can use the *OCF* to measure the performance gain associated with the swingbys and compare that with the time lost to determine whether the swingbys are worthwhile for a particular mission. Thus, the use of a Venus swingby for the Jupiter mission represents an increase in the available mass at Jupiter or a decrease in launch cost by a factor of approximately $10/6 \approx 1.7$. The question for the mission designer is then whether the added complexity and added time associated with these swingbys is worth the savings that are obtained.

The orbit cost function is related to the required ΔV by:

$$OCF = (1+K)\,e^{\Delta V / V_0} - K = (1+K)\,e^{\Delta V / g I_{sp}} - K \qquad (12\text{-}2)$$

where K is the fraction of the propellant mass assigned to tankage and other propellant hardware, typically 10%. I_{sp} is the specific impulse, g is the constant of gravity at the Earth's surface, and V_0 is the exhaust velocity of the propulsion system. An I_{sp} of 300 sec (typical for a bipropellant system) gives a V_0 value of 2.94 km/s. Depending on the purpose of the evaluation, we may choose to compare the Orbit Cost Function for simply getting to the mission orbit, through the useful life, or through de-orbit or disposal. If we calculate the *OCF* corresponding to the ΔV for multiple segments, then the cumulative cost function, $OCF_{A+B+C...}$, is just the product of the individual *OCF*s. Thus, a series of mission phases or maneuvers *A, B, C...*, with OCF_A corresponding to ΔV_A, and so on, then

$$\Delta V_{A+B+C...} = \Delta V_A + \Delta V_B + \Delta V_C + ... \qquad (12\text{-}3a)$$

and

$$OCF_{A+B+C...} = OCF_A \times OCF_B \times OCF_C \times ... \qquad (12\text{-}3b)$$

Figure 12-7 shows the orbit cost functions for typical Earth orbiting missions as a function of altitude and plane change. For more complex orbits, or interplanetary missions, the *OCF* is computed by first calculating the required ΔV, and then accounting for added tank mass and any other additional requirements such as the extra power required for electric propulsion. The *OCF* is tabulated for various Earth-oriented and interplanetary missions in Table 12-6.

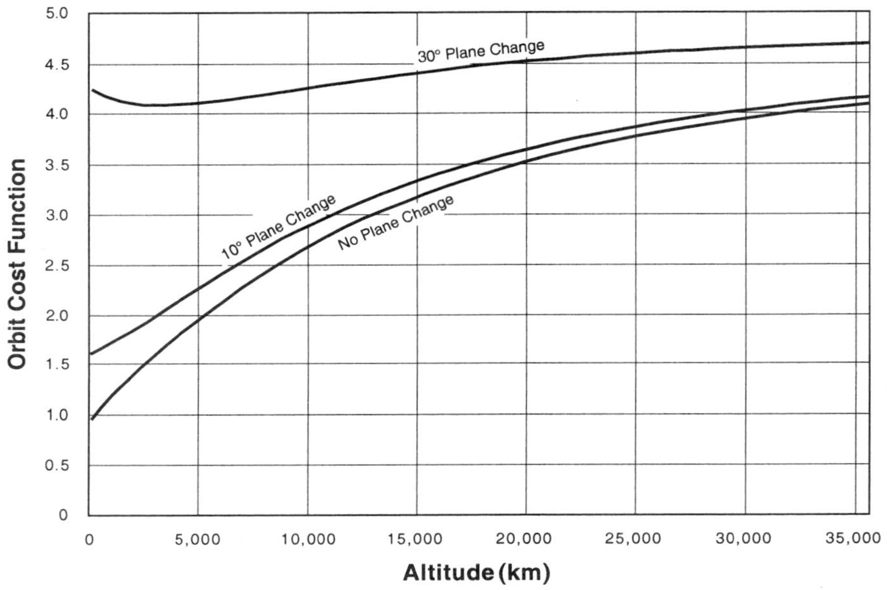

Fig. 12-7. Orbit Cost Function for Various Earth Orbiting Missions. The curves assume starting at a 185 km circular orbit and a circular orbit at the final mission altitude. The curves are for orbit acquisition only.

We can also construct the Orbit Cost Function for a launch vehicle alone from the data supplied by the manufacturers. For example, Fig. 12-8A shows the mass as a function of orbit parameters as provided by the launch vehicle manufacturer for the Delta 7925 launch vehicle. The orbit cost function is the ratio of this mass to the mass that can be launched due East to 185 km low-Earth orbit. This is plotted in Fig. 12-8B. As a specific example, the Delta II 7920 can put 5,140 kg into a 185 km circular orbit at 28.7 deg inclination and 3,220 kg into a Sun synchronous orbit at 800 km and 98.6 deg. Thus, the *OCF* for the Sun synchronous orbit is 5,140/3,220 = 1.60.

Typically, the highest mass to the final orbit can be achieved by using onboard propulsion. The reason for this is that we can then avoid putting the vehicle upper stage into the final spacecraft orbit. For example, if we launch a spacecraft to Jupiter using the traditional approach of a large upper stage, then the upper stage vehicle itself will also be put in the Jupiter transfer orbit. Using onboard propulsion, we will put only the spacecraft and some additional tankage into this very high energy orbit. An example of a high cost approach to orbit transfer is the Hubble Space Telescope, which was launched onboard the Space Shuttle and is re-boosted from time to time by the Orbiter

TABLE 12-6. Typical Orbit Cost Functions for Various Earth-Orbiting and Interplanetary Missions. Interplanetary missions assume a Hohmann transfer. *OCF* assumes I_{sp} of 300 sec and 10% tank mass.

Mission	Incremental ΔV			Cumulative Orbit Cost Function		
	Getting There	Mission Life	Disposal	Getting There	Mission Life	Disposal
200 km @ 90	0.75	12.66	0.045	1.32	107.01	108.83
407 km @ 51.6	0.39	0.192 0	0.104	1.16	1.24	1.29
500 km @ 28.7	0.24	0.043 2	0.130	1.09	1.11	1.17
500 km Sun-synchronous	1.04	0.043 2	0.130	1.47	1.49	1.57
500 km @ 90	0.89	0.043 2	0.130	1.39	1.41	1.48
1,000 km @ 28.7	0.51	0.000 2	0.257	1.21	1.21	1.33
1,000 km Sun-Synchronous	1.38	0.000 2	0.257	1.66	1.66	1.82
GTO (200 × 35,786 km)	2.80	0.411 4	0.024	2.75	3.20	3.23
GEO	4.95	0.521 5	0.018	5.82	7.06	7.11
Lunar Fly-By	3.14			3.10		
Lunar Orbit	3.23			3.20		
Lunar Lander	7.07			12.06		
Mars Fly-by	3.61			3.65		
Mars Orbit	5.69			7.51		
Mars Lander	9.30			25.86		
Mission Life $\Delta V = \Delta V$ required for 10 years						

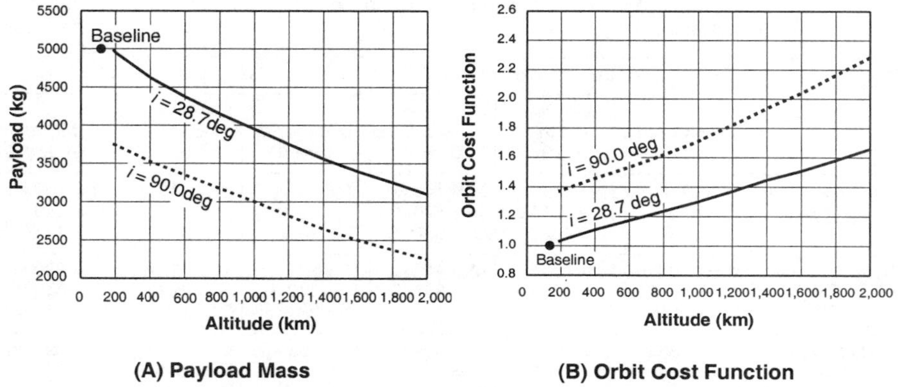

Fig. 12-8. Performance Data for the Delta 7925 Launch Vehicle (3 m fairing). (A) Mass vs. orbit as provided by the launch vehicle manufacturer. (B) The Orbit Cost Function is simply the ratio of the mass that can be launched due East to a 185 km LEO orbit to the mass that can be put in the mission orbit. See text for discussion.

at the same time instruments are changed out. The reasons for this approach were to avoid entirely an onboard propulsion system and the potential for contamination from thruster firings as well as to avoid the possibility of propellant slosh providing even a low level of vibration to the telescope. In this case, a higher cost approach to orbit acquisition and maintenance was used to meet the mission requirements for near-zero disturbances and absolute minimization of potential contamination.

In most cases, the dominant reasons for not using onboard propulsion are tradition and organizational structure. In a typical mission organization, the responsibility for launch is given to some segment of the organization or perhaps an entirely different organization or nation. In this case, the use of onboard propulsion to "fly" the spacecraft from an initial orbit to its final mission orbit constitutes a shifting of responsibility and budget from one organization to another. Consequently, there is a strong tendency to use the more traditional approach of upper stages, even though the available payload will be much less, or alternatively, the cost of launch much higher. In addition, some very simple spacecraft will not have an onboard propulsion system and, therefore, are fully dependent on whatever orbit is provided by the launch vehicle. If there is no inherent need for onboard propulsion, then the fundamental trade becomes the cost of the launch vehicle or the launch vehicle plus upper stage, versus the cost of adding an onboard propulsion system plus the gain in available mass at the destination.

Table 12-7 compares alternative scenarios for a low-cost Jupiter mission based on (a) the traditional approach of using the launch vehicle upper stage for final injection to the transfer orbit, (b) using a Venus-Earth-Earth swing-by as was done for the Galileo mission described in Sec. 1.1.3, and (c) using on-board propulsion to provide direct transfer to the target planet in a modified launch mode as proposed by Meissinger, et al. [1997, 1998]. The planetary swing-by approach provides 4 to 5 times the payload mass at Jupiter, but at the cost of increasing the transfer time from 2.3 years to over 6 years. The on-board propulsion approach increases the payload available from the traditional approach by 50 to 100%, but with no increase in transfer time.

TABLE 12-7. Alternative Launch Scenarios for a Low-Cost Jupiter Mission. The number below each vehicle is the baseline mass in a due east orbit at 185 km. See text for discussion.

	At Jupiter Arrival			In Jupiter Orbit		
	Traditional Direct	Venus-Earth-Earth	MLM Direct*	Traditional Direct	Venus-Earth-Earth	MLM Direct*
Taurus XL/S (1400 kg)	M = 62 kg T = 840 d C = 22.6	M = 316 kg T = 2240 d C = 4.4	M = 143 kg T = 840 d C = 9.8	M = 49 kg T = 840 d C = 28.6	M = 249 kg T = 2240 d C = 5.6	M = 109 kg T = 840 d C = 12.8
Delta II 7925 (5089 kg)	M = 280 kg T = 840 d C = 18.2	M = 1004 kg T = 2240 d C = 5.1	M = 443 kg T = 840 d C = 11.7	M = 221 kg T = 840 d C = 23.0	M = 792 kg T = 2240 d C = 6.4	M = 330 kg T = 840 d C = 15.4
Delta II 7925 H (6107 kg)	M = 336 kg T = 840 d C = 18.2	M = 1205 kg T = 2240 d C = 5.1	M = 520 kg T = 840 d C = 11.7	M = 265 kg T = 840 d C = 23.0	M = 950 kg T = 2240 d C = 6.4	M = 397 kg T = 840 d C = 15.4
M = mass at destination; T = transfer time in days; C = orbit cost function; MLM = modified launch mode						

* U.S. Patent No. 6,059,235, Microcosm, Inc.

Finally, the selection criteria for launch vehicles for interplanetary missions are similar to those for Earth orbit missions, but use a different set of parameters to characterize vehicle performance. As discussed further in Sec. 12.7.3, launch requirements are defined in terms of the velocity or energy of the spacecraft at the point at which it has just escaped the gravitational pull of the Earth. The velocity at this time is called the *hyperbolic excess velocity*, V_∞, and the energy per unit mass at this time is called the reference launch energy, $C_3 \equiv V_\infty^2$. Typical values of C_3 are 12 km^2/sec^2 for missions to Mars and 75 to 85 km^2/sec^2 for missions to Jupiter, corresponding to V_∞ values of 3.5 and 8.7 to 9.2 km/sec, respectively. Fig. 12-9 shows the payload mass of representative launch vehicles as a function of the C_3 provided. Because of the strong effect of the upper stage mass and staging process, there is no simple standard form of the rocket equation applicable to all of the vehicles. The data presented is based on detailed performance analysis by the vehicle manufacturers.

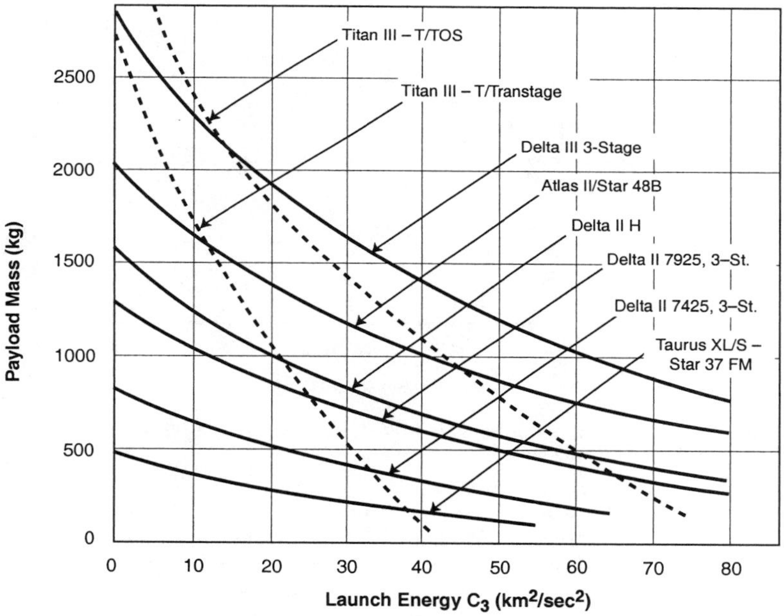

Fig. 12-9. Representative Range of U.S. Launch Vehicle Escape Mission Performance. Data should be compared with mass to LEO from Table 12-4 to determine the Orbit Cost Function.

12.3.3 Estimating Launch Cost

What does it cost to put a payload in orbit? In general, there are two answers, depending on how we view the problem. On the one hand, having selected a launch vehicle and possibly an upper stage or orbit transfer mechanism, the cost is a fixed dollar value. Changing the mass of the spacecraft will have no impact unless we ultimately are forced to use a larger vehicle, or find that we can launch on a smaller one. The basic message here is that once we have selected a launch vehicle, there is little point in reducing weight beyond what is needed to accommodate that vehicle.

The second view is to look at the launch capacity per kilogram, or *specific launch cost*. Generally, as shown in Fig. 12-10, launching twice as much mass will cost twice as much. From this perspective, reducing the mass of some portion of the spacecraft can allow us to either reduce the launch cost by potentially using a smaller vehicle, or alternatively, to increase the spacecraft mass in some other area, i.e., by flying an additional payload instrument or more propellant to allow a longer mission at the final destination.

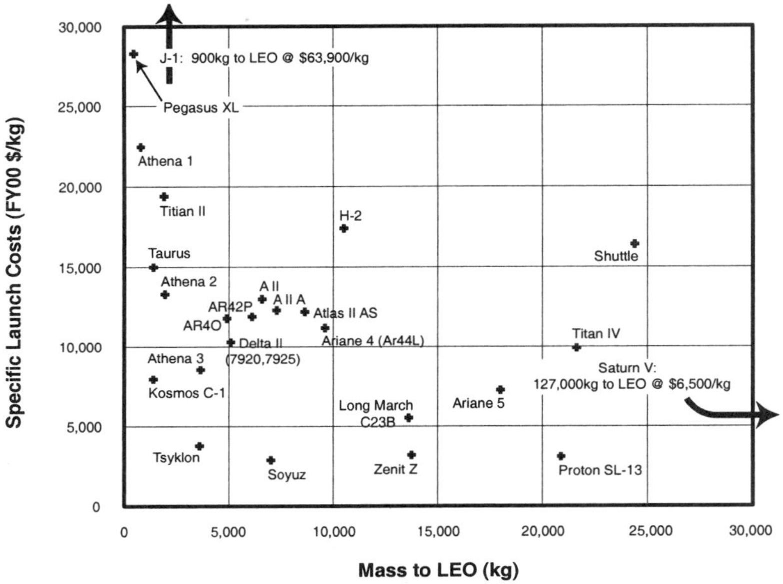

Fig. 12-10. Specific Launch Costs. Data from Tables 12-4 and 12-5. AII = Atlas II. See Fig. 12-7 for historical values.

There are two factors which make the specific launch cost inappropriate or at least a poor measure of effectiveness for launch cost. First is the quantization in launch vehicles. Launchers are not available in an infinite variety of sizes, so that once we have chosen a vehicle, the cost per kilogram is immaterial. Second, there are economies of scale as vehicles get bigger, as shown in Fig. 12-10. In general, launching a spacecraft which is 10 times as massive will cost less than 10 times as much, because of the efficiency associated with larger vehicles. Many of the commercial low-Earth orbit communications constellations have chosen to use a variety of launch vehicles and typically launch several spacecraft on a single large vehicle. This allows them to take advantages of the economies of scale and, at the same time, implies that the cost per kilogram continues to be an important measure. As the mass of an individual spacecraft is reduced, this effect is multiplied by the number of spacecraft per vehicle and can allow either additional propellant on board each of the spacecraft, or potentially, allow an additional spacecraft to be put on a given launcher.

Despite the shortcomings, the specific launch cost is a useful concept in mission design. It allows us to get a rough estimate of the cost of getting our payload into low-Earth orbit at a time before launch vehicle options have been selected. The biggest shortfall of the specific launch cost model is that it only gives the cost of getting into low-Earth orbit. To use this concept effectively, we need to be able to apply it to multiple orbit types—to low-Earth orbit, geosynchronous orbit, Sun-synchronous orbits, interplanetary, and so on, so that we have an effective means of comparing orbit cost. This is the purpose of the Orbit Cost Function defined in Sec. 12.3.2. We can make use of this function to assess the relative costs between, for example, high-inclination posigrade orbits and Sun-synchronous orbits which are retrograde.

Table 12-8 summarizes the step-by-step process of estimating the launch cost for a particular mission. Overall, it is an iterative process of selecting launch parameters, spacecraft mass, and launch cost. We need to adjust all of these factors to achieve our mission objectives at minimum cost and risk.

TABLE 12-8. Estimating Launch Cost. Specific launch costs will depend on multiple additional factors, such as the specific vehicle selected and the negotiating leverage of the organization buying the launch. Thus, this process is more accurate at estimating relative cost than absolute cost. (SMAD = Wertz and Larson [1999].)

Step	Where Discussed
1. Establish orbit parameters	Secs. 12.1–12.5
2. Establish spacecraft mass	SMAD, Chaps. 10–11
3. Estimate Orbit Cost Function for direct ascent and onboard propulsion, if applicable	Sec. 12.3.2
4. Obtain corresponding LEO mass	Result of (2) × (3)
5. Obtain rough estimate of launch cost from specific launch costs in Table 12-3	Sec. 12.3.1
5A. For dedicated launch, select vehicle or vehicles based on LEO mass or direct injection	Sec. 12.3.1, SMAD Chap. 18, Isakowitz [1999]
6. Determine launch cost and available mass margin	See text.

We begin the launch cost estimation process by determining the orbit parameters for the mission. We then estimate the spacecraft dry mass consisting of the operational payload and the spacecraft bus exclusive of the tankage required for any propellant used in orbit transfer. Next, we establish the Orbit Cost Function based on the ΔV budget as defined in Sec. 12.2. If possible, we would like to do this for both direct ascent using the launch vehicle and for using onboard propulsion. This process allows us to compute a corresponding mass into low-Earth orbit for our particular mission. Given an amount of mass in low-Earth orbit, we can then estimate the launch cost from the specific launch cost given in Fig. 12-10 or using the costs for an appropriate vehicle or range of vehicles listed in Table 12-3. For dedicated launch, we can then do a preliminary selection of a specific vehicle or range of vehicles based upon either the mass in low-Earth orbit or direct injection. This gives us the first estimate of our launch cost and available mass margin. We then proceed to iterate the process as appropriate. For example, we may be able to reduce our mass estimates somewhat in order to obtain a smaller, lower-cost launch vehicle. Alternatively, if we have large margins, we may choose to increase the system mass in order to provide more payload or greater propellant for other mission activities.

There are a number potential error sources in estimating launch costs. First, the cost of launch is a negotiated figure based in large part on the law of supply and demand. Thus, a user with a large number of payloads may be able to negotiate a lower price in exchange for a long term contract. However, the capacity to negotiate a lower price depends on the existence of at least some level of competition within the launch vehicle arena. Thus, if the political decision is made to use only national launch vehicles, then typically the competitive environment is substantially reduced and we can expect to pay significantly more for a given launch. Commercial launches, on the other hand, are usually not constrained to use vehicles from any particular nation or organization and, therefore, are in a better position to negotiate favorable prices based strictly on performance.

In addition to price negotiation, there is also the potential for dual payload launches. For example, we may choose to use a somewhat larger vehicle with substantial launch margin, and use that launch margin to include a secondary payload, which can cover a significant fraction of the cost of the launch vehicle. Third, there are overall evolutionary trends in launch costs that will impact the price which vehicle manufacturers can charge for vehicles of a given size. The net effect of these factors is to imply that the relative costs obtained by the above process will have a higher level of accuracy than the absolute costs.

For some missions, it is also useful to run the cost estimation process "backwards." To do this, we first select a representative launch vehicle, determine the mass available in low-Earth orbit, and use the Orbit Cost Function to estimate the mass available in the final mission orbit. This is a mechanism for sizing the payload to meet the capacity of a launch vehicle that falls within the budget constraints appropriate to the mission.

A third way to use the Orbit Cost Function is to use it to determine the orbit elements that can be achieved given a launch vehicle and a spacecraft mass. Thus, given a spacecraft mass that I want to put in orbit about Mars, and a launch vehicle that is being provided, I can use the Orbit Cost Function to determine excess mass that can be used as propellant in order to reduce the transfer time and therefore the operations cost of the mission.

In general, the Orbit Cost Function provides a much easier mechanism for including launch and orbit transfer costs in system trades than the traditional approach of selecting a vehicle and making the process work within this constraint. We would like to include the mission orbit itself as a part of the system trade process and determine the impact of the mission orbit on the overall mission cost. The Orbit Cost Function is an analytic mechanism doing this.

12.4 Design of Earth-Referenced Orbits

Earth-referenced orbits are typically among the most complex in terms of mission design for two reasons. First, there are a variety of specialized orbits that are design options which need to be evaluated and assessed. Second, the orbit parameters impact a large number of requirements in varying ways, such that no one orbit is ideal for all aspects of a mission. For example, a higher orbit typically provides better coverage, but is more expensive to get to in terms of the Orbit Cost Function, has lower resolution for observations, requires more power for communications, and is in a more adverse radiation environment.

Most of the steps in the orbit design process for Earth-referenced missions are the generic ones, defined in Table 12-3. The key issues which are specific to Earth-referenced missions are the orbit-related mission requirements, specialized Earth-referenced orbits, and the potential use of eccentric orbits. These are discussed in the three subsections below.

12.4.1 Mission Requirements for Earth-Referenced Orbits

As listed previously in Table 12-1, the first step in the orbit selection process after dividing the mission into phases is to accumulate the orbit-related mission requirements. The mission requirements which normally have the greatest effect on Earth-referenced orbits are listed in Table 12-9. The principal conclusion here is that a large number of mission requirements are orbit-dependent for Earth-orbiting missions. The second most important conclusion from the table is that the orbit parameter which is most important in orbit selection is the altitude, with the secondary parameter being the inclination. Altitude is a primary determining factor in nearly all of the orbit-related mission requirements. The altitude is the primary determinant of most aspects of coverage, performance, spacecraft environment, launch cost, and even the end-of-life options available to the spacecraft. Consequently, the most common trade here is one of coverage as a measure of performance versus ΔV or *OCF* as a measure of cost. The processes for evaluating these numerically were given in Secs. 9.5 and 12.2, respectively.

TABLE 12-9. Principal Mission Requirements that Normally Affect Earth-Referenced Orbit Design. See Sec. 12.1 for a discussion of the orbit design process. (from SMAD = Wertz and Larson [1999].)

Mission Requirement	Parameter Affected	Where Discussed
Coverage Continuity Frequency Duration Field Of View (Or Swath Width) Ground Track Area Coverage Rate Viewing Angles Earth Locations Of Interest	Altitude Inclination Node (only relevant for some orbits)	Chap. 9
Sensitivity or Performance Exposure Or Dwell Time Resolution Aperture	Altitude	SMAD Chaps. 9, 13 Sec. 11.2, 11.3
Environment and Survivability Radiation Environment Lighting Conditions Hostile Action	Altitude (Inclination usually secondary)	Chap. 11, SMAD Ch. 8
Launch Capability Launch Cost On-Orbit Weight Launch Site Limitations	Altitude Inclination	Sec. 12.3, SMAD Chap. 18
Ground Communications Ground Station Locations Use Of Relay Satellites Data Timeliness	Altitude Inclination	SMAD Chap. 13
Orbit Lifetime	Altitude Eccentricity	Sec. 2.4.4
Legal or Political Constraints Treaties Launch Safety Restrictions International Allocation	Altitude Inclination Longitude in GEO	SMAD Sec. 21.1

Another key factor in altitude selection is the satellite's radiation environment. As described in Sec. 2.3, the radiation environment undergoes a dramatic change at an altitude of approximately 1,000 km. (See Fig. 12-11.) Below this altitude, the atmosphere quickly clears out charged particles such that the radiation density is relatively low. Above this altitude are the Van Allen belts, where the high level of trapped radiation can greatly reduce the lifetime of spacecraft components. Consequently, most Earth-referenced mission orbits separate naturally into *low-Earth orbit* (LEO), below 1,000 km, and *geosynchronous orbit* (GEO), which is well above the Van Allen Belts. Mid-range altitudes have coverage characteristics which may make them particularly

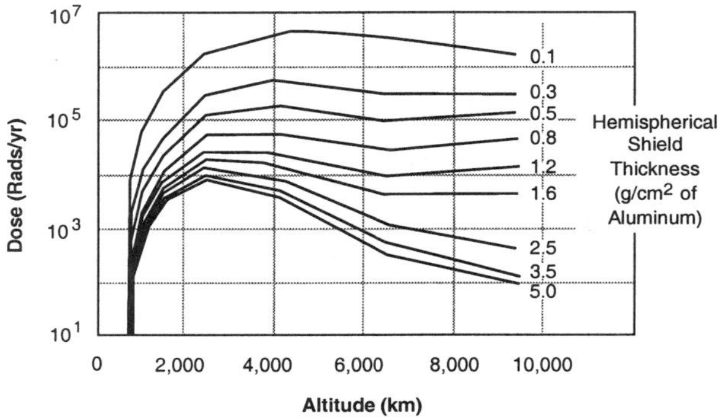

Fig. 12-11. In Practice, LEO is Defined at Below the Inner Edge of the Van Allen Radiation Belts.

valuable for some missions. However, the added shielding or reduced life stemming from this region's increased radiation environment also makes them more costly. Nonetheless, the increased coverage to be obtained at higher altitudes has tended to push up the minimum altitude defined as LEO. For example, LEO communications constellations are being considered at altitudes of up to 1,500 km. At these altitudes, not only is the radiation environment more harsh, but the potential options for end-of-life are also more difficult. Low-Earth orbit spacecraft are often de-orbited or allowed to reenter at the end of their useful life. Above 1,000 km, this process occurs extremely slowly when driven only by drag and requires a very substantial ΔV if it is to be done by an onboard propulsion system. Consequently, in the regime above 1,000 km, the end-of-life option often regarded as the most desirable is to raise the spacecraft 50 to 100 km higher in order to remove it from the constellation structure. Note however that this process creates one or more "graveyard" regimes in which a large number of spent non-functioning spacecraft will accumulate. Whether this will ultimately provide a long-term debris hazard remains to be determined.

12.4.2 Specialized Earth-Referenced Orbits

After having defined the orbit related mission requirements, the next step in finding an appropriate Earth-referenced orbit is to determine if any of the specialized orbits listed in Table 12-10 are appropriate. The advantages and disadvantages of these alternatives are summarized in Table 12-11 and discussed in more detail below. Chap. 2 provides a detailed discussion of the physical basis of each of these orbit types and will not be repeated here. Specific references are listed in Table 12-10. For purposes of mission design, we need to examine each of these specialized orbits individually to see if its characteristics will meet the mission requirements at a reasonable cost. Space missions do not need to be in specialized orbits, but these orbits have come into common use because of their valuable characteristics for many missions. Because they do constrain orbit parameters such as altitude and inclination, we first determine whether or not to use one of the specialized orbits before doing the more detailed design trades in Table 12-1.

TABLE 12-10. Specialized Orbits Used for Earth-Referenced Missions. Typically the orbit design process consists of deciding whether any of the specialized orbits should be used followed by a general trade on other orbits.* Chapter 2 references provide the physical basis for each orbit; Chap. 12 references discuss applications.

Orbit	Characteristic	Applications	Section
Geosynchronous (GEO)	Maintains nearly fixed position over equator	Communications, weather	Secs. 2.5.1, 12.4.2.1
Sun Synchronous	Orbit rotates so as to maintain approximately constant orientation with respect to Sun	Earth resources, weather	Secs. 2.5.3, 12.4.2.2
Molniya	Apogee/perigee do not rotate	High latitude communications	Secs. 2.5.4, 12.4.2.3
Frozen Orbit	Minimizes changes in orbit parameters	Any orbit requiring stable conditions	Secs. 2.5.6, 12.4.2.5
Repeating Ground Track	Subsatellite trace repeats	Any orbit where constant viewing angles are desirable	Secs. 2.5.2, 12.4.2.4

*Specialized orbits tend to divide orbit design into discrete regimes, each of which must be examined separately.

TABLE 12-11. Advantages and Disadvantages of Specialized Earth-Referenced Orbits

Orbit	Advantages	Disadvantages
Geosynchronous	Continuous viewing of one region	Poor polar region coverage, very high cost, very long range
Sun-Synchronous	Maintains roughly constant Sun angle	High cost
Molniya	Provides extended coverage of high latitude regions	High cost; widely varying ranges, Earth size, and rates drive up spacecraft cost; high radiation
Frozen Orbit	Maintains stable conditions	None
Repeating Ground Track	Coverage repeats	Orbit perturbations can resonate

It is frequently the existence of specialized orbits which yields very different solutions for a given space mission problem. Thus, a geosynchronous orbit may provide the best coverage characteristics but may demand too much propellant, instrument resolution, or power, or have too high an Orbit Cost Function. The trade of value vs. cost can lead to dramatically different solutions depending on mission needs. Thus, a Sun-synchronous orbit is typically 30% more expensive than a low-inclination prograde orbit. Nonetheless, for many observation satellites such as Earth resources or weather, the advantage of being able to see locations on the ground at the same time of day and under the same lighting conditions on a continuing basis outweighs the additional cost of this type of orbit.

12.4.2.1 Geosynchronous Orbits (GEO)

Prior to the introduction of low-Earth orbit communications constellations, geosynchronous orbit represented the single most used orbit in space. It accounted for approximately 50% of satellite launches during the early 1990s. The physical properties of geosynchronous orbit and orbit perturbations were discussed in Sec. 2.5.1; in addition, Pocha [1987] and Soop [1994] provide very detailed discussions of geosynchronous orbit design and stationkeeping approaches.

The principal applications for geosynchronous orbit are communications (both two-way and direct broadcast), weather, and Earth surveillance. However, as shown in Fig. 12-12, GEO is getting full. There are now relatively few orbital slots available over regions of particular interest, such as the mid-Atlantic or mid-Pacific areas used for communications between North America, Europe, and Japan. Similarly, slots over Europe and North America used for internal communications are also becoming full.

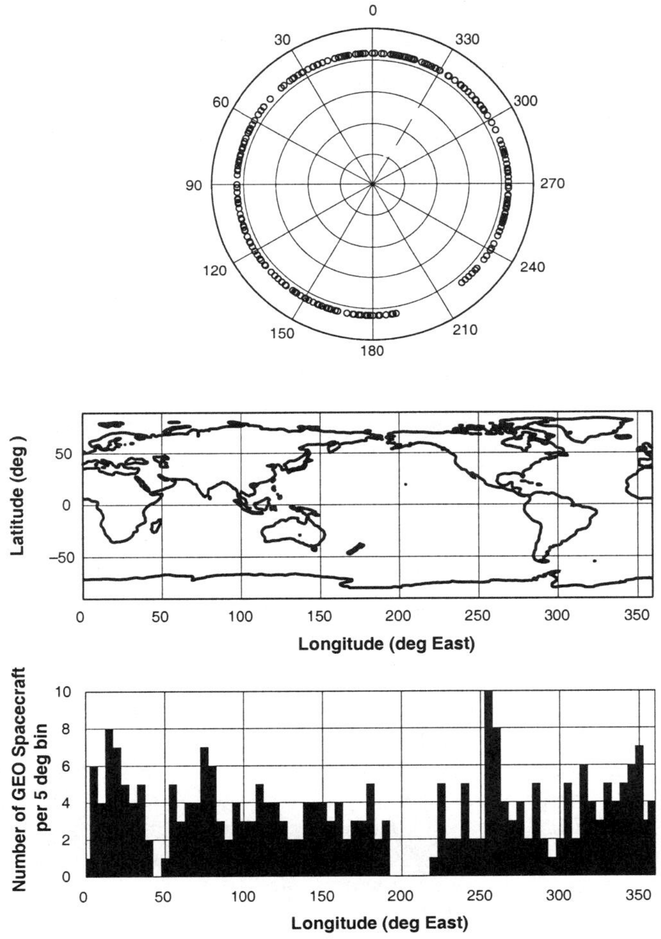

Fig. 12-12. Active Satellites in Geosynchronous Orbit as of 1/1/2000.

Overcrowding and the potential for satellite collisions represent major problems for geosynchronous orbit, as discussed in detail by Reijnen and De Graaff [1989]. In a sense, space is large and the potential for collisions between satellites is small. Nonetheless, the cost of getting spacecraft to GEO is extremely high and there is no current potential for being able to retrieve or actively recover either spent spacecraft or debris. In addition, there are essentially no natural perturbations that will remove debris from geosynchronous orbit. Consequently, any sequence of either spacecraft explosions or inadvertent collisions which produce a significant debris cloud in GEO may make the orbit effectively unusable for the foreseeable future.

Because there is currently no realistic mechanism for removing debris from GEO, the only viable mechanism for protecting it is to not allow actions which have the potential for generating debris. This means that spacecraft should be removed from geosynchronous orbit while they are still responding to commands and while there is still propellant available to do so. Thus, in order to preserve this unique resource, we must be willing to turn off operational spacecraft prior to the use of their last few grams of propellant. The "graveyard" for geosynchronous spacecraft is to put them in an orbit approximately 200 km above GEO. At this altitude, natural perturbations will cause the inclination to oscillate as discussed in Sec. 2.5.1. However, these oscillations in orbit elements will not bring the spacecraft back into the geosynchronous ring in any reasonable amount of time, i.e., within several hundred thousand years. In addition, the ΔV required to raise the altitude is extremely small. Increasing the altitude by 200 km requires a ΔV of only 7.4 m/sec.

As discussed in Sec. 2.5.1, the principal perturbative forces in GEO are solar/lunar perturbations, which cause a general North/South drift or change in inclination, and the effect of the out-of-roundness of the Earth's equator, which cause a very slow drift in the East/West direction. In both cases, the effects are extremely predictable and essentially continuous. Consequently, this represents an excellent application for electric propulsion for orbit maintenance. A nearly continuous low level of thrust can be used to maintain the spacecraft in geosynchronous orbit. Typically, the North/South stationkeeping is required for operational purposes so that the spacecraft can keep its target regime on Earth in view, and equally important, so that Earth antennas can be pointed at the spacecraft without having to be continuously steered. The East/West stationkeeping, while requiring only 10% of the ΔV of North/South stationkeeping, is perhaps more important in that it prevents either physical or communications interference with satellites in a neighboring orbital slot. Without nearly continuous East/West stationkeeping, geosynchronous satellites would continuously slide through the orbit slots assigned to other spacecraft, thus providing both significant communications interference and even the potential for satellite collisions.

Synchronous orbits are possible around other planets and satellites as well, although, like the Earth, they may be significantly influenced by various perturbations. Both the formulas to determine these orbits and the characteristics of synchronous orbits for a variety of other central bodies are listed in Table 2-11 in Sec. 2.5.1.

12.4.2.2 Sun-Synchronous Orbits

As discussed in Sec. 2.5.3, a Sun-synchronous orbit is one in which the perturbation due to the Earth's oblateness causes the orbit to rotate in inertial space at a rate equal to the average rate of the Earth's rotation about the Sun. Consequently, in a Sun-synchronous orbit, the position to the Sun relative to the orbit plane remains approximately constant. The general motion of the Sun relative to the orbit plane is shown in

Fig. 2-27 in Sec. 2.5.1. From an applications perspective, the Sun-synchronous orbit has the principal advantage of maintaining approximately constant Sun angles. This means that for Earth resources satellites, for example, the angle of illumination will be approximately constant as photographs of a given region are taken over time. Consequently, it is significantly easier to interpret the photos and look for changes over time.

Sun-synchronous orbits have also been used by some missions as a means of eliminating a second gimbal in the solar array drive. Thus, rather than requiring a 2-axis gimbal, a single-axis gimbal is sufficient and the cost of the spacecraft can be marginally reduced. This is an example of an application of the Sun-synchronous orbit which is probably inappropriate in most circumstances. The Sun-synchronous orbit requires an additional cost of approximately 30% to obtain this orbit. This cost is far in excess of the benefit achieved by having only a single gimbal in the solar array drive. In addition, it also adds an additional element of risk to the mission by creating a new failure mode. If the launch vehicle or propulsion system are unable to achieve or to maintain a Sun-synchronous orbit, then a failure of the mission is possible. If the system could operate under non-Sun-synchronous conditions, then there would have been no reason for the orbit in the first place. Consequently, choosing a Sun-synchronous orbit for purely spacecraft bus functions is an incorrect engineering choice in most circumstances.

Sun-synchronous orbits are also possible around other central bodies. Representative parameters for these orbits are given in Table 12-12. The advantages of these orbits are similar to their advantages when used on the Earth. That is, a constant level of illumination allows us to compare photographs taken at different times in order to more accurately determine physical changes which may be taking place on the planet or moon that we are orbiting. For example, Sun-synchronous orbits would be appropriate for examining seasonal variations on Mars, or variations as a function of volcanic activity or electromagnetic storms in the vicinity of Jupiter's moon, Io. Note that in the case of other planets and satellites, Sun-synchronous orbits are significantly less expensive to achieve. Generally, the orbit plane in which the spacecraft arrives can be adjusted by very small ΔVs applied during the orbit transfer. Consequently, the high cost associated with Sun-synchronous orbits on the Earth is not necessarily a problem for other central bodies. However, the parameters associated with Sun-synchronous orbits for other central bodies, such as the required altitude or inclination may make them inappropriate for other reasons, such as viewing distance or excessive perturbations.

TABLE 12-12. Representative Sun-Synchronous Orbits for Other Central Bodies.

Central Body	Altitude (km)	Inclination (deg)	Period (min)
Mars	1,000 5,000	94.85 144.52	147.2 388.4
Jupiter	1,000 5,000	90.08 90.09	181.5 196.7
Saturn	1,000 5,000	90.04 90.05	257.8 283.5
Uranus	1,000 5,000	90.01 90.02	183.3 232.4
Neptune	1,000 5,000	90.02 90.04	166.0 206.1

12.4.2.3 Molniya Orbits

A *Molniya orbit* is a highly elliptical orbit inclined at the critical inclination of 63.4 deg (or 180 – 63.4 = 116.6 deg) in order to prevent apogee and perigee from rotating. The fundamental equations and physical properties for Molniya orbits were discussed in Sec. 2.5.4. The basic application of these orbits is for communications or observations at high northern latitudes where geosynchronous spacecraft are ineffective or inaccessible. Consequently, Molniya orbits have been used for communications in Russia and the former Soviet Union for an extended period of time.

The properties of Molniya orbits for the Earth are summarized in Table 12-13 and the orbit ground track is shown in Fig. 12-13. Note that there are tick marks along the orbit at equal time intervals which clearly illustrates the long period of time that the spacecraft remains over high northern latitudes. Because each of the satellites tends to

TABLE 12-13. Properties of Representative Molniya Orbits.

Period Hours	Eccentricity	Apogee Height (km)	Perigee Height (km)	Fraction of Orbit with 90° < True Anomaly < 270°	Fraction of Orbit with 120° < True Anomaly < 240°
2	0.1722	3,076	300	80.45%	71.72%
6	0.6020	20,485	300	92.93%	86.81%
12	0.7493	40,178	300	96.38%	92.46%
24	0.8421	71,440	300	98.16%	95.87%
36	0.8795	97,661	300	98.77%	97.14%
48	0.9005	121,065	300	99.07%	97.81%
72	0.9241	162,688	300	99.38%	98.50%

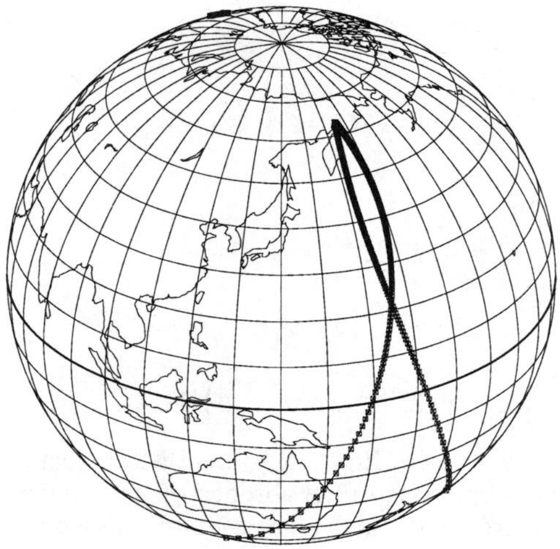

Fig. 12-13. A Molniya Orbit with a 12-Hour Period. With two satellites in this orbit, one of them will always be within 24 deg of apogee in true anomaly and with three satellites one will always be within 15 deg.

"hang" at apogee, it is straightforward to use two or three satellites in orbits of this type to provide good coverage of far northern or far southern regimes. Unfortunately, there are a number of disadvantages of the Molniya orbit, such as the non-stationary ground track with respect to the Earth, and the fact that it travels through the Van Allen radiation belts on a continuing basis, and consequently has a severe radiation environment. Nonetheless, the Molniya orbit provides the only realistic mechanism for providing extended coverage in high latitude regions, and therefore, is appropriate for any type of communication, observation, or sampling system that requires coverage of this type.

The period and eccentricity of the Molniya orbit depend on the gravitational parameters of the Earth. The fact that it is at the critical inclination of 63.4 deg, however, does not depend on any parameters of the Earth and is a function of the spherical harmonic expansion (i.e., an effect of the relative importance of larger gravitational effects at the equator and lower effects at the pole). Consequently, Molniya orbits about any of the other planets or satellites will always be at an inclination of 63.4 deg relative to the equator of that central body. Thus we might choose a Molniya-style orbit for monitoring the polar regions of Mars or providing communications or observations for scientific activities at the poles and the Moon.

12.4.2.4 Repeating Ground Track

A repeating ground track is simply an orbit in which the ground trace of the satellite will repeat itself after one or more days. This is extremely convenient for Earth observations and communications in that the general characteristics of the flight path with respect to a ground target or observer on the ground is a repeating pattern. Recall from Sec. 2.5.2 that a repeating ground track comes about when we go through an integral number of orbits in a sidereal day, taking into account the orbit rotation due to the oblateness of the Earth. Consequently, the fundamental requirement for a repeating ground track is:

$$H = \mu^{1/3}\left(\frac{n\pi}{180}\right)^{-2/3} - R \tag{12-4}$$

$$n = (j / k)\left(360 - \dot{\Omega}\right) - \left(\dot{\omega} + \dot{M}\right) \tag{12-5}$$

where

$$\dot{\Omega} = -2K_2 a^{-7/2} \cos i \left(1 - e^2\right)^{-2} \tag{12-6}$$

$$\dot{\omega} = K_2 a^{-7/2}\left(5\cos^2 i - 1\right)\left(1 - e^2\right)^{-2} \tag{12-7}$$

$$\dot{M} = K_2 a^{-7/2}\left(3\cos^2 i - 1\right)\left(1 - e^2\right)^{-3/2} \tag{12-8}$$

where the initial estimate of a for Eqs. (12-6) to (12-8) is just the repeating ground track value of the semimajor axis in the absence of the oblateness correction, i.e., $a_{initial} = K_1(j/k)^{-2/3}$, where j and k are integers. As discussed in Sec. 2.5.2, $\dot{\Omega}$ is the node rotation rate, $\dot{\omega}$ is the argument of perigee rotation rate, and $\dot{M}$ is the mean anomaly rotation rate due to oblateness. As usual, the parameters, a, e, and i are the semimajor axis, eccentricity, and inclination of the repeating ground track orbit and R is the radius of the central body. Values of K_1 and K_2 for various objects in the solar system are given in Table 12-14. (See Sec. 2.5.2 for the formulas for these constants.) Note that with the constants in the table, the rotation rates are all expressed in deg/sidereal day ≡ deg/day*, where "sidereal day" is the rotation period **of the body the satellite is orbiting about** relative to the fixed stars. The satellite completes j orbits in k sidereal days.

TABLE 12-14. Repeating Ground Track Parameters for Representative Central Bodies.

Body	Radius, R (km)	Day* (sec)	μ (km^3/sid day^2)	K_1 (km)	K_2 ($km^{3.5}$/sid day)
Moon	1,738	$2.360\,591 \times 10^6$	$2.732\,032 \times 10^{16}$	$8.023\,799 \times 10^5$	$7.590\,274 \times 10^{10}$
Mercury	2,439	$5.067\,032 \times 10^6$	$5.656\,674 \times 10^{17}$	$3.666\,292 \times 10^6$	$2.013\,338 \times 10^{11}$
Venus	6,052	$2.099\,606 \times 10^7$	$1.435\,799 \times 10^{20}$	$5.988\,628 \times 10^7$	$8.887\,296 \times 10^{12}$
Mars	3,397.2	$8.864\,266 \times 10^4$	$3.382\,663 \times 10^{14}$	$2.081\,545 \times 10^4$	$3.126\,615 \times 10^{11}$
Jupiter	71,492	$3.572\,986 \times 10^4$	$1.618\,757 \times 10^{17}$	$8.884\,214 \times 10^4$	$2.274\,883 \times 10^{16}$
Saturn	60,268	$3.780\,000 \times 10^4$	$5.421\,019 \times 10^{16}$	$6.405\,589 \times 10^4$	$1.043\,377 \times 10^{16}$
Uranus	25,559	$5.616\,000 \times 10^4$	$1.827\,396 \times 10^{16}$	$5.804\,523 \times 10^4$	$7.947\,793 \times 10^{14}$
Neptune	24,764	$6.635\,520 \times 10^4$	$2.998\,011 \times 10^{16}$	$7.651\,243 \times 10^4$	$3.185\,514 \times 10^{14}$
Pluto	1,151	$5.518\,109 \times 10^5$	$2.740\,457 \times 10^{14}$	$6.566\,573 \times 10^4$	N/A
Phobos	11.3	$2.755\,384 \times 10^4$	$5.385\,410 \times 10^5$	$1.115\,318 \times 10^1$	N/A
Deimos	6.3	$1.090\,749 \times 10^5$	$1.889\,503 \times 10^6$	$4.241\,016 \times 10^1$	N/A
Io	1,821.3	$1.528\,535 \times 10^5$	$1.392\,519 \times 10^{14}$	$2.226\,665 \times 10^4$	N/A
Europa	1,565	$3.068\,220 \times 10^5$	$3.015\,221 \times 10^{14}$	$4.583\,899 \times 10^4$	N/A

The principal merit of a repeating ground track is that we continue to sample the same region of the planet's surface on a repeating basis. This is useful, for example, in planet observations where I'm interested in determining changes from one time to the next. This can be particularly important for evaluating changes in vegetation, water levels, pollution parameters, population growth, or deforestation. The principal demerit of a repeating ground track orbit is that it also flies through the variations in the planet's geopotential in the same fashion on successive orbits. Thus, if I fly just to the left of the Himalayas on one day, I will do so on successive days as well. This allows the potential of resonance effects to build up, comparable to vibrations in a physical structure, which can greatly magnify the impact of the perturbations and cause significant larger variations in the motion of the satellite. Consequently, a repeating ground track should be chosen only if there is an operational reason to do so, since it may require significant propellant utilization to counter the cumulative perturbative forces.

For the Earth, an interesting subgroup of the repeating ground track orbits are those for which the inclination, and therefore node rotation rate, is adjusted so that the repeat occurs on precise multiples of the civil day of 24 hours. For these orbits, the ground track not only repeats but does so at the same time each day, every other day, or on a weekly basis, depending on the orbit parameters chosen. I call an orbit of this type a *civil orbit* because it is one in which the spacecraft is keeping time with civil functions, rather than requiring the many users on the ground to keep track of a spacecraft ephemeris. Thus, for example, for relaying data to the home office, we could catch the "5:10 to London" on a daily basis such that we could transmit data at the same time each day and have it received at a fixed, later time.

12.4.2.5 Frozen Orbits

As discussed in Sec. 2.5.6, frozen orbits come about because circular orbits are not inherently stable. On the other hand, stable or frozen orbits are available with very low values of eccentricity, such that they are nearly circular for most practical applications. Frozen orbits can be used with essentially any low-Earth orbit and are largely used as a means of maintaining a more precise orbit and reducing the propellant requirements for orbit maintenance. For applications in which a circular orbit is desirable, a frozen orbit will somewhat reduce the propellant utilization and has no significant drawbacks. For additional details on creating a frozen orbit, see for example Vallado [2001].

12.4.3 Eccentric Orbits for Earth Coverage

Eccentric orbits can be thought of in either of 2 ways: On the one hand, they add a level of complexity that increases the design cost of the spacecraft and the mission by requiring the spacecraft to work at multiple altitudes and at differing rotation rates if one side is to remain facing the Earth. On the other hand, eccentricity adds a degree of freedom in the design that can be used to adjust the orbit to best meet specific mission needs. Eccentric orbits can be used to minimize the number of satellites, maximize the coverage with respect to areas of interest, or combinations of these purposes. The use of eccentric orbits has been studied at length by Draim [1997, 1998], who has made an extremely strong case for using eccentric orbits to achieve maximum mission performance with a minimum number of satellites [Draim, 1999].

For any specific mission, the question becomes whether this additional level of performance is worth the increased cost and complexity of the spacecraft and mission parameters. As shown in Fig. 12-14, one of the most interesting examples of the use of eccentric orbits is using only 4 spacecraft to provide complete, continuous coverage of the surface of the Earth.* Another interesting example is the proposed, but not built

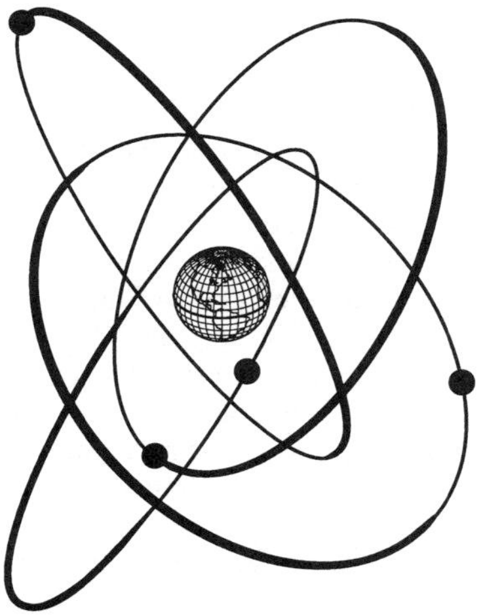

Fig. 12-14. Total Coverage of the Earth can be Obtained with Only 4 Satellite in Eccentric Orbits. Note, however, that the varying altitude may complicate the spacecraft design [Draim, 1985, 1987a, 1987b].

* This orbit has been patented by Draim, 1987a.

Ellipso communications constellation which uses eccentric orbits in combination with a supplemental equatorial orbit in order to optimize a low-Earth orbit communications system with only 18 operational satellites as shown in Fig. 13-8 in Sec. 13.2. As in the case of Molniya orbits, virtually all satellites in elliptical orbits will need to be at the critical inclination of 63.4 deg in order to prevent the line of apsides from rotating. Since this rotation rate can be up to 14 deg per day, it is important to maintain the critical inclination with good precision in order to maintain apogee and perigee over an extended mission life. This implies that orbit maintenance will typically be necessary for satellites in long term elliptical orbits. However, the ΔV requirements to maintain these parameters are very modest.

12.5 Design of Near-Earth Space-Referenced Orbits

In a space-referenced orbit, our objective is typically to be in space for manufacturing, low-gravity or high-vacuum experiments, or to observe celestial objects from above the Earth's atmosphere. These orbits are used by celestial observatories such as Space Telescope, Chandra, or SIRTF. In these orbits we typically have only a minimal concern with our orientation relative to the Earth. Consequently, we select such orbits to use minimum energy, while maintaining the orbit altitude and possibly to gain an unobstructed view of whatever celestial objects we may be observing. As listed in Table 12-15, the mission requirements that normally affect the design of such orbits tend to be less stringent than for Earth-referenced orbits. We are looking for a reasonable environment, easy accessibility, and good communications, all of which can be satisfied by a wide range of orbits. Consequently, the orbit design process is typically much more straightforward than it is for Earth-referenced orbits. Of course, some space-referenced mission orbits are designed specifically to sample space, such as magnetic field or solar wind explorers. In these cases, the orbit design is chosen to sample the region of interest on a schedule appropriate to the science return.

TABLE 12-15. Principal Requirements that Normally Affect the Design of Space-Referenced Orbits. Typically none of the requirements is as stringent as for Earth-referenced orbits.

Requirement	Where Discussed
Accessibility (ΔV or *OCF*)	Sec. 12.2
Orbit decay rate and long term stability	Sec. 2.4.4
Ground station communications, especially for maneuvers	Sec. 9.4
Radiation environment	Sec. 12.3
Thermal environment (Sun angle and eclipse constraints)	Secs. 6.3.3, 11.2
Accessibility by Shuttle or transfer vehicles	Sec. 12.1

As listed in Table 12-16, there are a few specialized space-referenced orbits that need to be considered in much the same fashion as specialized Earth-referenced orbits. The Sun-synchronous orbit was discussed previously in Sec. 12.4. This type of orbit may be appropriate for maintaining a constant Sun angle with respect to a satellite instrument such as an orbiting solar observatory.

TABLE 12-16. Specialized Space-Referenced Orbits.

Orbit	Characteristic	Application	Where Discussed
Sun-Synchronous	Orbit rotates so as to maintain approximately constant position with respect to Sun	Solar observations; Missions concerned about Sun interference or uniform lighting	Secs. 2.5.3, 12.4.2.2
Lagrange Point Orbit	Maintains fixed position relative to Earth/Moon system or Earth/Sun system	Interplanetary monitoring; potential space manufacturing	Secs. 2.5.5, 12.5
Statite	Solar radiation pressure balances gravity	Interplanetary monitoring and communications	[Forward, 1989]

An intriguing space-referenced orbit is the *statite*, designed and patented by Forward [1989]. The statite is not an orbit in the usual sense, since it uses solar radiation pressure to balance the Earth's gravitational force to maintain a spacecraft in an approximately fixed position relative to the Earth and the Sun. Such a spacecraft would have a rather remarkably large area to mass ratio and would be a substantial distance away from the Earth's gravitational field. Nonetheless, like nearly all specialized orbits, there are potential applications such as monitoring solar activity.

Perhaps the most interesting and most widely used of the space-referenced orbits are the Lagrange point orbits, described in Sec. 2.5.5. These are orbits which use the gravitational attraction of two orbiting bodies such as the Earth and the Moon or the Earth and the Sun to maintain the spacecraft in a constant orientation relative to the two bodies. The locations of Lagrange point orbits are shown in Fig. 12-15 and Fig. 2-29 in Sec. 2.5.5. Because of their long-term stability, these orbits have a wide variety of potential applications as summarized in Table 12-17.

Recall from Sec. 2.5.5 that the L_4 and L_5 Lagrange points are stable, such that objects orbiting these points will remain there indefinitely. In contrast, L_1, L_2, and L_3 are unstable equilibrium points such that an object placed there will ultimately drift away. However, it takes a relatively small amount of propellant to maintain a spacecraft in a *halo orbit* about one of the Lagrange points. In any case, the halo orbit is necessary in most cases in order to provide communications. For example, a spacecraft at the L_2 Lagrange point on the far side of the Moon will be useful for communications with any lunar far side stations but would need to be in a halo orbit in order to provide line of sight communications back to the Earth. Similarly, solar monitoring stations have been maintained for extended periods at the Earth-Sun L_1 Lagrange point in order to provide advance warning for solar storms. Again the halo orbit is required in order to keep the spacecraft away from a direct line with the Sun, which would prevent communications with the spacecraft due to the high level of radio noise from the solar disk.

The long term stability of the Earth-Moon L_4 and L_5 Lagrange points make these an ideal location for very large space colonies or space manufacturing facilities. Because they are at the distance of the Moon, the gravity-gradient forces will be extremely small such that a very large region of extremely low microgravity is possible. In addition, massive facilities are possible there, because no ΔV is necessary to maintain the orbit and there is no drag to provide orbit decay, as will occur for the Space Station. Material for constructing a large facility at the L_4 and L_5 Lagrange points can

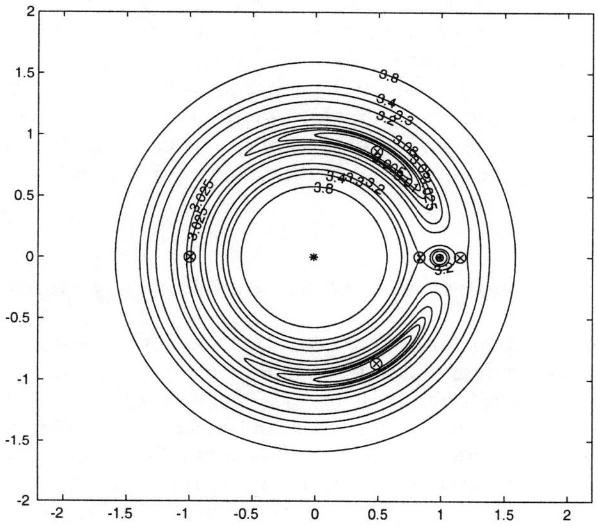

Fig. 12-15. Lagrange Point Orbits. These orbits are stable with respect to the 2-body system they are part of and are convenient locations for observations, communications, and manufacturing. (See also Fig. 2-29.)

TABLE 12-17. Potential Applications of Lagrange Point Orbits. E-S = Earth-Sun, E-M = Earth-Moon, H = Halo orbit

Lagrange Point	Application
E-M L_4, L_5	Space Manufacturing
E-M L_4, L_5	Space Observatory
E-M L_4, L_5	Lunar Communications
E-M L_4, L_5	Large Space Colonies
E-M L_2 H	Lunar Far Side Communications
E-S L_1 H	Monitoring solar activity
E-S L_3 H	Observing events not visible from Earth

be brought at relatively low ΔV cost from the surface of the Moon. The extensive work by O'Neill* and his colleages in the 1960s and 1970s has clearly established the feasibility and potential utility of large colonies at these locations. [Heppenheimer, 1977; O'Neill, 1976; O'Leary, 1982; Faughnam et. al, 1987]. Unfortunately, the continuing high cost of launch has prevented any of these from advancing beyond the mission study phase.

---

* O'Neill originated the concept as part of his undergraduate physics classes at Princeton in 1969. After several years working on technical details, he first published the concept of colonizing space itself (at L_4 or L_5), rather than a planetary surface, in the journal *Physics Today* in Sept., 1974 [O'Neill, 1974]. Substantial public enthusiasm led to the creation of the L-5 Society in 1975. In 1987 the L-5 Society merged with the National Space Institute to form the National Space Society.

Lagrange point orbits are also possible with respect to other pairs of celestial bodies. For example, spacecraft at the L_4 or L_5 Lagrange point with respect to Jupiter or the Sun could be used for monitoring the asteroid belt, Similarly, a Lagrange point orbit between any of the major planets and their larger moons could be used as a stable orientation with which to observe that planetary system. Thus, long-term stable (or nearly stable) observation platforms could be created at any of several of the Lagrange points within the systems of Jupiter, Saturn, Uranus, or Neptune.

12.6 Design of Transfer and Parking Orbits

Typically, the *parking orbit*, or *storage orbit*, is a low-Earth orbit high enough to reduce atmospheric drag, but low enough to be easy to reach. We may store satellites in these orbits, referred to as *on-orbit spares*, for later transfer to a higher altitude, or may use them as a place for test and check-out following launch or waiting for the appropriate transfer conditions to occur. Consequently, the principal issues for parking orbits are accessibility and matching the orbit conditions on either end to what is needed. For example, a Mars probe may be launched into low-Earth orbit for test and check-out while awaiting the appropriate opportunity to begin the Mars transfer phase.

The fundamental purpose of a *transfer orbit* is to get the spacecraft where it wants to be, when it wants to be there. Ordinarily, the design process is straightforward, and we'll want to do this with a minimum cost in terms of ΔV or propellant utilization. The physics of transfer orbits and the equations that govern them were described in Sec. 2.6.1. The principal requirements that normally affect the design of transfer orbits are shown in Table 12-18. As with space-referenced orbits, these are typically less stringent requirements than for Earth-referenced orbits, although there is often a requirement to match the desired end conditions with high precision in order to minimize the propellant cost of any corrective ΔV.

TABLE 12-18. Principal Requirements that Normally Affect the Design of Transfer Orbits. Typically none of the requirements is as stringent as for Earth-referenced orbits.

Requirement	Where Discussed
Transfer ΔV	Sec. 12.2
Transfer Time	Sec. 2.6
Departure and Arrival Conditions	Sec. 2.6.1
Ground Station Communications, Especially for Maneuvers	Sec. 9.4
Radiation Environment	Sec. 12.3
Thermal Environment (Sun Angle and Eclipse Constraints)	Secs. 6.3.3, 11.4
Required Navigation and Control Accuracy	Sec. 2.7

A further requirement that can arise in manned flight is for orbit transfer options that are "forgiving." For example, the Apollo program used a *free return trajectory* such that if the burn required to go into lunar orbit did not occur on the backside of the Moon, then the spacecraft would return to the Earth with no further ΔV. This was critical for the successful rescue of Apollo 13, in which the propulsion system in the command module was effectively destroyed by an explosion and the free return was necessary in order to bring the astronauts back to the vicinity of the Earth such that the lunar module propulsion system could be used to provide the appropriate deorbit ΔV for recovery of the astronauts.

Similarly, in anticipated manned Mars missions, there is a high premium for reducing the transfer time because of the high cost of maintaining people in orbit for extended periods. In addition, in any manned planetary mission, we need to plan the transfer time such that a return to Earth can be achieved in an appropriate time. Both of these requirements lead to somewhat higher energy transfers for manned flight than the traditional Hohmann transfer.

As shown in Table 12-19, there are specialized transfer orbits that are available to the mission designer. The physics of these transfers were discussed in Chap. 2. For each of the specialized transfer orbits, the fundamental objective is to reduce the ΔV required to achieve a particular set of mission objectives. Lunar or planetary flybys, for example, are used to provide additional energy by providing an effective elastic collision between the spacecraft and some other celestial object. Aeroassist trajectories are used principally to provide either a plane change or braking, as in the case of the Mars orbiter program.

TABLE 12-19. Specialized Transfer Orbits.

Orbit	Characteristic	Application	Section
Lunar or Planetary Fly-By	Same relative velocity approaching and leaving flyby body	Used to provide energy change or plane change	2.6.3
Aeroassisst Orbit	Use atmosphere for plane change or braking	Used for major energy savings for plane change or reentry	2.6.2
3-Burn Transfer (= bi-elliptic transfer)	Go to altitude above final orbit to reduce plane change ΔV	Reduce total ΔV for orbits with large plane change	2.6.2, 12.6

As was discussed in Sec. 2.6.2, the ΔV required for simultaneous plane changing and orbit raising can be reduced by combining these maneuvers such that the total ΔV is the vector sum rather than the linear sum of the individual maneuvers. However, in cases where the plane change is extremely large, this ΔV can be further reduced by using a 3-burn transfer, in which the spacecraft is first raised to an altitude significantly higher than the final orbit altitude. At extremely high altitude, the velocity will be very low and consequently a plane change can be done with very small ΔV. Thus the plane change is accomplished at the high altitude and the orbit is then returned to the final altitude. Similar to the 3-burn transfer, Belbruno, et al. [1991], has evaluated and patented several trajectories which make use of the Moon to further reduce the ΔV required for plane change maneuvers. The principal demerit of this approach is that it requires a fairly extended time for the maneuver, although substantial ΔV savings are possible in the case of large plane changes. The principal advantages and disadvantages of alternative plane change mechanisms are given in Table 12-20.

The various alternatives for direct orbit transfers have been described in detail in Sec. 2.6.1 (see specifically Fig. 2-32 and Table 2-16). Table 12-21 lists the relative advantages and disadvantages of using these alternative transfer methods and the principal applications to which they apply. High-energy direct transfers are useful principally when the transfer time is critical, as in manned flight or some military missions.

TABLE 12-20. Alternative Plane Change Mechanisms. See Table 12-17 for physical mechanisms and computations.

Orbit	Advantages	Disadvantages	Typical Application
Do ΔV at lowest velocity (highest altitude)	Smallest velocity is easiest to change	Altitude variation may be small	Orbit transfer
Combine ΔV with orbit raising	Vector sum is less than sum of components	Works best when large in-track ΔV is required	Orbit transfer
3-burn transfer	Plane change can occur at essentially no ΔV cost	Requires going to a higher altitude and then returning	Large plane change with moderate to high altitude final orbit
Use differential node rotation	No propellant cost	Time delay	Storage of satellites in a parking orbit
Aero-assist trajectories	No propellant cost	Requires precision maneuver and aerodynamic surfaces; may be heating	Planetary exploration
Planetary fly-by	No propellant cost	Requires planetary swing-by and typically long delays	Out of ecliptic mission (using Jupiter)

TABLE 12-21. Characteristics of the Alternative Direct Transfer Orbits Shown in Fig. 2-32 in Sec. 2.6.1. See Table 2-16 for transfer characteristics.

Type	Typical Accel.	Orbit Shape	Advantages	Disadvantages	Applications
High Energy	10g	Elliptical & hyperbolic	Rapid transfer	Uses more energy than necessary + Hohmann disadvantages	Manned flight, military intercept
Minimum Energy, High Thrust (Hohmann)	1 to 5g	Hohmann transfer	Traditional High efficiency Rapid transfer Low radiation exposure	Rough environment Thermal problems Can't use S/C subsystems	Used for nearly all orbit transfers
Low Thrust Chemical	0.02 to 0.10g	Hohmann transfer segments	High efficiency Low engine weight Low orbit deployment & check-out Better failure recovery Can use spacecraft subsystems	Moderate radiation exposure 3 to 4 day transfer to GEO	Use when needed to reduce cost, weight, risk, or disturbances
Electric Propulsion	0.0001 to 0.001g	Spiral transfer	Can use very high I_{sp} engines = major weight reduction Low orbit deployment & check-out Can have reusable transfer vehicle	2 to 6 month transfer to GEO High radiation exposure Needs autonomous transfer for cost efficiency	Rarely used. Has been proposed for GEO and interplanetary transfer

Typically, the ΔV penalty associated with high-energy transfer is small for minor increases in transfer time, but becomes very large for any major reduction in transfer time, such that very short transfers are prohibitively expensive in terms of ΔV. The other alternatives of successive burns using low-thrust chemical or a spiral transfer using electric propulsion both take significantly longer than the Hohmann transfer and are of use principally when transfer time is not a major constraint. The low thrust chemical transfer offers the significant advantage of providing a much more benign environment for the spacecraft, since the principal disturbance forces and maximum loads frequently occur during orbit transfer. In addition, low thrust transfer allows the spacecraft to be fully deployed prior to transfer, such that it can be tested and checked out before being put in a totally inaccessible orbit. Electric propulsion transfer has the merit of extremely high efficiency but can take a very long time. Consequently, electric propulsion is an extremely efficient approach for orbit maintenance but has not yet been widely used for orbit transfer.

In the design of orbit transfer, it is important to keep in mind the distinction between the basic requirements for launch vehicles and the requirements for in-orbit transfer. In launch vehicle design, high thrust is absolutely imperative in order to get to space as quickly as possible and minimize gravity losses which occur when thrusting is not done at right angles to the central body. In a number of launch attempts in the early space program, the thrust to weight ratio was very close to 1, such that the launch vehicle lifted a short distance off the pad, burned all of its propellant, held itself in the air, and crashed as soon as the propellant supply was consumed. Thus, a driving characteristic for launch vehicles is the need for a high thrust system.

In contrast, once we have gotten into space, high thrust is no longer important and can be a major detriment to an in-orbit transfer system. A high thrust transfer stage frequently imparts the largest loads the spacecraft will ever see. Thus it has a strong potential for damaging the spacecraft. In addition, in any high thrust system, performance is critical and all maneuvers must be done with precision both in terms of the maneuver itself and the timing of the maneuver. Typically, any failures of high thrust transfer will lead directly to mission failure. Similarly, because the forces are extremely large, high thrust orbit transfer stages need their own separate control system to control the very large disturbance torques that are generated. Consequently, the transfer stage is nearly a separate spacecraft with a very large propulsion and control system. However, in the on-orbit environment, much of this performance is either wasted or detrimental. An onboard propulsion system, for example, can provide the ΔV appropriate to orbit transfer but do so at much lower thrust levels. For most orbit transfers, the time required for the burn is small relative to the transfer time and is unimportant in successfully completing the maneuver. If the orbit transfer is done by a sequence of low thrust burns, then individual burns become far less critical and an error or misfire on one burn may be able to be corrected on subsequent burns. Consequently, low thrust orbit transfer tends to be significantly more fail-safe than high thrust transfer. In addition, the disturbance torques imparted by a low thrust system are far less, such that it may be possible to control the transfer using the control system already on board the spacecraft itself. This can significantly reduce the amount of ancillary equipment that needs to be flown, thus reducing both the weight and cost of the mission. As described at the end of Sec. 12.2, the use of onboard propulsion can have a dramatic impact on the mass available in the mission orbit, or, alternatively, on the launch cost because the entire mass of the transfer stage doesn't need to be sent all the way to the mission orbit.

The important point here is to make a clear distinction between the requirements for launch and the requirements for orbit transfer once we have achieved low-Earth orbit. These frequently are regarded as nearly the same process because they are often assigned to a single organization which has the responsibility for putting the spacecraft in its final mission orbit. While this has some possible organizational advantages, it typically provides a system which is less robust, higher risk, more expensive, and lower performing than would be the case using a low thrust system once we have achieved orbit. The critical issue here is to regard in-orbit transfer not as simply an extension of the launch process, but as a separate mission phase. As always, we want to achieve the overall mission objectives at minimum cost and risk. In many cases, we may be able to substantially reduce both cost and risk by making use of straightforward, low-cost, low-thrust technology for in-orbit transfer.

12.7 Design of Interplanetary Orbits

Hans F. Meissinger, *Microcosm, Inc.*

The selection and design of ballistic interplanetary mission trajectories have some aspects in common with Earth orbital missions, namely the use of classical Keplerian two-body orbit dynamics around a central gravity field (see Chap. 2), except that successive mission phases involve different central bodies, such as first the Earth, then the Sun, and finally, a target planet such as Jupiter. The alternative of using non-Keplerian interplanetary trajectories will be briefly discussed later in this section.

The transition between the motion within essentially one central force field, e.g., the initial geocentric motion, the subsequent heliocentric motion, and finally, the planetocentric orbit at destination, must be taken into account for a more precise trajectory definition. However, the very short transition phases have only a secondary influence on the overall trajectory design, typically involving few days in a mission that spends many hundreds of days in heliocentric space. A key parameter here is the *sphere of influence* of the planets in question which is the region in which the gravitational attraction of the planet is greater than that of the Sun. In the spacecraft-Earth-Sun orbit mechanics applying during the departure phase the radius of the Earth's sphere-of-influence, of the order of 0.9 million km, as discussed by Wiesel [1998], is the parameter of principal concern.

For preliminary trajectory design purposes it often is sufficiently accurate to use the *patched conic approximation*, as discussed by Bate et al. [1971], Prussing and Conway [1993], Vallado [2001], and others. This technique consists of determining the planetocentric hyperbolic excess velocities at the departure and arrival planets, in the above example those at Earth and Jupiter, that match the heliocentric departure and arrival velocities, respectively, both in direction and magnitude, while the brief transition phases at departure and arrival are ignored. Computation of precision orbits is a trial-and-error procedure that involves numerical integration of the complete equations of motion in which all perturbation effects are included.

Principal mission objectives lead to the selection of specific trajectory characteristics, mission durations, preferred launch dates, and the choice of flyby, atmospheric entry, orbiting or landing at the target. Other factors of concern in this process are the past exploration history and known characteristics of the target, the available (or projected) technology level required to perform the mission, and any scientific and operational priorities. Budget constraints generally are dominant. Trades between desired and achievable mission objectives generally involve a wide range of alternatives in mission specifications and are an essential part of the mission definition process.

Appendix D.4 lists principal orbit parameters and physical characteristics of the planets from Mercury, with a semimajor axis of 0.390 Astronomical Units (AU), to Pluto, with a semimajor axis of 39.5 AU, about one hundred times farther from the Sun than Mercury. (1 AU ≅ 150 million km is the semimajor axis of the Earth's orbit). Both of these planets have significant orbital eccentricities of 0.206 and 0.249, respectively, and inclinations relative to the ecliptic plane whereas all other planets move in nearly circular orbits, and very nearly in the ecliptic.

Planetary exploration, starting in the 1960s with visits to Mars and Venus, has since included flyby or orbiter missions to the other planets as well, except Pluto to which a mission is projected in the early 2000s. Launch energy requirements to reach the planets, especially Mercury at its close solar distance, and the outer planets, i.e., Jupiter and beyond, are extremely high (see below). To reduce the required energy planetary gravity assist is often applied, as will be discussed later in this section (see also Sec. 2.6.3).

In the exploration of Jupiter and other outer planets, the first missions were flyby missions, like Pioneer 10 and 11, launched in 1972 and 1973, and Voyager 1 and 2, launched in 1977. The Voyager missions (also known as "Grand Tour Missions") included successive flybys of Jupiter, Saturn, Uranus and Neptune (see Fig, 12-16). All four of these deep-space probes ultimately left the solar system after passing the orbit of Pluto, traveling at hyperbolic velocities relative to the sun. In this final phase of moving through the *heliosphere* in four different directions they have been used to gather astrophysical data on particles and fields, and other phenomena. Ultimately, it is of considerable interest to find the *heliopause*, where galactic influences begin to dominate, a range assumed to be of the order of 100 astronomical units (AU), depending on each vehicle's direction of travel relative to the Sun's own motion within the galaxy.

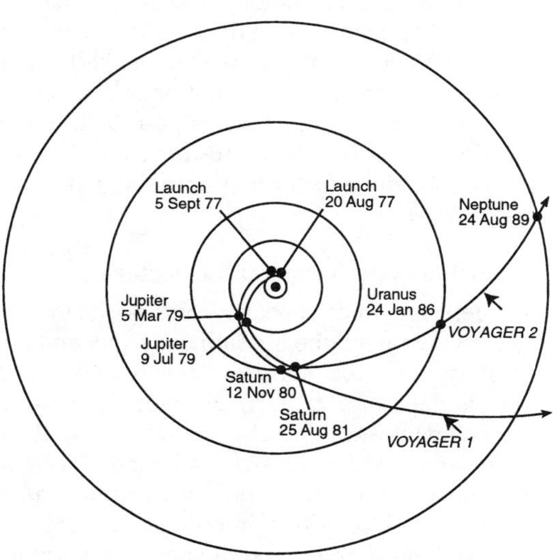

Fig. 12-16. Ground Tour Trajectories by Voyager 1 and 2.

Having reached distances of more than 70 AU, and still functioning in 1998 after more than 25 years of operation, Pioneer 10 has no longer been actively tracked from Earth (in part for budgetary reasons), since its gradually deteriorating radio-isotope power generator only allows a greatly diminished transmission of scientific data. However, Pioneer 10 was still contacted occasionally for Deep Space Network (DSN) station test purposes. Pioneer 11 ceased to maintain radio contact with the Deep Space Network from its position outside the solar system, in the mid-1990s, i.e., prior to Pioneer 10, because of its more rapidly diminishing operating power. The Voyager spacecraft, with a system design much more complex than Pioneer and hence more subject to subsystem failure, have had a somewhat shorter (20-year) mission life, although they achieved a remarkable overall mission success.

This section primarily covers ballistic missions with high-thrust departure from Earth, followed by a free-flight heliocentric transfer phase, i.e., missions that have been flown to-date or are projected to be flown in the near future. In addition, the section also briefly discusses "non-ballistic" mission profiles with prolonged low-thrust transfer phases that use solar-electric propulsion or solar-sailing (see Sec. 12.7.6). They offer the principal advantage of large launch cost savings due to either a greatly reduced propellant mass, in the case of electric propulsion, or the use of solar radiation pressure alone for providing propulsion in deep space. Earth-based-laser illumination is being contemplated also as a way to augment solar-sail effectiveness.

The first solar-electric propulsion mission in deep space, the Discoverer comet exploration mission, DS-1, was launched in 1999 and is performing as intended on its way to close encounters of comets Wilson-Harrington and Borelly. Alternate concepts using nuclear power for electric propulsion also are being considered for deep-space exploration, at distances where solar power is no longer sufficient. However, adequately dependable, long-life nuclear-electric power sources need considerable further development for this purpose.

Table 12-22 gives a summary of some U.S. planetary missions since the launch of Pioneer 10 to Jupiter in early 1972. These missions give evidence of the great progress in space mission sophistication and technology evolution since the 1970s. The trend to ever-greater mission cost has been slowed down, and in some cases has even been reversed, to reflect the current space exploration planning philosophy. In spite of being among the earliest, ambitious deep-space exploration spacecraft, the Pioneer 10 and 11 and Voyager 1 and 2 surviving for many years past the initial mission goals have transmitted astrophysical science observation results from distances up to and more than 70 AU. This was undoubtedly a factor in proceeding with even more demanding planetary mission developments.

12.7.1 Overview of Interplanetary Transfer Trajectories

Key parameters in defining interplanetary mission characteristics include the desired flight time to reach the target, the mission departure and arrival dates within a given mission opportunity, i.e., the specific launch and arrival "windows," as mentioned before, and the departure and arrival velocities that are involved. These parameters affect the type and cost of launch vehicles having the performance capability suitable for the desired spacecraft size and mass. They also determine the amount of onboard propellant required for critical deep-space maneuvers, such as orbit insertion at the target planet. Also of critical importance are the velocity vector orientations in planetocentric and heliocentric coordinates, and various orientation angles like those of the lines-of-sight to the Sun, to the target planet, and to Earth which de-

TABLE 12-22. Representative U.S. Planetary Missions, 1972–2000.

Mission Name	Mission Objectives	Launch Vehicle; Date	Target Encounter Dates	Spc Mass (kg)	Trajectory Info	Comments
Pioneer 10, Jupiter Flyby	Jupiter flyby. Safety of crossing asteroid belt determined.	Atlas/Centaur/ TE-364; 3/3/72	Jupiter 12/3/73	258	Direct flight to Jupiter. 1st to escape Solar System. ≈ 76 AU from Earth in 2001.	Survival to 10x specified mission life. Discovered gravitational perturbation from a Kuiper Belt object (1995). Pioneer 11 followed Pioneer 10 passing Saturn (9/79) after Jupiter swingby (12/74).
Viking 1, Mars Orbiter/Lander	Mars orbital observation, surface sample analysis. Look for life.	Titan IIIE/ Centaur; 8/20/75	Mars orbit insertion 6/19/76, landing 9/3/76	572	Direct mission to Mars. Lander descends from orbiter for surface obser.	Mars observation from orbit and surface. No signs of life detected. Followed by similar Viking 2 Mission.
Voyager 1 and 2, Outer Planet Flyby	Close Jupiter and outer planet observations during flyby.	Titan IIIE/ Centaur; 9/5, 8/20 1977	At Jupiter 2/79 and 7/79. At Saturn 11/80 and 8/81.	722 each	Swingby of Jupiter, Saturn (1). Grand Tour of Jupiter, Saturn, Uranus, Neptune (2).	Closeup images of planets/moons. Survived > 20 yrs after launch. Voyager 2 renamed Voyager Interstellar Mission. Farthest man-made object from Sun.
Galileo, Jupiter Orbiter and Entry Probe	Detailed exploration of Jupiter and satellites.	Shuttle/ IUS; 11/4/89	12/7/95	Orbiter 2223. Probe 339.	Used multiple swingby via Venus, Earth (2x), to reach Jupiter.	Observation from orbit of Jupiter environment and moons. Discovered additional moons, Io volcanoes, Jupiter rings. 1st use of Earth swingby. Reduces launch energy, C_3, from 78 to 13 km^2/sec^2. Close flyby of asteroid Gaspra.
*Ulysses, Solar Polar Mission**	Observation of solar polar regions from high latitudes.	Shuttle/ 2 upper stages; 10/6/90	Jupiter swingby 2/9/92. Solar passes 9/13/94, 7/31/95. Again 00/01.	370	Used Jupiter swingby to achieve required high orbit inclination (79 deg), for solar polar passages.	First look at solar emission in polar directions. Measured particles and fields far from ecliptic plane. Highest injection energy ever used.
Cassini, Saturn Orbiter and Huygens Probe	Exploration of Saturn atmosphere, magneto- sphere, satellites, Titan surface.	Titan IV/Centaur. 2 added solid stages; 10/15/97	Saturn orbit insertion, 7/1/04. Huygens Probe at Titan 11/27/04.	Orbiter 2150, Probe, 350	Used Venus-Venus-Earth swingbys to reach Saturn.	Extended exploration of Saturn's atmosphere, environment, rings, moons. Surface data of Titan.
Near-Earth Asteroid Rendezvous (NEAR)†	Rendezvous with and orbit Eros.	Delta II-7925; 2/17/96	Eros orbit insertion 4/30/00	805	Initial excursion to 2.2 AU, return for Earth swingby after 23 mos.	First mission to orbit and land on an asteroid. Flyby, images of asteroid 253 Mathilde (6/27/97). Initial Eros rendezvous aborted; orbit insertion on 2nd approach. Landed 2/01.
Mars Pathfinder Mission	Mars surface exploration, use of microrover (Sojourner).	Delta II-7925/PAM; 12/4/96	Mars arrival 7/4/97	890 at launch. 360, Lander	Conventional 8-month trajectory to Mars.	NASA low-cost Discovery mission. First "microrover" on Mars (Sojourner). Left names of 100,000 members of Planetary Society.

* Developed by ESA, launched and managed by NASA. †Renamed NEAR-Shoemaker.

termine the required spacecraft orientation for uplink and downlink communication, for performing critical maneuvers, for solar power generation, and for other mission-specific objectives.

A comprehensive set of reference handbooks for (ballistic) missions to different planetary targets, covering past, present, and future launch and arrival dates have been published by the Jet Propulsion Laboratory starting in the 1980s by Sergeyevsky et al. [1983 and later], showing charts of all relevant parameters for these mission dates. These handbooks cover missions to Venus, Mars, Jupiter, and Saturn for many successive launch opportunities. The manuals include detailed definitions of all parameters involved and their geometrical relations. Only a few of these factors will be covered here. Readers who wish to study detailed aspects of planetary missions and their trajectories are urged to become familiar with this important reference material.

A dominant trajectory characteristic, and one of the first to be considered in selecting the mission profile to a planetary target, is the required amount of launch energy, and specifically, the energy required beyond Earth escape. This *departure energy*, C_3,* defined as the square of the *hyperbolic excess velocity*, V_∞, is one of the two terms in the equation of the escape orbit *vis-viva-energy*

$$V_i^2 = V_{esc}^2 + V_\infty^2 = V_{esc}^2 (1 + V_\infty^2 / V_{esc}^2) \equiv V_{esc}^2 (1 + C_3 / V_{esc}^2) \qquad (12\text{-}9)$$

where V_i is the path velocity, and $V_{esc} = \sqrt{2\mu/r_P}$, the escape velocity at the periapsis (perigee) distance r_P. [See Eq. (2-6) in Sec. 2.1.4.] Minimum energy transfers to Mars typically require $V_\infty = 3.5$ km/s, those to Jupiter require at least 8.5 km/s, or energies C_3 of 12 and 72 km^2/s^2, respectively. The transfer time to the target planet, an important mission parameter, is close to 0.6 years for a minimum energy Mars mission, and 2.4 years for a minimum-energy Jupiter mission corresponding to these C_3-values.

The time interval between successive (minimum energy) launch opportunities to a target planet depends on the synodic period of the Earth's and that planet's orbit, as previously discussed in Chap. 2. The inverse of that period is equal to the difference between the inverse of the orbit periods of Earth and target planet. The synodic period is 1.60 years for launch opportunities to Venus, 2.13 years to Mars, 1.09 years to Jupiter, and 1.04 years to Saturn. For the large orbit periods of the outer planets the synodic periods decrease to values that are closer and closer to 1.0 year the more distant that planet is from the Sun.

An important launch-time constraint in any planetary mission is the required phase angle at launch of the target planet relative to Earth, i.e., the angular difference in heliocentric space between the orbital positions of Earth and the planet in question. This is illustrated in Fig. 12-17 for the case of Earth-to-Mars transfer. With an assumed transfer time of the Earth-to-Mars trajectory, $t_T = t_2 - t_1$, the orbital motion of Mars between the launch time t_1 (at Earth) and the arrival time t_2 (at Mars) is given by $\omega_t (t_2 - t_1)$, where ω_t is the average Mars orbital rate during that time interval. The phase angle γ_1 is the difference between the spacecraft transfer angle and the angular motion of Mars during the transfer, as shown in the diagram. A launch delay of several days implies a phase angle reduction, and hence will require a shorter transfer time, and, generally, an increase in departure energy.

---

* The subscript of the term C_3 derives from an earlier designation in the literature of energy components, such as C_1 and C_2, that are no longer in use.

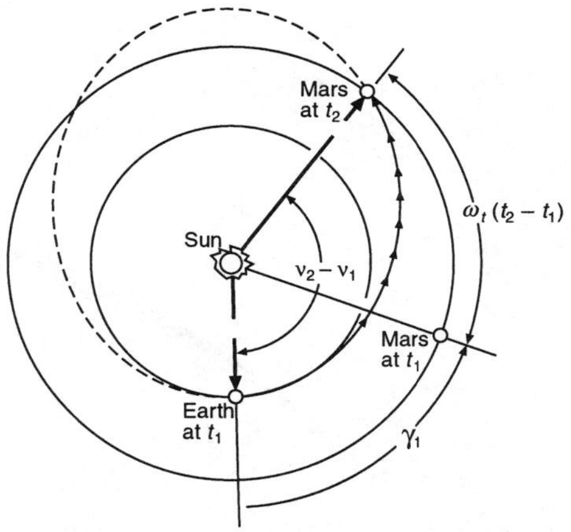

Fig. 12-17. Phase Angle at Launch, Earth-to-Mars Transfer.

The minimum energy and flight-time to a specific target planet varies between mission opportunities because of the slight eccentricity of the Earth's and that planet's orbits and the corresponding slight variations of the perihelion and aphelion distances of the transfer trajectories that are used in different mission years. Thus, the required minimum energy C_3-requirements can vary as much as 5 to 10 km^2/s^2 and more in missions to Jupiter. An additional factor is the generally slight planetary orbit inclination relative to the ecliptic plane as will be discussed below.

An ideal minimum energy Hohmann transfer, with a 180-deg central angle, involves co-tangential departure and arrival. (See Sec. 2.6.1.) For an actual transfer between planetary orbits the conditions of a strict Hohmann transfer are often not attainable, since the target planet, at the time of arrival, is almost always above or below the ecliptic plane due to its orbit inclination. In a mission to Mars, a planet with an orbit inclination of 1.85 deg relative to the ecliptic plane and a mean orbit radius of 1.52 AU, the maximum distance out-of-plane is only 0.0491 AU or 7.36 million km. Even for conditions with much smaller out-of-plane distances, with the target planet being close to its ascending or descending nodes at the spacecraft arrival time, a coplanar 180-deg transfer will not be possible. For transfer angles near 180 deg the spacecraft's transfer orbit, in fact, must have an inclination that is considerably larger than that of the target planet and would increase very rapidly the closer the transfer angle approached 180 deg.

A very useful illustration of the relationships between departure energy C_3, departure date and transfer time, and hence arrival date is shown by the chart of departure energy contours, Fig. 12-18A, for a mission to Mars launched in the year 2011 and 2012. This type of chart, often referred to as a *pork chop plot* because of its distinctive energy contour shapes, shows two separate regions of launch windows, with arrival dates in mid and late 2011 and beyond.* (See Sec. 4.1.). The two nested sets of launch

---

* In the *JPL Planetary Mission Handbooks* by Sergeyevsky et al. [1983 and later] referred to in the beginning of this section, the C_3-contours are plotted in terms of departure and arrival dates, with transfer time indicated by sloping lines. Their appearance, therefore, is somewhat different from those shown here.

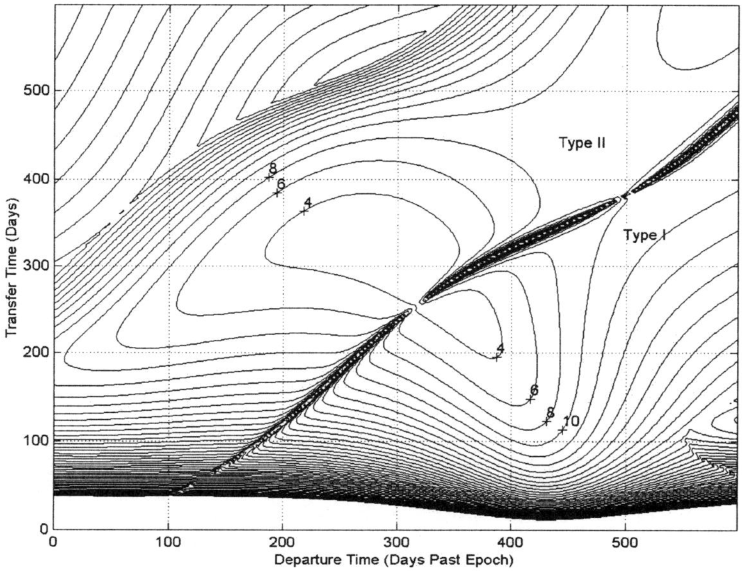

(A)

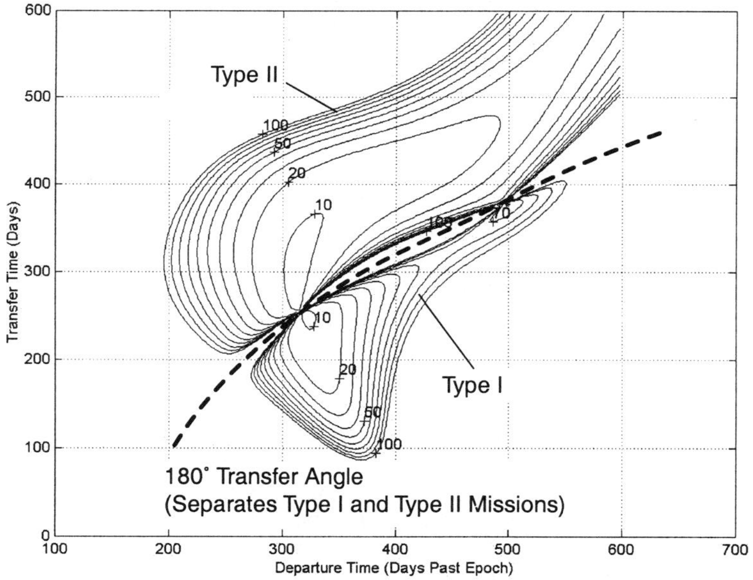

(B)

Fig. 12-18. Representative Earth-to-Mars Mission Parameters ("Pork Chop Plots") for 2011–2012 Launch Opportunity. Epoch is 1 Jan 2011. (A) Contours of departure energy C_3(in km^2/s^2), and (B) Contours of Mars arrival velocity (in km/sec). Type-I and Type II mission contours are shown, separated by a curve of 180 deg transfer angle.

energy contours characterize the faster *Type-I missions*, with heliocentric transfer angles less than 180 deg and the slower *Type-II missions*, with transfer angles greater than 180 deg. The minimum launch energies fore these mission types are about 9 to 10 km^2/sec^2, with flight times of about 250 and 320 days, respectively.

Fig. 12-18B shows two corresponding nested sets of contours that indicate the hyperbolic arrival velocities, V_∞, at Mars for the same range of launch dates and flight times as the departure energy, C_3, contours, for Type-I and Type-II missions. The minimum arrival velocities are about 3 km/sec for Type-I and Type-II transfer trajectories. These minima occur at departure dates and flight times that differ somewhat from the minima of the departure energy contours in Fig. 12-18A. The selection of a preferred launch date and flight time depends on which of the two parameters should best be minimized, the departure energy or the arrival velocity. A compromise date and flight time between the two minima generally will be the preferred choice.

The hypothetical Hohmann transfer from Earth to an ideally coplanar Mars orbit would have a flight time of 259 days, between those of the two actual minimum-energy transfer-orbits given in the chart, i.e., in the swath that separates the two mission sets. As indicated by the very steep contour line variation designating this "separating wall" between Type-I and Type-II missions, very much larger launch energies would be required for transfer angles close to 180 degrees. Actually, a purely ballistic transfer would require a departure at a very large, out-of-ecliptic angle, (see Fig. 12-19A) and hence, with an unacceptably high C_3-value and, therefore, entirely unaffordable launch vehicle performance requirements. In interplanetary mission swhere no specific target object is to be reached at the required heliocentric distance, i.e., missions with general astrophysical observation objectives in the ecliptic plane, these restrictions do not apply, and the lower-cost Hohmann transfer can be used. (The pork chop contours in Fig. 12-18 correspond to those in the JPL Handbooks referred to above, but differ in terms of the launch, arrival date and transfer time coordinates shown).

The geometry constraints that preclude a co-planar departure trajectory can be circumvented by performing a midcourse plane change maneuver as illustrated in Fig. 12-19B (from Fimple [1963]). The minimum amount of plane change that will be required for a given out-of-plane position of the target planet occurs at the location 90 deg prior to the target arrival, as indicated by the broken-plane transfer trajectory diagram. However, because of the precise magnitude and direction and the precise location of this plane change being of critical concern, this option is generally not used.

Non-Direct Trajectories with Planetary Gravity Assist

A very different class of mission profiles includes one or several encounters with other planets on the way to the target for the purpose of getting an energy boost from the effect of planetary gravity assist obtained at each swingby. This technique can greatly reduce launch energy requirements in some missions, specifically by making the initial target of the mission profile a planet with a much smaller launch energy requirement than a direct mission to the final target (see also discussion in Sec. 2.6.3).

The concept of using planetary gravity assist to increase mission energy was first described in 1963 by M. A. Minovitch with reference to a Mars swingby on the way to Jupiter. The first spacecraft that actually used a large Jupiter swingby effect was Pioneer 11, launched in 1973, on its way to Saturn and beyond, as discussed earlier in this Section. Jupiter, Saturn, and their moons were the main objects of observation. To

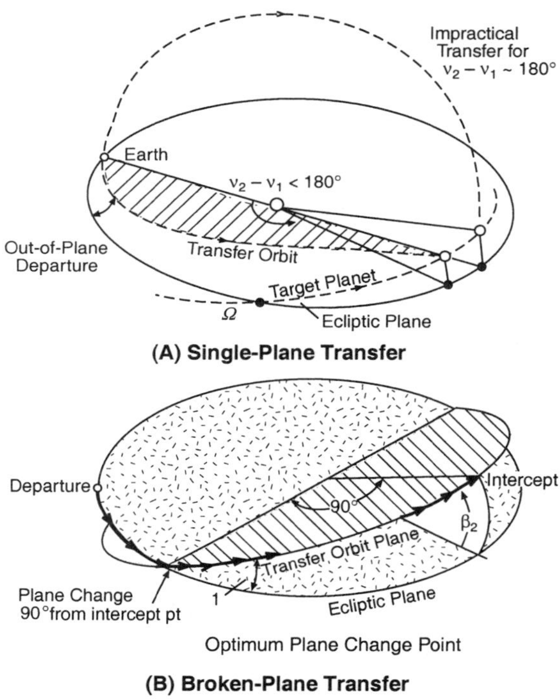

Fig. 12-19. Broken-Plane Transfer to Target Above Ecliptic Plane.

reach Saturn in 1979 after the Jupiter encounter, the spacecraft followed a trajectory between Jupiter and Saturn with a transfer angle of about 145 deg, returning en-route to about 4 AU solar distance.

Other missions that used planetary swingbys to reach their targets are the Galileo Jupiter orbiter and entry probe mission, launched in 1989, as shown in Fig. 12-20 [D'Amario et al., 1989], and the Cassini Saturn orbiter mission launched in 1997 [Peralta and Smith, 1993]. With a gross mass of 2,560 kg and 2,470 kg, respectively, these missions could not have been launched directly to their destinations without the benefit of multiple planet swingbys. Galileo used one Venus and two Earth swingbys, the Cassini mission requires swingbys of Venus, Earth and Jupiter. The Earth departure energy, C_3, of about 13 km^2/sec^2 allows a near-Hohmann transfer trajectory to Venus, as the first target, with the Shuttle/Inertial Upper Stage used for launching Galileo, and Titan IV for launching Cassini. This large reduction in departure energy and the associated lowering of launch vehicle performance requirements, however, can only be achieved by accepting the considerably more complex and time-consuming mission profile and added design requirements such as extra thermal protection to withstand the 0.7 AU solar distance at the Venus encounter, as compared with solar distances ≥ 1 AU in direct missions to the outer planets.

An extreme case of planetary gravity assist was used by the Ulysses solar-polar mission, launched in Oct. 1990, with Jupiter chosen as the interim target, to allow a close solar approach of 1.3 AU with a departure energy of 128 km^2/s^2 using the Shuttle/Upper Stage as launch vehicle, see Fig. 12-21 [Luthey et al., 1989]. Its departure

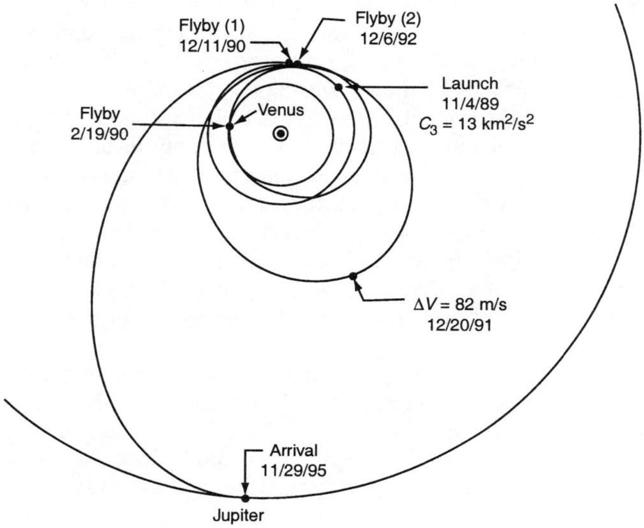

Fig. 12-20. Galileo 1989 Trajectory to Jupiter via Venus-Earth-Earth Swingby.

energy was by far the highest one used up to that date. The mission included the unique space exploration objectives of passing through interplanetary space at a high (78 deg) inclination relative to the ecliptic plane and of observing phenomena over the Sun's South and North polar regions that had remained previously unexplored. These observations enhanced our understanding of surface phenomena at and near the Sun's poles, their propagation into the solar system, and especially those affecting particles and fields phenomena near Earth. Without Jupiter's gravity assist the high out-of-ecliptic orbit inclination of this mission could not have been achieved. It would have required the entirely unrealizable launch energy.

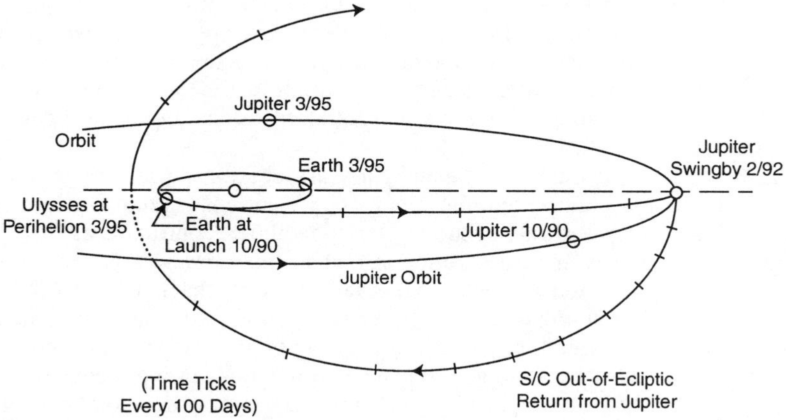

Fig. 12-21. Ulysses Trajectory (1990), Solar Polar Mission via Jupiter.

As mentioned before, Sec. 2.6.3 discusses the orbital mechanics of planetary gravity assist. Of particular concern is the turn angle, ψ (and its supplement φ), which is the angle change of the planetocentric asymptotic velocity V_∞ during the encounter, and the resulting change in the heliocentric velocity between arrival and departure during the swingby event [Minovitch, 1963]. This velocity change can provide a significant increase in magnitude and a direction change either in-plane or out-of-plane, or both. Such changes depend primarily on the direction and magnitude of the hyperbolic velocity and on the closest approach distance, i.e., the periapsis radius, r_P.

Table 2-19 in Sec.2.6.3 includes a list of turn angles and velocity changes for representative swingbys. For Jupiter and Saturn swingby closest approach distances of 5 to 10 planet radii are preferred to avoid unacceptably large, potentially damaging effects from planetary radiation belts during the encounter. In the case of Saturn, this also avoids a potential interaction with the planet's rings.

For example, in a Jupiter swingby, at 5.6 km/sec relative velocity, the asymptotic velocity direction changes by 135 deg for a closest-approach distance of 5 planet radii, [see Fig. 12-22], and by 116 deg for 10 planet radii. With a heliocentric arrival velocity of 8 km/sec in this case, the departure velocity would be increased to about 15 km/sec by the trajectory change due to the swingby effect. [Also see Eq. (2-82) to (2-84) in Sec. 2.6.3.]

A small delta-V maneuver at the closest approach to the planet produces a *powered swingby* that can significantly increase the outbound asymptotic velocity at only a minor propellant cost. This mode, therefore, can achieve a much greater gravity-assist effect than the more commonly used *passive swingby*.

12.7.2 Navigation, Guidance and Control

Earth-based tracking of the spacecraft to determine and correct any deviations from the intended flight path has been practiced from the time of the earliest interplanetary missions in the 1960s. More recently, emphasis is being shifted to include autonomous navigation over extended time intervals during the heliocentric phase of the mission and especially during the approach to the target, based on the use of onboard sensing instruments and onboard navigation and guidance computers, with this technology steadily advancing. Optical navigation techniques were used in the Voyager Neptune encounter [Reidel, et al., 1990], the Cassini Saturn orbiter mission [Gray and Hahn, 1995], and the NEAR mission [Miller, et al., 1995]. Serrano et al, [1996] provide a general assessment of various autonomous navigation techniques for interplanetary missions. DS-1, the first in NASA's New Millennium series, used solar-electric propulsion to reach its two cometary targets, and autonomous navigation during the deep-space cruise [Wolff et al., 1998].

Considering the long duration of many planetary missions, a shift to greater navigation, guidance and control autonomy is a significant cost-saving concern. These operations, if performed entirely by ground-based facilities, contribute significantly to the overall mission cost. Increased autonomy of navigation and guidance serves to reduce this cost element and also helps to mitigate problems that may be caused by unforeseen communication link outages between the ground station and the spacecraft.

There generally is a need for several mid-course guidance maneuvers to correct trajectory errors, followed by approach guidance corrections several weeks or months prior to arriving at the target. Typical guidance maneuvers require a total budget of up to several hundred m/sec in some missions depending on the mission complexity, especially when interim target encounters are included for gravity assist purposes.

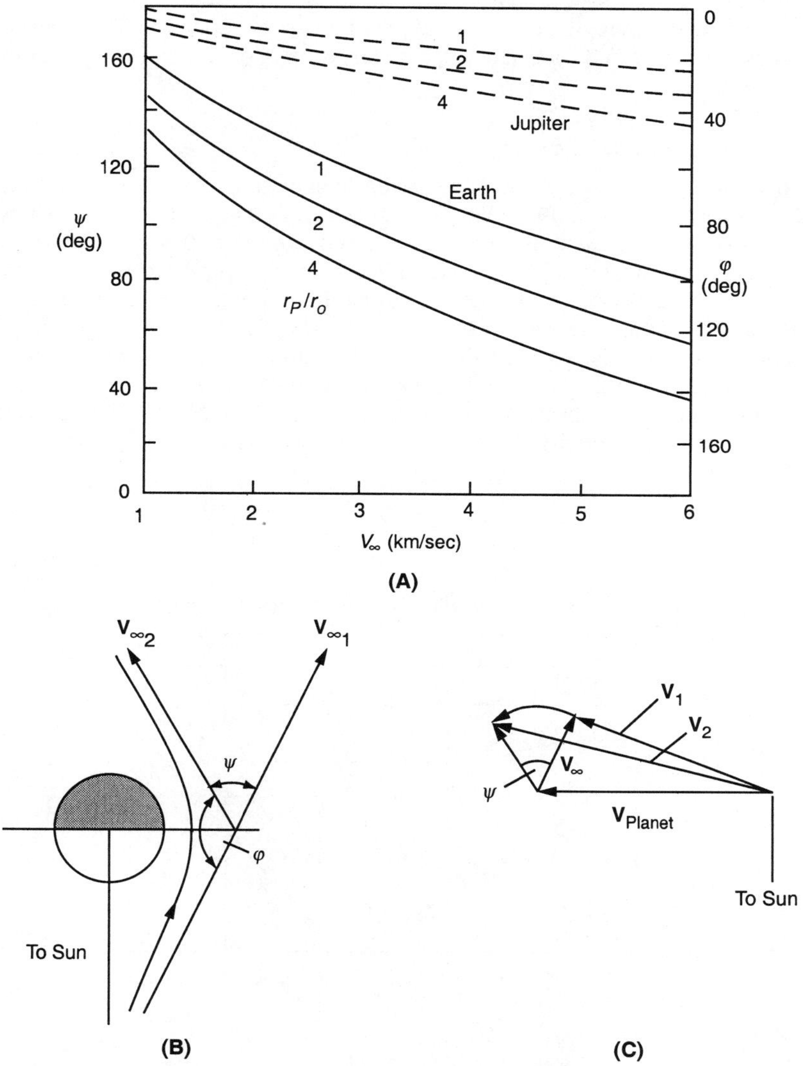

Fig. 12-22. Swingby Angle Change vs. V_∞ and r_P. (A) Angles ψ and φ change with V_∞ and r_p,(B) Trajectory deflection, (C) Velocity directions.

Communication between the spacecraft and ground stations on Earth, i.e., NASA's Deep Space Network (DSN), is always needed for timely status checks and commands, and for telemetry of data acquired by the science payload instruments. DSN tracking to derive navigation data may be performed at these and other times, but much less frequently, if the spacecraft has autonomous navigation capabilities.

The DSN stations involved in tracking and communication are distributed around the globe to provide round-the-clock access as required. The three principal DSN stations are located at Goldstone (California), Madrid (Spain), and Canberra (Australia).

Each of these stations in turn can give up to 10 hr of communication coverage, in accordance with the changing Earth-to-spacecraft viewing geometry. The Space Flight Operations Facility (SFOF) located at JPL controls the global tracking and communication activities.

12.7.3 Additional Launch Energy Considerations

An overview of the transfer time and the Earth departure velocity required for outbound missions in the ecliptic plane as a function of target distance is shown in Fig. 12-23. This chart (which includes the idealized minimum-energy Hohmann transfers with 180-deg transfer angles) is useful in providing a preliminary assessment of launch energy requirements and flight times and their variations with target distance. Type I and II trajectory classes are represented in this figure by the segments of the fixed-velocity curves shown here that are below and above the minimum-energy points indicated by a dashed line connecting the points of maximum target distance on each velocity curve. Based on the energy equation (12-9) in Sec. 12.7.1, the relation between the injection velocity, V_i, and V_∞, is readily derived (with V_{esc} = 10.9 km/s, assumed fixed).

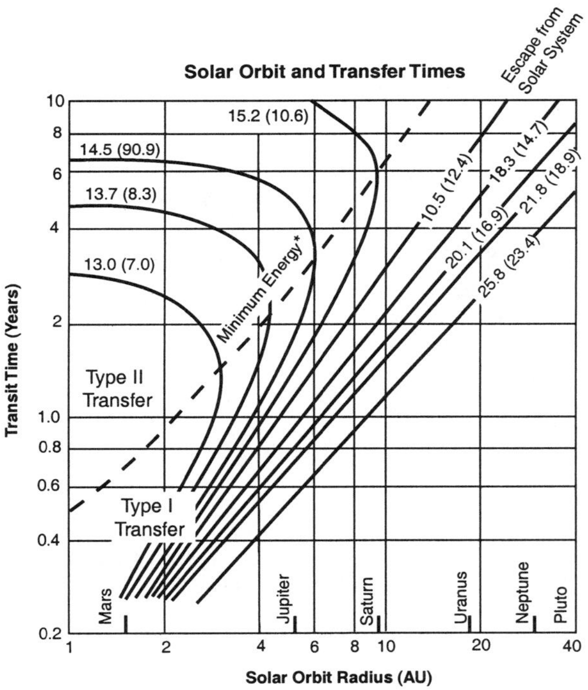

Note:
1. Numbers on curves are injection velocities V_i (hyperbolic velocities V_∞) in km/sec
2. Earth Departure from 300 km altitude parking orbit
* Hohmann Transfer, Assuming Co-Planar Orbits

Fig. 12-23. Transfer Time to Targets vs. Distance (in AU), for Various Launch Velocities.

Figure 12-23 illustrates the important fact that near the minimum-energy Hohmann transfer the flight time varies greatly with only a minor change of the target distance or the departure velocity. This shows, for example, that in a Type-I transfer only little extra launch energy is required to reduce the flight time significantly from that required for the minimum-energy case. Corresponding flight-time and launch-energy variations can also be observed in Fig. 12-18 (see above) between C_3-contours near the two minimum-energy points shown.

Some interesting relationships between the velocity terms involved in the launch phase—as well as those occurring on arriving at the target planet—can be readily derived from Eq. (12-9) through a geometrical interpretation shown in Fig. 12-24. Figure 12-24A depicts the three velocity terms, V_{esc}, V_∞, and V_i, as the two sides and the hypotenuse of a right triangle ABC. (Note: this is a geometrical "construct" which does not reflect any physical velocity directions.) The magnitude of V_{esc} corresponds to a given perigee radius. A circular arc of radius AB, constructed around point A and intersecting the hypotenuse AC at point P, subdivides the path velocity V_i into two segments of magnitude V_{esc} and ΔV_i. The latter is the comparatively small velocity increment to be added to the escape velocity to achieve the desired amount of V_∞ which reflects the algebraic definition of the velocity increment

$$\Delta V_i = V_i - V_{esc} = \sqrt{V_{esc}^2 + V_\infty^2} - V_{esc} \tag{12-10}$$

as derived from Eq. (12-9). The figure also shows an arc of radius 0.707 V_{esc} that designates the corresponding circular velocity and indicates the total velocity increment required to reach V_i from a a circular orbit of radius r_P. Its magnitude is $\Delta V_i + 0.293\ V_{esc}$.

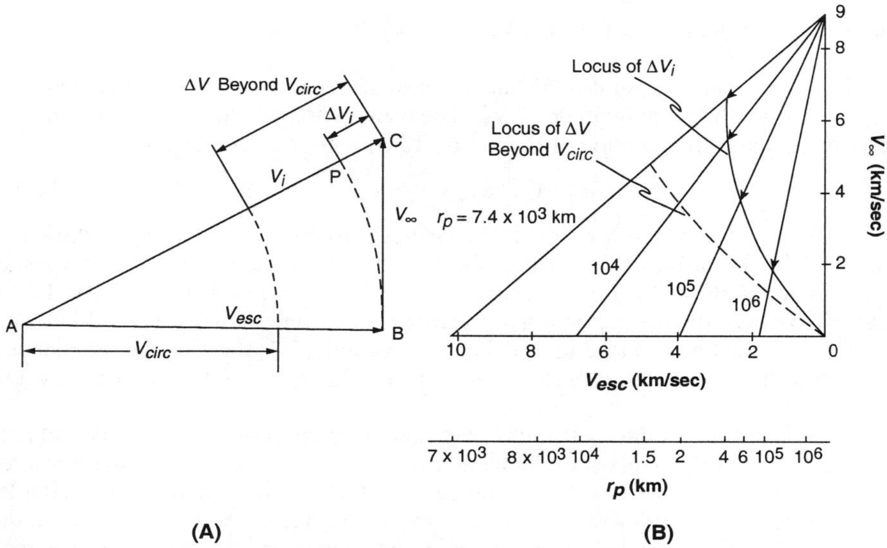

Fig. 12-24. Velocity Relationships at Earth Departure for Various Values of Escape Velocity. See text for discussion.

A second diagram, Figure 12-24B shows the effect on ΔV_i of decreasing V_{esc} associated with increasing the perigee radius r_P (see the scales shown below this figure). It is apparent that ΔV_i increases rapidly as V_{esc} is decreased until, with V_{esc} approaching zero for $r_P \rightarrow \infty$, the velocity increment ΔV_i approaches the value of V_∞. Figure 12-25 shows the resulting values of ΔV_i as function of r_p for several values of V_∞, e.g., in a Jupiter mission with $V_\infty = 9$ km/s ΔV_i increases from about 3.5 km/s for low perigee distances to 7.6 km/s for $r_P = 20$ Earth radii, and to 9 km/s for $r_P \rightarrow \infty$.

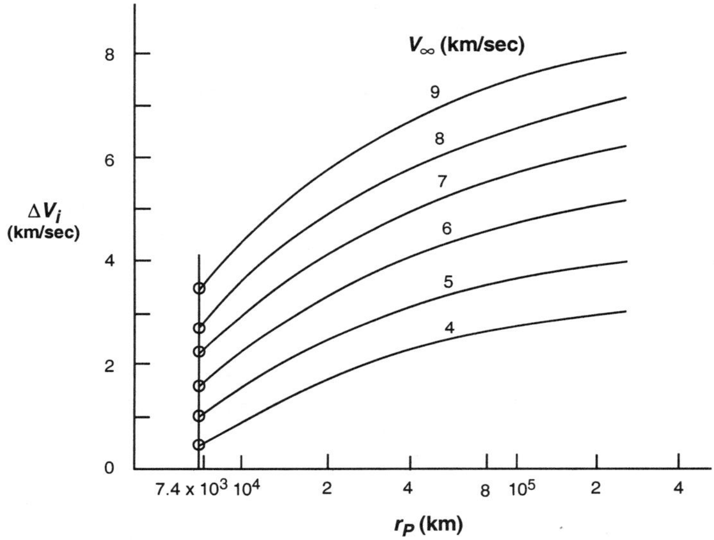

Fig. 12-25. ΔV_i Variation with r_P and V_∞. Horizontal axis is on a log scale.

Figure 12-24 also illustrates the fact that a small variation of V_i typically leads to a larger variation of the magnitude of V_∞. This gain factor, G, can be obtained analytically by partial differentiation of V_∞ in Eq. (12-9) with respect to V_i, viz.,

$$G = \partial V_\infty / \partial V_i = V_i / V_\infty \tag{12-11}$$

This gain factor is the ratio of the side AC to BC in the triangle shown in Fig. 12-24A. For a Jupiter mission, with $V_\infty = 9$ km/s and departure at low perigee, the gain is about 14/9 = 1.56. It decreases to 1.0 as r_p approaches infinity. In the interest of obtaining the maximum V_∞-gain, the departure maneuver should be performed at a location as close to the planet as possible, i.e., deep inside the planet's "gravity well." These characteristics are further illustrated by the curves shown in Fig. 12-25.

A key factor in evaluating launch energy requirements concerns the payload performance capability and cost of the launch vehicles that are under consideration for a specific mission. There is a wide range of launch vehicle candidates available, with injection capabilities ranging from a few hundred to several thousand kg at the reference launch energy $C_3 = 0$ km^2/s^2. Launch vehicle types and performance characteristics, and their relation to mission performance and cost are discussed in Secs. 12.2 and 12.3.

12.7.4 Earth Departure Geometry and Constraints

As discussed in Sec. 12.7.1 the launch window selection for a given mission opportunity deals with the year, month and calendar dates, based on near-minimum launch energy characteristics, as indicated by the C_3-contours given in Fig.12-18 and also on a trade between minimum launch and arrival velocities. An additional time constraint is imposed by the one or two *daily launch windows* of typically 10 to 20 minutes. These windows are related to the orientation, in Earth-centered coordinates, of the departure trajectory's asymptotic velocity vector. Coordinates of concern are the declination and right ascension of this launch asymptote, designated as DLA and RLA, respectively. Figure 12-26 illustrates the launch geometry constraints imposed by the launch site and the orientation, in geocentric coordinates, of the hyperbolic departure velocity asymptote V_∞. Figure 12-26A shows the departure trajectory in two dimensions, starting at the launch site L, briefly remaining in a circular parking orbit, and then undergoing injection at P into the desired hyperbolic departure orbit. The direction of the departure asymptote is the V_∞-vector which is reached after going through the transfer angle η_L.

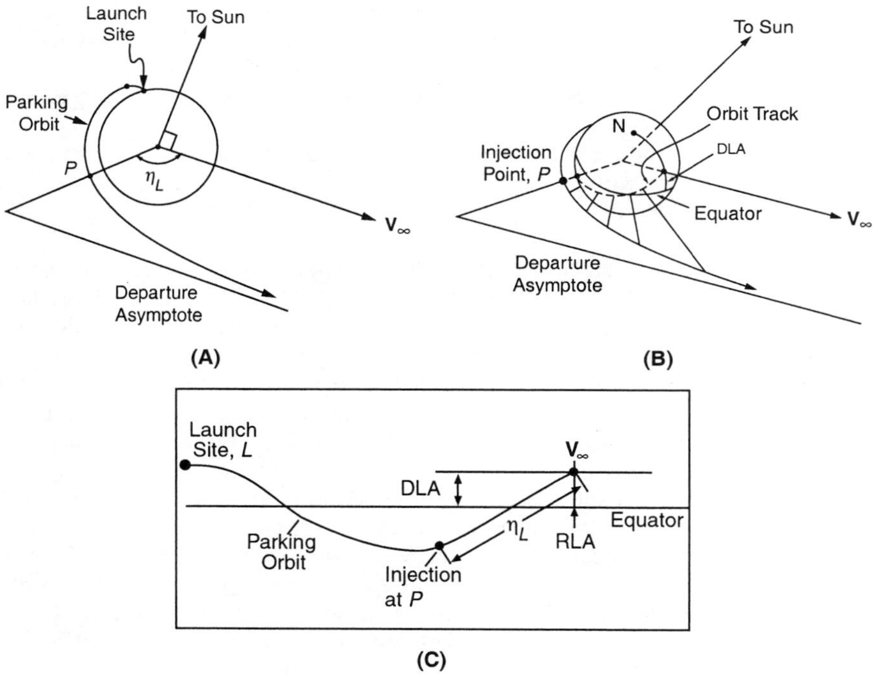

Fig. 12-26. Launch Constraints. (A) Departure trajectory in 2 dimensions, (B) In 3 dimensions, (C) ground track, in Earth coordinates.

Figure 12-26B shows the corresponding three-dimensional departure geometry, with the planar motion of Fig. 12-26A now depicted at some inclination relative to the Earth's equator. This inclination is dictated by the requirement of the trajectory passing through L and V_∞.

The geometry constraints are further illustrated in Fig. 12-26C which shows the departure trajectory ground track, passing through L and V_∞. The departure asymptote is shown here as a point (V_∞) with given longitude and latitude coordinates relative to the launch site coordinates from which the ground track of the departure trajectory originates. The assumed launch site is Cape Canaveral. A due-East launch is assumed in this diagram, which uses a 90-deg launch-azimuth to make best use of the Earth's axial rotation rate. The first segment of this ground track is the arc between the launch site and the perigee, *P*, of the hyperbolic departure trajectory, essentially the time interval during which the spacecraft remains in its parking orbit. The second ground track segment extends from *P* and has the central angle η_L, i.e., the angle which designates the limiting true anomaly of the departure hyperbola.

It is important to realize that as a result of launch delay the launch site moves eastward in Fig. 12-26C, which requires a gradual change in launch azimuth. Thus, departure ground tracks with different inclinations to the equator and different parking orbit durations will be involved. (This is discussed further below). In any case, as long as the departure trajectory passes through V_∞, the three-dimensional heliocentric direction of the departure trajectory will be the same, regardless of differences in geocentric orbit inclination. As an important consequence, no plane change maneuver to compensate for different Earth orbit inclinations, and any associated launch velocity penalty, will be required, although this may appear somewhat paradoxical: Actually the orbit orientation around Earth (i.e. the orbit inclination relative to the equator), is not relevant as long as the proper departure direction, along the V_∞-vector, is reached when leaving Earth.

Corresponding conditions also apply to planetary arrival and entry into a planetary orbit of any inclination without requiring a plane change. This will be achieved simply by selecting an appropriate arrival point near the planet, as illustrated in Fig. 12-28, in the next section.

Taking the 15 deg/hr eastward shift of the launch site due to Earth rotation into account means that the ground track shown in Fig. 12-26C would miss the target coordinates RLA and DLA even after only a short time interval, unless corrected by launching at a different azimuth angle that increases with time from the preferred 90 deg. This may add a noticeable take-off velocity penalty. However, by restricting the allowable daily launch window duration to about 20 min, 10 min before and after the optimum takeoff time, only a minor azimuth penalty is incurred.

The coordinates DLA and RLA of the target point in Fig. 12-26C are of concern here. Typically DLA is within the range of –30 to +30 deg. For a launch that is coplanar with Earth's heliocentric orbit DLA varies seasonally between –23.4 and +23.4 deg, due to the inclination of the celestial equator relative to the ecliptic plane. Zero declination occurs at the times of spring and fall equinox. Ground tracks for a launch from Cape Canaveral can cover a DLA range between +28.4 and –28.4 deg without an azimuth penalty. For departure trajectories that are more highly inclined relative to the ecliptic the required DLA can exceed this range by at least 10 to 15 deg. This may impose a correspondingly larger azimuth penalty in order to assure reaching the launch asymptote without requiring a significant plane change at point *P*. Useful references for further information are the series of NASA handbooks entitled *Launch Vehicle Estimating Factors* [McGolrick, 1971], *TRW Flight Operations Handbook* [White, 1963], and *Orbital Operations Handbook* [Wolverton, 1963].

One launch-geometry aspect, readily explained by Fig. 12-26, concerns the number and spacing of daily launch windows. Again assuming a due-East launch, as shown in that diagram, it is apparent that the ground track generally intercepts a given set of target coordinates RLA and DLA twice a day, at times that are at most 12 hours apart. The closer the value of DLA is to the upper limit of due-East launch coverage, the smaller is the time difference between the two available daily launch windows. In the limit, i.e., if DLA equals the maximum northern or southern latitudes of a ground track launched due East, the two daily launch windows coincide. A DLA beyond these limits necessitates a launch azimuth that is above or below 90 deg.

12.7.5 Planetary Arrival Geometry, Orbit Insertion, Orbit Shaping

In defining the arrival geometry at a planetary target, the transition from heliocentric to planetocentric velocity characteristics must be considered. The process is analogous to the conversion from geocentric to heliocentric reference coordinates during Earth departure, but in reverse order. Figure 12-27 shows representative directions of the heliocentric and planetocentric velocities at the time of arrival. These velocities are the heliocentric velocities of the target, $\mathbf{V}_T$, and of the arriving spacecraft, $\mathbf{V}_2$. Generally, they are neither co-tangential nor co-planar with the arrival trajectory. A velocity triangle can be formed that includes these velocities and the relative velocity, $\mathbf{V}_3$, shown in Fig. 12-27A, the latter being the planetocentric hyperbolic excess velocity. Typically, this velocity is oriented at an acute angle, θ, relative to $\mathbf{V}_T$, with a component pointing in opposite direction. In the case of cotangential arrival, i.e., in a Hohmann transfer, the relative velocity would be anti-parallel to both $\mathbf{V}_2$ and $\mathbf{V}_T$. The diagram in Fig. 12-27A defines conditions with an offset or miss distance at arrival. A minimum offset is necessary to avoid a direct impact. Fig. 12-27B shows the hyperbolic approach orbit in planetocentric coordinates. The offset distance normal to the arrival asymptote is designated as the *impact parameter*, *b*, shown here in a two-dimensional diagram (see Bate et al. [1971]).

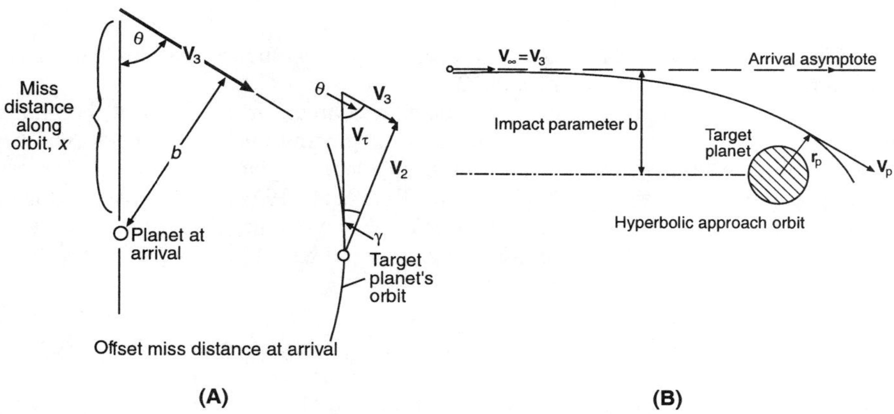

Fig. 12-27. Planet Arrival Geometry, Velocity Definitions. (A) Velocity directions and offset miss distance *x*, (B) Corresponding approach trajectory.

Figure 12-28 shows the corresponding three-dimensional arrival geometry. Two parallel arrival vectors are shown, as well as a plane normal to them, the so-called *B-plane*, or *impact-plane*. The figure shows the impact point *B* of a specific arrival asymptote, with an offset *b* from the planet center, i.e., the point in 3-D space that the planetocentric arrival velocity $\mathbf{V}_3$ must be guided to, so as to produce a specified encounter trajectory ground track that is indicated by the heavy trace. Other such traces shown in the diagram are various ground tracks, either of a flyby trajectory or a planetary orbit that are achievable by choosing different impact points on the B-plane. Only a small offset terminal guidance maneuver, to be performed some weeks before arrival, is required to produce any of these ground-tracks, and the corresponding flyby or orbital trajectories. As visualized in this diagram, the set of ground tracks shown form a beach-ball-like pattern that intersect at the *vertical impact point* of the undeflected arrival trajectory.

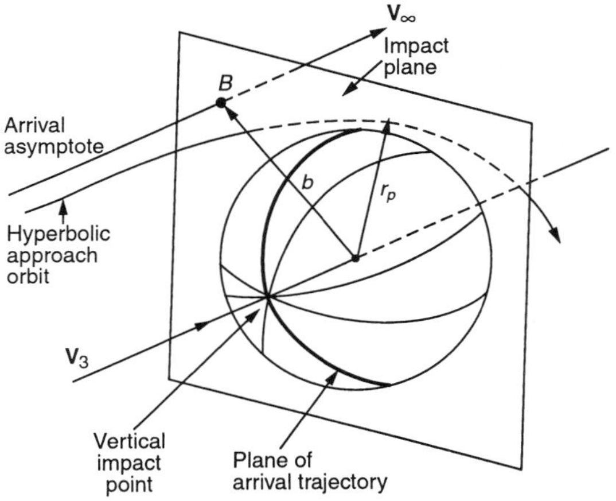

Fig. 12-28. Planet Arrival Geometry in 3 Dimensions Showing Impact Plane and Trajectory Ground Tracks, Depending on Choice of Impact Point B.

Table 12-23 lists the various orbital mechanics and geometry relations relevant to the diagrams shown in Figs. 12-27 and 12-28.

An important characteristic of the planetary encounter phase is that of the *planet impact size*, which is defined by the envelope of grazing approach trajectories that separates trajectories that, at the closest approach, clear the planet's surface from those that impact the planet, see Fig. 12-29 (also see Bate et al. [1971]). The cross section of that envelope is called the *collision cross section*, *b*, having the radius at large distances from the planet. As an example, for a Mars mission with V_{esc} = 5.1 km/s and V_∞ = 3 km/s, the ratio b/r_c is given by

$$b/r_c = \sqrt{1 + (\mathrm{V_{esc}} / \mathrm{V_\infty})^2} = \sqrt{1 + 25.31/9} = 2.93 \qquad (12\text{-}12)$$

Here, the collision cross-section is nearly three times the cross section of the planet itself. For a large planet such as Jupiter this ratio is very much larger, i.e., typically 10 for V_{esc} = 60.2 km^2/s^2 and V_∞ = 6 km^2/s^2. The collision cross section at Earth, for

TABLE 12-23. Equations Used for Defining Planetary Arrival Conditions. See Figs. 12-26 and 12-27 for definition of V_T, V_2, V_3. r_T is target planet distance from Sun, a_T is its orbits's semimajor axis. See App. D.4 for additional equations.

Quantity	Equation	Relationship	Relates to Fig. No
Heliocentric Arrival Velocity Equation, V_2	$V_2 = \sqrt{(\mu_s / r_T)(2 - r_T / a_T)}$ (μ_s is Sun's grav. constant)	Orbital velocity at target planet	12-27A
Heliocentric Flight Path Angle, γ	$\gamma = \tan^{-1}\left[e \sin\nu / (1 + e\cos\nu)\right]$ (where ν is true anomaly at intercept, *e* is eccentricity)		12-27A
Rel. Encounter Velocity (= asympt. velocity) , V_∞	$V_\infty = \sqrt{V_2^2 + V_T^2 - 2V_2V_T\cos\gamma}$ (V_T is target planet velocity)	Law of cosines	12-27A
Offset Distance *(Impact Parameter)*, *b*	$b = x\sin\theta$	Produced by miss distance along planet orbit	12-27A
Orientation of Relative Velocity, θ	$\sin\theta = \sin\gamma\,(V_2 / V_3)$	Law of sines	12-27A
Offset Distance, *b*, as Related to Closest Approach Distance r_p	$b = r_P V_P / V_3$ (V_P is arrival velocity at r_P)	Law of constant angular momentum	12-27B and 12-28

returning planetary spacecraft, is about 2.4 times the Earth diameter, if the arrival velocity is 5 km/sec. It is interesting to note that for meteoroids, or even an asteroid on a collision course, approaching the Earth at a high velocity, e.g., 20 km/sec, the collision cross section would only be about 10 percent larger than Earth's diameter. This means that on Earth we are not receiving as many meteoroid impacts per unit time as we might if the space debris were to arrive at very small velocities.

Note that the collision cross section, as shown in Fig. 12-29, at a finite distance from the central body, actually is slightly smaller than its full size that is determined by the corresponding arrival asymptotes. Fig. 12-29 also shows the entry corridor, for planets that are surrounded by an atmosphere, a region of relatively small width adjacent to the collision cross section. Objects arriving inside this corridor enter the atmosphere and may descend to the surface. The width of the *entry corridor* is greater than the atmospheric height in the same ratio [Eq. (12-12)] that determines the size of the collision cross section relative to the planet's diameter.

Maneuver requirements for planetary orbit insertion depend on the closest approach distance, the orbit dimensions, the escape velocity at closest approach, and the arrival velocity. Table 12-24 lists the equations to be used in calculating the required retro-maneuver velocity.

Figure 12-30 shows the normalized retro-velocity $\Delta V/V_{eP}$ versus the normalized arrival velocity V_∞ / V_{eP} for various values of the apoapsis-to-periapsis ratio R (where V_{eP} is the escape velocity at the periapsis of the arrival trajectory). These are two extreme cases:

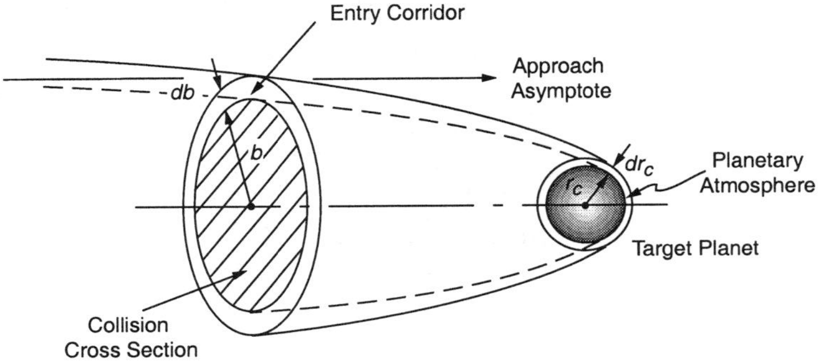

Fig. 12-29. Collision Cross Section and Entry Corridor. (See also Bate et al. [1971].)

TABLE 12-24. Equations Used for Orbit Insertion at Planet Periapsis r_P. (See Fig. 12-29).

Quantity	Equation	Relationship
Retro-impulse, ΔV	$\Delta V = V_{P1} - V_{P2}$ (where $V_{P1} = \sqrt{V_\infty^2 - V_{eP}^2}$)	Difference between arrival and orbit velocities at periapsis Arrival velocity at periapsis (V_{P2} is orbit velocity at periapsis)
Escape Velocity at Periapsis, V_{eP}	$V_{eP} = \sqrt{2\mu_p / r_P}$ (μ_p is planet's grav. constant)	Orbit equation
Periapsis Velocity of intended Elliptical Orbit, V_{P2}	$V_{P2} = V_{eP}\sqrt{r_A / (r_A + r_P)} = V_{eP}\sqrt{R/(R+1)}$ (where $R = r_A / r_P$)*	Orbit equation
Retro-impulse, ΔV, Relative to Escape Velocity at Periapsis, V_{eP}	$\Delta V / V_{eP} = \sqrt{(V_\infty / V_{eP})^2 + 1} - \sqrt{R/(R+1)}$	See also characteristics of large and small planets indicated in Fig. 12-30

*r_A is apoapsis and r_P is periapsis radius of orbit around planet. See also Table 12-23.

(a) For small values of V_∞ / V_{eP} (typical for large planets) circular orbits, with $R = 1$, require a very much greater ΔV than highly eccentric orbits. However, capture is generally less costly than for small planets.

(b) For large V_∞ / V_{eP} values (typical for small planets) the normalized retro-velocity $\Delta V / V_{eP}$ is much larger than for case (a), and the ΔV savings by the choice of a highly eccentric orbit are much smaller than in case (a).

An interesting example is the initial choice and the subsequent modifications of the orbit dimensions of the Galileo orbit at Jupiter, shown in Fig. 1-11 in Sec. 1.1.3. The

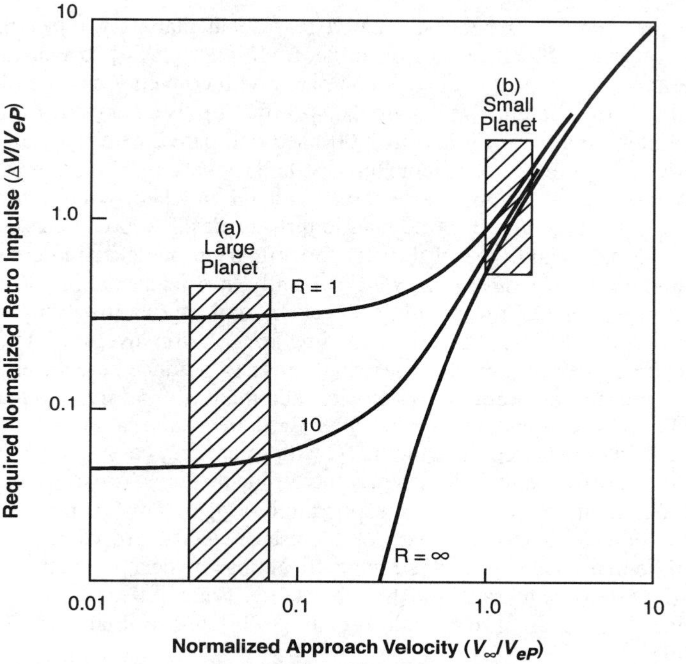

Fig. 12-30. Retro-Impulse Requirements vs. Approach Velocity.

highly eccentric initial orbit has an extremely large apojove-to-perijove ratio calling for a low orbit insertion ΔV-requirement. Subsequent multiple flybys of Jupiter's moons allow their close observation and also serve to obtain a gravity assist from each encounter. This is used to gradually shrink the orbit dimensions and reduce the time intervals between subsequent close encounters. The process is known as *orbit pumping*, with emphasis on orbit shrinking, *pumping down* in this case. A different gravity assist effect, known as *orbit cranking* that would result in successively changing the orbit inclination, is not being emphasized in this mission.

The Cassini Saturn Orbiter with its Huygens Titan Probe, was launched on October 15, 1997, to reach Saturn on July 1, 2004 [Peralta and Smith, 1993]. It is one of the largest and most complex interplanetary spacecraft. Its flight included gravity assists by two Venus swingbys, an Earth and a Jupiter swingby in Dec. 2000. After orbit insertion at Saturn it will follow a series of "flower-petal orbits" around Saturn comparable to those flown around Jupiter by the Galileo Orbiter, again using the orbit pumping technique.

12.7.6 Other Propulsion Techniques Used in Planetary Mission Design

This section covers mission profiles that employ low-thrust propulsion, rather than high-thrust chemical propulsion to achieve the energy required for transfer to distant planetary and other targets. This includes the use of electric propulsion, at a high specific impulse, and solar sailing which uses large, light-weight, deployed sail surfaces rather than propellant to produce thrust in the desired direction.

Solar-Electric Propulsion

Electric propulsion has been advocated for use in planetary missions since the beginning of space exploration (for example, Stuhlinger [1964]) because of the very large propellant mass savings it offers compared with conventional chemical propulsion. This due to its inherently much greater specific impulse. I_{sp}-values which for typical ion engines range from 3,000 to 5,000 sec compared with the 300 to 450 sec representative of storable or cryogenic bipropellant rocket engines. Electric propulsion technology and its applications are described in detail in a later volume of this series.

Various electrostatic and electrodynamic thruster designs have been developed to date. The most promising type of thruster for primary propulsion in deep-space missions is the *electrostatic*, or *ion thruster*. Typically, it produces about 40 to 50 millinewtons of thrust per kW of operating power. In applications involving a spacecraft mass of the order of 1,000 kg the corresponding acceleration level is 40 to 50 micro-g. Thus, by using 10 kW of constant operating power to produce an acceleration of 450 micro-g in a mission that requires a velocity increment of 9.5 km/s, typical for direct low-thrust propulsion transfer to Jupiter after Earth departure, a net thrust duration of about 8 months would be required. Actually, with solar-arrays as a likely power source, the power level decreases with the steadily increasing distance from the sun, and hence, the total thrust duration would be correspondingly longer. This example indicates the nature of mission characteristics based on the use of electric propulsion. Detailed discussions of the many factors involved in practical mission design and performance are covered in the extensive literature on the subject (e.g., Sauer [1993], and Sauer and Yen, [1994]). Meissinger et al. [1968], Uphoff et al. [1993], and Williams and Coverstone-Carroll [1997].

A fundamental trade must be performed regarding I_{sp}-selection between the desired propellant mass savings and the required extra mass of the power source, such as a large solar array. In any solar-electric propulsion application the propellant mass decreases in inverse proportion with I_{sp}, while the required power and, hence the solar array size and mass increase in proportion with I_{sp} and desired thrust magnitude. An additional factor is the variation of propulsion efficiency with I_{sp}. Without discussing specifics of this trade, the results show that optimal I_{sp}-values typically are 2,500 to 3,500 sec for ion engine efficiencies of 60 to 70%, rather than higher I_{sp}-values that would be suggested if propellant saving objectives are considered alone. At the optimum I_{sp}-value the propellant mass and the power-dependent mass elements are of equal magnitude, and consequently, the minimum total mass of the propulsion system and power source plus propellant mass is twice the mass of these I_{sp}-dependent parts of the system. A thrust level increase shifts the optimum I_{sp} to lower values, whereas an increase of the total impulse requirement shifts it to higher values.

Major incentives for the use of solar-electric propulsion in future high-energy missions are the expected cost savings afforded by using smaller launch vehicles for a given net spacecraft mass and, conversely, the much greater net spacecraft mass that can be delivered with a given launch vehicle size and cost.

In many application the flight time of the low-thrust trajectory is nearly the same as that of a corresponding trajectory produced with conventional high thrust at Earth departure. This is explained by the cumulative effect of prolonged low-thrust application. Thus, electric propulsion when used in interplanetary missions is not associated with a flight time penalty, a disadvantage that would affect Earth orbital missions with low-thrust primary propulsion.

Advances in ion engine technology as well as in solar arrays and power conditioning subsystems have led to plans for applying primary solar-electric propulsion in the coming decades in high-energy missions to the outer planets, to Mercury, and to comets and asteroids, and especially in missions that include a rendezvous with these targets. Representative propulsion power requirements of such missions have been reduced to the range of 5 to 10 kW at Earth departure, i.e., at 1-AU initial solar distance, which typically can be provided by solar array sizes of 50 to 150 m^2, depending on the solar cell type, the solar-array design and other design factors. Earlier studies, in the '60s and '70s, had projected propulsion power levels that were larger by up to an order of magnitude and therefore offered less of a practical advantage.

An important consideration in current solar-electric mission plans is to use the low thrust propulsion only after Earth escape rather than starting with a spiral ascent phase from low Earth orbit. This would add many months of extra flight time and place a much greater demand on continuous thrust time requirements, and hence, propulsion system life. Obviously, thrusting at acceleration levels of 50 to 100 micro-g will be much more efficient after Earth escape at distances where the effective (solar) gravity force is smaller by two to three orders of magnitude. Barber and Meissinger [1969] have shown that optimal departure energies, C_3, for Jupiter missions range from to 3 to 5 km^2/s^2. This reflects the increased injection-velocity gain, discussed in Sec. 12.7.3 (see Fig. 12-24), for departure velocities V_i that are slightly greater than the Earth escape velocity V_{esc} at low altitude.

Related studies by JPL and elsewhere [Sauer 1997, and Meissinger, 1970] have shown the performance advantages of including gravity assists from Earth and other planets in the electric-propulsion mission profile. Meissinger and Dawson [2001] show the benefit in outer planet missions of adding an initial out-of-ecliptic mission phase, followed by an Earth swingby, and the advantages of this mission mode relative to one staying entirely in the ecliptic plane, but also using Earth swingby [Sauer, 1997]. Figure 12-31 shows typical trajectory plots for (a) a rendezvous mission to asteroid Ceres, (b) a sample return mission to Comet Temple 1, and (c) a Jupiter orbiter mission with Earth swingby.

Solar Sailing

An entirely different technology is involved in missions that would use large solar sails for "passive" low-thrust propulsion as contrasted with active, solar-electric propulsion. Such missions have been under investigation for more than two decades. Solar-sail mission applications have been discussed in the literature by Sauer [1976], Wright and Warmke[1976], Leipold et al. [1996, 1998], Friedman [1978, 1988], McInnes [1993, 1999] and others. The principle of using the solar pressure effect is analogous to wind-sailing on water. It permits spiraling inward or outward in the solar system once the sailcraft has left the Earth's gravitational sphere of influence. As an example, a square sail about 200 m × 200 m in size, made of 7.5 mil Kapton film, and deployed by diagonal carbon-fiber-reinforced plastic booms, has been studied under auspices of NASA/JPL and the German Space Agency DLR [Leipold, 1998]. The flight system includes about 200 kg for the sail system and 115 kg net spacecraft mass, with the sailcraft to be launched by a Taurus rocket. The sail specific-mass is 5.2 g/m^2. A potential application is a fast Pluto flyby mission to be launched in the next decade. It would include a "solar-photonic assist" phase with an inbound excursion to 0.45 AU solar distance. Because of the difficulties involved in performing ground-based tests of the solar sailing technique, a preliminary demonstration in Earth orbit is envisioned

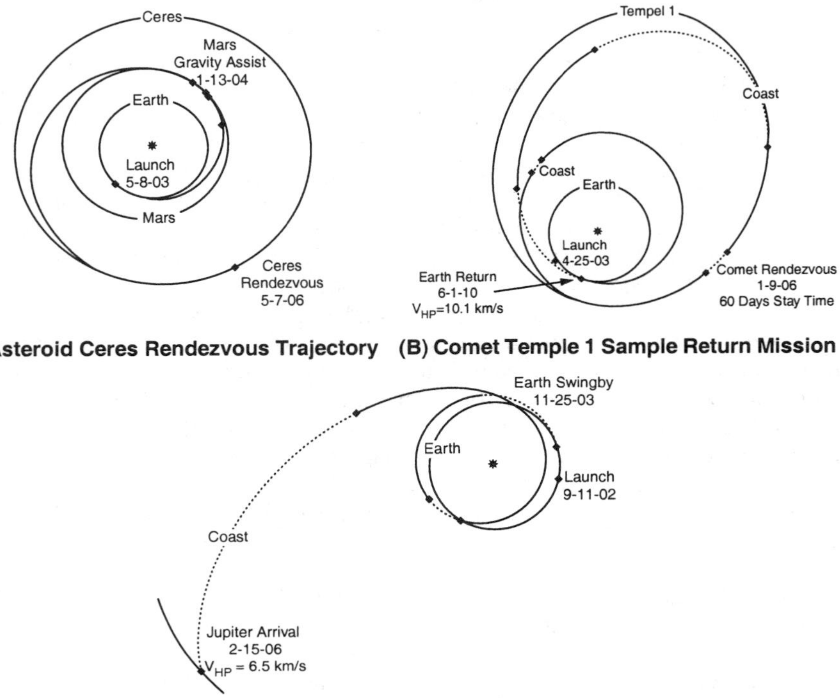

(A) Asteroid Ceres Rendezvous Trajectory **(B) Comet Temple 1 Sample Return Mission**

(C) SEP Earth Gravity Assist Jupiter Orbiter Trajectory

Fig. 12-31. SEP Transfer Trajectories for Three Mission Types: Ceres, Comet Temple 1, and Jupiter. (Sauer [1997].)

[Leipold, 1998]. Materials technology development, system deployment and control processes, and mission design continue to be studied at this time, with further progress expected to lead to greater acceptance of this novel technology by the space exploration community and government agencies.

12.8 Interstellar Exploration*

Pioneer 10 was launched on March 3, 1972. In 1991, it became the first spacecraft to go beyond the solar system and enter interstellar space. In a sense, the exploration of the galaxy has begun. However, Pioneer 10, and Pioneer 11 which followed closely

* Interstellar travel is not a realistic option in the near-term. Many people believe it to be impossible, in much the same way that many thoughtful scientists and engineers 100 years ago believed that space travel was impossible. Indeed, 100 years ago, space travel was impossible. And today, many of the ideas put forward for interstellar travel fail the basic test of violating physics. However, many do not. Physicist Robert Forward spent a number of years at the Hughes Research Laboratories studying the problem of interstellar travel and summarized the problem very well: "Interstellar travel is difficult, but it is not impossible" [Forward, 1986]. The purpose of this section is to understand the basic reasons that the problem is so hard, the relativistic equations of motion needed for working in this area and, at a very high level, the nature of a few of the possible solutions.

behind, were only symbolic in terms of interstellar travel. At the time it left the solar system, Pioneer was traveling at about 13 km/sec. If it were headed in the right direction, which it isn't, Pioneer could get to the nearest star in a bit more than 100,000 years, a somewhat longish time when programs are funded with public money and reviewed on a annual basis.

TABLE 12-25. The 20 Stars Nearest the Sun.* Only 8 of them are visible to the naked eye and 6 are multiple stars. ε Eridani and τ Ceti are often thought of as a good place to begin exploration because they are reasonably "sun-like".

Star	Distance (lt yrs)	Apparent Magnitude	Absolute Magnitude	Spectral Type
Sun		–26.72	4.85	G2 V
Centauri C (Proxima)	4.22	11.05	15.49	M5 V
Alpha Centauri A	4.39	–0.01	4.37	G2 V
Alpha Centauri B	4.39	1.33	5.71	K1 V
Barnard's Star	5.94	9.54	13.22	M5 V
G1 411	8.31	7.50	10.50	M2 Ve
Sirius A	8.60	–1.46	1.42	A1 V
Sirius B	8.60	8.30	11.20	wd
G1 729	9.70	10.45	13.14	M4.5 Ve
Epsilon Eridani	10.48	3.73	6.14	K2 V
G1 887	10.72	7.35	9.76	M2 Ve
Ross 128	10.86	11.10	13.47	M4.5 V
61 Cygni A	11.36	5.22	7.56	K5 Ve
61 Cygni B	11.36	6.03	8.37	K7 Ve
Procyon A	11.40	0.37	2.64	F5 IV-V
Procyon B	11.40	10.70	13.00	wd
G1 725 A	11.45	8.90	11.15	M4 V
G1 725 B	11.45	9.69	11.94	M5 V
GX And	11.64	8.08	10.39	M2 V
Epsilon Indi	11.81	4.68	8.37	K5 V
Tau Ceti	11.89	3.50	5.72	G8 Vp
G1 54.1	12.12	12.04	14.12	M5.5 Ve
Luyten Star	12.39	9.84	11.94	M3.5
Kapteyn's Star	12.78	8.84	10.88	M0 V
AX Mic	12.88	6.66	8.74	M0 Ve
Krüger 60 A	13.04	9.85	11.87	M2 V
Krüger 60 B	13.04	11.30	13.30	wd

* In the table, *absolute magnitude* is a measure of actual brightness of the star and *apparent magnitude* is how bright it appears in the sky (i.e., depending on absolute magnitude and distance). Smaller numbers correspond to brighter stars. (See Sec. 11.6.) The *spectral type* is a classification of stars by their spectra (depending primarily on temperature, size, age, and composition). The *main sequence* of stars follow the classification O, B, A, F, G, K, and M with type O being the very hot blue-white stars and types K and M being cool, reddish stars. The classes are further subdivided by tenths and a Roman numeral is added to show the *luminosity class* which is an indicator of intrinsic brightness. Alpha Centauri is very similar to the Sun. Unfortunately, its also part of a triple star system such that there would be dramatically varying temperatures on any planets in the system. Of our nearest neighbors, ε Eridani and τ Ceti are the non-multiple stars most like the Sun.

Within the solar system, the basic problem to be overcome is how much energy is required to get there and, therefore, how much fuel must be put into orbit at very high cost to accomplish what wants to be done. For interstellar travel, the problem is not cost, but whether the objective can be achieved at all on time scales consistent with human activities. On a human scale, the distances to the stars are enormous and the time scales very long. To get a sense of the magnitude of the problem, Table 12-25 gives the distances to the 20 stars nearest the Sun. Our closest neighbor is Proxima Centauri, one of the 3 components of the Alpha Centauri system, at a distance of 4.22 light years. This is the distance light travels in 4.22 years, which is about 100,000 times the distance from the Earth to Mars when they're on opposite sides of the Sun, or around 40,000,000,000,000 km. It's a long way.

Of course, a long distance just means I need to use a bigger rocket and go faster. Rockets can provide accelerations of several g's, but that's not particularly comfortable for people. If we assume a rocket accelerates continuously at 1g for 13 min, this is sufficient to get to low Earth orbit. In only 20 min at 1g we will get to the Earth's escape velocity of around 11 km/sec and will have traveled 7,000 km. If we fire our rocket continuously so as to maintain the 1g acceleration for 3 months, we will have gotten to a velocity of about 100,000 km/sec, or 30% of the speed of light (usually written as "0.3 c"). We will have traveled 500 billion km, 3000 times the distance from the Earth to the Sun, or a bit more than 1% of the distance to Proxima Centauri. At this point, we might as well turn off the rocket. Pushing more will increase the velocity only slightly and most of the energy will go into increasing the mass of the rocket. (See Sec. 12.8.1 for an explanation and relevant equations.) Cruising to Proxima Centauri at the speed we've gotten to will now take another 14 years.

Unfortunately, the scenario is even less appealing from an energy or propellant mass perspective. Using a very efficient hydrogen/oxygen rocket with a specific impulse of 450 sec, the rocket equation tells us that we can get to low Earth orbit with a propellant mass which is 5 times the mass of the empty rocket plus its payload, ignoring entirely any loses due to gravity or atmospheric drag. (See, for example, Sackheim and Zafran [1999].) In practice this is a challenging, but workable, problem. However, to keep our rocket going at 1g for 3 months requires a propellant mass $10^{10,000}$ times the mass of the rocket plus its payload. It is not just a matter of building better, more efficient, or more massive rockets. Getting to even the nearest stars requires a whole new process.

The basic problem of interstellar travel is a combination of distance, time, and amount of energy required. This has led Forward [1986] to come to four broad conclusions about the potential for interstellar travel:

1. **We can't do rapid interstellar travel with simple rocket technology.** If standard rockets are used, either the amount of propellant required will be orders of magnitude too large or the maximum velocity will be a very small fraction of the speed of light, such that the trip times will be many centuries. To make the trip within a reasonable human lifetime, we must use something other than normal rockets to avoid carrying all of the required reaction mass along on the trip.

2. **We can't do interstellar travel at 1g acceleration.** As discussed in the next section, a continuous 1g acceleration is simply not practical. After having reached some significant fraction of the speed of light, nearly all the propulsion energy goes into making the rocket heavier and harder to push, rather than making it go faster. (Explanations and equations are in Sec. 12.8.1.) This means that a reasonable mission will accelerate to some cruise velocity in the general vicinity of 0.2 c to 0.8 c, and will then coast for the remainder of the trip.

3. **We can't do interstellar travel in round-trip times of less than 10 years.** Traveling at 0.8 c to the nearest star and back, with no exploration or turn-around time, will take just over 10 years. This implies that interstellar travel and exploration will be a process spread out over many years or decades. However, information can be returned from an interstellar probe at the speed of light. Thus, traveling at 0.5 c means that information can be returned in 3 times the 1-way light travel time. At this speed, we could get information back from Proxima Centauri in 12.5 years and from any of the 20 to 30 nearest stars in less than 40 years.
4. **We can't do interstellar travel using only resources brought from the surface of the Earth.** Interstellar vehicles could certainly be built on the surface of the Earth. However, the energy source or reaction mass must almost certainly come from space. While this is a limitation, it is not necessarily a severe one. There is an enormous amount of mass and energy available in the solar system. There are about 10 million asteroids with a diameter greater than 1 km and a mass of more than 10^{12} kg [Cox, 2000]. At the distance of the Earth, the Sun is continuously providing 1,368 W/m^2 or 1.4 million kW/km^2. Of course, this falls off as $1/r^2$ as we leave the vicinity of the Sun. Thus, large quantities of energy and mass cannot be brought up from the surface of the Earth and are scarce in interstellar space. However, both are plentiful within the solar system. Energy and mass are not a major limitation, but cannot be brought from the surface of the Earth.

12.8.1 Relativistic Space Travel

As we have seen above, traveling to even the nearest stars requires going at speeds that are a substantial fraction of the velocity of light. At these speeds, ordinary Newtonian mechanics is no longer a good approximation and we need to use relativistic mechanics to do interstellar travel computations. The physical phenomena associated with both special and general relativity are covered in a variety of texts, such as Einstein [1936, 1952], Mermin [1968], and Kaufman [1973]. Relativistic time is discussed in Sec. 4.1.5 and a detailed discussion is provided by Seidelmann [1992]. The most important relativistic effects for interstellar space travel are as follows:

- **Absolute upper limit of the velocity of light.** No matter how hard or how long we push on a spacecraft, the velocity of light, c, is an upper limit to the spacecraft velocity, v. As we approach the velocity of light, the spacecraft velocity will increase ever more slowly and the mass of the spacecraft will increase. (The relevant equations are given below.)

- **Time dilation.** Moving clocks run slow. The clock on the spacecraft runs slower than the clock on the ground by the factor $\gamma \equiv (1 - v^2 / c^2)^{0.5}$. This means that on a long trip less time will have passed for the astronaut than will have passed for someone remaining behind on Earth. (This leads to the famous twin paradox described in the boxed example.) Thus, it is possible that trips of hundreds of years can be completed within the lifetime of a single crew. Time measured by a clock at rest with respect to the observer is called *proper time*, i.e., time as measured by the astronaut on board the spacecraft. With respect to the proper time, all moving clocks run slow.

- **The Lorentz contraction.** Moving objects are shorter. For the astronaut, the distance to the stars has contracted by the same factor of $\gamma = (1-v^2 / c^2)^{0.5}$ and, therefore, it won't take as long to get there. The various relativistic effects "work together" to produce strange results. Thus, what is a slowing down of the astronaut's clock as measured by an observer on Earth is a shrinking of the distance to be traveled by the astronaut. The distance in the frame for which the object is at rest is called the *proper distance.*
- **The lack of absolute simultaneity.** Whether or not two distant events are simultaneous (i.e., happen at the same time), depends on the velocity of the observer. Specifically, if two synchronized clocks are at rest with respect to each other at a proper distance, D, apart, then for an observer moving at velocity v parallel to the line joining them, the clock in the rear will be behind by Dv / c^2. It is this feature of special relativity that "resolves" many of the apparent paradoxes in relativity, including the twin paradox. It is also one of the hardest to accept because we want to believe that time has some absolute meaning—either events are simultaneous or they are not. Unfortunately, this is simply not the case when dealing with velocities that aren't small with respect to c.
- **The increase in mass of moving objects.** If we continue to push on our spacecraft, the velocity eventually approaches the velocity of light. As we get close to c, the velocity increases only slightly, but the mass of the spacecraft increases, such that the energy continues to increase as we continue to push.* The ratio of the *proper mass*, or rest mass, to the moving mass is, once again, γ. As discussed above, this makes space travel close to the velocity of light very inefficient—we are putting all of our energy into increasing the mass of the spacecraft while having very little effect on the velocity.

It is important to recognize that the relativistic concept of a "clock" doesn't mean just a mechanical or digital watch, but the flow of time however it is measured. A compelling demonstration of this was done in the 1960s at the Education Development Center for a film on time dilation [Frisch and Smith, 1963]. μ-mesons are elementary particles with a short half-life that are produced when cosmic rays hit the upper atmosphere. In the demonstration the number of μ-mesons arriving per hour is first determined on a mountain top at an elevation of 2000 m. Based on the measured laboratory decay rate only about 5% of the μ-mesons should survive until they reach sea level. However, when the experiment is repeated at sea level the count is more than 70% of the count on the mountain top. The μ-mesons are traveling very near the velocity of light. Time dilation has caused the μ-meson's internal clock to slow down such that many fewer have decayed. (From the perspective of the μ-meson, the Lorentz contraction has shortened the distance from the mountain top to sea level.) Thus, even remarkably fundamental clocks, such as those internal to elementary particles, run slow when moving at velocities close to c.

---

* Just as we like to think of time and length as intrinsic properties of the world around us, we tend to think of mass as an intrinsic property of matter. The problem with this is as follows. As we continue to apply force to our rocket, the momentum and energy increase indefinitely as they should. However, as we approach the speed of light, the velocity increases only very slowly. Therefore, we have to either introduce a new "fudge factor" in the definition of momentum and energy or redefine our concept of "mass" to mean the constant of proportionality between velocity and momentum such that the mass is a function of the velocity. While either is possible, physicists have chosen to adopt the latter approach.

The physical interpretation of relativistic space travel is more complex than the equations. Specifically, assume that a spacecraft of length, L_0, and mass, m_0, when at rest is traveling at constant velocity, v. Then the length, L, of the spacecraft when it is moving is given by:

$$L = L_0\sqrt{1 - v^2 / c^2} \equiv \gamma L_0 \tag{12-13}$$

where, as usual, c is the velocity of light. As discussed above, L_0 is called the *proper length* or *rest length.* The Lorentz contraction applies only in the direction of motion. The two axis perpendicular to the direction of motion do not change.

Similarly, a time interval, $\Delta\tau$, measured by a clock on board the spacecraft will be shorter than the same interval, Δt, measured by a clock which is at rest with respect to the observer on Earth:

$$\Delta\tau = \gamma\,\Delta t \tag{12-14}$$

where Δt is called the *proper time* **for the Earth observer**. Either an observer on the ground or one on the spacecraft is allowed to consider himself at rest. Thus, for both observers the other clock runs slow. (If this seems strange, see the boxed example on the twin paradox.)

If two distant clocks are synchronized (i.e., read the same time) when they are at rest with respect to each other, then in a frame of reference moving at velocity, v, with respect to the clocks, the trailing clock will be ahead by:

$$\Delta T = Dv / c^2 \tag{12-15}$$

where ΔT is the difference in absolute time* between the two clocks and D is the proper distance between them.

Finally, the increase in mass, m, and energy, E, with increasing velocity are given by:

$$m = m_0 / \gamma \tag{12-16}$$

and, of course, one of the most famous equations in physics:

$$E = mc^2 = m_0c^2 / \gamma \tag{12-17}$$

where, as usual, m_0 is the proper mass or rest mass, m is the spacecraft mass which now increases with increasing velocity, and E is the total energy consisting of the rest energy (m_0c^2) plus the kinetic energy. These and additional equations are derived in nearly all texts on Special Relativity. Particularly good explanations are those of Mermin [1968] and French [1968].

Given the equations above, and some care in interpretation of variables, we can determine the equations for time, distance, and mass for a rocket undergoing a constant acceleration, a, measured by an observer on board the rocket. Since the acceleration must be present for months to reach velocities approaching c, we generally assume that the acceleration will be close to 1 g, but of course this may or may not be true for any specific spacecraft solution. Let τ be time as measured on the rocket and t be time as measured on Earth. Then

$$d\tau = \gamma\, dt \tag{12-18}$$

* By absolute time we mean, for example, January 13th, 2014, at 1:00 pm UT. This is to distinguish it from a time interval of, for example, 2 hours 30 minutes.

where, as above, $\gamma \equiv (1 - v^2 / c^2)^{0.5}$ and v is the velocity of the rocket as measured from Earth or from the spacecraft. (The spacecraft velocity as measured from Earth is the same as the Earth velocity measured from the spacecraft, but in opposite directions, of course.) We also have:

$$a = \frac{d}{dt}\left[\frac{v}{\gamma}\right] \tag{12-19}$$

from which the velocity as a function of Earth time is

$$v(t) = \frac{at}{\sqrt{1 + (at / c)^2}} \tag{12-20}$$

This leads to the equation for distance traveled, x, as measured in the Earth frame of reference:

$$x(t) = \int_0^t v\, dt = \frac{c^2}{a}\left[-1 + \sqrt{1 + \left(\frac{at}{c}\right)^2}\right] \tag{12-21}$$

Finally, we have the interesting equation for time as a function of time:

$$\tau(t) = \int_0^t \gamma\, dt = \frac{c}{a}\left[\operatorname{arc\,sinh}\left(\frac{at}{c}\right)\right] \tag{12-22a}$$

$$= \frac{c}{a}\ln\left(\frac{at}{c} + \sqrt{1 + \left(\frac{at}{c}\right)^2}\right) \tag{12-22b}$$

where again τ is measured in the spacecraft frame, t is measured in the Earth frame, and a is the constant acceleration measured in the spacecraft frame. For a more detailed discussion of these equations see, for example, von Hoerner [1962, 1963].

In order to obtain the relativistic equivalent of the rocket equation [Eq. (12-1) in Sec. 12.2)], we need one more element from relativistic kinematics—the addition of velocities. Specifically, if a rocket is moving at velocity v relative to the Earth and shoots a bullet out the front at a velocity u with respect to the rocket, then the velocity of the bullet with respect to the Earth, w, is given by:

$$w = \frac{u + v}{1 + \left(uv / c^2\right)} \tag{12-23}$$

which reduces to the normal addition of velocities if both u and v are small with respect to c. In the case of a small velocity increment, du, provided by the rocket (and measured in the rocket frame of reference), we get:

$$\mathrm{d}v = \gamma^2\, \mathrm{d}u \tag{12-24}$$

This can then be combined with the conservation of momentum to obtain the *relativistic rocket equation* [von Hoerner, 1963; Oliver, 1990]:

$$\mathrm{d}v / \mathrm{d}m = -(u_e / m)\gamma^2 \tag{12-25}$$

The Twin Paradox

One of the most famous paradoxes in physics is the *twin paradox*, introduced by Einstein [1905] in his first paper on relativity. The *principle of relativity* states that one cannot tell by any experiment the difference between two frames of reference that are moving uniformly with respect to each other, i.e., an observer in either frame is allowed to consider himself at rest and the other frame as moving. Combining this principle with the results of the *Michelson-Morley experiment*, which showed that the velocity of light was constant in any frame of reference, led Einstein to conclude that time dilation must also occur, i.e., moving clocks run slow. This leads to a paradox in which one twin leaves Earth on a rocket and returns to find that the twin who remained behind is older than the one who traveled out and back. This appears to violate both common sense and the original principle of relativity.

In a way, we can resolve the twin paradox by saying that special relativity applies only to frames of reference that are in uniform motion with respect to each other and the twin who has traveled has had to undergo a large change in velocity to return home. Thus, in a formal sense, we can worm our way around having to numerically explain the twin paradox. However, if we do not wish to hide behind general relativity, we can still tackle the problem quantitatively within the framework of special relativity.

To make it simple, let's assume the rocket leaves Earth and accelerates instantly to 0.995 c. It arrives at Alpha Centauri, 4 light years away, and decelerates instantly to 0. It immediately repeats the process, accelerating to 0.995 c towards home and decelerating to 0 when it arrives. While traveling, $\gamma = 0.1$, so the arithmetic is easy, if not the logic. To the observer on Earth, the rocket has gone 8 light years (out and back) at a velocity of 0.995 c, so the trip takes 8.04 years. However, he measures the moving clock running slow by a factor of 10, so when the astronaut returns he is only 0.804 years older.

What happens from the perspective of the astronaut on the rocket? He steps into the rocket at time $t = 0$ at Earth and is immediately transformed into the moving reference frame of the rocket. In this frame the distance to Alpha Centauri is only 0.4 light years, so it will take 0.4 / 0.995 = 0.402 years to get there. At the time he left, the clocks on the Earth and Alpha Centauri were synchronized in the frame of reference in which they weren't moving. However, our clever astronaut knows about the lack of absolute simultaneity and, therefore, knows that in his current frame the clock on Earth must be $Dv/c^2 = 4 \times 0.995 = 3.98$ years behind. Since he got on board at $t = 0$, it must now be $t = 3.98$ years at Alpha Centauri. However, the Centaurian clock (and the Earth clock, of course) are running slow by a factor of $1/\gamma = 10$. Therefore, he will arrive at Alpha Centauri at $t = 0.402$ years on his clock and $t = 3.98 + 0.402/10 = 4.02$ years on the Centaurian clock.

Our intrepid traveler immediately transfers to the next rocket back. Having changed his frame of reference again, he knows the Centaurian clock will now be behind the Earth clock by 3.98 years, so it is now $t = 4.02 + 3.98 = 8.00$ years on Earth. Of course, it takes him 0.402 years to get home by his clock, which, since the Earth clock is still running slow, corresponds to only 0.04 years on Earth. Thus, he arrives home at $t = 0.804$ years on his clock and $t = 8.00 + 0.04 = 8.04$ years on the Earth.

Both twins come to the same conclusion, but for significantly different reasons. The basic problem we have trouble overcoming is that not only do moving clocks run slow (which seems a bit strange), but also what time it is at some distant place depends on how fast we're moving with respect to that distant clock. Another way to look at the twin paradox is to have both twins send out radio pulses to the other at 1 second intervals. We can go through much the same logic as above, counting the pulses that are emitted and received and come to the same conclusion as above. Both approaches to the twin paradox are explained in more detail by Mermin [1968]. French [1968] and Terletskii [1968] also provide excellent discussions of this and similar paradoxes in relativity theory.

where m is the rest mass of the rocket and u_e is the exhaust velocity relative to the rocket. Two specific cases are of interest for interstellar travel. If the exhaust velocity remains constant with respect to the rocket, then integrating over time yields:

$$\mu \equiv \frac{m_i}{m_f} = \left(\frac{1 + v/c}{1 - v/c}\right)^{c/2u_e} \tag{12-26}$$

$$\frac{v}{c} = \frac{\mu^{2u_e/c} - 1}{\mu^{2u_e/c} + 1} = \tanh\left(\frac{u_e}{c}\ln\mu\right) \tag{12-27}$$

where the rocket is assumed to start from rest and accelerate to velocity v. Here $\mu \equiv m_i / m_f$, where m_i is the initial proper mass of the rocket and m_f is the final proper mass. The second case is a photon rocket for which $u_e = c$. Here Eqs. 12-26 and 12-27 become:

$$\mu = \sqrt{\frac{1 + v/c}{1 - v/c}} \tag{12-28}$$

$$\frac{v}{c} = \frac{\mu^2 - 1}{\mu^2 + 1} \tag{12-29}$$

Oliver [1990] derives the above equations and provides substantial additional discussion on the performance of interstellar rockets.

12.8.2 Getting to the Stars

It is clear from the above discussion that interstellar travel will require not just building bigger and better rockets, but a fundamentally new approach to space travel in at least some respects. The problems of building a spacecraft or, for human missions, creating long-term life support can be solved by the application or extrapolation of technology that we understand today. The problem of propulsion is more fundamental. We need to build up a velocity at least 1,000 times greater than any current rockets provide and, if we want to stop and explore at the other end, get rid of it again. If we want to return, then we have to start again and stop again. At best, the technology to do this is conceptual and many of the proposed approaches may prove impossible to implement. The systems most often considered are:

- **Nuclear Electric Propulsion.** Nuclear fission systems that could be launched in the near term could reach the nearest stars in perhaps 10,000 years, cutting 90% off the Pioneer 10 transit time. Solar electric and laser electric are also possible, but even less efficient.
- **Nuclear Pulse Propulsion.** This approach, originally called "Orion," uses a series of nuclear fusion bombs to push the spacecraft to its destination. It was originally proposed at Los Alamos National Laboratory and has been worked on by, among others, Freeman Dyson [1968], the developer of the geodesic dome.
- **Antiproton Propulsion.** This is potentially a remarkably efficient energy source. A 1 ton interstellar probe could be accelerated to 0.1 c by using only 4

tons of liquid hydrogen and 10 kg of antihydrogen as the energy source. Antiprotons are being produced (in remarkably small quantities) and stored for days in current particle physics laboratories.

- **Fusion Rockets.** Controlled fusion is not yet available. If it does become possible, then there is the potential for using it for interstellar rocketry.
- **Interstellar Ramjet.** This concept uses a large magnetic scoop (on the order 10,000 km^2) to collect interstellar hydrogen and use it for controlled nuclear fusion such that the vehicle can effectively push against the interstellar medium to reach relativistic velocities. There are several variants on this approach. All remain in the realm of science fiction at the present time.
- **Beamed Power Propulsion.** In these systems the source of energy remains fixed in the Solar System and power is beamed to the interstellar starship. The three most promising approaches use a stream of small pellets, microwave beams, and lasers. The laser system is particularly interesting in that it can provide all four needed phases—acceleration, deceleration, return acceleration, and return deceleration [Forward, 1984]. It requires no new physics, but simply large scale engineering extrapolation of known technologies.

An excellent summary of the above approaches is provided by Forward [1986]. All of them represent travel to only the nearest stars. It is the huge distances and the remarkably slow speed limit of the velocity of light that restricts our capacity for far ranging interstellar travel. Table 12-26 summarizes the fundamental problem of travel

TABLE 12-26. Travel Data for Representative Destinations. Distances and travel times are all one-way. Travel at the relatively high spacecraft velocity of 25 km/sec is impractical because of the large distances to the stars. Travel at 1 g acceleration is impractical because of the enormous amounts of energy it would require.

Destination	Moon	Sun	Pluto	Alpha Centauri	Galactic Center	Magellenic Clouds	Andromeda Galaxy
Distance							
km	384,000	1.5×10^8	5.9×10^9	4.12×10^{13}	2.8×10^{17}	1.7×10^{18}	2.3×10^{19}
*AU**	0.00257	1.00	39.5	275,000	1.9×10^9	1.1×10^{10}	1.5×10^{11}
Light Years	4.06×10^{-8}	1.58×10^{-5}	6.2×10^{-4}	4.35	3.0×10^4	1.8×10^5	2.4×10^6
Travel at 25 km/sec							
Time Ellapsed	4.3 hr	69 days	7.5 yr	52,000 yr	3.6×10^8 yr	2.2×10^9 yr	2.9×10^{10} yr
Travel at 0.5 c							
Time Ellapsed on Earth	2.6 sec	16.6 min	11.0 hr	8.7 yr	60,000 yr	3.6×10^5yr	4.8×10^6yr
Time Ellapsed on Rocket	2.2 sec	14.4 min	9.5 hr	7.5 yr	52,000 yr	3.1×10^5yr	4.2×10^6yr
Travel at 1 g acceleration							
Time Ellapsed on Earth	3.5 hr	2.9 days	18 days	6.0 yr	30,000 yr	1.8×10^5yr	2.4×10^6yr
Maximum Velocity	0.0002 c	0.0040 c	0.026 c	0.95 c	1.00 c	1.00 c	1.00 c
Time Ellapsed on Rocket	3.5 hr	2.9 days	18 days	3.6 yr	20.0 yr	23.5 yr	28.5 yr

*1 AU (Astronomical unit) = mean distance from the Earth to Sun = 150,000,000 km

to more distant destinations. One of our nearest extragalactic neighbors is the Andromeda galaxy which contains on the order of 10 billion stars. You can see it with the naked eye on a dark night as a fuzzy patch in the northern sky. (Visually, the galaxy isn't small, it's simply faint. The dramatic long exposure photos we see of Andromeda are more than 6 times the size of the full Moon.) But even nearby galaxies are **very** far away. The light we see from Andromeda left there 2.4 million years ago. Even traveling at nearly the speed of light, it's a 5 million year round trip.

The literature base on interstellar exploration is enormous. Much of the professional technical literature on this topic appears in the *Journal of the British Interplanetary Society, JBIS*, which often runs complete issues on various aspects of interstellar travel. Robert Forward published a series of bibliographies, one of which took up an entire issue of *JBIS* and lists 2,699 articles, books, and reports conveniently sorted by subtopic, including more bibliographies [Mallove, et al., 1980]. Several similarly sorted updates have added a few thousand more entries [Paprotny, et al., 1983, 1984, 1986]. Good summaries of the state of the art in this area, along with more references, are provided by Forward [1986] and Vulpetti [1999].

References

Austin, R. E., M. I. Cruz, and J. R. French. 1982. "System Design Concepts and Requirements for Aeroassisted Orbital Transfer Vehicles." AIAA Paper 82-1379 presented at the AIAA 9th Atmospheric Flight Mechanics Conference.

Barber, T. A. and H. F. Meissinger. 1969. "Simplification of Solar-Electric Propulsion Missions by a New Staging Concept." AIAA Paper 69-251 presented at the AIAA 7th Electric Propulsion Conference, Williamsburg, VA, March 3–5.

Bate, R. R., D. D. Mueller, and J. E. White. 1971. *Fundamentals of Astrodynamics*. New York: Dover Publications.

Belbruno, Edward A., Rex. W. Ridenoure, and Jaime Fernandez. 1991. "To the Moon from a B-52: Robotic Lunar Exploration Using the Pegasus Winged Rocket and Ballistic Lunar Capture." Presented at the 5th Annual AIAA/Utah State University Conference on Small Satellites, Aug. 27–29.

Cefola, P.J. 1987. "The Long-Term Orbital Motion of the Desynchronized Westar II." AAS Paper 87-446 presented at the AAS/AIAA Astrodynamics Specialist Conference, Aug. 10.

Cox, Arthur N, ed. 2000. *Allen's Astrophysical Quantities* (4th ed.). New York: Springer-Verlag.

D'Amario, L.A., D.V. Byrnes, J. R. Johannesen, and B.G. Nolan. 1989. "Galileo 1989 VEEGA Trajectory Design." *Journal of the Astronautical Sciences*, 37:281–306.

Draim, John. 1985. "Three- and Four-Satellite Continuous Coverage Constellations." *Journal of Guidance, Control, and Dynamics*, 6:725–730.

————. 1987a. "A Common-Period Four-Satellite Continuous Global Coverage Constellation." *Journal of Guidance, Control, and Dynamics*, 10:492–499.

————. 1987b. "A Six-Satellite Continuous Global Double Coverage Constellation." AAS Paper 87-497 presented at the AAS/AIAA Astrodynamics Specialist Conference, Aug. 10.

————. 1997. "Optimization of the ELLIPSO and ELLIPSO 2G Personal Communications Systems." Paper C-4 presented at the IAF International Workshop on Mission Design and Implementation of Satellite Constellations, Nov. 17–19, 1997, Toulouse, France.

————. 1998. "Design Philosophy for the ELLIPSO Satellite System." Paper presented at the 17th AIAA International Communications Satellite Conference. Yokohama, Japan.

Draim, J., Helman, G., and Castiel, D. 1997. "The ELLIPSO Mobile Personal Communications System; It's Development History and Current Status." Paper IAF 97-M.3.03. Presented at the 48th International Astronautical Congress, Oct. 6–8, Turin, Italy.

Dyson, F. J. 1968. "Insterstellar Transport." *Physics Today,* October, 41–45.

Einstein, Albert. 1905. *The Principle of Relativity*. Translated by W. Perrett and G. B. Jeffrey. New York: Dover.

————. 1936. "Physics and Reality." *J. Franklin Inst.*, Vol. 221, P. 349–382.

Einstein, Albert. 1952, 1961. *Relativity: The Special and General Theory*. Translated by Robert W. Lawson. New York: Crown Publishers.

Farquhar, R. W. 2001. "The Flight of ISEE-3/ICE: Origins, Mission History, and a Legacy." *The Journal of the Astronautical Sciences*, Vol. 49, No. 1, January –March, pp. 23–73.

Faughnam, Barbara and Gregg Maryniak. 1987. *Space Manufacturing 6 Nonterrestrial Resources, Biosciences, and Space Engineering*. Proceedings of the Eighth Princeton/AIAA/SSI Conference, May 6–7, 1987. Washington D.C.: AIAA.

Fimple, W.R. 1963. "Optimum Midcourse Plane Change for Ballistic Interplanetary trajectories." *AIAA Journal,* 1:430-434.

Forward, Robert L. 1984a. "Round-Trip Interstellar Travel by Laser-Pushed Lightsails." *J. Spacecraft & Rockets.* Vol. 21.

————. 1986. "Feasibility of Interstellar Travel." *Journal of the British Interplanetary Society,* Vol. 39, No. 9, September.

————. 1989. "Statite Spacecraft that Utilizes Light Pressure and Method of Use." U.S. Patent No. 5,183,225. Issued Feb. 2, 1993.

French, A. P. 1968. *Special Relativity.* MIT Introductory Physics Series. NY: W. W. Norton and Company.

Friedman, L. 1978. "Solar Sailing—The Concept Made Realistic." Paper 78-82, AIAA 16th Aerospace Sciences Meeting, Huntsville, Alabama, January.

————. 1988. *Starsailing—Solar Sails and Interstellar Travel*. New York, NY: J. Wiley and Sons.

Frisch, D. H. and J. H. Smith. 1963. Film entitled *Time Dilation—An Experiment with μ-Mesons*, Education Development Center, Newton, MA.

————. 1963. *American Journal of Physics*, Vol. 31.

Gray, D. L. and Y. Hahn. 1995. "Maneuver Analysis of the Cassini Mission." AIAA Paper 95-3275. AIAA Guidance and Control Conference, Boston, MA, Aug.

Heppenheimer, T. A. 1977. *Colonies in Space*. Harrisburg, PA: Stackpole Books.

Hujsak, Edward. 1994. *The Future of U.S. Rocketry*. La Jolla, CA: Mina-Helwig Company.

Humble, Ronald W., Gary N. Henry, and Wiley J. Larson. 1995. *Space Propulsion Analysis and Design*. New York: McGraw-Hill.

Isakowitz, Steven J. 1999. *International Reference Guide to Space Launch Systems*, (3rd ed.). Reston, VA: American Institute of Aeronautics and Astronautics.

Kaufman, B., C. R. Newman, and F. Chromey. 1966. *Gravity Assist Optimization Techniques Applicable to a Variety of Space Missions*. NASA Goddard Space Flight Center. Report No. X-507-66-373.

Kaufmann III, William J. 1973. *Relativity and Cosmology*. NY: Harper and Row.

Koelle, Dietrich E. 1991. *TRANSCOST, Statistical-Analytical Model for Cost Estimation and Economic Optimization of Space Transportation Systems*. Munich, Germany: MBB Space Communications and Propulsion Systems Division, Deutsche Aerospace.

————. 2000. *Handbook of Cost Engineering for Space Transportation Systems*. Germany: TCS—Trans Cost Systems.

Leipold, M. 1998. "To the Sun and Pluto with Solar Sails and Micro-Sciencecraft." ACTA ASTRONAUTICA, Vol. 45, Aug.–Nov.

Leipold, Manfred E., Otto Wagner. 1996. "Mercury Sun Synchronous Polar Orbits Using Solar Sail Propulsion." *Journal of Guidance, Control and Dynamics*, Vol. 19, No. 6, Nov–Dec.

Leipold, M., et al. 1999. "ODISEE—A Proposal for Demonstration of a Solar Sail in Earth orbit." *Acta Astronautica*, Vol. 45, Aug.–Nov.

London, III, John R. 1994. *LEO on the Cheap—Methods for Achieving Drastic Reductions in Space Launch Costs*. Maxwell Air Force Base, AL: Air University Press.

————. 1996. "Reducing Launch Cost." In Wertz, James R., and Wiley J. Larson (eds.). *Reducing Space Mission Cost*. Torrance, CA, and Dordrecht, The Netherlands: Microcosm, Inc., and Kluwer Academic.

Luthey, J. L., F. Peralta, and J. L. Pojman. 1989. "Ulysses Mission Design After Challenger." AAS Paper 89-432 presented at the AAS/AIAA Astrodynamics Conference, Stowe, VT, August 7–10.

Mallove, Eugene F., Robert L. Forward. 1980. Zbigniew Paprotny, and Jurgen Lehmann. "Interstellar Travel and Communication: A Bibliography." *Journal of the British Interplanetary Society.* Vol. 33, No. 6, June.

McGolrick, J. E. (ed.). 1971. *Launch Vehicle Estimating Factors—For Use in Advanced Space Mission Planning.* NASA Headquarters Publication NHB 7100.5, January.

McInnes, Colin R. 1993. "Solar Sail Trajectories at the Lunar L Sub 2 Lagrange Point." *Journal of Spacecraft and Rockets*, Vol. 30, No. 6, Nov.–Dec.

————. 1999. *Solar Sailing: Technology, Dynamics and Mission Applications.* London: Springer.

Mease, K. D. 1988. "Optimization of Aeroassisted Orbital Transfer: Current Status." *The Journal of the Astronautical Sciences.* 36:7–33.

Meissinger, H.F., R.A. Park, and H.M. Hunter. 1968. "A 3-kw Solar Electric Spacecraft for Multiple Interplanetary Missions." *Journal of Spacecraft and Rockets*, Vol. 5, June.

Meissinger, Hans F. 1970. "Earth Swingby—A Novel Approach to Interplanetary Missions Using Electric Propulsion." AIAA Paper No. 70-1117, presented at the AIAA 8th Electric Propulsion Conference, Stanford, CA, August 31–September 2.

Meissinger, H.F., S. Dawson, and J.R. Wertz. 1997. "A Low-Cost Modified Launch Mode for High-C_3 Interplanetary Missions." AAS Paper No. 97-711, presented at the AAS/AIAA Astrodynamics Specialist Conference, Sun Valley, Idaho, August 4–7.

Meissinger, Hans F. and Simon Dawson. 1998. "Reducing Planetary Mission Cost by a Modified Launch Mode." Presented at the Third IAA International Conference on Low-Cost Planetary Missions, Pasadena, CA, April 27–May 1.

Meissinger, H. F. and S. Dawson. 2001. "Solar-Electric Planetary Missions with an Initial Out-of-Ecliptic Thrust Phase." AIAA *Journal Spacecraft and Rockets*, Vol. 38, No. 2, March–April.

Mermin, David N. 1968. *Space and Time in Special Relativity.* NY:McGraw-Hill Book Company.

Miller, J. K., B. G. Williams, W. E. Bollman, R. P. Davis, C. E. Helfrich, D. J. Scheeres, S. P. Synnott, T. M. Wang, and D. K. Yeomans, "Navigation of the Near Earth Asteroid Rendezvous Mission." AAS Paper 95-111 presented at AAS/AIAA Spaceflight Mechanics Meeting, Feb. 13–16.

Minovitch, M. A. 1963. "Determination and Characteristics of Ballistic Interplanetary Trajectories under the Influence of Multiple Planetary Attractions," Technical Report No. 32-464, Jet Propulsion Laboratory.

O'Leary, Brian O. 1982. *Space Industrialization, Vol. 1.* Boca Rotan, FL: CRC Press.

Oliver, B. M. 1990. "A Review of Interstellar Rocketry Fundamentals." *Journal of the British Interplanetary Society*, Vol. 43, pp. 259–264.

O'Neill, Gerard K. 1974. "The Colonization of Space." *Physics Today*, Vol. 27, No. 9, pp. 32–41.

————. 1976. *The High Frontier: Human Colonies in Space.* NY: William Morrow and Company.

Paprotny, Zbigniew and Jurgen Lehmann. 1983. "Interstellar Travel and Communication Bibliography: 1982 Update." *Journal of the British Interplanetary Society.* Vol. 36, No. 7, pp. 311–329, July.

Paprotny, Zbigniew, Jurgen Lehmann, and John Prytz. 1984. "Interstellar Travel and Communication Bibliography: 1984 Update." *Journal of the British Interplanetary Society.* Vol. 37, No. 11, pp. 502–512.

———. 1986. "Interstellar Travel and Communication Bibliography: 1985 Update." *Journal of the British Interplanetary Society.* Vol. 39, No. 3, July, pp. 127–136.

Peralta, F. and J. C. Smith, Jr. 1993. "Cassini Trajectory Design Description." AAS Paper 93-968 presented at AAS/AIAA Astrodynamics Conference, Victoria, B.C., Canada, Aug. 16–19.

Pocha, J. J. 1987. *An Introduction to Mission Design for Geostationary Satellites.* Dordrecht, The Netherlands: Kluwer Academic.

Prussing, J. E., and B. A. Conway. 1993. *Orbital Mechanics.* New York: Oxford University Press.

Reidel, J., W. Owen, J. Stuwe, S. Synnott, and R. Vaughan. 1990. "Optical Navigation During the Voyager Neptune Encounter." AIAA Paper 90-2877 presented at AIAA/AAS Astrodynamics Conference, Portland, OR, Aug. 20–22.

Reijnen, G. C. M. and W. De Graaff. 1989. *The Pollution of Outer Space, in Particular of the Geostationary Orbit:* Dordrecht, The Netherlands:Kluwer/Martinus Nijhoff Publishers

Sackheim, Robert, L. and Sidney Zafran. 1999. "Space Propulsion Systems." Chap. 17 in Wertz, J.R. and Larson, W.J. (eds). *Space Mission Analysis and Design* (3rd ed.). Torrance, CA, and Dordrecht, The Netherlands: Microcosm Press, and Kluwer Academic.

Sauer, C. D. 1976. "Optimum Solar Sail Interplanetary Trajectories." AIAA/AAS Astrodynamics Conference, San Diego, CA, Aug. 18–20.

————. "Planetary Mission Performance for Small Solar-Electric Propulsion Spacecraft." Paper AAS 93-561, presented at the AAS/AIAA Astrodynamics Specialist Conference, Victoria, BC, Canada, August 16–19.

————.. "Solar Electric Propulsion Performance for Medlite and Delta Class Planetary Missions." *Advances in the Astronautical Sciences*, Vol. 97, Part II. Proceedings of the AAS/AIAA Astrodynamics Conference, Sun Valley, Idaho, August 4–7.

Sauer, C.D., and Chen-Wan Yen. 1994. "Planetary Mission Capability of Small Low-Power Solar Electric Propulsion Systems." Paper IAA-L-0706. International Conference on Low-Cost Planetary Missions, Laurel, MD, April 12–25.

Serrano, J. B., J. Prieto, and S. E. Strandmoe. 1996. "A Preliminary Assessment of Various Autonomous Navigation Techniques for Interplanetary Missions." Presented at 3rd ESA International Conference on Spacecraft Guidance, Navigation and Control Systems, ESTEC, Noordwijk, Netherlands, Nov. 26–29.

Sergeyevsky, A. B., G. C. Snyder, and R. A. Cuniff. 1983. *Interplanetary Mission Design Handbook*, V*ol. 1, Part 2, Earth to Mars Ballistic Mission Opportunities, 1990-2005*. JPL Publication 82-43, NASA, Sept. 15. And subsequent Handbook series on Missions to Venus, Mars, Jupiter and Saturn published by Jet Propulsion Laboratory, Pasadena, CA.

Soop, E. M. 1994. *Handbook of Geostationary Objects*. Dordrecht, The Netherlands: Kluwer Academic.

Stuhlinger, E. 1964. *Ion Propulsion*. New York: McGraw-Hill.

Terletskii, Ya P. 1968. *Paradoxes in the Theory of Relativity*. NY: Plenum Press.

Uphoff, C. Reinert, R., and French, J. R. 1993. "Is it SEP Yet?" 30th Space Congress, Cocoa Beach, FL. April.

Vallado, David A. 2001. *Fundamentals of Astrodynamics and Applications* (2nd ed.). El Segundo, CA and Dordrecht the Netherlands; Microcosm Press and Kluwer Academic.

von Hoerner, Sebastian. 1962. "The General Limits of Space Travel." *Science*, Vol. 137, July.

————. 1963. "The General Limits of Space Travel." In *Interstellar Communication: A Collection of Reprints and Original Contributions*. A. G. W. Cameron, editor. pp. 144–159.

Vulpetti, Giovanni. 1999. "Problems and Perspectives in Interstellar Exploration." *Journal of the British Interplanetary Society*. Vol. 52, No. 9/10, July.

Wiesel, William E. 1989. *Spaceflight Dynamics*. New York: McGraw-Hill.

Wertz, James R., and Wiley J. Larson. 1996. *Reducing Space Mission Cost*. Torrance, CA, and Dordrecht, The Netherlands: Microcosm Press, and Kluwer Academic Publishers.

————. 1999. *Space Mission Analysis and Design* (3rd ed.). Torrance, CA, and Dordrecht, The Netherlands: Microcosm Press, and Kluwer Academic Publishers.

White, J. F. 1963. *Flight Performance Handbook for Powered Flight Operations*. NY: John Wiley & Sons.

Williams, S. N., and Coverstone-Carroll, V. 1997. "Benefits of Solar Electric Propulsion for the Next Generation of Planetary Mission." *Journal of the Astronautical Sciences*, Vol. 45, No. 2.

Wolff, P. J., F. Pinto, B. G. Williams, and R. M. Vaughan. 1998. "Navigation Considerations for Low-Thrust Planetary Missions." AAS Paper 98-201 presented at AAS/AIAA Space Flight Mechanics Meeting, Monterey, CA, Feb. 9–12.

Wolverton, R. W. ed. 1963. Space Technology Laboratories, Inc. *Flight Performance Handbook for Orbital Operations*. New York: John Wiley & Sons, Inc.

Wright, J., and J. Warmke. 1976. "Solar Sail Mission Applications." Presented at the AIAA/AAS Astrodynamics Conference, San Diego, CA, August 18–20.

Chapter 13

Constellation Design

A *constellation* is a set of satellites distributed over space intended to work together to achieve common objectives. If the satellites are close together, such as a flying interferometer, or spacecraft next to each other exchanging data or material, then it is called a *cluster* or *formation*, rather than a constellation. A number of past and proposed constellations are listed in Table 13-1. Notice that nearly all of the characteristics of the constellations vary dramatically, including size, altitude, and inclination. Because constellations are inherently very expensive, most are used for communications, navigation, or similar functions that take advantage of the global Earth coverage provided by satellites and difficult to achieve by other means.

The key background material on Earth coverage, large and small scale relative motion of satellites, and the design process for single satellite orbits has been covered in Chaps. 9, 10, and 12. This chapter provides additional relevant information on stationkeeping, collision avoidance, and constellation build-up, replenishment, and end-of-life, and makes use of this material to provide specific recommendations on constellation design. Finally, Sec. 13.7 provides an overview of the constellation design process and how to go about achieving this in a systematic way.

A major trend in the evolution of satellite systems is an increase in the number of smaller, lower-cost satellites. This has led to a dramatic increase in the number of Earth-orbiting constellations for observations, communications, navigation, and science. Consequently, constellation design has become a topic of considerable current work and will continue to grow in importance, both as constellations become more achievable and as the potential problems of collision avoidance and debris mitigation become more critical.

TABLE 13-1. Representative Past and Proposed Satellite Constellations.*

Name	Operator	Purpose	Status	Alt. (km)	Inc. (deg)	# of Sats	# of Planes
Aries	Constellation Comm Inc.	comm (voice, data, radiolocation)	planned	1,022	90	48	4
Astrolink	TRW	comm (broadband)	planned	GEO	—	4	—
Bankir	NPO Larochkine	comm (data)	planned	LEO	—	6/8	—
Celsat	Celsat Inc	comm (voice, video, data, radiolocation)	planned	GEO	0	1/2 + 1 spare	1
Coscon	KB Polyet	comm (data, radiolocation)	demo	1,000	83	32	—
Discoverer II	US DoD	Earth obs radar	planned	TBD (LEO)	TBD	TBD	TBD
DMSP	Military	meteorological	operational	822	99	2	—
Draim 4	N/A	continuous whole Earth coverage	theoretical	>38,736	31.3	4	4
DSP	Military	comm	deploying	GEO	—	16	1
ECCO	Constellation	comm	planned	1,018		48	
Ellipso	MCHI	comm (mobile voice)	planned	7.506 8,050	116.6 0	10 7	2 1
E-Sat	E-Sat Inc.	comm (message)	planned	1,262	—	6	—
FAISAT	Final Analysis	comm (message	planned	1,000	66/83	36 (+4), 2	—
FLTSATCOM	USN	UHF comm	operational	35,800	4–5	4	1
GalileoSat		navigation	planned	24,000	57–65	24	3
Gander	BNSC	ocean obs	planned	—	90	16	—
GGS	Japan/ESA	scientific	operational	—	—	2–5	—
Globalstar	Loral	comm (voice)	planned	1,386	47,55	24/48	14
Glonass	Russian govt	navigation	operational	—	—	24	—
GOES	NASA/NOAA	meteorological	operational	GEO	0–7	—	1
Gonetz	NPO Prikadnoy	comm (voice, data)	planned	1,400	82.6	24	4
GPS Block I	USAF/USN	navigation	operational	20,200	63	24	3
GPS Block II	USAF/USN	navigation	deploying	20,200	63	55	21
GPS III	USAF/USN	navigation	planned	—	—	—	—
New ICO	ICO Teledesic Global	comm (voice, broadband)	planned	10,335	45	10	3
Inmarsat	Private	comm (mobile voice)	operational	—	—	—	—
Intelsat	COMSAT, Intel	comm (voice, data, TV)	operational	GEO	0	17	1
Iridium	Motorola	comm	bankrupt	805	90	66	6
INX	Iridium LLC	comm (voice)	planned	850	90	96	—
iSky	iSky	comm	planned	—	—	—	—
Leo-One	LEO One USA	comm (message)	planned	950	50	48	8
LEOSAT	Low-Earth Orbit Satellite Corp	comm (data radio-message)	operational	1,000	42	24	
Magellan	ESA/EC	navigation	planned	—	—	—	—
Marathon	Marathon-Zemlia, NPO	comm (voice, telex, telecopy)	operational	3 GEO, 8 elliptic	0, 63	11	—
Molniya	USSR	comm	operational	1,000/ 26,600	63.4	many	—
M-SAT	American Mobile Satellite Corp, Telesat Mobile	comm (voice, data)	operational	GEO	0	2	1
MSSP	Military	comm	proposed	LEO	various	200–400	many
Norstar 1	Norris Satellite Communication	comm (voice, data)	operational	GEO	0	1	1

TABLE 13-1. Representative Past and Proposed Satellite Constellations.* (Continued)

Name	Operator	Purpose	Status	Alt. (km)	Inc. (deg)	# of Sats	# of Planes
Odyssey	TRW	comm (voice)	planned	10,354	50	12 + 3 spare	3
ORBCOMM	Orbital Comm Corp	comm (radio-message)	operational	970	40	20	3
Orbview	Orbital	Earth obs (visual)	in design	—	—	—	—
Pentriad	Denali Telecom		planned	elliptical	—	14	—
Project 21	Inmarsat	comm (voice, data)	planned	—	—	35/40	—
RapidEye	Kayser-Threde	Earth obs (agricul)	planned			4	
Resource 21		Earth obs (agricul)					
S-80	CNES	comm (radio-location & message)	planned	1,000–1,500	45–55	—	—
SBIRS	US DoD	Earth obs (IR)	planned	GEO/MEO /LEO	TBD	TBD	TBD
Skybridge	Skybridge Ltd, Alcatel	comm (broadband, data)	planned	1,469.3	53	80	20
Spaceway	Hughes	comm (broadband)	planned	10,352	—	20	—
Starnet	Starsys Inc	comm (voice, radiolocation)	planned	1,300	50/60	—	—
TDRS	NASA	comm	operational	GEO	0–2	5	1
TechSat 21	USAF AFRL	Earth obs (SAR)	planned	TBD	TBD	—	constel
Virgo	Virtual Geosatellite	—	planned	800 × 27,000	—	15 + 3 spare	—
Vitasat	Volunteers in Technical Assistance	comm (data)	planned	LEO	—	—	—
Walker 5	NA	continuous whole Earth coverage	theoretical	>38,655	43.7	5	5

* Status as of January 1, 2000.

One of the most important results of decades of constellation studies has been that no absolute rules exist for constellation design. As described in the boxed example in Sec. 13.1, a constellation of satellites in randomly spaced low-Earth orbits is a possibility for a survivable communications system. One of the most interesting characteristics of the low-Earth orbit communications constellations is that constellation builders have invested billions of dollars and come up with distinctly different solutions. For example, a higher altitude means fewer satellites, but a much more severe radiation environment, such that the cost of each satellite will be higher, and the life potentially shorter. Both solutions are being used by commercial constellations. Similarly, circular orbits provide a simple, low-cost satellite design. However, elliptical orbits allow an additional degree of freedom, which allows the constellation to be optimized for multiple factors, but requires a more complex satellite operating over a range of altitudes and velocities, and passing through heavy radiation regimes. (See, for example, Draim et al. [1996, 1999].) Again, both solutions are being used by modern constellations. Because the constellations' size and structure strongly affect system cost and performance, we must carefully assess alternative designs and document the reasons for trades which are made. It is this list of reasons that allows the constellation design process to continue in order to achieve the system objectives at minimum cost and risk.

While there are no absolute rules, there are a number of key issues which dominate constellation design trades, as listed in Table 13-2. These are discussed briefly below, and in more detail later in the chapter. Because virtually any multi-satellite system will be inherently expensive, all constellation design trades are ultimately based on cost vs. performance. Thus, each of the issues in Table 13-2 is a major determinant of system cost, performance, or both.

TABLE 13-2. Principal Issues which Dominate Constellation Design. Virtually all constellations are designed on a cost vs. performance basis. See Secs. 13.3 and 13.7 for a detailed discussion of the contellation design process.

Issue	Why Important	What Determines It	Principal Issues or Options	Where Discussed
Coverage	Principal performance parameter	Altitude, minimum elevation angle, inclination, constellation pattern	Gap times for discontinuous coverage; Number of satellites simultaneously in view for continuous coverage	Chap. 9, Sec. 13.3
Number of Satellites	Principal cost driver	Altitude, minimum elevation angle, inclination, constellation pattern	Altitude, minimum elevation angle, inclination, constellation pattern	Sec. 13.3
Launch Options	Major cost driver	Altitude, inclination, spacecraft mass	Low altitude, low inclination costs less	Secs. 12.3, 13.3
Environment	Radiation level and, therefore, lifetime and hardness requirements	Altitude	Options are below, in, or above Van Allen radiation belts	Fig. 2-12, Sec. 12.4
Orbit Perturbations (Stationkeeping)	Causes constellations to disassociate over time	Altitude, inclination, eccentricity	Keep all satellites at common altitude and inclination to avoid drifting apart	Secs. 2.4, 13.4
Collision Avoidance	Snowball effect can destroy entire constellation	Constellation pattern, orbit control	No option—must design entire system for collision avoidance	Sec. 13.5
Constellation Build-Up, Replenishment, and End-of-Life	Determines level of service over time and impact of outages	Altitude, constellation pattern, build-up and sparing philosophy	Sparing: on-orbit spares vs. launch on demand; End-of-life: Deorbit vs. raise to higher orbit	Secs. 2.6.4, 13.6
Number of Orbit Planes	Determines performance plateaus	Altitude, inclination	Fewer planes means more growth plateaus and more graceful degradation	Secs. 2.6.2, 13.6

Coverage

Coverage is ordinarily the principal performance parameter. (See Chap. 9, Sec. 13.3.) It is normally the reason we are creating a constellation in the first place. If the coverage requirement is not continuous, then we are typically interested in minimizing the gap times for coverage of regions of interest. Continuous coverage most often requires that a region of interest, and perhaps the whole world, be seen at all times by at least one satellite in the constellation. However, multiple continuous coverage may also be required in some circumstances. For example, GPS requires continuous coverage of the entire world by a minimum of four non-coplanar satellites.

Number of Satellites

Typically, the number of satellites is seen as the principal cost driver, and the cost is usually assumed to be proportional to this number. (See Sec. 13.3.) Thus, the most common goal in constellation design is to achieve the desired coverage with the minimum number of satellites. Nonetheless, a minimum number of satellites may not represent minimum cost. A smaller constellation may require larger or more complex satellites. Since constellations with fewer satellites are typically higher, they may also have greater launch costs. Thus, a constellation of 20 satellites in low-Earth orbit may or may not be significantly cheaper than a constellation of 3 or 4 satellites in geosynchronous orbit.

Launch Options

After the number of satellites, the launch requirements normally represent the principal cost driver for the system, and may also represent the largest risk, since only about 90% of all launches are successful. (See Secs. 12.3, 13.3.) Typically, a given level of coverage can be achieved with fewer satellites at a higher altitude. However, the higher altitude and increased mass due to increased power and performance requirements tends to drive up the launch costs, which in turn, pushes the altitude down again.

Environment

For purposes of constellation design, the vacuum, thermal, and zero-g environment are largely independent of orbit. (See Fig. 2-12 in Secs. 2.3, 12.4.) However, the radiation environment is dramatically dependent on the altitude. Being in or above the Van Allen belts can increase the radiation by several orders of magnitude and therefore put demanding and expensive requirements on the spacecraft and potentially limit the lifetime of radiation-sensitive components, such as solar arrays or computers.

Orbit Perturbations (Stationkeeping)

The dominant perturbations for most Earth satellites are drag, which is a function principally of altitude, and the Earth's oblateness effects, which are a function of altitude, inclination, and eccentricity. (See Secs. 2.4, 13.4.) Because we cannot realistically use propellant to cancel the effects of oblateness, constellations with satellites at different altitudes, inclinations, or eccentricities will drift apart rapidly over time. In order to maintain the constellation structure, nearly all constellations have satellites at a common altitude, inclination, and eccentricity, except for a few special cases, such as the addition of an equatorial orbit for which orbit rotation does not matter. In addition, constellations of satellites in eccentric orbits will nearly always be at the critical inclination of 63.4 deg, so that apogee and perigee do not rotate.

Collision Avoidance

The single largest threat to constellations in the long term is the problem of satellite collisions as discussed further in Sec. 13.5. Specifically, collisions within a constellation can have a cascading or snowball effect in which a debris cloud remains within the constellation structure, thereby dramatically increasing the probability of subsequent collisions. Thus, while the probability of collision is inherently low because space is large and spacecraft are small, it is nonetheless critical to design the entire system (i.e., the constellation, the spacecraft, and the launch and de-orbit processes) for collision avoidance.

Constellation Build-Up, Replenishment, and End-of-Life

Historically, most constellations spend most of their time in a less-than-complete configuration. Consequently, it is critical to consider as a fundamental part of constellation design the process of how the constellation is to be constructed and what happens when spacecraft fail. In practice, this area is frequently given only minimal attention. However, it may represent a major operations cost driver. Equally critical is the end-of-life problem because dead satellites must be removed from the constellation pattern or unacceptable collision probabilities will result. (See Secs. 2.6.4 and 13.6.)

Number of Orbit Planes

The key issue in terms of the number of orbit planes is that moving satellites within a plane takes extremely small amounts of propellant, whereas changing the orbit plane takes very large amounts of propellant. Consequently, rephasing within planes is economical, and can be done often. This allows much more flexibility for the in-plane structure, and means that constellations with a smaller number of orbit planes will have more performance plateaus as the system is built up, and more graceful degradation if there are spacecraft failures. In general, higher constellations can have fewer orbit planes, and there will be a series of altitude plateaus below which additional planes will be required. (See Secs. 2.6.2 and 13.6.)

13.1 Coverage in Adjacent Planes

Before discussing constellation patterns, we need additional background on coverage in adjacent orbit planes of a constellation. Chapter 10 provided a detailed discussion of spacecraft relative motion and of the coverage and viewing angles by satellites in adjacent planes. Most constellations involve multiple satellites per plane and a series of planes spaced more or less uniformly along the equator. One way to view this problem is to look at a series of relative motion analemmas, as described in Sec. 10.1. For satellites in the same plane, there will be no relative motion to first order, and the relative motion analemma reduces to simply a dot in the orbit plane, ahead of or behind the reference satellite. The series of satellites in adjacent planes will each move on an analemma for which the half-height is equal to the relative inclination between the two planes. Note that all of the satellites in an adjacent plane will move on relative motion analemmas which are identical in size and shape. (See Fig. 10-9 in Sec. 10.1.1.) Differing phases in the adjacent plane will simply move the relative motion analemma along the reference orbit plane. Thus, choosing any satellite in the constellation as our reference satellite, all other satellites which are not in the same plane will move back and forth across the plane of the reference satellite, reflecting the fact that any two orbit planes either coincide or intersect at two points 180 deg apart. The larger the relative inclination, the larger the relative motion analemma.

An alternative approach to the relative motion analemma is discussed here, in which we look at the relationship between coverage circles both within a single orbit plane and between adjacent planes. The simplest coverage relationship between satellites is, of course, for those in the same orbit plane as shown in Fig. 13-1. As can be seen from the figure, the spacing between satellites in a single orbit plane determines whether coverage in that plane will be continuous, and the width of the continuous coverage region.

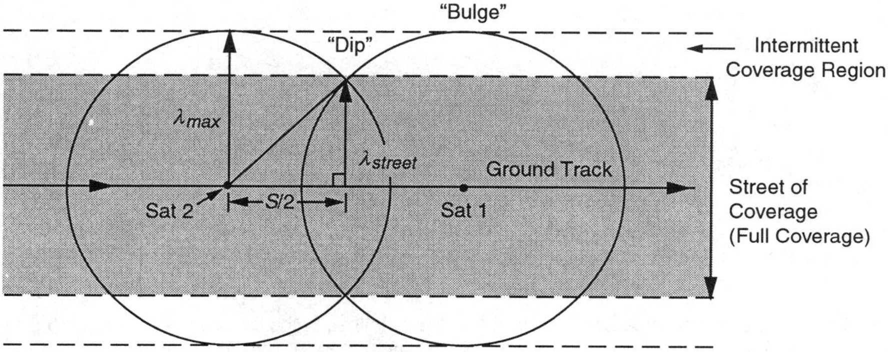

Fig. 13-1. The "Street of Coverage" is a Swath Centered on the Ground Track for which there is Continuous Coverage.

Assume that there are N satellites equally spaced at $S = 360/N$ deg apart in a given orbit plane and that λ_{max} is the maximum Earth central angle, as defined in Sec. 9.1. [See Eqs. (9-2) to (9-7).] There will be intermittent coverage throughout a swath of half-width λ_{max}. If $S > 2\ \lambda_{max}$, the coverage is intermittent throughout the entire swath. If $S < 2\ \lambda_{max}$, there is a narrower swath, often called a *street of coverage*, centered on the ground trace and of width $2\ \lambda_{street}$, in which there will be continuous coverage. This width is given by:

$$\cos \lambda_{street} = \cos \lambda_{max} / \cos (S/2) \tag{13-1}$$

In the coverage diagrams such as Fig. 13-1, the ground traces and coverage circles are projected onto a fictitious, non-rotating Earth (i.e., one fixed in inertial space). If we are interested in continuous coverage, this is not an issue. If the system continuously covers all of the surface of a non-rotating Earth, then it will also cover all of the surface of the real Earth, and we do not need to take into account the rotation of the Earth to determine coverage. However, if coverage gaps are allowed in a particular constellation, then we need to be concerned about the rotation of the Earth carrying one coverage gap into another, such that the gap is longer than we would otherwise have calculated.

A second issue for the figures is how to treat elliptical orbits. In this case, the ground trace in inertial space will still be a great circle. However, the rate of travel along the great circle and the size of the coverage circle will both vary. For moderate eccentricities, we can use the series expansion in Sec. 2.1.8 (see Eq. 2-12). λ_{max} will then be a function of the altitude and, therefore, of the position along the ground trace.

Returning to the coverage patterns themselves, if the satellites in adjacent orbit planes are going in the same direction, then the "bulge" in one orbit can be used to offset the "dip" in the adjacent orbit, as shown in Fig. 13-2. In this case, the maximum

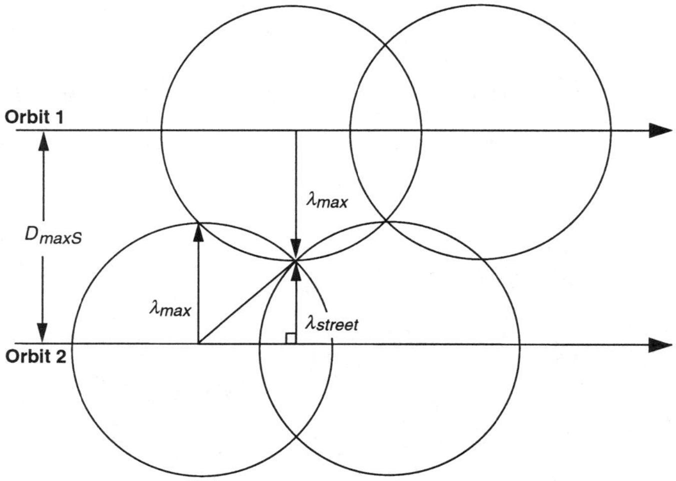

Fig. 13-2. Coverage in Adjacent Planes. If the satellites in the planes are moving in the same direction, the coverage pattern can be designed to provide maximum overlap.

perpendicular separation, D_{max}, between orbit planes with continuous coverage is

$$D_{maxS} = \lambda_{street} + \lambda_{max} \quad \text{(moving in the same direction)} \quad (13\text{-}2)$$

If the satellites are moving in opposite directions, then the bulge and the dip cannot be made to continuously line up and, therefore,

$$D_{maxO} = 2\,\lambda_{street} \quad \text{(moving in opposite directions)} \quad (13\text{-}3)$$

Note that the equations above are correct only in terms of the perpendicular distance between the orbit planes at their maximum separation. Because the ground traces are great circles, this maximum separation occurs at only two points in both orbits, 90 deg on either side of the point where the two orbits cross. While this is apparent for polar orbits, it is true for any pair of orbits. For most constellations, the inclination of adjacent orbit planes will be the same in order to maintain the same node rotation rate. Consequently, the relevant orbit parameters will be the spacing between the nodes, ΔN, and the common inclination of the orbits, i. This geometry is shown in Fig. 13-3. Each orbit crosses the equator at inclination i, reaches its maximum latitude 90 deg later, then comes back toward the equator. The *relative inclination,* discussed in more detail in Sec. 10.1, is the angle at which the two orbits intersect and is also the angular separation between the orbit planes, 90 deg from this intersection. If we draw the great circle arc connecting the two orbits at their greatest separation, this arc will cross the equator midway between the two nodes, forming two right spherical triangles that are convenient for computation. From this triangle, we find:

$$\sin(i_R/2) = \sin(\Delta N/2)\sin i \quad (13\text{-}4)$$

Similarly, we define the phase offset, $\Delta\phi$, between the two orbits as the difference in path length along the two orbits from the nodes to the point at which the orbits intersect. This would also be the relative phase between two satellites in these orbits which cross the ascending nodes at the same time. Again, from the small spherical

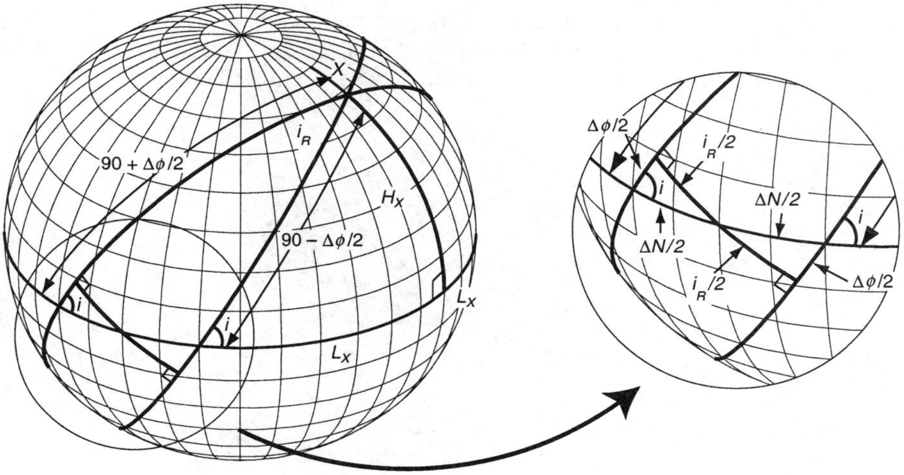

Fig. 13-3. Relative Geometry Between Two Planes at the Same Inclination. The great circle 90 deg from the intersection of the two planes crosses the equator midway between the two nodes and forms two identical right spherical triangles.

triangles in Fig. 13-3, we have:

$$\tan(\Delta\phi/2) = \tan(\Delta N/2)\cos i \qquad (13\text{-}5)$$

To connect Fig. 13-3 with Figs. 13-2 and 13-1, note that the maximum spacing between the two orbit planes, D, is just equal to the relative inclination, i_R; thus:

$$D = i_R \qquad (13\text{-}6)$$

We can then use Eq. (13-4) to solve for the node spacing corresponding to two orbits of inclination i and maximum separation D, as follows:

$$\sin(\Delta N/2) = \sin(D/2) / \sin i \qquad (13\text{-}7)$$

Finally, it is convenient to determine the longitude shift L_x, and latitude H_x, of the point at which the two orbits intersect. From Fig. 13-3, we see immediately:

$$L_x = 90 \text{ deg} - \Delta N/2 \qquad (13\text{-}8)$$

$$\tan H_x = \cos(\Delta N/2)\tan i \qquad (13\text{-}9)$$

Surrounding each ground trace in Fig. 13-3 is a swath of half-width λ_{max} or λ_{street}, depending on the application. These swaths are illustrated in Fig. 13-4, in which the ground trace is now the dashed line in the center of each swath. In some respects, Fig. 13-4 is simply a more accurate representation of Fig. 13-2, in which the geometry on the sphere is now taken into account. Note that the swaths between adjacent orbit planes overlap substantially, as shown by the shaded region in Fig. 13-4. This overlap is at a maximum where the two orbit planes cross, and at a minimum at the equator. The shaded area is the region of double coverage in which satellites from either orbit plane can be used. Similarly, if the spacing between nodes is sufficiently far apart, there will be a similar diamond-shaped gap in coverage centered on the equator. The size of the overlap region or uncovered region can be easily determined for any particular problem using the geometry of Figs. 13-3 and 13-4. This allows us to do the basic coverage calculations for any two orbit planes in a constellation.

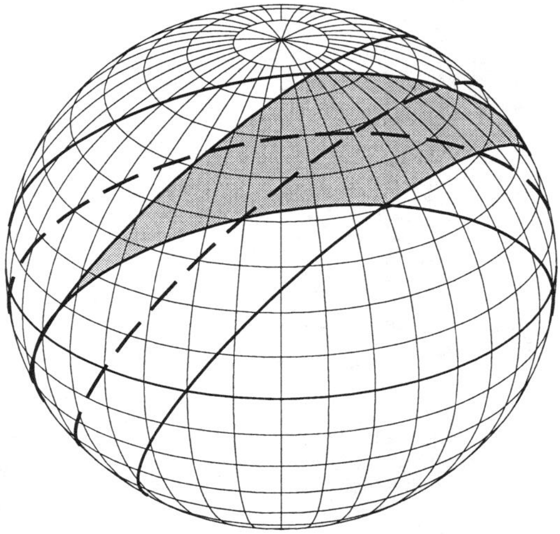

Fig. 13-4. Two Swaths with the Geometry Defined in Fig. 13-3. Overlapping coverage is shaded. The minimum overlap occurs at the equator. This provides a more realistic view than the schematic representation in Fig. 13-2.

13.2 Constellation Patterns

As discussed briefly in the introduction, one of the most remarkable facets of constellation design is the diversity of both constellation patterns and methods of analyzing them. Table 13-3 from Mora et al. [1997] provides an excellent summary of this historical process. Conceptually, we like to think of there being a small number of possible constellation configurations, roughly equivalent to the five regular solid geometry figures, and beyond that the number of satellites needed would simply decrease smoothly and uniformly with increasing altitude. Of course the problem is more complex because each of the satellites is in an orbit and therefore is moving with respect to the other satellites in the pattern, unless the others are simply leading or trailing in the same orbit.

In practice, there has been no single universal constellation pattern. Instead, there are multiple issues that tend to drive constellation design, each leading to somewhat different characteristics. For example, we may want complete global coverage but may also want to concentrate a higher fraction of our resources on high northern latitudes where most of the world's population resides. In most constellations, we would like to minimize the number of satellites, but would also prefer to stay below the Van Allen radiation belts to reduce the cost and complexity of each satellite. These diverse requirements have led to diverse solutions.

TABLE 13-3. Review of Constellation Design.†

Author	Year	Orbit type	Design method*	Remarks
Lüders	1961	circ., inclined, symmetrical	SoC	full single coverage
Ullock, Schoen	1963	circ., polar, non-symmetr.	SoC	phasing of co-rotating planes
Walker	1970 1977	star pattern delta pattern	satellite triad	T/P/F and inc. 5 sat. for global cov.
Mozhaev	1972	circular	symm. group	hard to find
Emara, Leondes	1976	circular, inclined	pt cov simul.	optimum 4×2 and 3×4
Beste	1977	circ., polar, non-symmetr.	SoC	systematic, mult. cov.
Ballard	1980	rosette (delta pattern)	satellite triad	systematic, mult. cov.
Lang, Hanson	1983	delta pattern	pt cov simul.	minimum revisit time
Rider	1986	delta pattern	SoC	analyt. closed form, mult. cov.
Draim	1986	elliptic, high altitude	tetrahedron	4 s/c continuous cov.
Adams, Rider	1987	polar, circular, non-symm.	SoC	systematic computational approach
Lang	1987	circular, inclined	point cov + s/c triad	2 step approach.
Hanson, Linden	1988	circular, inclined	SoC	BTH double, ATH single
Mainguy et al.	1989	geos., elliptic, inclined	zonal cov.	SYCOMORES, 2–3 s/c constellation
Rondinelli et al.	1989	GEO (3) + TUNDRA(2)	zonal cov.	orbit control analysis
Hanson, Higgins	1990	geosynchronous	pt cov simul.	geostationaty, Walker, elliptic, com.
Maral et al.	1990	LEO circular	zonal cov.	network topology
Baranger et al.	1991	GPS like	pt cov simul.	adaptative random search, PDOP
Hanson et al.	1992	circular, inclined	cov. timeline meshing	time gap, partial cov, repet. g. track
Lang	1993	circ., polar, non-symmetr.	pt cov simul.	up to 100 s/c
Werner et al.	1995	LEO – ICO	analytical approx.	network topology sim.
Radzik, Maral	1995	Walker and Beste types	SoC	min. revisit time
Sabol et al.	1996	ELLIPSO	refinement	orbital perturbations
Ma, Hsu	1997	Repeat. ground track	cov. timeline meshing	part. cov, oblate earth
Kelley, Fischer	1997	GPS orbit type	simulated annealing	VDOP optimization
Pablos, Martin	1997	GEO + IGSO	zonal coverage	availability, integrity
Lansard, Palmade	1997	LEO circular	Design to cost	Cost/efficiency, spares, availability

TABLE 13-3. Review of Constellation Design.† (Continued)

Author	Year	Orbit type	Design method*	Remarks
Palmade et al.	1997	LEO circular	Double Walker	GEO interference constraint
Boudier et al.	1997	GEO + MEO	Hybrid	Communication, stationkeeping
Renault	1997	GEO + IGSO	Hybrid	Navigation const., HDOP, VDOP
Micheau, Thiebolt	1997	GEO + LEO	Walker	Accuracy, integrity, continuity
Perrota et al.	1997	LEO circular	Walker	Nav., 75 s/c constel.
Palmerini	1997	Elliptical	Hybrid	Addl. local cov.
Draim	1997	Elliptical + circular	Hybrid systems	Stationkeeping, collision avoidance
Cornara et al.	1997	GEO, LEO	Various	Geom. and dynamics s/c interaction
Ulivieri et al.	1997	LEO sun-sync. Circ.	Optimal revisit time	Earth observation
Lang, Adams	1997	LEO circular	pt cov simul.	Comparative table of opt. Const.
Lucarelli et al.	1998	circular	Hippopede	General analytic approach

* SoC = street of coverage pt cov = point coverage simulation
† Adapted from Mora et al. [1997], which also includes a detailed list of references.

An interesting example of this solution diversity is the straightforward question for constellation design, "What is the minimum number of satellites required to provide continuous coverage of the Earth?" In the late 1960s, Easton and Brescia [1969] of the United States Naval Research Laboratory analyzed coverage by satellites in two mutually perpendicular orbit planes and concluded that at least **six** satellites were needed to provide complete Earth coverage. In the 1970s, John Walker [1971, 1977, 1984] at the British Royal Aircraft Establishment expanded the types of constellations considered to include additional circular orbits at a common altitude and inclination. He concluded that continuous coverage of the Earth would require **five** satellites. Because of his extensive work, *Walker constellations* are a common set to evaluate for overall coverage as discussed below. Finally, in the 1980s, John Draim [1985, 1987a, 1987b] found and patented a constellation of **four** satellites in elliptical orbits which would provide continuous Earth coverage. A minimum of four satellites is required at any one instant to provide full coverage of the Earth. Consequently, while the above progression looks promising, the 1990s didn't yield a three-satellite full Earth coverage constellation and the 2000s are unlikely to provide a two-satellite constellation.

In principle, specifying a constellation pattern means specifying the number of satellites and the six orbit elements for each. Thus, in some sense, the process of constellation design is the process of filling in an $n \times 6$ matrix where n is the number of satellites. In practice, it rarely works that way. Because of the need for symmetry, there are usually far fewer free parameters. At the same time, a great many practical constellations, such as GPS, are not fully symmetric, such that more than the minimum number of parameters is often needed. In addition, a non-orbit parameter, the swath width or minimum working elevation angle, is a key element of constellation design and should be specified as a constellation parameter, although this is rarely done. As discussed numerically in Secs. 13.1 and 13.3, the swath width is a function of the elevation angle and the altitude. In turn, the node spacing for the constellation is a function of the swath width and the inclination.

We discuss below the most common constellation patterns and then summarize some other patterns which have been proposed, including a constellation pattern which has no structure at all. (See the boxed example at the end of the section.)

Geosynchronous Constellations

The simplest constellation pattern is a set of geosynchronous satellites that work together to perform a common function. For example, TDRS consists of multiple satellites in geosynchronous orbit that cover a large fraction of the Earth as shown in Fig. 13-5. The basic coverage parameters are defined in Eqs. (13-1) to (13-4) above. Geosynchronous constellations have been used extensively for many purposes, including communications, weather, and tracking of low-Earth orbit satellites.

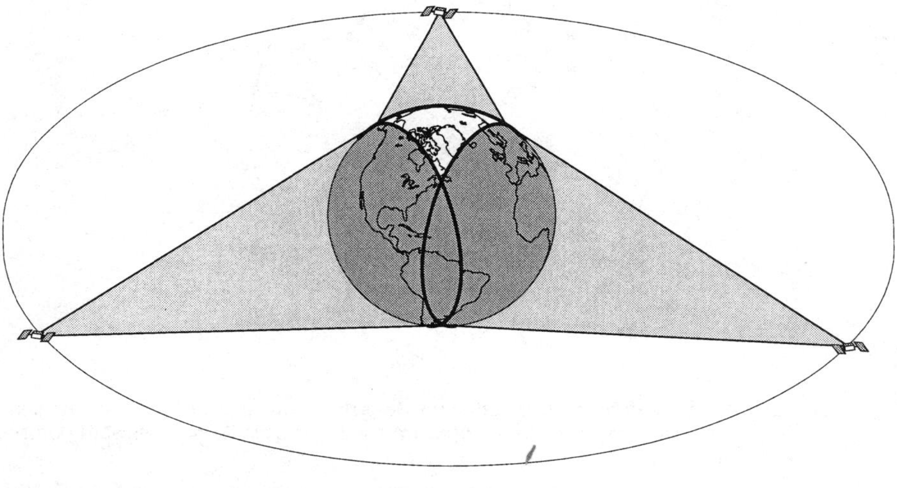

Fig. 13-5. Geosynchronous Constellation. This is the simplest of the constellations, consisting of several satellites in geosynchronous orbit working together to achieve a common purpose, such as TDRS.

Geosynchronous constellations require very few satellites. However, they are in very high energy orbits and occupy prime real estate in the space arena. These constellations cover equatorial and mid-latitude regions extremely well but do poorly over high latitude regions. The biggest advantage of geosynchronous constellations is that the individual satellites remain essentially fixed with respect to the surface of the Earth, and therefore provide continuous coverage of one region and antennas on the Earth's surface can maintain a fixed orientation when pointing at the satellite.

Streets of Coverage Constellations

The concept of streets of coverage, introduced in Sec. 13.1, can be used to define a constellation pattern also known as *"streets of coverage,"* in which n satellites in each of m approximately polar orbit planes are used to provide continuous global coverage. As illustrated in Fig. 13-6, at any given time satellites over half of the world are going northward and satellites over the other half are going southward. Within both regions, the orbit planes are separated by D_{maxS} as defined in Eq. (13-2). Between the two halves is a seam in which the satellites are going in opposite directions. Consequently, the spacing between planes on opposite sides of the seam must be reduced to D_{maxO} as defined in Eq. (13-3) in order to maintain continuous coverage. In order to provide global continuous coverage for a streets of coverage pattern using m planes of polar orbits, we must have:

$$(m + 1)\,\lambda_{street} + (m - 1)\,\lambda_{max} > 180 \text{ deg} \tag{13-10}$$

where λ_{street} and λ_{max} are defined in Eqs. (13-1) and (9-2).

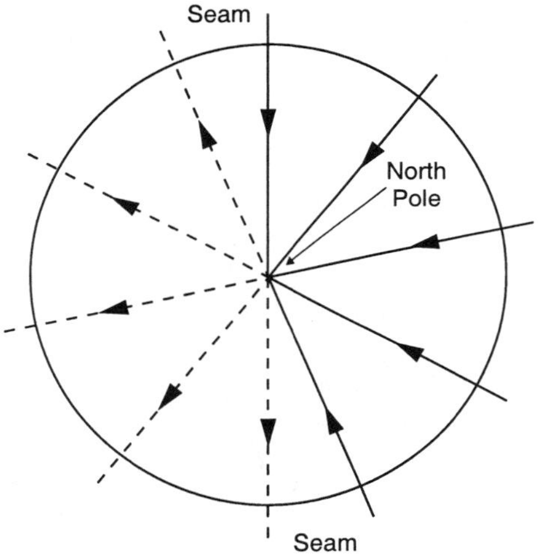

Fig. 13-6. "Streets of Coverage" Constellation Pattern. View seen from above the North Pole. Northward portions of each orbit are shown as solid lines; southward portions are dashed.

Notice that it is the swath width and not the altitude which determines the number of orbit planes and ultimately the number of satellites required to provide global coverage. This illustrates clearly one of the most critical characteristics of constellations—**coverage does not vary continuously and smoothly with altitude**. There are discrete jumps in coverage which depend primarily on λ_{max} which in turn depends upon the minimum elevation angle ε_{min} and the altitude [see Eqs. (9-2) to (9-7)]. If we keep ε_{min} fixed and lower the constellation altitude, then we will reach an *altitude plateau* at which we will need to add another orbit plane and n more satellites to cover the Earth. The Iridium communications constellation was originally intended to have 77 satellites in a streets of coverage pattern. (The element iridium has atomic number 77.) By slightly increasing the altitude and decreasing the minimum elevation angle, the number of orbit planes was reduced by 1, and the number of satellites required for continuous coverage was reduced to only 66. (Unfortunately, dysprosium is not a good constellation name.)

Figure 13-6 illustrates another key constellation characteristic—what appears to be a major collision problem at the poles. One can almost see the satellites colliding there. Many practical constellations spread the intersections out somewhat over the polar region to avoid this. Intersatellite collisions are indeed a problem, as discussed in Sec. 13.7. However, they are no more of a problem for the streets of coverage pattern than for any other constellation pattern made of circular orbits. Every great circle orbit will intersect every other great circle orbit exactly twice. Whether those intersections are bunched together at the pole or spread out over the globe doesn't matter. It is the pairwise probability of collision that matters and this depends only on the fact that all pairs of orbits intersect. Thus, there are just as many collision possibilities in any constellation pattern with a given number of satellites and a given number of orbit planes as there are in any other pattern with the same number of satellites and orbit planes.

The streets of coverage pattern is generally very efficient, allowing good overlap between adjacent satellites, and allowing the space between adjacent planes to be increased by taking advantage of the bulge in one plane accommodating the dip in the adjacent plane. There are two principal drawbacks to this pattern. First, the seam represents an asymmetry in coverage and satellite relative motion. Consequently, satellites on either side of the seam must behave differently than those in other parts of the pattern. Second, and perhaps most important, the streets of coverage constellation has the greatest coverage over the pole where there are few people or facilities needing its services. This overcoverage at the pole leads us to look for ways to reduce the inclination so as to have more coverage at mid-latitudes where there is greater demand.

Walker Constellations

The most symmetric of the satellite patterns is the *Walker constellation*, named after John Walker, who made an extensive study of their properties at the Royal Air Force Establishment from the late 1960s to the early 1980s [Walker, 1971, 1977, 1984]. The most common of these constellations is the *Walker Delta Pattern*, containing a total of T satellites with S satellites evenly distributed in each of P orbit planes. All of the orbit planes are assumed to be at the same inclination, i, relative to the equator. (For constellation design purposes, the reference plane need not be the Earth's equator, however, since orbit perturbations depend on the inclination relative to the equator, this is the most practical reference plane.) Unlike the streets of coverage pattern, the ascending nodes of the P orbit planes in Walker patterns are uniformly distributed around the equator at intervals of 360 deg/P. Within each orbital plane, the S satellites are uniformly distributed at intervals of 360 deg/S.

The only remaining issue is to specify the relative phase between the satellites in adjacent orbit planes. To do this, we define the *phase difference*, $\Delta\phi$, in a constellation as the angle in the direction of motion from the ascending node to the nearest satellite at a time when a satellite in the next most westerly plane is at its ascending node. In order for all of the orbit planes to have the same relationship to each other, $\Delta\phi$ must be an integral multiple, F, of 360 deg/T, where F can be any integer from 0 to $P - 1$. So long as this condition holds, each orbit will bear the same relationship to the next orbit such that there is no starting or ending point in the constellation. The pattern is fully specified by giving the inclination, and the three parameters T, P and F. Usually such a constellation will be written in a shorthand notation of i:T/P/F. For example, Fig. 13-7 illustrates Walker constellations of 65:15/3/2 and 65:15/5/4. Table 13-4 gives the general rules for Walker Delta Pattern parameters.

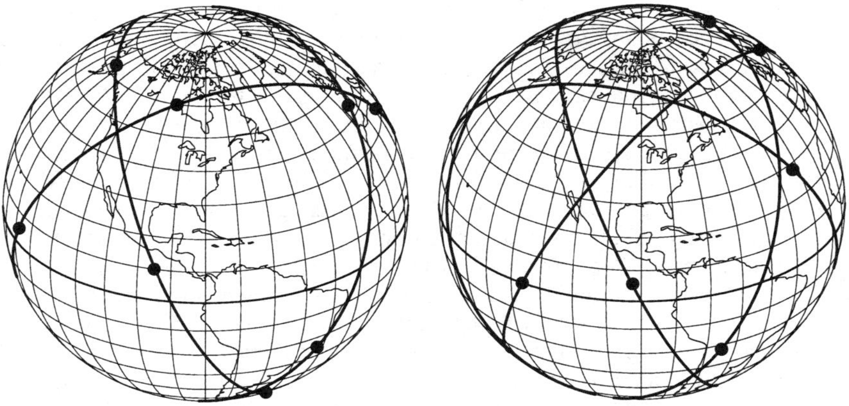

(A) 15/3/2 Configuration **(B) 15/5/4 Configuration**

Fig. 13-7. Typical Walker Constellations for *i* = 65 deg.

TABLE 13-4. Characteristics of a Walker Delta Pattern Constellation [Walker, 1984].

T/P/F—Walker Delta Patterns
T = Number of satellites P = Number of orbit planes evenly spaced in node F = Relative spacing between satellites in adjacent planes
Define $S = T/P$ = Number of satellites per plane (evenly spaced)
Define *Pattern Unit*, $PU \equiv 360$ deg/T
Planes are spaced at intervals of S *PU*s in node. Satellites are spaced at intervals of P *PU*s within each plane.
If a satellite is at its ascending node, the next most easterly satellite will be F *PU*s past the node. F is an integer which can take on any value from 0 to $(P - 1)$.
Example: 15/5/4 constellation shown in Fig. 13-7B 15 satellites in 5 planes (T = 15, P = 5) 3 satellites per plane ($S = T/P = 3$) $PU = 360/T = 360/15 = 24$ deg In-plane spacing between satellites = $PU \times P = 24 \times 5 = 120$ deg Node spacing = $PU \times S = 24 \times 3 = 72$ deg Phase difference between adjacent planes = $PU \times F = 24 \times 4 = 96$ deg

Walker constellations have the advantage of having complete symmetry in longitude. Because both the ascending and descending nodes cover the full equator, they give up some efficiency relative to the polar orbit streets of coverage patterns. However, they gain efficiency by allowing the inclination to be reduced to provide the highest level of coverage at mid latitudes, which has by far the largest population concentration.

Perhaps the greatest advantage of Walker constellations is that there is a finite number of them and all can be identified and investigated. This has made them popular with mission designers, since a "complete" analysis can be done for any specific characteristic of interest. This completeness has made them one of the most analyzed constellation designs, but does not necessarily make them better or more successful than other patterns.

Elliptical Orbit Patterns

The oldest elliptical orbit constellations are *Molniya orbits*, used by the former Soviet Union for communications since the opening of the Space Age. (See Sec. 2.5.4.) While geosynchronous satellites are inherently useful as single spacecraft, communications systems using Molniya orbits require multiple satellites to provide continuous coverage of any region. Nonetheless, they can provide coverage of high northern latitudes which cannot be successfully served from geosynchronous orbit. It is this characteristic that caused their use by the Soviet Union which has extensive territory at high latitudes.

As discussed in Sec. 12.4.3, elliptical orbits add complexity to both the system and spacecraft design and, at the same time, add an additional degree of freedom to allow the constellation designer to optimize coverage to fit specific needs. Draim, et al. [2000] have done an extensive analysis of these trades in order to use this additional design freedom to maximize the performance benefits in terms of coverage of appropriate latitudes, longitudes, and time of day. The Ellipso constellation shown in Fig. 13-8 takes full advantage of this freedom to optimize coverage for both the locations of the Earth and the time of day at which peak traffic is anticipated.

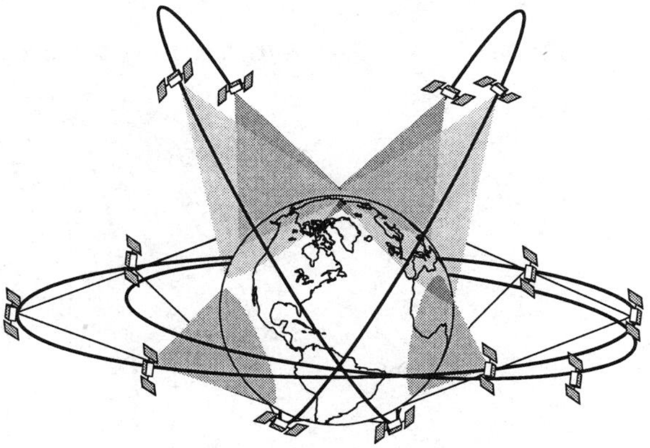

Fig. 13-8. The Ellipso Communications Constellation. Elliptical orbits are used to optimize coverage as a function of longitude, latitude, and time of day. As discussed in the text, there will also be a significant cost. (Adapted from Draim [2000].)

The largest advantage of elliptical constellations is that they provide additional free parameters to optimize the constellation. The penalty for this added freedom is a greater level of spacecraft complexity, because it must work at varying altitudes which, in turn, means variations in range, angular size of the Earth's disk, in-track velocity, and relative position for satellites in the same orbit. Elliptical orbits are effectively restricted to the critical inclination of 63.4 deg, and will be in the Van Allen belts much of the time. Consequently, components for these spacecraft will need extensive radiation hardening.

Other Constellation Patterns

There are many types of non-standard constellation patterns, some of which may be much better suited to specific problems than either Walker or streets of coverage patterns. For example, the Ellipso constellation described above adds an equatorial ring to improve coverage characteristics at low latitudes. Similarly, a polar ring could be added to a constellation for high latitude coverage, in conjunction with an inherently low latitude or low altitude constellation. Figure 13-9 shows specific examples of non-Walker constellations, i.e., ones which break specific symmetries in order to achieve other objectives.

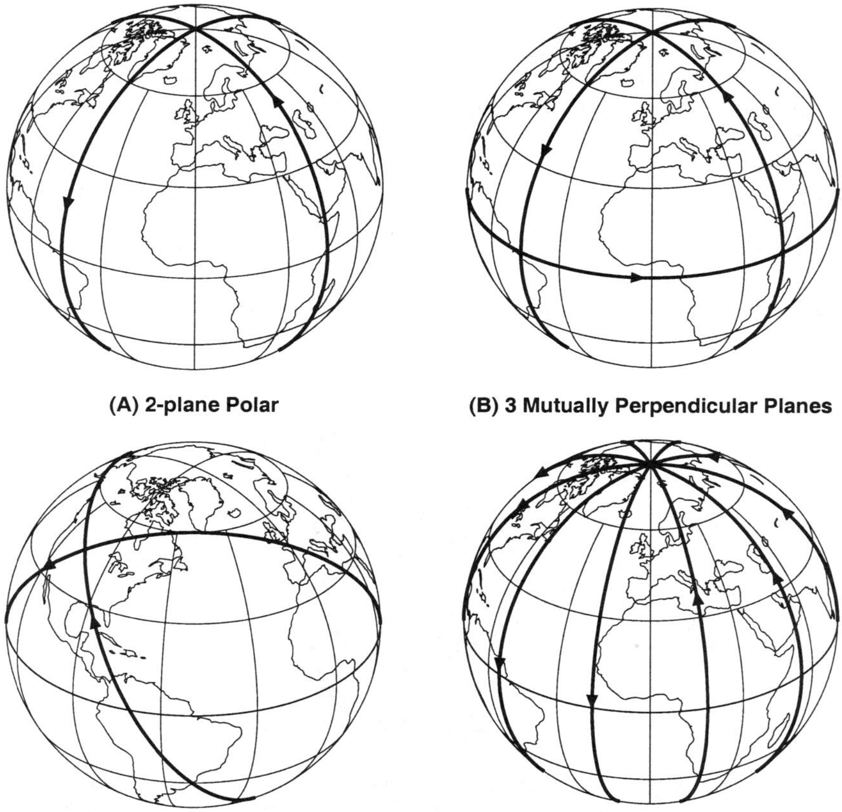

(A) 2-plane Polar **(B) 3 Mutually Perpendicular Planes**

(C) 2 Perpendicular Non-polar Planes **(D) 5-plane Polar "Streets of Coverage"**

Fig. 13-9. Examples of Typical Non-Walker Constellations. All orbits are assumed to be circular. There is also a variety of constellations with non-circular orbits as discussed in the text.

A major problem for constellation design is the fact that it is not a systematic study. Many variations are possible. GPS follows nearly a Walker pattern. Ellipso provides excellent coverage characteristics with eccentric orbits. Iridium and others have demonstrated how the asymmetric streets of coverage constellation can also provide excellent coverage. One of the most intriguing examples for a constellation which defies nearly all of the rules of constellation design is the Multi-Satellite System Program described in the boxed example.

MSSP—A Counterexample for All the Rules of Constellation Design

Constellations use symmetry to provide well defined relationships between satellites that persist over time so that the total number of satellites can be minimized. Thus the streets of coverage pattern provides a series of satellites which moved "together" over the surface of the Earth and the Walker patterns provide a regularly recurring coverage mechanism. However, it is this very symmetry which represents a weakness from the perspective of providing continuous coverage. For example, if one or two satellites in the GPS navigation constellation are destroyed, there will be long and regular breaks in coverage that are easily predicted and could in principle be used for a military advantage.

One way around this problem of allowing an opponent to take advantage of coverage holes is to create a constellation consisting of satellites in random or pseudorandom orbits, such that the constellation pattern does not repeat but is continuously changing. Although it requires a larger number of satellites than ones having a high degree of symmetry, it has the advantage that the loss of even a significant number of satellites either intentionally or by accident will not significantly disrupt the communications system as a whole, since the system does not depend on a regular pattern to provide communications. This was the basic concept of the Multi-Satellite System Program, which was an inherently survivable communications constellation illustrated in Fig. 13-10.

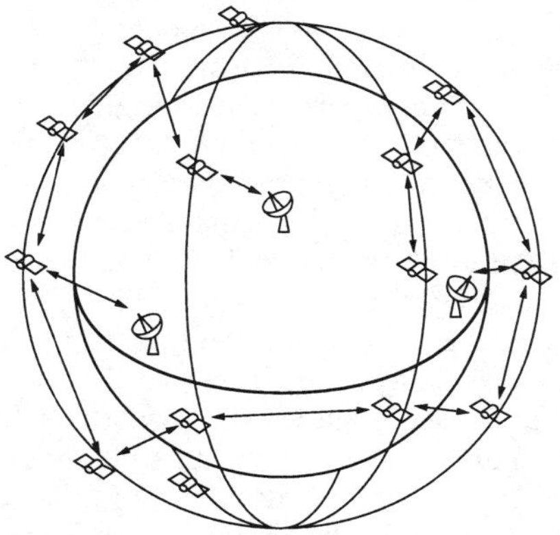

Fig. 13-10. **MSSP**. This constellation consists of a large number of satellites in random orbits. Drawing from Fleeter [1999].

While MSSP requires a larger number of satellites than most other constellation patterns, it has a number of inherent advantages in addition to fundamental survivability. Because the orbits are random, they do not need to be controlled or maintained. This significantly reduces the operations cost and complexity. In addition, insertion into specific orbits is not required so that piggyback launches or other cheap mechanisms of putting spacecraft in orbit can be used because the orbits themselves are not critical. Similarly, any launch dispersion that comes from errors or anomalies in the launch process makes no difference, so long as the satellites have achieved orbit. The idea of deploying MSSP was dropped because of the large number of satellites required. However, it remains an interesting possibility, as microsatellites and nanosatellites become more competent. Certainly one characteristic of this type of constellation is that it violates virtually all of the rules of constellation design.

13.3 Selection of Constellation Parameters

Constellation parameters are frequently thought of as the orbit elements of the satellites in the constellation. Nonetheless, one of the most critical of the constellation parameters is the swath width or maximum Earth central angle, which defines the coverage for each of the satellites in the constellation. The eccentricity of the orbits is also a key parameter although in most cases it is set to zero or near-zero (i.e., a frozen orbit. See Sec. 2.5.6). Non-zero eccentricity orbits are discussed in Sec. 13.2 and the references therein. In this section, we will discuss the basis for selecting the other principal constellation parameters consisting of:

- Swath width (maximum Earth central angle)
- Altitude
- Inclination
- Node spacing

Formulas for the relevant parameters were defined in Chaps. 2, 9 and Sec. 13.1. This section defines the logic and trades ordinarily used in the parameter selection process.

Swath Width (Maximum Earth Central Angle)

The key coverage parameter for any constellation is the area that can be covered by each individual satellite. For discontinuous coverage, this is most conveniently measured by the swath width or maximum Earth central angle. For constellations requiring continuous coverage, the maximum Earth central angle represents the circle of coverage that can be seen by the satellite and the minimum swath width or width of the street of coverage represents the required spacing between orbit planes.

We tend to regard the altitude as the principal determinant of coverage for satellite systems. However, it is the swath width or the maximum Earth central angle which actually determines the coverage for individual satellites. The maximum Earth central angle is a function of both the altitude and the minimum elevation angle or grazing angle at which the system operates. (See Table 13-5.) Particularly at low elevation angles, the maximum Earth central angle is a very strong function of the minimum elevation angle. As shown in Fig. 13-11, a given swath width can result from a variety of combinations of elevation angle and altitude. Formulas for the maximum swath width as a function of both altitude and minimum elevation angle were provided in Sec. 13.1 and 9.4. Recall that the maximum swath width is simply twice the maximum Earth central angle. As shown in Fig. 13-12, the minimum swath width or width of the street of coverage is determined by both the maximum Earth central angle and the spacing between satellites, as defined in Eq. (13-1).

Depending on the application, we want either the coverage circles or the swaths to overlap in order to maintain good satellite coverage. If this does not occur, then there will be gaps in coverage between the orbit planes. Similarly, the swath width and maximum Earth central angle will also determine the reach of constellation coverage between the ground track and the Earth's poles. Thus, the wider the swath width, the lower the orbit inclination can be, while still maintaining coverage at high latitudes.

The minimum elevation angle is fundamentally determined by payload performance. Nearly all payload types will perform better at higher elevation angles because of the angle above the horizon, distance, and atmospheric absorption. Consequently, payload designers would prefer to limit the minimum elevation to relatively high

TABLE 13-5. Swath Width (deg) as a Function of Altitude and Minimum Working Elevation Angle. It is the swath width that is the most basic determinant of coverage.

Attitude (km)	Minimum Working Elevation Angle (deg)					
	0	5	10	15	20	30
100	20.16	12.48	8.32	6.02	4.61	3.00
200	28.33	2001	14.56	11.04	8.68	5.78
300	34.48	25.86	19.71	15.40	12.34	8.39
400	39.56	30.76	24.15	19.29	15.68	10.84
500	43.96	35.03	28.09	22.80	18.76	13.15
600	47.87	38.84	31.65	26.02	21.61	15.34
700	51.39	42.29	34.90	28.99	24.28	17.41
800	54.62	45.46	37.90	31.75	26.78	19.38
900	57.59	48.38	40.68	34.34	29.13	21.26
1,000	60.36	51.10	43.29	36.77	31.35	23.05
1,500	71.89	62.49	54.25	47.11	40.93	30.96
2,000	80.85	71.36	62.87	55.33	48.65	37.51
2,500	88.15	78.60	69.94	62.12	55.08	43.05
3,000	94.30	84.70	75.90	67.87	60.55	47.83
3,500	99.57	89.93	81.03	72.83	65.29	52.00
4,000	104.16	94.50	85.51	77.17	69.45	55.69
4,500	108.21	98.52	89.46	81.01	73.13	58.97
5,000	111.81	102.11	92.99	84.43	76.43	61.91
10,000	134.16	124.35	114.90	105.81	97.07	80.58
15,000	145.28	135.42	125.83	116.50	107.44	90.05
20,000	152.01	142.12	132.45	122.99	113.73	95.83

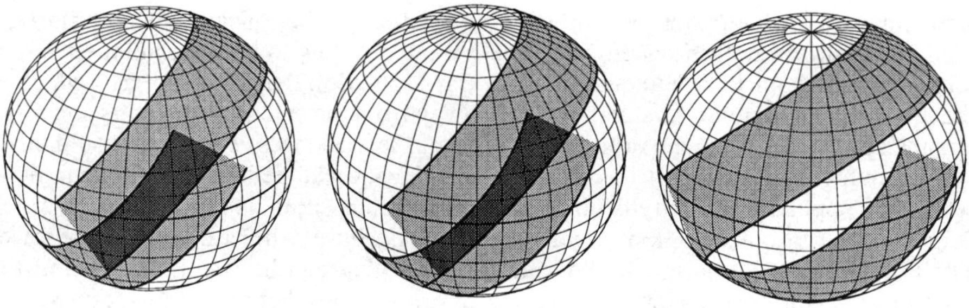

(A) (B) (C)

Fig. 13-11. Three Systems with Equal Swath Width but Different Altitude. The only difference is the orbit period and, therefore, the longitude shift per orbit. Swath width = 4,000 km for all three orbits: (A) altitude = 525 km, minimum elevation angle = 5 deg; (B) altitude = 735 km, minimum elevation angle = 10 deg; (C) altitude = 1,225 km, minimum elevation angle = 20 deg.

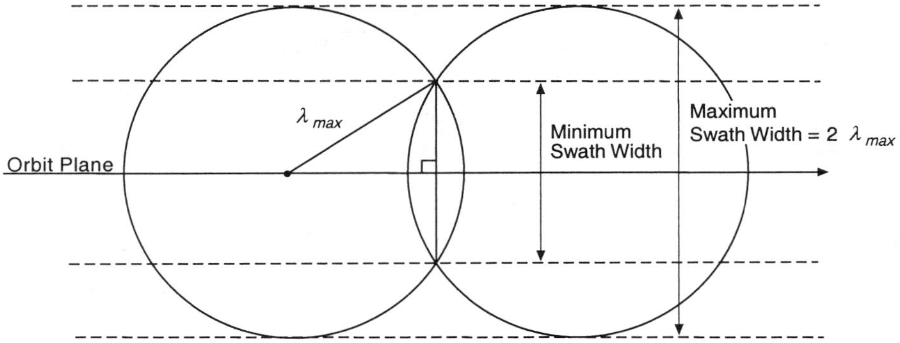

Fig. 13-12. Characteristic Maximum Swath Widths. The minimum swath width or width of the street of coverage will depend on the in-plane spacing between satellites, but is typically chosen as approximately 70% of maximum swath width.

values. From a constellation design perspective, however, a high minimum elevation angle implies either a larger number of satellites or a higher altitude, both of which significantly impact cost. Consequently, a key issue in the constellation design process is to find a reasonable compromise between altitude and minimum elevation angle in order to achieve the widest possible swath width for a given constellation. This becomes one of the most important system engineering trades in the design of most constellations.

Because of the importance of swath width in determining the number of satellites required and the payload performance, a reasonable alternative is to consider using more than one performance plateau. For example, in observation systems, it might be acceptable to have one level of performance to provide complete Earth coverage on a daily basis if better performance (i.e., a higher elevation angle) can be provided every several days. This would allow frequent coverage at moderate resolutions with less frequent coverage at higher resolution with a smaller number of satellites. Similarly, a communications satellite system might be willing to allow lower minimum elevation angles in the vicinity of the equator where the population density is not as high as in the mid-latitude regions. As satellites move away from the equator, the orbits converge and the spacing between the orbit planes becomes less. Consequently, one could envision a satellite system with a 10-deg minimum elevation angle in high latitude regions where the population density is high and an 8-deg minimum elevation angle over the equator. Such a constellation could potentially be built with a significantly fewer satellites because of the much wider swath width that can be accommodated at the equator and, therefore, the smaller number of orbit planes that would be required.

Altitude

Generally, all of the satellites will need to be at the same altitude in order to have the same period. This is important in order to maintain a uniform relationship between the satellites over time. If all of the orbit periods in the constellation are the same, then the pattern will repeat every orbit. Otherwise, it will not and a variety of different patterns will need to be accommodated. While this is not impossible, most constellations tend to work at a single common altitude. A second reason for this is that it also keeps the node rotation rate the same such that the orbit planes continue to maintain their relative orientation.

If the minimum elevation angle has been fixed by the payload (typically as a result of extensive trades as discussed above), then the altitude is the key driver for constellation design. Specifically, higher altitudes will mean a smaller number of satellites and a smaller number of orbit planes. However, the number of satellites and number of planes is not continuously variable with the altitude. Rather, there are a series of altitude plateaus below which an additional plane will be required. For example, for circular polar orbits and a 0-deg minimum elevation angle, the following plateaus exist:

- Above 2,642 km, complete coverage can be provided with two perpendicular planes
- Below 2,642 km, at least three planes are required for full Earth coverage
- Below 987 km, at least four planes are required for full coverage
- Below 526 km, at least five planes are required for full coverage

Altitude plateaus are a function of both the minimum working elevation angle and the inclination. As the minimum elevation angle becomes higher, the swath width becomes smaller, and the altitude plateaus for a given number of orbit planes become higher. Conversely, at lower inclinations, the required node spacing at the equator becomes larger and a smaller number of planes can suffice. Table 13-6 provides representative examples of altitude plateaus for various minimum elevation angles and inclinations. In general, systems will need to be at somewhat higher altitudes than those specified to accommodate the stationkeeping box. The values in this table should be taken only as representative limits. The actual values depend not only on the minimum elevation angle but also on the portions of the Earth to be covered, the overlap area needed for stationkeeping and margin, and the desired coverage pattern.

The values in Table 13-6 are representative for streets of coverage constellations in which coverage at both ascending and descending nodes are used. Walker constellations will need approximately twice as many planes because the Walker patterns are meant to provide complete coverage at both the ascending and descending nodes. Also note that less planes may be required in a lower inclination orbit in order to cover the equator. However, they may leave coverage gaps in some higher latitude regions in the streets of coverage type patterns. In addition, more planes may also be required due to the need for overlap.

The altitude plateaus for any particular constellation pattern will be unique to that pattern. The principal point to bear in mind is that for any coverage objective and constellation pattern a series of altitude plateaus exists. As we go down in altitude, we will get less and less overlap until at some point the overlap will disappear entirely and we will need to add one more plane, or revise the constellation pattern in some other way in order to ensure coverage.

The altitude plateaus in Table 13-6 take only coverage into account. However, as described in detail in Chap. 12, a variety of other issues are strongly affected by the altitude. Of particular importance are the launch capability and the radiation environment. Above approximately 1,000 km, the radiation environment increases extremely rapidly. This significantly drives up the complexity and cost of individual spacecraft.

TABLE 13-6. Altitude Plateaus (km). These plateaus represent the minimum number of planes required for complete equatorial coverage in a streets of coverage pattern. Walker constellations will typically require twice as many planes. The actual altitude for a given constellation will typically be higher. See text for limitations and discussion.

Minimum Elevation Angle = 0 deg

Inc.	90 deg	75 deg	60 deg
Planes	Altitude (km)	Altitude (km)	Altitude (km)
10	80	74	59
9	98	92	73
8	125	116	93
7	164	153	122
6	225	209	167
5	328	305	241
4	526	486	382
3	987	906	698
2	2,642	2,354	1,690

Minimum Elevation Angle = 5 deg

Inc.	90 deg	75 deg	60 deg
Planes	Altitude (km)	Altitude (km)	Altitude (km)
10	170	162	137
9	200	189	160
8	240	227	192
7	297	281	235
6	384	361	301
5	524	493	406
4	785	734	596
3	1,379	1,275	1,008
2	3,507	3,132	2,276

Minimum Elevation Angle = 10 deg

Inc.	90 deg	75 deg	60 deg
Planes	Altitude (km)	Altitude (km)	Altitude (km)
10	265	253	218
9	306	292	251
8	361	344	295
7	438	416	355
6	552	523	443
5	736	695	582
4	1,069	1,004	828
3	1,821	1,691	1,353
2	4,573	4,078	2,966

Minimum Elevation Angle = 20 deg

Inc.	90 deg	75 deg	60 deg
Planes	Altitude (km)	Altitude (km)	Altitude (km)
10	475	454	397
9	543	519	451
8	633	604	524
7	757	721	622
6	939	892	764
5	1,228	1,163	986
4	1,751	1,648	1,373
3	2,946	2,735	2,197
2	7,804	6,860	4,857

In addition, launch costs also increase significantly with altitude. For example, the payload available in geosynchronous orbit is only one-fifth of that available in low-Earth orbit for a given launch system. Consequently, higher altitudes will generally imply a smaller number of satellites in a constellation; however, the satellites themselves may be significantly more expensive to build or launch and therefore the total system cost may or may not be less than with a low-altitude constellation. See Table 12-9 in Sec. 12.4.1 for a list of the principal system parameters impacted by the altitude. In constellation design studies, each of these issues should be addressed in terms of their impact on overall system cost and performance as a part of the altitude selection process.

Inclination

One of the most important "rules" of constellation design is driven by the oblateness of the Earth. As discussed in detail in Sec. 2.5 and 12.4, the oblateness, represented by J_2 in the spherical harmonic expansion of the Earth's gravitational potential, causes both the node and argument of perigee to rotate rapidly with respect to the lifetime of most constellations. This rotation rate is a function of the altitude, the inclination, and the eccentricity. However, **rotation itself is typically not a problem so long as the whole constellation rotates together. This will occur if the satellites are all at the same altitude, inclination, and eccentricity.**

For example, if we construct a constellation at 700 km with some satellites at an inclination at 70 deg and some at 30 deg, those at 70 deg will have a node rotation rate of 2.62 deg per day, and those at 30 deg will have a node rotation rate of 6.63 deg per day. This means the planes will move with respect to each other at the rate of 4 deg per day. While it may not be impossible, this certainly makes the construction of a long-term constellation challenging.

If the orbits are noncircular, than the rotation of the argument of perigee due to J_2 also becomes important. This implies that constellations with satellites in eccentric orbits will almost certainly be at the critical inclination of 63.4 deg, so that perigee doesn't rotate.

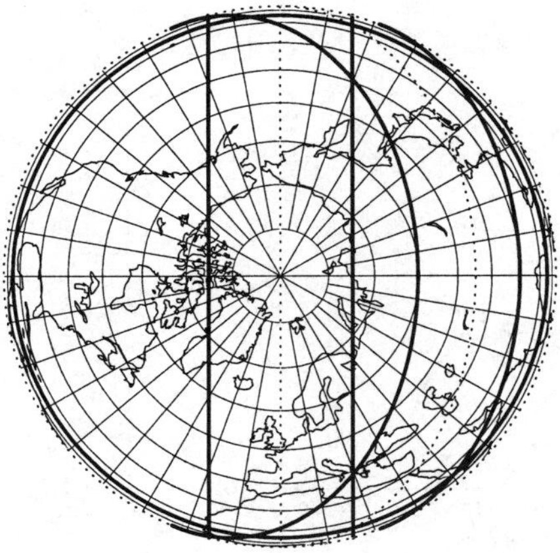

(A) Viewed from Pole

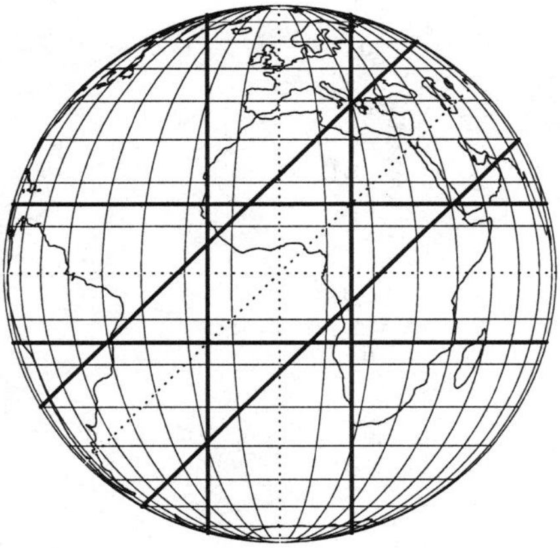

(B) Viewed from Equator

Fig. 13-13. Ground Swaths as Seen from Equator and from the Pole for Satellites with a Swath Width of 30 deg and Inclination of 0 deg, 45 deg, and 90 deg.

The inclination has a strong impact on both how coverage patterns are formed and on coverage as a function of latitude. Figure 13-13 shows the ground swath as seen from both the pole and the equator for satellites in orbits with inclinations of 0, 45, and 90 deg. The coverage as a function of latitude for these ground swaths is shown in Fig. 13-14. Note that it is not simply the coverage as a function of latitude but also the character of the coverage curves that changes significantly between the three cases. For equatorial orbits, coverage is essentially constant as a function of latitude. At latitudes below the half width of the streets of coverage, the coverage will be 100% and at latitudes above the maximum Earth central angle there will be no coverage. Of course the width of the equatorial band will depend on both the altitude and the minimum elevation angle, as discussed above. For the polar orbit, the highest level of coverage is at the pole itself, which will be covered by every swath in the constellation. Coverage of the equatorial regions will be divided into two symmetric segments at the ascending and descending nodes. The streets of coverage constellation pattern is typically formed by multiple near-polar orbits. The moderate inclination orbits provide asymmetric coverage over the mid-latitude regions. Along the equator, there are two bands of coverage similar to the polar orbit. However, coverage is best at mid-latitude regions centered approximately on the inclination, which is also the maximum latitude of the ground track of the satellite. The actual maximum coverage is achieved at a latitude equal to the inclination minus the swath width. Above a latitude equal to the inclination plus the swath width there will be no coverage. Algebraic formulas for the coverage and breakpoints were provided in Sec. 9.5.1.3. The key issue here is to note the asymmetry of the coverage and how the inclination can be adjusted to provide varying levels of coverage at varying latitudes.

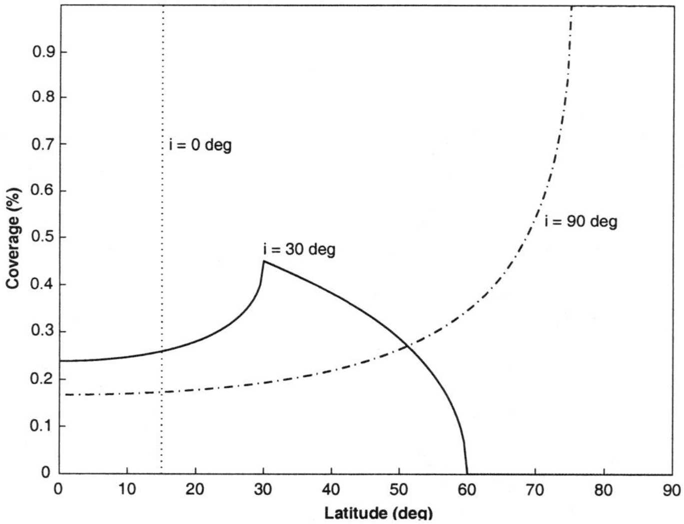

Fig. 13-14. Single Satellite Coverage vs. Latitude. All three curves are for a satellite with a swath width of 30 deg. See also Tables 13-14 and 13-15.

An interesting constellation design that provides complete global coverage could be provided by a combination of polar and equatorial orbits. So long as the altitude is above the plateau for which only two planes are required, then an equatorial orbit can be combined with a polar orbit with any node orientation to provide complete global coverage. For these orbits, the orbit rotation due to the oblateness of the Earth will not be important and complete continuous coverage can be maintained over time with a relatively small number of satellites. For example, at an altitude of 8,660 km and a minimum elevation angle of 5 deg, the maximum Earth central angle is 60 deg and the half width of the streets of coverage is 45 deg for 4 satellites. For this constellation, complete continuous global coverage can be provided by four satellites in an equatorial orbit and four satellites in a polar orbit, with the maximum overlapping coverage occurring in the general vicinity of 45 deg latitude.

Node Spacing

The actual location of the ascending node for individual orbits in a constellation is generally irrelevant, since the whole constellation will rotate with respect to inertial space and with respect to the Earth's surface. (For some repeating ground track orbits, the node location may be important in order to provide appropriate coverage at specific longitudes). The key issue is to have all of the nodes rotate at the same rate, which implies a single altitude and inclination for the entire constellation, except for the possibility of adding an equatorial ring to improve coverage there, since node rotation doesn't matter for equatorial satellites.

Four types of node spacing are most commonly used:

- Equal node spacing over the complete equator as done for Walker constellations
- Equal node spacing over half the equator to avoid coverage gaps between orbits (see Fig. 13-8). Except for polar orbits, this process tends to leave a hole in one region of the Earth
- Equal node spacing except for a seam between satellites going up and coming down, as used in streets of coverage patterns (see Fig. 13-9D)
- Node spacing adjusted in pairs or triplets to provide "fill-in coverage" for successive satellites. For example, a synthetic aperture radar can not see targets which lie along the ground track. Thus, a system of this type intended to provide nearly complete coverage would need successive satellites having the nodes shifted slightly to fill in the nadir hole for the preceding satellite.

While equal node spacing around the equator is the one most often evaluated, it is not necessarily the only or best choice. There may well be clever selections of node and inclination which provide strong coverage characteristics for specific applications. The key issue in node spacing is to look at the coverage patterns to see how best to achieve the specific mission objectives. For example, Fig. 13-9C illustrates a coverage pattern with asymmetric nodes which is achieved by using a two-plane polar constellation and simply reducing the inclination in order to provide greater launch mass.

13.4 Stationkeeping

Stationkeeping is the process of maintaining a satellite within a well defined box or position relative either to inertial space or to other satellites. In formation flying, the position is always maintained relative to another spacecraft, such as maintaining close proximity to the Space Station or building a multi-satellite interferometer. In global constellations, stationkeeping may be done either relative to other satellites or, as in the case of geosynchronous spacecraft, relative to inertial space or the surface of the Earth. The principal reason for stationkeeping is to maintain the overall constellation structure. At the same time, it also provides collision avoidance and allows intersatellite communications.

Within constellations, the objective of stationkeeping is to maintain the relative position between satellites. We want to minimize the propellant utilization and the system cost and complexity needed to do this. The need for stationkeeping arises from two sources:

- *Orbit Perturbations*
  Atmospheric drag causes overall system decay that must be compensated in an long-lived LEO constellation to keep the constellation from ultimately decaying and reentering. In addition, drag and other orbit perturbations impact each satellite in the constellation differently. These differences can accumulate with time such that small variations in perturbations can lead to large separations over the course of many orbits.

- *Variations in Initial Conditions*
  Variations in the initial conditions for each individual satellite cause the satellites to drift in time with respect to each other. If these drifts are oscillatory or accumulate only small differences, we may be able to simply live with them. However, small differences in altitude, for example, cause different periods such that the in-track error grows exponentially with time. Small differences in inclination cause differences in the node drift rate which also grows with time.

There are several different ways to evaluate stationkeeping. Geosynchronous stationkeeping is well understood and will be treated only briefly here. For extended discussions, see for example Pocha [1987] or Soop [1994]. We will concentrate primarily on stationkeeping in low-Earth orbit. Ultimately, the implementation will be divided into *in-track stationkeeping*, which controls the true anomaly or phase in the orbit, and *cross-track stationkeeping*, which controls the component perpendicular to the orbit plane, i.e., the inclination and node. The radial component (corresponding to the semimajor axis) is maintained as a part of in-track stationkeeping, since the mean altitude determines the orbit period.

Each of the orbit perturbations described in Sec. 2.4 will have an impact on the motion of the spacecraft and the stationkeeping requirements. Generally, each perturbation can be dealt with separately using one of three possible approaches.

1. ***Leave the Perturbation Uncompensated***

   This is the best method for accommodating any perturbation, since it requires no propellant and no control. We simply increase the stationkeeping budget to incorporate variations that occur over time. It is the only realistic method for accommodating short-period oscillations in the positions of the satellites, such as those due to higher order harmonics. There is simply not enough propellant on board any spacecraft to do otherwise for an extended period.

2. ***Control the Perturbing Disturbance to be the Same for All Satellites in the Constellation***

   In this case satellites will maintain the same relative position but will not follow a perfectly Keplerian orbit. Providing the same level of perturbation for all of the satellites requires less propellant than negating the perturbation, and is the best approach if the perturbation cannot be ignored. For example, in low-Earth orbit, the node drift rate will be controlled to be the same for all satellites by controlling the inclination. There is insufficient propellant (and no reason) to attempt to stop the node drift rate.

3. ***Negate the Perturbing Force***

   This approach maintains the orbit characteristics over time. Consequently, it requires continuous propellant usage and should be used only when necessary. For example, atmospheric drag in low-Earth orbit must be negated in order to maintain the constellation altitude and prevent the system from decaying. In geosynchronous orbit, both the north-south perturbations due to solar-lunar effects and the east-west perturbations due to the non-spherical character of the Earth's equator are negated in order to maintain the satellite within a well defined box over the equator.

TABLE 13-7. Recommended Methods for Handling the Principal Perturbations in Low-Earth Orbit.

Perturbation	Impact	How Handled
Atmospheric Drag	Secular decay ranging from 1–100 m/day	Negated by altitude maintenance
J_2 (Oblateness)	Secular node rotation of ~6 cos *i* deg/day	Controlled by inclination maintenance
	Secular phase rotation of up to 14 deg/day	Controlled as part of altitude maintenance
	Changes in shape of orbit up to ~5 km variation between adjacent satellites	Uncompensated
Higher Order Harmonics (Zonal)	Eccentricity oscillation of 0.001 about a mean value of 0.0013—a value of ~0.0013 can be maintained naturally	$e \approx 0.0013$ maintained naturally
Solar/Lunar	Secular drift in inclination and node of up to 3.5×10^{-5} deg/day	Negated by inclination maintenance or reduced by inclination change
	Low amplitude oscillations in inclination and node	Uncompensated
Solar Radiation Pressure	Small	Typically uncompensated

Section 10.1.1 provided a detailed discussion of the consequences of each of the perturbations. The basic stationkeeping process is to look at each of these orbit perturbations within the context of the specific mission and determine how it should be handled. Table 13-7 provides recommendations for handling the principal perturbations in low-Earth orbit. Table 13-8 provides similar recommendations for geosynchronous spacecraft. Similar tables can be constructed for other orbits such as interplanetary ones or orbits around a comet or asteroid by examining the effect of the individual perturbations and determining whether it should be left uncompensated, controlled, or negated.

TABLE 13-8. Recommended Methods for Handling the Principal Perturbations in Geosynchronous Orbit.

Perturbation	Impact	How Handled
Drag	Negligible	Uncompensated
J_2 and Higher Order Harmonics	Negligible	Uncompensated
Sectorial Harmonics	East-West drift about stable longitudes	Negated by East-West stationkeeping
Solar/Lunar	North-South (inclination) drift of ~0.9 deg/year	Negated by North-South stationkeeping
Solar Radiation Pressure	Small	Secular component handled as part of stationkeeping

13.4.1 Controlled Orbits and Absolute vs. Relative Stationkeeping

To begin, it is critical to understand the distinction between alternative approaches to stationkeeping and orbit maintenance. Specifically, *absolute stationkeeping* maintains each satellite in a predefined mathematical box relative to the Earth or inertial space (this is equivalent to geosynchronous stationkeeping, but in low-Earth orbit). *Relative stationkeeping* maintains only the relative positions of the satellites with respect to each other and not the absolute positions. Thus, relative stationkeeping is what would be done in formation flying. *Orbit maintenance* is the general process of maintaining the average orbit elements over time except that the in-track phase or true anomaly is not necessarily maintained. In contrast, *orbit control* maintains the value of all of the orbit parameters including the in-track phase. Thus, in a *controlled orbit,* we will know in advance the future positions of the spacecraft because they will be controlled to have specific values to within the stationkeeping errors. We will return to the importance of these distinctions shortly.

In constellation maintenance, our only goal is to maintain the **relative** positions of the satellites. Thus, it is natural to ask whether it is possible to save propellant by doing relative stationkeeping rather than absolute stationkeeping. A great deal of effort has been expended, both analytically and in real constellation maintenance, to achieve this. However, in most cases this is not necessary and may be counterproductive in terms of saving propellant. That is, in most practical orbit maintenance applications, absolute stationkeeping uses less ΔV and less propellant than relative stationkeeping.

The answer to the issue of absolute vs. relative stationkeeping depends upon another key question—whether we wish to maintain the system altitude or allow the constellation to slowly "fall" to lower altitudes because of atmospheric drag. Allowing the system to fall saves propellant only in the short term (i.e., several years). Presumably replacement satellites would be launched at the lower altitude, drag would continuously increase as the altitude decreases, and coverage holes would begin to appear as the constellation goes lower. Eventually, if left for a long enough period, the constellation would reenter. Maintaining the altitude and negating atmospheric drag is the only way to give the system long-term viability without having performance degradation grow with time. For many individual low-Earth orbit satellites, the altitude is not maintained. The orbit is allowed to decay and the spacecraft eventually reenters, typically well after the end of its useful life. For most low-Earth orbit constellations, however, the altitude should be maintained over the long term in order to maintain constellation utility.

If the decision is made to **never** do altitude maintenance, then it is possible to save propellant by doing relative stationkeeping. In this case, we would, for example, allow all the satellites in the constellation to decay at the same rate as the most slowly decaying one. It would be undesirable to use any other satellite as the basis since that would mean pushing some satellites downward and augmenting rather than compensating for drag. If the decision is made to do altitude maintenance **at any time**, including reboosting the satellites after they've decayed for many years, then there are no substantial advantages, and quite a few disadvantages, to relative stationkeeping. Ultimately, if we are to maintain the satellite altitude, we have no choice but to put back in the ΔV which the atmosphere takes out. If we do relative stationkeeping such that we allow the constellation to "decay" for a period of time, then the constellation will be moving further down into the atmosphere and the level of atmospheric drag and rate of decay will increase significantly. At the altitude of most constellations, the atmospheric density decreases exponentially with altitude, with a doubling of the density every 20 to 50 km. Thus, allowing the constellation to decay even a few kilometers can significantly increase the decay rate and require a greater amount of propellant to raise the satellite back to its original altitude. If the constellation is maintained at its higher altitude, the impact of atmospheric drag will be minimized and the total ΔV and propellant required will also be minimized.

Table 13-9 summarizes the advantages and disadvantages of absolute vs. relative stationkeeping for the circumstance where the altitude of a constellation will be maintained over time. In this case, nearly all of the advantages favor absolute stationkeeping. The absolute stationkeeping process itself is inherently simple in that we continuously push on each satellite in order to put back the ΔV taken out by atmospheric drag. Each satellite is flown by itself and does not require interaction with the rest of the constellation. Because I'm generally using a larger number of smaller burns, the size of the thrusters is also smaller for absolute stationkeeping. With both smaller thrusters and shorter burns, the disturbance torque on the spacecraft is smaller, which reduces the size and speed required of the attitude control system, since thruster firings are normally the largest disturbance the spacecraft sees once it is on orbit. Propellant utilization is also minimized, since I am firing only in one direction to combat atmospheric drag, and am maintaining the constellation at its highest altitude (lowest density and lowest drag) at all times.

TABLE 13-9. Absolute vs. Relative Stationkeeping Trade. See text for discussion.

Method	Additional Propellant Cost	Advantages	Disadvantages
Relative Stationkeeping	May be some added propellant cost depending on implementation	• Minimizes maneuver frequency	• Stationkeeping depends on interrelationship between all satellites in the system • Complex commanding may lead to command errors and greater risk • High operations cost • Different logic for system build-up than operations
Absolute Stationkeeping	None, assuming drag makeup is the only in-plane stationkeeping	• Simple commanding • Each satellite maintains itself in the pattern • Position of all other satellites are known without sending data around continuously • Can be fully autonomous • Same logic for build-up as for normal operations • Easily monitored from ground • Stationkeeping will not interfere with normal system operations	• More frequent stationkeeping (may be an advantage since burns will be smaller and more easily controlled).

The principal advantage to relative stationkeeping is that it minimizes the maneuver frequency and, therefore, minimizes the amount of commanding required of the spacecraft. Note that the advantages of absolute stationkeeping go away if it is appropriate to allow the entire constellation to decay. In this case, we can do relative stationkeeping only and, in some cases, may even be able to achieve this with differential drag, such that the propulsion system can be eliminated entirely. This approach has been used for the ORBCOMM constellation [Burgess and Gobrieal, 1996].

There is a secondary but potentially substantial benefit to absolute stationkeeping. In this case, we can create a purely deterministic constellation with a deterministic pattern in which the positions of all of the satellites are known at all future times. Because we are controlling the absolute position of all of the satellites, the long-term error in our ability to project these positions is simply the size of the stationkeeping control box. This has the advantage of dramatically simplifying the planning and scheduling process for both housekeeping and payload operations. Ordinarily, this scheduling process is dominated by multiple iterations as we're able to more accurately propagate the future position of the spacecraft. Thus we may begin with a preliminary plan for a particular stationkeeping pass or observation activity 2 to 3 weeks in advance, based on an approximate propagation of what we believe the orbit will be. For a critical operation, this would then be refined, say, 72 hours before the planned observations, and refined again 24 hours before, with a final update a few hours or minutes prior to the actual event. This is how we establish where the satellite will be at various critical events, such as acquisition of the satellite by a ground station, or photographing a ground target. In absolute stationkeeping, this replanning process can be entirely eliminated. Because we know the positions of the satellites in advance, we can do our "final" observations and communications scheduling as far in advance as is convenient for business purposes, say at the beginning of the month, or on Monday afternoons. In most cases, the absolute stationkeeping algorithms are sufficiently simple that the ground station, or even a hand-held receiver can know where the satellites are at future times without having that information conveyed or updated. Essentially, the satellites run on time because they are controlled to run on time. This is what we call a *controlled orbit*.

The Controlled Orbit Concept

The basic distinction between orbit maintenance and orbit control is important in terms of how a constellation functions. In normal orbit maintenance, the orbit elements are maintained only in an average sense. We need an orbit propagator to estimate where the satellite will be at any future time. We use the word "estimate" since the actual future positions of the satellite will depend on drag and other variables which are normally poorly known in advance. Orbit propagation is inherently inaccurate in terms of predicting future positions of spacecraft primarily because of the difficulty in being able to predict the levels of drag.

In contrast, a *controlled orbit* is one which uses absolute stationkeeping to maintain all of the elements of the orbit, including the in-track phase. An orbit propagator is not needed to determine future positions, and indeed will not work over an extended period, since small burns are being made on a regular basis to force the satellite to follow a predefined mathematical algorithm. This means that the position of the satellite at any future time is easily determined, as discussed in Sec. 13.4.2. This determination is not done by an orbit propagator, but by a much simpler mathematical projection. A relatively simple orbit propagator can be used to determine the position of the stationkeeping box, if it is desired to know the position of the satellite to a higher level of accuracy than the short-term variations produced by higher order harmonics. Even in this case, the orbit propagator would not be run from the current time to some future time, but only for one orbit corresponding to the time at which the information was needed.

In many respects, a controlled orbit is similar to the attitude control system on board most spacecraft. In most communications satellites, for example, we know that 3 years from now, if the spacecraft is functioning, the spacecraft's z-axis will be pointed at nadir, simply because it is a nadir-oriented spacecraft, and a particular axis is controlled to be in that direction at all times to within the control system accuracy. We can at best crudely estimate the sum of all of the disturbance torques which the spacecraft feels over that extended period of time. However, irrespective of the magnitude or sequence of these torques, we expect the spacecraft to be nadir pointed at any given future date. Similarly, in a controlled orbit, we do not know all of the orbit perturbations that the satellite will need to overcome. Atmospheric drag will vary in unpredictable ways; there may be a small leak or an explosive bolt which will change the orbit. Irrespective of these effects, if the system is operating, the spacecraft in a controlled orbit will be at a well defined position at any given future date and time, just as the spacecraft attitude will be.

13.4.2 In-Track Stationkeeping

In low-Earth orbit, we can use either relative or absolute in-track stationkeeping. In relative stationkeeping, we will maintain each satellite to follow the most drag-free, i.e., the one which decays the most slowly. Otherwise, we would be using the thrusters to increase the rate of decay for some satellites, thereby wasting system propellant. The most direct approach to achieving this is to determine which satellite is decaying the most slowly and fire thrusters in the other satellites in the system so as to match as closely as possible this decay rate. A particularly clever alternative approach is to make use of differential drag to adjust the decay rates to be the same for all of the satellites, as was done on the ORBCOMM constellation.* For many spacecraft the amount of drag can vary by up to a factor of 10, depending on the orientation of the spacecraft, and particularly the solar arrays, with respect to the velocity vector. If the arrays are turned sidewise to the velocity vector, the drag level and decay rate will be significantly reduced relative to what will occur if the arrays are normal to the velocity vector. Adjusting the angle of the arrays by even small amounts can impact the decay rate of the satellite with only minor impacts on the power output of the arrays. In addition, during eclipse periods the arrays can be adjusted to whatever angle is needed to achieve the most appropriate decay rate. The ORBCOMM satellites shown in Fig. 13-15 used this approach to provide relative orbit maintenance without the use of propellants.

For most constellations, altitude maintenance is required such that absolute in-track stationkeeping is more appropriate than relative stationkeeping.† (See Fig. 13-16.) In in-track stationkeeping in which the altitude is maintained, the fundamental problem is to put back the ΔV that drag takes out. This is equivalent to bouncing a pingpong ball with a paddle and maintaining it in the air. Gravity is continuously pulling the pingpong ball downward. I hit the ball upwards such that it follows a small parabolic arc; it returns to the position of the paddle, where it is hit again, and the process repeats.

* U.S. Patent No. 5,806,801.

† The process described here is covered by patents by Microcosm (U.S. Patent Nos. 5,528,502 and 5,687,084) and Glickman (U.S. Patent No. 5,267,167).

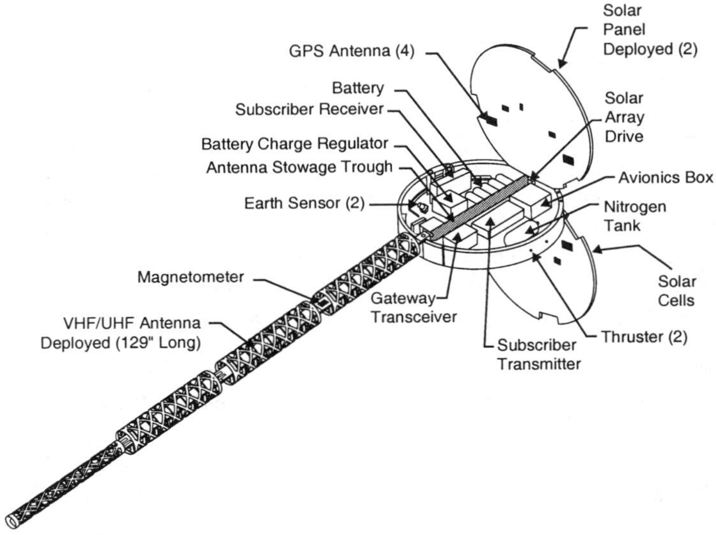

Fig. 13-15. ORBCOMM Satellites use the Rotational Position of the "Ears" for Differential Drag Control. (See Burgess, [1996].)

Similarly, I maintain the satellite in a stationkeeping box by letting it drift to one side of the box, "hitting" it with a thruster, letting it drift across the box and back, and then hitting it again, as illustrated in Fig. 13-17.

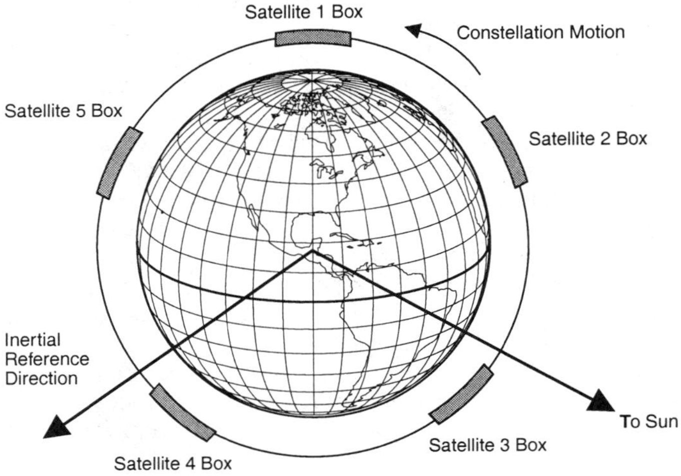

Fig. 13-16. Absolute Stationkeeping Maintains Each Satellite Within a Pre-Defined Mathematical Box. The boxes are equivalent to stationkeeping boxes in GEO, except that they are moving with respect to the surface of the Earth.

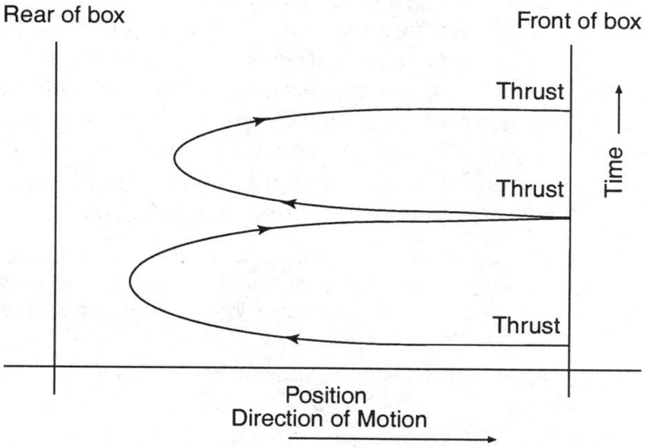

Fig. 13-17. Satellite In-Track Stationkeeping.

The total ΔV which we must apply to the spacecraft does not depend on how often the stationkeeping maneuvers are made. At each maneuver, I must put back the ΔV that the atmosphere has taken out since the last maneuver. Consequently, the total ΔV over any given time period will be the same irrespective of the number of maneuvers used to apply this ΔV.

The size of the stationkeeping box and the timing and frequency of in-track burns is a function of the atmospheric drag, which in turn is a strong function of the altitude and the phase in the solar cycle as described in Sec. 2.4. At low altitudes, where drag is strong, the disturbance is substantial and the control process is straightforward. Thruster burns are made at frequent regular intervals such as once per orbit, and tight control can be maintained. As the altitude increases, the drag perturbing force goes to zero. As this occurs, propellant utilization goes down, but the control process itself becomes more difficult to manage. At the point where there is no effective drag, the in-track control process becomes equivalent to the cross-track stationkeeping discussed in Sec. 13.4.3, where burns in both directions must be done in order to maintain the satellite within a well-defined box.

As illustrated in Fig. 13-18, the size of the stationkeeping box depends in part on how it is defined and what it will be used for. If the stationkeeping box is to be used for determining or controlling the relative distances between satellites, it must include the differential in-track perturbations discussed in Sec. 10.1. If the only requirement is position knowledge, then these terms are not required. Similarly, if we wish to model the center of the position of the box with a simple circular model, then the size of the box must be increased to take into account the non-circular character of a true spacecraft orbit. On the other hand, these variations from pure circular motion can be easily computed such that we can also consider a smaller stationkeeping box moving in a more complex path. Generally, an ideal (Keplerian) reference orbit is used to define an overall mission plan or constellation pattern. This reference orbit can be either elliptic or circular. This idealized orbit is perturbed by the complex structure of the Earth's geopotential field. These higher order perturbations are not controlled because of the enormous amount of propellant that it would require, and the fact that their effect is cyclic, returning to the original values when the spacecraft again passes over the same place on the Earth. While this more complex motion cannot be eliminated, it can be known very precisely because the Earth's geopotential field is extremely well known. This more complex orbit shape defines the center of the orbit control box in which the satellite is maintained. The maximum variation between the motion of the control box and the much smoother Keplerian reference orbit is about ±5 km. This variation can be thought of as the sum of a smooth longitude-independent variation of nearly ±5 km due to the oblateness of the Earth, and a small, much more complex motion due to higher order harmonics of approximately ±2 km.

In-plane stationkeeping should be done by controlling the orbit elements as determined at a fixed time (e.g.), at the node crossing). This results in the following error budget build-up:

Control of node crossing times to within specified measured values

+

Measurement error in node crossing times

results in

Absolute box for node crossing times

+

Position variations throughout the orbit due to errors in orbital elements

+

Position variations throughout the orbit due to natural perturbations

results in

Absolute whole orbit stationkeeping box for the constellation

This must be less than the stationkeeping requirement box.
Typically, stationkeeping box must be 10 km to 50 km long.

Fig. 13-18. Build-up of the Stationkeeping Box. Which terms are included depends on the purpose for which the stationkeeping box is used.

Stationkeeping accuracy depends on both the navigation accuracy and the control mechanization. Generally the repeatable accuracy with respect to an absolute standard is on the order of ±0.15 sec = ±1 km for low-Earth orbit in-track stationkeeping. Typical results are shown in Fig. 13-19. Note that there is also a problem with keeping absolute positions relative to the surface of the Earth because the rotation of the Earth itself is non-uniform.* This variation is compensated by leap seconds, which are added or not added to civil time at 6-month intervals. The leap second causes a 1 sec perturbation in the stationkeeping problem if we wish to maintain coverage with respect to a civil clock.

In geosynchronous orbit, stationkeeping is done both in-track (also called *east-west stationkeeping*) and cross-track (*north-south stationkeeping*). While the nature of the perturbing forces is substantially different, the process is essentially the same for both of these as it is for in-track control in low-Earth orbit. The reasons for the geosyn-

*There is a general slowing of the Earth's rotation caused primarily by tidal friction with the Moon. In addition, there is an irregular non-uniformity in the rotation caused primarily by freezing and thawing of the polar ice caps. When the ice caps recede, water is transferred from the polar regions to the equator, and the Earth slows down. See Fig. 4.1 on Sec. 4.1.

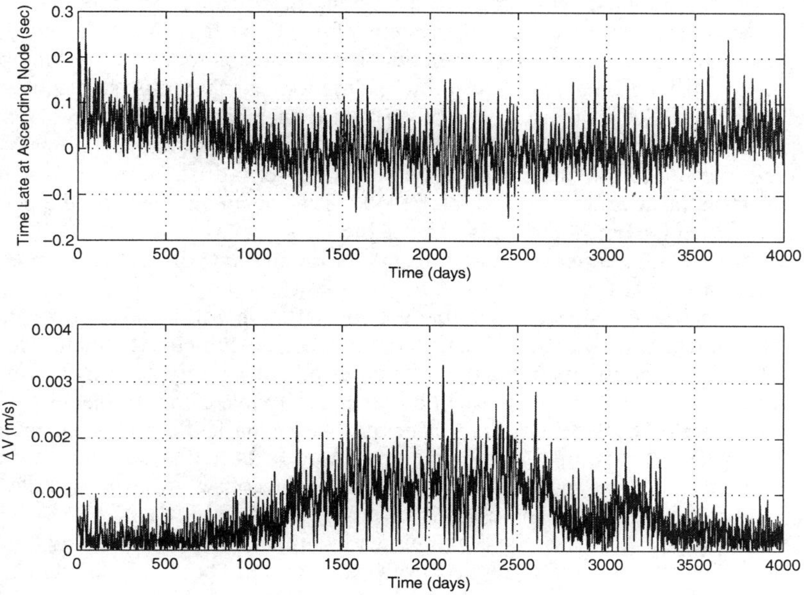

Fig. 13-19. Simulation Results of In-track Stationkeeping over a 10-Year Period.

chronous orbit perturbations were discussed in Sec. 2.5.1. In both cases, there is a perturbing force pushing the satellite continuously in one direction. Therefore, the stationkeeping box and stationkeeping process are essentially similar to that defined above.

13.4.3 Cross-Track Stationkeeping

Cross-track stationkeeping refers to maintaining the orientation of the orbit plane. This is done by maintaining the inclination and the right ascension of the ascending node, or, with respect to the Earth, the longitude of the ascending node. These two parameters are coupled due to the perturbation caused by the Earth's oblateness. Specifically, the J_2 term representing the Earth's oblateness causes the ascending node to drift at a rate that is proportional to the cosine of the inclination (see Secs. 2.4 and 2.5). This means that small differences in the inclination of each satellite will cause a cumulative differential drift in node due to the oblateness. This in turn implies that the inclination must be maintained in order to control the node rate. For example, in a polar orbit at 700 km, an 0.1 deg difference in inclination will cause a relative drift rate in the value of the node of 0.01 deg per day = 4.4 deg per year. For a 5-year mission life, this small difference in inclination would cause a 22-deg separation in ascending node which is more than enough to destroy the structure of nearly any constellation.

It is neither necessary nor realistic to attempt to drive the node drift rate to zero. All that needs to be done is to make the node drift rate the same for all of the satellites in the constellation. This in turn means adjusting the inclination as needed to provide a common drift rate.

The cross-track control problem is fundamentally different in character than in-track control. In the in-track direction in low-Earth orbit there is a continuous perturbing force (atmospheric drag) always acting in the same direction that must be negated. This in turn gives the control system a force to push against in order to maintain tight control. In the cross-track direction, there is no continuously growing perturbation that must be balanced. The orbit inclination is inherently stable over long periods of time. The problem to be solved is that each satellite will have a slightly different inclination when it is delivered to orbit. These inclination variations must be corrected in order to provide the same level of long-term drift. How this is achieved depends upon the accuracy with which the node is to be maintained and the period of time over which the constellation is to be stable.

If we can measure either the node drift rate or inclination with sufficient precision, then we can make fine adjustments in the inclination so as to provide each satellite with nearly the same drift rate, such that the constellation will be stable over the lifetime of the spacecraft. Typically, this would imply establishing the inclination to better than 0.01 deg. If the inclination cannot be adjusted sufficiently accurately when the satellites are placed in orbit, then it will be necessary to make control maneuvers from time to time through the life of the spacecraft. This is basically a bang-bang control process in which the inclination is pushed back and forth with a very long time constant to try and achieve a mean value appropriate to the constellation as a whole. Once a nearly correct value has been established at the beginning, it will take very small amounts of propellant to provide continuing adjustments. However, it may be necessary to burn in the cross-track direction from time to time. Therefore, thrusters need to be mounted in this direction or alternatively, a mechanism needs to be provided such that the spacecraft can be rotated to use the in-track thrusters in the cross-track direction on an occasional basis. The typical logic involved in the process would be to sense the inclination error by sensing the difference in drift rate of the ascending node relative to the desired value. This drift rate error then leads to an adjustment by correcting the inclination.

This type of control approach is appropriate whenever there is no continuing perturbing force that must be balanced. This occurs in the cross-track direction in low-Earth orbit and in both the in-track and cross-track when I get sufficiently far from low-Earth orbit that atmospheric drag is no longer a significant perturbation. However, when the orbit goes all the way to geosynchronous altitudes, then we need the "in-track style" stationkeeping approach for both in-track and cross-track components, due to the continuing perturbations caused by the Sun and the Moon, and by the Earth's higher order harmonics. Again, the type of control is determined by the nature of the perturbing forces which are being balanced.

13.5 Collision Avoidance

On a first look, collisions between spacecraft should not be a problem, and, in general, they are not. Space is remarkably big, spacecraft are small, and there are only small numbers of them. If we had only a few hundred cars scattered over the surface of the world and moving at random, car collisions would be unheard of, even though there are only two dimensions for avoiding collisions, rather than three, as in space. However, if we confine all of the automotive traffic to a small number of well defined high velocity superhighways and if the superhighways intersect each other with no traffic lights, then not only do collisions become more likely, but as the traffic density increases, they become nearly inevitable. This is the fundamental problem for collision avoidance in constellations. For the satellite population in general, it is a relatively minor problem. Historically, collisions between spacecraft or spacecraft and large pieces have been very rare. However, constellations force spacecraft into narrowly defined intersecting orbits. Because constellations frequently have a high level of symmetry, there is often a desire to design the pattern in such a way that in principle, two satellites will end up at the same position at the same time at some point in the orbit. The obvious alternatives of, for example, putting satellites in eccentric orbits so that they pass over and under each other, may serve to make the problem worse, rather than better. Continuing our automotive analogy, if a collision does occur, then we leave a large amount of debris scattered about the roadway which dramatically increases the potential of secondary collisions. As discussed in detail in Sec. 2.5, the increasing problem of artificial space debris has received significant attention. Johnson and McKnight [1991], Reijnen and de Graaff [1989], and Simpson [1994] provide detailed assessments of the artificial debris and collision problem. Akella and Alfriend [2000] discuss alternative computations for debris collisions with the Space Station. Finally Chobotov et al. [1997], Kamprath and Jenkin [1998], and Jenkin [1995, 1993a, 1993b] discuss specifically the problem of collision and debris hazards for constellations, including the geostationary ring which, for purposes of collision analysis, can be thought of as a one-orbit constellation in a very unique environmental regime. Thus, while collision avoidance is a workable problem in constellation design, it is one that should be given serious consideration as a part of the fundamental systems engineering of constellations.

In order to assess the importance of collision avoidance, we need to estimate two key elements. First, what is the probability of a collision, and second, what are the consequences of a collision? We will find that the consequences of a collision are potentially very detrimental and that the number of collision opportunities in constellations is extremely large. This in turn implies that a key issue in constellation design is to drive the probability of collision per opportunity to be extremely small.

We define a *collision opportunity* as an incident in which two satellites pass more or less close to each other. Assume that we have two satellites, A and B, which are in different orbits but at approximately the same altitude. Each satellite passes through the orbit plane of the other satellite twice per orbit. In most cases, the crossing satellite, say A, will pass over, under, in front of, or behind the other satellite, B. However, if the center of mass of the two satellites come within a distance of each other which is less than the sum of the radii of the two satellites, then a collision will occur. This process of one satellite passing through the orbit plane of another is a collision opportunity.

For computations, it is convenient to think of the two satellites as spheres of radii R_1 and R_2. The *collision cross section*, σ, is the area surrounding the center of mass of satellite A such that if the center of mass of satellite B falls within that area, a collision will occur. For the case of spherical satellites of radii R_A and R_B, the cross sectional area will be $\pi(R_A + R_B)^2$. Thus, if the two satellites are both 10 m in diameter, the collision cross section will be approximately 300 square meters. Assume that satellite A is confined to a stationkeeping box 3 km long and 100 m high. Therefore, it must be within an area of 300,000 m^2. Any time satellite B passes randomly through that stationkeeping box, there will be a probability of $300 \div 300{,}000 = 0.001$ that the two satellites will collide.

How many collision opportunities will there be in a given constellation? Consider as an example a low-Earth orbit constellation of 100 satellites with 10 satellites in each of 10 orbit planes. Assume that we have spread our satellites out within each orbit plane but are unconcerned about collisions so we have decided not to control the satellites in different planes with respect to each other. Further, let us assume that each time a satellite crosses one of the other orbit planes, it has a non-zero probability of colliding with only one other satellite, i.e., whichever of the 10 in that plane is the closest. Each satellite crosses 9 other planes twice and, therefore, faces 18 collision opportunities per orbit, with approximately 15 orbits per day. Therefore, the constellation as a whole has $100 \times 18 \times 15 = 27{,}000$ collision opportunities per day $= 10^7$ per year $= 10^8$ in a 10-year constellation life. If we want less than a 1% probability that there will be a collision in 10 years of the constellation life, then the probability of a collision in any single opportunity should be less than 10^{-10}, and less than 10^{-12} would certainly be more comforting, given the extremely adverse consequences of a collision. This is a remarkably small number. The chances of anything man-made working correctly every time in a trillion failure opportunities is not good.

Table 13-10 gives the collision opportunities and collision probabilities for representative constellations. Note that these calculations assume that the satellites are randomly located in a stationkeeping box and that the centers of these boxes are designed to collide in order to provide the proper coverage characteristics. In a realistic constellation, we will not do this. We will design the stationkeeping boxes such that they do not collide. However, the large number of collision opportunities implies that we must do more than this. We should attempt to maximize the probability that collisions will **not** occur.

In the above discussion, we have implied that the consequences of a collision are extremely deleterious. There are two reasons for this. First, as illustrated in Table 13-11, the energy associated with colliding objects in space is extremely large. This comes about because the energy imparted by the colliding particles is proportional to the square of the relative velocity. The orbital velocities are extremely high and the velocity with which they collide will be proportional to the linear velocities and the sine of the angle between their velocity vectors. As can be seen from the table, 7 km/s times the sine of almost anything is a large number, such that even particles far too small to be tracked carry dramatically large amounts of kinetic energy. By and large, spacecraft do not do well when hit by high speed bullets, cannonballs, trains, other satellites, or fragments of satellites.

The second problem with collisions is the consequence of that collision over time. An explosion of a satellite creates a large number of fragments of various sizes and imparts an additional velocity relative to the previous center of mass. However, the velocity imparted by the explosion is extremely small relative to the orbital velocity. Consequently, the particles will form a *debris cloud* consisting of fragments of various sizes and moving fundamentally in the same orbit as the satellite which exploded.* What the explosion has done is transform a spacecraft which is trackable and potentially controllable into a large cloud of fragments in a nearly identical orbit, many of

* The natural analog to this process is comets, which tend to evaporate and break up as they near the Sun. The dust and rock left behind stays in the comet orbit and produces a *meteorite swarm*. When the Earth crosses the comet's orbit and encounters this swarm, it results in a *meteor shower*, which will be more or less spectacular depending on the density of particles in that particular portion of the comet's orbit.

TABLE 13-10. Collision Opportunities and Collision Probabilities for Representative Constellations. Collision probability represents how often a collision would occur if the satellites were randomly located in a stationkeeping box and the centers of the stationkeeping box occupied the same space at the same time—i.e., if we ignore the potential for collisions and simply use the "space is big, satellites are small" philosophy.*

System Modeled	2 Random Co-Alt. Sats[1]	100 Random Co-Alt. Sats[2]	100 Sats In-Plane Control Only[3]	100 Sats in Intersecting Boxes, Poor Cntl.[4]	100 Sats in Intersecting Boxes, Mod. Cntl.[5]
No. of sats considered	2	100	100	100	100
No. of orbit planes	2	100	10	10	10
Satellite diameter (m)	5	5	5	5	5
Diam. of keep-out box (m)	10	10	10	10	10
Collision cross-sect. (m^2)	100	100	100	100	100
Vertical dispersion (km)	1	1	1	1	0.1
In-track dispersion (km)	45,000	45,000	4,500	10	2
Potential impact area (km^2)	45,000	45,000	4,500	10	0.2
Collision prob. per opport.	2.22×10^{-9}	2.22×10^{-9}	2.22×10^{-8}	1.00×10^{-5}	5.00×10^{-4}
Collision opport. per orbit	4	19,800	1,800	1,800	1,800
$\times$ 0.5 for joint collisions	2	9,900	900	900	900
Orbit period (min)	100	100	100	100	100
Collision opport. per yr	10,519	5.21×10^7	4.73×10^6	4.73×10^6	4.73×10^6
Collision opport. per 10 yrs	1.05×10^5	5.21×10^8	4.73×10^7	4.73×10^7	4.73×10^7
Mean no. of collisions per yr	2.34×10^{-5}	0.12	0.11	47.34	2,367
Mean no. of years between collisions	42,780	8.64	9.51	0.021	0.00042
Mean no. of days between collisions	1.56×10^7	3,157	3,472	7.72	0.15

* Collision probabilities are exceptionally low under ordinary circumstances. A controlled constellation is dramatically different—without a collision avoidance strategy, collisions are essentially inevitable in the two rightmost columns

1 2 satellites in random circular orbits at the same altitude

2 100 satellites in random circular orbits at the same altitude

3 100 satellites in 10 planes, controlled in phase within each plane, but uncontrolled with respect to the other orbit planes

4 100 satellites in 10 km × 1 km stationkeeping boxes with boxes allowed to intersect

5 100 satellites in 2 km × 0.1 km stationkeeping boxes with boxes allowed to intersect

TABLE 13-11. Consequences of a Collision Between a Spacecraft and Small Debris Fragments. The fragments are assumed to have a density of 1 g/cc and an impact angle of 30 deg. A 10 cm fragment is approximately the smallest that can be tracked by ground radar systems.

Fragment Diameter	Equivalent Kinetic Energy of Impact
1 mm	marble @ 25 mph
1 cm	baseball @ 500 mph
10 cm	bowling ball @ 2,000 mph
1 m	truck @ 4,000 mph

which will be too small to be tracked. As shown in Fig. 13-20, this debris cloud evolves over time, due to both the differential initial velocities from the explosion and differential drag due to the varying properties of the individual fragments. Initially, the cloud grows, following closely the path of the original satellite. Over time the debris will spread throughout the orbit plane of the original satellite. Thus we create a debris ring similar in many respects to components of Saturn's rings, although, of course, with far fewer particles. This dramatically increases the collision cross section with other spacecraft, since each of the individual fragments now has the potential for a collision.* While these fragments will eventually decay, the lower the level of drag, the longer that decay process will take.

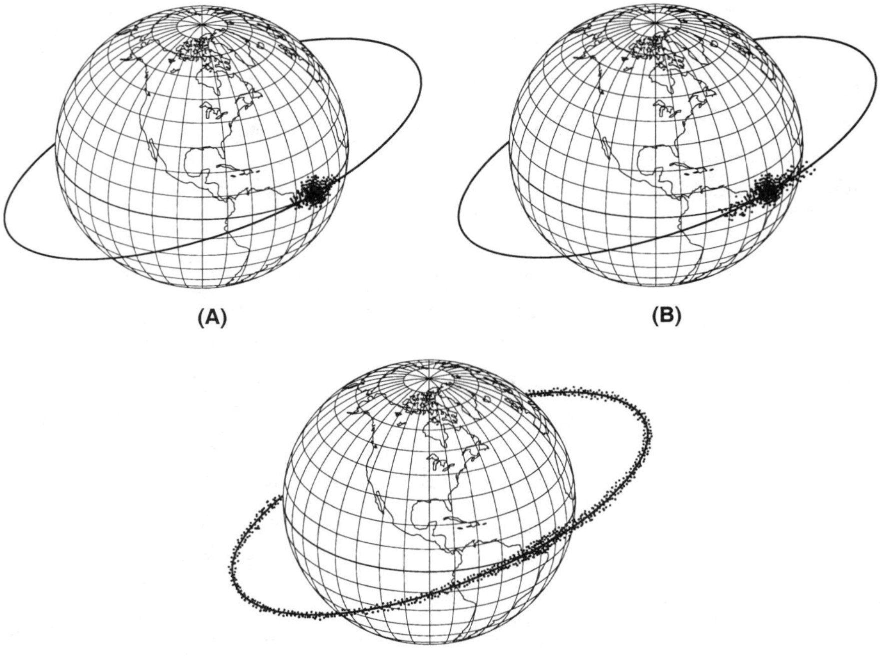

Fig. 13-20. Evolution of a Collision Debris Cloud. Immediately after the collision (A), there is a dense cloud of pieces traveling in essentially the same orbit as the original satellite with small differential velocities imparted by the explosion. Because of the differential velocities and differential drag, the particles spread out (B) and eventually form a ring (C) in the original orbit and then decay due to atmospheric drag.

* In the earlier example, two spacecraft each of 10 m diameter had a collision cross section of 300 m^2. Assume one of these has exploded or hit a fragment and been transformed into 10,000 small pieces, each of negligible size but substantial kinetic energy. The collision cross section per fragment is now $\pi \times 5^2 \approx 80$ m^2, so the collision cross section for the entire set of fragments that used to be a satellite has increased to 800,000 m^2. This increases the collision probability by a factor of more than 1,000. As an analogy, your chance of being hit by a shotgun fired in your general direction is far higher than the chance of being hit by a single rifle shot fired in the same direction.

The possible consequences of a collision with another satellite in the constellation, or even with a small fragment are distinctly bad. A 10 cm diameter fragment deposits as much energy as a bowling ball hitting the spacecraft at 3,000 miles per hour, or a large car hitting it 250 miles per hour. In either case, there will not be a lot left of the satellite that is hit, other than another debris cloud. This greatly increases the probability of secondary collisions, which in turn can result in a chain reaction, or snowball effect. A single collision creates a debris cloud that greatly increases the collision probability. This, in turn, creates more collisions and a larger cloud, such that over time the entire constellation may be transformed into a debris cloud. This cloud slowly decays, proceeding to take out large portions of those constellations which are beneath it and, after a large number of years, the International Space Station. On the whole, this would make for a very bad day. Of course, this is a hypothetical result. An assessment of the potential for this occurring for any specific constellation requires a detailed analysis and modeling of the constellation, both in terms of the collision probabilities and the consequences of any collisions that do occur. Our principal message is that such an assessment is clearly worth doing before investing billions of dollars in a low-Earth orbit constellation.

All of the above implies two specific issues for constellation design. First, collision avoidance analysis should be given significant attention. For your constellation, how important is collision avoidance, in terms of both probability and consequences? Secondly, the constellation design should be such that the probability of collision is extremely low, even for satellites that are no longer functioning. Thus, we want to consider collision avoidance, not only in normal satellite operations, but also in the process of putting satellites in orbit, taking them out of orbit, and working with or around satellites which have died in place.

Fortunately, the importance of collision avoidance is straightforward to evaluate. Using the techniques described above, we can assess the collision probabilities for most types of orbits, at least in a first approximation. The leftmost column in Table 13-10 is applicable, for example, for a satellite in a geosynchronous transfer orbit. Here, we are going through virtually all of the low-Earth orbit constellations. Nonetheless, we are doing so only a very small number of times such that the total probability of collision is remarkably small. Clearly it would be worthwhile in such a transfer to avoid large trackable particles. Nonetheless, collisions are not generally a problem for single satellites or spacecraft in transfer orbits. Space is indeed big, and spacecraft are small. The real problem arises with constellations, which are constrained to operate within a narrowly defined space, and which will occupy that space for an extended period. In these cases, we need to proactively design the constellation to avoid collisions.

Designing the Constellation to Avoid Collisions

Table 13-12 summarizes the critical issues for designing a constellation for collision avoidance. The most basic problem is to design the constellation so that the stationkeeping boxes do not intersect. This in turn means that we must keep track of all of the mutual intersections of all possible pairs of planes. Generally, the larger and more symmetric a constellation, the more difficult this problem will be. This is illustrated in Fig. 13-21, which shows our hypothetical constellation of 100 satellites in 10 orbit planes, 10 satellites per plane. The heavy lines on each orbit represent the stationkeeping box for each satellite. Our problem then is to design the constellation such that none of the 900 interactions between the varying orbits occurs when a second stationkeeping box is at the point of intersection. How to do this will be discussed below.

TABLE 13-12. Key Issues in Designing a Constellation for Collision Avoidance.

Approach or Issue	Comment
1. Maximize the spacing between satellites when crossing other orbit planes.	May impact phasing between planes and, therefore, coverage.
2. Remove satellites at end-of-life.	Either deorbit or raise them above the constellation, if still functioning.
3. Determine the motion through the constellation of a satellite that "dies in place."	Constellations at low altitude have an advantage.
4. Remove upper stages from the orbital ring or leave them attached to the satellite.	Do not leave uncontrolled objects in the constellation pattern.
5. Design the approach for rephasing or replacement of satellites with collision avoidance in mind.	All intersatellite motion should address the collision potential.
6. Capture any components which are ejected.	Look for items such as explosive bolts, lens caps, or Marmon clamps.
7. Avoid the potential for self-generated explosions.	Vent propellant tanks of spent spacecraft.

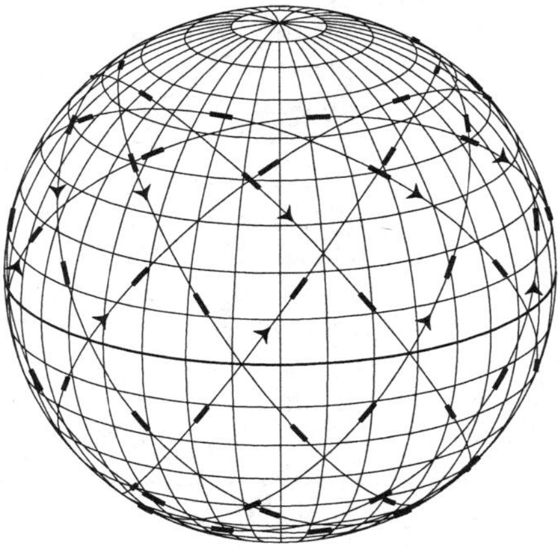

Fig. 13-21. Constellation with 10 Orbit Planes and 10 Satellites per Plane has 90 Different Locations Where Two Planes Intersect Which Results in 900 Potential Collisions per Orbit.

In addition to simply avoiding collisions between the stationkeeping boxes, we want to maintain the largest possible minimum separation between satellites for two reasons. First, we would like to provide the largest possible stationkeeping margin because of the dramatically adverse consequences of a collision. Second, maintaining a large minimum separation provides the most time and greatest safety margin if a satellite fails in place, as is virtually certain to occur many times in any large constellation.

It is important to understand the motion of a satellite that "dies in place," i.e., that loses the capacity for control while it is still in the constellation pattern. This would occur, for example, if the satellite power system fails, or if the command link fails for a satellite which is controlled from the ground. Relative to the rest of the constellation pattern, the dead satellite moves both down and forward as illustrated in Fig. 13-22. We would like the satellite to be below the rest of the constellation when it moves

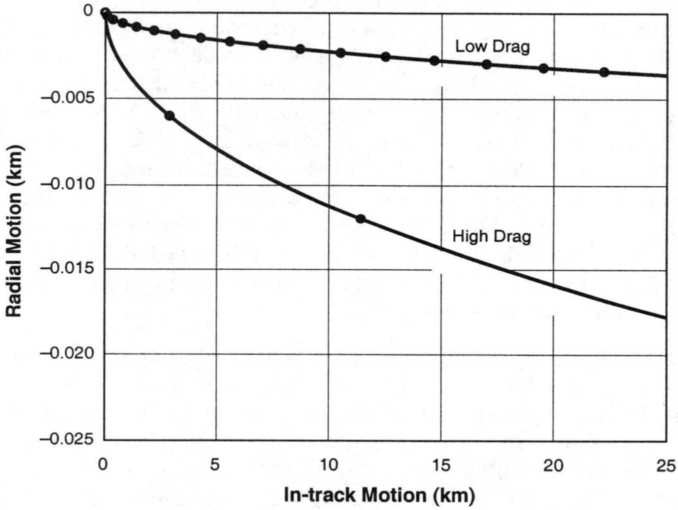

Fig. 13-22. Consequences of a Satellite "Dying in Place." In a high drag environment, the satellite moves down and forward more steeply than in a low drag environment. On both curves, dots are at an interval of 7 days.

forward enough to intersect the next stationkeeping box crossing its orbital path. If this occurs, then the dead satellite will dive under the constellation and we will have a greater assurance of avoiding collisions which might generate debris within the constellation. This "cleaning" of the constellation occurs best at low altitudes. In a high drag environment, the satellite will move forward rapidly. However, it also moves downward faster than it moves forward, moving the satellite on a steeper slope relative to the constellation. In a very low drag environment, the satellite moves downward slowly with only a very small amount of downward motion. Therefore, the dead satellite slices the next forward stationkeeping box which crosses its orbit very finely, maximizing the inherent probability of a collision. Spacecraft in a low drag environment will evolve out of their pattern very slowly, and will do so in a way that is potentially very detrimental to the constellation as a whole.

At first, it might appear that collision avoidance is best done by the choice of constellation design pattern. For example, the fundamentally polar orbits in the streets of coverage pattern imply all of the satellites come together at the poles, which appears to maximize the collision potential. However, this is not the case. Any two distinct orbit planes will intersect twice and only twice, irrespective of their relative inclination or positions of the node. Consequently, major changes in the constellation structure, such as polar vs. low inclination, will have no fundamental impact on collision opportunities. Reducing the number of orbit planes will reduce the collision opportunities simply because satellites will not collide with other satellites in the same plane. Thus, collision avoidance is not done by making major changes in the constellation pattern, but rather by "fine tuning" the locations of the stationkeeping boxes. There are three ways to make these fine adjustments in how the stationkeeping boxes intersect:

1. **Eccentricity**. Maintaining the satellites in eccentric orbits such that stationkeeping boxes pass over and under each other seems like an inherently strong solution but has significant problems. Eccentricity gives the constellation pattern thickness such that it takes far longer for a dead satellite to decay through the constellation. Recall that for a dead satellite in an eccentric orbit, drag initially maintains perigee at an approximately constant altitude and lowers apogee until it is the same height as perigee. The satellite then spirals inward (see Fig. 2-18 in Sec. 2.4.4). During the entire time apogee is being reduced, the satellite is continuously within the constellation pattern. Further, because the orbit is eccentric and is drifting in terms of argument of perigee and eccentricity, it is also sliding in phase throughout the constellation. This provides a very large number of collision opportunities over an extended period, which is the opposite of what we desire.

2. **Inclination**. Changing the inclination shifts the along-track position relative to the equator at which the orbit planes intersect. Since constellations are typically defined by the relative phase when they cross the equator, changing the inclination will shift where the satellites are at the time the orbit planes intersect. The geometry of this phase shift is shown in Fig. 13-23. Here we assume the two planes are at the same inclination i and have a node spacing ΔN. We wish to determine the phase shift, $\Delta\phi_c \equiv \Delta\phi_{c2} - \Delta\phi_{c1} = -2\Delta\phi_{c2}$ corresponding to a small change in inclination, Δi. From the right spherical triangle in the figure we have:

$$\tan \phi_{c1} = 1 / [\tan (\Delta N / 2) \cos i] \qquad \text{(13–11a)}$$

$$\phi_{c2} = 180 \text{ deg} - \phi_{c1} \qquad \text{(13-11b)}$$

from which we find:

$$\Delta\phi_c = \Delta\phi_{c2} - \Delta\phi_{c1} = -2\Delta\phi_{c1} \qquad \text{(13–12a)}$$

$$= -2 \sin2(\phi_c) \tan (\Delta N / 2) \sin i \qquad \text{(13-12b)}$$

For high inclination orbits and $\Delta N \approx 30$ deg, so that $\Delta\phi_c \approx 0.5\ \Delta i$.

3. **In-Plane Phasing Between Adjacent Planes**. Shifting the phase between adjacent orbit planes shifts the relative time at which the satellites cross the equator. This shift has the same effect as a change in inclination in that it slides the intersection between the stationkeeping boxes forward and backward. Note that a shift in in-plane phasing will typically break the symmetry that ordinarily occurs as we go from the last plane to the first in a given constellation.

The inclination and phase shift (options 2 and 3 above) are typically the most practical approaches for designing a constellation for collision avoidance. These can

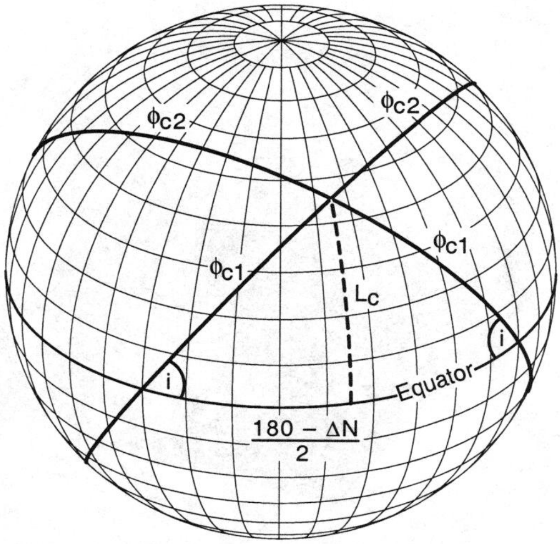

Fig. 13-23. Effect of Inclination on the Orbit Crossing Location. Both orbits are assumed to be at the same inclination.

be mixed as needed to maximize the spacing at the time of plane crossings. This problem is most conveniently done numerically by examining the closest approach between the constellation satellites as a function of inclination and phase offset. The results of a typical analysis of this type are shown in Fig. 13-24. The horizontal coordinates are the inclination and phase offset for a near polar constellation. The vertical coordinate is the closest approach between any two satellites in the constellation, assuming that each is maintained at the center of its defined stationkeeping box. Thus the valleys in the plot represent collisions between stationkeeping boxes. At an absolute minimum, we must be at a higher "elevation" on the plot than the size of the stationkeeping box. Our real goal for collision avoidance is to live on the highest mountaintop, in order to give ourselves margin, and to minimize the potential problem with dead satellites within the constellation. Within the figure, each of the valleys represents a specific collision. Thus the valley labeled 11 is the potential collision between satellites in plane 1 (the base satellite) and the nearest satellite in plane 11. Valley 11^- is a collision between the base satellite and the next satellite behind the closest one in plane 11. Plane 11^+ would be collisions with the next satellite in front of the closest satellite. Consequently, with various combinations of orbit planes, there are many "valleys" to be avoided. In the particular pattern illustrated, we can design the constellation to have a minimum separation between satellites of as much as 2.5 deg, or ~300 km.

Note that these are fine-tuning adjustments that are imposed on the overall structure of the constellation. While they ordinarily break the perfect symmetry of the constellation, they are at a small scale, and will typically have minimal impact on system coverage as a whole. For example, assume that we have a baseline streets of coverage constellation with perfectly polar orbits. In this case, satellites in the adjacent plane will be midway between satellites in the base plane in order to maximize the overlap in the coverage areas. However, if each plane has satellites midway between those in

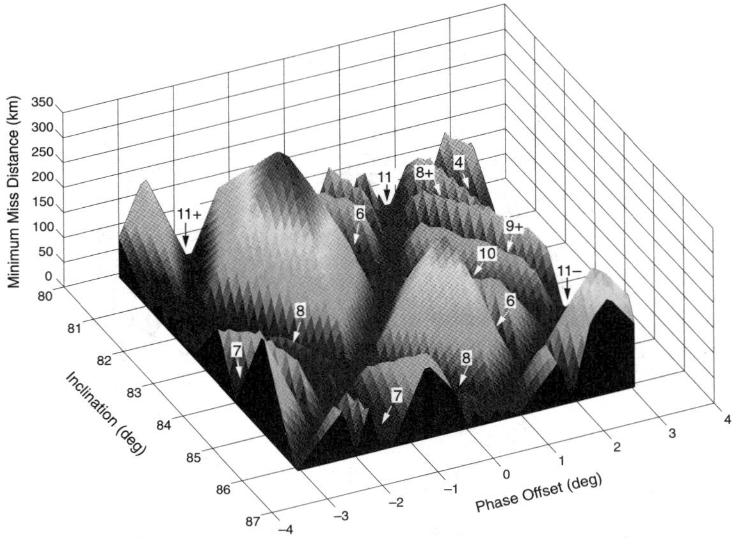

Fig. 13-24. Closest Approach Between Satellites as a Function of Inclination and Phase Offset for a Streets of Coverage Constellation with 10 Satellites in each of 11 Orbit Planes. Numbers on the "valleys" indicates which plane interfaces with plane 1. See text for explanation.

the adjacent plane, then satellites two planes over will have the same phase as the base plane, and will result in collisions between stationkeeping boxes at the pole. It is this symmetry which needs to be broken by some combination of small adjustments in inclination and phase offset. In addition, an adjustment which is too large will result in potential collisions between stationkeeping boxes further out in the pattern, say, between plane 1 and plane 6. Thus we need to evaluate the pattern as a whole in terms of collision avoidance probabilities.

Finally, we can evaluate the cost of collision avoidance by assessing the impact of lack of symmetry on coverage. Basically, the lack of symmetry that is necessary to meet our collision avoidance criteria will cause nonuniform coverage that must be compensated by going to a smaller elevation angle, higher constellation altitude, or both. However, these numbers are typically small and can ordinarily be accommodated by changing the altitude by only a few kilometers, or the minimum elevation angle by a fraction of a degree.

13.6 Constellation Build-Up, Replenishment, and End-of-Life

Most constellations spend a major portion of their lives in less than their full configuration. It may take several years to launch and test the constellation; spacecraft die on orbit; and new configurations take over for old ones. Consequently, it is important to understand both how to build the constellation in a configuration sense and how to achieve incremental performance.

One of the most fundamental goals of building up a constellation is providing performance plateaus, incremental performance, and graceful degradation. We cannot have a 100-satellite constellation in which all of the performance comes only when the last satellite is in place. The funding source would never be willing to build the constellation, and a single satellite failure would be catastrophic. What we need is an incremental improvement in performance with each small group of satellites, both for building up the constellation initially, and to provide as much residual performance as possible when satellites fail.

Recall that moving satellites within the orbit plane is easy, while moving between planes is hard. Putting up multiple satellites in one orbit plane is much easier for launch but provides limited utility because the coverage will tend to be very non-uniform. If we put up one satellite in each orbit plane, we get much more uniform coverage. More important, as we add one more satellite to each plane, we can rephase the satellites to maintain consistent spacing, with almost no propellant usage. If we have 4 satellites per plane at an early stage of constellation building, it would be desirable to have them 90 deg apart. When a 5th satellite is added, we can rephase all of the satellites such that they are 72 deg apart with a very small amount of propellant. As we add one more satellite to each orbit plane, we will achieve a performance plateau with overall better performance than we had before.

The ease of moving satellites within an orbit plane provides a significant advantage in system utility to having a constellation with a smaller number of orbit planes. With two planes, we will have performance plateaus at 1, 2, 4, 6, 8, 10, 12, 14, and 16 satellites. With eight planes, there will be plateaus at 1, 8, and 16 satellites. This reinforces the importance of altitude plateaus as discussed in Sec. 13.3. Because of this, there is a significant advantage in constellation design to having a small number of orbit planes in terms of both incremental performance and graceful degradation.

We can build up the full constellation in a wide variety of ways. The detailed process of buildup tends to be unique to each constellation and is strongly related to the choice of launch vehicle and the number of satellites that it can place on orbit in a single launch. Nonetheless, there are several general characteristics applicable to most constellations:

- Constellations often begin with a test satellite or set of test satellites which usually become a part of the subsequent constellation

- An attempt is made to build some utility at an early stage in the buildup process (i.e., performance plateaus)

- Rapid completion occurs after the initial slow test and evaluation phase

These general criteria are driven primarily by the economics of constellation buildup. We need an initial test satellite to verify that the system functions as intended and that all of the components are correctly working before committing to launching the entire constellation. Having shown that the system works, we would like to obtain at least some initial utility so that the system can begin generating useful results, either money for a commercial system or scientific or military results for a government system. Finally, having begun the process, we would like to complete it rapidly so that the entire constellation can be in place as soon as possible. Constellations are dramatically expensive, and a large amount of money is tied up in nonrecurring and development which will only be recovered after the constellation becomes operational. In addition, the early satellites launched will be going through their operational life. If the buildup process is very slow, the early satellites may die before the constellation is complete.

Spacecraft Outages and Satellite Replacement

What happens when a satellite dies? The response will depend upon the nature of the constellation and the importance of having complete coverage. We will consider as an example the case of a constellation intended to provide continuous coverage such as a low-Earth orbit communications constellation.

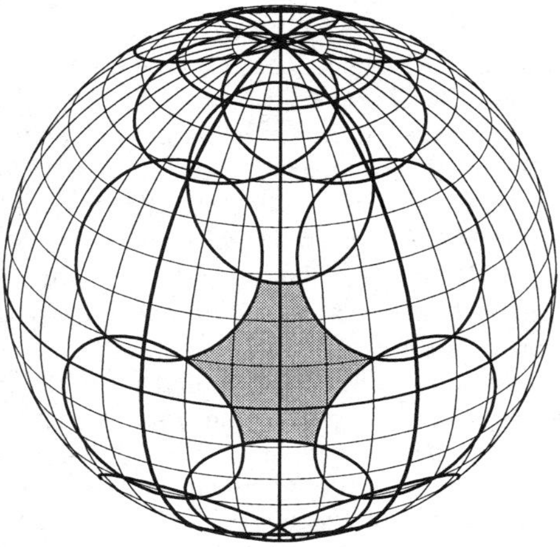

Fig. 13-25. Typical Coverage Outage Due to Loss of a Single Spacecraft. This assumes a continuous coverage constellation with an approximately polar orbit.

As shown in Fig. 13-25, when a single satellite in a constellation dies, a hole is created in the coverage pattern at the equator. The hole typically becomes smaller, and may disappear entirely at higher latitudes. Depending on the constellation altitude and pattern, points near the equator will experience outages at one or two successive ascending nodes, and then again approximately 12 hours later at the descending node of the failed satellite. Consequently, the result of a single satellite failure is typically 1 to 4 outages per day for points on the equator, with durations on the order of 5 to 20 min. As we move away from the equator, the outages will become less frequent and shorter. With a well designed constellation, we may experience either very brief or no outages at high northern latitudes where much of the population is centered. (See Fig. 13-26.)

How do we accommodate a satellite outage? The answer depends on the level of need to maintain full coverage. The only instantaneous solution available to the constellation operator is to change the minimum working elevation angle so that neighboring satellites pick up more of the burden, as illustrated in Fig. 13-27. In this case, performance may be degraded within the coverage hole but this may be more desirable than a performance outage. The principle advantage of changing the minimum elevation angle is that it can be done immediately by simply changing the operating parameters of the system. This reduces the size of the hole at the equator and reduces the latitude at which the hole closes. It will shift a number of areas from "no coverage" to "possibly degraded coverage." This can have a major impact on coverage interruptions. The service will, of course, not be as good in regions which have gone to a lower working elevation angle. For marginal users (i.e., those with limited signal strength), it may be that the degraded performance mode will prove unacceptable. However, for

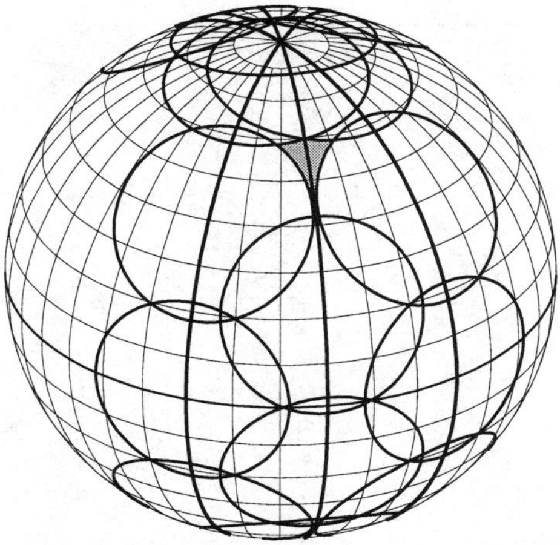

Fig. 13-26. Coverage Hole at High Latitude for the Same Constellation Shown in Fig. 13-25.

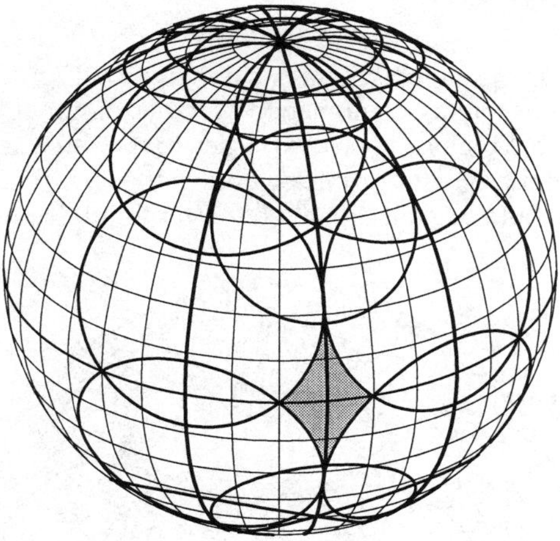

Fig. 13-27. Outage Reduction due to Using Lower Minimum Elevation Angle for Nearby Satellites.

users with significant margin, it may be that the coverage will remain indistinguishable from the previous uninterrupted coverage. Thus, while not ideal, changing the minimum working elevation angle can provide an excellent short term solution.

We can further reduce the outage due to a dead satellite by rephasing the satellites on all sides of the coverage hole while at the same time increasing their coverage region by going to a lower working elevation angle. Recall that this rephasing can be done with relatively little propellant and that the fuel required to rephase is proportional to the rephasing time as shown in Fig. 13-28. (See Sec. 2.6.2 for the relevant equations.) As we slide neighboring satellites along their orbits toward the coverage

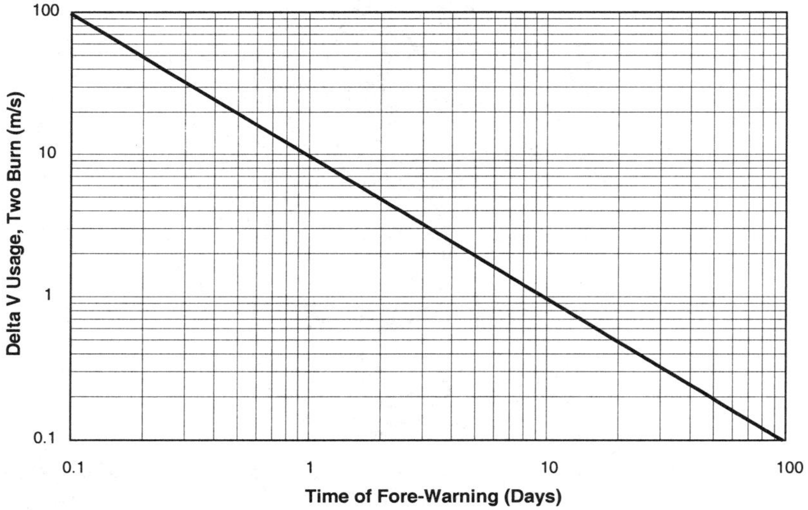

Fig. 13-28. ΔV Required for to Rephase Satellite by 10 deg In-Track. The satellite is assumed to be at 800 km.

hole, we begin to fill in the coverage gap and as shown in Fig. 13-29, and may be able to eliminate the gap entirely by combination of lower minimum elevation angles and rephasing. However, the rephasing process needs to be well established in advance in order to avoid potential problems of intersatellite collisions. Thus, the satellite outage and rephasing plan should be well thought out prior to implementation.

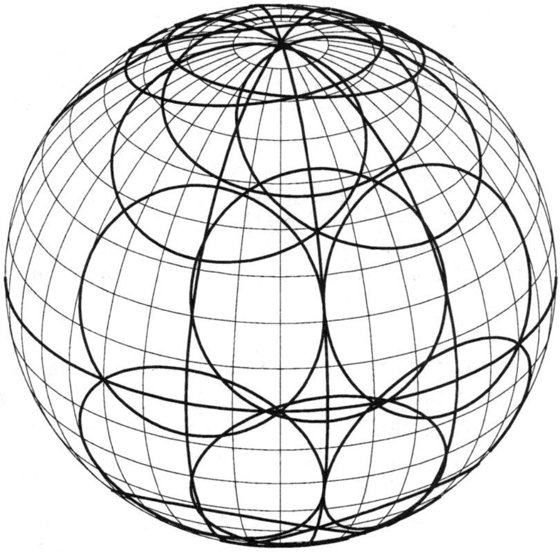

Fig. 13-29. Elimination of Outage by Shifting to Lower Minimum Elevation Angle Plus Rephasing of Nearby Satellites.

For most constellations, we will ultimately choose to replace a satellite which has died on orbit. The two basic approaches for satellite replacement are an *on-orbit spare* and *launch on demand. On-orbit spares* are typically stored above or below the baseline constellation, since storing them within the constellation poses a potential collision hazard. Storage above the constellation requires extra propellant for both raising and lowering but reduces the drag makeup requirements while the satellite is on orbit. Storage below the constellation reduces the demand on raising and lowering propellant but subjects the satellite to greater atmospheric density and, consequently, higher drag and more propellant utilization during the period of on-orbit storage.

Launch on demand, in which a satellite is ready to be launched when needed, reduces the number of spacecraft required on orbit and the on-orbit propellant cost, but places a much heavier (i.e., more expensive) burden on the launch segment. In an extreme circumstance, we would have the spacecraft ready to be launched and a vehicle prepared to go on an as-needed basis.

In practice, both on-orbit spares and having spacecraft available for launch on demand are used by most constellations. Thus some spares will be available on orbit and some spare spacecraft will have been built up on the ground such that they are prepared to be launched quickly. Thus, if a satellite fails on orbit, one of the on-orbit spares will be moved into the empty slot as promptly as possible and a new spacecraft will be moved to the launch site and put into the position of the spare which has been used.

End-of-Life

Finally, it is important to address the issue of removing satellites at end-of-life. As discussed in detail in Sec. 2.6.4, de-orbiting the satellite is certainly the best solution. If this is impractical due to the altitude, then raising the dead satellites above the constellation minimizes the probability of future collisions. The ΔV for this process has been previously calculated and is relatively small. (See Sec. 2.6.1.) The fundamental problem is that raising the satellite or lowering it requires that the satellite be moved while it is still operational. If the satellite dies in orbit, then removing it becomes significantly more difficult. Whatever the method chosen, the fundamental rule for all constellations is the same:

When you're done with it, take it out of orbit.

13.7 Summary—The Constellation Design Process

In most chapters, we begin by setting out a process and then discuss the various steps in that process. Because of its complex character, constellation design is best done in reverse. We began by defining the key elements of constellation design, discussing the reasons for them, and how they are selected. We are now in a position to go back and summarize the constellation design process, the principal factors which need to be defined, and the general rules for a good design.

The overall process of constellation design is summarized in Table 13-13. The key requirement in this process is to understand the mission objectives and what is needed to fulfill the mission, particularly with respect to coverage. This means understanding both the coverage needs for the mission and the spacecraft needs to provide that coverage, such as swath width or constraints on lighting, power, or communications. Can the system operate in the Van Allen belts? A second key part of the requirements is the growth and degradation goals. Are outages acceptable if a satellite dies on orbit? How soon is a replacement required? How soon will the constellation as a whole be replaced and upgraded?

TABLE 13-13. The Constellation Design Process. See also Tables 13-14 and 13-15.

Step	Where Discussed
1. Establish constellation-related mission requirements, particularly – Latitude-dependent coverage – Goals for growth and degradation plateaus – Requirements for different modes or sensors – Limits on system cost or number of satellites	Chap.5 Secs. 12.1, 13.1
2. Do all single satellite orbit trades except coverage	Chap. 12, Sec. 13.3
3. Do trades between swath width (or maximum Earth central angle), coverage, and number of satellites. Evaluate candidate constellations for: – Coverage Figures of Merit vs. Latitude and mission mode – Coverage excess – Growth and degradation – Altitude plateaus – End-of-life options Consider the following orbit types – Walker Delta pattern – Polar constellations with seam – Equatorial – Equatorial supplement – Elliptical	Chap. 9 Secs. 13.3, 13.6, 13.7
4. Evaluate ground track plots for potential coverage holes or methods to reduce the number of satellites	Sec. 9.5.1.2
5. Adjust inclination and in-plane phasing to maximize the intersatellite distances at plane crossings for collision avoidance	Sec. 13.5
6. Review the rules of constellation design in Tables 13-14 and 13-15.	Sec. 13.7
7. Document reasons for choices and iterate.	

The principal factors to be defined during constellation design are listed in Table 13-14, along with the major selection criteria for each. These factors have been discussed in detail earlier in the chapter. A key point to keep in mind here is that constellation design consists of more than just orbit elements. The minimum working elevation angle is perhaps the single most critical parameter in defining constellation coverage. Collision avoidance parameters, including the method for stationkeeping and size of the stationkeeping box are key to insuring the integrity of the constellation over its lifetime. While we often think of a constellation as a single, coherent pattern, it may be that some combination of patterns will satisfy our mission objectives at a lower cost and risk. This approach has been adapted, for example, by Ellipso with a mix of inclined eccentric and circular equatorial orbits.

TABLE 13-14. Principal Factors to be Defined During Constellation Design.

Factor	Effect	Selection Criteria	Where Discussed
Principal Design Variables:			
Number of Satellites	Principal determinant of cost and coverage	Minimize number consistent with meeting other criteria	Chap. 9 Sec. 13.3
Constellation Pattern	Determines coverage vs. latitude, plateaus	Select for best coverage	Sec. 13.1
Minimum Elevation Angle	Principal determinant of single satellite coverage	Minimum value consistent with payload performance and constellation pattern	Secs. 9.1, 13.3
Altitude	Coverage, environment, launch, and transfer cost	System level trade of cost vs. performance	Chap. 9, Sec. 12.4, 13.3
Number of Orbit Planes	Determines coverage plateaus, growth and degradation	Minimize consistent with coverage needs	Sec. 13.6
Collision Avoidance Parameters	Key to preventing constellation self-destruction	Maximize the intersatellite distances at plane crossings	Sec. 13.5
Secondary Design Variables:			
Inclination	Determines latitude distribution of coverage	Compare latitude coverage vs. launch costs*	Sec. 13.3
Between Plane Phasing	Determines coverage uniformity	Select best coverage among discrete phasing options*	Sec. 13.1
Eccentricity	Mission complexity and coverage vs. cost	Normally zero; non-zero may reduce number of satellites needed	Sec. 13.3
Size of Stationkeeping Box	Coverage overlap needed; cross-track pointing	Minimize consistent with low cost maintenance approach	Sec. 13.4
End-of-Life Strategy	Elimination of orbital debris	Any mechanism that allows you to clean up after yourself	Secs. 2.6.4, 13.6

* Fine tune for collision avoidance

Typically the purpose of creating a constellation is to provide Earth coverage, or at times, coverage of near-Earth space. The demerit of a constellation is that you need multiple satellites, and therefore, multiple reaction wheels, communication systems, and so on. A typical goal of constellation design is to provide the needed coverage with a minimum number of satellites. Consequently, the principal system trade is most frequently coverage as a measure of performance vs. number of satellites as a measure of cost. Nonetheless, it is important to bear in mind that the number of satellites is not necessarily an accurate representation of system cost. For example, raising the altitude of the constellation will normally result in needing fewer satellites. However, as the altitude increases, the launch cost for each satellite increases, and the radiation hardening requirements increase dramatically as we enter the Van Allen radiation belts. Minimizing the number of satellites may or may not minimize the system cost and it is the cost which is typically of most interest to constellation sponsors, both government and commercial.

Coverage and coverage figures of merit were described in detail in Chap. 9. Perhaps the most important coverage issue to remember in terms of constellation design is that compiling statistical data on orbit coverage may not provide useful physical insight into the constellation design problem and can, in many cases, be dramatically misleading. The mission designer must always be aware that in constellation design, statistical data is being used to represent a dramatically non-Gaussian process. A number of examples of this problem have been given throughout the book. See, for example, Secs. 9.5.1.2 and 9.5.1.4.

There are two fundamentally different types of constellations —those that demand continuous coverage and those that do not. The former group represents the more straightforward design problem. What is the minimum number of satellites (or minimum total system cost) needed to provide the necessary single or multiple coverage? For example, GPS wants continuous coverage of the entire world by a minimum of four satellites.

An interesting figure of merit for continuous coverage constellations is the *excess coverage*—i.e., the total instantaneous coverage available as a percentage of the total required. For N satellites in circular orbits at a common altitude with coverage defined as being within λ_{max} of the subsatellite point, the total instantaneous coverage, COV, is given by:

$$COV = N\,(1 - \cos \lambda_{max}) \,/\, 2K \qquad (13\text{-}13)$$

where K is the coverage multiplicity that is needed (i.e., K = 4 for GPS). Our goal is to drive COV toward 1.

For the 24-satellite GPS constellation, the satellites are all at half GEO (a = 26,561.75 km) and the assumed minimum elevation angle is 5 deg. From Eqs. (9-4) and (9-5), we find that λ_{max} = 71.2 deg and COV = 2.03. This means that it takes approximately twice as many satellites as would be needed if the coverage were static and could be perfectly distributed. Iridium is a communications constellation with 66 satellites at 780 km. Here K = 1 and the minimum working elevation angle is 9.5 deg corresponding to λ_{max} = 19.0 deg and COV = 1.80. Although the two constellations are very different in use and in coverage pattern, the excess coverage in the implemented constellations is nearly the same.

For constellations which do not demand continuous coverage, the most representative figure of merit is typically the mean and maximum response time as a function of the number of satellites (see Sec. 9.5.1.4). This is a substantially more difficult trade because it now needs to be worked iteratively with the basic objectives of the constellation and may require extended interaction with the end user to determine how those needs are best met.

The complexity of choosing orbit parameters for noncontinuous coverage is illustrated in Fig. 13-30, which illustrates the hypothetical mean response time vs. number of satellites for a satellite system for detecting forest fires. If we assume that the initial goal of the system was to have a mean response time of no more than 5 hours, we see from the plot that a system of 6 satellites can meet this goal, while a 4-satellite system can achieve a mean response time of 6 hours. Is the smaller response time worth the increased number of satellites and the money required to build them? Only the ultimate users of the system can judge. The additional fire warning may be critical to fire containment, and therefore, a key to mission success. However, it is also possible that the original goal was somewhat arbitrary and a response time of **approximately** 5 hours is what is really needed. In this case, firefighting resources could probably be

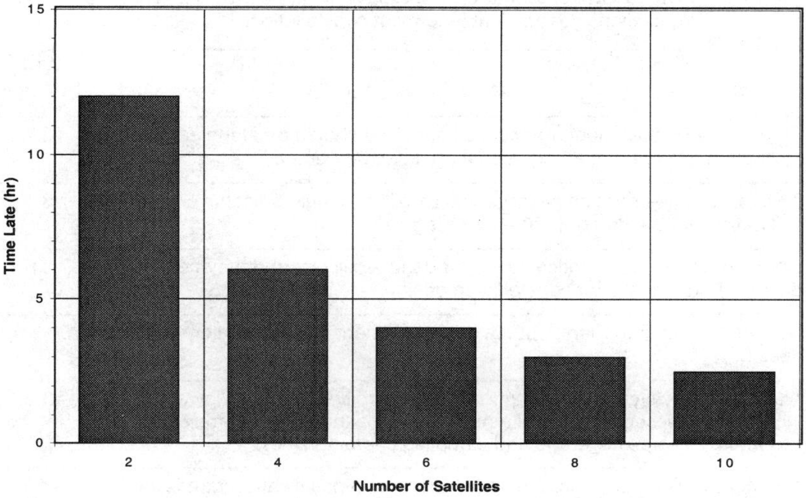

Fig. 13-30. Hypothetical Coverage Data for Fire Detection System. See text for definitions and discussion. As discussed in Sec. 13.6, satellite growth comes in increments or plateaus. These are assumed to be two-satellite increments for the example shown.

used better by flying a 4-satellite system with 6 hours response time and applying the savings to other purposes, such as more ground equipment or a larger number of firefighters. We can only determine how this is best done by working closely with the end users.

The Rules for Constellation Design

It is clear from the above discussion, and particularly the example of the MSSP program at the end of Sec. 13.2, that there are no absolute rules for constellation design. It is not a systematic process, where we can simply take, for example, all possible Walker constellations and enumerate how well they do, and then select an absolute winner for the best constellation. The constellation design process is much fuzzier than that. The key is to look at the fundamental mission objectives and determine how these objectives can best be met at minimum cost and risk.

Ordinarily, our goal would be to minimize the number of satellites while achieving the appropriate level of coverage. Nonetheless, as discussed above, this may not be the lowest cost approach. For example, we may be able to achieve our coverage objectives with 20 satellites in the Van Allen radiation belts, where 25 would be required below the belts. The key question then becomes whether the lower cost and longer life per satellite for the lower constellation is worth the additional number of satellites. The constellation design process per se cannot answer that question. It can only be answered within the broader context of mission, system, and spacecraft design.

While there are not absolute rules, there are broad guidelines which assist in the process of constellation design. These are summarized in Table 13-15. In the end, constellation design is coupled only moderately to astrodynamics, and strongly to the process of meeting mission objectives at minimum cost and risk.

TABLE 13-15. Rules for Constellation Design. While there are no absolute rules, these broad guidelines are applicable to most constellations.

Rule	Where Discussed
1. To avoid differential node rotation, all satellites should be at the same inclination, except that an equatorial orbit can be added.	Sec. 13.1
2. To avoid perigee rotation, all eccentric satellites should be at the critical inclination of 63.4 deg or (180 – 63.4)deg.	Sec. 13.1
3. Collision avoidance is critical, even for dead satellites, and may be a driving characteristic for constellation design.	Sec. 13.5
4. Symmetry is an important, but not critical element of constellation design.	Secs. 13.0, 13.1
5. Altitude is typically the most important of the orbit elements, followed by inclination. 0 eccentricity is the most common, although eccentric orbits can improve some coverage and sampling characteristics.	Sec. 13.1
6. Minimum working elevation angle (which determines swath width) is as important as the altitude in determining coverage.	Sec. 9.1, 13.3
7. Two satellites can see each other if and only if they are able to see the same point on the ground.	Sec. 10.1.1
8. Principal coverage Figures of Merit for constellations: • Percentage of time coverage goal is met • Number of satellites required to achieve the needed coverage • Mean and maximum response times (for non-continuous coverage) • Excess coverage percent • Excess coverage vs. latitude	Secs. 9.5.1.4, 13.1
9. Size of stationkeeping box is determined by the mission objectives, the perturbations selected to be overcome, and the method of control.	Sec. 13.2
10. For long-term constellations, absolute stationkeeping provides significant advantages and no disadvantages compared to relative stationkeeping.	Sec. 13.2
11. Orbit perturbations can be treated in 3 ways: • **Negate** the perturbing force (use only when necessary) • **Control** the perturbing force (best approach if control is required) • Leave perturbation **uncompensated** (best for cyclic perturbations)	Sec. 13.2
12. Performance plateaus and the number of orbit planes required are a function of the altitude.	Sec. 13.1
13. Changing position within the orbit plane is easy; changing orbit planes is hard; implies that a smaller number of orbit planes is better.	Sec. 13.4
14. Constellation build-up, graceful degradation, filling in for dead satellites, and end-of-life disposal are critical and should be addressed as part of constellation design.	Sec. 13.4
15. Taking satellites out of the constellation at end-of-life is critical for long-term success and risk avoidance. This is done by: • Deorbiting satellites in LEO • Raising them above the constellation above LEO (including GEO)	Sec. 13.4

References

Akella, Maruthi R., and Kyle T. Alfriend. 2000. "Probability of Collision Between Space Objects." *Journal of Guidance, Control, and Dynamics*, Vol. 23, No. 5, pp. 769–772, September–October.

Burgess, E. L. and H. S. Gobrieal. 1996. "Integrating Spacecraft Design and Cost-Risk Analysis Using NASA Technology Readiness Levels," The Aerospace Corporation. Presented at the 29th Annual DoD Cost Analysis Symposium, Leesburg, VA. February 21–23.

Burgess, Gregg E. 1996. "ORBCOMM." In *Reducing Space Mission Cost*. J.R. Wertz and W. J Larson (eds.) Torrance, CA: Microcosm Press and Dordrecht, The Netherlands: Kluwer Academic Publishers.

Chobotov, V. A., D. E. Herman, and C.G. Johnson. 1997. "Collision and Debris Hazard Assessment for a Low-Earth-Orbit Constellation." *Journal of Spacecraft and Rockets*. 34(2): 233–238, March–April.

Draim, John. 1985. "Three- and Four-Satellite Continuous Coverage Constellations." *Journal of Guidance, Control, and Dynamics*. 6:725–730.

———. 1987a. "A Common-Period Four-Satellite Continuous Global Coverage Constellation." *Journal of Guidance, Control, and Dynamics*. 10:492–499.

———. 1987b. "A Six-Satellite Continuous Global Double Coverage Constellation." AAS Paper 87-497 presented at the AAS/AIAA Astrodynamics Specialist Conference.

———. 1998. "Optimization of the ELLIPSO™ and ELLIPSO 2G™ Personal Communications System, Mission Design & Implementation of Satellite Constellations." In *Space Technology Proceedings*, Jozef van der Ha, editor. Dordrecht, The Netherlands: Kluwer Academic Publishers.

Draim, J., and D. Castiel. 1996. "Optimization of the Borealis and Concordia Sub-Constellations of the Ellipso Mobile Communications System." Paper No. IAF-96-A.1.01, presented at the 47th International Astronautical Congress, Beijing, China October 7–11.

Draim, John E., Cecile Davidson, and David Castiel. 1999. "Evolution of the ELLIPSO™ and ELLIPSO 2G™ GMPCS Systems." Paper No. IAF-99-M.4.02, presented at the 50th International Astronautical Congress, Amsterdam, The Netherlands, October 4–8.

Draim, John, Paul J. Cefola, and David Castiel. 2000. "Elliptical Orbit Constellation—A New Paradigm for Higher Efficiency in Space Systems."

Easton, R. L., and R. Brescia. 1969. *Continuously Visible Satellite Constellations*. Naval Research Laboratory Report 6896.

Fleeter, Rick. 1999. "Design of Low-Cost Spacecraft," Chap. 22 in *Space Mission Analysis and Design,* 3rd ed., James R. Wertz and Wiley J. Larson, eds. Torrance, CA, and Dordrecht, the Netherlands: Microcosm, Inc. and Kluwer Academic Publishers.

Jenkin, A. B. 1993a. "DEBRIS: A Computer Program for Debris Cloud Modeling." Paper No. IAA.6.3-93-746, presented at the 44th Congress of the International Astronautical Federation, Graz, Austria, October.

———. 1993b. "Analysis of the Non-Stationary Debris Cloud Pinch Zone." Paper No. AAS-93-625, presented at the AAS/AIAA Astrodynamics Conference, Victoria, BC, Canada, August.

———. 1995. "Probability of Collision During the Early Evolution of Debris Clouds." Presented at the 46th Congress of the International Astronautical Federation, Oslo, Norway, October.

Johnson, Nicholas L. and Darren McKnight. 1991. *Artificial Space Debris*. Malabar, FL: Orbit Book Company.

Kamprath, M. F. and A. B. Jenkin. 1998. "Debris Collision Hazard from Breakups in the Geosynchronous Ring." In *Proceedings of the SPIE Conference on Characteristics and Consequences of Space Debris and Near Earth Objects*, San Diego, CA, 23 July.

Mora, Miguel Belló, José Prieto Muñoz, and Genevieve Dutruel-Lecohier. 1997. "Orion—A Constellation Mission Analysis Tool." International Workshop on Mission Design and Implementation of Satellite Constellations, International Astronautical Federation, Toulouse, France. Nov. 17–19.

Pocha, J. J. 1987. *An Introduction to Mission Design for Geostationary Satellites.* Boston: D. Reidel Publishing Company.

Reijnen, G. C. M. and W. de Graaff. 1989. *The Pollution of Outer Space, in Particular of the Geostationary Orbit.* Dordrecht, The Netherlands: Kluwer/Martinus Nijhoff Publishers.

Simpson, John A. (ed.). 1994. *Preservation of Near-Earth Space for Future Generations.* Cambridge, UK: Cambridge University Press

Soop, E. M. 1994. *Handbook of Geostationary Orbits.* Dordrecht, The Netherlands: Kluwer Academic Publishers.

Walker, J. G. 1971. "Some Circular Orbit Patterns Providing Continuous Whole Earth Coverage." *Journal of the British Interplanetary Society*. 24: 369–384.

———. 1977. *Continuous Whole-Earth Coverage by Circular-Orbit Satellite Patterns.* Royal Aircraft Establishment Technical Report No. 77044.

———. 1984. "Satellite Constellations." *Journal of the British Interplanetary Society*. 37:559–572.

Chapter 14

Operations Considerations in Orbit Design —Launch, Orbit Acquisition, and Disposal

Lauri Kraft Newman, ***NASA Goddard Space Flight Center***

Chapters 12 and 13 discussed in detail the process of defining orbit parameters based on mission requirements. However, in most cases the fundamental mission requirements will define only a subset of the orbit parameters. Nonetheless, each spacecraft must ultimately be launched into a specific orbit for which all of the parameters are chosen and assigned allowed error limits. Trajectory designers are faced with the prospect of choosing values for those elements for which there have been no specifications. Of the many factors which feed into this choice, operations considerations are key. In other words, knowledge of how the spacecraft will be operated, how it will perform on orbit, and how it will interact with the launch vehicle are used to make element selection in the absence of other criteria. Sec. 14.1 addresses some of these secondary criteria that may be used to choose a complete set of orbit parameters, including error boundaries. Once the element values are chosen in the early phase of mission design, the focus shifts to planning for operations. The remaining sections of the chapter discuss the launch, orbit acquisition, and end-of-life disposal phases, and form a link between the definition of the initial elements and the mission operations. Sec. 14.2 provides the process for translating detailed orbit criteria into launch parameters and launch window boundaries. The process of achieving the mission orbit after launch is highly mission dependent. The various elements of this process have been previously discussed in Secs. 2.6, 12.6, and 12.7. Sec. 14.3 provides detailed disposal methods which implement the general approach outlined in Sec. 2.6.4. Finally, Sec. 14.4 documents the definition of orbit parameters for the Earth Observing System Terra while Sec. 14.5 covers the analysis and execution of an end-of-life disposal scenario for the Compton Gamma Ray Observatory.

14.1 Definition of Complete Orbit Parameters

Typically, the orbit designer is faced with a set of mission and or payload requirements that must be met by the final orbit design. However, not all of the classical Keplerian elements are driven by requirements in every case, and those that are not may be selected arbitrarily or used to achieve secondary mission goals. The flexibility in how these elements are driven by primary mission requirements usually depends on the trajectory design complexity and typically differs from mission to mission. Trade studies are performed, costs are evaluated, and the desired values are chosen. Often these decisions are not documented well, if at all, since they occur early in the mission design and are often the result of informal analysis or taken from previous experience. As in all mission elements, documentation of these decisions would be helpful to the spacecraft support team in understanding the rationale behind what eventually become untraceable "requirements" on the orbit elements.

The values of various orbit elements have different importance for different classes of orbits. However, the most common requirement is on altitude, whether it be chosen to support an instrument field of view, to yield a particular period (such as for geosynchronous spacecraft), to maximize time in sunlight, to avoid high drag, or to synchronize the orbit with a particular ground trace or with another spacecraft. The second most common requirement is on inclination, which is often chosen based on the desire to view certain portions of the Earth or the celestial sphere.

Small payloads are often flown "piggyback" on the same launch vehicle as larger missions in order to share the launch cost. These missions often cannot choose any of their orbital elements. Since they are not paying the majority of the launch cost, they must choose to piggyback with a spacecraft that has orbit requirements similar to their own desires and be flexible in how closely they achieve the desired orbit. Many of these spacecraft have no propulsion system with which to change their orbit once they are injected by the launch vehicle. However, the primary payload often has some flexibility in orbit mission parameters. For instance, the SAC-C mission is in a Sun-synchronous orbit, but is limited in the local mean time it can use because it is flying piggyback with EO-1 , which is required to fly in constellation with Landsat-7. Since changing the mean time is costly, SAC-C will not have much flexibility in altering this parameter.

The following paragraphs discuss the operational considerations that may effect the selection of mission parameters not defined by the primary mission requirements.

Semimajor Axis. If the altitude of the orbit is not defined by mission requirements, other factors which could be used to choose the altitude include avoiding the Van Allen radiation belts, increasing on-orbit mass, determining the length of eclipses, or providing optimal ground station coverage. For interplanetary missions, the semimajor axis is often driven by the time of flight desired, avoiding eclipses, or minimizing fuel use by employing a lunar or planetary swingby. For instance, for the MAP mission, a lunar swingby is required for the spacecraft to reach the L2 Earth-Moon libration point within the available fuel budget. The timing of this swingby is critical, so *phasing loops*, a series of Earth orbits following injection and prior to the swingby, are used to allow the swingby to occur at the appropriate time. The semimajor axis of each loop is determined to achieve the correct timing of the swingby.

Eccentricity. If the orbit eccentricity is not specified by mission requirements, it is generally set to 0. However, a frozen eccentricity could be chosen to minimize altitude variations over a given latitude. (See Secs. 2.5.6 and 12.4.3.5.) Often, a near-frozen orbit can be implemented. This is one in which the eccentricity and argument of perigee vary slightly, but not enough to affect the accuracy of instrument measurements. Since an exact frozen point is not being maintained, near-frozen orbits allow more flexibility in maneuver placement, timing, and, potentially, fuel use. In the case of a geosynchronous mission, eccentricity affects the range of east-west drift over the course of a day. (See Sec. 12.4).

Inclination. If the orbit inclination is not pre-determined, several factors can be considered in choosing it. Launch vehicle capability is maximized if the inclination equals the latitude of the launch site, which is the normal default if no specific value is required. Choosing a polar orbit minimizes the amount of time spent in the diurnal bulge, therefore decreasing atmospheric drag and lengthening mission lifetime. Choosing a Sun-synchronous inclination, if it is available at the mission altitude, provides thermal and power stability. For geosynchronous orbits, a near-zero inclination provides minimal north-south excursions over the course of a day. This reduces distortion in image data such as that provided by weather satellites. However, choosing any inclination other than the latitude of the launch site will reduce the available on-orbit mass.

Right Ascension of the Ascending Node. Regression of the nodes will cause the ascending node to rotate continuously for non-polar missions. If the node is not defined by the mission, it is often left as a free variable for the launch vehicle. However, there may be benefits in choosing the initial node because it defines the eclipse cycle. For missions with lifetimes of less than a year or very sensitive power requirements during the checkout, choosing an initial right ascension to maximize sunlight times at launch could be advantageous. Geosynchronous spacecraft normally require an initial right ascension that will maximize the amount of time that the spacecraft remains below the maximum allowable inclination. This optimum node will cause the inclination to approach zero, then return to the maximum desired value before the first north-south stationkeeping maneuver is required.

Argument of Perigee. The argument of perigee could be selected along with the eccentricity to freeze the orbit, or to place the perigee above a particular sub-satellite point such as a ground station. For critically-inclined elliptical orbits (Sec. 12.4) the argument of perigee is chosen to maximize the desired coverage, typically by placing apogee over the desired latitude.

Anomaly. The anomaly is often not something that can be chosen by the mission because most launch vehicles use this as a free variable for trajectory design. This can pose challenges for spacecraft attempting to rendezvous with another or being placed into a constellation. Often those missions have to carry enough fuel to alter their anomaly after launch by either injecting low and raising the orbit at the correct time, or by performing a pair of maneuvers to raise and lower the orbit at the proper time. However, the added fuel requirement is typically small.

Once the orbit elements have been broadly determined, we must decide how to compute the specific value of each. Often this decision is based on the development phase of the mission, which drives the accuracy level required. Missions in early phases of development only require a coarse orbit definition to feed the design of orbit-dependent subsystems, such as power, thermal, propulsion, and altitude control. However, missions in final phases of development, especially during integration and test phases, will require that the orbit be defined in much greater detail to ensure, for example, that the correct mass of fuel is loaded. Section 14.5 gives a detailed example of how the orbit elements were chosen for the Terra mission.

14.1.1 Orbit Error Boundaries

Each mission parameter also has error bars on how tightly it must be achieved in order to meet mission requirements. These error boundaries drive operational parameters such as maneuver size, location, and frequency, as well as launch window duration. Although the choice of error bounds for a given orbit is very mission-specific, the following paragraphs provide general examples of requirements which could drive the error bounds for some of the orbit elements.

Semimajor Axis. A simple example would be the choice of altitude bounds for an earth-looking scientific payload. The instrument may require a viewing range of between 400 and 450 km to take accurate images. Therefore, the altitude bounds are set by the instrument requirement, the orbit raising maneuver frequency is determined by how often the orbit decays to the lower edge of the box, and the maneuver size is determined by how much ΔV is required to achieve the upper edge of the box.

As another example, a spacecraft which controls its ground track to within ±5 km of a reference ground track may have chosen those bounds to keep the image angle or size within science requirements. This ground track accuracy translates directly into bounds on the orbit altitude, since as the altitude changes, so does the ground track error. The initial altitude is chosen such that the error with respect to the reference is +5 km, the eastern edge of the control box. As atmospheric drag causes the altitude to decay, the orbit period decreases, causing the equator crossing to drift westward relative to the reference track. Eventually, the altitude will reach the value that yields a –5 km error. At this point, the orbit altitude starts to fall below the nominal value, causing the period to be less than nominal and hence causing the drift to turn around and become eastward. Once the track has drifted back to the eastern control boundary, a maintenance maneuver is required to raise the orbit altitude and begin the cycle again. The difference in altitude between the value at the +5 km edge of the box and the value at the –5 km edge of the box then form the error bounds for the mission. Mission requirements are sometimes specified in terms of derived requirements, such as a ground track accuracy, instead of an actual requirement on the orbit altitude itself, since that value can vary, as in this case in which it would depend on the expected solar flux level during the decay time between maneuvers. However, requirements defined in this manner actually require further analysis. For instance, while a satellite may wish to control its ground track to within ±5 km of a reference, instead of choosing the exact orbit altitudes which yield the edges of this box to the altitude bounds, the actual altitudes chosen are usually within the box, so that the ground track is controlled more tightly than the requirement. This operational consideration prevents uncertainties in predicting the solar flux, and hence the altitude rate of change, from causing an unexpected violation of constraints. Thus, many orbit error boundary definitions depend on the perturbations expected on that orbit element throughout the mission life. Orbit perturbations are discussed in more detail in Sec. 2.4.

Inclination. A Sun-synchronous spacecraft may have a requirement to maintain a 10:30 am descending mean local time within ±15 min. This 30 min error boundary could be used by a launch vehicle with variable targeting capabilities to place the spacecraft in any orbit plane between 10:15 and 10:45, allowing an approximately 30 min launch window duration.

Anomaly. Sometimes the orbit error boundaries do not determine operational parameters to meet the mission requirements, but, conversely, are driven by operational considerations. For instance, satellites in a formation or constellation may experience different orbit perturbations due to differences in mass properties and atmospheric drag. Therefore, they may oscillate with respect to each other over a period of weeks or months. If two such spacecraft desire to use the same ground station without conflicts, they need to be separated by at least 20 min, allowing time for the ground station to take a 10 min pass from one spacecraft and then repoint to acquire the next. Normally this means that the two spacecraft should be placed 20 min (~70 deg) apart in mean anomaly. However, if the error boundary on the mean anomaly is 8 deg due to the oscillations of the spacecraft from perturbations, then the spacecraft should be placed 78 deg apart to prevent any conflicts at the station.

14.2 Launch Window Parameters

The *launch window* is the time during which a spacecraft may be launched to meet all mission requirements. The *launch period* is the set of dates on which there exists a viable launch window. For many low Earth spacecraft, there exists a launch window every day of the year, so launch period is not a factor. However, for many interplanetary missions the launch period becomes critical because of the changing relative position of the planets. Choosing a vehicle and launch site also often plays a key role in launch window determination.

The launch site depends on the chosen launch vehicle as well as the orbit to be achieved. Each launch vehicle has facilities in certain geographic locations, some in more than one. Figure 14-1 shows a selected set of launch sites and Table 14-1 lists data about these and other available sites. These sites can change and should be con-

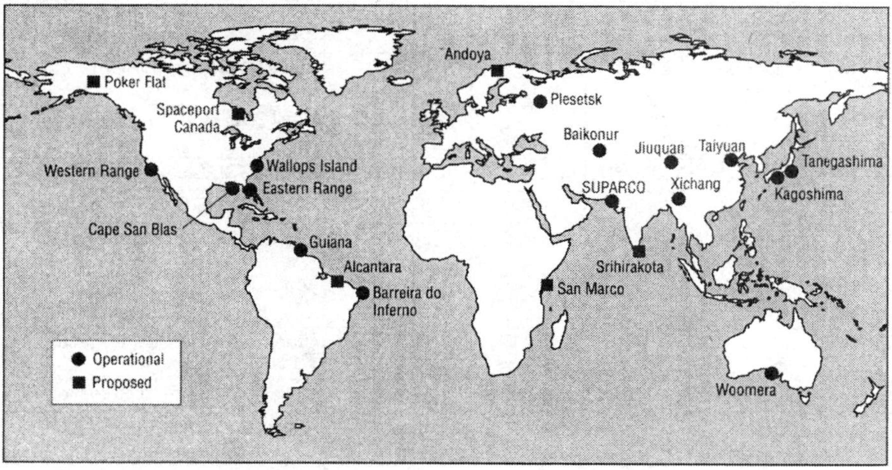

Fig. 14-1. World Launch Sites [Chiulli, 1994]. (Reprinted with permission of The Aerospace Corporation.)

TABLE 14-1. World Launch Sites. Data from Kraft [1996], Isakowitz [1999], and Chiulli [1994].

Launch Site	Latitude	Longitude	Allowed Inclinations	Vehicles
Alcantara, Brazil	2.28°S	44.38°W	2.2°–100°	VLS, sounding rockets
Andoya, Norway	69.28°N	16.02°E		Sounding rockets, orbital capability planned
Baikorur Cosmo-drome, Kazakhstan	45.6°N	63.4°E	50.5°–99° (not contiguous)	Dnepr, Ikar, Molniya/Soyuz, Proton, Rokot, Tsyklon, Zenit
Russian submarine launch	69.3°N (mobile)	35.5°E (mobile)	79°	Shtil
Cape Canaveral AFB, USA	28.5°N	80.57°W	28.5°–57°	Athena, Atlas, Delta, Pegasus, Taurus, Titan
Cape York, Australia	12°S	143°E		Zenit
Esrange, Sweden	68°N	21°E		Sounding rockets
Kourou, Guiana	5.23°N	52.77°W	5.2° –100°	Ariane 4 and 5
Hammaguir, Algeria	30.9°N	3.1°W	34°–40°	Diamant (closed)
Jiuquan Sat. Launch Cen., China	40.7°N	100.0°E	57° –70°	LM-1D, LM-2C, LM-2E, LM-2F, LM2E(A)
Kagoshima Space Center, Japan*	31.2°N	131.1°E	31°–100°	M-V
Kapustin Yar, Russia	48.4°N	45.8°E	51°	Kosmos 3M
Kodiak Island, AK, USA	57.5°N	152.2°W	63°–116°	Athena I and II
Marshall Islands	19.5°N	166.1°W	<10°	Pegasus XL
NASA Kennedy Space Center, USA	28.5°N	81.0°W	28.5° –57°	Space Shuttle (STS)
Nevada Test Site, USA	37.2°N	116.3°W	45–60°, 84–99°	Kistler K-1 (not active)
Poker Flat, AK, USA	65.12°N	147.47°W		Sounding rockets
Palmachim AFB, Israel	31.9°N	34.7°E	143°	Shavit 1
Plesetsk, Russia	62.8°N	40.1°E		Kosmos, Molniya/Soyuz, Tsyklon, Zenit
San Marco Platform, Indian Ocean, Italy	2.9°S	40.3°E	2.9–38°	Inactive, planned for Vega
Pacific Ocean	0°N (mobile)	154°W (mobile)	0–100°	Zenit 3SL
Sriharikota, India	13.68°N	80.23°E	18–50°, SSO	PSLV, GSLV, sounding rockets
Svobodny, Russia	51.8°N	128.4°E	SSO	Start, Start-1, Strela
Taiyuan Launch Center, China	37.8°N	111.5°E	87°, 96–98°	LM-4, LM-2C/SD
Tanegashima Space Center, Japan*	30.4°N	130.6°E	30–100°	H-II, H-IIA, J-I
Vandenberg AFB, USA	34.7°N	120.6°W	63.4–110°	Athena, Atlas, Delta, Pegasus, Taurus, Titan II and IV
Wallops Island, VA	37.85°N	75.47°W	38–55°	Pegasus XL, sounding rockets
Woomera, Australia	31.1°S	136.6°E	45–60°, 84–99°	Kistler K-1 (not active)
Xichang Launch Center, China	28.2°N	102.0°E	27.5–31.1°	LM-2E, LM-3, LM-3A, LM-3B, LM-3C

*Seasonal launch periods of 45 days in Jan/Feb & Aug/Sept due to range safety and the fishing fleet.

firmed with the launch vehicle provider. The inclination achievable from a site is a function of its latitude. The latitude of a site is the minimum orbit inclination that can be achieved, unless the vehicle performs a plane-change maneuver during ascent or the spacecraft performs one after insertion. If the inclination required is greater than the latitude of the launch site, two launch windows are available, one yielding a descending orbit, the other an ascending orbit. Range safety limits the set of inclinations that can be achieved from a site based on surrounding land masses. Geosynchronous or other low inclination spacecraft are launched from equatorial or low-latitude sites, since the inclination of these spacecraft needs to be near zero degrees and the maneuver to adjust the inclination to that value is cheaper from low-inclination sites.

Typical performance values for various vehicles are provided in Sec. 12.3.2 and by, for example, Isakowitz [1999]. However, only the launch vehicle manufacturer can provide the most current and most accurate information regarding launch vehicle capabilities. Detailed performance information must be obtained from a users guide which is typically updated every 3 to 4 years. Users guides for the Delta [Boeing, 1996, 1999a, 1999b], Atlas [International Launch Services, 1998], Pegasus [Orbital Sciences Corp., 2000] and Taurus [Orbital Sciences Corp., 1999] are given in the references.

Once a site and vehicle have been selected, the launch window may be determined. The optimum launch time is when the desired inertial orbit plane rotates through the launch site. The orbit plane is defined by the orbit inclination and right ascension, while the launch site is defined by the latitude and longitude of the launch pad. Figure 14-2 shows the geometry of a launch site and inclination of the orbit. The latitude of

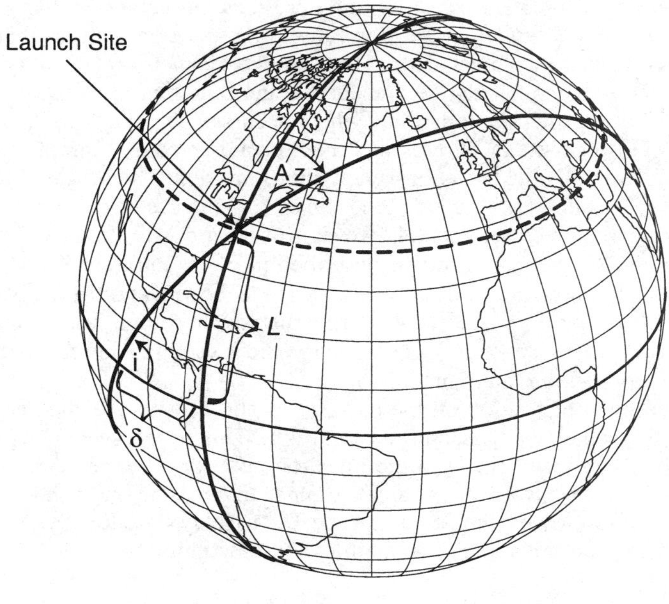

Fig. 14-2. Launch Site Geometry. See text for explanation.

the site is given by L, while the longitude difference between the site and the orbit node is given by δ. Az is the *launch azimuth*, the angle measured clockwise from north to the velocity vector. If the inclination of the desired orbit is less than the latitude of the launch site, the desired orbit cannot be achieved. (Small differences may be accommodated by the powered flight of the launch vehicle, but large differences are too expensive to correct.) The launch azimuth required to achieve the desired inclination from the latitude of the launch site is given by Wertz & Larson [1999] as:

$$Az = Az_I \pm \gamma \approx Az_I \qquad (14\text{-}1)$$

where

$$\sin Az_I = \cos i \,/\, \cos L \qquad (14\text{-}2)$$

$$\tan \gamma = V_L \cos Az_I /(V_o - V_{eq} \cos i) \approx (V_L/V_o)\cos Az_I \qquad (14\text{-}3)$$

$$V_L = (464.5 \text{ m/s}) \cos L \qquad (14\text{-}4)$$

Here V_L is the inertial velocity of the launch site, $V_{eq} = 464.5$ m/s is the velocity of the Earth's rotation at the equator, and $V_o \approx 7.8$ km/s is the velocity of the satellite immediately after launch. γ is a small correction to account for the velocity contribution caused by the Earth's rotation, and has a value of 0 deg for a due east launch, and 3 deg for a polar launch. Equation 14-3 is accurate to within 0.1 deg for low Earth orbits. In Eq. 14-1, the plus sign is used for ascending node orbits, and the minus sign is used for descending node orbits.

Interplanetary and deep space trajectories have very tightly constrained windows based on the alignment of celestial bodies with the spacecraft trajectory. Often fuel costs for adjusting these trajectories are high, so accuracy of launch time is important to meet mission goals. The boxed example describes the launch window design for Clementine, a military lunar probe. For low-Earth spacecraft, often there are few requirements on either the launch date or time, unless the mission is Sun-synchronous. In that case, the spacecraft must be launched at the time that the desired orbit plane passes through the launch site longitude, which occurs once per day in the appropriate (ascending or descending) direction. The second boxed example shows the computation of launch time for a Sun-synchronous mission. The length of the window may be widened around the exact launch time by making use of the permissible error range on the mean time requirement; however, this error box is often used to eliminate inclination maintenance maneuvers as described in the example in Sec. 14.4. In that case, the launch window must be as short as possible (seconds) or make use of guided targeting for widening the window by altering the powered flight trajectory. Powered flight trajectories are designed by the launch vehicle supplier due to the proprietary nature of the propulsion system models.

Another possible restriction on the powered flight trajectory is the desire to have contact with the vehicle or spacecraft during flight. This coverage can be provided by Instrumented Aircraft, which fly to the injection point or other relevant point in the trajectory to provide coverage; by local ground antennas if one is available in an appropriate location; or by the Tracking and Data Relay Satellite System, TDRSS, which are geosynchronous tracking satellites with a continuous view of most of the Earth.

Launch Window Determination for Clementine*

Clementine, launched on January 25, 1994, was intended to map the lunar surface and then to perform a flyby of the asteroid 1620 Geographos. The nominal mission plan involved spending 7 days in LEO, then injecting into a cislunar transfer orbit consisting of 2.5 phasing loops about the Earth. The first loop had a 5-day period, the second loop a 10-day period, and the last half-loop had a 5-day period as illustrated in Fig. 14-3. At the end of this half-loop, the spacecraft was inserted into a polar lunar mapping orbit, where it remained for two months. At the end of the mapping phase, Clementine left the Moon on a planned asteroid-intercept trajectory and was lost during the first post-lunar burn.

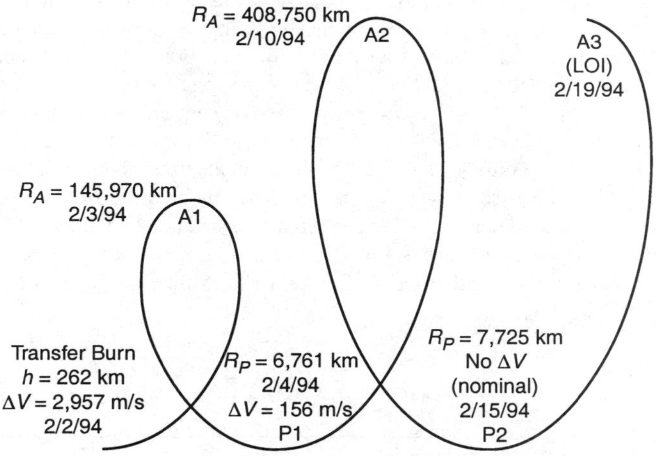

Fig. 14-3. Clementine Transfer Phase Trajectory Schematic [Schiff, 1993].

The Clementine launch window had to accommodate all of the mission requirements, including lunar mapping and the Geographos encounter which was a time-critical rendezvous; therefore, the trajectory was designed assuming a specific date for the Geographos encounter and working backward. The launch window was designed to allow the spacecraft to meet its mapping orbit constraints by controlling which lunar longitude was achieved at lunar injection and to meet its asteroid rendezvous constraints by controlling the time of maneuvers. Phasing orbits were used for the transfer phase to allow flexibility of launch date, since changing the size and number of phasing orbits allowed flexibility on when to perform the fixed ΔV transfer insertion maneuver and still reach the moon on the target date. The launch period was determined by performing analysis to see how late or early the transfer maneuver could be

*Adapted from Richon [1995].

performed and still have enough fuel to perform the necessary additional maneuvers. Moving the initial maneuver date caused the phasing loops to change size in order to meet the mission constraints, and this change in size drove the ΔV budget.

Based on available ΔV, a preferred launch date of January 25, 1994 was determined that allowed 7.5 days in the parking orbit before the transfer maneuver. The launch period was divided into two parts: the nominal period, and an extended period. The nominal period, from January 25 to 31, consisted of the launch opportunities when the transfer maneuver occurred on February 2. The stay in the parking orbit decreased throughout the period, from 7.5 days to 1.5 days. The extended launch period, from February 1 to 8, consisted of the launch opportunities during which the transfer maneuver epoch moved one day later for each day into the extended period. In order to maintain lunar arrival on the same date, the time of flight was shortened by decreasing the period of the second phas-ing loop. This was accomplished by removing ΔV from the first phasing perigee and applying an essentially equal ΔV at the second perigee to ensure the correct lunar arrival conditions. On February 8, the first phasing perigee maneuver reached zero, and all of the ΔV was applied at the second perigee.

To determine the daily launch window for each day within the launch period, a nominal trajectory for that day, the "daily nominal," was designed. This was not necessarily the center of the window open and close box, but the time when all of the spacecraft ΔV occurred at the first perigee for the nominal launch window, or where all ΔV occurred at the second perigee on February 8 for the extended window. A contingency allowance of 10 m/s from the baseline 603 m/s ΔV requirement was used to calculate the daily window open and close. Figure 14-4 shows the daily launch window as a function of launch date.

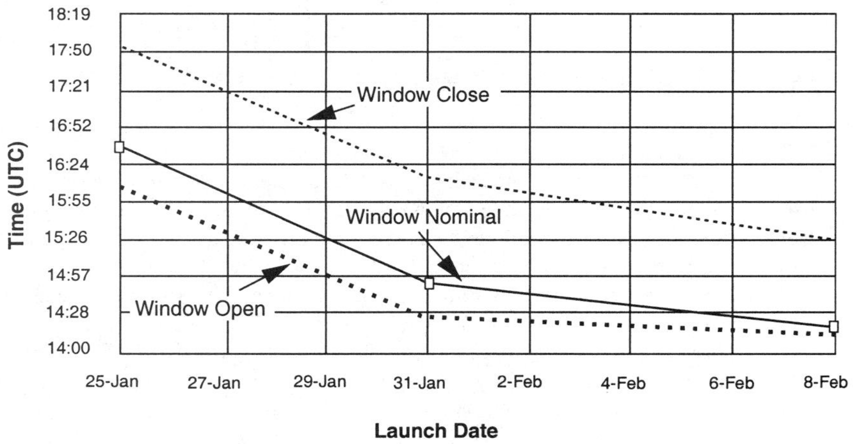

Fig. 14-4. Clementine Launch Window for 2966 m/s Transfer Burn [Richon, 1995].

Launch Time Computation for Sun-synchronous Missions

The equation for computing the Greenwich Mean Time (GMT) of launch for a Sun-synchronous orbit is:

$$GMT_{LO} = GMT_{AN} - \Delta t_1 - \Delta t_2 \tag{14-5}$$

where GMT_{LO} is the GMT of liftoff, Δt_1 is the nominal time of launch vehicle flight from launch to spacecraft separation, and Δt_2 is the nominal time from spacecraft separation to the descending node.

GMT_{AN} is the GMT of the ascending node. If times are expressed in sec, then:

$$GMT_{AN} = [LMST_{AN} - LAN \times (86{,}400 \text{ sec}/360 \text{ deg})]_{\text{mod } 86{,}400 \text{ sec}} \tag{14-6}$$

where $LMST_{AN}$ is the local mean solar time of ascending node, LAN is the East longitude of ascending node (in deg). It is the angle measured east from the Greenwich meridian to the ascending node at the time of the ascending node crossing. (For more information about time systems and the Earth's rotation, see Sec. 4.1.)

For example, for the Earth Observing System Aqua spacecraft, which has a 1:30 pm ascending node local mean time requirement and a launch date of Dec. 30, 2000, the above equations can be used to compute the launch time as follows. From the trajectory data provided by the Delta launch vehicle, the LAN is 39.74°, Δt_1 = 150.0 sec, and Δt_2 = 3114.0 sec. Also, 1:30 pm converted to seconds of the day equals 48600 sec. Then,

$$GMT_{AN} = [48{,}600 - 39.74 \times (86{,}400 \text{ sec}/360 \text{ deg})]_{\text{mod } 86{,}400 \text{ sec}} = 39{,}062.4 \text{ sec} \tag{14-7}$$

and

$$GMT_{LO} = 39{,}062.4 - 150 - 3114 = 35{,}798.4 \text{ sec} = 9 \text{ hours, } 56 \text{ min, } 38.4 \text{ sec} \tag{14-8}$$

14.2.1 Operational Considerations for Launch Vehicle Targeting

For some missions, a direct ascent to the mission orbit is available due to the performance capabilities of the launch vehicle. For other spacecraft, the vehicle cannot provide enough lift to attain the desired orbit, so the spacecraft must carry sufficient fuel in its own propulsion system to perform ascent maneuvers. Spacecraft with no propulsion systems must use a direct transfer to the desired mission orbit, thus dictating the choice of a launch vehicle with sufficient capability.

For spacecraft having propulsion systems, various targeting strategies are available for choosing the orbit into which the vehicle places the spacecraft. It is sometimes desirable to plan for the launch vehicle to place the spacecraft into a 3σ low injection orbit. This low targeting prevents the need for negative ΔV maneuvers to achieve the desired mission orbit, even if a 3σ high injection is achieved. Negative ΔV maneuvers are those which require the spacecraft to burn in a direction opposite to the velocity direction. These maneuvers waste propellant and often require yawing the spacecraft 180 deg to align the thrusters properly, a potentially risky and typically avoided operational practice. For instance, a spacecraft requiring an orbit altitude of 700 km and is targeted for an altitude of 690 km. Then, even a 10 km injection error would not require the spacecraft to perform a negative ΔV maneuver. However, if the launch vehicle performs flawlessly, the spacecraft will have to raise the orbit from 690 km to 700 km—i.e. the probability of needing to do a maneuver to achieve the mission orbit is increased. Even if the target orbit is not chosen to be 3σ low, choice of a slightly low target allows the opportunity to perform some small trim maneuvers to place the spacecraft precisely on station. Allowing atmospheric drag to lower the altitude over time is an alternative to performing a negative ΔV maneuver; however, the amount of time required to achieve the desired altitude may be undesirably long, preventing the collection of data during the drag period. The risks versus benefits of which targeting scenario to use must be weighed based on the spacecraft's maneuvering capabilities and operational constraints.

For spacecraft that cannot obtain a direct transfer, an ascent scenario must involve combinations of transfer orbits. Given the types of transfer orbits discussed in Chap. 12 and the ability to compute the ΔV required to maneuver from one to the other, a combination of transfer orbits may be determined. Various factors must be taken into account during this planning process, including the drift rates of the orbit elements while in the transfer orbits to ensure meeting all mission requirements once on orbit. Note that if a spacecraft is planned to be in a certain transfer orbit for a given period of time, and this time is based on achieving a certain amount of drift in one of the orbit elements, the element could drift to an undesirable value if the spacecraft is forced to remain in the transfer orbit longer or shorter than planned.

One example of ascent planning is the GOES mission, which uses restartable engines to affect the transfer from injection to mission orbit. Constraints used in planning a geosynchronous ascent include the number and magnitude of maneuvers which must be performed (both in- and out-of-plane), the number of orbit revolutions between maneuvers, the Sun-spacecraft geometry, ground station coverage, and the longitude drift rate. Other launch and early orbit operational concerns must also be addressed. For instance, each maneuver in the sequence is time critical if the spacecraft is to be placed on station correctly due to the drift rates experienced in each orbit. Also, between each maneuver, orbit determination must be performed to ensure the next maneuver will be accurate. In order to feed the orbit determination process, 4 to 8 hours of tracking data are required from a combination of 2 or 3 ground stations. Finally, the attitude must be determined between each maneuver, usually to within ± 2 deg, requiring an amount of time which depends on the subsystem configuration and required accuracy.

14.3 End-of-Life Disposal

The growing amount of orbital debris surrounding the Earth poses a potential hazard to all Earth orbiting spacecraft. Some space agencies have established policies for minimizing orbital debris. One method of doing this includes ensuring proper end-of-life disposal for a spacecraft to reduce the number of spacecraft being left on orbit after the end of their useful lifetimes. NASA Policy Directive 8710.3 states that spacecraft must reenter the Earth's atmosphere within 25 years of the end of their mission life. Guidelines on performing analysis to ensure compliance with 8710.3 were published to aid compliance [NASA, 1995]. The trade studies performed to arrive at the 25 year requirement were also published [Reynolds, 1995]. The most current version of the policy can be obtained from the NASA Code Q website.

Spacecraft designers must be aware of the policies limiting orbital debris because they may have an impact on the required fuel load, as well as other design features. Often a great deal of analysis must be performed to design a spacecraft to meet debris limitation policies. These analyses are complicated by the inherent uncertainties in predicting events that will occur many years after the spacecraft is launched. Choosing an analysis method that provides sufficient accuracy while minimizing the necessary effort requires care. This section provides a comparison of three available disposal analysis methods and recommends which reentry analysis method to choose for a given situation.

14.3.1 Predictability of Impact

It is impossible to accurately predict the way a spacecraft will behave during decay, the way it will break up, or the altitude and time at which breakup will occur. The spacecraft attitude during decay significantly affects the decay time but is often unpredictable because most attitude control systems are designed to function only above a minimum threshold altitude. Once the spacecraft passes below this threshold, any deboost maneuvers could not be reliably pointed, and tumbling may cause variations in the frontal area which are hard to model and which affect the impact time. Breakup factors depend on the material composition and structural integrity of the spacecraft components [Newman, 1993]. However, it is possible to adequately bound the problem using judicious choice of analysis methods. It is important to know the limitations and appropriate applications of the available methods, and to choose the method for performing a given piece of analysis accordingly. The trajectory and lifetime of a few pieces of the spacecraft, such as the largest and smallest, may be computed to determine the area over which the debris is expected to impact the Earth. Sometimes the choice of pieces to study is made by the fact that certain materials are known to survive reentry, such as a telescope mirror which is fairly large and made of a solid base metal.

If available, a thermal analysis can predict which pieces could survive reentry heating. Johnson Space Center has the capability to perform such analyses (see Newman [1993]). Then the trajectory of each of the surviving pieces can be propagated from the breakup point. Variations in mass and frontal area will affect the landing site, creating the scatter field. If breakup and thermal models are not available, the whole spacecraft may be assumed to reenter simultaneously and survive to impact.

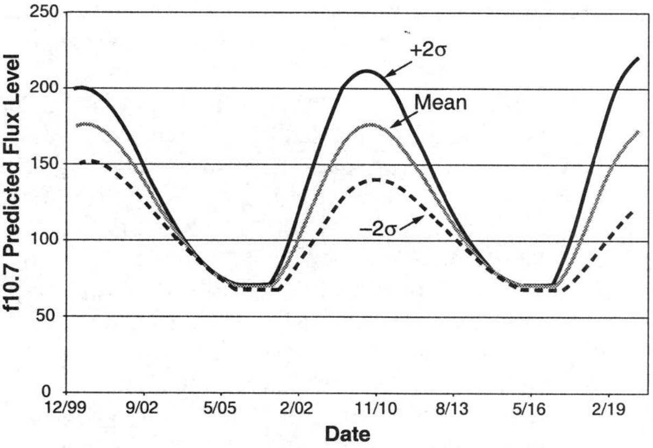

Fig. 14-5. Solar Flux Predictions as of April, 2001. See also Fig. 2-19 in Sec. 2.4.

It is also very difficult to predict the solar flux far into the future, and even the best models are updated frequently to account for changes. Yet this factor has the greatest effect on the lifetime calculations. Figure 14-5 shows the solar flux levels as predicted in April, 2001 by Schatten [2001]. Note that predictions are available for mean and ±2 sigma flux levels. In addition, early and late timing of the solar maximum are predicted similarly to the nominal timing values shown here. For historical variations, see Fig. 2-19 in Sec. 2.4. For further information concerning the historical and future prediction of solar flux, see Schatten [2001].

14.3.2 Disposal Options

During the initial design phase for a spacecraft, programs that follow the NASA guidelines must perform a lifetime analysis to determine whether the spacecraft will be able to meet existing disposal requirements. If it is determined that the spacecraft cannot meet the end-of-life time on-orbit constraint through natural decay, several disposal options are available. These include:

- Uncontrolled Reentry
- Controlled Reentry
- Place in Disposal Orbit
- Retrieval
- Reuse

Uncontrolled reentry is an option for spacecraft that, due to their ballistic coefficients and the level of solar activity at their end of life, are able to reenter the Earth's atmosphere within 25 years. If initial analysis shows that a spacecraft will not reenter within this time, there are still ways to take advantage of an uncontrolled reentry, which is the cheapest of the disposal options. The spacecraft area to mass ratio may be altered sufficiently to change the decay lifetime of the spacecraft. This could be done before launch by physically changing the mass or area, although this is generally not feasible due to spacecraft design constraints. After the spacecraft has finished its mission life it could be put into a high drag attitude to promote rapid decay. However, this alternative assumes an ability to control this attitude throughout the decay period. In addition, the spacecraft orbit could be lowered to one which will decay during the required time frame. This option can be relatively cheap if only a small orbit change is required.

If the spacecraft is unable to reenter naturally within an appropriate time, a *controlled reentry* may be performed.* "Controlled" means that the ground operators plan maneuvers which drive the spacecraft back to a specific location on Earth. This requires that the spacecraft carry the necessary fuel, and so must be planned before the spacecraft is fully designed and built. There must also be sufficient attitude control at low altitudes to ensure that the final maneuvers are executed in the proper direction. These operations are potentially hazardous, as not all spacecraft completely burn up during reentry. Components that are very large, have materials with high melting points, or have a shape which helps reduce atmospheric heating may survive reentry, posing a threat to those on Earth. Statistics regarding the probability of the reentering components striking a human being are used in determining the size and location of the disposal location needed to perform a controlled reentry of a spacecraft, based on models of how the spacecraft is expected to break up and which parts are expected to reenter (for more information, see Mrozinski [2001]. This option is very expensive from a fuel point of view. Carrying such a large amount of propellant is generally prohibitive for small, low-budget spacecraft. However, some larger spacecraft may carry the extra fuel to perform a controlled reentry to avoid causing casualties on impact or the perception that damage could occur. Section 14.5 contains a detailed discussion of the reentry analysis and execution for CGRO, a NASA spacecraft designed to be

* This option may also be preferred to ensure that the spacecraft doesn't reenter overpopulated areas.

reentered at the end of its useful lifetime due to its large lead components which could potentially injure someone if left to reenter in an uncontrolled fashion.

For orbits such as geosynchronous which are too high to use the reentry methods, the spacecraft may be placed in a disposal orbit that is out of the way of other spacecraft in the vicinity. Geosynchronous spacecraft are usually boosted to a higher orbit at the end of their useful life to keep them out of the path of new spacecraft in geosynchronous transfer orbits. This option is also available to low Earth spacecraft which do not carry enough fuel to reenter completely, but which can be taken out of crowded orbits. The region allocated by NSS 1740.14 for disposal of LEO spacecraft is between 2,500 km and 18,833 km altitude. Since most LEO spacecraft have orbits well below 2,500 km, placing these spacecraft in such a storage orbit would be more costly than maneuvering to an orbit which will allow decay within 25 years.

Some spacecraft may take advantage of the retrieval option in which the spacecraft is captured by the Space Shuttle and brought back to Earth for testing or reuse. However, this can only be done for spacecraft within reach of the Shuttle, which typically goes only to a maximum altitude of 300 km and an inclination of 28 deg to 57 deg. Retrieval requires substantial rendezvous planning and special hardware on the spacecraft to enable grappling by astronauts. The LDEF retrieval is an example of this technique. However, the purpose was not to eliminate debris, but to retrieve the information LDEF had collected about the space environment.

A final option is to reuse the spacecraft bus for a new mission. This can be accomplished through extensive initial planning to allow various payloads to use the same support systems. The Explorer Platform was designed in this manner, to first carry the EUVE payload, then have that replaced by the XTE payload. However, this capability was not used and XTE was launched aboard a different bus. The Hubble Space Telescope is also an example of reuse, since its instruments are switched out every few years, potentially extending the lifetime of the telescope indefinitely.

Disposal of the Mir Space Station

In 2001, the Russian space agency, Rosaviakosmos, decided to reenter the Mir space station, successfully placing the station in a planned deorbit box in the Pacific Ocean on March 23, 2001. At the end of its useful lifetime, the Russians had allowed Mir to decay naturally from its mission orbit until they were ready to perform the reentry operation. Mir's altitude had gradually dropped from 350 km in the end of December to about 250 km before the final reentry sequence began. The station was then reentered using a control sequence powered by fuel contained in a Progress vehicle docked to the station for that purpose. Three reentry maneuvers lasting approximately 20 min each were executed by Russian Mission Control at 6:35 pm EST on March 22, 9:01 pm and 12:07 am March 23 [Sietzen, 2001]. Splashdown occurred about 50 min after Burn 3 began. This method of providing extra fuel for the operation was available due to the flexible nature of docking ports on the station. A typical satellite may not be equipped with such a feature that would allow the addition of extra fuel for end-of-life disposal. The center of the Mir debris impact area was approximately 3,700 km south of Tahiti and 4,500 km east of New Zealand in an area completely free of islands, human habitation, shipping lanes, or air traffic. Controllers expected that most of the 135-ton station would burn up in the atmosphere, but that up to 30 tons of debris, including some pieces the size of an automobile, would reach the surface. Observers near Fiji noted large fireballs streaking through the sky that broke into smaller pieces as they dropped toward the Pacific.

14.3.3 Choosing an Orbit for Uncontrolled Reentry

As discussed in Sec. 2.4.1 satellite decay varies dramatically with time relative to the solar cycle. (See Fig. 2-21 in Sec. 2.4.1). Consequently choosing an end-of-life orbit altitude that will meet the NASA guidelines of reentry within 25 years can be analysis-intensive. Three methods are readily available: the method presented in NASA guidelines [NASA, 1995], the modified NASA method developed at GSFC, and the full numerical approach. The NASA guidelines method is easy to use and requires virtually no knowledge of orbit perturbations and decay. The analysis is quick using software available with the guidelines. However, the results obtained are coarse and conservative, as they do not model the varying solar flux levels. The numerical method is most accurate because it accounts for orbit perturbations such as the solar flux cycle and the diurnal bulge. However, it is complicated and time consuming and requires experience in orbit analysis and reentry planning. The GSFC method is a compromise between the other two. It uses solar flux predictions to model the solar cycle and the timing of orbit decay, yet is still simple and easy to use.

Differences in fuel calculated between methods could drive mission cost, mass margins, tank sizes, or other spacecraft design concerns. The method used for analysis of the uncontrolled reentry option should be chosen based on the level of development of the spacecraft. The NASA guidelines and GSFC methods are appropriate for spacecraft undergoing feasibility studies, in which a worst case estimate of the disposal ΔV required would be used for tank volume and mass calculations. A more accurate approach may be needed for spacecraft in the design and test phase, when the spacecraft configuration has been established and disposal planning becomes necessary to determine fuel budgets.

The NASA guidelines method uses a series of plots and the spacecraft ballistic properties to determine whether the spacecraft meets the 25 year lower lifetime requirement, or if moving the spacecraft to a disposal orbit or reentering it will be required. From these results, the fuel required for spacecraft lowering or reentry may be computed. Figure 14-6 is one step in the process. The figure shows, for a given spacecraft mass and area, how much ΔV and hydrazine are required for reentry. The plot was generated assuming a constant solar flux of 130×10^{-22} W/m^2/Hz over periods of up to 50 years, a physical impossibility given that the solar flux varies between approximately 75 and 250 during a typical 11 year solar cycle. (See Fig. 14-5 or Fig. 2-19 in Sec. 2.4.) Therefore, the lifetimes calculated using the NASA guidelines method are erroneously long. While the long lifetime may be viewed as a conservative estimate, it may also cause unnecessary mitigation techniques to ensure the spacecraft will be able to comply with the guidelines, since under true solar conditions the spacecraft might meet the 25 year requirement more economically.

Reynolds [1995] states that the fuel required for reentry is on the order of the amount usually put on board as margin in case of emergency. However, this is not always the case. The percent of the Terra fuel budget required for the uncontrolled reentry option ranges between 16% and 38%, much greater than the 10% typically held in reserve (see Table 14-4). Therefore, each spacecraft should examine its disposal options to find the one that is most efficient and least costly.

The GSFC method involves scaling the NASA guidelines results to be more consistent with a full numerical analysis. By fitting predicted solar flux data with a 9th order polynomial, the NASA guidelines calculations can be scaled to the numerical data. The polynomial is of the form:

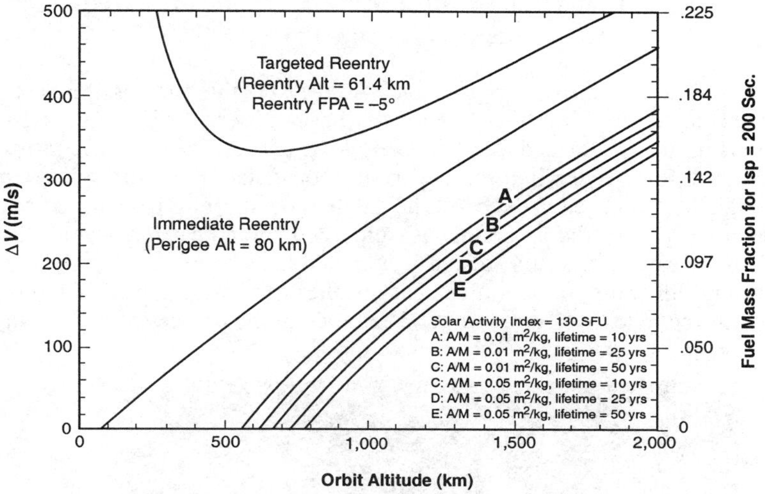

Fig. 14-6. NASA Guidelines Method [Reynolds, 1995]. Select the area to mass ratio (A/M) for a spacecraft design and use this chart to determine the required reentry fuel (right axis) or ΔV (left axis).

$$flux = c + c_1 x + c_2 x^2 + ... + c_9 x^9 \tag{14-9}$$

where x is the time in years from the epoch of the solar flux predictions. The mean value over the appropriate interval should be found by evaluating the polynomial over the desired time interval and dividing by the NASA Guidelines solar flux value of 130×10^{-22} W/m^2/Hz to compute the scale factor. The interval to be used should begin at end-of-life and include at least one complete solar cycle. The perigee determined from the NASA Guidelines is then multiplied by the scale factor.

The full numerical method is most accurate but very time consuming. It applies all perturbations to the propagation over the entire predicted lifetime of the spacecraft to determine when reentry will occur. This method need only be applied once a configuration is well defined and an exact fuel budget is needed for the reentry trajectory. Table 14-2 compares all three methods for the Terra spacecraft, showing the perigee height to which the 705 km circular mission orbit would have to be lowered for the spacecraft to reenter within 25 years. The higher the perigee height, the less ΔV required, so the NASA Guidelines approach is the most fuel-expensive while the GSFC and numerical methods provide good agreement for a lower cost solution.

TABLE 14-2. Terra End-of-Life Uncontrolled Reentry Orbits Based on Varying Models.

EOL Conditions	NASA Guidelines Perigee Height (km)	GSFC Perigee Height (km)	Numerical Perigee Height (km)
EOL on 6/2003, mean flux	550	571	571
EOL @solar max, mean flux	550	580	587
EOL @solar max, +2s flux	550	634	638

14.4 Example 1: Defining Launch, Orbit, and Disposal Parameters for Terra

In order to illustrate the design principles discussed in this chapter, this section describes the selection of orbit elements for the Earth Observing System (EOS) Terra spacecraft (Fig. 14-7) launched Dec. 18, 1999. Terra carries five scientific instruments and is designed for a 6-year lifetime as part of a constellation of Earth-observing satellites. Originally proposed in the late 1980's to be a polar orbiting platform as part the Space Station program, the program was called POP-A and carried dozens of instruments. In the early 1990's, this design was scaled back to eventually become EOS Terra. Through all of the configuration changes, the orbit design stayed fairly constant. Because of its complexity, Terra is a good example of the process of orbit design.

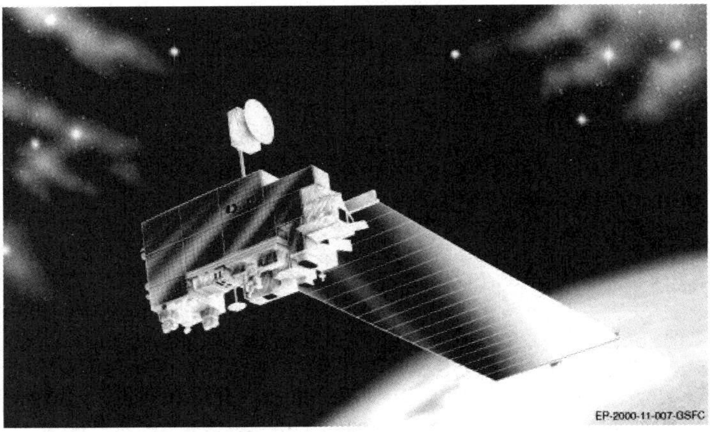

Fig. 14-7. The Terra Spacecraft.

14.4.1 Definition of Complete Orbit Parameters

The Terra mission orbit requirements are:

1. Sun-synchronous
2. Repeating ground track with cycle of 233 orbits in 16 days
3. 705 km mean altitude over the equator
4. Frozen Orbit
5. 10:30 am (±15 min) descending node mean local solar time
6. ±20 km ground track control accuracy with respect to the World Reference System
7. ±5 km radial constraint
8. Fly the same ground track as Landsat-7 within 15 min to 1 hour

As discussed in Sec. 14.1, not all of the classical Keplerian orbit elements are explicitly defined by the mission requirements listed above; however, all are defined implicitly and some are over-defined. Table 14-3 shows which elements are affected by which requirements. The equations which define these relationships are covered in Chaps. 2 and 12. While argument of perigee and mean anomaly are only affected by one requirement, the semimajor axis and inclination are affected by many. Obviously, Terra has a very strictly defined set of mission requirements with little room for further choices. In fact, the requirements need to be checked to make sure they are not over-constraining the orbit element selection. The best place to start is to determine mean values for the elements, beginning with the altitude and inclination. The mean values will account for basic orbital forces such as the geopotential, but will not take into account higher order terms such as atmospheric drag or lunar and solar gravitation. Those types of forces affect the maintenance of the orbit elements as opposed to the initial selection.

TABLE 14-3. Mapping of Terra Orbit Requirements to Orbit Elements Affected.

Requirement	a	e	i	Ω	ω	M
1. Sun-synchronous	X		X			
2. Repeating Ground Track	X		X			
3. 705 km Altitude	X					
4. Frozen Orbit		X			X	
5. 10:30 am Mean Time	X		X	X		
6. ±20 km Cross Track	X					
7. ±5 km Radial		X				
8. Some Ground Track as LandSat-7				X		X

The first step in the mean element selection process is to see if it is possible to choose an inclination that meets both the repeat cycle and Sun-synchronous node rate requirements for the required altitude. Figure 14-8 illustrates combinations of altitude and inclination that result in various ground track repeat cycles and also those which result in a Sun-synchronous node rate. For Terra the repeat cycle of 233 orbits in 16 days equals 14.56 revs/day, and the mean altitude is required to be 705 km. These requirements can both be met at an inclination of 98.2 deg. Since one unique solution was successfully found, mission orbit requirements 1 through 3 have now been met.

The second step in the design process is to choose the values of argument of perigee and eccentricity for a frozen orbit. In order for this to occur, the change in eccentricity and change in argument of perigee must be zero.

As discussed in Sec. 2.5.6, in order for the change in eccentricity to be zero, the argument of perigee must be either 90 deg or 270 deg, that is, fixed above the Northernmost or Southernmost latitudes, respectively. The chosen argument of perigee is then plugged into Eq. 2-67 in Sec. 2.5.6, along with the altitude and inclination determined above. In the case of Terra, a value of 90 deg is chosen for the argument of perigee based on the science desire to have perigee over the Northernmost latitude for data calibration purposes. The frozen eccentricity is computed to be 0.0012 and requirement number 4 has now been met.

The third step is to select the node such that the mean local time meets the 10:30 am descending node mission requirement. The node may be computed using:

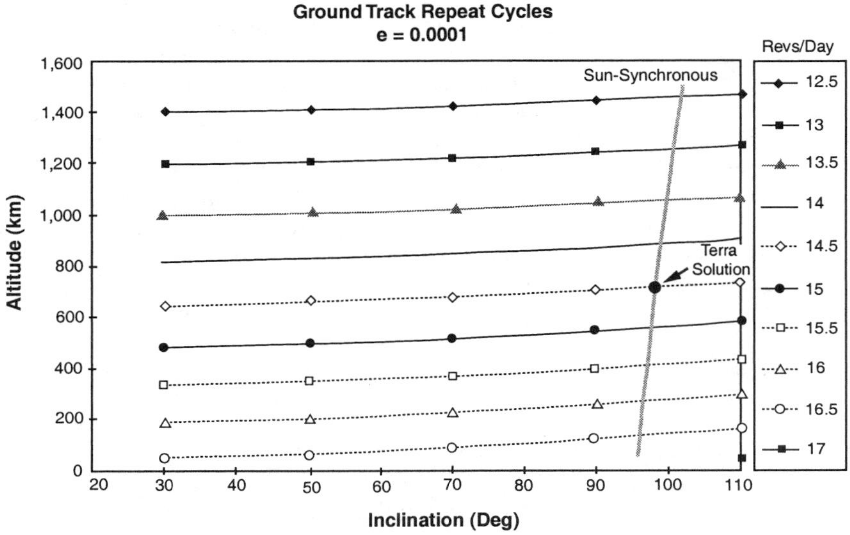

Fig. 14-8. Sun-Synchronous and Repeating Altitude/Inclination Combinations.

$$\Omega = \left[\left(\text{MLT}_{AN} - 12\right) \cdot \left(\frac{360\,\text{deg}}{24\,\text{hours}} \right) + \Omega_{SUN} \right]_{\text{mod}\,360} \tag{14-10}$$

where MLT_{AN} is the mean local time of the ascending node Ω_{SUN}, is the right ascension of the Sun on the epoch date, and Ω is right ascension of the ascending node. Assuming a launch date for Terra of 6/20/98, the original target launch date, we obtain Ω = 246.19 deg.

If the mean local time requirement is specified as a descending node time, as is the case for Terra, simply add 12 hours to get the corresponding ascending node time before applying Eq. 14-10. This process meets requirement number 5.

The above analysis fully defines a stand-alone mission for the Terra spacecraft to meet all the original science requirements. However, we have not yet addressed requirement 8, to fly in constellation with Landsat-7, which was levied a few years before launch but well after the design and fabrication of the spacecraft parts. The only orbit element not yet specified is the mean anomaly. Fortunately, Landsat-7 has identical orbit requirements to Terra, except that it is in a 10:00 am descending orbit. Therefore, specifying the mean anomaly allows Terra to fly in constellation with Landsat-7 such that the two spacecraft trace the same ground track within 15 to 60 min of each other. While none of the other orbit elements are affected. In order for both spacecraft to see the same point on the ground and still meet their respective mean time requirements, they must be separated in mean anomaly enough so that as the Earth rotates under the two orbit planes such that a given point on the equator is at 10:00 am as Landsat-7 crosses over head, and at 10:30 am when Terra is overhead. This geometry is shown in Fig. 14-9.

The two orbit planes are separated by 30 min in mean local time corresponding to 7.5 deg of right ascension. A separation of 108 deg (360 × 30 min/100 min orbit period

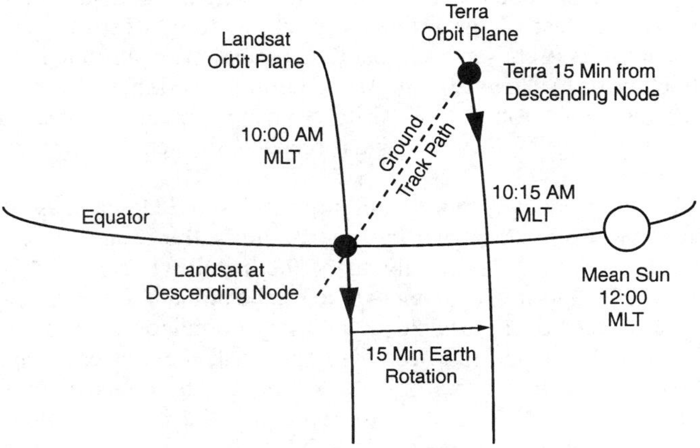

Fig. 14-9. Relative Positions of Terra and Landsat-7 for 15-min Separation on Same Ground Track [McIntosh, 2000].

≈ 108 deg) in anomaly will permit the two spacecraft to be separated by 30 min in mean local time. Any value can be assumed for the anomaly pre-launch, with the understanding that the anomaly of the final orbit must be constrained. No particular value should be chosen during the pre-launch phase because the anomaly of the first spacecraft at the time that the second reaches orbit determines the target anomaly for the second spacecraft. In addition, most launch vehicles will not permit a particular value of mean anomaly to be used as a target because it is a free variable for the launch vehicle trajectory. Variations in launch time, date, and powered flight trajectory experienced by the second spacecraft prevent the specific value from being known in advance.

These steps have yielded a mean element set that meets mission requirements. Now, the elements must be refined to include higher order terms and perturbation effects and be converted from mean to osculating elements for the launch vehicle to target.

14.4.2 Orbit Error Boundaries

Requirements 6 and 7 have not yet been addressed. They affect not the initial choice of orbit elements, but the maintenance of these values over time. (Orbit maintenance is discussed in Sec. 2.7.2 and 13.4.) These requirements do not over-constrain the choice of orbit altitude or eccentricity, but define error bounds on them. As discussed in Sec. 14.1, the orbit error bounds for a given mission are often a measure of the flexibility of the requirements driving a particular orbit element, and thus the selection of those bounds is very mission specific. In order to determine how tightly each element must be achieved, it is necessary to analyze the long-term perturbations on the elements. The following paragraphs provide a definition and analysis of the Terra orbit error bounds in an effort to provide a complete case study for the mission.

Semimajor Axis Error Bound. The orbit altitude varies due to atmospheric drag. Requirement 6 simply defines how much the altitude is allowed to drop before being raised. In order to control the ground track to within the ±20 km box stipulated by requirement 6, it is necessary for the spacecraft to perform frequent altitude raising maneuvers. An initial altitude is chosen that is above the nominal and which places the ground track 20 km east of the reference track, drifting westward as the altitude decreases. The altitude is chosen such that the nominal mean altitude is reached when the ground track error reaches –20 km. As the altitude continues to decrease, the orbit perturbations cause the ground track drift to change directions and drift eastward towards the +20 km edge. When that edge is reached, the next maneuver is performed to restart the cycle.

To keep the burn frequency to a minimum, it is desirable to have as large a control box as possible. However, the larger the control limits, the greater the chance of violating the ground track limits, primarily due to the inability to accurately predict solar flux activity in the long term. The maneuver to set the initial altitude is chosen by propagating the ground track over the cycle period using a prediction of the solar flux level. If the actual solar flux value is lower than expected, the western boundary of the control box will be violated. Therefore, a box must be chosen based on the ability to predict the solar flux level. This new box represents the error bound on the ground track control box and, hence, on the orbit altitude.

In order to ensure that changes in flux level would not cause Terra to violate its ground track control box, analysis was performed to determine longitude errors in the ground track repeat cycle using different flux prediction levels to develop an understanding of the possible range in ground track errors. Simulations were run using a numerical propagator with worst-case low flux levels and average daily prediction errors to choose the lower control box limit, since a lower than expected solar flux could cause the ground-track to violate the western boundary of the control box. To further mitigate the possibility that a decrease in the solar flux would cause a violation of the western ground-track error limit, average solar flux prediction errors were introduced. Using these models, a range of ground-track control sub-limits were evaluated to determine if the post-maneuver ground-track error would exceed the western limit of –20 km. In the case that a violation occurred, a new sub-limit was chosen and the targeter rerun to determine the new burn duration. This process was repeated until an acceptable ground-track resulted.

Figure 14-10 shows the results for each flux level examined. As expected, the lower flux cases allowed more westward drift. Notice that the majority of the solar flux cases result in nearly identical eastern drift rates, as indicated by the similar upward positive slopes in the ground track error. Drift rates near the eastern edge of the box averaged approximately 1.5 km per day. Given this information and the desire to have a burn delay buffer of 2 to 3 days prior to violating the eastern ground track boundary, an eastern control limit of +15 km was chosen. In this manner, the Terra ground-track control box limits of +15 km and –5 km were chosen to prevent violating the ground-track error limits of ± 20 km. The upper control limit of +15 km was chosen to allow a 2 to 3 day burn delay without violating the eastern boundary. The lower control limit of –5 km was chosen to prevent a lower than expected solar flux from causing a violation of the western boundary.

Eccentricity and Argument of Perigee Error Bounds. Requirement 7, a radial constraint, affects how tightly the orbit must be frozen, or the allowable variation in eccentricity. This requirements does not affect the altitude maintenance or error bounds on the semimajor axis because the ground track control (requirement 6) requires that the altitude at a given latitude be maintained within about 1 km. Thus, meeting requirement 6 ensures that requirement 7 wouldn't be violated as long as perigee remains fixed at the same latitude. However, perigee rotates to some degree as the

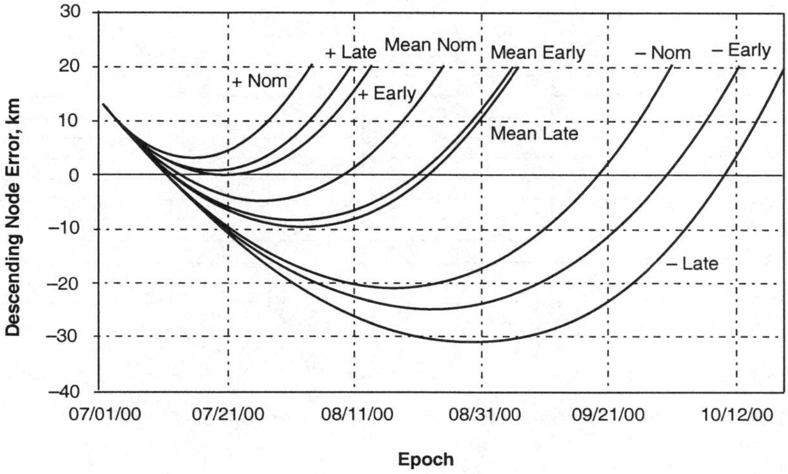

Fig. 14-10. Effect of Various Solar Flux Levels on Terra Ground Track Error [Wilkin, 1998].

eccentricity changes, even in a frozen orbit. Therefore, further analysis was required to determine the acceptable amount of rotation of the argument of perigee and the associated eccentricity variation.

There was a desire among project scientists for Terra to minimize the science down time by minimizing the number of maneuvers. To ameliorate the situation, performing ground track control using one maneuver instead of the traditional two burn pair was proposed. To validate this operations scenario, it was necessary to investigate whether the frozen orbit would degrade after many ground track maneuvers had taken place, resulting in violation of the radial position constraint. Optimization of the near frozen orbit condition was examined by selective placement of a single ground track maintenance maneuver at the mean anomaly that produced mean eccentricity and argument of perigee values closest to mission nominal (eccentricity = 0.00116, argument of perigee = 90 deg). Results indicated that allowing a worst-case altitude deviation of ±5 km for these maneuvers corresponded to an eccentricity deviation from nominal of +0.0008/–0.0006 as shown in Fig. 14-11. This eccentricity results in the frozen orbit boundary indicated on Fig. 14-12. The corresponding argument of perigee variation is ±40 deg for the above nominal case and ±33 deg for below nominal [Noonan, 1996]. Therefore, conservative values of the mean argument of perigee error bounds of ±20 deg and mean eccentricity error bounds of ±0.0004 were chosen to maintain the altitude to within ±5 km at a given latitude. It was determined that performing the required ground track control maneuvers in a place in the orbit chosen to optimize the frozen condition meets the radial constraint without imposing further restrictions on the orbit.

Inclination Error Bound. The Terra inclination requirement did not specify error bounds; however, the inclination is implicitly bounded by maintaining the mean local time. Over the life of the mission, solar and lunar perturbations on the orbit will cause the inclination to gradually decrease. This will alter the node rate, which will cause the local time to change. The inclination can be controlled actively, using maneuvers perpendicular to the orbit velocity. These maneuvers are costly in fuel and operationally complex, often involving yawing the spacecraft in a manner not used for any other

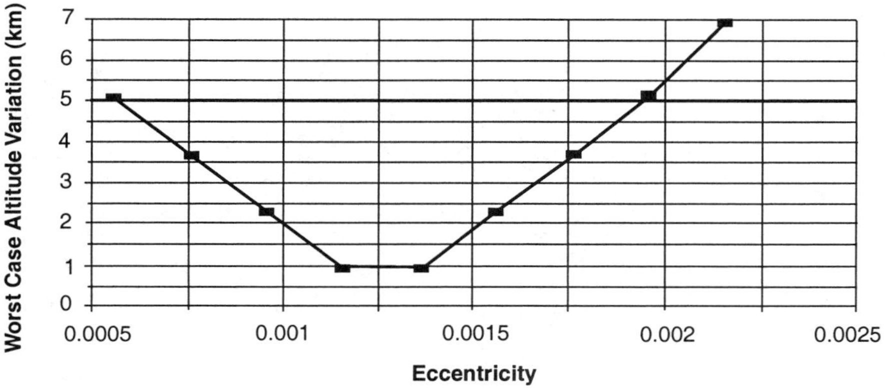

Fig. 14-11. Terra Altitude Variation vs. Eccentricity [Noonan, 1996].

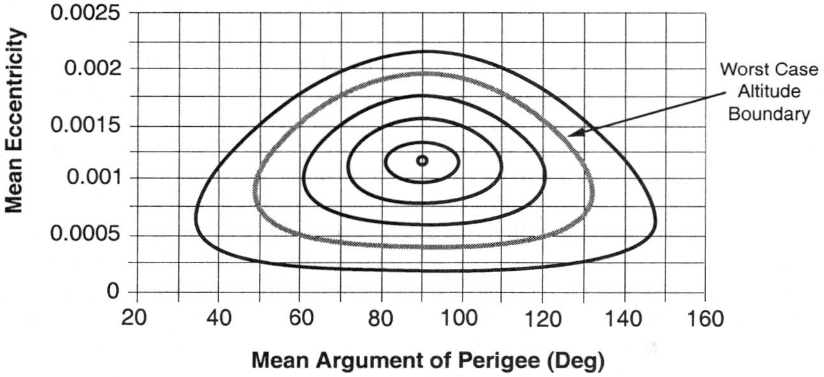

Fig. 14-12. Effect of Various Solar Flux Levels on Ground Track Error [Noonan, 1996].

mission activities. Therefore, inclination maneuvers are often avoided by spacecraft that can take advantage of passive control [Folta, 1992]. In passive control, the inclination is offset from the optimal Sun-synchronous one by a small amount (on the order of hundredths of a degree). Lunar and solar forces then cause the inclination to move in a beneficial direction, similar to the philosophy of ground track control. The turnaround period is on the order of several years, making it possible to complete an entire mission without performing an inclination maneuver if the initial inclination is sufficiently accurate. Most launch vehicles only guarantee inclination accuracy to 0.03 to 0.10 deg. Changes from the nominal of this size would not achieve the passive control goals, so a small initial inclination change maneuver may be necessary.

As discussed in Sec. 14.4.3, Terra had multiple inclination targets given a launch time within its 25-min window. Figure 14-13 shows the mean local time drift produced through passive inclination control assuming optimal inclination targets were achieved for 10:20 am and 10:40 am orbits.

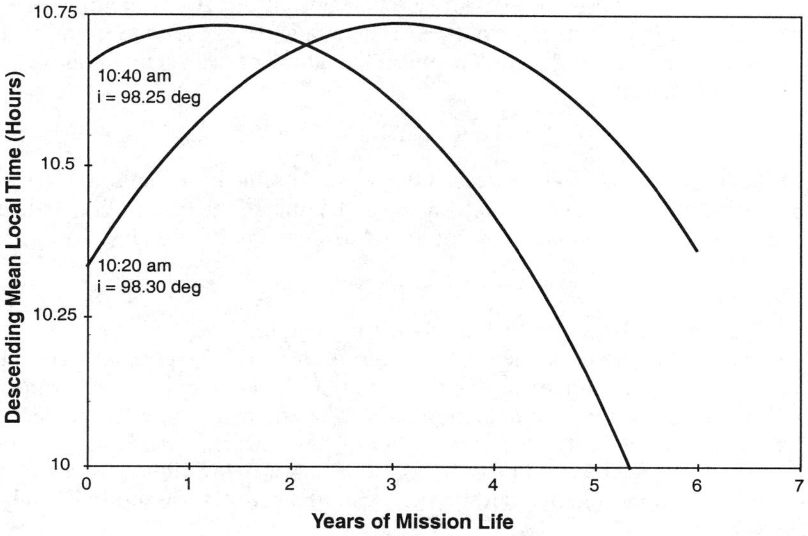

Fig. 14-13. Terra Mean Local Time Drift for Various Initial Values [McIntosh, 1998].

14.4.3 Launch Window Parameters

The Terra launch window is predominantly defined by the requirement for a Sun-synchronous orbit with a mean local time of 10:30, ±15 min. In order to achieve a particular local time, the spacecraft much launch when that plane is in the right position with respect to the launch site. Terra launched on an Atlas IIAS, which had the capability to do guided targeting. This means that for each minute of the window, the vehicle could target different values of inclination that would maximize the time spent within the local time control box. This allowed the window to be widened to a 25-min block instead of only being able to target a 10:30 orbit. The Terra launch window times corresponded to achievable local times of 10:15 to 10:40 am. A buffer was left for possible injection errors as sized by the vehicle contractor. Landsat-7, which launched on a Delta II, did not have this flexibility, as the Delta could only use one target. Therefore, the Landsat-7 window was much narrower, on the order of 5 min, despite having the same local time error bound requirement.

To compute the launch vehicle targets, optimum inclinations were determined for every minute of a launch window opening at 10:15 and closing at 10:40. For each minute, mean orbital elements were propagated for 6 years and the inclination was varied until a value was found that resulted in a maximum mean local time of 10:44 (1 min short of the control limit) at some point during the 6 years. The mean elements were converted to osculating and a polynomial was fit to the osculating inclinations. The polynomial coefficients were then loaded into the vehicle flight software, where they were used after liftoff to compute the target inclination through the following process.

When the vehicle senses liftoff, the GMT of the descending node can be calculated from:

$$GMT_{DN} = GMT_{LO} + \Delta t_1 + \Delta t_2 \tag{14-11}$$

where GMT_{LO} is the GMT of the software detected liftoff, Δt_1 is the time of launch vehicle flight from liftoff to spacecraft separation, and Δt_2 is the time from spacecraft separation to the descending node. The mean local time of descending node, MLT_{DN}, is then computed from:

$$MLT_{DN} = GMT_{DN} - [(360 \text{ deg} - LDN) \times (86{,}400 \text{ sec}/360 \text{ deg})] \tag{14-12}$$

where GMT_{DN} is the GMT at the descending node crossing in seconds and LDN is the East longitude of the descending node in deg at the time of the descending node crossing. Finally, the target inclination is computed using the polynomial

$$y = C_0 + C_1x + C_2x^2 \tag{14-13}$$

where x is the MLT_{DN} and y is the osculating inclination.

Note that this method assumes constant values for LDN, Δt_1, and Δt_2 for all Terra launch times. This is not exactly true given that the vehicle trajectory times may vary due to winds and launch date geometry. The constant values used were computed by the launch vehicle contractor assuming a nominal powered flight trajectory. Analysis showed that variations in the times were sufficiently small to allow inclination targeting scheme within the desired accuracy, assuming no launch vehicle errors.

Terra actually launched at the end of its launch window. The inclination targeting scheme successfully chose the target to maximize the time spent in the control box as shown in Fig. 14-14. However, a maneuver is necessary at about 3 years into the mission to change the mean local time drift direction and remain in the control limits for the rest of the 6-year mission. Figure 14-14 shows one possible local time profile which could be used to achieve mission goals.

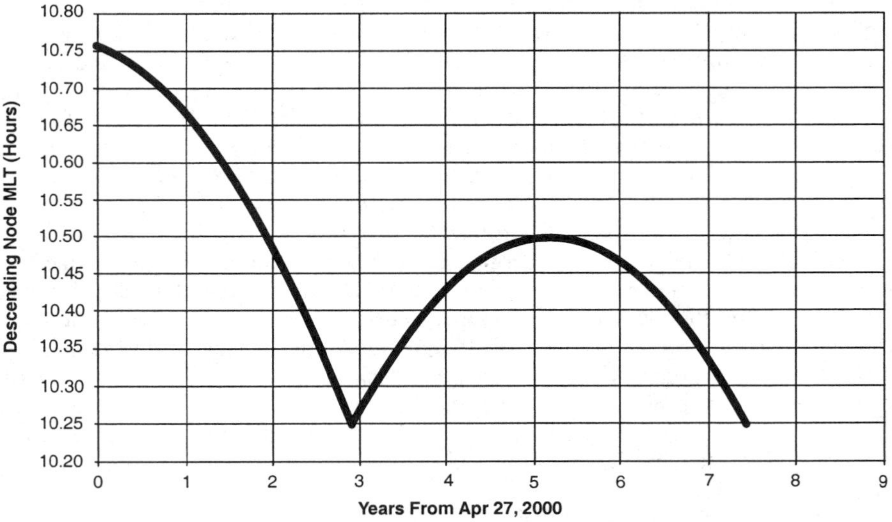

Fig. 14-14. Terra Mean Local Time Drift Following Mission Orbit Acquisition. Assumes an inclination maneuver performed at 3 years.

14.4.4 Achieving Mission Orbit

Although Terra did not have any rendezvous or docking requirements, there was an orbit phasing requirement, which is similar to a rendezvous problem. Strategy for the ascent planning is based on the need to achieve a Sun-synchronous, frozen, ground track control, and Landsat-7 phasing requirements simultaneously. The World Reference System, the target ground track reference path system used by Landsat, consists of 233 equally spaced descending node "paths." Achieving the mission orbit for a satellite attempting to control its ground track to this reference usually requires a series of maneuvers to raise the spacecraft to the proper altitude to synchronize with the system grid. The final trim maneuver is timed so that the spacecraft ground track will align with the nearest reference system path within the allowed control limits. Usually it does not matter which path is achieved at the start. Phasing with another spacecraft, however, requires that the ascent be targeted to a specific path.

In addition, the Terra anomaly is dictated by the difference in mean local time between the two spacecraft. The nominal launch window for Terra could result in a range from 10:15 am to 10:40 am. With the Landsat-7 mean local time near 10:00 am at the time of Terra launch, the two orbit planes could be separated anywhere from 15 to 40 min. The actual launch time and local time difference dictate where Terra must be positioned relative to Landsat-7. For example, if launch occurs at the end of the window, Terra must ascend to a target point 40 min behind Landsat-7 in order to achieve the same World Reference System path.

In addition, the initial phase angle between Terra and Landsat-7 varies with the given launch date in a 16-day repeat pattern. The ascent maneuver plan had to be flexible enough to accommodate all possible configurations. Figure 14-15 shows the relative positions of Terra and Landsat-7 after the ascent has been completed; resulting positions for launches at the opening and closing of the window are indicated (spacecraft

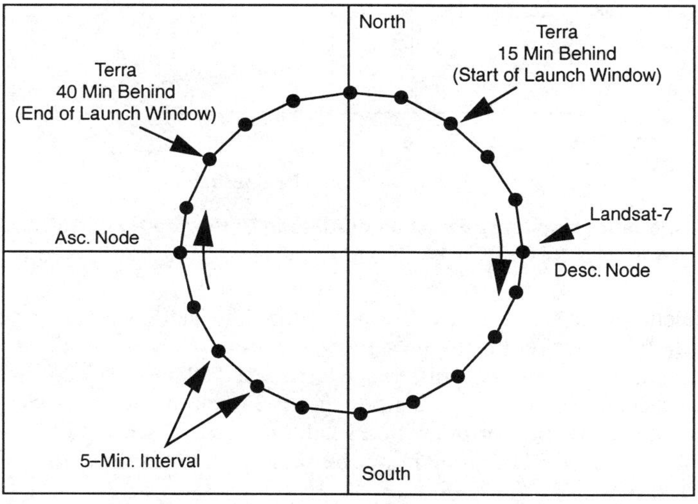

Fig. 14-15. Final Relative Positions Resulting from Launch at Opening and Closing of Window [McIntosh, 2000].

are shown in the same plane for simplicity). While Terra sits on the ground waiting for launch, the relative phasing with Landsat-7 repeats on a 16-day cycle. Thus, a set of 16 maneuver sequences can be computed that will cover all nominal initial conditions. Once launch occurs and the nominal injection orbit is achieved, the synodic period is on the order of 10 days. Therefore, if the initial opportunity to begin the maneuver sequence is missed, the sequence can be started again 10 days later with little change. The synodic period is important in determining the frequency of opportunities for performing the ascent (see discussion in Sec. 2.2). As the altitude is raised, this period becomes longer. If the ascent sequence is interrupted, it may be a long time before the two spacecraft return to the required phase angle. Figure 14-16 shows the synodic period as a function of altitude difference. While Terra remains in the nominal parking orbit, the synodic period is about 10 days. If Terra ascends to an altitude 2 km below Landsat-7, the synodic period becomes 65 days; this means there would have to be a wait of more than 2 months before completing the ascent if the final burn is missed. Phasing could be adjusted by lowering the orbit, but this wastes fuel, and would require an undesirable 180-deg yaw of the spacecraft.

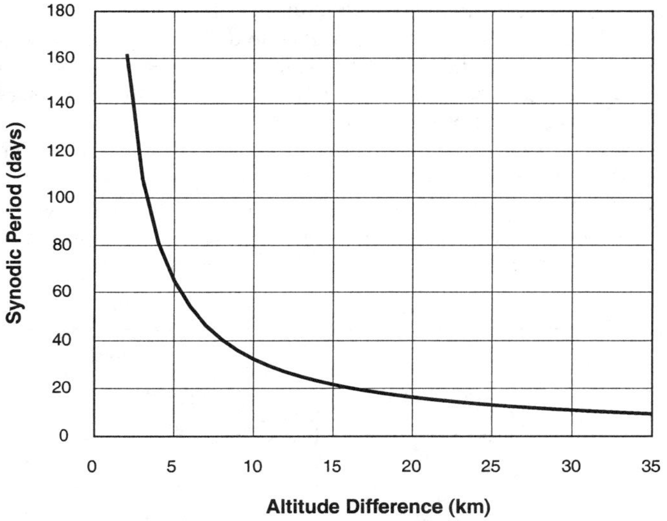

Fig. 14-16. Synodic Period as a Function of Altitude Difference for Terra and Landsat-7. Semimajor Axis is 7,078 km [McIntosh, 2000].

Until the end of the ascent phase, Terra is below Landsat-7 and flying faster. Each time the path difference returns to the same value, Terra has revolved one extra orbit relative to Landsat-7. A zero path difference is achieved at the end of the ascent phase. Since both spacecraft will perform periodic ground track maintenance maneuvers to keep their own ground track errors within small ranges (±20 km for Terra and ±5 km for Landsat-7), they will both remain on the same path and follow the same repeat cycle until end of life.

The exact orbital period required to stay on the World Reference System is closely correlated with node rate. As the node rate changes, very small adjustments to the orbital period will be required to keep the spacecraft on track. As the mean local time of Landsat-7 and Terra evolve differently, separation between the two spacecraft will also change with time. As both spacecraft maintain their respective ground track errors within bounds, a natural byproduct will be to keep an along-track separation equal to the mean local time difference. If the orbit planes drift farther apart, the spacecraft along-track separation will also increase; if the orbit planes move closer together, the along-track separation will decrease.

Ground track control and phasing are accomplished by varying the number of orbits between maneuvers, keeping the burn magnitudes fixed. This proved to be the simplest method from a spacecraft operations standpoint. The frozen orbit eccentricity is achieved by positioning the maneuvers at two optimum locations on nearly opposite sides of the orbit. The number of orbits between burns is adjusted until Terra is on the same path as Landsat-7 and the ground track error is less than 20 km. The final burn is also fine-tuned to give the desired ground track drift that will keep the spacecraft within bounds for the longest possible time.

The actual liftoff time (18:57:36 UT) was within 20 sec of the end of the window. This meant that the goal for the ascent was now set for a point nearly 40 min behind Landsat-7. After launch, analysts used the current orbital states of Terra and Landsat-7 to plan ascent maneuvers. The ascent was completed on Feb. 23, 2000. The final ascent burn stopped the ground track drift at +17 km, near the western boundary of the error box, and started the spacecraft on a normal drift cycle.

14.4.5 End-of-Life Disposal.*

Terra was built at the time when the NASA guidelines on orbit debris were first written. Therefore, although a disposed analysis was completed, no requirement was placed on the spacecraft to be deorbited because it was determined that the amount of additional fuel required could not be placed onboard given the existing mass margins.

In order to compare the three methods described in Sec. 14.4, the Terra spacecraft and orbit characteristics were used to perform a parametric end-of-life disposal analysis. Analyzing the spacecraft orbit to determine guideline adherence as described in Sec. 14.4 involves first computing the natural decay lifetime of the spacecraft to determine if the 25 year constraint is met. The mass and frontal area used were 4652.5 kg and 42.5 m^2, giving an area to mass ratio of 0.009 m^2/kg. Using the NASA guidelines method plots [Reynolds, 1995], a 705 km circular orbit with a lifetime of 25 years corresponds to an area to mass ratio of 0.03 m^2/kg. Since this is greater than the Terra value of 0.009 m^2/kg, the spacecraft will not naturally reenter within 25 years. For 0.009 m^2/kg and an apogee height of 705 km, a 25 year lifetime corresponds to a perigee height of 550 km. Thus, according to the NASA guidelines method, Terra would have to be maneuvered from its 705 km circular orbit to a 705 $\times$ 550 km orbit in order to comply. This would require a ΔV of 41.6 m/s.

For comparison, a numerical analysis using full force modeling and expected solar flux conditions was then performed. With mean solar flux predictions, the spacecraft was found to require an end-of-life orbit of 705 x 571 km to meet the 25 year limit with decay beginning on the scheduled end-of-life date of 6/30/03. This would require a ΔV of 35.9 m/s, a savings of 5.7 m/s relative to the NASA quidelines method. However, a

* Adapted from Newman [1995].

likely end-of-life date must be selected with the understanding that if the mission slips to a period of lower solar flux, disposal will cost more fuel. For comparison, fuel costs were determined for at solar maximum using a mean solar flux level and $+2\sigma$ flux levels on both dates. Table 14-4 presents the results, as well as the percentage of the total fuel budget that must be used to place the spacecraft into the appropriate orbit for uncontrolled reentry. Obviously, the NASA guideline method yields the most conservative and costly solution.

At the time, it was determined that the fuel required for any of these methods, which ranges between 16% and 38%, would be prohibitive, since all of the budgeted fuel is needed to perform the mission. Hence, Terra was allowed to not adhere to the new NASA guidelines.

TABLE 14-4. Terra Starting Orbits for Uncontrolled Reentry Based on Varying Model Assumptions. EOL=end-of-life. Fuel budget = 110 m/s.

Model	Disposal Orbit (km)	ΔV (m/s)	Change in ΔV from NASA Method (m/s)	Change in Perigee Height from NASA Method (km)	Required Deorbit Fuel for Isp=200s (kg)	Position of Fuel Budget Required for Reentry (%)
NASA Method	705 x 550	41.6	N/A	N/A	99.7	37.7
EOL on 6/2003, mean flux	705 x 571	35.9	5.7	21	85.9	32.5
EOL @solar max, mean flux	705 x 587	31.6	10.0	37	75.5	28.6
EOL on 6/2003, $+2\sigma$ flux	705 x 614	24.3	17.3	64	58.0	22.0
EOL @solar max, $+2\sigma$ flux	705 x 638	17.8	23.8	88	42.4	16.1

Reynolds [1995] states that "For cases where post-mission disposal is required, and for mission orbit altitudes below ~1200 km, typically no more than 3%–5% of the final mass is required for this disposal maneuver. This mass fraction is comparable to flight performance reserves." The final mass of Terra is 4652.5 kg, of which 3%–5% would be 139.6 kg–232.6 kg. While the fuel required for disposal given in Table 14-4 is less than these percentages, it is also a large portion of the fuel budget. Most spacecraft allot approximately 10% of their fuel budget to reserves, values more on the order of 25 kg. While this reserve amount, based on the Terra fuel budget of 241.5 kg, would suffice for the disposal cases which use the $+2\sigma$ predictions shown in Table 14-4, it would not suffice if solar activity was on the level of the mean predictions. For comparison, the GSFC method was also used to scale the perigee height values. As shown in Table 14-2, the results are very similar to the numerical method results.

14.5 Example 2: End-of-Life Disposal of CGRO

The Compton Gamma Ray Observatory (CGRO) was designed from inception to have the ability to reenter at the end of its useful life. A portion of the propellant was reserved for this purpose. When the fuel remaining reached this limit, the observatory would be reentered. Figure 14-17 shows the nominal predicted reentry scenario for CGRO, in which breakup of the spacecraft occurs at 122 km, and the remaining debris reenters over a pre-designated scatter zone in the Pacific Ocean. The CGRO debris footprint is shown in Fig. 14-18. Calculations must be performed to ensure that the debris scatter will remain within this footprint.

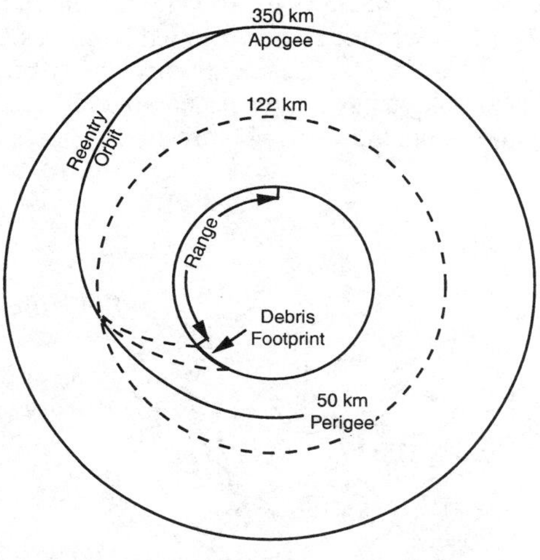

Fig. 14-17. Reentry Trajectory for CGRO [Brown-Conwell, 1989].

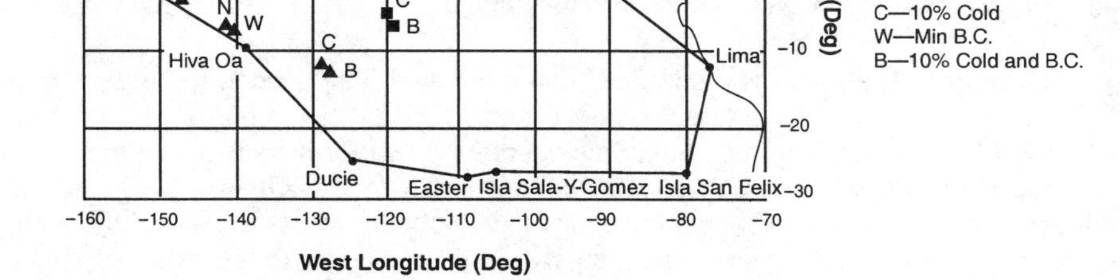

Fig. 14-18. CGRO Footprint and Predicted Debris Scatter. [Brown-Conwell, 1989]. B.C. = Ballistic coefficient.

Two factors affect the debris scatter—the altitude at which breakup of the spacecraft occurs, and the altitude at which the spacecraft is assumed to reenter. Higher breakup altitudes will produce more debris scatter, yielding a larger footprint. Lowering the perigee height for reentry decreases footprint size but increases the required ΔV. An analysis of the debris footprint [CSC, 1986], assumed CGRO would break up at 122 km to be conservative, although actual breakup was predicted at 80 km.

The acceptable level of casualty expectation resulting from a given piece of debris impacting the ground is a common parameter used in evaluating the disposal options for a spacecraft. This parameter may be calculated using the instructions given by NASA [1995].

Flight Experience.* On June 4, 2000, CGRO entered the Earth's atmosphere over the Pacific Ocean target. This was the first controlled re-entry of an unmanned spacecraft from low Earth orbit by NASA. The complexity and criticality of this operation was enhanced by the 14,000 kg mass of the spacecraft and the loss of 2 of the 4 orbit control thrusters soon after launch in 1991. Figure 14-19 shows the spacecraft.

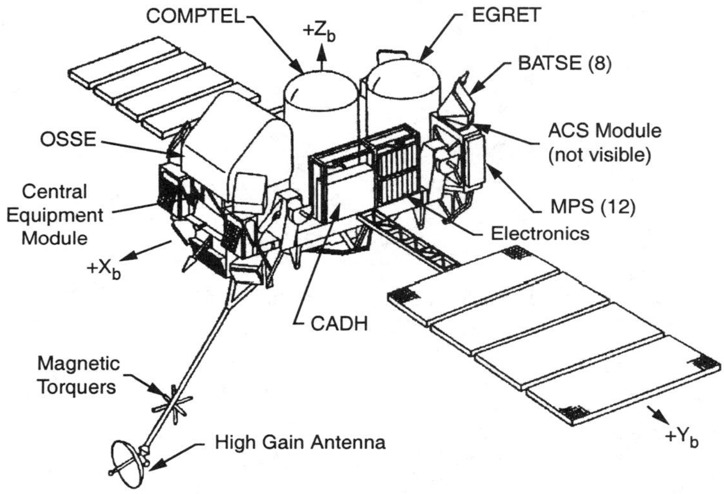

Fig. 14-19. The Compton Gamma Ray Observatory.

In December 1999, it was recognized that a detailed plan needed to be developed for a controlled re-entry. A target date of summer 2000 was chosen as a balance between allowing enough time to plan the complex operation versus trying to accomplish the activities before hardware on the spacecraft failed. One of the gyros had failed already, causing mission planners to worry about the ability to control the pointing of the spacecraft during the maneuvers if another gyro were to fail. Approximately one month before re-entry, all procedures where frozen and rehearsed with the final mission profile.

The re-entry maneuver scenario consisted of an engineering burn and four 26+ min burns, each centered at apogee, that dropped the spacecraft from it's 510 km circular orbit to a 510×50 km terminal orbit. On May 28, 2000, 19:44:00 GMT, the engineering burns were executed. These consisted of short firings of the 20N and 220N thrusters to verify performance. Re-entry burn #1 was conducted on May 31, 01:51:05 GMT

* Adapted from Mangus [2000]

and put the spacecraft in a 510km × 350km orbit. Burn #2 on June 1, 02:36:52 GMT placed the spacecraft in a 510km × 250km orbit. The final two re-entry burns were done on June 4 at 03:56:00 GMT and 05:22:21 GMT, dropping perigee to 150 km and finally to 50 km. Within 30 min after burn #4, the spacecraft had completed its re-entry into the Pacific.

Figure 14-20 shows a simplified version of the burn sequence. Between Burns 1, 2 and 3, the spacecraft remained in a power positive "Parking Attitude" under wheel control. Six min before the burn, the spacecraft entered thruster control. At the burn minus 2 min mark, the spacecraft pitched at 1 revolution per orbit to maintain the thrusters parallel to the velocity vector. A command from the ground fired the 220 N Orbit Adjust Thrusters.

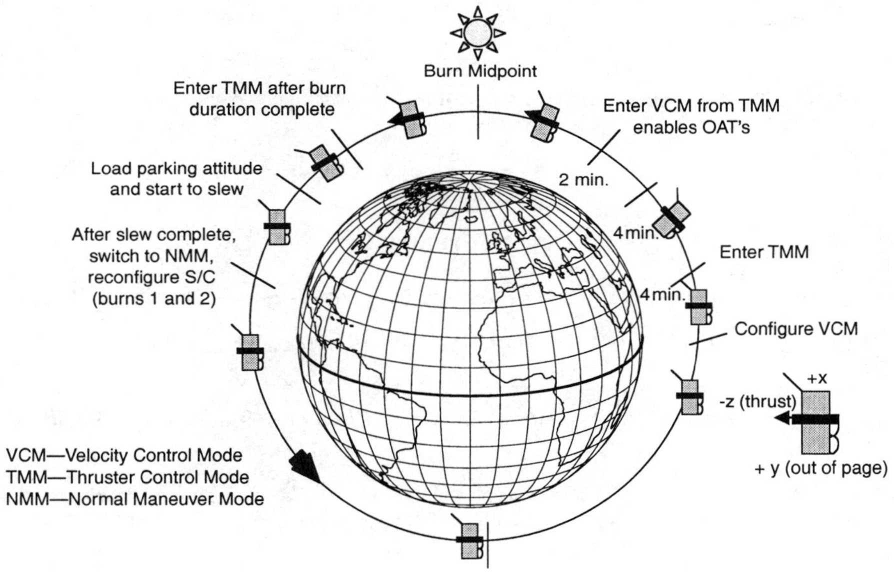

Fig. 14-20. Simplified Burn Sequence.

After Burn 3, aerodynamic torques would cause the controller to saturate the wheels at perigee. Therefore, the spacecraft remained under thruster control during a final perigee pass.

Figure 14-21 shows the predicted footprint, represented as the three symbols connected by a line in the ocean. The circles and line along the American coast represent the boundaries of the safety zone that the debris had to remain within. Since the burns were of nominal performance, the spacecraft objects fell around the star at the center of the line. The objects with a low mass to area ratio, i.e. the solar arrays, fell on the upper left side of the star and the objects with a high mass to area ratio, i.e. the titanium bolts, fell downstream from the star. All objects fell within the plus sign and the circle along the line. Visual contact from an U.S. Air Force plane, contracted by NASA to track re-entry, verified the proper time and location of impact.

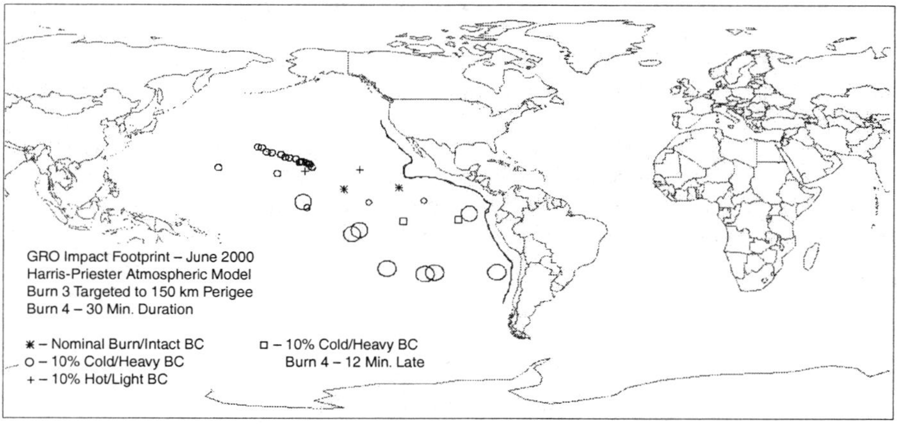

Fig. 14-21. CGRO Predicted Debris Footprint. BC = Ballistic coefficient.

References

The Boeing Company. 1996. *Delta II Payload Planner's Guide*, MDC H3224D. April.

The Boeing Company. 1999. *Delta III Payload Planner's Guide*, MDC 99H0068. October.

The Boeing Company. 1999. *Delta IV Payload Planner's Guide*, MDC 99H0065. October.

Brown-Conwell, Evette R. 1989. *GRO Mission Flight Dynamics Analysis Report: Controlled Reentry of the Gamma Ray Observatory*, CSC/TM-90/6001. November.

Chiulli, Roy M. 1994. *International Launch Site Guide*. El Segundo, CA. The Aerospace Press.

Computer Sciences Corporation. 1986. *Gamma Ray Observatory (GRO) Flight Dynamics Report: Analysis of Debris Impact Footprint for GRO Controlled Reentry*, CSC/TM-86/6042.

Folta, David and Lauri Kraft. 1992. "Methodology for the Passive Control of Orbital Inclination and Mean Local Time to Meet Sun-Synchronous Orbit Requirements," AAS 92-143, AAS/AIAA Spaceflight Mechanics Meeting, Colorado Springs, CO. February 24–26.

International Launch Services, Inc. 1998. *Atlas Launch System Mission Planner's Guide*, Revision 7. December.

Isakowitz, Steven J. 1999. *International Reference Guide to Space Launches* (3rd ed.), American Institute of Aeronautics and Astronautics, Washington, D.C.

Kraft, J. Donald. 1996. "Launch Vehicle Selection, Performance and Use," Applied Technology Institute. April.

Mangus, David and Susan Hoge. 2000. "CGRO Reentry Summary Report" in the *Flight Dynamics Analysis Branch End of Fiscal Year 2000 Report*, NASA GSFC Code 572. November.

McIntosh, Richard J., Noonan, Paul J., and Lauri K. Newman. 2000. "Terra Ascent Planning to Meet Landsat-7 Phasing Requirements," AIAA 2000-4342, AIAA Astrodynamics Specialist Conference, Denver, CO. August 14–17.

McIntosh, Richard J. 1998. Computer Sciences Corporation, Analysis "Mean Local Time Drift Analysis," April 2.

Mrozinski, Richard B. 2001. "Entry Debris Field Estimation Methods and Application to Compton Gamma Ray Observatory Disposal," NASA CP-2001-209986, 2001 Flight Mechanics Symposium Proceedings. June 19–21.

NASA Office of Safety and Mission Assurance. 1995. "NASA Safety Standard: Guidelines and Assessment Procedures for Limiting Orbital Debris," NASA Headquarters, Washington D.C., NSS 1740.14, August.

NASA Code Q. 1997. *Policy for Limiting Orbital Debris Generation*, NPD 8710.3 (formerly NMI 1700.8).

Newman, Lauri K., Brian P. Ross, et al. 1993. "Reentry Analysis for Low Earth Orbiting Spacecraft," AAS 93-307, Flight Mechanics/Estimation Theory Symposium, Greenbelt, MD.

Newman, Lauri K. and David C. Folta. 1995. "Evaluation of Spacecraft End-of-Life Disposal to Meet NMI Guidelines," AAS 95-325, Astrodynamics Specialist Conference, Halifax, NS, Canada, August 14–17.

Noonan, Paul. 1996. "EOS AM-1 Ground-Track Control and Frozen Orbit Analysis," Computer Sciences Corporation, CSC/TM-56816-02. September 9.

Orbital Sciences Corporation. 2000. *Pegasus User's Guide*, Release 5.0.

Orbital Sciences Corporation. 1999. *Taurus Launch System Payload User's Guide*, Release 3.0.

Reynolds, R. C., Lockheed Corporation. 1995. *Rationale for Guideline Limit of 25 Years for Post-Mission Removal from Orbit*, NASA Code Q, Johnson Space Center, and Lockheed Engineering and Science.

Richon, Karen V. and Lauri K. Newman. 1995. "Flight Dynamics Support For The Clementine Deep Space Program Science Experiment (DSPSE) Mission," AAS 95-444, Astrodynamics Specialist Conference, Halifax, NS, Canada. August 14–17.

Schatten, Kenneth. 2001. "Solar Activity Forecasting for use in Orbit Prediction." NASA CP-2001-209986, 2001 Flight Mechanics Symposium Proceedings. June 19–21.

Sietzen, Jr., Frank. 2001. "Mir: Resting in Peace." *Aerospace America*. May.

Wertz, James R., and Wiley J. Larson (ed). 1999. *Space Mission Analysis and Design*, (3rd ed.). Torrance, CA: Microcosm Press and Dordrecht, The Netherlands: Kluwer Academic Publishers.

Wilkin, Paul. 1998. *EOS AM-1 Ground-Track Control Box Study*, Computer Sciences Corporation, CSC/TM-28292-02. August 20.

APPENDICES

The appendices summarize the equations and data needed for mission engineering of spacecraft orbit and attitude systems and the analysis of payload and spacecraft mission geometry.

Appendices

These appendices provide the basic formulas and data needed to implement the algorithms in this book for nearly any space mission. Most of the spherical geometry and orbit formulas are standard ones that can be found in many references. The full-sky geometry formulas (Sec. A.7) and spherical-to-spherical coordinate transformations were developed by Microcosm and have not previously been published.

All numerical data is given to its full available accuracy or, in the case of infinite series, to a minimum of 16 places so that in nearly all cases values can be used without accuracy being an issue. The fundamental physical constants and conversion factors based on them are those determined by the National Bureau of Standards using a least squares fit to the best available experimental data [Mohr and Taylor, 1999; 2000]. A complete listing is given on the NIST website at *physics.nist.gov/constants*. Their intent is to create a set of constants that is mutually consistent to within the experimental accuracy. Other constants or conversion factors, such as the speed of light in vacuum or the conversion between inches and meters, are exact definitions of the units involved. (See, for example, Taylor [1991].)

For astronomical and astronautical constants, values adopted by the International Astronomical Union are given. Many of these are quoted from *Astrophysical Quantities* [Cox, 2000], which contains a great deal of additional astrophysical data. We highly recommend this volume for those who need additional quantitative detail about the solar system or other astronomical quantities. Similarly, those looking for precise definitions of coordinate systems, time systems, or the computational aspects of astronomical ephemerides should consult the excellent reference by Seidelmann [1992].

Finally, the tabular summary of properties of orbits about the Earth (inside rear pages), Sun, Moon, and Mars (Appendix F) are derived from formulas and constants elsewhere in this volume. The formulas used are given at the front of each of the tables. We would, of course, appreciate any errors or omissions in any of the material being brought to our attention at *bookproject@smad.com*.

References

Mohr, Peter J. and Barry N. Taylor. 2000. "CORDÅTA Recommended Values of the Fundamental Constants." *Reviews of Modern Physics*. Vol. 72, No. 2.

______. 1999. "CODATA Recommended Values of the Fundamental Constants." *Journal of Physical and Chemical Reference Data*. Vol. 28, No. 6.

Cox, Arthur N, ed. 2000. *Allen's Astrophysical Quantities (4th Edition)*. New York: Springer-Verlag.

Seidelmann, Kenneth P., ed. 1992. *The Explanatory Supplement to the Astronomical Almanac*. Mill Valley, CA: University Science Books.

Taylor, Barry N. 1991. *The International System of Units (SI)*. National Institute of Standards and Technology (NIST), Special Publication 811, U.S. Department of Commerce: U.S. Government Printing Office.

Appendix A

Spherical Geometry

Chapter 6 provides the basis for using spherical geometry for a great many problems in orbit and attitude analysis, space mission geometry, and angles-only measurement analysis. Unfortunately, prior works have been oriented primarily toward manual computation or older computer systems in which the evaluation of trig functions was painfully slow. Analytic approaches tended to be forced into vector terms, irrespective of whether this was analytically convenient, easily tested, or computationally efficient. The analyst choosing to use a correct spherical geometry solution for angles-only geometry was constantly reinventing the wheel (or at least the rounded triangle) by using the law of sines or cosines. Too often, a longer and more computationally complex vector solution or plane geometry approximation will be used rather than a simpler, exact formula because of the lack of an easily applied set of spherical geometry formulas. The purpose of this appendix is to eliminate that problem.

Of course, many problems are conveniently worked using unit vectors or are more-or-less equally easy in vector or spherical geometry formulations. Consequently, arc length and rotation formulas are expressed both ways. However, the solution to general spherical triangles is not conveniently done in terms of unit vectors and no simple formula for angular areas comparable to the spherical excess rule exists in vector terms.

Previously, angular measurements which included arc lengths or rotation angles greater than 180 deg required keeping track of the quadrant of each of the components, which rapidly becomes very inefficient in either spherical or vector terms. This problem is now entirely eliminated by introducing solutions to all possible full-sky triangles in which any of the sides or angles can range from 0 to 360 deg. These triangles are discussed at length in Sec. 8.1 and the full set of solutions is given in Sec. A.7, below. In turn, these solutions make possible the analysis of the dual-axis spiral, introduced in Sec. 8.2 and applied throughout much of the rest of the book.

The formulas here are intended to provide practical, usable receipes for geometrical problems. We have attempted to provide formulas and solution conditions that can be simply plugged into a hand calculator, spreadsheet, or computer routine with little or no thought—i.e., allowing you to concentrate on the problem at hand and not the spherical geometry. If more background is needed, Chap. 6 provides a general introduction to using spherical geometry in mission analysis and orbit and attitude problems, Chap. 7 discusses the theory of angular measurements, and Chap. 8 introduces full-sky geometry and provides a complete taxonomy of full-sky triangles.

A.1 Arc Length and Rotation Angle Formulas

Let P_i , $i = 1, 2, 3$, be three points on the unit sphere with coordinates (α_i , δ_i). The **arc-length** distance, θ_{12}, between P_1 and P_2 is given by:

$$\begin{aligned}\cos\theta_{12} &= \cos\theta_{21} \qquad 0 \le \theta \le 180^\circ \\ &= \sin\delta_1 \sin\delta_2 + \cos\delta_1 \cos\delta_2 \cos(\alpha_1 - \alpha_2) \qquad \text{(A-1a)}\end{aligned}$$

If $\hat{\mathbf{P}}_i$ are unit vectors corresponding to P_i , then

$$\cos\theta = \hat{\mathbf{P}}_1 \cdot \hat{\mathbf{P}}_2 \qquad 0 \le \theta \le 180^\circ \qquad \text{(A-1b)}$$

The **rotation angle**, $\Phi\,(P_1, P_2, P_3)$, from P_1 to P_2 about P_3, is cumbersome to calculate and is most easily obtained from spherical triangles (see Secs. A.4 to A.7) if any of the triangle components are already known. To calculate directly from coordinates, obtain as intermediaries the arc-length distances θ_{ij}, between pairs of points P_i, P_j. Then

$$\cos\Phi(P_1, P_2; P_3) = \frac{\cos\theta_{12} - \cos\theta_{13}\cos\theta_{23}}{\sin\theta_{13}\sin\theta_{23}} \qquad 0 \le \Phi \le 360^\circ \qquad \text{(A-2a)}$$

with the quadrant determined by inspection. For automated quadrant resolution use the side-side-side triangle solution in Sec. A.7.1

If the three points are expressed as unit vectors, then

$$\tan\Phi = \frac{\hat{\mathbf{P}}_3 \cdot \left(\hat{\mathbf{P}}_1 \times \hat{\mathbf{P}}_2\right)}{\left(\hat{\mathbf{P}}_1 \cdot \hat{\mathbf{P}}_2\right) - \left(\hat{\mathbf{P}}_3 \cdot \hat{\mathbf{P}}_1\right)\left(\hat{\mathbf{P}}_3 \cdot \hat{\mathbf{P}}_2\right)} \qquad \text{(A-2b)}$$

with the quadrant of Φ determined by the signs of the numerator and denominator, as done by the ATAN2 computer function. (See Sec. A.6 and A.7.)

A.2 Equations of Great and Small Circles

The **equation for a small circle** of angular radius ρ and centered at $P_0 = (\alpha_0, \delta_0)$ in terms of the coordinates, $X = (\alpha, \delta)$, of the points on the small circle is, from Eq. (A-1a),

$$\cos\rho = \sin\delta \sin\delta_0 + \cos\delta \cos\delta_0 \cos(\alpha - \alpha_0) \qquad \text{(A-3a)}$$

If the center and points on the small circle are expressed as unit vectors, then from Eq. (A-1b),

$$\hat{\mathbf{X}} \cdot \hat{\mathbf{P}}_0 = \cos \rho \qquad \text{(A-3b)}$$

The **arc length**, β, **along the arc of a small circle** of angular radius ρ and between two points on the circle separated by the rotation angle, Φ, measured at the center of the circle is

$$\beta = \Phi \sin \rho \qquad \text{(A-4)}$$

The **chord length**, γ, along the great circle chord of an arc of a small circle of angular radius ρ is given by

$$\cos \gamma = 1 - (1 - \cos \Phi) \sin^2 \rho \qquad 0 \leq \gamma \leq 180 \text{ deg} \qquad \text{(A-5)}$$

The **equation for a great circle** with pole at (α_0, δ_0) is, from Eq. (A-3a) with $\rho =$ 90 deg,

$$\tan \delta = -\cot \delta_0 \cos (\alpha - \alpha_0) \qquad \text{(A-6a)}$$

In terms of unit vectors, the equation for a great circle is, from Eq. (A-3b)

$$\hat{\mathbf{X}} \cdot \hat{\mathbf{P}}_0 = 0 \qquad \text{(A-6b)}$$

α_0 and δ_0 are related to the coordinates of $\hat{\mathbf{P}}_0$ by:

$$\delta_0 = \text{asin}\, z_0$$

$${}_0 = \alpha\text{tan}\, (y_0/x_0) \qquad \text{(A-6c)}$$

The **inclination,** i_0, and **azimuth of the ascending node,** ϕ_0, (point crossing the equator from south to north then moving along the great circle toward increasing azimuth) of the great circle are

$$i_0 = 90° - \delta_0$$

$$\phi_0 = 90° + \alpha_0 \qquad \text{(A-6d)}$$

In terms of the coordinates of the pole, $\hat{\mathbf{P}}_0$, the expressions for i_0 and ϕ_0 are:

$$i_0 = \text{acos}\, z_0$$

$$\phi_0 = -\text{atan}\, (x_0/y_0) \qquad \text{(A-6e)}$$

The **equation for the great circle in terms of inclination and ascending node** is

$$\tan \delta = \tan i_0 \sin (\alpha - \phi_0) \qquad \text{(A-6f)}$$

The **equation of a great circle through two arbitrary points** is given by Eq. (A-8a). Along a great circle, the arc length, the chord length, and the rotation angle, Φ, are all equal, as shown by Eqs. (A-4) and (A-5) with $\rho = 90$ deg.

The **direction of the cross product between two unit vectors** associated with points P_1 and P_2 on the unit sphere is the **pole of the great circle passing through the two points**. The intermediary, β_1, is

$$\cot\beta_1 = \left(\frac{\tan\delta_2}{\tan\delta_1}\right)\frac{1}{\sin(\alpha_2-\alpha_1)} - \cot(\alpha_2-\alpha_1) \tag{A-7a}$$

As shown in Fig. A-1, β_1 is the azimuth of point P_1 relative to the ascending node of the great circle through P_1 and P_2. The coordinates, (α_c, δ_c), of the cross product $\hat{\mathbf{P}}_1 \times \hat{\mathbf{P}}_2$ are given by

$$\alpha_c = \alpha_1 - 90° - \beta_1 \tag{A-7b}$$

$$\tan\delta_c = \begin{cases} \dfrac{\sin\beta_1}{\tan\delta_1} & (\delta_1 \neq 0) \\ \dfrac{\sin(\alpha_2-\alpha_1)}{\tan\delta_2} & (\delta_1 = 0) \end{cases} \tag{A-7c}$$

In terms of unit vectors, the direction of the cross product, $\hat{\mathbf{C}}$, is:

$$\hat{\mathbf{C}} = \frac{\hat{\mathbf{P}}_1 \times \hat{\mathbf{P}}_2}{\left|\hat{\mathbf{P}}_1 \times \hat{\mathbf{P}}_2\right|} \tag{A-7d}$$

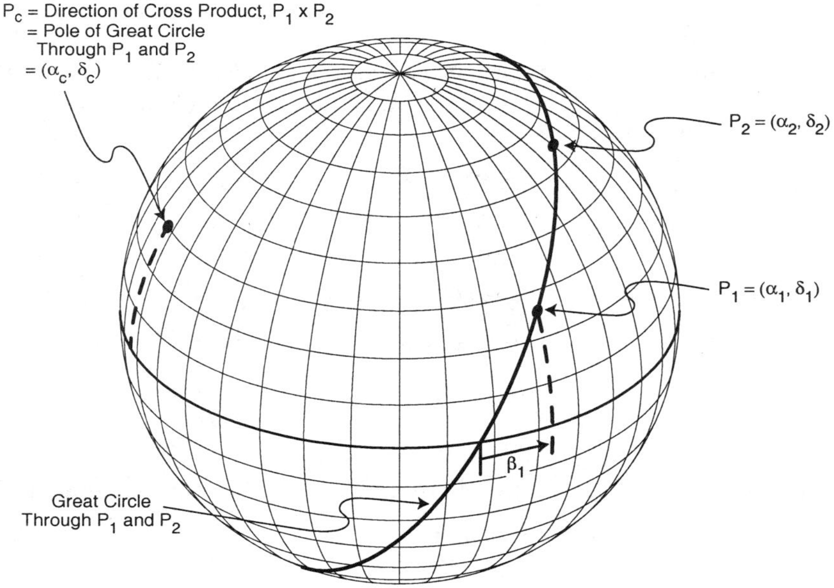

Fig. A-1. Finding the Pole of a Great Circle. $\hat{\mathbf{P}}_c$ is the pole of the great circle passing through $\hat{\mathbf{P}}_1$ $\hat{\mathbf{P}}_2$ and is also in the direction of the cross product $\hat{\mathbf{P}}_1 \times \hat{\mathbf{P}}_2$. β_1 is an intermediate variable used for computation.

Combining Eqs. (A-7b) and (A-6f) gives the equation for a great circle through points P_1 and P_2:

$$\tan\delta = \begin{cases} \dfrac{\tan\delta_1}{\sin\beta_1}\sin(\alpha - \alpha_1 + \beta_1) & (\delta_1 \neq 0) \\ \dfrac{\tan\delta_2}{\sin(\alpha_2 - \alpha_1)}\sin(\alpha - \alpha_1 + \beta_1) & (\delta_1 = 0) \end{cases} \qquad \text{(A-8a)}$$

Finally, in terms of unit vectors, the equation of a great circle through $\hat{\mathbf{P}}_1$ and $\hat{\mathbf{P}}_2$ is:

$$\hat{\mathbf{X}} \cdot (\hat{\mathbf{P}}_1 \times \hat{\mathbf{P}}_2) = 0 \qquad \text{(A-8b)}$$

A.3 Area Formulas

All areas are measured on the curved surface of the unit sphere. See Sec. 8.1 and Table 8-3 for a discussion of angular area. For a sphere of radius R, multiply each area by R^2. In the area formulas, all arc lengths are in radians and all angular areas are in steradians (sr), where

1 sr $\equiv$ solid angle enclosing an area equal to the square of the radius
$= (180/\pi)^2 \text{ deg}^2 \approx 3{,}282.806\ 350\ 011\ 743\ 794 \text{ deg}^2$

The **surface area of the sphere** is

$$\Omega_s = 4\pi \qquad \text{(A-9)}$$

The **area of a lune** bounded by two great circles which intersect at an angle of Θ radians is

$$\Omega_l = 2\Theta \qquad \text{(A-10)}$$

The **area of a spherical triangle** whose three rotation angles are θ_1, θ_2, and θ_3, is

$$\Omega_t = \theta_1 + \theta_2 + \theta_3 - \pi \qquad \text{(A-11)}$$

The **area of a spherical polygon** of n sides, where S is the sum of its rotation angles in radians, is

$$\Omega_p = S - (n-2)\,\pi \qquad \text{(A-12)}$$

The **area of a small circle** of angular radius ρ is

$$\Omega_c = 2\pi\,(1 - \cos\rho) \qquad \text{(A-13)}$$

The **area of a segment of rotation angle, ϕ,** in a small circle of angular radius ρ (i.e., a "pie piece") is

$$\Omega_{sc} = \phi\,(1 - \cos\rho) \qquad \text{(A-14)}$$

The **area of a ring or annulus** of inner radius ρ_1 and outer radius ρ_0 is

$$\Omega_r = 2\pi\,(\cos\rho_1 - \cos\rho_0) \qquad \text{(A-15)}$$

The **area of a segment of rotation angle, ϕ,** in an annulus of inner radius ρ_1 and outer radius ρ_0 is

$$\Omega_{sr} = \phi\,(\cos\rho_1 - \cos\rho_0) \quad \text{(A-16)}$$

The **overlap area between two small circles** of angular radii ρ and ε, separated by a center-to-center distance, α, is

$$\begin{aligned}\Omega_0 &= 2\pi - 2\cos\rho\,\mathrm{acos}\left[\frac{\cos\varepsilon - \cos\rho\cos\alpha}{\sin\rho\sin\alpha}\right]\\ &\quad - 2\cos\varepsilon\,\mathrm{acos}\left[\frac{\cos\rho - \cos\varepsilon\cos\alpha}{\sin\varepsilon\sin\alpha}\right]\\ &\quad -2\,\mathrm{acos}\left[\frac{\cos\alpha - \cos\varepsilon\cos\rho}{\sin\varepsilon\sin\rho}\right] \qquad \left(|\rho-\varepsilon| \le \alpha < \rho+\varepsilon\right)\end{aligned} \quad \text{(A-17)}$$

If ε goes to 90 deg, then the above simpliefies to the formula for the **overlap area between a great circle and a small circle** of angular radius ρ, separated by a center-to-center distance, α:

$$\Omega_0 = 2\pi - \cos\rho\,\mathrm{acos}(\cot\alpha\cot\rho) - 2\,\mathrm{acos}(\cos\alpha / \cot\rho) \qquad |90^\circ - \rho| \le \alpha < 90^\circ + \rho \quad \text{(A-18)}$$

Recall that area is measured on the curved surface.

A.4 General Rules for Spherical Triangles

The laws of sines and cosines apply to all spherical triangles. For *normal spherical triangles* (as discussed in Sec. 8.1), all of the sides and angles fall in the range of 0 to 180 deg and inverse trig functions should be taken over this range. Quadrant ambiguities within this range (i.e., the inverse sine function, $\sin^{-1}$, or asin) can be resolved by the rules at the end of the section. Solutions for the quadrants in full-sky triangles (i.e., all sides and angles ranging from 0 to 360 deg) follow automatically from the full-sky spherical triangle formulas in Sec. A.7.

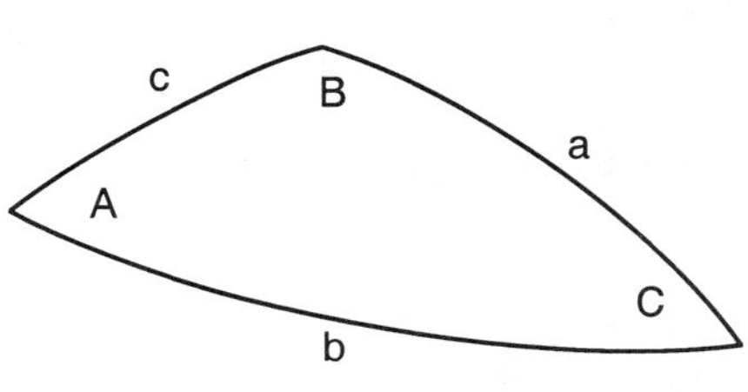

Fig. A-2. Standard Notation for a Spherical Triangle.

The following rules hold for any spherical triangle:

The Law of Sines:

$$\frac{\sin a}{\sin A} = \frac{\sin b}{\sin B} = \frac{\sin c}{\sin C} \qquad \text{(A-19)}$$

The Law of Cosines for Sides:

$$\cos a = \cos b \cos c + \sin b \sin c \cos A \qquad \text{(A-20a)}$$
$$\cos b = \cos c \cos a + \sin c \sin a \cos B \qquad \text{(A-20b)}$$
$$\cos c = \cos a \cos b + \sin a \sin b \cos C \qquad \text{(A-20c)}$$

The Law of Cosines for Angles:

$$\cos A = -\cos B \cos C + \sin B \sin C \cos a \qquad \text{(A-21a)}$$
$$\cos B = -\cos C \cos A + \sin C \sin A \cos b \qquad \text{(A-21b)}$$
$$\cos C = -\cos A \cos B + \sin A \sin B \cos c \qquad \text{(A-21c)}$$

Napier's Analogies:

$$\tan\tfrac{1}{2}(A+B) = \left(\cot\tfrac{1}{2}C\right)\left[\frac{\cos\frac{1}{2}(a-b)}{\cos\frac{1}{2}(a+b)}\right] \qquad \text{(A-22a)}$$

$$\tan\tfrac{1}{2}(A-B) = \left(\cot\tfrac{1}{2}C\right)\left[\frac{\sin\frac{1}{2}(a-b)}{\sin\frac{1}{2}(a+b)}\right] \qquad \text{(A-22b)}$$

$$\tan\tfrac{1}{2}(a+b) = \left(\tan\tfrac{1}{2}c\right)\left[\frac{\cos\frac{1}{2}(A-B)}{\cos\frac{1}{2}(A+B)}\right] \qquad \text{(A-22c)}$$

$$\tan\tfrac{1}{2}(a-b) = \left(\tan\tfrac{1}{2}c\right)\left[\frac{\sin\frac{1}{2}(A-B)}{\sin\frac{1}{2}(A+B)}\right] \qquad \text{(A-22d)}$$

Gauss's Formula:

$$\sin\left[\tfrac{1}{2}(A-B)\right] = \frac{\sin\left[\frac{1}{2}(a-b)\right]}{\sin\left(\frac{1}{2}c\right)}\cos\left(\tfrac{1}{2}C\right) \qquad \text{(A-23)}$$

Equations (A-22) and (A-23) can be extended to other components by cyclic conversion of all sides and angles. Cyclically changing a formula means that "a" is replaced by "b", "b" by "c", and "c" by "a." The pattern follows a cycle, as in Fig. A-3.

These quadrant rules can be used to resolve quadrant ambiguities in the trigonometric functions:

- If one side differs from 90 deg by more than another side, it is in the same quadrant as its opposite angle.
- If one angle differs from 90 deg by more than another angle, it is in the same quadrant as its opposite side.
- Half the sum of any two sides is in the same quadrant as half the sum of the opposite angles.

For example, $c = \text{atan}(\tan b \cos A) \pm \text{atan}(\tan a \cos B)$
becomes $b = \text{atan}(\tan a \cos C) \pm \text{atan}(\tan c \cos A)$
and then $a = \text{atan}(\tan c \cos B) \pm \text{atan}(\tan b \cos C)$

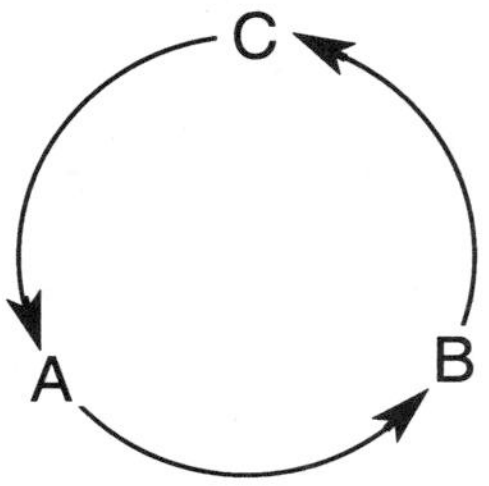

Fig. A-3. Cyclic Conversion.

A.5 Napier's Rules

The law of cosines and law of sines reduce to simpler relations, known as *Napier's Rules**, for *right spherical triangles* in which one of the angles is a right angle and *quadrantal spherical triangles* in which one of the sides is 90 deg long. (Unlike plane triangles, spherical triangles can have 1, 2, or 3 right angles and 1, 2, or 3 sides that are 90 deg long.) Any two of the remaining components, including the two remaining angles, serve to completely define the triangle.

Navigation based on spherical geometry was an important element of math in the early 20th century. At that time Napier's rules were often included in high school texts. They are normally formulated in a way intended for easy memorization by putting each of the 5 unknown components in a circle and expressing the rules in terms related to their position in the circle (i.e., "the sine of any angle is equal to the product of the cosines of the two opposite angles," and so on). The details can be found in many old high school texts or the references in the bibliography in Sec. A.10.

To make life easier for today's students and engineers, we have written out explicitly all possible permutations of Napier's Rules, including the quadrants. These are given in Sec. A.6. For right and quadrantal spherical triangles, the quadrant of the solution can also be determined by three simple rules:

- In a right spherical triangle or a quadrantal spherical triangle, a rotation angle and the side opposite are in the same quadrant.
- When the hypotenuse of a right spherical triangle or the angle opposite the hypotenuse of a quadrantal spherical triangle is less than 90 deg, the legs are in the same quadrant; when the hypotenuse (or opposite angle) is greater than 90 deg, the legs are in different quadrants.
- When the two given parts are a leg and its opposite angle, there are always two solutions.

---

* Introduced by 17th century Scottish mathematician and Baron of Merchiston, John Napier. Napier also invented logarithms and introduced the decimal point into mathematical notation.

A.6 Right and Spherical Quadrantal Triangles

Right Spherical Triangles

The line below each formula indicates the quadrant of the answer. Q(A) = Q(a) means that the quadrant of angle A is the same as that of side a. "2 possible solutions" means that either quadrant provides a correct solution to the defined triangle.

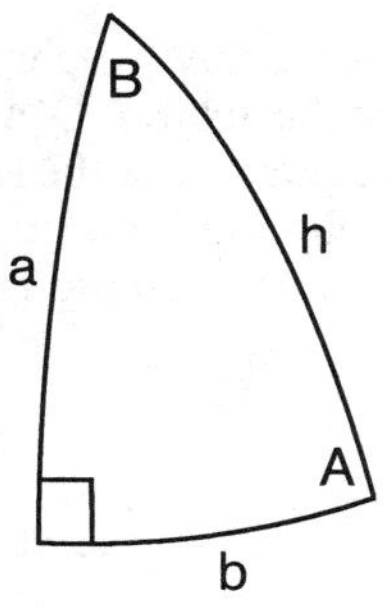

Given	Find		
a, b	**$\cos h = \cos a \cos b$** $Q(h) = \{Q(a)\,Q(b)\}^*$	**$\tan A = \tan a / \sin b$** $Q(A) = Q(a)$	**$\tan B = \tan b / \sin a$** $Q(B) = Q(b)$
a, h	**$\cos b = \cos h / \cos a$** $Q(b) = \{Q(a)/Q(h)\}^{**}$	**$\sin A = \sin a / \sin h$** $Q(A) = Q(a)$	**$\cos B = \tan a / \tan h$** $Q(B) = \{Q(a)/Q(h)\}^{**}$
b, h	**$\cos a = \cos h / \cos b$** $Q(a) = \{Q(b)/Q(h)\}^{**}$	**$\cos A = \tan b / \tan h$** $Q(A) = \{Q(b)/Q(h)\}^{**}$	**$\sin B = \sin b / \sin h$** $Q(B) = Q(b)$
a, A	**$\sin b = \tan a / \tan A$** 2 possible solutions	**$\sin h = \sin a / \sin A$** 2 possible solutions	**$\sin B = \cos A / \cos a$** 2 possible solutions
a, B	**$\tan b = \sin a \tan B$** $Q(b) = Q(B)$	**$\tan h = \tan a / \cos B$** $Q(h) = \{Q(a)\,Q(B)\}^*$	**$\cos A = \cos a \sin B$** $Q(A) = Q(a)$
b, A	**$\tan a = \sin b \tan A$** $Q(a) = Q(A)$	**$\tan h = \tan b / \cos A$** $Q(h) = \{Q(b)\,Q(A)\}^*$	**$\cos B = \cos b \sin A$** $Q(B) = Q(b)$
b, B	**$\sin a = \tan b / \tan B$** 2 possible solutions	**$\sin h = \sin b / \sin B$** 2 possible solutions	**$\sin A = \cos B / \cos b$** 2 possible solutions
h, A	**$\sin a = \sin h \sin A$** $Q(a) = Q(A)$	**$\tan b = \tan h \cos A$** $Q(b) = \{Q(A)/Q(h)\}^{**}$	**$\tan B = 1 / \cos h \tan A$** $Q(B) = \{Q(A)/Q(h)\}^{**}$
h, B	**$\sin b = \sin h \sin B$** $Q(b) = Q(B)$	**$\tan a = \tan h \cos B$** $Q(a) = \{Q(B)/Q(h)\}^{**}$	**$\tan A = 1 / \cos h \tan B$** $Q(A) = \{Q(B)/Q(h)\}^{**}$
A, B	**$\cos a = \cos A / \sin B$** $Q(a) = Q(A)$	**$\cos b = \cos B / \sin A$** $Q(b) = Q(B)$	**$\cos h = 1 / \tan A \tan B$** $Q(h) = \{Q(A)\,Q(B)\}^*$

* $\{Q(x)\,Q(y)\} \equiv$ 1st quadrant if $Q(x) = Q(y)$, 2nd quadrant if $Q(x) \neq Q(y)$

** $\{Q(x)/Q(h)\} \equiv$ quadrant of x if $h \leq 90$ deg, quadrant opposite x if $h > 90$ deg

Quadrantal Spherical Triangles

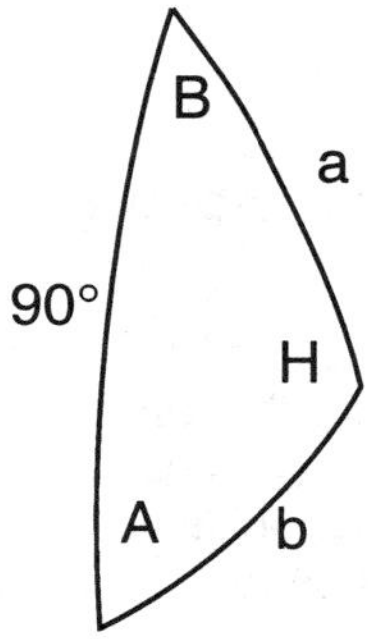

The line below each formula indicates the quadrant of the answer. $Q(A) = Q(a)$ means that the quadrant of angle A is the same as that of side a. "2 possible solutions" means that either quadrant provides a correct solution to the defined triangle.

Given	Find		
A, B	$\cos H = -\cos A \cos B$ $Q(H) = \{Q(A)\, Q(B)\}^*$	$\tan a = \tan A / \sin B$ $Q(a) = Q(A)$	$\tan b = \tan B / \sin A$ $Q(b) = Q(B)$
A, H	$\cos B = -\cos H / \cos A$ $Q(B) = \{Q(A) \setminus Q(H)\}^{**}$	$\sin a = \sin A / \sin H$ $Q(a) = Q(A)$	$\cos b = -\tan A / \tan H$ $Q(b) = \{Q(A) \setminus Q(H)\}^{**}$
B, H	$\cos A = -\cos H / \cos B$ $Q(A) = \{Q(B) \setminus Q(H)\}^{**}$	$\cos a = -\tan B / \tan H$ $Q(a) = \{Q(B) \setminus Q(H)\}^{**}$	$\sin b = \sin B / \sin H$ $Q(b) = Q(B)$
A, a	$\sin B = \tan A / \tan a$ 2 possible solutions	$\sin H = \sin A / \sin a$ 2 possible solutions	$\sin b = \cos a / \cos A$ 2 possible solutions
A, b	$\tan B = \sin A \tan b$ $Q(B) = Q(b)$	$\tan H = -\tan A / \cos b$ $Q(H) = \{Q(A)\, Q(b)\}^*$	$\cos a = \cos A \sin b$ $Q(a) = Q(A)$
B, a	$\tan A = \sin B \tan a$ $Q(A) = Q(a)$	$\tan H = -\tan B / \cos a$ $Q(H) = \{Q(B)\, Q(a)\}^*$	$\cos b = \cos B \sin a$ $Q(b) = Q(B)$
B, b	$\sin A = \tan B / \tan b$ 2 possible solutions	$\sin H = \sin B / \sin b$ 2 possible solutions	$\sin a = \cos b / \cos B$ 2 possible solutions
H, a	$\sin A = \sin H \sin a$ $Q(A) = Q(a)$	$\tan B = -\tan H \cos a$ $Q(B) = \{Q(a) \setminus Q(H)\}^{**}$	$\tan b = -1 / \cos H \tan a$ $Q(b) = \{Q(a) \setminus Q(H)\}^{**}$
H, b	$\sin B = \sin H \sin b$ $Q(B) = Q(b)$	$\tan A = -\tan H \cos b$ $Q(A) = \{Q(b) \setminus Q(H)\}^{**}$	$\tan a = -1 / \cos H \tan b$ $Q(a) = \{Q(b) \setminus Q(H)\}^{**}$
a, b	$\cos A = \cos a / \sin b$ $Q(A) = Q(a)$	$\cos B = \cos b / \sin a$ $Q(B) = Q(b)$	$\cos H = -1 / \tan a \tan b$ $Q(H) = \{Q(a)\, Q(b)\}^*$

$^*\{Q(x)\, Q(y)\} \equiv$ 1st quadrant if $Q(x) = Q(y)$, 2nd quadrant if $Q(x) \neq Q(y)$

$^{**}\{Q(x) \setminus Q(H)\} \equiv$ quadrant of x if $H > 90$ deg, quadrant opposite x if $H \leq 90$ deg

A.7 Oblique Full-Sky Spherical Triangles*

An *oblique spherical triangle* has arbitrary sides and angles. Sides and angles are typically defined over the range of 0 to 180 deg. However, in this section we provide general rules, not previously published, for *full-sky spherical triangles* in which any sides or angles can be anywhere in the full range of 0 to 360 deg. (See Sec. 8.1 for a complete list of properties of all of the full-sky triangles.) This full range of angles makes computer implementation particularly simple. We define the relevant triangle or triangles in a problem and set up computer routines based on the formulas below. The range of the input variables is unlimited† and the output will automatically provide the correct angle, including the quadrant.

The nomenclature for the sides and angles for full-sky triangles is the same as that shown in Fig. A-3 in Sec. A.5. Given any three components in an oblique spherical triangle, the remaining three components can be determined. All of the components (both known and unknown) can lie in the full range of 0 to 360 deg. There are 6 possible combinations of known and unknown components, as listed in Table A-1. See Sec. 8.1 for a complete discussion of the taxonomy of full-sky triangles and specifically Table 8-4 in Sec. 8.1 for a list of solutions depending on how the triangles are defined.

TABLE A-1. The 6 Categories of Oblique Spherical Triangles.

Type	Given	Find	No. of Solutions	Where Solved
Side-Side-Side	*a, b, c*	*A, B, C*	0 or 2	Sec. A.7.1
Side-Side-Angle	*a, b, A*	*B, C, c*	0 or 2	Sec. A.7.2
Side-Angle-Side	*a, C, b*	*A, B, c*	2	Sec. A.7.3
Angle-Angle-Side	*A, B, a*	*b, c, C*	0 or 2	Sec. A.7.4
Angle-Side-Angle	*A, c, B*	*a, C, b*	2	Sec. A.7.5
Angle-Angle-Angle	*A, B, C*	*a, b, c*	0 or 2	Sec. A.7.6

Full-sky solutions are given below for each of the categories. Conditions under which solutions exist and singularities which occur are also listed for each case. **Note:** the solution conditions represent those conditions for which a triangle exists and are not related to the approach used to solve for the missing components. For example, 3 known sides of 10 deg, 20 deg, and 60 deg can not form a spherical triangle because one side is longer than the sum of the other two. Similarly the singularity conditions represent singularities in the triangles themselves (such as a side going to 0), not in the solution approach.

Whenever a solution exists in a full-sky triangle, a second solution also exists. Formulas for both are given in each subsection along with an illustration of how the

---

* The full-sky formulas presented in this section are due to Rob Bell, Leo Early, Hans Meissinger, Herb Reynolds, and James Wertz of Microcosm.

† Trig functions are defined over an unlimited domain. However, for computers or calculators (which use series approximations), better precision will be obtained if the variables are first reduced to the range 0 to 360 deg with modulo arithmetic. In some cases, the modulo function may be a part of the definition of the trig series.

second solution arises. When the solved for component can range from 0 to 360 deg, there must be some method, such as the FORTRAN atan2 function, to allow inverse trig functions to uniquely cover this full range. The approach used in this appendix is the newly created acos2 function, defined in Table 8-5 in Sec. 8.1.

A.7.1 Side-Side-Side Spherical Triangles

For these triangles, the three sides are given and we wish to determine the three rotation angles. That is,

Given *a, b, c* Find *A, B, C*

The requirement for a solution is that if one end of two of the sides, say a and b, are attached to the ends of side c, then the remaining ends of a and *b* must be able to meet. For each solution, the second solution is the inverse spherical triangle in which each of the angles is replaced by 360 deg minus the angle. This simply reverses the roles of "inside" and "outside" for the triangle as shown in Fig. A-4.

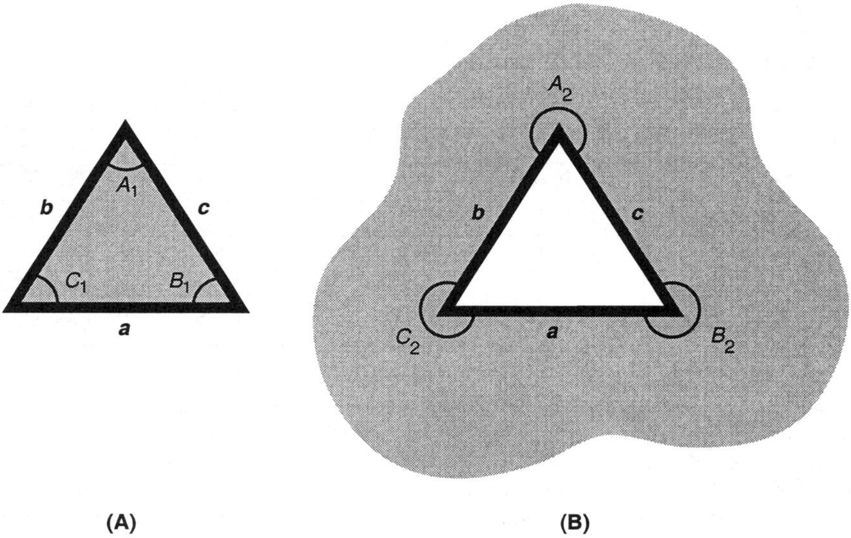

Fig. A-4. The Two Solutions for the Side-Side-Side Triangle. For ease of identification in Figs. A-4 to A-9, The "given" variables are bold italics and the "given" lines and angles are bold on the figure.

Solution Conditions:

The three given sides form a triangle if, and only if:

$$\left| |180^\circ - a| - |180^\circ - b| \right| \;\le\; |180^\circ - c| \;\le\; \left| |180^\circ - a| + |180^\circ - b| \right| \qquad \text{(A-24)}$$

If this condition holds (or does not hold) for any permutation of *a, b,* and *c*, then it will hold (or not hold) for the two remaining permutations.

As listed in Table A-2, a singular case occurs whenever one of the specified sides is 0, 180 deg, or 360 deg. For the side-side-side triangle, all of the singularities are, of course, cyclic permutations of each other. Nonetheless, they are all listed in the table for completeness. The various degenerate spherical triangles that result from singularities are shown in Fig. A-10 in Sec. A.7.9.

TABLE A-2. Singular Cases for Side-Side-Side Spherical Triangles. As with all of the solutions in Sec. A.7, the singularities are due to the nature of the triangle, not the fact that it is being solved via spherical geometry. See Sec. A.7.9 for singularity types and how to handle them in practice.

If	Then			Type
$a \to 0°$	$b \to c$	$A \to 0°$	$B + C \to 180°$	Type 1 Arc
or	$b \to c$	$A \to 360°$	$B + C \to 540°$	Type 1 Arc
$b \to 0°$	$a \to c$	$B \to 0°$	$A + C \to 180°$	Type 1 Arc
or	$a \to c$	$B \to 360°$	$A + C \to 540°$	Type 1 Arc
$c \to 0°$	$a \to b$	$C \to 0°$	$A + B \to 180°$	Type 1 Arc
or	$a \to b$	$C \to 360°$	$A + B \to 540°$	Type 1 Arc
$a \to 180°$	$b + c \to 180°$	$A \to 180°$	$B \to C$	Lune
$b \to 180°$	$a + c \to 180°$	$B \to 180°$	$A \to C$	Lune
$c \to 180°$	$a + b \to 180°$	$C \to 180°$	$A \to B$	Lune
$a \to 360°$	$b \to c$	$A \to 0°$	$B + C \to 540°$	Double Arc
or	$b \to c$	$A \to 360°$	$B + C \to 180°$	Double Arc
$b \to 360°$	$a \to c$	$B \to 0°$	$A + C \to 540°$	Double Arc
or	$a \to c$	$B \to 360°$	$A + C \to 180°$	Double Arc
$c \to 360°$	$a \to b$	$C \to 0°$	$A + B \to 540°$	Double Arc
or	$a \to b$	$C \to 360°$	$A + B \to 180°$	Double Arc

First Solution:

If a non-singular solution exists, then there are two solutions. One is given by:

$$A_1 = \text{acos2}\left[\frac{\cos a - \cos b \cos c}{\sin b \sin c}, \text{H}(a)\right] \tag{A-25a}$$

$$B_1 = \text{acos2}\left[\frac{\cos b - \cos a \cos c}{\sin a \sin c}, \text{H}(b)\right] \tag{A-25b}$$

$$C_1 = \text{acos2}\left[\frac{\cos c - \cos a \cos b}{\sin a \sin b}, \text{H}(c)\right] \tag{A-25c}$$

The acos2 function is defined in Sec. A.7.7 and discussed further in Sec. 8.1.

Second Solution:

The second solution is given by:

$$A_2 = 360° - A_1 \tag{A-26a}$$

$$B_2 = 360° - B_1 \tag{A-26b}$$

$$C_2 = 360° - C_1 \tag{A-26c}$$

A.7.2 Side-Side-Angle Spherical Triangles

For these triangles, we know two sides and one of the two angles not included between the sides. That is,

Given a, b, A Find B, C, c

For simplicity, assume unknown side c_1 lies along the equator of a coordinate system as shown schematically in Fig. A-5. (See also Fig. 8-6 in Sec. 8.1.) Known angle A and side b bring us to a vertex at C_1. We then construct a circle centered on C_1 of radius a, the length of the remaining known side. The solution condition [Eq. (A-27)] corresponds to the requirement that the circle touch the "equator" that contains side C_1. If a is either too short or too long, then there is no solution. The two solutions for this case correspond to the two locations at which the circle crosses the equator. Note that by the way we have defined the problem, side c_1 starts out to the right. Therefore if one or both of the crossings is to the left of A, then side c_1 will be a long arc greater than 180 deg.

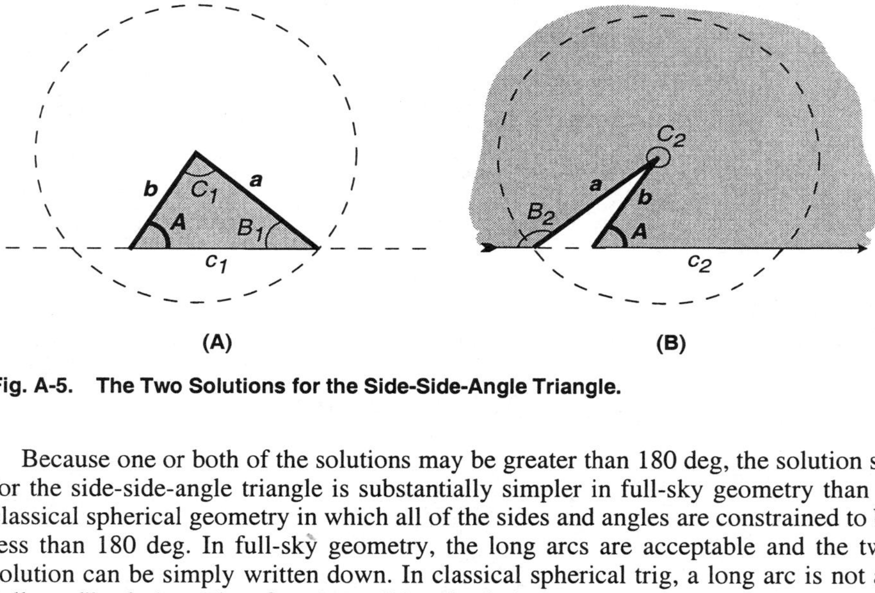

Fig. A-5. The Two Solutions for the Side-Side-Angle Triangle.

Because one or both of the solutions may be greater than 180 deg, the solution set for the side-side-angle triangle is substantially simpler in full-sky geometry than in classical spherical geometry in which all of the sides and angles are constrained to be less than 180 deg. In full-sky geometry, the long arcs are acceptable and the two solution can be simply written down. In classical spherical trig, a long arc is not an "allowed" solution. Therefore, in traditional solutions we must compute an intermediate variable and potentially throw away one or both of the solutions.

Solution Conditions:

The three given components form a triangle if, and only if:

$$|\sin b \sin A| \leq |\sin a| \tag{A-27}$$

As listed in Table A-3, a singular case occurs whenever one of the specified sides or angles is 0, 180 deg, or 360 deg. The various degenerate spherical triangles that result from singularities are shown in Fig. A-10 in Sec. A.7.9.

TABLE A-3. Singular Cases for Side-Side-Angle Spherical Triangles. *a*, *b*, and *A* are given. *B*, *C*, and *c* are unknown. See Sec. A.7.9 for singularity types and how to handle them in practice.

If		Then			Type
$a \to 0°$		$A \to 0°$	$c \to b$	$B + C \to 180°$	Type 1 Arc
	or	$A \to 360°$	$c \to b$	$B + C \to 540°$	Type 1 Arc
$b \to 0°$		$c \to a$	$B \to 0°$	$A + C \to 180°$	Type 1 Arc
	or	$c \to a$	$B \to 360°$	$A + C \to 540°$	Type 1 Arc
$A \to 0°$		$a \to 0°$	$c \to b$	$B + C \to 180°$	Type 1 Arc
	or	$a \to 360°$	$c \to b$	$B + C \to 540°$	Double Arc
$a \to 180°$		$b + c \to 180°$	$A \to 180°$	$B \to C$	Lune
$b \to 180°$		$a + c \to 180°$	$B \to 180°$	$C \to A$	Lune
$A \to 180°$		$c \to a - b$	$C \to 0°$	$A \to 0°$	Type 2 Arc
	or	$c \to a - b$	$C \to 360°$	$A \to 360°$	Type 2 Arc
	or	$b + c \to 180°$	$a \to 180°$	$B \to C$	Lune
	or	$a + b + c \to 360°$	$B \to 180°$	$C \to 180°$	Great Circle
$a \to 360°$		$c \to b$	$A \to 0°$	$B + C \to 540°$	Double Arc
	or	$c \to b$	$A \to 360°$	$B + C \to 180°$	Double Arc
$b \to 360°$		$c \to a$	$B \to 0°$	$A + C \to 540°$	Double Arc
	or	$c \to a$	$B \to 360°$	$A + C \to 180°$	Double Arc
$A \to 360°$		$c \to b$	$a \to 0°$	$B + C \to 540°$	Type 1 Arc
	or	$c \to b$	$a \to 360°$	$B + C \to 180°$	Double Arc

First Solution:

If a non-singular solution exists, then there are two solutions. One is given by:

$$B_1 = \operatorname{asin}\left(\frac{\sin b \sin A}{\sin a}\right) \bmod 360° \qquad \text{(A-28a)}$$

$$c_1 = \text{MSL}\ (a, b, A, B_1) \qquad \text{(A-28b)}$$

$$C_1 = \text{MAL}\ (A, B_1, a, b) \qquad \text{(A-28c)}$$

where the asin function is defined over the range –90 deg to +90 deg and MSL and MAL are the Middle Side Law and Middle Angle Law defined in Sec. A.7.8.

Second Solution:

The second solution is given by:

$$B_2 = (180° - B_1) \bmod 360° \qquad \text{(A-29a)}$$

$$c_2 = \text{MSL}\ (a, b, A, B_2) \qquad \text{(A-29b)}$$

$$C_2 = \text{MAL}\ (A, B_2, a, b) \qquad \text{(A-29c)}$$

where, as above, MSL and MAL are defined in Sec. A.7.8.

A.7.3 Side-Angle-Side Spherical Triangles

In this case, we know two sides and the included angle. Thus,

Given *a, C, b* Find *A, B, c*

In this case there are two solutions for all possible combinations of known components. As shown in Fig. A-6, one solution corresponds to connecting the known endpoints with a short arc (less than 180 deg) and the other solution corresponds to connecting them with a long arc of greater than 180 deg.

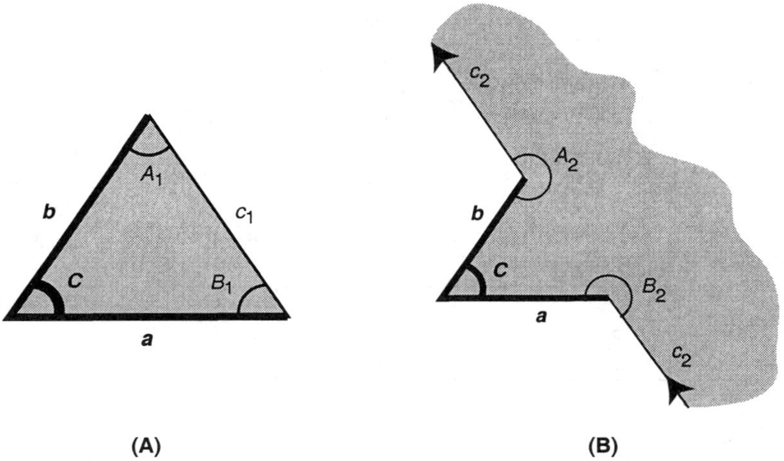

Fig. A-6. The Two Solutions for the Side-Angle-Side Triangle.

Solution Conditions:

There are two solutions for all possible combinations of known components covering the full range of 0 to 360 deg.

As listed in Table A-4, a singular case occurs whenever one of the specified sides or angles is 0, 180 deg, or 360 deg. The various degenerate spherical triangles that result from singularities are shown in Fig. A-10 in Sec. A.7.9.

First Solution:

If a non-singular solution exists, then there are two solutions. One is given by:

$$c_1 = \text{acos2}\,[\cos a \cos b + \sin a \sin b \cos C, \text{H}(C)] \tag{A-30a}$$

$$A_1 = \text{acos2}\left[\frac{\cos a - \cos b \cos c}{\sin b \sin c}, \text{H}(a)\right] \tag{A-30b}$$

$$B_1 = \text{acos2}\left[\frac{\cos b - \cos a \cos c}{\sin a \sin c}, \text{H}(b)\right] \tag{A-30c}$$

where the acos2 function is defined in Sec. A.7.7 and further discussed in Sec. 8.1.

TABLE A-4. Singular Cases for Side-Angle-Side Spherical Triangles. *a*, *C*, and *b* are given. *A*, *c*, and *B* are unknown. See Sec. A.7.9 for singularity types and how to handle them in practice.

If		Then			Type
$a \to 0°$		$A \to 0°$	$c \to b$	$B + C \to 180°$	Type 1 Arc
	or	$A \to 360°$	$c \to b$	$B + C \to 540°$	Type 1 Arc
$b \to 0°$		$c \to a$	$B \to 0°$	$A + C \to 180°$	Type 1 Arc
	or	$c \to a$	$B \to 360°$	$A + C \to 540°$	Type 1 Arc
$C \to 0°$		$c \to 0°$	$a \to b$	$A + B \to 180°$	Type 1 Arc
	or	$c \to 360°$	$a \to b$	$A + B \to 540°$	Double Arc
$a \to 180°$		$b + c \to 180°$	$A \to 180°$	$B \to C$	Lune
$b \to 180°$		$a + c \to 180°$	$B \to 180°$	$A \to C$	Lune
$C \to 180°$		$c \to a + b$	$A \to 0°$	$B \to 0°$	Type 2 Arc
	or	$c \to a + b$	$A \to 360°$	$B \to 360°$	Type 2 Arc
	or	$a + b \to 180°$	$c \to 180°$	$A \to B$	Lune
	or	$a + b + c \to 360°$	$A \to 180°$	$B \to 180°$	Great Circle
$a \to 360°$		$c \to b$	$A \to 0°$	$B + C \to 540°$	Double Arc
	or	$c \to b$	$A \to 360°$	$B + C \to 180°$	Double Arc
$b \to 360°$		$c \to a$	$B \to 0°$	$A + C \to 540°$	Double Arc
	or	$c \to a$	$B \to 360°$	$A + C \to 180°$	Double Arc
$C \to 360°$		$a \to b$	$c \to 0°$	$A + B \to 540°$	Type 1 Arc
	or	$a \to b$	$c \to 360°$	$A + B \to 180°$	Double Arc

Second Solution:

The second solution is given by:

$$c_2 = 360° - c \tag{A-31a}$$

$$A_2 = (A + 180°) \bmod 360° \tag{A-31b}$$

$$B_2 = (B + 180°) \bmod 360° \tag{A-31c}$$

A.7.4 Angle-Angle-Side Spherical Triangles

For these triangles, the known components are two angles and one of the sides not between them. That is,

Given *A, B, a*   Find *b, c, C*

For convenience of illustration, assume unknown side c_1 lies along the equator of a coordinate system as shown schematically in Fig. A-7. Known angle B and side a bring us to a vertex at C_1. To complete the triangle, we find vertex A along the equator, such that the remaining unknown side b_1 intersects C_1. There will be no solution if the vertex C_1 is far enough above the equator that great circles making an angle A with the equator do not come that close to the pole. The two solutions correspond to intersecting C_1 on the ascending or descending portions of the arc as illustrated in Fig. A-7.

As with the case of the side-side-angle triangle described in Sec. A.7.2, either or both solutions for some of the unknown components may be greater than 180 deg. This

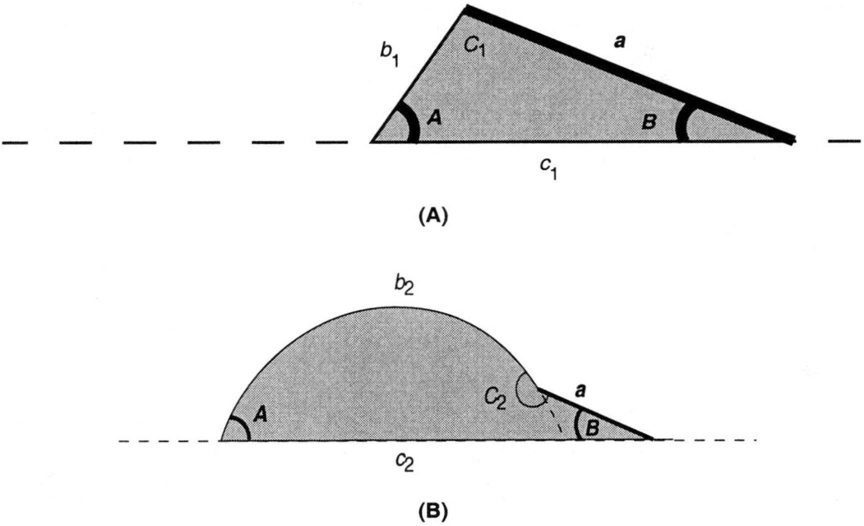

Fig. A-7. The Two Solutions for the Angle-Angle-Side Triangle.

is not a problem for the full-sky triangles. However, in classical spherical trig, in which all of the angles and sides are required to less than 180 deg, some of the real solutions will need to computed and then discarded, because they are not "allowed." This means that the full-sky solutions will be simpler to both compute and interpret than the more restrictive classical solutions.

Solution Conditions:

The three given components form a triangle if, and only if:

$$|\sin B \sin a| \leq |\sin A| \tag{A-32}$$

As listed in Table A-5, a singular case occurs whenever one of the specified sides or angles is 0, 180 deg, or 360 deg. The various degenerate spherical triangles that result from singularities are shown in Fig. A-10 in Sec. A.7.9.

First Solution:

If a non-singular solution exists, then there are two solutions. One is given by:

$$b_1 = \text{asin}\left(\frac{\sin B \sin a}{\sin A}\right) \bmod 360° \tag{A-33a}$$

$$c_1 = \text{MSL}\,(a, b_1, A, B) \tag{A-33b}$$

$$C_1 = \text{MAL}\,(A, B, a, b_1) \tag{A-33c}$$

where the asin function is defined over the range –90 deg to +90 deg and MSL and MAL are the Middle Side Law and Middle Angle Law defined in Sec. A.7.8.

TABLE A-5. Singular Cases for Angle-Angle-Side Spherical Triangles. *A*, *B*, and *a* are given. *b*, *c*, and *C* are unknown. See Sec. A.7.9 for singularity types and how to handle them in practice.

If		Then			Type
$a \to 0°$		$A \to 0°$	$b \to c$	$B + C \to 180°$	Type 1 Arc
	or	$A \to 360°$	$b \to c$	$B + C \to 540°$	Type 1 Arc
$A \to 0°$		$a \to 0°$	$b \to c$	$B + C \to 180°$	Type 1 Arc
	or	$a \to 360°$	$b \to c$	$B + C \to 540°$	Double Arc
$B \to 0°$		$b \to 0°$	$a \to c$	$A + C \to 180°$	Type 1 Arc
	or	$b \to 360°$	$a \to c$	$A + C \to 540°$	Double Arc
$a \to 180°$		$b + c \to 180°$	$A \to 180°$	$C \to B$	Lune
$A \to 180°$		$b + c \to a$	$B \to 0°$	$C \to 0°$	Type 2 Arc
	or	$b + c \to a$	$B \to 360°$	$C \to 360°$	Type 2 Arc
	or	$b + c \to 180°$	$a \to 180°$	$C \to B$	Lune
	or	$a + b + c \to 360°$	$B \to 180°$	$C \to 180°$	Great Circle
$B \to 180°$		$b \to a + c$	$A \to 0°$	$C \to 0°$	Type 2 Arc
	or	$b \to a + c$	$A \to 360°$	$C \to 360°$	Type 2 Arc
	or	$a + c \to 180°$	$b \to 180°$	$C \to A$	Lune
	or	$a + b + c \to 360°$	$A \to 180°$	$C \to 180°$	Great Circle
$a \to 360°$		$b \to c$	$A \to 0°$	$B + C \to 540°$	Double Arc
	or	$b \to c$	$A \to 360°$	$B + C \to 180°$	Double Arc
$A \to 360°$		$b \to c$	$a \to 0°$	$B + C \to 540°$	Type 1 Arc
	or	$b \to c$	$a \to 360°$	$B + C \to 180°$	Double Arc
$B \to 360°$		$a \to c$	$b \to 0°$	$A + C \to 540°$	Type 1 Arc
	or	$a \to c$	$b \to 360°$	$A + C \to 180°$	Double Arc

Second Solution:

The second solution is given by:

$$b_2 = (180° - B_1) \bmod 360° \quad \text{(A-34a)}$$

$$c_2 = \text{MSL}\ (a, b_2, A, B) \quad \text{(A-34b)}$$

$$C_2 = \text{MAL}\ (A, B, a, b_2) \quad \text{(A-34c)}$$

where, as above, MSL and MAL are defined in Sec. A.7.8.

A.7.5 Angle-Side-Angle Spherical Triangles

For these triangles, the known components are two angles and the included side. That is,

Given *A, B, c* Find *a, b, C*

As in the case of the side-angle-side triangle from Sec. A.7.3, there are two solutions for all possible combinations of known components. As shown in Fig. A-8, the known components define the two planes of the unknown sides *a* and *b*. These planes will intersect in two locations, 180 deg apart. Either intersection can be the unknown vertex, C_1.

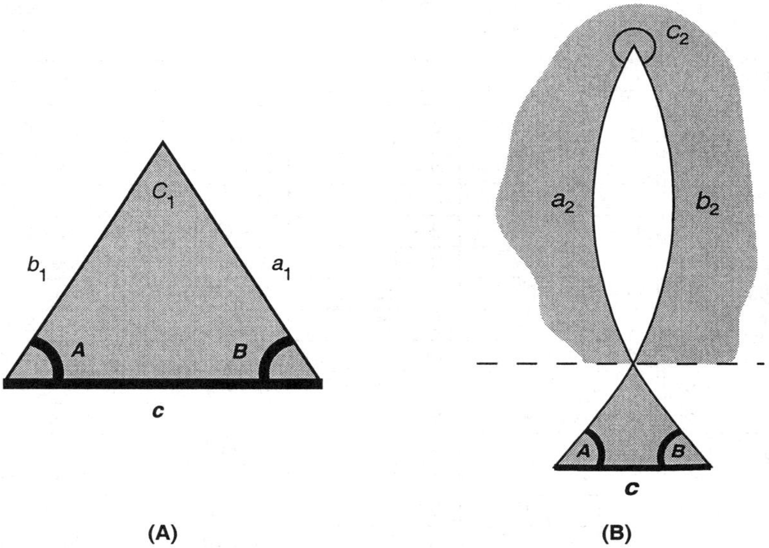

Fig. A-8. The Two Solutions for the Angle-Side-Angle Triangle.

Solution Conditions:

There are two solutions for all possible combinations of known components covering the full range of 0 to 360 deg.

As listed in Table A-6, a singular case occurs whenever one of the specified sides or angles is 0, 180 deg, or 360 deg. The various degenerate spherical triangles that result from singularities are shown in Fig. A-10 in Sec. A.7.9.

First Solution:

If a non-singular solution exists, then there are two solutions. One is given by:

$$C_1 = \text{acos2}\,[-\cos A \cos B + \sin A \sin B \cos c,\ \text{H}(c)] \qquad \text{(A-35a)}$$

$$a_1 = \text{acos2}\left[\frac{\cos A + \cos B \cos C_1}{\sin B \sin C_1},\ \text{H}(A)\right] \qquad \text{(A-35b)}$$

$$b_1 = \text{acos2}\left[\frac{\cos B + \cos A \cos C_1}{\sin A \sin C_1},\ \text{H}(B)\right] \qquad \text{(A-35c)}$$

where the acos2 function is defined in Sec. A.7.7 and discussed further in Sec. 8.1.

Second Solution:

The second solution is given by:

$$C_2 = 360° - C_1 \qquad \text{(A-36a)}$$

$$a_2 = (a_1 + 180°) \bmod 360° \qquad \text{(A-36b)}$$

$$b_2 = (b_1 + 180°) \bmod 360° \qquad \text{(A-36c)}$$

TABLE A-6. Singular Cases for Angle-Side-Angle Spherical Triangles. *A*, *c*, and *B* are given. *a*, *C*, and *b* are unknown. See Sec. A.7.9 for singularity types and how to handle them in practice.

If		Then			Type
$c \to 0°$		$C \to 0°$	$a \to b$	$A + B \to 180°$	Type 1 Arc
	or	$C \to 360°$	$a \to b$	$A + B \to 540°$	Type 1 Arc
$A \to 0°$		$a \to 0°$	$b \to c$	$B + C \to 180°$	Type 1 Arc
	or	$a \to 360°$	$b \to c$	$B + C \to 540°$	Double Arc
$B \to 0°$		$b \to 0°$	$a \to c$	$A + C \to 180°$	Type 1 Arc
	or	$b \to 360°$	$a \to c$	$A + C \to 540°$	Double Arc
$c \to 180°$		$a + b \to 180°$	$C \to 180°$	$A \to B$	Lune
$A \to 180°$		$a - b \to c$	$B \to 0°$	$C \to 0°$	Type 2 Arc
	or	$a - b \to c$	$B \to 360°$	$C \to 360°$	Type 2 Arc
	or	$b + c \to 180°$	$a \to 180°$	$C \to B$	Lune
	or	$a + b + c \to 360°$	$B \to 180°$	$C \to 180°$	Great Circle
$B \to 180°$		$b - a \to c$	$A \to 0°$	$C \to 0°$	Type 2 Arc
	or	$b - a \to c$	$A \to 360°$	$C \to 360°$	Type 2 Arc
	or	$a + c \to 180°$	$b \to 180°$	$C \to A$	Lune
	or	$a + b + c \to 360°$	$A \to 180°$	$C \to 180°$	Great Circle
$c \to 360°$		$a \to b$	$C \to 0°$	$A + B \to 540°$	Double Arc
	or	$a \to b$	$C \to 360°$	$A + B \to 180°$	Double Arc
$A \to 360°$		$b \to c$	$a \to 0°$	$B + C \to 540°$	Type 1 Arc
	or	$b \to c$	$a \to 360°$	$B + C \to 180°$	Double Arc
$B \to 360°$		$a \to c$	$b \to 0°$	$A + C \to 540°$	Type 1 Arc
	or	$a \to c$	$b \to 360°$	$A + C \to 180°$	Double Arc

A.7.6 Angle-Angle-Angle Spherical Triangles

In this case, the 3 rotation angles are given and we wish to determine the 3 sides. That is,

Given *A, B, C* Find *a, b, c*

Analogous to the side-side-side triangles, there is an inverse solution in which each of the sides is replaced by 360 deg minus the side. (See Fig. A-9.) This transforms a regular spherical triangle into a star and a notch into a fish. (See the discussion in Sec. 8.1)

This case has no analogy in plane geometry. If the three angles are known, then only the ratios of the sides can be determined. However, in spherical geometry the sum of the rotation angles minus 180 deg is proportional to the area of the triangle. (See Sec. A.4.) Therefore, the three rotation angles uniquely determine the sides to within the twofold ambiguity of all full-sky triangles.

Solution Conditions:

The three given rotation angles form a triangle if, and only if:

$$\left|180° - |A| - |B|\right| \leq |C| \leq 180° - \left||A| - |B|\right| \tag{A-37}$$

If this condition holds (or does not hold) for any permutation of *a*, *b*, and *c*, then it will hold (or not hold) for the two remaining permutations.

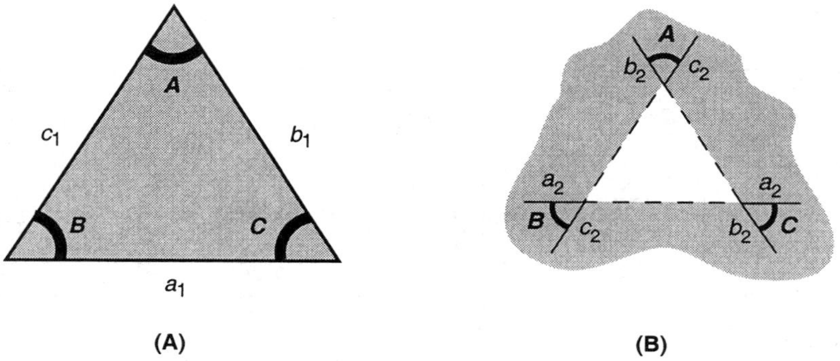

Fig. A-9. The Two Solutions for the Angle-Angle-Angle Triangle.

As listed in Table A-7, a singular case occurs whenever one of the specified angles is 0, 180 deg, or 360 deg. The various degenerate spherical triangles that result from singularities are shown in Fig. A-10 in Sec. A.7.9.

TABLE A-7. Singular Cases for Angle-Angle-Angle Spherical Triangles. *A*, *B*, and *C* are given. *a b*, and *c* are unknown. See Sec. A.7.9 for singularity types and how to handle them in practice.

If		Then			Type
$A \to 0°$		$a \to 0°$	$b \to c$	$B + C \to 180°$	Type 1 Arc
	or	$a \to 360°$	$b \to c$	$B + C \to 540°$	Double Arc
$B \to 0°$		$b \to 0°$	$a \to c$	$A + C \to 180°$	Type 1 Arc
	or	$b \to 360°$	$a \to c$	$A + C \to 540°$	Double Arc
$C \to 0°$		$c \to 0°$	$a \to b$	$A + B \to 180°$	Type 1 Arc
	or	$c \to 360°$	$a \to b$	$A + B \to 540°$	Double Arc
$A \to 180°$		$b + c \to a$	$B \to 0°$	$C \to 0°$	Type 2 Arc
	or	$b + c \to a$	$B \to 360°$	$C \to 360°$	Type 2 Arc
	or	$b + c \to 180°$	$a \to 180°$	$B \to C$	Lune
	or	$a + b + c \to 360°$	$B \to 180°$	$C \to 180°$	Great Circle
$B \to 180°$		$a + c \to b$	$A \to 0°$	$C \to 0°$	Type 2 Arc
	or	$a + c \to b$	$A \to 360°$	$C \to 360°$	Type 2 Arc
	or	$a + c \to 180°$	$b \to 180°$	$A \to C$	Lune
	or	$a + b + c \to 360°$	$A \to 180°$	$C \to 180°$	Great Circle
$C \to 180°$		$a + b \to c$	$A \to 0°$	$B \to 0°$	Type 2 Arc
	or	$a + b \to c$	$A \to 360°$	$B \to 360°$	Type 2 Arc
	or	$a + b \to 180°$	$c \to 180°$	$A \to B$	Lune
	or	$a + b + c \to 360°$	$A \to 180°$	$B \to 180°$	Great Circle
$A \to 360°$		$b \to c$	$a \to 0°$	$B + C \to 540°$	Type 1 Arc
	or	$b \to c$	$a \to 360°$	$B + C \to 180°$	Double Arc
$B \to 360°$		$a \to c$	$b \to 0°$	$A + C \to 540°$	Type 1 Arc
	or	$a \to c$	$b \to 360°$	$A + C \to 180°$	Double Arc
$C \to 360°$		$a \to b$	$c \to 0°$	$A + B \to 540°$	Type 1 Arc
	or	$a \to b$	$c \to 360°$	$A + B \to 180°$	Double Arc

First Solution:

If a non-singular solution exists, then there are two solutions. One is given by:

$$a_1 = \text{acos2}\left[\frac{\cos A + \cos B \cos C}{\sin B \sin C}, \text{H}(A)\right] \tag{A-38a}$$

$$b_1 = \text{acos2}\left[\frac{\cos B + \cos A \cos C}{\sin A \sin C}, \text{H}(B)\right] \tag{A-38b}$$

$$c_1 = \text{acos2}\left[\frac{\cos C + \cos A \cos B}{\sin A \sin B}, \text{H}(C)\right] \tag{A-38c}$$

where the acos2 function is defined in Sec. A.7.7 and discussed further in Sec. 8.1.

Second Solution:

The second solution is given by:

$$a_2 = 360° - a \tag{A-39a}$$

$$b_2 = 360° - b \tag{A-39b}$$

$$c_2 = 360° - c \tag{A-39c}$$

A.7.7 atan2 and acos2 Functions

The atan2 function has been used in computer programming languages for many years and is intended to resolve the problem of quadrant ambiguities in inverse trig functions. Specifically, if ϕ is an angle defined over the range 0 to 360 deg and sin ϕ and cos ϕ are known, then the atan2 function is defined by:

$$\text{atan2}\,(\cos\phi, \sin\phi) \equiv \phi \tag{A-40a}$$

$$= [\text{atan}\,(\sin\phi/\cos\phi) + 90°\,(1 - \text{sign}\,(\cos\phi))]\text{mod}\,360° \tag{A-40b}$$

where atan is defined over the usual range of –90 deg to +90 deg and the atan2 function is defined over the range 0 to 360 deg.

While the above expression is correct, it is not well-defined when cos ϕ goes to 0 and can result in mathematical singularities when used in practice. An alternative definition which avoids these singularities and is well-defined over the entire range is as follows:

$$\begin{aligned}
\text{atan2}(x, y) &\equiv \text{atan}(y/x) && \text{if } 0 \le y \le |x| \text{ and } x > 0 \\
&\equiv 360° + \text{atan}(y/x) && \text{if } -|x| \le y \le 0 \text{ and } x < 0 \\
&\equiv 180° + \text{atan}(y/x) && \text{if } -|x| \le y \le |x| \text{ and } < 0 \\
&\equiv 90° - \text{atan}(y/x) && \text{if } y \ge |x| \\
&\equiv 270° - \text{atan}(y/x) && \text{if } y < |x|
\end{aligned} \tag{A-41}$$

where, as above, atan is defined over the usual range of –90 to +90 deg and atan2 is defined over the range 0 to 360 deg.

The acos2 function has been introduced in this volume to serve the same function as atan2 (i.e., be uniquely defined over the range 0 to 360 deg) when using the law of cosines. As discussed in Sec 8.1, the acos2 function is defined by:

$$\text{acos2}[\cos\phi, H(\phi)] \equiv [H(\phi)\ \text{acos}(\cos\phi)]\text{mod}_{360\ \text{deg}} \tag{A-42}$$

where

$$0\ \text{deg} \leq \text{acos}(\phi) < 180\ \text{deg} \tag{A-43}$$

and

$$\begin{aligned} H(\phi) &\equiv +1 \text{ if } 0\ \text{deg} \leq \phi\ \text{mod}_{360\ \text{deg}} < 180\ \text{deg} \\ H(\phi) &\equiv -1 \text{ if } 180\ \text{deg} \leq \phi\ \text{mod}_{360\ \text{deg}} < 360\ \text{deg} \end{aligned} \tag{A-44}$$

Properties of the acos2 function are summarized in Table 8-5 in Sec. 8.1.

A.7.8 Middle Side Law and Middle Angle Law*

To simplify the solution of angle-angle-side and side-side angle triangles, it is convenient to define middle component laws when two sides (a, b) and their opposite angles (A, B) are known. Specifically, the Middle Side Law, MSL, is:

$$\sin c = \frac{\sin a \cos b \cos B + \sin b \cos a \cos A}{1 - \sin a \sin b \sin A \sin B} \tag{A-45a}$$

$$\cos c = \frac{\cos a \cos b - \sin a \sin b \cos A \cos B}{1 - \sin a \sin b \sin A \sin B} \tag{A-45b}$$

$$c = \text{atan2}\left(\cos c,\ \sin c\right) \tag{A-45c}$$

Similarly, the Middle Angle Law, MAL, is:

$$\sin C = \frac{\sin A \cos B \cos b + \sin B \cos A \cos a}{1 - \sin a \sin b \sin A \sin B} \tag{A-46a}$$

$$\cos C = \frac{-\cos A \cos B + \sin A \sin B \cos a \cos b}{1 - \sin a \sin b \sin A \sin B} \tag{A-46b}$$

$$C = \text{atan2}\left(\cos C,\ \sin C\right) \tag{A-46c}$$

where the notation is the same as that used throughout the section as defined in Fig. A-2 and the atan2 function is defined in Sec. A.7.7.

A.7.9 Singularities and Degenerate Triangles

As listed in the tables throughout Sec. A.7.1 to A.7.6, a large number of singularities can arise in spherical trigonometry. An important point to keep in mind is that these singularities arise from the nature of the problem or measurement set, not because of the fact that it is being solved using spherical trig rather than vectors or

---

* These relationships are due to Leo Early.

some other approach. To see this, consider the airplane problem introduced at the beginning of Sec. 8.1. Suppose that our pilot takes off from Los Angeles and flies 100 deg along a great circle arc in some arbitrary direction. For the second leg of his flight he simply proceeds along the same great circle path that he has been following for another 79 deg. How does he turn so as to go directly home? He has two choices—he can turn around through 180 deg and go back the way he came or he can proceed ahead (0 deg turn) and go 181 deg. These are his only options if he wishes to fly a great circle route.

Now suppose his second leg of the trip had been exactly 80 deg. He will have arrived at the antipoint of Los Angeles. The solution is no longer well-defined. He can turn in any direction and fly 180 deg on a great circle arc to get home. It doesn't matter whether we do the problem using vectors, spherical trig, or any other mathematically correct approach. There are an infinite number of directions the pilot can use to get back. It's the nature of the problem, not the process we're using to solve it, that created the singularity.

Fig. A-10 illustrates all of the singular solutions and the corresponding degenerate spherical triangles. The fundamental problem for each of them is that two or more of the components are not well-defined. For example, if one of the known sides is 0 and the two remaining sides are both unknown, then the triangle reduces to a segment of great circle. So long as the two remaining sides are equal, they can be arbitrarily long. We first discuss each of the 6 types of degenerate triangles and then the general approach to solving them.

Type 1 Arc Segment

If one (and only one) of the known sides becomes 0, then the remaining two sides collapse into a single great circle arc. This means that the remaining two sides must be of equal, but arbitrary, length. The angle opposite the 0 length side must also be 0 and the sum of the two remaining angles (the ones adjacent to the 0 length side) must be 180 deg. There is also an inverse angle solution in which the roles of "inside" and "outside" are reversed. In this case, the angle opposite the 0 length side becomes 360 deg and the sum of the two adjacent angles is 540 deg.

Double Arc

If one (and only one) of the known angles becomes 0, then the two adjacent sides collapse into a single great circle arc. This means that the remaining two sides must be of equal, but arbitrary, length. If the side opposite the 0 angle is also 0, then the figure is the Type 1 Arc Segment. However, if the side opposite is 360 deg, then the figure is a Double Arc, effectively a great circle with an arc segment attached to it. (See Fig. A-10.) The remaining two angles must sum to 540 deg. In the inverse angle solution, the singular angle becomes 360 deg and the sum of the remaining angles becomes 180 deg.

Type 2 Arc Segment

If one of the known angles becomes 180 deg, and the side opposite is not 180 deg, then the triangle again collapses into a great circle arc. The two remaining angles must be 0 (or 180 deg in the Great Circle case below), and the sum of the two adjacent sides must be equal to the third side. However, that length is arbitrary. In the inverse angle solution, the "inside" and "outside" are reversed, and the remaining angles are both 360 deg.

Small Triangle			Large Triangle	
$a = b$ $c = 0$	$A + B = 180°$ $C = 0$	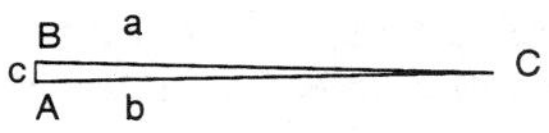 Type 1 Arc Segment	$A + B = 540°$ $C = 360$	$a = b$ $c = 0$
$a = b$ $c = 360°$	$A + B = 540°$ $C = 0$	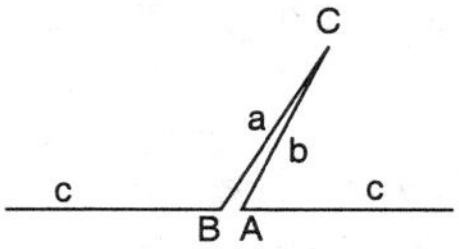 Double Arc	$A + B = 180°$ $C = 360°$	$a = b$ $c = 360°$
$a + b = c$	$A = B = 0$ $C = 180°$	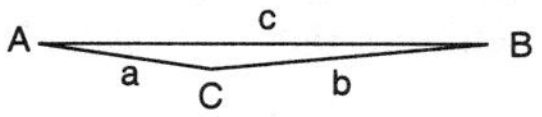 Type 2 Arc Segment	$A = B = 360°$ $C = 180°$	$a + b = c$
$a + b + c = 360°$	$A = B = C$ $= 180°$	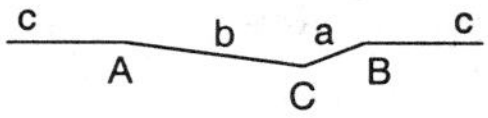 Great Circle	$A = B = C$ $= 180°$	$a + b + c = 360°$
$a + b = 180°$ $c = 180°$	$A = B$ $C = 180°$	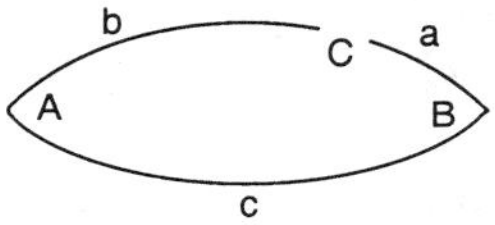 Lune	$A = B$ $C = 180°$	$a + b = 180°$ $c = 180°$
$a = b = c = 0$	$A + B + C =$ $180°$	 Point	$A + B + C =$ $900°$	$a = b = c = 0$

Fig. A-10. Singularities and Degenerate Spherical Triangles. See text for discussion of each and how to best handle the resulting singularities.

Great Circle

If one of the known angles becomes 180 deg, then an alternative solution to the Type 2 Arc Segment is for the two adjacent sides to sum to 360 deg minus the opposite side. In this case, the 3 sides are again arbitrary, but sum to 360 deg and the figure is simply a great circle. All three angles are 180 deg. The inverse angle solution is now identical and is simply a matter of which side of the great circle we choose to pick as the "inside."

Lune

If one of the known sides becomes 180 deg, then the triangle becomes a lune with two of the vertices at antipoints of each other (i.e., opposite poles of a spherical coordinate system). The remaining two sides are arbitrary, but must sum to 180 deg and the angle opposite the 180 deg side must also be 180 deg. The two angles at the antipoints are also arbitrary, but must be equal. Unlike the other degenerate triangles, the sum of the angles and, therefore, the area of the triangle, is arbitrary and can range from 0 to the full sphere. The inverse angle triangle for a lune is simply another lune.

Point

Finally, if two of the known sides become 0, then the third side must either be 0, reducing the triangle to a point, or 360 deg, creating a Great Circle. In the point, the three angles are arbitrary but sum to 360 deg. The inverse of the point is the full sky in which the three sides remain 0 and the three angles sum to 900 deg.

Dealing with Singularities and Solving Degenerate Triangles

The most important issue in dealing with singular solutions is to recognize that they are real. Thus, if one side of a spherical triangle goes to 0 and the other two sides are unknown, then those two sides must be equal, but can be arbitrarily long. There are infinitely many solutions for the specified problem. It is generally inconvenient to write out all of these solutions. Nonetheless, we need some practical approach to dealing with this circumstance because it can arise in realistic problems, such as finding the spacecraft attitude using the Sun and Earth as reference vectors when they are 180 deg apart in the sky. There are three reasonable alternatives:

Set a Flag. One alternative is to simply set a flag indicating the presence of the singularity. For completeness, that flag should also convey what is known about the solution, i.e., that the unknowns are equal or that they sum to a specific value.

Set Solutions to a Representative Value. For discrete solutions (i.e., where individual triangles are being solved) the only reasonable alternative to a simple flag is to pick a reasonable value for the unknowns which is consistent with the solution conditions. Thus, if two unknown sides are arbitrary, but must be equal, we could set them both to 90 deg. The same approach would work if they were arbitrary, but must sum to 180 deg.

Preserve Solution Continuity. There is an additional option if the problem involves either analytic or numerical functions such that one or more of the components approaches a singular state (0 or 180 deg) along a continuous, smooth curve. In this case, the best approach is to allow the solved for sides or angles which become arbitrary at the singularity to remain continuous through the singularity. For example, if a vanishing side approaches 0 along a curve for which the remaining solved for sides both approach 60 deg, then they should retain this value when the third side vanishes. As a practical example, assume that we are using the Earth and Sun for spacecraft attitude determination and control, with the Sun being used to measure the yaw angle about nadir. If the Sun is in the orbit plane, then it will pass through the zenith as the spacecraft goes around in its orbit and the yaw solution will be undefined at that point. The most practical approach is to assume that the yaw angle does not change (or, if it is changing, that it continues to change at a uniform rate) during the brief period that the Sun is at the zenith. While this may not be mathematically "correct," it is a reasonable solution for most practical applications.

A.8 Differential Spherical Trigonometry

The development here follows that of Newcomb [1960], which contains a more extended discussion of the subject.

A.8.1 Differential Relations Between the Parts of a Spherical Triangle

In general, any part of a spherical triangle may be determined from three other parts. Thus, we may determine the error in any part produced by infinitesimal errors in the three given parts. This may be done by determining the partial derivatives relating any four parts of a spherical triangle from the following differentials, where the notation of Fig. A-2 is retained.

Given three angles and one side:

$$-\sin b \sin A \, dc + dC + \cos a \, dB + \cos b \, dA = 0 \tag{A-47}$$

Given three sides and one angle:

$$-dc + \cos A \, dB + \cos B \, da + \sin a \sin B \, dC = 0 \tag{A-48}$$

Given two sides and the opposite angles:

$$\cos c \sin A \, dc - \cos b \sin C \, da + \sin c \cos A \, dA - \sin a \cos C \, dC = 0 \tag{A-49}$$

Given two sides, the included angle, and one opposite angle:

$$-\sin A \, da + \cos b \sin C \, da + \sin b \, dC + \cos A \sin c \, dB = 0 \tag{A-50}$$

As an example of the determination of partial derivatives, consider a triangle in which the three independent variables are the three sides. Then, from Eq. (A-48),

$$\left.\frac{\partial C}{\partial a}\right|_{b,c} = -\frac{\cos B}{\sin a \sin B} = -\frac{\cot B}{\sin a} \tag{A-51}$$

A.8.2 Infinitesimal Triangles

The simplest infinitesimal spherical triangle is one in which the entire triangle is small relative to the radius of the sphere. In this case, the spherical triangle may be treated as a plane triangle if the three rotation angles remain finite quantities. If one of the rotation angles is infinitesimal, the analysis presented below should be used.

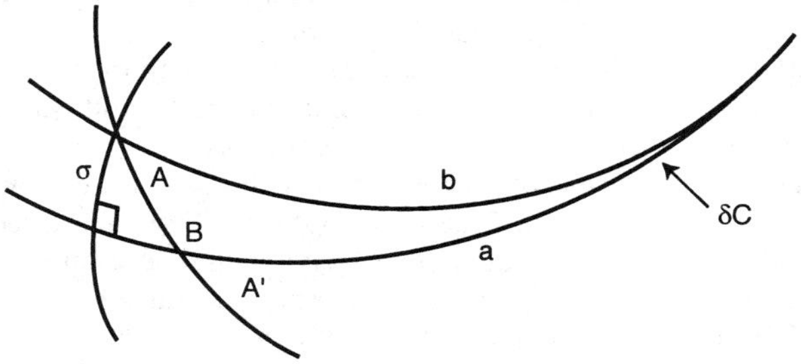

Fig. A-11. Spherical Triangle With One Infinitesimal Angle.

Figure A-11 shows a spherical triangle in which two sides are of arbitrary, but nearly equal, length and the included rotation angle is infinitesimal. Then the change in the angle by which the two sides intercept a great circle is given by

$$\delta A \equiv A' - A = 180° - (B + A) = \delta C \cos b \tag{A-52}$$

The perpendicular separation, σ, between the two long arcs is given by

$$\sigma = \delta C \sin b \tag{A-53}$$

If two angles are infinitesimal (such that the third angle is nearly 180 deg), the triangle may be divided into two triangles and treated as above.

A.9 Common Relations Between Trig Functions

The following relationships hold between the trigonometric functions and, consequently, are true in either plane or spherical geometry.

A.9.1 Relations Among the Functions

$$\tan x = 1 / \cot x = \sin x / \cos x \quad \text{(A-54a)}$$

$$\sin^2 x + \cos^2 x = 1 \quad \text{(A-54b)}$$

$$1 + \tan^2 x = 1 / \cos^2 x \quad \text{(A-54c)}$$

$$1 + \cot^2 x = 1 + 1/ \tan^2 x = 1 / \sin^2 x \quad \text{(A-54d)}$$

$$\sin x = \cos (90° - x) = \sin (180° - x) \quad \text{(A-54e)}$$

$$\cos x = \sin (90° - x) = -\cos (180° - x) \quad \text{(A-54f)}$$

$$\tan x = \cot (90° - x) = -\tan (180° - x) \quad \text{(A-54g)}$$

$$\cot x = 1 / \tan x = \tan (90° - x) = -\cot (180° - x) \quad \text{(A-54h)}$$

$$1 / \sin x = \cot (x / 2) - \cot x \quad \text{(A-54i)}$$

A.9.2 Sums and Differences of Angles

$$\sin (x + y) = \sin x \cos y + \cos x \sin y \quad \text{(A-55a)}$$

$$\sin (x - y) = \sin x \cos y - \cos x \sin y \quad \text{(A-55b)}$$

$$\cos (x + y) = \cos x \cos y - \sin x \sin y \quad \text{(A-55c)}$$

$$\cos (x - y) = \cos x \cos y + \sin x \sin y \quad \text{(A-55d)}$$

$$\tan(x + y) = \frac{\tan x + \tan y}{1 - \tan x \tan y} \quad \text{(A-55e)}$$

$$\tan(x - y) = \frac{\tan x - \tan y}{1 + \tan x \tan y} \quad \text{(A-55f)}$$

$$\cot(x + y) = \frac{\cot x \cot y - 1}{\cot x + \cot y} \quad \text{(A-55g)}$$

$$\cot(x - y) = \frac{\cot x \cot y + 1}{\cot x - \cot y} \quad \text{(A-55h)}$$

A.9.3 Double and Half Angle Formulas

$$\sin 2x = 2 \sin x \cos x = \frac{2\tan x}{1+\tan^2 x} \tag{A-56a}$$

$$\cos 2x = \cos^2 x - \sin^2 x = 2\cos^2 x - 1 = 1 - 2\sin^2 x = \frac{1-\tan^2 x}{1+\tan^2 x} \tag{A-56b}$$

$$\tan 2x = \frac{2\tan x}{1-\tan^2 x} \tag{A-56c}$$

$$\cot 2x = \frac{\cot^2 x - 1}{2\cot x} \tag{A-56d}$$

$$\sin (x/2) = \pm\sqrt{\frac{1-\cos x}{2}} \tag{A-56e}$$

$$\cos (x/2) = \pm\sqrt{\frac{1+\cos x}{2}} \tag{A-56f}$$

$$\tan (x/2) = \pm\sqrt{\frac{1-\cos x}{1+\cos x}} = \frac{1-\cos x}{\sin x} = \frac{\sin x}{1+\cos x} \tag{A-56g}$$

$$\cot (x/2) = \pm\sqrt{\frac{1+\cos x}{1-\cos x}} = \frac{1+\cos x}{\sin x} = \frac{\sin x}{1-\cos x} \tag{A-56h}$$

A.9.4 Reduction Formulas

$$\sin x = +\cos (x - 90°) = -\sin (x - 180°) = -\cos (x - 270°) \tag{A-57a}$$

$$\cos x = -\sin (x - 90°) = -\cos (x - 180°) = +\sin (x - 270°) \tag{A-57b}$$

$$\tan x = -\cot (x - 90°) = +\tan (x - 180°) = -\cot (x - 270°) \tag{A-57c}$$

$$\cot x = -\tan (x - 90°) = +\cot (x - 180°) = -\tan (x - 270°) \tag{A-57d}$$

See Table A-8 for additional reduction formulas.

A.9.5 Series Expansions

$$\sin x = x - \frac{x^3}{3!} + \frac{x^5}{5!} - \frac{x^7}{7!} + \dots$$

TABLE A-8. Reduction Formulas. Example: Find sin (270° – x): Look in the row marked (270° – x), and the column marked "sine," and get: – cos x.

	sine	cosine	tangent	cotangent
$-x$	$-\sin x$	$+\cos x$	$-\tan x$	$-\cot x$
$90°+x$	$+\cos x$	$-\sin x$	$-\cot x$	$-\tan x$
$90°-x$	$+\cos x$	$+\sin x$	$+\cot x$	$+\tan x$
$180°+x$	$-\sin x$	$-\cos x$	$+\tan x$	$+\cot x$
$180°-x$	$+\sin x$	$-\cos x$	$-\tan x$	$-\cot x$
$270°+x$	$-\cos x$	$+\sin x$	$-\cot x$	$-\tan x$
$270°-x$	$-\cos x$	$-\sin x$	$+\cot x$	$+\tan x$
$360°+x$	$+\sin x$	$+\cos x$	$+\tan x$	$+\cot x$
$360°-x$	$-\sin x$	$+\cos x$	$-\tan x$	$-\cot x$

$$= x-\frac{x^3}{6}+\frac{x^5}{120}-\frac{x^7}{5{,}040}+\ldots \qquad \text{(A-58a)}$$

$$\cos x = 1-\frac{x^2}{2!}+\frac{x^4}{4!}-\frac{x^6}{6!}+\ldots$$

$$= 1-\frac{x^2}{2}+\frac{x^4}{24}-\frac{x^6}{720}+\ldots \qquad \text{(A-58b)}$$

$$\tan x = x+\frac{x^3}{3}+\frac{2x^5}{15}+\frac{17x^7}{315}+\frac{62x^9}{2{,}835}+\ldots \qquad |x| < 90°$$

$$\cot x = \frac{1}{x}-\frac{x}{3}-\frac{x^3}{45}-\frac{2x^5}{945}-\frac{x^7}{4{,}725}-\ldots \qquad |x| < 180° \qquad \text{(A-58c)}$$

A.10 Bibliography of Spherical Trigonometry

Bell, Clifford and Tracy Y. Thomas. 1946. *Essentials of Plane and Spherical Trigonometry*. New York: Henry Holt and Company.

Beyer, William H., ed. 1984. *CRC Standard Mathematical Tables, 27th Edition.* Boca Raton: CRC Press, Inc.

Bowditch, Nathaniel. 1966. *American Practical Navigator.* Washington, DC: US Government Printing Office.

Granville, William A. 1942. *Spherical Trigonometry.* Rev. by Percey F. Smith. Boston: Ginn and Company.

Green, Robin M. 1985. *Spherical Astronomy*. Cambridge: Cambridge University Press.

Kells, Lyman M., William F. Kern, and James R. Bland. 1942. *Spherical Trigonometry with Naval and Military Applications*. New York: McGraw-Hill Book Company, Inc.

Newcomb, Simon. 1960. *A Compendium of Spherical Astronomy*. New York: Dover.

Taff, Laurence G. 1991. *Computational Spherical Astronomy*. Florida: Krieger Publishing Company.

Appendix B

Coordinate Transformations

For problems in mission geometry, the most common representations of directions as seen from the spacecraft (or other observer) are in terms of either spherical coordinates or unit vectors in a Cartesian (rectangular) coordinate frame. This appendix provides the four relevant coordinate transformations, i.e., Cartesian → Spherical (Sec. 1), Spherical → Cartesian (Sec. 1), Cartesian → Cartesian (Sec. 2), and Spherical → Spherical (Sec. 3).

B.1 Transformation Between Cartesian and Spherical Coordinates

The components of a vector, **R**, in cartesian (x, y, z) and spherical (r, θ, ϕ) coordinates are shown in Fig. B-1 and listed below. (See also Fig. 6-9 in Sec. 6.1.)

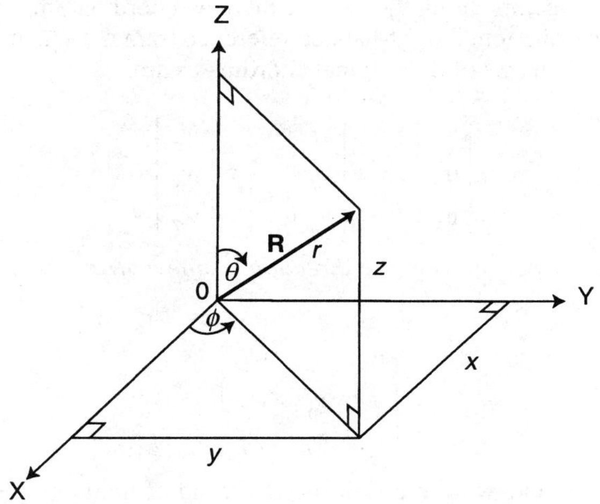

Fig. B-1. Components of a Vector, R, of length *r* in Cartesian (*x, y, z*), and Spherical (*r, θ, φ*) Coordinates.

The *declination*, δ, used in celestial coordinates is measured from the equatorial (x–y) plane and is related to θ by

$$\delta \equiv 90° - \theta \tag{B-1}$$

The components in cartesian and spherical coordinates are related by the following equations:

Arbitrary Vector	Unit Vector ($|\mathbf{R}| \equiv 1$)	
$x = r \sin\theta \cos\phi$	$x = \cos\phi \sin\theta$	(B-2a)
$y = r \sin\theta \sin\phi$	$y = \sin\phi \sin\theta$	(B-2b)
$z = r \cos\theta$	$z = \cos\theta$	(B-2c)
$r = (x^2 + y^2 + z^2)^{1/2}$	$r = 1$	(B-2d)
$\theta = \text{acos}\{z/(x^2 + y^2 + z^2)^{1/2}\}$	$\theta = \text{acos}\, z$	(B-2e)
$\phi = \text{atan2}(y, x)$	$\phi = \text{atan2}(y, x)$	(B-2f)

The correct quadrant for ϕ in Eq. (2f) is obtained from the signs of x and y by, for example, using the FORTRAN atan2 function. See Sec. A.7.7 for nonsingular formulas for atan2.

B.2 Transformation Between Cartesian Coordinates

Given a cartesian rectangular coordinate frame (x, y, z) as defined in Sec. B-1, we can define a second cartesian coordinate frame (u, v, w) by defining three mutually perpendicular unit vectors along the axes of the new coordinate frame. (Both frames are assumed to be orthogonal, right-handed reference frames.) The unit vectors defining the new frame in terms of the original coordinates are:

$$\hat{\mathbf{u}} \equiv \begin{bmatrix} u_x \\ u_y \\ u_z \end{bmatrix} \quad \hat{\mathbf{v}} \equiv \begin{bmatrix} v_x \\ v_y \\ v_z \end{bmatrix} \quad \hat{\mathbf{w}} \equiv \begin{bmatrix} w_x \\ w_y \\ w_z \end{bmatrix} \tag{B-3}$$

Given these vectors, we can form the *direction cosine matrix**, or *attitude matrix*, *A*, as follows:

$$A \equiv \begin{bmatrix} u_x & v_x & w_x \\ u_y & v_y & w_y \\ u_z & v_z & w_z \end{bmatrix} \tag{B-4}$$

So long as $\hat{\mathbf{u}}$, $\hat{\mathbf{v}}$, and $\hat{\mathbf{w}}$ form a right-handed triad of mutually perpendicular unit vectors, A will be a proper real orthogonal matrix. Only three of the nine elements are independent and $\det A = 1$. The attitude matrix is a coordinate transformation that maps

* The matrix A is called the direction cosine matrix because each of the elements is the cosine of the angle between the two relevant vectors. For example, $u_x = \hat{\mathbf{u}} \bullet \hat{\mathbf{x}} = \cos\theta$, where θ is the angle between $\hat{\mathbf{u}}$ and $\hat{\mathbf{x}}$.

vectors from the original frame to the new frame. Thus, if **b** is an arbitrary vector with components b_x, b_y, and b_z, then the components in the new frame are given by:

$$\begin{bmatrix} b_u \\ b_v \\ b_w \end{bmatrix} = \begin{bmatrix} \hat{\mathbf{u}} \bullet \mathbf{b} \\ \hat{\mathbf{v}} \bullet \mathbf{b} \\ \hat{\mathbf{w}} \bullet \mathbf{b} \end{bmatrix} = A\mathbf{b} \equiv \begin{bmatrix} u_x & v_x & w_x \\ u_y & v_y & w_y \\ u_z & v_z & w_z \end{bmatrix} \begin{bmatrix} b_x \\ b_y \\ b_z \end{bmatrix} \tag{B-5}$$

The inverse matrix, A^{-1}, is the coordinate transformation that maps vectors from the new frame (u, v, w) back into the original frame (x, y, z). For the attitude matrix, the inverse is simply the transpose. That is:

$$A^{-1} = A^T \equiv \begin{bmatrix} u_x & u_y & u_z \\ v_x & v_y & v_z \\ w_x & w_y & w_z \end{bmatrix} \tag{B-6}$$

and

$$\begin{bmatrix} b_x \\ b_y \\ b_z \end{bmatrix} = A^{-1} \begin{bmatrix} b_u \\ b_v \\ b_w \end{bmatrix} \tag{B-7}$$

B.3 Transformation Between Spherical Coordinates

We can use the formalism developed for full-sky geometry to significantly reduce the complexity of transforming between two spherical coordinate systems. Specifically, assume that two spherical coordinate systems are related as shown in Fig. B-2, with the variables defined as follows:

$\rho \equiv$ arc length between the two positive poles ($0 < \rho < 180$ deg)

$\psi_1 \equiv$ azimuth of the second pole in the first coordinate system ($0 < \psi_1 < 360$ deg)

$\psi_2 \equiv$ azimuth of the first pole in the second coordinate system ($0 < \psi_2 < 360$ deg)

Given the coordinates (ϕ_2, δ_2') of a point, **P**, in the second coordinate system, we wish to find the coordinates (ϕ_1, δ_1') of **P** in the first system, where δ' is the co-elevation angle = 90 deg – δ. We first define the triangle shown in Fig. B-3, with:

$$\Delta\phi_1 = \psi_1 - \phi_1 \tag{B-8}$$

and

$$\Delta\phi_2 = \psi_2 - \phi_2 \tag{B-9}$$

From the general solution for side-angle-side spherical triangles [see A.7.3 and Eqs. (8-4) to (8-6) in Sec. 8.1], we have two solutions:

$$\delta_1' = \text{acos}2[\cos\rho\cos\delta_2' + \sin\rho\sin\delta_2'\cos\Delta\phi_2, H(\Delta\phi_2)] \tag{B-10}$$

$$\Delta\phi_1 = \text{acos}2\left[\frac{\cos\delta_2' - \cos\rho\cos\delta_1'}{\sin\rho\sin\delta_1'}, H(\delta_2')\right] \tag{B-11}$$

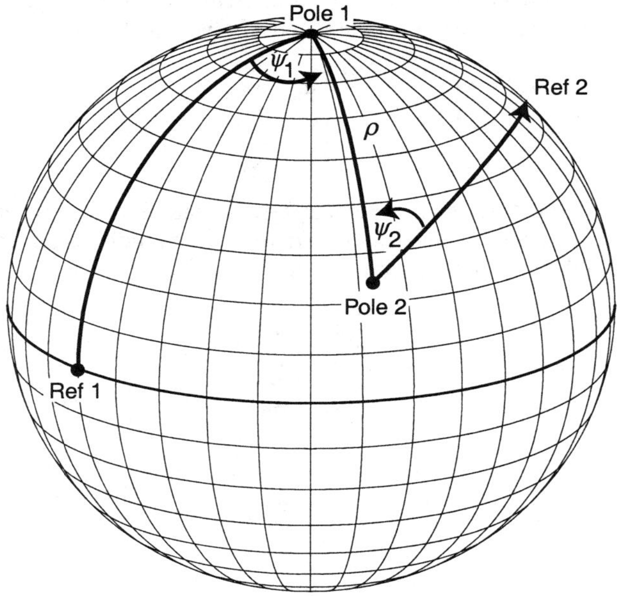

Fig. B-2. Relationship Between the Coordinate Systems.

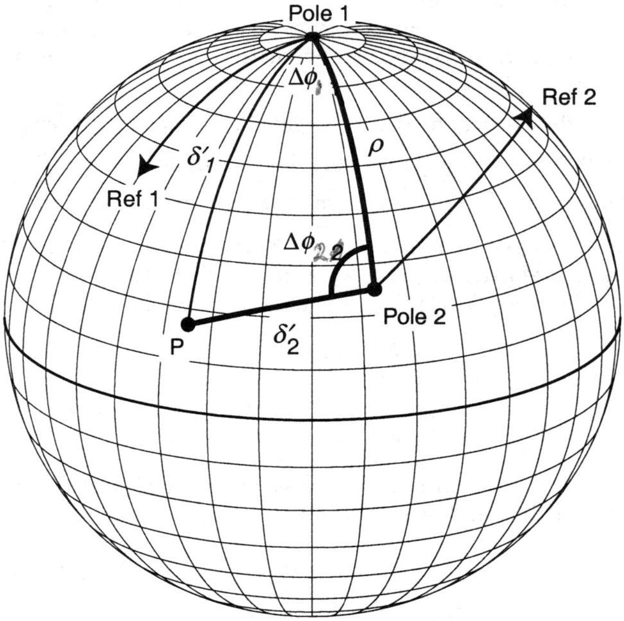

Fig. B-3. Definition of the Spherical Triangle for Coordinate Transformations.

and

$$\delta_1'^* = 360 \text{ deg} - \delta_1' \tag{B-12}$$

$$\Delta\phi_1^* = \Delta\phi_1 + 180 \text{ deg} \tag{B-13}$$

If we allow the angles to range from 0 to 360 deg, but restrict the sides to the range of 0 to 180 deg, then we have a unique solution [see Eq. (8-6) in Sec. 8.1)], except in the singular case in which the poles are identical or 180 deg apart:

$$\delta_1' = \text{acos}[\cos\rho\cos\delta_2' + \sin\rho\sin\delta_2'\cos\Delta\phi_2] \tag{B-14}$$

$$\Delta\phi_1 = \text{acos}\left[\frac{\cos\delta_2' - \cos\rho\cos\delta_1'}{\text{H}(\Delta\phi_2)\sin\rho\sin\delta_1'}\right] - 90\,\text{deg}[\text{H}(\Delta\phi_2) - 1] \tag{B-15}$$

This can be further reduced to the normal coordinate expressions (α, δ), as:

$$\delta_1 = \text{acos}(\cos\rho\ \sin\delta_2 + \sin\rho\ \cos\delta_2\cos\Delta\phi_2) - 90 \text{ deg} \tag{B-16}$$

$$\Delta\phi_1 = \text{acos}\left[\frac{\sin\delta_2 - \cos\rho\sin\delta_1}{\text{H}(\Delta\phi_2)\sin\rho\cos\delta_1}\right] - 90\text{ deg }[\text{H}(\Delta\phi_2) - 1] \tag{B-17}$$

By symmetry, the reverse transformation will be:

$$\delta_2 = \text{acos}(\cos\rho\sin\delta_1 + \sin\rho\cos\delta_1\cos\Delta\phi_2) - 90\text{ deg} \tag{B-18}$$

$$\Delta\phi_2 = \text{acos}\left[\frac{\sin\delta_1 - \cos\rho\sin\delta_2}{\text{H}(\Delta\phi_1)\sin\rho\cos\delta_2}\right] - 90\text{ deg}[\text{H}(\Delta\phi_1) - 1] \tag{B-19}$$

where acos is the normal inverse cosine function defined on the range of 0 to 180 deg and H is the hemisphere function defined in Secs. A.7.7 and 8.1.

Appendix C

Statistical Error Analysis

Geoffrey N. Smit, *The Aerospace Corporation*

This appendix is an analytic introduction to error analysis. The flow of topics is summarized in Fig. C-1. Section 5.4 provides an introduction to error analysis and a general recipe for adding errors in an error budget. The process of creating an error budget is introduced in Sec. 5.3 and discussed in detail with tables of error sources in Sec. 5.5. Chapter 7 provides an introduction to spacecraft position and attitude measurements. Specifically, Sec. 7.2 provides a detailed assessment of the evaluation of measurement uncertainty on the celestial sphere and Sec. 7.6 describes good and bad measurement sets (in terms of uncertainty) and a set of practical tests to determine them.

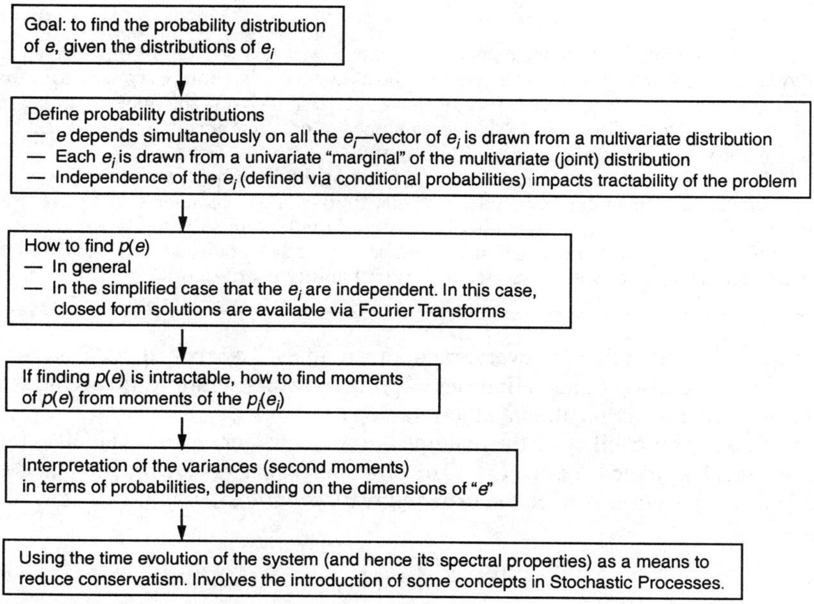

Fig. C-1. Sequence of Topics in this Appendix.

C.1 Probability Considerations

The basic problem to be addressed is:
Given: a set of components with errors e_1, e_2, ... with known probability distributions. The components are combined in a system such that the output error is

$$e = e_1 + e_2 + \ldots + e_n \tag{C-1}$$

Find: the probability distribution of e.

As noted in Sec. 5.4, the more general problem is

$$e = F(e_1, e_2, \ldots, e_n) \tag{C-2}$$

F may, in general, depend on the state of the system—i.e. if the component contributions are

$$x_i = d_i + e_i, \; (i = 1, \ldots, n) \tag{C-3}$$

then the system output is some function, $G(x)$, which can be decomposed into the nominal output, $G(d)$, and the error,

$$G(x) = G(d) + F(x) \tag{C-4}$$

G can usually be expanded in a Taylor series. When this is the case, we have

$$G(x) = G(d) + eG'(x) + \text{higher order terms} \tag{C-5}$$

This gives the system error,

$$F = G(x) - G(d) \approx eG'(x) \tag{C-6}$$

which is a weighted sum of the e_i, with coefficients which are functions of the state, x.

A weighted sum can always be scaled to be a pure sum. Therefore we will concentrate on the case of a pure sum, since we have seen that it covers the majority of cases of interest. Also, it allows us to derive a number of concrete results which would be less understandable in a more general setting.

If, for some reason, it is desired to retain a functional form other than a sum, this does not impact the conceptual basis for much that follows. For example, a worst case estimate of the system error can readily be produced (and it typically will be too conservative), and computational schemes can be devised to estimate the probability distribution of e or quantities related to this probability distribution.

Note that e is a function of several random variables. To proceed, we first summarize some of the concepts and definitions of probability distributions involving several variables in order to fix notation and terminology.

Consider first probability on the real line (i.e. we consider "events" labelled by real numbers—such as a measurement, x). The probability that $x \le y$, $\text{Prob}(\{x \le y\})$, is denoted $P(y)$. $P(y)$ is defined to be the *probability distribution.* Assuming that the derivative exists

$$dP \,/\, dy \equiv p(y) \tag{C-7}$$

is called the *probability density function*, or *pdf.* $p(y)\,dy$ is the probability that x lies between y and $y + dy$ and

$$\int_{-\infty}^{\infty} p(x)dx = 1 \tag{C-8}$$

In the definition of the probability distribution, there are two variables (I've called them x and y). The variable y is the actual argument of the probability distribution. x is a "dummy variable", introduced for explanatory reasons. Thus, $P(y) = \text{Prob}\{x \leq y\}$, means that any "experiment" performed on the system described by P will yield an outcome less than or equal to y on P fraction of the trials. Thus, as shown in Fig. C-2, P is monotonically increasing. In the case of the probability density, we are focussing attention on the neighborhood of a single point, "y". It is not uncommon to see terminology like "the probability that y lies between y and $y + dy$ is given by $p(y)dy$".

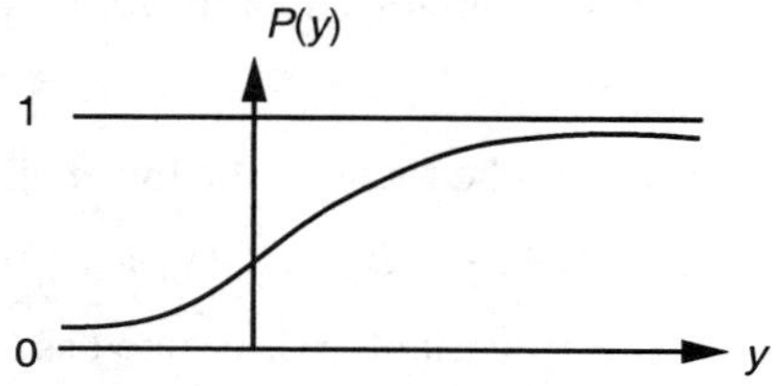

Fig. C-2. Probability Distribution *P*(*y*) vs. *y*.

The variable, x, used to label points or "events" in our probability sample space is called a *random variable* or *variate*. I use the terms "variable," "random variable," and "variate" interchangeably.* The sample space need not be the real line. It could be n-dimensional space (i.e. n copies of the real line), or, in general, any suitable set.

Measurements of angles, distances, brightnesses, or frequencies are all random variables. The result of any particular measurement would be a single real number, the value of which includes some element of chance. The associated probability densities would usually be peaked around the true value of the item being measured, and would be negligible far away from the true value as shown in Fig. C-3.

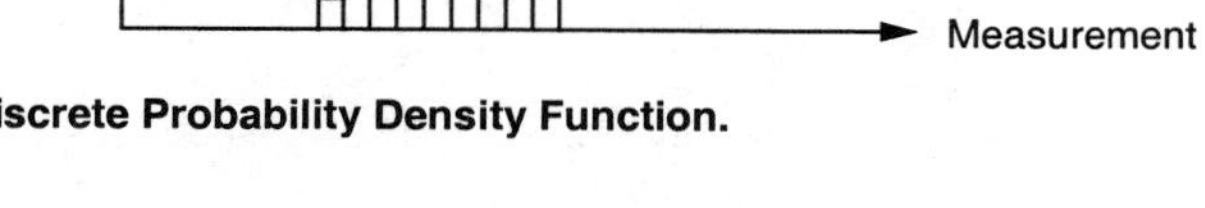

Fig. C-3. A Discrete Probability Density Function.

* Intuitively, the idea of a random variable is fairly clear—there is an element of chance in any given "reading" of x, i.e. x is drawn from some probability space ("black bag") at random, and the likelihood that it will have any particular value is given by its probability density. The mathematical theory was originally developed to describe various games of chance. The subject only became mathematically respectable after its foundations had been worked out independent of references to these intuitive notions. A rapid increase in the rate of progress occurred at this point. (See [Kac, 1989].)

Examples of multidimensional random variables include measurements of "physical" vectors such as the 3-dimensional velocity vector of an object and the arguments of functions of several 1-dimensional random variables. For example, to determine the area of a rectangle, we have to measure two lengths. This input "vector" would be a 2-dimensional random variable. The pointing errors of a spacecraft typically depend on the value of numerous parameters (such as sensor readings, temperatures, structural deformations) and this input vector would be a multidimensional random variable. Random variables can also be *discrete,* i.e. limited to a finite number of values. Examples are the outputs of coin or die tossings. The output from a digital sensor is discrete.

For a multi-dimensional random variable, the probability density has the form

$$p(x_1, x_2, \ldots, x_n) \tag{C-9}$$

This gives the probability that x will be found in the hypercube

$$\{(x_1, x_1 + dx_1), (x_2, x_2 + dx_2), \ldots, (x_n + dx_n)\} \tag{C-10}$$

The multi-dimensional probability distribution is defined as

$$P(y) = \text{Prob}\{x_1 \le y_1, \ldots., x_n \le y_n\} \tag{C-11}$$

and we have $p(x)$

$$p(x) = \frac{\partial^n P}{\partial x_1 \partial x_2 \ldots \partial x_n} \tag{C-12}$$

The system errors that we are trying to estimate depend on the input errors contributed by numerous components, i.e. the system error depends on a multivariable probability distribution. In general, we don't have any data on this multivariable distribution, per se. What we have is data on the distribution of each of the inputs. We may also have some information on whether some of these inputs interact with each other so that the value measured by one input may be coordinated with that measured by another. We are thus faced with the task of building up the multivariable distribution from its "projection" on each of the input axes. This brings us to the topic of such projections (marginal distributions), and the topic of interdependence between the inputs (conditional probabilities).

Marginal Distributions

One can "integrate out" some of the variables of a multivariate distribution function, leaving a probability distribution in the remaining variates.*

For example,

$$\int_{-\infty}^{\infty} p(x_1, \ldots, x_n)\, dx_2\, dx_3 \ldots dx_n \tag{C-13}$$

leaves a density

---

* The significance of the integration is as follows. For simplicity consider the two variable case. The multivariate probability distribution function, $p(x_1, x_2)dx_1dx_2$ is the probability that x_1 and x_2 will lie in $\{(x_1, x_1 + dx_1), (x_2, x_2 + dx_2)\}$. $\{\int[p(x_1, x_2)dx_2]\}dx_1$ is the probability that x_1 and x_2 will lie in the strip $\{(x_1, x_1+dx_1)$, any $x_2\}$, i.e. we'll "accept" any measurement which has x_1 in $(x_1, x_1 + dx_1)$ regardless of the x_2 value.

$$p_1(x_1) = \frac{dP_1(x_1)}{dx_1} \tag{C-14}$$

P_1 and p_1 are called the *marginal distribution function* and *marginal density* of x_1 associated with $p(x_1, \ldots, x_n)$ and $P(x_1, \ldots, x_n)$. Marginal distributions of $x_2, x_3, \ldots$ can be similarly defined. The figure below illustrates the marginals of a bivariate probability density. (The geometry of the figure also illustrates why they are called marginals.)

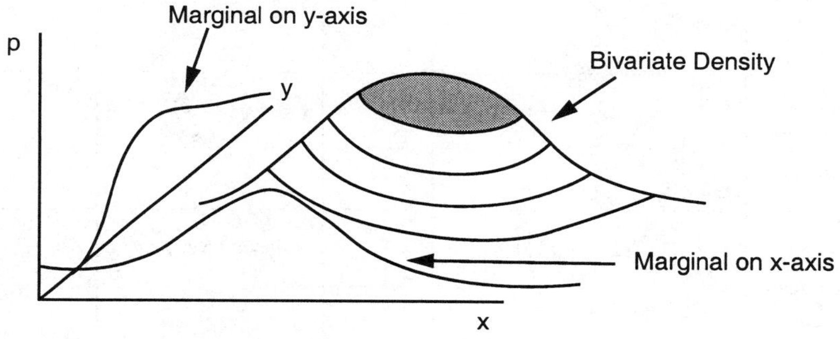

Fig. C-4. Joint (Bivariate) Probability Density Showing Marginals on Each of the Axes.

The multivariate density, p, is called the *joint density* associated with these variates. Similarly we can define the *joint distribution*.

While a given multivariate distribution function (or density) will have unique marginals, the inverse problem of finding a joint distribution given the marginals does not have a unique solution. In the error analysis problem being addressed in this section, the information that we have about the joint distribution of the errors, e_i, comes from its marginals, the p_i, and the correlations between the e_i.* In addition to the uniqueness issue mentioned above, for some marginal distributions not all correlation coefficients (between -1 and $+1$) are possible, so that we must also observe bounds on the correlations we input to the problem. Assuming that we have posed the problem properly, we can in principle generate a joint distribution (e.g. via a Monte Carlo simulation) consistent with the marginals. Table C-1 lists a number of common probability distributions used in statistics.

Conditional Probabilities and Independence

Random variables can be coupled, so that the values taken on by one may give us information about the others. For example, a spacecraft structural distortion may be related to a temperature change. The probability that an event A occurs, given that event B has occurred, is written $P(A|B)$ and said "probability of A, given B." From the definition,

$$P(A,B) = P(A|B)P(B) \tag{C-15}$$

---

* The word "correlation" has a technical meaning which will be defined later. It refers to the degree to which the values of random variables are interrelated.

TABLE C-1. Some Common Probability Distributions.

Name, Comments	Probability Density Function	Graph	Mean, *M* Variance, *V*	Characteristic Function
Uniform Distribution Arises during quantization	$p(x) = 1/(b-a)$, $a<x<b$ $= 0$, otherwise	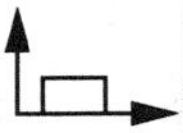	$M = (a+b)/2$ $V = (b-a)^2/12$	$(\exp(sb) - \exp(sa))/(b-a)s$
Normal Ubiquitous: arises via sums, also as the limit of some distributions	$\left(1/\sqrt{2\pi s^2}\right)e\left(-(x-a)^2/2s^2\right)$	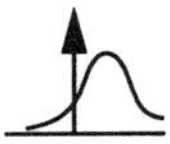	$M = a$ $V = s^2$	$\exp(at + s^2/2)$
Rayleigh Distribution of radial error with normal components	$\left(x/s^2\right)e\left(-x^2/2s^2\right)$ $(x > 0)$ (zero for $x < 0$)	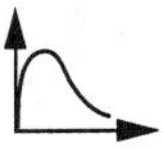	$M = s\sqrt{(\pi/2)}$ $V = ((4-\pi)/2)s^2$	Complicated
Cauchy Ratio of two normal variates. Also, geometric meaning (tan of a uniformly distributed variate)	$a/\left[\pi\left\{(x-b)^2 + a^2\right\}\right]$	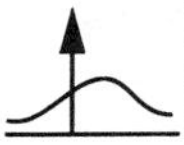	$M = b$ Variance diverges	$\exp(-bs - a\|s\|)$
Poisson Prob. of getting k of independent events (discrete)—model of shot noise, etc.	$\lambda^k e(-\lambda)/k!$ (prob of a negative number of occurrences = 0)	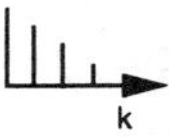	$M = \lambda$ $V = \lambda$	$\exp[\lambda\{\exp(s) - 1\}]$
*Binomial** Prob. of getting k wins in m trials, each with prob of success, $p = 1 - q$	$C_m^k p^k q^{m-k}$	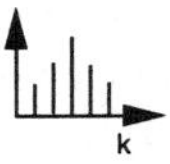	$M = mp$ $V = mpq$	$[1 + p\{\exp(s) - 1\}]^m$

*The *Bernoulli* distribution is a binomial distribution with $m = 1$

i.e. the probability of A and B is the probability of B times the probability of A given B.

The events A and B are called *independent* if

$$P(A|B) = P(A) \tag{C-16}$$

which is the same as

$$P(A,B) = P(A)P(B) \tag{C-17}$$

In this case, the densities can also be written as products, e.g.*

* Independent variates have many mathematical similarities to orthogonal coordinate systems. In particular, they tend to make the algebra much simpler than coupled variates and non-orthogonal coordinates, respectively.

$$p(x_1, x_2) = p(x_1)p(x_2) \tag{C-18}$$

Later, we will introduce the moments of probability densities. These provide simple measures of various attributes of the density function. The "correlation" will be a moment quantifying the extent to which the variates in a multivariate density are independent.

Functions of Random Variables

Given a random variable, x, with density $p(x)$ or a set of random variables, $x_1, x_2, \ldots, x_n$, with density $p(x_1, x_2, \ldots, x_n)$, we frequently need to determine the density corresponding to some function of x or of $x_1, x_2, \ldots, x_n$. This is the central issue of the error combination problem.

First look at the one dimensional case. Let

$$y = y(x) \tag{C-19}$$

If y is a monotonic function, we have

$$P_y(y) = P_x[x(y)] \tag{C-20}$$

and

$$p_y(y)\,|dy| = p_x\,[x(y)]\,|dx| \tag{C-21}$$

i.e.

$$p_y(y) = p[x(y)]\,|dx/dy| \tag{C-22}$$

For example, if x has density function $p(x)$, and

$$y = 3x + 1 \tag{C-23}$$

then y has density function

$$q(y) = p((y - 1)/3)/3 \tag{C-24}$$

As a second example, if x has density function $p(x)$, and $y = x^2$, then y has the density function

$$q(y) = \left[p\left(\sqrt{y}\right) + p\left(-\sqrt{y}\right)\right] / \left[2\sqrt{y}\right] \tag{C-25}$$

The pairing of terms here derives from the fact that y is not monotonic.

Similarly, in the multivariate case, if

$$x = (x_1, \ldots, x_n) \tag{C-26}$$

and

$$y = (y_1, \ldots, y_n) \tag{C-27}$$

are related by a one-to-one transformation, then

$$P_y(y) = P_x[x(y)] \tag{C-28}$$

and

$$p_y(y) = p_x[x(y)]\,|\partial x/\partial y| \tag{C-29}$$

where $|\partial x/\partial y|$ is the Jacobian. The basic idea is that we solve for x in terms of y and substitute this into the argument for the density (in the obvious way) to yield a function of y, and we also rescale the function so that the integral of the density is one.

The process becomes more complicated if we map onto a space of fewer dimensions, e.g.

$$y = (y_1, \ldots, y_m) \tag{C-30}$$

and

$$x = (x_1, \ldots, x_n),\ m < n. \tag{C-31}$$

A special case of this is the sum, $y = x_1 + \ldots + x_n$. We are taking a generalized sort of marginal, and we need to integrate out some of the variables. The problem is to determine what needs to be integrated out. This is usually more easily done in the case of the probability distribution, as opposed to the density. For example, assume we have:

$$y_i = y_i(x_1, \ldots, x_n),\ i = 1, .., m \tag{C-32}$$

The marginal distribution, $P_{y_1}(y_1)$ is, by definition, the probability that "$y_1 \leq Y_1$" as shown in Fig. C- 5, for 2-dimensions. In "y – space", the set of all appropriate y's is the shaded area.

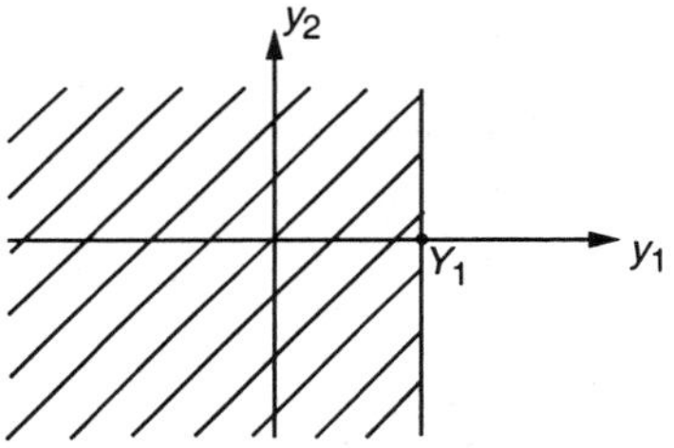

Fig. C-5. Shaded Region Represents the Set of Points for Which the y_1 Component is Less than or Equal to Y_1.

To find $P_{y_1}(y_1)$ we need to associate a probability density with each part of the shaded region, and then integrate (see Fig. C-6). Since we only know the density function in the x-space, we must find the corresponding region there, and integrate there. Thus, for the distribution, $P_{y_1}(y_1)$ = probability that $y_1 \leq Y_1$, we need to integrate over all combinations of the x's which yield a $y_1 \leq Y_1$:

$$P_{y_1}(y_1) = \underset{y_1(x_1 \ldots x_n) \leq Y_1}{\int \ldots \int} p_x(x_1, \ldots, x_n)\, dx_1 \ldots dx_n \tag{C-33}$$

(similarly for $y_2, y_3, \ldots$). The corresponding joint probabilities are

$$P_{y_i \dots y_k}(Y_i \dots Y_k) = \int \dots \int_{\substack{y_i(x_1 \dots x_n) \le Y_i \\ \vdots \\ y_k(x_1 \dots x_n) \le Y_k}} p_x(x_1, \dots, x_n)\, dx_1 \dots dx_n \quad \text{(C-34)}$$

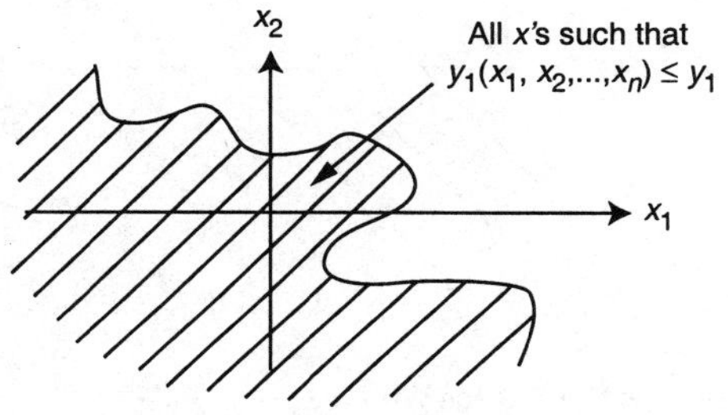

Fig. C-6. Shaded Region is the Set of Points for which $y_1(x_1 \dots x_n) \le Y_1$.

Depending on the nature of the function y, this can take some effort. Similarly, the densities can be found by either (1) differentiating the P's, or (2) integrating the p_x's over suitable subsets of x space. The next section illustrates this for the special case where $y = x_1 + x_2 + \dots + x_n$.

C.2 Addition of Random Variables

Here we have a single function, $y = y(x_1, x_2, \dots x_n)$ given by

$$y = x_1 + x_2 + \dots + x_n. \quad \text{(C-35)}$$

We shall first reproduce the above analysis for this special case. It turns out that when the variables are independent, the analysis can be significantly simplified—in fact, all the standard "textbook" results for the addition of random variables are for independent random variables. We will point out below how these simplifications occur.

For simplicity, first consider the case of two variables. Let the joint distribution of x_1 and x_2 be $P_x(x_1, x_2)$ and the density be $p_x(x_1, x_2)$. As shown graphically in Fig. C-7, the probability that $x_1 + x_2 \le Y$ say is given by the integral of p_x over the shaded region, i.e. over all points x_1, x_2 such that $x_1 + x_2 \le Y$.

Hence,

$$P_y(Y) = \iint_{x_1 + x_2 \le y} p_x(x_1, x_2)\, dx_1\, dx_2 \quad \text{(C-36)}$$

The density is given by:

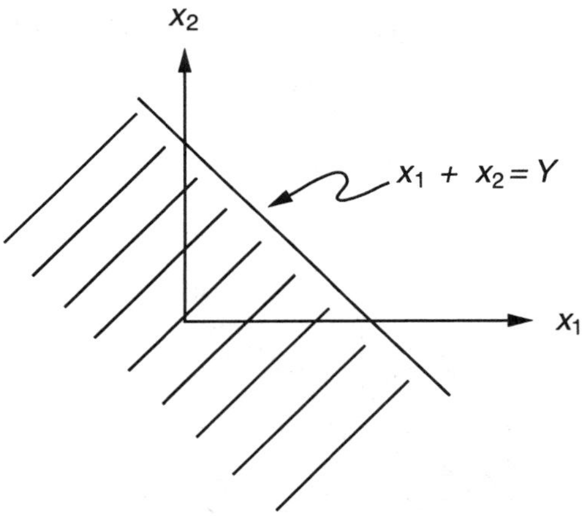

Fig. C-7. Shaded Region is the Set for Which $x_1 + x_2 \le Y$

$$p_y(Y) = \int\int dx_1\, dx_2\; p(x_1, x_2)\,\delta(Y - x_1 - x_2)$$

$$= \int p(x_1, Y - x_1)\, dx_1 \qquad \text{(C-37)}$$

This type of analysis is easily extended to more than two variables. In general, the formulas get very complicated unless the variables are independent. The main exception is if P_x is multivariate Gaussian. The underlying reason for the normal distribution retaining its tractability, even in the presence of correlations, is the fact that we can always transform to a new set of variates which are independent.

In the case where the x_i are independent, the analysis can be simplified as follows. Starting again with the two variate case, we have

$$p(x_1, x_2) = p_1(x_1)\, p_2(x_2) \qquad \text{(C-38)}$$

and

$$y = x_1 + x_2 \qquad \text{(C-39)}$$

$$P_y(y) = \int p_x(x_1, y - x_1)\, dx_1$$

$$= \int p_1(x_1) p_2(y - x_1)\, dx_1 \qquad \text{(C-40)}$$

This is suggestive of the convolution of p_1 and p_2, and invites the use of Fourier transforms. In probability theory, the Fourier transform of a density is called its *characteristic function.**

---

* Characteristic functions or Fourier Transforms are ubiquitous in probability theory and statistics. In fact it has been said that knowledge of statistics, like Electrical Engineering, reduces to a knowledge of the Fourier Transform.

The Fourier Transform of a convolution is the product of the Fourier Transforms.

$$FT\left[p_y(y)\right]=FT\left[\int p_1(x_1)p_2(y-x_1)\,dx_1\right]$$

$$=\int e^{i(q+x_1)s}\,p_1(x_1)\,p_2(q)\,dx_1\,dq$$

$$=FT\left(p_1(x)\right)\,FT\left(p_2(x)\right)=G_{x_1}(s)\,G_{x_2}(s)=G_y(s) \tag{C-41}$$

Hence the distribution of y can be found by inverting the Fourier Transform. This is easily extended to n independent variables—we simply get more terms in the product

$$G=G_1G_2G_3.....G_n \tag{C-42}$$

Examples

(1) The sum of n normal independent random variables is a normal random variable:

$$x=x_1+x_2+\ldots+x_n \tag{C-43}$$

$$p(x_i)=\frac{1}{\sqrt{2\pi}\,\sigma_i}\,\exp\left(-\frac{1}{2}\left[\frac{x_i-\xi_i}{\sigma_i}\right]^2\right)$$

$$\Rightarrow\quad p(x)=\frac{1}{\sqrt{2\pi}\,\sigma}\,\exp\left(-\frac{1}{2}\left[\frac{x-\xi}{\sigma}\right]^2\right) \tag{C-44}$$

where

$$\xi=\xi_1+\ldots+\xi_n$$

$$\sigma^2=\sigma_1^2+\ldots+\sigma_n^2 \tag{C-45}$$

The sum of n statistically independent random variables is normal if and only if each of the variables is normal.

(2) The binomial, Poisson and Cauchy distributions also "reproduce themselves" under addition of independent variates:

If

$$p_i(x_i)=\binom{n_i}{x_i}q^{x_i}(1-q)^{n_i-x_i} \tag{C-46}$$

Then

$$p(x)=\binom{N}{x}q^x(1-q)^{N-x},\ N=n_1+\ldots+n_n \tag{C-47}$$

If

$$p_i(x_i)=e^{-\xi_i}\,\frac{\xi_i^{x_i}}{x_i!} \tag{C-48}$$

Then

$$p(x) = e^{-\xi} \frac{\xi^x}{x!} \quad , \xi = \xi_1 + \ldots + \xi_n \tag{C-49}$$

If

$$p_i(x_i) = \frac{1}{\pi\alpha} \frac{1}{1 + \left(\frac{x_i - \xi_i}{\alpha}\right)^2} \tag{C-50}$$

Then

$$p(x) = \frac{1}{\pi\alpha} \frac{1}{1 + \left(\frac{x - \xi}{\alpha}\right)^2} \tag{C-51}$$

(3) If we add an arbitrary random variable, x, to a *uniformly* distributed random variable, y, the sum, $z = x + y$ yields the moving average of x, assuming x and y are independent. Let

$$\begin{aligned} p(y) &= \frac{1}{2a} \qquad -a \le y < a \\ &= 0 \qquad \text{otherwise} \end{aligned} \tag{C-52}$$

Then

$$\begin{aligned} \mathrm{P_z(z)} &= \int p_x(x)\, p_y(z - x)\, dx = \frac{1}{2a} \int_{z-a}^{z+a} p_x(x)\, dx \\ &= \frac{1}{2a}\left[P_x(z + a) - P_x(z - a)\right] \end{aligned} \tag{C-53}$$

In general, the probability distributions of sums $x_1 + x_2 + \ldots$, where the x_i come from different distribution types, can yield messy algebra.

Other Functions of Random Variables

We have already presented the general approach to finding the probability distributions of functions of random variables other than sums. We have emphasized sums because they are important, particularly since we have indicated that most error combination problems can be reduced to sums, and also because they are tractable. In a few cases, analytical results can be obtained for other functions, as the following examples show.

To find the distribution of a product of two independent random variables, let the variables be x and y, with joint density $f(x,y) = p(x)q(y)$ since they are independent. We want to find the density, $w(z)$, of $z = xy$. We have

$$w(z) = \int_{-\infty}^{\infty} p(x)\, q(z / x) \left|\frac{1}{x}\right| dx \tag{C-54}$$

To find the distribution of a quotient of two independent random variables, with x, y, $p(x)$, $q(y)$ as above, and with $z = x/y$ and the density of z being $w(z)$, we have:

$$W(z) = \int_{-\infty}^{\infty} p(yz)\,q(y)\,|y|\,dy \tag{C-55}$$

For p and q normal, W reduces to a Cauchy distribution.

Once we have the probability distribution of the output (i.e. the system performance), we are in a position to estimate the probability that the system error will lie within the required bounds. The generation of this probability cannot be accomplished analytically, except for some special cases, such as independent, identically distributed e_i, with the p_i given by some of the standard types. It will in general require the use of a Monte Carlo simulation plus some insight to ensure that the basic problem is well defined. This can be time consuming. Also, often the input data (e.g. the p_i) are not particularly well known, and it might not make sense to expend tremendous amounts of computational effort analyzing their consequences. For these reasons, it is often of interest to find simplified ways of assessing the system performance. It turns out that the moments of e can be calculated quite simply in many situations as discussed in the next section.

C.3 Expectations and Moments

It is often convenient to find a few numbers which summarize the key features of a probability distribution. For example, consider the following density functions. In Fig. C-8(A), the density is centered about the origin and is fairly spread out. This indicates that "on average" readings of this variable will give zero, but that there will be a lot of scatter. In Fig. C-8(B), we also have a variable centered about the origin, but in this case there will be much less scatter. In Fig. C-8(C), the density is centered about a non-zero value—i.e. on average, we expect these measurements to give a reading displaced from zero. In Fig. C-8(D), the probability density is "skewed"—there is more scatter for positive than for negative values. The basic point is that the behavior of the random variable can be summarized via a few general features of the density—i.e. measures of location, scatter and symmetry. Invoking the analogy of the mass moments of a rigid body, these features are usually quantified by taking the "moments" of the density function.

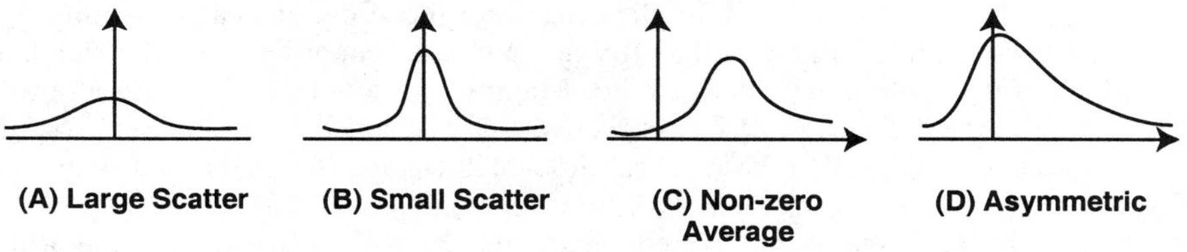

Fig. C-8. Qualitative Features of Distributions.

We start with some definitions. The *expectation* of a function f of a random variable x with probability density $p(x)$ is defined to be:

$$E[f(x)] \equiv \int f(x)\,p(x)\,dx \tag{C-56}$$

The *nth moment* of the probability density $p(x)$ is then defined as

$$m_n(x) \equiv E\left[x^n\right] \tag{C-57}$$

The following rules for expectations are easily established:

$$E(c) = c \tag{C-58}$$

$$E(cf) = cE(f) \tag{C-59}$$

$$E(f_1 + f_2) = E(f_1) + E(f_2) \tag{C-60}$$

If

$$f_1(x) \leq f_2(x) \tag{C-61}$$

for all x then,

$$E(f_1) \leq E(f_2) \tag{C-62}$$

$$|(E(f(x))| \leq E(|f(x)|) \tag{C-63}$$

These results are completely independent of the probability distributions of the random variables.

The first moment, μ, given by

$$\mu \equiv \int xp(x)dx \tag{C-64}$$

corresponds to the "center of mass" of the probability density. It is called the *mean* or *expected value* of the random variable, x. The second moment is called the variance

$$Var(x) \equiv \int (x-\mu)^2 p(x)dx \tag{C-65}$$

The variance is the square of the standard deviation, σ. The variance corresponds to the moment of inertia of p, and the standard deviation to the radius of gyration. They give a measure of how spread out p is, and hence how scattered the observations of the random variable, x, will be. Specifications of error bounds are often given in terms of standard deviations i.e. "n times the standard deviation should not exceed a certain value," where n is typically 1, 2 or 3. Implicit in such a specification is a probability figure. For a given density, p, the probability that a measurement lies within n standard deviations of the mean is well defined. For example, for a normal distribution, these values are 68.3%, 95.5%, and 99.7% respectively as given in Table 7-3 in Sec. 7.2.2.2. We discuss later the fact that these probabilities will change if a different distribution is used.

We now return to the problem of characterizing the probability distribution of the system error, given those of the components. We can use the above rules to calculate some moments of sums:

$$E\left[\Sigma x_i\right] = \Sigma E\left(x_i\right)$$

$$E\left[\Sigma x_i^2\right] = \Sigma\left(Ex_i^2\right) + 2 \sum_{i>j} \sum E\left(x_i\, x_j\right) \tag{C-66}$$

Hence,

$$\mathrm{Var}\left(\Sigma x_i\right) = \Sigma\left(\mathrm{Var}\left(x_i\right)\right) + 2 \sum_{i>j} \Sigma \mathrm{Cov}\left(x_i x_j\right) \tag{C-67}$$

If the x_i are independent, the covariances are zero, and we have

$$\mathrm{Var}(\Sigma\ (x_i)) = \Sigma\ (\mathrm{Var}(x_i)) \tag{C-68}$$

Taking square roots, we have

$$\sigma_{x_1+x_2\ldots x_n} = \sqrt{\sigma_{x_1}^2 + \sigma_{x_2}^2 + \ldots + \sigma_n^2} \tag{C-69}$$

If we have perfect correlation, the standard deviations sum:

$$\mathrm{Var}\left(x_1 + x_2\right) = \mathrm{Var}\left(x_1\right) + \mathrm{Var}\left(x_2\right) + 2\sigma_1\sigma_2 = \sigma_1^2 + \sigma_2^2 + 2\sigma_1\sigma_2 = \left(\sigma_1 + \sigma_2\right)^2 \tag{C-70}$$

Hence

$$\sigma_{x_1+x_2} = \sigma_{x_1} + \sigma_{x_2} \quad (\text{for } r = -1, \text{ this becomes} \left|\sigma_1 - \sigma_2\right|) \tag{C-71}$$

Similar analyses can be carried out for more variables. Hence, if we know the means and standard deviations (or variances) of our inputs, it is easy to calculate the mean and standard deviation of the output, particularly if the inputs are either independent or perfectly correlated.

When the variables are uncorrelated, the system standard deviation is the square root of the sum of the squares, called the *root sum square* or *RSS*, of the individual standard deviations. When the variables are correlated, the system error starts to take on more of the appearance of a sum of the errors of the input variables. The interpretation is that the statistical "smoothing" no longer takes place, and the variables add algebraically. Between these two extremes lie systems with partial correlations. The results also lie in between, and the algebra becomes messier.

If the output is a weighted sum of the individual inputs, we can perform a similar analysis. For uncorrelated inputs, we get a weighted sum of squares for the variance, and for perfect correlation, we get a weighted sum.

Note that in this case we can always rescale the inputs so that the weights are all equal to one—i.e. the weightings really introduce no new concepts or complications.

These results form the basis for some powerful ideas in probability theory and its applications:

(1) Law of Large Numbers

Take the average of a large number of samples,

$$\mu_n = (x_1 + x_2 + \ldots + x_n)/n \tag{C-72}$$

then

$$\mathrm{Var}(\mu_n) = \mathrm{Var}(x)/n \tag{C-73}$$

Thus, the variance of the sample means is $(1/n)$ times the variance of the population. By taking large enough samples we can cluster as close to the mean as desired. However, there are some bounds on "how close". For example, *Chebychev's inequality* says that the probability that we lie within $c\sigma^2\sqrt{n}$ of the mean is greater than $1 - 1/c^2$, for any c. This idea underlies a number of filtering approaches.

(2) Central Limit Theorem

If the x_i are independent and identically distributed, each with mean μ, and variance σ^2, then

$$z_n = \left(x_1 + x_2 + \ldots + x_n\right) / \sqrt{n\sigma^2} \tag{C-74}$$

is normally distributed as $n \to \infty$ **regardless of the distributions of the** $\mathbf{x_i}$. This is used, for example, to justify the use of normal distributions in the theory of errors. The basic idea is that errors of measurement in most physical systems are due to a large number of small influences, so that one can argue that their combination is normally distributed. Experimentally, this is borne out in a wide variety of situations. It is somewhat of a miracle, because the normal distribution also happens to be extremely convenient mathematically. A very large portion of all that has been written on statistics assumes that samples are drawn from normally distributed populations.

(3) Stable distributions

We have already noted that the binomial, Cauchy, Poisson and normal distributions are self reproducing under summation (and hence averaging)—i.e. sums of such variates are also so distributed. This concept can be generalized to that of a *stable* distribution.

Let x, x_1, ..., x_n be independent identically distributed random variables with density $p(x_i)$. Let

$$s_n \equiv x_1 + x_2 + \ldots + x_n \tag{C-75}$$

The density $p(x)$ is *stable* if there exist constants $c_n > 0$ and γ_n (for all $n \geq 2$) such that s_n has the same density as $c_n x + \gamma_n$. If $\gamma_n = 0$, $p(x)$ is called *strictly stable*.

For the normal distribution, $c_n = n^{1/2}$. For the Cauchy, $c_n = n$. One can show [Feller, 1957, 1966]: that c_n can only be of the form

$$n^{1/\alpha}, \quad 0 < \alpha \leq 2 \tag{C-76}$$

where $\alpha = 1$ for Cauchy, 2 for Normal. The distribution

$$\begin{aligned} p(x) &= \frac{1}{\sqrt{2\pi x^3}} e^{-1/2x} && (x > 0) \\ &= 0 && (x < 0) \end{aligned} \tag{C-77}$$

is stable with $\alpha = 1/2$. The stable densities with $\alpha < 2$ do not have variances, i.e. their second moments are unbounded.

(4) Computing Higher Moments

The calculation of the higher moments of sums of independent random variables is usually accomplished using the characteristic function. The log of a characteristic function is easy to differentiate. We define the *nth cumulant* of a random variable, x, as

$$K_n[x] \equiv \frac{1}{i^n} \frac{d^n}{du^n} \log G_x(u) \qquad u = 0 \tag{C-78}$$

The cumulants of independent random variables are additive, i.e.

$$K_r[x_1 + x_2 + \ldots + x_n] = K_r[x_1] + K_r[x_2] + \ldots + K_r[x_n] \tag{C-79}$$

Even if the Fourier Transform of the sum cannot be inverted, we can evaluate the cumulants and express the moments in terms of them. In fact, the first three moments about the mean equal the first three cumulants. This also shows that the first three moments are additive for independent summands.

If we take the Laplace transform of a density function (analogously to taking the Fourier transform to form the *characteristic function*) the result is called the *moment generating function* (*MGF*). The reason for this is that the moments turn out to be the coefficients in the Taylor series for the MGF. Let $G(s)$ be the MGF of the probability density $p(x)$. Then

$$G(s)=\int\left[e^{sx}p(x)dx\right]=E\left[e^{sx}\right] \tag{C-80}$$

Now note that

$$G'(s)=E\left[xe^{sx}\right],\ G''(s)=E\left[x^2e^{sx}\right],\ldots,G^{(n)}(s)=\left[x^ne^{sx}\right] \tag{C-81}$$

Hence

$$G'(0)=E[x],\ G''(0)=E\left[x^2\right],\ldots,G^{(n)}(0)=\left[x^n\right] \tag{C-82}$$

Finally note that

$$G(s)=1+G'(0)s+G''(0)s^2/2!+\ldots=1+E[x]s+E\left[x^2\right]s^2/2!+\ldots \tag{C-83}$$

Two and Three Dimensional Target Spaces

We have seen that if the target location must be specified as a 2 or 3 dimensional vector, we can readily calculate the standard deviation of the error in terms of the standard deviations of the 1-dimensional components. We now discuss the significance of the fact that this system error will have a different probability density from those of the components. To illustrate the ideas involved, we shall present the simplest possible case—a bivariate normal distribution—and then briefly indicate what happens in general.

Suppose the target is nominally at (0,0) in the (x, y) plane, and that the x and y error densities are given by normal densities:

$$p(x)=\frac{1}{\sqrt{2\pi}\sigma_x}e^{-x^2/2\sigma_x^2} \tag{C-84}$$

$$p(y)=\frac{1}{\sqrt{2\pi}\sigma_y}e^{-y^2/2\sigma_y^2} \tag{C-85}$$

Suppose, further, that these are independent, and that $\sigma_x = \sigma_y = \sigma$. Then the probability of making a measurement in an element of area, $dxdy$ is given by

$$p(x,y)dxdy=p(x)p(y)dxdy=\frac{1}{2\pi\sigma^2}e^{-(x^2+y^2)/2\sigma^2}dxdy \tag{C-86}$$

We can convert to polar coordinates (r, θ) and integrate out the θ-dependence, leaving the distribution of radial errors:

$$p(r)dr=\frac{r}{\sigma^2}e^{-r^2/2\sigma^2}dr \tag{C-87}$$

This is called a *circular normal* or *Rayleigh* probability density. It is usually tabulated in terms of the *circular error probability*, or *CEP*.

Assume that the cumulative distribution function, $P\{r \le R\}$ is given by

$$\int_0^R p(r)dr=1-e^{-R^2/2\sigma^2} \tag{C-88}$$

The *CEP* is defined as the *R* such that $P(R) = 0.5$. Hence

$$CEP = \sigma\sqrt{2\ln 2} = 1.177\sigma \tag{C-89}$$

We have also seen that the standard deviation of *r* is

$$\sigma_r = \sqrt{2}\sigma \tag{C-90}$$

Let us now calculate the probability that

$$r \leq \sigma_r = \sqrt{2}\sigma \tag{C-91}$$

We have

$$P\left(\sqrt{2}\sigma\right) = 1 - e^{-1} = 0.6321 \tag{C-92}$$

Similarly the "2σ" probability is $1 - e^4 = .9817$, and the "3σ" probability is 0.9998. Numerical values for 1, 2, 3, and 4σ variations in 1, 2, and 3-dimensional problems are given in Table 7-3 in Sec. 7.2.2. The large print is that the probabilities associated with *n*-sigma errors vary with dimension and with the probability distributions. Note that in two dimensions there is an extra "*r*" factor in the area element. For small *r* we enclose fewer points, while at large *r* we enclose more. In three dimensions we get a similar effect, except that now the extra factor involves r^2. **The main message of this discussion is that the probabilistic significance of n-sigma error bounds changes with the dimensionality of the problem and with the assumed probability distributions.**

Adding Errors of Different Frequencies

Any measurement on a system can be regarded as drawing a sample from an *ensemble* of systems, a population with the statistical properties we have derived. Up to now we have not said anything about how these samples are drawn. We now consider to what extent the sampling procedure can affect the errors. In an actual system, this sampling procedure is realized as a time series of measurements. Apart from providing us with a string of readings (and hence the opportunity to do statistics) a time series has extra structure. Readings taken close together in time can be more closely related than those taken far apart. As a result, the probability distributions of the output will depend on the time scales used in taking the readings. Since time domain and frequency domain behavior can be related through the Fourier transform, the spectral structure of the errors can influence the way in which we combine them.

From a systems engineering point of view, one of our goals in error budgeting is to eliminate excessive conservatism. We don't want to impose unnecessarily strict requirements on the subsystems, since this drives up cost. The "extra degree of freedom" obtained by considering frequency can sometimes be exploited to reduce conservatism. The basic idea is that at any given time only a limited fraction of the total error variance may actually be accessible. This is illustrated schematically in Fig. C-9. We may think of the shaded area (the short term available error variation) as wandering around the total area. At small time scales, our error variance is defined by the shaded area. At long time scales, we can observe errors anywhere in the larger, unshaded area. For this to make sense, there must be two time scales in the problem—a short time scale associated with activity within the shaded area, and a longer one associated with the motion of the shaded area. We also require that the motion of the shaded area be classified as "noise"—i.e. not as a deterministic motion which we should have accounted for in the measurement process.

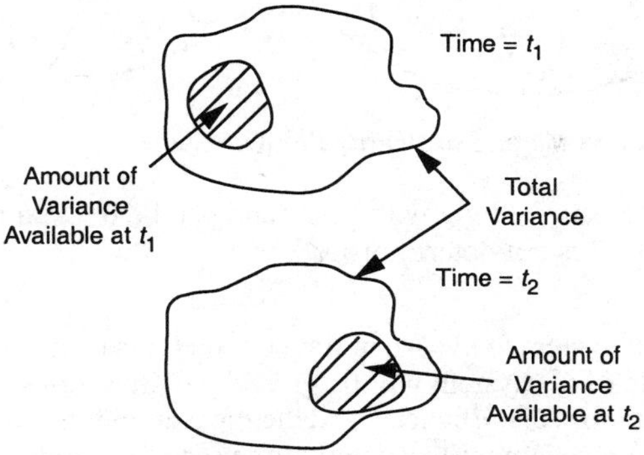

Fig. C-9. The Amount of Variation Available to a System in the Short Term (Shaded Region) May (1) be Smaller than the Total Amount Available in the Long Term (Unshaded Region), and (2) May Move Around with Time.

For a simple illustration, consider adding two pure sinusoids. If the frequencies are far apart, the sum will look like the curve in Fig. C-10.

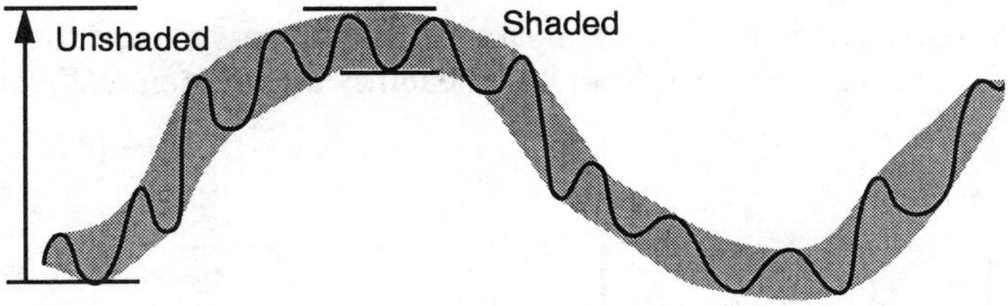

Fig. C-10. Sinusoidal Example of Short Term Variation (Shaded) vs. Long Term Variation (Unshaded).

Measuring over a long time scale, we'll pick up the total variation. Over a short time scale we'll get a smaller "local" variation, plus a slowly varying bias. However, if the frequencies are close together, we'll get a beat pattern as shown in Fig. C-11. In principle, if the frequencies were very steady (in which case they wouldn't be "noise") we could take advantage of the small amplitudes at the nodes of the beats. In practice, there is a band of frequencies, and the beats don't occur. In both these examples, the total sample space available is large (essentially the total variation of the combined signal). In the first case, however, because of the spread in frequencies, the perceived variance can be less than the total variance if an appropriate time scale is used.

It is possible to have "random analogs" to the sinusoids used in the discussion above—an example would be integrated white noise as it appears on a gyro angle out-

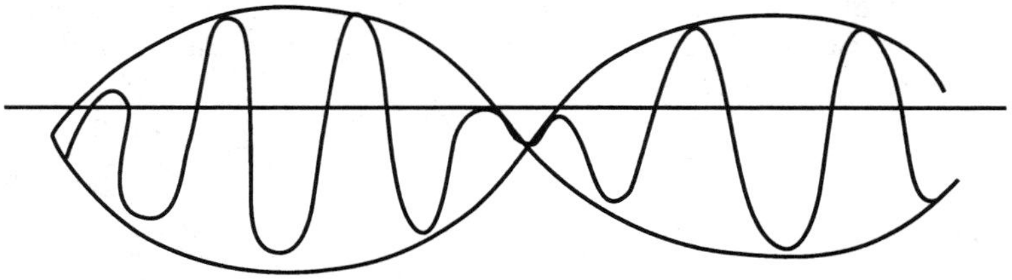

Fig. C-11. Beat Pattern in Mixture of Nearby Frequencies.

put. Here the bias can shift slowly with time (and can be tracked and eliminated from the error budget), but it is not deterministic.*

Stochastic Processes

If we consider our system to evolve in time but that it is influenced by some random effects, then the state of the system will be given by a time series of random variables. Also, the series of random disturbances, and the measurements with random errors that we use to describe our system will also yield time series of random variables. Such series are called *random processes.* We will show how the frequency content of such processes can be measured, and that processes with various frequency contents can be constructed. We will then give an analog of our sinusoidal example.

A *stochastic process* (stochastic means random) is a family $\{X_t: t \varepsilon T\}$ of random variables. For our purposes, the index set, T, will either be a continuous or a discrete time variable. The X_t will typically represent the state of our system. A random process is *strongly stationary* if its probability distributions are invariant under time shifts. It is *weakly stationary* if the first two moments (i.e. the means and covariances) are invariant under time shifts.

For a discrete time variable, a stationary random process is easy to visualize. For each time step, t_i, we draw an X from its probability distribution, $p(X)$, and plot it as shown in Fig. C-12.

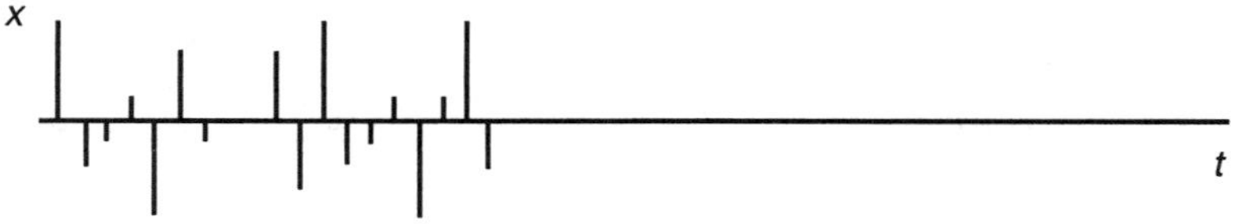

Fig. C-12. A Discrete Time Stationary Random Process, $x = x(t)$. See text for definitions.

If we observe the process for a long time, and count the number of times the ordinate lies between X and $X + dX$ for various X we will find that the probabilities of the various X values match $p(X)$.

Next, we want to see how a frequency spectrum can be associated with such a process. Start in the time domain, and introduce a measure of how much the X's are correlated with their neighbors. A high positive correlation would imply that X does not

---

* There are also a number of deterministic situations in which a slowly varying bias might occur. Typical examples include disturbances that are periodic with the spacecraft orbit, such as thermal or lighting effects.

change rapidly with time. The *autocorrelation function* of a univariate process is defined as

$$R(t) \equiv E\{X(s-t)X^*(s)\} \tag{C-93}$$

It measures the correlation between readings taken a time interval t apart. Given two processes, $x(t)$ and $y(t)$, their *cross-correlation* is

$$R_{xy}(s) \equiv E\{x(t+s)y^*(t)\} \tag{C-94}$$

We now look at how this temporal behavior translates into the frequency domain. The *power spectral density* of a process $x(t)$ is the Fourier Transform of its autocorrelation:

$$S(\omega) \equiv \int_{-\infty}^{\infty} e^{-i\omega t} R(t)dt \tag{C-95}$$

$$R(t) = \frac{1}{2\pi}\int S(\omega)\, e^{i\omega t} d\omega \tag{C-96}$$

The *cross-power spectrum*, or *coherence*, of two processes, $x(t)$ and $y(t)$ is

$$S_{xy}(\omega) \equiv \int R_{xy}(t)e^{-i\omega t}dt \tag{C-97}$$

$$R_{xy}(t) = \frac{1}{2\pi}\int S_{xy}(\omega)\, e^{i\omega t} d\omega \tag{C-98}$$

As the name implies, this measures the power in our signal as a function of frequency, and hence indicates its frequency content.

For example, a theoretical model of *white noise*, $W(t)$, is given by

$$S_{ww}(\omega) = 1,\ R_{ww}(t) = \delta(t) \tag{C-99}$$

There is no correlation over time. For Gaussian white noise, the probability density of each $W(t)$ is Gaussian.* The total power in white noise is

$$\text{Power} = \frac{1}{2\pi}\int S_{ww}(\omega)\, d\omega = \infty \tag{C-100}$$

Any real physical system would attenuate the high frequencies. Modifications of white noise by filtering are termed *colored noise*.

As a second example, a *random walk*, also called *Brownian motion* is integrated white noise. Many physical processes can be modeled as linear systems driven by white noise. *Autoregressive models* are an example of this. They have the form

$$\Sigma a_n x_{t-n} = \omega_t \tag{C-101}$$

Moving average models are another example. They have the form

$$x_t = \Sigma b_n \omega_{t-n} \tag{C-102}$$

---

* In the noise literature, "Normal" distributions are usually called "Gaussian".

These can be combined to yield *moving average autoregressive* models:

$$\sum a_n \, x_{t-n} = \sum b_n \, \omega_{t-n} \tag{C-103}$$

Similar definitions involving stochastic differential equations apply in the continuous case. It should be noted that the "stochastic calculus" involved in the continuous case involves some subtleties. See, for example, Karatzas and Shreve [1997], and Oksendal [1998].

Since many stochastic processes can be built up by passing white noise through various kinds of filters, the inverse problem suggests itself—finding a filter which will reduce a given stochastic process to white noise. Such filters are commonly used in estimation theory—once we get down to white noise, we have essentially squeezed all the information out of the process.

We now return to the "stochastic analog" of the sinusoidal example given previously. We first need to generate a pair of stochastic processes which have very different frequencies, and then discuss how they can be combined. In a real situation, the stochastic processes would be provided by nature. We shall use a pair of mathematically very simple autoregressive processes. (See Box and Jenkins [1970].) Let

$$x_i = a \, x_{i-1} + u_i \tag{C-104}$$

and

$$y_i = -a \, y_{i-1} + v_i \tag{C-105}$$

be two stationary processes. It can be shown that this requires $|a| < 1$. u and v are supposed to both be white noise with variance σ^2. As shown in Fig. C-13, heuristically, x tries to match itself, and hence is relatively smooth, with slow meanderings. y reverses sign at each time step, and hence has a much higher frequency appearance. This is confirmed by calculating the power spectra (the Fourier transforms of the autocovariance functions). See Fig. C-14.

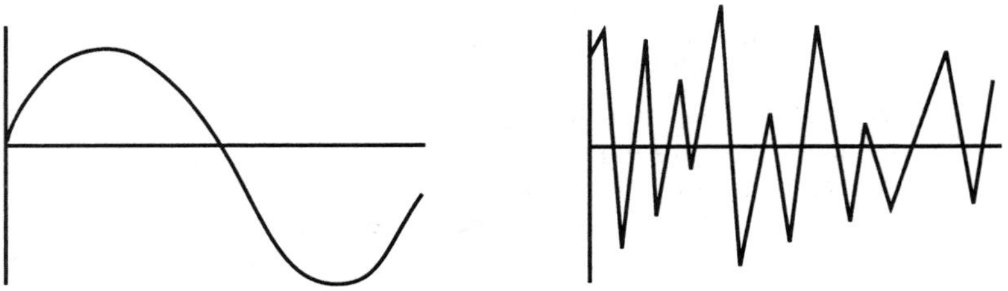

(A) (B)

Fig. C-13. (A) Realization of $x_i = ax_{i-1} + u_i$ $(o<a<1)$. (B) Realization of $y_i = ay_{i-1} + v_i$ $(o<a<1)$.

If we sum x and y we obtain a process with ostensibly the sum of their variances. This is most easily seen by transforming these autoregressive processes into moving average processes. We have

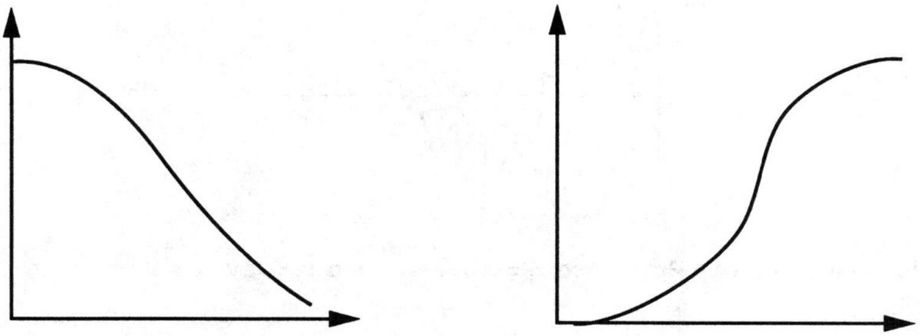

(A) (B)

Fig. C-14. (A) Power Spectra of $x_i = ax_{i-1} + u_i$. (B) Power spectra $y_i = ay_{i-1} + v_i$.

$$(1 - aB)x_i = u_i \tag{C-106}$$

where B is the back-shift operator,

$$Bx_i \equiv k_{i-1} \tag{C-107}$$

Hence

$$x_i = u_i\,(1 + aB + [aB]^2 + \ldots.) \tag{C-108}$$

and

$$\mathrm{Var}(x_i) = \mathrm{Var}(u)(1 + a^2 + a^4 + \ldots) = \sigma^2/(1 - a^2) \tag{C-109}$$

Similarly,

$$y_i = v_i(1 - aB + [aB]^2 - \ldots) \tag{C-110}$$

and

$$\mathrm{Var}\,(y_i) = \mathrm{Var}\,(v)(1 + a^2 + a^4 + \ldots) = \sigma^2/(1 - a^2) \tag{C-111}$$

If we call

$$z = x + y \tag{C-112}$$

we have

$$z_i = u_i(1 + aB + [aB]^2 + \ldots) + v_i(1 - aB + [aB]^2 - \ldots) \tag{C-113}$$

and

$$\mathrm{Var}(z_i) = \mathrm{Var}\,(u)/(1 - a^2) + \mathrm{Var}\,(v)/(1 - a^2) = \sigma_{xi}^2 + \sigma_{yi}^2 \tag{C-114}$$

This corresponds to the unshaded area alluded to in the introduction to this section. To see quantitatively that the short term variance is lower we can proceed in various ways. First, we can simply add the two plots, obtaining the results shown in Fig. C-15.

We essentially get y modulated by x. For short time periods, the local variation is predominantly that of y. Alternatively, we can note that the spectrum at high frequencies is essentially that of y as shown in Fig. C-16.

Fig. C-15. Sum of the Two Processes $x_i = ax_{i-1} + u_i$ and $y_i = -ay_{i-1} + V_i$

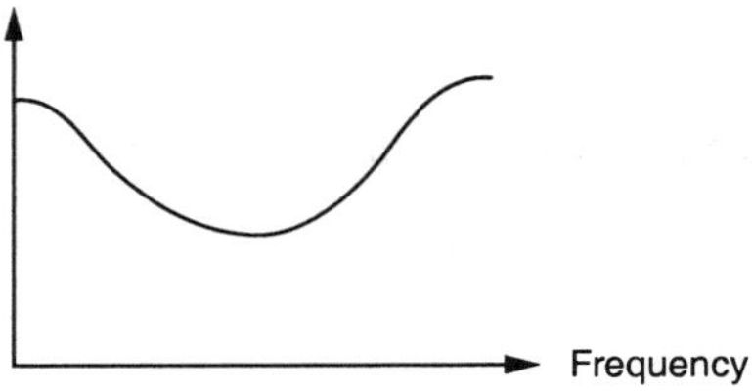

Fig. C-16. Spectrum of Combined Process.

This again implies that the short term fluctuations are mainly those due to y. Finally, we can look at the autocorrelation function, as seen in Fig. C-17, and note that for short time differences, deviations of the autocorrelation function from unity (i.e. "smoothness") are due to y:

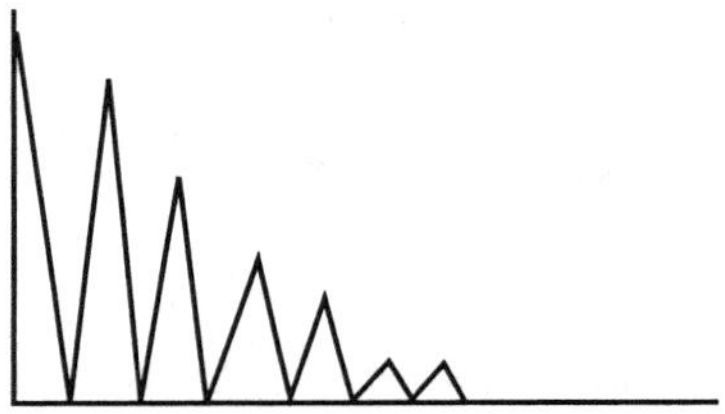

Fig. C-17. Autocorrelation Function for Combined Process.

In summary, the basic point is that we can "achieve" σ_y^2 even though the net variance of the system is $\sigma_x^2 + \sigma_y^2$, over time scales short compared with the main frequency content of "x". Hence, in coming up with an error budget (for short time scales) we can reduce the variance from the "nominal value".

For example, if we return to Table 5-15, we would expect errors (2) and (7) to vary much more slowly than the others. On the shorter time scale of the other errors we would thus expect to be able to estimate these "biases" and correspondingly reduce the system error. The effect of time scale on variance can be conveniently summarized in terms of the Allen Variance $\sigma_A(t)$, which gives the variance in output measurements when those measurements are averaged over a time scale, t. If the output is a sum of inputs with different spectra, these can be identified in a plot of $\sigma_A(t)$. At different time scales, different spectra become dominant. There is an optimum time scale that involves a minimum variance. From the standpoint of error budgeting, we need to identify an appropriate frequency band. This, in turn will yield the corresponding output variance.

C.4 Example: Minimizing Cost

Up to this point, we have not discussed how the error budget is distributed among the various components. We have only shown how a given set of errors contributed by the components can be added. Normally the flowdown of requirements to the components is accomplished by simply spreading the pain as evenly as possible. In this section we briefly describe how the budget can be optimized in terms of cost.

An error budget should be formulated with an eye toward the sensitivity of the cost of each component to its accuracy requirement. However, cost figures are hard to come by. If an item can be bought off the shelf, there should be no problem. If a new item has to be developed, the risk and cost go up. The more challenging the requirement, the more surprises can arise which tend to add to the cost.

For costing analyses, these distributions are often approximated by triangular distributions as shown in Fig. C-18. As the annotations in the figure indicate, the shape of the triangle will correspond to the amount of risk, and the location to the expected cost. As the requirements on a given object are made more stringent, its triangle will start looking more risky. Fig. C-19 shows a hypothetical family of distributions for a given type of instrument, as the error bounds are tightened. Note that the highest possible cost grows much more rapidly than the "expected cost", and the corresponding distributions become more and more skewed. The idea is to come up with a family of such curves for each of the components. Having compiled all this information, we now must come up with our error budget—i.e. we must apportion out the total allowable system error to the various components in such a way as to minimize the cost. Conceptually, we want to superimpose curves of constant system cost onto a plot of the error budget constraint (Fig. C-20), and find the lowest cost consistent with the constraint, i.e. the point of tangency. From this we can read off the optimal error budget process as follows:

1. For each component, we can translate the family of cost curves into a curve of accuracy vs cost. We then sum these to obtain curves of system cost. The summation procedure will require care, since it should account for correlations, and, perhaps more important, account for risk. This amounts to deciding which curves to add. A conservative approach would be to use the upper bound curves. This is usually too conservative. Note, for example, that if we push the performance of one item, we may be able to back off on another—i. e. the costs tend to be correlated. We have seen that it is simple to add mean values, and standard deviations. Hence, we can find "mean plus n-sigma" curves for the system cost.
2. Finding the error budget constraint curve, i.e. combinations of component errors which are compatible with the allowed system error, is straightforward assuming we characterize the errors via their standard deviations. For example, if we have n components, then the surface of all combinations of sigmas which will RSS to a given system sigma is an n-sphere. For example, in 2-dimensions we have a circle. This can be compared with the more conservative sum, given by the straight line in Fig. C-21. Other correlation values will give intermediate curves. These can now be overlaid on the cost curves to find the optimum vector of sigmas to create the error budget.

In a cost setting it is common to have to provide a probability distribution of system cost—i.e. not simply an expected value or a mean plus n-sigma. Such distributions are

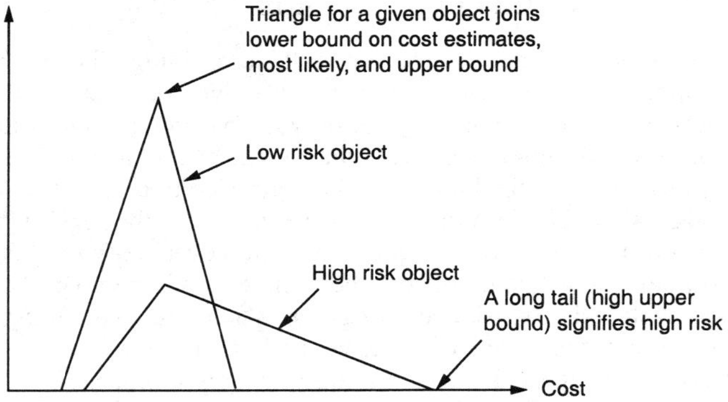

Fig. C-18. Idealized Probability Density Functions for Low and High Risk Items.

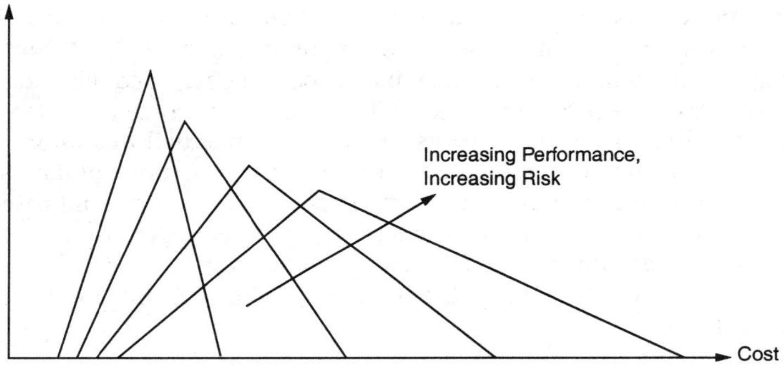

Fig. C-19. Family of Probability Density Functions Parametrized Accordingly to Risk (or Performance)

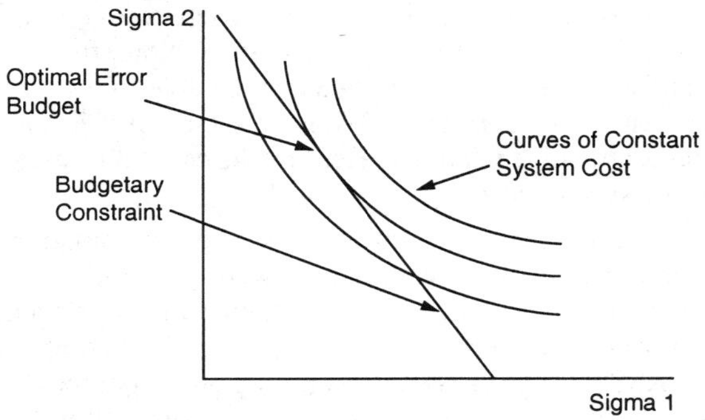

Fig. C-20. Curves of Constant System Cost as a Function of Component Performance Requirements—and Hence Risk—as Derived from the Cost-Risk Curves in Fig. C-19. Superimposed on a Curve of the Error Budget Constraint (Combination of Component Performances which Yield a Given System Performance). The optimal error budget can be read off from this plot.

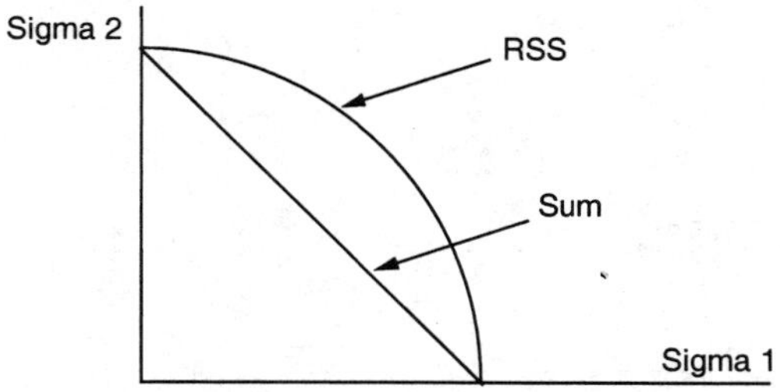

Fig. C-21. Curves of Constant System Error Budget (Sum and RSS).

usually generated using Monte Carlo techniques based on the triangular distributions described above. The cost portion of the error budgeting problem described in this example can also be handled directly via Monte Carlo methods.

It should be noted that error budgets are not typically developed as outlined in this example. The error is often uniformly distributed among the components, or else is allocated based on the known capabilities of existing components. We will generally have some awareness of the state of the art, and will avoid setting unreasonable and, hence, expensive requirements. The error budgeting process usually involves some iterations and negotiation of "terrible injustices" [Williams, 1992].

References

Feller, W. 1957, 1976. *An Introduction to Probability Theory and its Applications*. Vol.1 (1957), Vol.2 (1966), Wiley.

Meyer, P.L. 1972. *Introductory Probability and Statistical Applications*. Addison-Wesley.

Papoulis, A. 1965. *Probability, Random Variables and Stochastic Processes*. McGraw-Hill.

Parzen, E. 1960. *Modern Probability Theory and its Applications*. Wiley .

Kac, M. 1989. *Statistical Independence in Probability, Analysis and Number Theory*. MAA.

Box, G. and G. Jenkins. 1970. *Time Series Analysis*. Holden-Day.

Karatzas, I. and S. Shreve. 1997. *Brownian Motion and Stochastic Calculus*. Springer.

Oksendal, B. 1998. *Stochastic Differential Equations*. Springer.

Williams, Michael. 1992. "Requirements Definition." In Larson, Wiley J. and Wertz, James R. (eds.). *Space Mission Analysis and Design,* 2nd ed. Dordrecht, The Netherlands and Torrance, CA: Kluwer Academic and Microcosm, Inc.

Appendix D

Summary of Keplerian Orbit and Coverage Equations

This appendix provides summary formulas in addition to those given in Table 2-4 in Sec. 2.1. Formulas are provided for all four types of Keplerian orbits—circular, elliptical, parabolic, and hyperbolic. See Sec. 2.1 for definition of orbit variables, derivations, and conditions. See Table D-1 for values of the gravitational constant, μ, for the Earth, Moon, Sun, and Mars. See Table E-1 in App. E for values of μ for all of the major bodies in the solar system. See Sec. 9.1 for definition of most of the geometric variables. Finally, numerical evaluations of most of the characteristics of the motion are contained in Appendix F for orbits about the Sun, Moon, and Mars and on the pages preceding the inside rear cover for orbits about the Earth.

μ = GM is the gravitational constant of the central body and is much more accurately known than either the mass, M, or the universal gravitational constant, G, the least accurately known of the fundamental physical constants.

For all of the orbit types, ν is the true anomaly = the angle from perifocus to the orbiting body and $M = n(t - T)$ is the mean anomaly, where t is the time of observation, T is the time of perifocal passage, and n is the mean angular motion. Other parameters are defined in the table and discussed at the text reference cited in the table.

TABLE D-1. Values of the Gravitational Constant, μ, for the Earth, Sun, Moon, and Mars. Values are those given by Cox [2000], which are in close agreement with those in use by the International Astronomical Union. See Table E-1 in App. E for other central bodies.

Central Body	μ (m^3/s^2)	$\sqrt{\mu}$ ($m^{1.5}/s$)
Earth	$3.986\,004\,41 \times 10^{14}$	19,964,980.4
Moon	$4.902\,798\,98 \times 10^{12}$	2,214,226.5
Mars	$4.283\,200\,00 \times 10^{13}$	6,544,616.1
Sun	$1.327\,124\,38 \times 10^{20}$	11,520,088,436

D.1 Equations for Circular Orbits

See Sec. 2.1 for definition of orbit variables, Sec. 9.1 for definition of geometric variables, and Sec. 8.3.3 for application of the Euler axis formula as to satellite ground tracks. See rear end-papers for numerical evaluation of most Earth satellite formulas and App. F for properties of orbits about the Moon, Sun, and Mars.

Note: A bold **"C"** is put in front of each descriptor to denote formulas for circular orbits.

C. Defining parameter: a = semimajor axis = r = radius (D-1)

(For a discussion of Keplerian orbits, see Sec. 2.1; for transformations between orbital elements and position and velocity, see Sec. 2.7.1.1 and 2.7.1.2; for the apparent shape of a circular orbit viewed from near-by, see Sec. 6.3.4.)

C. Parametric equation: $x^2 + y^2 = a^2$ (D-2)

C. Distance from focus, *r*: $r = a$ (D-3)

C. Specific energy, ε (= Total energy per unit mass):

$$\varepsilon = -\frac{\mu}{2a} = \frac{V^2}{2} - \frac{\mu}{a} \qquad \text{(D-4)}$$

C. Specific angular momentum, *h*: $h = |\mathbf{h}| = \sqrt{\mu a}$ (D-5)

C. Angular momentum vector, h: $\mathbf{h} = \mathbf{r} \times \mathbf{V}$ (D-6)

C. Nodal vector, N: $\mathbf{N} = \hat{\mathbf{z}} \times \hat{\mathbf{h}} = \hat{\mathbf{z}} \times \mathbf{h} / h$ (D-7)

C. Inclination, *i*: $i = \text{acos}\,(h_z / h)$ (D-8)

(For a discussion of apparent inclination, see the Boxed Example at the end of Sec. 9.3.1.)

C. Right ascension of the ascending node, Ω : $\Omega = \text{atan2}\,(N_y, N_x)$ (D-9)

C. Flight path angle, ϕ_{fpa}: $\phi_{fpa} = 0$ (D-10)

C. Perifocal distance, *q*: $q = \text{a}$ (D-11)

C. Semi-parameter, *p*: $p = a$ (D-12)

C. Semimajor axis, *a*: $a = r$ (D-13)

C. Eccentricity, *e*: $e = 0$ (D-14)

C. Mean motion, *n*: $n = \sqrt{\mu / a^3} = 2\pi / P$ (D-15)

C. Mean anomaly, *M*: $M = M_0 + nt$ (D-16)

C. True anomaly, ν: $\nu = M$ (D-17)

C. Rate of change of true anomaly, $\dot{\nu}$: $\dot{\nu} = n$ (D-18)

C. Period, P : $P = 2\pi / n = 2\pi\sqrt{a^3 / \mu}$ (D-19)

$= 1.658\ 669\ 010 \times 10^{-4}\ a^{3/2}$ (for Earth; P in min, a in km)

$= 1.495\ 569\ 413 \times 10^{-3}\ a^{3/2}$ (for Moon; P in min, a in km)

$= 5.059\ 429\ 211 \times 10^{-4}\ a^{3/2}$ (for Mars; P in min, a in km)

$= 1.996\ 228\ 781 \times 10^{-10}\ a^{3/2}$ (for Sun; P in days, a in km)

C. Velocity, V : $V = \sqrt{\mu / a} = an$ (D-20)

C. Range • range rate, $r\dot{r}$: $r\dot{r} = 0$ (D-21)

C. Areal velocity, $\dot{A}$: $\dot{A} = 0.5\sqrt{\mu a} = 0.5\ a^2 n$ (D-22)

C. Escape velocity, V_E : $V_E = \sqrt{2\mu / a} = \sqrt{2}V$ (D-23)

C. Euler axis co-latitude, δ'_E : $\delta'_E = \text{atan}\left(\dfrac{n \sin i}{-\omega_E + n \cos i}\right)$ (D-24)

ω_E = inertial rotation rate of central body
= 0.004 178 074 deg/sec (Earth)
= 0.000 152 504 deg/sec (Moon)
= 0.004 061 249 deg/sec (Mars)

(For a complete set of closed-form ground track equations, see Table 8-9 in Sec. 8.3 and Sec. 9.3.1.)

C. Euler rotation rate, ω_E : $\omega_E = n \sin i / \sin \delta'_E$ (D-25)

$= \sqrt{\omega_E^2 + n^2 + 2n\omega_E \cos i}$

C. Angular radius of the Earth, ρ : $\rho = \text{asin}(R_E/a)$ (D-26)

R_E = radius of central body
= 6378.140 km (Earth)
= 1738.2 km (Moon)
= 3397 km (Mars)

(Assumes a spherical Earth. For the effect of oblateness, see Sec. 9.1.5.)

C. Distance to the horizon, D : $D = a \cos \rho$ (D-27)

$= \sqrt{a^2 - R_E^2}$

(For calculation of angles and distance for targets not on the horizon, see Sec. 9.1.1.)

C. Maximum Earth central angle, λ_{max} : λ_{max} = 90 deg – ρ (D-28)

= acos (R_E/a)

C. Instantaneous Access Area, *IAA* : $IAA = K_A(1 - \cos \lambda_{max})$ (D-29)

$K_A = 2\pi \approx 6.283\ 185\ 311$ for area in steradians
$= 360^2 / (2\pi) \approx 20{,}626.480\ 62$ for area in deg^2
$= 2.556\ 041\ 87 \times 10^8$ for area in km^2 (Earth)

$= 1.898\,363 \times 10^7$ for area in km^2 (Moon)
$= 7.250\,550 \times 10^7$ for area in km^2 (Mars)

(For alternative ways to calculate ground coverage, see Sec. 9.5.1; for other ground area formulas, see Table 9-7 in Sec. 9.5.1; for transformations between geocentric and access area coordinates, see the Boxed Example in Sec. 9.1; for projections of sensor fields of view onto the central body, see Sec. 9.1.4.)

C. Area Access Rate, *AAR* :

$$AAR = 2K_A \frac{\sin \lambda_{max}}{P} \tag{D-30}$$

C. Maximum time in view, T_{max} :

$$T_{max} = P\lambda_{max} / 180 \text{ deg} \tag{D-31}$$

(For a complete set of target or ground station coverage formulas, see Table 9-4 in Sec. 9.4.1.)

C. Maximum angular rate seen from ground, $\dot{\theta}_{max}$:

$$\dot{\theta}_{max} = \frac{a \; 360^\circ}{P(a - R_E)} \tag{D-32}$$

C. Node precession rate due to J_2, $\Delta\Omega_{J2}$:

$$\Delta\Omega_{J2} = -1.5 n J_2 n (R_E / a)^2 \cos i \equiv K_{J2}\, a^{-7/2} \cos i \tag{D-33}$$

$= -2.064\,74 \times 10^{14}\, a^{-7/2} \cos i$ (Earth, a in km)
$= -3.220 \times 10^{11}\, a^{-7/2} \cos i$ (Moon, a in km)
$= -3.483 \times 10^{13}\, a^{-7/2} \cos i$ (Mars, a in km)

(In the numerical forms, $\Delta\Omega_{J2}$ is in deg / calendar day)

C. Sun-synchronous inclination, i_{SS}:

$$i_{ss} = \text{acos}\left(\frac{360\, a^{7/2}}{K_{J2} SP}\right) \tag{D-34}$$

$= \text{acos}(-4.773\,7 \times 10^{-15}\, a^{7/2})$ (Earth, a in km)
$= \text{acos}(-3.061 \times 10^{-12}\, a^{7/2})$ (Moon, a in km)
$= \text{acos}(-1.505 \times 10^{-14}\, a^{7/2})$ (Mars, a in km)

(Where *SP* is the sidereal period of the planet about the Sun in calendar days. For a discussion of Sun synchronous orbits, see Sec. 2.5.3.)

C. Revolutions per day, *Rev/d*:

$$Rev/d = \text{Day} / \text{P} \tag{D-35}$$

$= 1{,}436.07 / P$ (Earth, P in min)
$= 39{,}343 / P$ (Moon, P in min)
$= 1{,}477.38 / P$ (Mars, P in min)

(This is the number of orbit revolutions for each rotation of the planet on its axis relative to the fixed stars (i.e., the inertial rotation period). "Day" is the length of the sidereal day for the given central body. For more accurate expressions, see the discussion of repeating ground tracks in Sec. 2.5.2.)

C. Node spacing, ΔN:

$$\Delta N = 360 \text{ deg } (P / \text{Day}) \tag{D-36}$$
$$= 0.250\,684\ P \quad \text{(Earth, } P \text{ in min)}$$
$$= 0.009\,150\,3\ P \quad \text{(Moon, } P \text{ in min)}$$
$$= 0.243\,675\ P \quad \text{(Mars, } P \text{ in min)}$$

(For the equations for repeating ground track orbits, see Sec. 2.5.2.)

C. Maximum eclipse, T_E:

$$T_E = P(\rho / 180 \text{ deg}) = P \operatorname{asin}(R_E / a)/180 \text{ deg} \tag{D-37}$$

(For computation of eclipse duration for any Sun angle, see Sec. 6.3.2; for the formulas for eclipse conditions, see Sec. 11.4.)

C. Sun angle constraints for terminator visibility, β':

$$90° + \xi - \rho < \beta' < 90° - \xi + \rho \tag{D-38}$$

(ξ is the dark angle defined in Sec. 11.5.2. For general conditions of terminator visibility, see Table 11-3 in Sec. 11.5.2.)

C. Transit time for a spacecraft whose celestial coordinates are known, T:

$$T = \alpha + L - \text{GST} \tag{D-39}$$

(where α is the right ascension, L is the observer East longitude, and GST is the Greenwich Sidereal Time. For computation of observability times of spacecraft for which the celestial coordinates are known, see Table 9-6 in Sec. 9.4.4.

D.2 Equations for Elliptical Orbits

See Sec. 2.1 for definition of orbit variables, Sec. 9.1 for definition of geometric variables, and Sec. 8.3.3 for application of the Euler axis formulas to satellite ground tracks. See rear end-papers for numerical evaluation of most Earth satellite formulas and App. F for properties of orbits about the Moon, Sun, and Mars.

Note: An "E" is put in front of each descriptor to denote formulas for Ecliptical Orbits. Subscript A stands for evaluation of parameters at apogee; subscript P stands for evaluation of parameters at perigee.

E. Defining parameters:

$$a = \text{semimajor axis} \tag{D-40}$$
$$b = \text{semiminor axis}$$

(For a discussion of Keplerian orbits, see Sec. 2.1; for transformations between orbital elements and position and velocity, see Sec. 2.7.1.1 and 2.7.1.2.)

E. Parametric equation:

$$\frac{x^2}{a^2} + \frac{y^2}{b^2} = 1 \tag{D-41}$$

E. Distance from focus, r:

$$r = \frac{q(1+e)}{(1+e\cos\nu)} = a(1 - e\cos E) = \frac{p}{1+e\cos\nu} = \frac{r_A(1-e)}{1+e\cos\nu} \tag{D-42}$$

E. Specific energy, ε (= Total energy per unit mass):

$$\varepsilon = \frac{V^2}{2} - \frac{\mu}{r} = -\frac{\mu}{2a} < 0 \qquad \text{(D-43)}$$

E. Specific angular momentum, h:

$$h = |h| = \sqrt{\mu p} = rV\cos\phi_{fpa} = r^2\dot{\nu} = r_A V_A = r_p V_p \qquad \text{(D-44)}$$

E. Angular momentum vector, h: $\mathbf{h} = \mathbf{r} \times \mathbf{V}$ (D-45)

E. Nodal vector, N: $\mathbf{N} = \hat{\mathbf{z}} \times \hat{\mathbf{h}} = \hat{\mathbf{z}} \times \mathbf{h} / h$ (D-46)

E. Eccentricity vector, e: $\mathbf{e} = \dfrac{\mathbf{V} \times \mathbf{h}}{\mu} - \dfrac{\mathbf{r}}{r}$ (D-47)

E. Inclination, *i*: $i = \text{acos}(h_z / h)$ (D-48)

(For a discussion of apparent inclination, see the Boxed Example at the end of Sec. 9.3.1.)

E. Right ascension of the ascending node, Ω: $\Omega = \text{atan2}(N_y, N_x)$ (D-49)

E. Flight path angle, ϕ_{fpa}:

$$\phi_{fpa} = \text{atan2}\,(\cos\phi_{fpa}, \sin\phi_{fpa}) = \text{acos}\left(\sqrt{\mu p} / rV\right) \qquad \text{(D-50)}$$

$$\sin\phi_{fpa} = \frac{e \sin E}{\sqrt{1 - e^2\cos^2 E}}$$

$$\cos\phi_{fpa} = \sqrt{\frac{1 - e^2}{1 - e^2\cos^2 E}}$$

E. Perifocal distance, q = radius of perigee, r_P :

$$q = r_p = a(1-e) = \frac{p}{1+e} = r_A\left(\frac{1-e}{1+e}\right) = \frac{b^2}{r_A} = r_A\left(V_A / V_P\right) \qquad \text{(D-51)}$$

E. Semi-parameter, p:

$$p = a(1-e^2) = r(1 + e\cos\nu) = q(1+e) = b^2/a = h^2/\mu \qquad \text{(D-52)}$$

E. Radius of apogee, r_A:

$$r_A = a(1+e) = 2a - r_P = b^2 / r_P = q\left(\frac{1+e}{1-e}\right) = \frac{b^2}{a-c} \qquad \text{(D-53)}$$

E. Semimajor axis, a:

$$a = \frac{r_A + r_P}{2} = \frac{r_P}{1-e} = \frac{r_A}{1+e} = \frac{p}{1-e^2} = -\frac{\mu}{2\varepsilon} = \left(\frac{\mu}{n^2}\right)^{1/3} \qquad \text{(D-54)}$$

E. Semiminor axis, b: $$b = a\sqrt{1-e^2} = \sqrt{ap} = \sqrt{r_A r_P} = \sqrt{\mu p / h} \qquad \text{(D-55)}$$

E. Eccentricity, e:

$$e = |\mathbf{e}| = \sqrt{1 + \frac{2\varepsilon h^2}{\mu^2}} = \frac{\sqrt{a^2 - b^2}}{a} = \frac{r_A - r_P}{r_A + r_P} = \frac{r_A}{a} - 1 = 1 - \frac{r_P}{a} = \frac{c}{a} \qquad \text{(D-56)}$$

$0 < e < 1$

E. Mean motion, n: $$n = \sqrt{\mu / a^3} = \frac{2\pi}{P} \qquad \text{(D-57)}$$

E. Mean anomaly, M: $$M = M_o + nt = E - e \sin E \qquad \text{(D-58)}$$

E. Eccentric anomaly, E:

$$E = \operatorname{atan2}(\cos E, \sin E) = 2 \operatorname{atan}\left[\sqrt{\frac{1-e}{1+e}} \tan(\nu / 2)\right] \qquad \text{(D-59)}$$

$$= \operatorname{acos}\left(\frac{a - r}{ae}\right) = \operatorname{asin}\left(\frac{r}{b} \sin \nu\right) = \operatorname{acos}\left(\frac{a - r}{a - r_p}\right)$$

$$\cos E = \frac{e + \cos\nu}{1 + e\cos\nu} \qquad \sin E = \frac{\sin\nu\sqrt{1-e^2}}{1 + e\cos\nu}$$

as an iterative equation with successive estimates E_i:

$$E_{i+1} = E_i + \frac{M - E_i + e\sin E_i}{1 - e\cos E_i}$$

E. True anomaly, ν: $$\nu = \operatorname{atan2}(\cos\nu, \sin\nu) = 2 \operatorname{atan}\left[\sqrt{\frac{1+e}{1-e}} \tan(E / 2)\right] \qquad \text{(D-60)}$$

$$= \operatorname{acos}\left(\frac{p / r - 1}{e}\right) = \operatorname{acos}\left(\frac{\cos E - e}{1 - e\cos E}\right)$$

$$\cos\nu = \frac{\cos E - e}{1 - e\cos E} \qquad \sin\nu = \frac{\sin E\sqrt{1-e^2}}{1 - e\cos E}$$

as a power series in M:

$$\nu \approx M + 2e\sin M + \frac{5}{4}e^2 \sin 2M - \frac{1}{4}e^3 \sin M \qquad \text{(D-61)}$$

$$+ \frac{13}{12}e^3 \sin 3M + \mathcal{O}\left(e^4\right)$$

E. Rate of change of true anomaly, $\dot{\nu}$:

$$\dot{\nu} = \frac{\sqrt{\mu p}}{r^2} = \frac{V_P r_P}{r^2} = \frac{V_A r_A}{r^2} = \frac{na^2}{r^2}\sqrt{1-e^2} \qquad \text{(D-62)}$$

E. Period, P: $P = 2\pi / n = 2\pi\sqrt{a^3 / \mu}$ (D-63)

$= 1.658\,669\,010 \times 10^{-4}\, a^{3/2}$ (for Earth; P in min, a in km)
$= 1.495\,569\,413 \times 10^{-3}\, a^{3/2}$ (for Moon; P in min, a in km)
$= 5.059\,429\,211 \times 10^{-4}\, a^{3/2}$ (for Mars; P in min, a in km)
$= 1.996\,228\,781 \times 10^{-10}\, a^{3/2}$ (for Sun; P in days, a in km)

E. Velocity, V:

$$V = \sqrt{\frac{2\mu}{r} - \frac{\mu}{a}} = \sqrt{2\left(\frac{\mu}{r} + \varepsilon\right)} = \sqrt{\frac{\mu}{r}\left(2 - \frac{1 - e^2}{1 + e\cos\nu}\right)} \qquad \text{(D-64)}$$

$$= \sqrt{\mu p} \,/\, \left(r\cos\phi_{fpa}\right)$$

$$\frac{V_A}{V_P} = \frac{r_P}{r_A}$$

$$V_P = \sqrt{\frac{\mu}{r_P}(1 + e)} = \sqrt{\frac{2\mu r_A}{r_P\left(r_A + r_P\right)}} = \sqrt{\frac{\mu}{r_P}\left(2 - \frac{r_P}{a}\right)} = V_A\left(\frac{r_A}{r_P}\right)$$

$$V_A = \sqrt{\frac{\mu}{r_A}(1 - e)} = \sqrt{\frac{\mu r_P}{a\, r_A}} = \sqrt{\frac{\mu}{r_A}\left(2 - \frac{r_A}{a}\right)} = V_P\left(\frac{r_P}{r_A}\right)$$

E. Azimuthal velocity, V_{az}: $V_{az} = V\cos\phi_{fpa} = r\dot{\nu}$ (D-65)

E. Radial velocity, V_r: $V_r = V\sin\phi_{fpa} = V_{az}\dfrac{e\sin\nu}{q}$ (D-66)

$$= \frac{r\,\dot{\nu}\, e\sin\dot{\nu}}{1 + e\cos\nu}$$

E. Range • range rate, $r\dot{r}$: $r\dot{r} = e\sqrt{a\mu}\,\sin E$ (D-67)

E. Areal velocity, $\dot{A}$: $\dot{A} = 0.5\sqrt{a\mu\left(1 - e^2\right)} = 0.5\, r^2\dot{\nu}$ (D-68)

E. Escape velocity, V_E: $V_E = \sqrt{2\mu / r}$ (D-69)

E. Euler axis co-latitude, δ'_E: $\delta'_E = \operatorname{atan}\left(\dfrac{\dot{\nu}\sin i}{-\omega_E + \dot{\nu}\cos i}\right)$ (D-70)

ω_E = inertial rotation of central body
= 0.004 178 074 deg/sec (Earth)
= 0.000 152 504 deg/sec (Moon)
= 0.004 061 249 deg/sec (Mars)

(For a complete set of ground track equations, see Table 8-9 in Sec. 8.3 and Sec. 9.3.1, which also includes a discussion of approximations for small eccentricities.)

E. Euler rotation rate, ω_E:

$$\omega_E = \dot{v} \sin i / \sin \delta_E' = \sqrt{\omega_E^2 + \dot{v}^2 + 2\dot{v}\omega_E \cos i} \quad \text{(D-71)}$$

E. Angular radius of the Earth, ρ: $\rho = \text{asin}\,(R_E / r)$ (D-72)

R_E = radius of central body
= 6378.140 km (Earth)
= 1738.2 km (Moon)
= 3397 km (Mars)

(Assumes a spherical Earth. For the effect of oblateness, see Sec. 9.1.5.)

E. Maximum angular radius of the Earth, ρ_{max}: $\rho_{max} = \text{asin}(R_E / r_P)$ (D-73)

E. Minimum angular radius of the Earth, ρ_{min}: $\rho_{min} = \text{asin}(R_E / r_A)$ (D-74)

E. Distance to the horizon, D: $D = r \cos \rho = \sqrt{r^2 - R_E^2}$ (D-75)

(For calculation of angles and distance for targets not on the horizon, see Sec. 9.1.1.)

E. Maximum distance to the horizon, D_{max}:

$$D_{max} = r_A \cos \rho_{min} = \sqrt{r_A^2 - R_E^2} \quad \text{(D-76)}$$

E. Minimum distance to the horizon, D_{min}:

$$D_{min} = r_P \cos \rho_{max} = \sqrt{r_P^2 - R_E^2} \quad \text{(D-77)}$$

E. Maximum Earth central angle, λ_{max}:

$$\lambda_{max} = 90 \text{ deg} - \rho = \text{acos}(R_E / r) \quad \text{(D-78)}$$

E. Instantaneous Access Area, IAA: $IAA = K_A(1 - \cos\lambda_{max})$ (D-79)

$K_A = 2\pi \approx 6.283\ 185\ 311$	for area in steradians
$= 360^2 / (2\pi) \approx 20{,}626.480\ 62$	for area in deg^2
$= 2.556\ 041\ 87 \times 10^8$	for area in km^2 (Earth)
$= 1.898\ 363 \times 10^7$	for area in km^2 (Moon)
$= 7.250\ 550 \times 10^7$	for area in km^2 (Mars)

(For alternative ways to calculate ground coverage, see Sec. 9.5.1; for other ground area formulas, see Table 9-7 in Sec. 9.5.1; for transformations between geocentric and access area coordinates, see the Boxed Example in Sec. 9.1; for projections of sensor fields of view onto the central body, see Sec. 9.1.4.)

E. Area Access Rate, AAR:

$$AAR = \left(\frac{K_A \dot{v}}{\pi}\right) \sin \lambda_{max} \quad \text{(D-80)}$$

E. Maximum time in view, T_{max}: $T_{max} \approx 2\lambda_{max} / \dot{v}$ (D-81)

(For a complete set of target or ground station coverage formulas for elliptical orbits, see Table 9-5 in Sec. 9.4.2.)

E. Maximum angular rate seen from ground, $\dot{\theta}_{max}$:

$$\dot{\theta}_{max} = \frac{\dot{v}\, r}{\left(r - R_E\right)} \quad \text{(D-82)}$$

E. Node precession rate due to J_2, $\Delta\Omega_{J2}$:

$$\begin{aligned}
\Delta\Omega_{J2} &= -1.5\, J_2 n\, (R_E / a)^2 (1 - e^2)^{-2} \cos i \equiv K_{J2}\, a^{-7/2} (1 - e^2)^{-2} \cos i && \text{(D-83)}\\
&= -2.064\,74 \times 10^{14}\, a^{-7/2} (1 - e^2)^{-2} \cos i && \text{(Earth, } a \text{ in km)}\\
&= -3.220 \times 10^{11}\, a^{-7/2} (1 - e^2)^{-2} \cos i && \text{(Moon, } a \text{ in km)}\\
&= -3.483 \times 10^{13}\, a^{-7/2} (1 - e^2)^{-2} \cos i && \text{(Mars, } a \text{ in km)}
\end{aligned}$$

(In the numerical forms, $\Delta\Omega_{J2}$ is in deg/calendar day.)

E. Sun-synchronous inclination, i_{SS}:

$$i_{SS} = \text{acos}\left(\frac{360\, a^{7/2}}{K_{J2}\left(1 - e^2\right)^2 SP} \right) \quad \text{(D-84)}$$

$$\begin{aligned}
&= \text{acos}\,(-4.773\,7 \times 10^{-15}\, a^{7/2} (1 - e^2)^2) && \text{(Earth, } a \text{ in km)}\\
&= \text{acos}\,(-3.061 \times 10^{-12}\, a^{7/2} (1 - e^2)^2) && \text{(Moon, } a \text{ in km)}\\
&= \text{acos}\,(-1.505 \times 10^{-14}\, a^{7/2} (1 - e^2)^2) && \text{(Mars, } a \text{ in km)}
\end{aligned}$$

(Where SP is the sidereal period of the planet about the Sun in calendar days. For a discussion of Sun synchronous orbits, see Sec. 2.5.3.)

E. Perigee rotation rate due to J_2, $\Delta\omega_{J2}$:

$$\Delta\omega_{J2} = 1.5\, J_2 n \left(R_E / a\right)^2 \left(1 - e^2\right)^{-2} \left(2 - \frac{5}{2} \sin^2 i\right) \quad \text{(D-85)}$$

$$= K_{J2}\, a^{-7/2} \left(1 - e^2\right)^{-2} \left(2 - \frac{5}{2} \sin^2 i\right)$$

where K_{J2} is the same as for $\Delta\Omega_{J2}$

(In the numerical forms, $\Delta\omega_{J2}$ is in deg/calendar day. Note that the perigee rotation rate depends on the central body. However, the fact that perigee rotation goes to 0 at the critical inclination of 63.4 deg is independent of the central body.)

E. Revolutions per day, *Rev/d*:

$$\begin{aligned}
\text{Rev}/d &= \text{Day}/P && \text{(D-86)}\\
&= 1{,}436.07 / P && \text{(Earth, } P \text{ in min)}\\
&= 39{,}434 / P && \text{(Moon, } P \text{ in min)}\\
&= 1{,}477.38 / P && \text{(Mars, } P \text{ in min)}
\end{aligned}$$

(This is the number of orbit revolutions for each rotation of the planet on its axis relative to the fixed stars (i.e., the inertial rotation period). "Day" is the length of the sidereal day for the given central body. For more accurate expressions, see the discussion of repeating ground tracks in Sec. 2.5.2.)

E. Node spacing, ΔN: $\Delta N = 360\ \text{deg}(P / \text{Day})$ (D-87)

$= 0.250\,684\ P$ (Earth, P in min)

$= 0.009\,150\,3\ P$ (Moon, P in min)

$= 0.243\,675\ P$ (Mars, P in min)

(For the equations for repeating ground track orbits, see Sec. 2.5.2.)

E. Maximum eclipse at a specified true anomaly, T_E:

$$T_E \approx 2\rho / \dot{v} = (2 / \dot{v})\,\text{asin}(R_E / r) \tag{D-88}$$

(For computation of eclipse duration for any Sun angle, see Sec. 6.3.2; for the formulas for eclipse conditions, see Sec. 11.4.)

E. Sun angle constraints for terminator visibility, β':

$$90° + \xi - \rho < \beta' < 90° - \xi + \rho \tag{D-89}$$

(ξ is the dark angle defined in Sec. 11.5.2. For general conditions of terminator visibility, see Table 11-3 in Sec. 11.5.2.)

E. Transit time for a spacecraft whose celestial coordinates are known, T:

$$T = \alpha + L - \text{GST} \tag{D-90}$$

(where α is the right ascension, L is the observer East longitude, and GST is the Greenwich Sidereal Time. For computation of observability times of spacecraft for which the celestial coordinates are known, see Table 9-6 in Sec. 9.4.4.)

D.3 Equations for Parabolic Orbits

As discussed in Sec. 2.1 which defines the orbit variables, parabolic orbits represent the boundary between closed, negative total energy elliptical orbits and unbounded, positive total energy hyperbolic orbits. Sec. 9.1 defines the geometric variables involved.

Note: A "**P**" is put in front of each descriptor to denote formulas for Parabolic orbits. Subscript P stands for the value of the parameter at perigee.

P. Defining parameters: p = semi-latus rectum = semiparameter

q = perifocal distance (D-91)

(For a discussion of Keplerian orbits, see Sec. 2.1; for transformations between orbital elements and position and velocity, see Sec. 2.7.1.1 and 2.7.1.2.)

P. Parametric equation:

$$x^2 = 4qy \tag{D-92}$$

P. Distance from focus, r:

$$r = \frac{p}{1 + \cos v} = \frac{q(1 + e)}{1 + e \cos v} = q + D^2 / 2 \tag{D-93}$$

P. Specific energy, ε (= Total energy per unit mass): $\varepsilon = 0$ (D-94)

P. Specific angular momentum, h:

$$h = |\mathbf{h}| = \sqrt{\mu p} = rV \cos\phi_{fpa} = r^2 \dot{v} = r_P V_P \tag{D-95}$$

P. Angular momentum vector, h: $\mathbf{h} = \mathbf{r} \times \mathbf{V}$ (D-96)

P. Nodal vector, N: $\mathbf{N} = \hat{\mathbf{z}} \times \hat{\mathbf{h}} = \hat{\mathbf{z}} \times \mathbf{h} / \mathrm{h}$ (D-97)

P. Eccentricity vector, e: $\mathbf{e} = \dfrac{\mathbf{v} \times \mathbf{h}}{\mu} - \dfrac{\mathbf{r}}{r}$ (D-98)

P. Inclination, *i*: $i = \mathrm{acos}\,(h_z / h)$ (D-99)

(For a discussion of apparent inclination, see the Boxed Example at the end of Sec. 9.3.1.)

P. Right ascension of the ascending node, Ω: $\Omega = \mathrm{atan2}(N_y, N_x)$ (D-100)

P. Flight path angle, ϕ_{fpa}: $\phi_{fpa} = \nu / 2 = \mathrm{acos}\left(\sqrt{\mu P} / rV\right)$ (D-101)

P. Perifocal distance, *q* = radius of perigee, r_P: $q = r_P = p/2$ (D-102)

P. Semi-parameter, *p*: $p = 2q = h^2/\mu = r(1 + \cos\nu)$ (D-103)

P. Semimajor axis, *a*: $a = \infty$ (D-104)

P. Semiminor axis, *b*: $b = \infty$ (D-105)

P. Eccentricity, *e*: $e = 1$ (D-106)

P. Mean motion, *n*: $n = 2\sqrt{\mu / p^3} = \left(\dfrac{1}{t}\right)\left[\tan\left(\dfrac{\nu}{2}\right) + \dfrac{1}{3}\tan^3\left(\dfrac{\nu}{2}\right)\right]$ (D-107)

where t = time from perigee passage.

P. Mean anomaly, *M*: $M = M_0 + nt = qD + D^3/6$ (D-108)

P. Parabolic anomaly, *D*: $D = \sqrt{2q}\,\tan(\nu / 2)$ (D-109)

P. True anomaly, ν: $\nu = \mathrm{atan}\,2(\cos\nu, \sin\nu)$ (D-110)

$$\cos\nu = (p - r) / r$$

$$\sin\nu = D_p / r\sqrt{2q}$$

P. Rate of change of true anomaly, $\dot{\nu}$: $\dot{\nu} = \sqrt{\mu p} / r^2 = V_P r_P / r^2$ (D-111)

P. Period, *P*: $P = \infty$ (D-112)

P. Velocity, *V*: $V = V_E = \sqrt{2\mu / r} = \sqrt{\mu p} / (r\cos\phi_{fpa})$ (D-113)

P. Velocity at perigee, V_P: $V_P = \sqrt{\dfrac{2\mu}{r_P}}$ (D-114)

P. Parabolic velocity = Escape Velocity, V_E: $V_E = \sqrt{2\mu / r}$ (D-115)

P. Azimuthal velocity, V_{az}: $V_{az} = V\cos\phi_{fpa} = r\dot{\nu}$ (D-116)

P. Radial velocity, V_r: $$V_r = V \sin \phi_{fpa} = V_{az} \frac{\sin \nu}{q} = \frac{r\, \dot{\nu}\, e \sin \nu}{1 + e \cos \nu} \quad \text{(D-117)}$$

P. Range • range rate, $r\dot{r}$: $$r\dot{r} = \sqrt{\mu}\, D \quad \text{(D-118)}$$

P. Areal velocity, $\dot{A}$: $$\dot{A} = \sqrt{\mu q / 2} = 0.5 r^2\, \dot{\nu} \quad \text{(D-119)}$$

(For a complete set of ground track equations, see Table 8-9 in Sec. 8.3 and Sec. 9.3.1.)

All Euler Axis and coverage formulas for Parabolic Orbits are the same as for Hyperbolic Orbits

D.4 Equations for Hyperbolic Orbits

As discussed in Sec. 2.1 which defines the orbit variables, hyperbolic orbits are unbounded with positive total energy. As shown in Figs. 2-1 and 2-3 in Sec. 2.1.1, the hyperbola has two discrete segments, only one of which represents the orbit. Section 9.1 defines the geometric variables involved. Section 12.7.3 discusses hyperbolic orbit parameters with respect to planetary arrival and departure.

Note: An "H" is put in front of each descriptor to denote formulas for Hyperbolic orbits. Subscript P stands for the value of the parameter at perigee.

H. Defining parameters: a = semi-transverse axis ($a < 0$) (D-120)
b = semi-conjugate axis

(For a discussion of Keplerian orbits, see Sec. 2.1; for transformations between orbital elements and position and velocity, see Secs. 2.7.1.1 and 2.7.1.2; for planetary arrival and departure, see Sec. 12.7.3.)

H. Parametric equation: $$x^2/a^2 - y^2/b^2 = 1 \quad \text{(D-121)}$$

H. Distance from focus, r:

$$r = \frac{q(1+e)}{1 + e\cos\nu} = a(1 - e\cosh F) = a\left(\frac{e}{\cos H} - 1\right) = a\sqrt{e^2 - 1}\,\frac{\tan H}{\sin \nu} \quad \text{(D-122)}$$
$$= \frac{p}{1 + e\cos\nu}$$

H. Specific energy, ε (= Total energy per unit mass):

$$\varepsilon = -\frac{\mu}{2a} = \frac{V^2}{2} - \frac{\mu}{r} > 0 \quad \text{(D-123)}$$

H. Specific angular momentum, h:

$$h = |\mathbf{h}| = \sqrt{\mu p} = rV\cos\phi_{fpa} = r^2\,\dot{\nu} = r_P V_P \quad \text{(D-124)}$$

H. Angular momentum vector, h: $$\mathbf{h} = \mathbf{r} \times \mathbf{V} \quad \text{(D-125)}$$

H. Nodal vector, N: $$\mathbf{N} = \hat{\mathbf{z}} \times \hat{\mathbf{h}} = \hat{\mathbf{z}} \times \mathbf{h} / h \quad \text{(D-126)}$$

H. Eccentricity vector, e: $$\mathbf{e} = \frac{\mathbf{v} \times \mathbf{h}}{\mu} - \frac{\mathbf{r}}{r} \quad \text{(D-127)}$$

H. Inclination, *i*: $$i = \operatorname{acos}(h_z / h) \quad \text{(D-128)}$$

(For a discussion of apparent inclination, see the Boxed Example at the end of Sec. 9.3.1.)

H. Right ascension of the ascending node, Ω: $$\Omega = \operatorname{atan2}(N_y, N_x) \quad \text{(D-129)}$$

H. Flight path angle, ϕ_{fpa}: $$\phi_{fpa} = \nu / 2 = \operatorname{acos}\left(\sqrt{\mu P} / rV\right) \quad \text{(D-130)}$$

H. Auxiliary angle of the hyperbola, *H*:

$$H = \operatorname{acos}\left(\frac{e}{a + r}\right) = \operatorname{acos}\left(\frac{e}{1 + rh / \mu}\right) \quad \text{(D-131)}$$

H. Turn angle, ψ:

$$\psi = 2 \operatorname{asin}\left(\frac{1}{e}\right) = 2 \operatorname{asin}\left(\frac{1}{1 + V_\infty^2 q / \mu}\right) = 2 \operatorname{atan}\left(\frac{a}{b}\right) \quad \text{(D-132)}$$

$$= 2 \operatorname{atan}\left(\frac{\mu}{V_P V_\infty r_P}\right) = 2 \operatorname{atan}\left(\frac{\mu}{\rho V \sqrt{\eta} \cos\phi_{fpa}}\right)$$

(For a discussion of planetary fly-bys, see Secs. 2.6.3 and 12.7.1.)

H. Perifocal distance, *q* = radius of perigee, r_P:

$$q = r_P = a(1 - e) = \frac{p}{1 + e} = \frac{\mu}{V_P^2}(1 + e) = \frac{\mu}{V_\infty^2}(e - 1) \quad \text{(D-133)}$$

H. Semi-parameter, *p*:

$$p = a\left(1 - e^2\right) = r(1 + e\cos\nu) = q(1 + e) = \frac{b^2}{a} = \frac{h^2}{\mu} \quad \text{(D-134)}$$

H. Semimajor axis, *a*: $$a = -\frac{\mu}{2\varepsilon} = \left(\frac{\mu}{n^2}\right)^{1/3} = \frac{\mu}{V_\infty^2} = \frac{q}{e - 1} = \frac{p}{e^2 - 1} \quad \text{(D-135)}$$

$$a < 0$$

H. Semiminor axis = semi-conjugate axis, *b*:

$$b = a\sqrt{e^2 - 1} = \sqrt{ap} = \sqrt{\mu p / h} = \frac{V_P}{V_\infty} r_P = \frac{a}{\tan(\psi / 2)} \quad \text{(D-136)}$$

H. Eccentricity, *e*:

$$e = |\mathbf{e}| = \sqrt{1 + \frac{2\varepsilon h^2}{\mu^2}} = \sqrt{\frac{a^2 + b^2}{a}} = 1 + \frac{r_P}{a} = \sqrt{1 + \frac{P}{a}} = 1 + \frac{r_P}{\mu} V_\infty^2 \quad \text{(D-137)}$$

$e > 1$

H. Mean motion, *n*: $$n = \sqrt{-\mu / a^3} \quad \text{(D-138)}$$

H. Mean anomaly, *M*: $$M = M_0 + nt = e \sinh F - F \quad \text{(D-139)}$$

H. Hyperbolic anomaly, *F*: $$F = 2\,\text{atanh}\left[\sqrt{\frac{e-1}{e+1}} \tan\frac{\nu}{2}\right] \quad \text{(D-140)}$$

$$\sinh F = \frac{\sin\nu\sqrt{e^2 - 1}}{1 + e\cos\nu}$$

$$\cosh F = \frac{e + \cos\nu}{1 + e\cos\nu}$$

as an iterative equation with successive estimates F_i:

$$F_{i+1} = F_i + \frac{M - e\sinh F_i + F_i}{e\cosh F_i - 1}$$

H. True anomaly, ν:

$$\nu = \text{atan2}(\cos V, \sin V) = 2\,\text{atan}\left[\sqrt{\frac{e+1}{e-1}} \tanh\frac{F}{2}\right] \quad \text{(D-141)}$$

$$= 2\,\text{asin}\left(\frac{a}{r}\sqrt{e^2 - 1}\tan H\right) = 2\,\text{atan}\left[\sqrt{\frac{e+1}{e-1}} \tan\frac{H}{2}\right]$$

$$\cos\nu = \frac{\cosh F - e}{1 - e\cosh F}$$

$$\sin\nu = \frac{-\sinh F\sqrt{e^2 - 1}}{1 - e\cosh F}$$

H. Rate of change of true anomaly, $\dot{\nu}$: $$\dot{\nu} = \sqrt{\mu p} / r^2 = V_P r_P / r^2 \quad \text{(D-142)}$$

H. Period, *P*: $$P = \infty \quad \text{(D-143)}$$

H. Velocity, *V*: $$V = \sqrt{\frac{2\mu}{r} - \frac{\mu}{a}} = \frac{\sqrt{\mu p}}{(r\cos\phi_{fpa})} = \sqrt{\frac{2\mu}{r} + V_\infty^2} \quad \text{(D-144)}$$

H. Velocity at perigee, V_P: $$V_P = \sqrt{\frac{2\mu}{r_P} + V_\infty^2} = \sqrt{\frac{\mu}{r_P}(1 + e)} \quad \text{(D-145)}$$

H. Hyperbolic excess velocity, V_∞ :

$$V_\infty = \sqrt{V^2 - \frac{2\mu}{r}} = \sqrt{V_P^2 - \frac{2\mu}{r_E}} = \frac{r_P V_P}{b} = \sqrt{\frac{\mu}{r_P}(e-1)} \qquad \text{(D-146)}$$

(The role of V_∞, C_3 , and related parameters in interplanetary mission analysis is discussed in Secs. 12.3.2 and 12.7.3 to 12.7.5.)

H. Reference launch energy, C_3 : $C_3 = V_\infty^2$ (D-147)

H. Azimuthal velocity, V_{az}: $V_{az} = r\dot{\nu} = V\cos\phi_{fpa}$ (D-148)

H. Radial velocity, V_r: $V_r = V\sin\phi_{fpa} = \left(\frac{V_{az}e}{q}\right)\sin\nu = \frac{r\dot{\nu}e\sin\nu}{1 + e\cos\nu}$ (D-149)

H. Range • range rate, $r\dot{r}$: $r\dot{r} = e\sqrt{-a\mu}\sinh\ F$ (D-150)

H. Areal velocity, $\dot{A}$: $\dot{A} = \frac{1}{2}\sqrt{a\mu\left(1 - e^2\right)}$ (D-151)

H. Escape velocity, V_E: $V_E = \sqrt{2\mu / r}$ (D-152)

H. Euler axis co-latitude, δ_E': $\delta_E' = \operatorname{atan}\left(\frac{\dot{\nu}\sin i}{-\omega_E + \dot{\nu}\cos i}\right)$ (D-153)

ω_E = inertial rotation of central body
= 0.004 178 074 deg/sec (Earth)
= 0.000 152 504 deg/sec (Moon)
= 0.004 061 249 deg/sec (Mars)

(For a complete set of ground track equations, see Table 8-9 in Sec. 8.3 and Sec. 9.3.1.)

H. Euler rotation rate, ω_E: $\omega_E = \dot{\nu}\sin i / \sin\delta_E'$ (D-154)

$$= \sqrt{\omega_E^2 + \dot{\nu}^2 + 2\dot{\nu}\omega_E\cos i}$$

H. Angular radius of the Earth, ρ: $\rho = \operatorname{asin}\left(R_E / r_P\right)$ (D-155)

R_E = radius of central body
= 6378.140 km (Earth)
= 1738.2 km (Moon)
= 3397 km (Mars)

(Assumes a spherical Earth. For the effect of oblateness, see Sec. 9.1.5.)

H. Maximum angular radius of the Earth, ρ_{max}: $\rho_{max} = \operatorname{asin}\left(R_E / r_P\right)$ (D-156)

H. Distance to the horizon, D: $D = r\cos\rho = \sqrt{r^2 - R_E^2}$ (D-157)

(For calculation of angles and distance for targets not on the horizon, see Sec. 9.1.1.)

H. Minimum distance to the horizon, D_{min}:

$$D_{min} = r_P \cos \rho_{max} = \sqrt{r_P^2 - R_E^2} \qquad \text{(D-158)}$$

H. Maximum Earth central angle, λ_{max}:

$$\lambda_{max} = 90 \text{ deg} - \rho = \text{acos}\,(R_E/r) \qquad \text{(D-159)}$$

H. Instantaneous Access Area, *IAA*:

$$IAA = K_A(1 - \cos\lambda_{max}) \qquad \text{(D-160)}$$

$K_A = 2\pi \approx 6.283\ 185\ 311$	for area in steradians
$= 360^2 / (2\pi) \approx 20{,}626.480\ 62$	for area in deg^2
$= 2.556\ 041\ 87 \times 10^8$	for area in km^2 (Earth)
$= 1.898\ 363 \times 10^7$	for area in km^2 (Moon)
$= 7.250\ 550 \times 10^7$	for area in km^2 (Mars)

(For alternative ways to calculate ground coverage, see Sec. 9.5.1; for other ground area formulas, see Table 9-7 in Sec. 9.5.1; for transformations between geocentric and access area coordinates, see the Boxed Example in Sec. 9.1; for projections of sensor fields of view onto the central body, see Sec. 9.1.4.)

H. Area Access Rate, *AAR*:

$$AAR = \left(\frac{K_A \dot{v}}{\pi}\right) \sin \lambda_{max} \qquad \text{(D-161)}$$

H. Maximum time in view, T_{max}:

$$T_{max} \approx 2\lambda_{max} / \dot{v} \qquad \text{(D-162)}$$

(This approximation holds only when the rate of change of true anomaly and the distance to the Earth do not change strongly over the time in view. For more precise calculations the start time and stop time of a viewing event should be calculated independently.)

H. Maximum angular rate seen from ground, $\dot{\theta}_{max}$:

$$\dot{\theta}_{max} = \frac{\dot{v}\, r}{(r - R_E)} \qquad \text{(D-163)}$$

H. Maximum eclipse at a specified true anomaly, T_E:

$$T_E \approx 2\rho / \dot{v} = \left(\frac{2}{\dot{v}}\right) \text{asin}\left(\frac{R_E}{r}\right) \qquad \text{(D-164)}$$

(This approximation holds only when the rate of change of true anomaly and the distance to the Earth do not change strongly over the eclipse duration. For more precise calculations, the start time and stop time of the eclipse should be calculated independently. For computation of eclipse duration for any Sun angle, see Sec. 6.3.2; for the formulas for eclipse conditions, see Sec. 11.4.)

H. Sun angle constraints for terminator visibility, β':

$$90° + \xi - \rho < \beta' < 90° - \xi + \rho \qquad \text{(D-165)}$$

(ξ is the dark angle defined in Sec. 11.5.2. For general conditions of terminator visibility, see Table 11-3 in Sec. 11.5.2.)

H. Transit time for a spacecraft whose celestial coordinates are known, *T*:

$$T = \alpha + L - \mathrm{GST} \qquad \text{(D-166)}$$

(where α is the right ascension, L is the observer East longitude, and GST is the Greenwich Sidereal Time. For computation of observability times of spacecraft for which the celestial coordinates are known, see Table 9-6 in Sec. 9.4.4.)

Appendix E

Physical and Orbit Properties of the Sun, Earth, Moon, and Planets

This appendix provides physical and orbit data for the Sun, Moon, and planets. Properties of orbits about these bodies are listed in tables throughout the text. Most of these tables are listed on page facing the inside front cover. Numerical properties of orbits about the Sun, Moon, and Mars are given in Appendix F and for orbits about the Earth in the pages preceding the inside rear cover. For additional data on virtually all aspects of the Solar System, astrophysics, and astronomy, we highly recommend that the reader consult Cox [2000]. For a detailed explanation and high accuracy numerical methods and tables for computing planetary orbit ephemerides, see Seidelmann [1992]. For lower accuracy, but computationally convenient techniques, see Meeus [1998].

E.1 Gravitational Constants of Major Solar System Bodies

In Table E-1, values of μ = GM are given to their full available accuracy. Other values are rounded. Values for the smaller satellites are estimates based on a typical density and the object's size. Except for the Sun, the last 3 columns are evaluated at the object's surface (or at the largest dimension for irregular bodies). Data from Cox [2000] and Seidelmann [1992].

TABLE E-1. Gravitational Parameters for Orbits About Major Solar System Bodies.

Object	μ = GM (m^3/s^2)	Orbital Velocity (km/s)	Orbit Period (min)	Escape Velocity (km/s)
Sun (at surface)	$1.327\,124\,3 \times 10^{20}$	436.822	167.0	617.760
Sun (at 1 AU)	$1.327\,124\,3 \times 10^{20}$	29.716	529,642	42.024
PLANETS AND SATELLITES				
Mercury	$2.203\,4 \times 10^{13}$	3.005	85.0	4.250
Venus	3.249×10^{14}	7.327	86.5	10.362

TABLE E-1. Gravitational Parameters for Orbits About Major Solar System Bodies.

Object	μ = GM (m^3/s^2)	Orbital Velocity (km/s)	Orbit Period (min)	Escape Velocity (km/s)
Earth	$3.986\ 004\ 41 \times 10^{14}$	7.905	84.5	11.180
Moon	$4.903\ 226 \times 10^{12}$	1.680	108.3	2.376
Mars	$4.283\ 2 \times 10^{13}$	3.551	100.2	5.022
Phobos	7.093×10^5	0.007	192.9	0.010
Deimos	1.59×10^5	0.005	170.7	0.007
Jupiter	1.2669×10^{17}	42.097	177.8	59.534
Io	5.9597×10^{12}	1.805	106.2	2.552
Europa	3.202727×10^{12}	1.431	114.6	2.023
Ganymede	9.88786×10^{12}	1.938	142.4	2.740
Callisto	7.17925×10^{12}	1.728	145.6	2.444
Amalthea	4.8×10^8	0.061	226.5	0.086
Himalia	6.3×10^8	0.086	103.1	0.122
Elara	5.3×10^7	0.037	114.7	0.052
Pasiphae	1.3×10^7	0.027	69.2	0.039
Sinope	5.3×10^6	0.020	75.1	0.028
Lysithea	5.3×10^6	0.021	59.6	0.030
Carme	6.0×10^6	0.020	78.5	0.028
Ananke	2.7×10^6	0.016	64.1	0.023
Leda	4.0×10^5	0.009	58.5	0.013
Thebe	5.3×10^7	0.031	184.9	0.044
Adrastea	1.3×10^6	0.010	134.4	0.014
Metis	6.0×10^6	0.017	120.9	0.025
Saturn	3.7934×10^{16}	25.088	251.6	35.480
Mimas	2.50×10^9	0.109	200.2	0.155
Enceladus	4.7×10^9	0.135	198.8	0.191
Thethys	4.18×10^{10}	0.279	200.7	0.395
Dione	7.3×10^{10}	0.362	162.0	0.512
Rhea	1.54×10^{11}	0.449	178.1	0.635
Titan	8.9780×10^{12}	1.867	144.4	2.641
Hyperion	1.3×10^9	0.086	218.9	0.122
Iapetus	1.1×10^{11}	0.386	195.0	0.545
Phoebe	2.7×10^7	0.016	739.5	0.022
Janus	1.28×10^8	0.036	279.5	0.051
Epimetheus	3.6×10^7	0.023	316.2	0.032
Helene	1.3×10^6	0.009	218.9	0.012
Telesto	7.7×10^5	0.007	218.9	0.010
Calypso	7.7×10^5	0.007	218.9	0.010
Atlas	1.45×10^6	0.009	218.9	0.013
Prometheus	9.34×10^6	0.011	689.7	0.016
Pandora	8.67×10^6	0.013	458.6	0.018
Pan	2.3×10^5	0.005	218.9	0.007

TABLE E-1. Gravitational Parameters for Orbits About Major Solar System Bodies.

Object	$\mu = GM$ (m^3/s^2)	Orbital Velocity (km/s)	Orbit Period (min)	Escape Velocity (km/s)
Uranus	5.7951×10^{15}	15.058	177.8	21.295
Ariel	9.01×10^{10}	0.394	154.6	0.557
Umbriel	7.81×10^{10}	0.365	167.6	0.517
Titania	2.36×10^{11}	0.546	151.2	0.773
Oberon	2.01×10^{11}	0.514	155.2	0.726
Miranda	4.4×10^{9}	0.135	186.0	0.191
Cordelia	9.2×10^{5}	0.008	161.5	0.012
Ophelia	1.4×10^{6}	0.010	161.5	0.014
Bianca	3.9×10^{6}	0.014	161.5	0.019
Cressida	1.3×10^{7}	0.020	161.5	0.028
Desdemona	8.3×10^{6}	0.018	161.5	0.025
Juliet	3.1×10^{7}	0.027	161.5	0.039
Portia	6.6×10^{7}	0.035	161.5	0.050
Rosalind	8.3×10^{6}	0.018	161.5	0.025
Belinda	1.5×10^{7}	0.021	161.5	0.030
Puck	1.9×10^{8}	0.050	161.5	0.071
Caliban	1.1×10^{7}	0.019	161.5	0.028
Sycorax	9.1×10^{7}	0.039	161.5	0.055
Neptune	6.8354×10^{15}	16.614	156.1	23.496
Triton	1.43×10^{12}	1.027	137.9	1.453
Nereid	1.3×10^{9}	0.089	200.9	0.125
Naiad	1.0×10^{7}	0.019	160.8	0.027
Thalassa	2.7×10^{7}	0.026	160.8	0.037
Despina	1.7×10^{8}	0.048	160.8	0.068
Galatea	2.1×10^{8}	0.051	160.8	0.073
Larissa	4.77×10^{8}	0.068	160.8	0.096
Proteus	4.40×10^{9}	0.142	160.8	0.201
Pluto	8.7×10^{11}	0.852	146.9	1.205
Charon	1.08×10^{11}	0.427	145.4	0.604
ASTEROIDS LARGER THAN 300 KM DIAMETER				
Ceres	7.83×10^{10}	0.414	115.4	0.586
Pallas	1.46×10^{10}	0.236	115.9	0.334
Vesta	1.59×10^{10}	0.252	104.0	0.357

E.2 Physical Properties of the Sun

TABLE E-2. Physical Properties of the Sun. Data from Cox [2000].

Radius of the photosphere	$6.960\ 33 \times 10^5$ km
Angular diameter of the photosphere at 1 AU	0.530 69 deg
Mass	$1.989\ 1 \times 10^{30}$ kg
Mean density	1.409 g/cm^3
Gravity at surface	2.740×10^4 cm/sec^2
Moment of inertia	5.7×10^{53} g cm^2
Angular rotation velocity at equator	2.85×10^{-6} rad/sec
Angular momentum (based on surface rotation)	1.63×10^{48} g cm^2 /sec
Escape velocity at solar surface	6.177×10^7 g cm/sec
Total radiation emitted	3.845×10^{26} W
Total radiation per unit area at 1 AU	1367 W/m^2
Apparent visual magnitude at 1 AU	–26.75
Absolute visual magnitude (magnitude at distance of 10 parsecs)	+4.82
Color index, B-V	+0.65
Spectral type	G2 V
Effective temperature	5777 K
Inclination of the equator to the ecliptic	7.25 deg
Adopted period of sidereal rotation	25.38 days
Corresponding synodic rotation period (relative to Earth)	27.275 days
Oblateness: semidiameter equator-pole difference	0."0086
Velocity relative to nearby stars	19.7 km sec

TABLE E-3. Sunspot Cycles, Maxima, and Minima.

Sunspot Cycle Number	Year of Minimum	Smallest Smoothed Monthly Mean	Year of Maximum*	Largest Smoothed Monthly Mean†	Rise to Max (Years)	Fall to Min (Years)	Cycle Length (Years)
–12	1610.8	—	1615.5	—	4.7	3.5	8.2
–11	1619.0	—	1626.0	—	7.0	8.0	10.5
–10	1634.0	—	1639.5	—	5.5	5.5	13.5
–9	1645.0	—	1649.0	—	4.0	6.0	9.5
–8	1655.0	—	1660.0	—	5.0	6.0	11.0
–7	1666.0	—	1675.0	—	9.0	4.5	15.0
–6	1679.5	—	1685.0	—	5.5	4.5	10.0

TABLE E-3. Sunspot Cycles, Maxima, and Minima. (Continued)

Sunspot Cycle Number	Year of Minimum	Smallest Smoothed Monthly Mean	Year of Maximum*	Largest Smoothed Monthly Mean†	Rise to Max (Years)	Fall to Min (Years)	Cycle Length (Years)
–5	1689.5	—	1693.0	—	3.5	5.0	8.0
–4	1698.0	—	1705.5	—	7.5	6.5	12.5
–3	1712.0	—	1718.2	—	6.2	5.3	12.7
–2	1723.5	—	1727.5	—	4.0	6.5	9.3
–1	1734.0	—	1738.7	—	4.7	6.3	11.2
0	1745	—	1750.3	92.6	5.3	4.9	11.6
1	1755.3	8.4	1761.5	86.5	6.2	5.0	11.1
2	1766.5	11.2	1769.8	115.8	3.3	5.7	8.3
3	1775.5	7.2	1778.4	158.5	2.9	6.4	8.6
4	1784.8	9.5	1788.2	141.2	3.4	10.2	9.8
5	1798.4	3.2	1805.2	49.2	6.8	5.5	17.0
6	1810.7	0.0	1816.3	48.7	5.6	7.1	11.1
7	1823.4	0.1	1829.9	71.7	6.5	4.0	13.6
8	1833.9	7.3	1837.3	146.9	3.4	6.3	7.4
9	1843.6	10.5	1848.2	131.6	4.6	7.8	10.9
10	1856.0	3.2	1860.2	97.9	4.2	7.1	12.0
11	1867.3	5.2	1870.7	140.5	3.4	8.3	10.5
12	1879.0	2.2	1883.9	74.6	5.0	6.3	13.3
13	1890.3	5.0	1894.1	87.9	3.8	8.0	10.1
14	1902.1	2.6	1906.2	64.2	4.1	7.5	12.1
15	1913.7	1.5	1917.7	105.4	4.0	6.0	11.5
16	1923.7	5.6	1928.3	78.1	4.6	5.5	10.6
17	1933.8	3.4	1937.3	119.2	3.5	6.9	9.0
18	1944.2	7.7	1947.4	151.8	3.2	6.9	10.1
19	1954.3	3.4	1958.3	201.3	4.0	6.5	10.9
20	1964.8	9.6	1968.9	110.6	4.1	7.6	10.6
21	1976.5	12.2	1980.0	164.5	3.5	6.8	11.1
22	1986.8	12.3	1989.6	158.5	2.8	7.2	9.6
23	1996.8	5	2000.6	170.1	3.8	—	11.0
Mean Cycle		**6**		**112.9**	**4.7**	**6.3**	**10.9**

* When observations permit, a date selected as either a cycle minimum or maximum is based in part on an average of the times extremes are reached in the monthly mean sunspot number, in the smoothed monthly mean sunspot number, and in the monthly mean number of spot groups alone. Two more measures are used at time of sunspot minimum: the number of spotless days and the frequency of occurrence of "old" and "new" cycle spot groups.

† The smoothed monthly mean sunspot number is defined here as the arithmetic average of two sequential 12-month running means of monthly mean numbers.

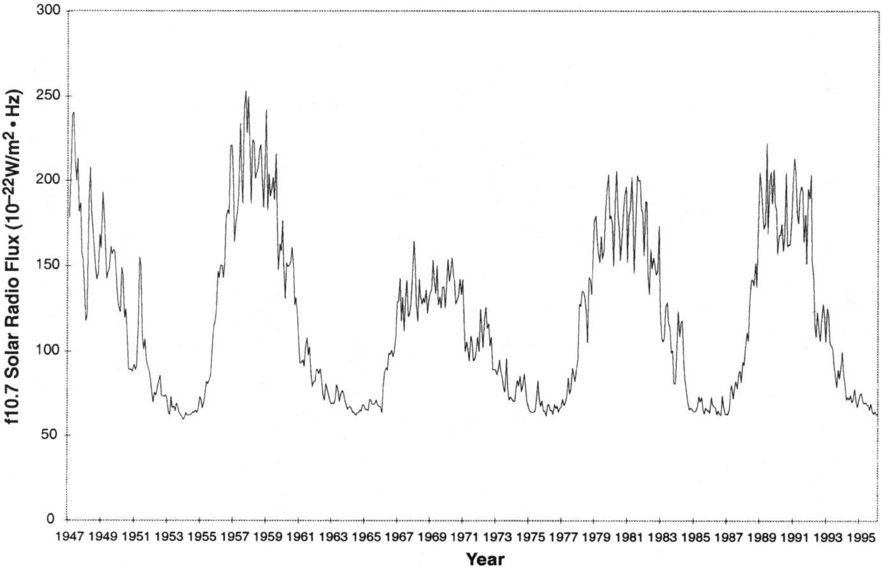

Fig. E-1. Historical Monthly 10.7 cm Radio Flux from the Sun (F10.7 Index) Since January 1947. For daily variations, see Fig. 2-19 in Sec. 2.4.

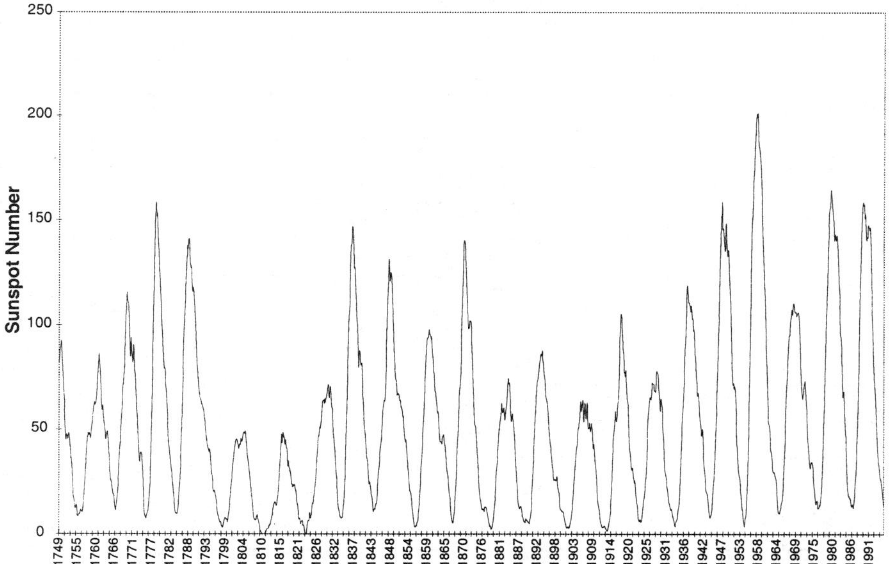

Fig. E-2. Historical Smoothed Sunspot Values from the 18th Century to Present.

E.3 Physical and Orbit Properties of the Earth

TABLE E-4. Physical and Orbit Properties of the Earth. Data from Cox [2000], Muller and Jappel [1976]; Astronomical Almanac [1999].

Equatorial radius, a	6,378.136 km
Flattening factor (ellipticity), $f \equiv (a - c)/a$	$1/298.257 \approx 0.003\,352\,81$
Polar radius,* c	$6.356\,753 \times 10^6$ m
Mean radius,* $(a^2c)^{1/3}$	6,371.00 km
Eccentricity,* $(a^2 - c^2)^{1/2}/a$	0.081 818
Surface area	$5.100\,657 \times 10^8$ km^2
Volume	$1.083\,207 \times 10^{12}$ km^3
Ellipticity of the equator $(a_{max} - a_{min})/a_{mean}$	$\sim 1.6 \times 10^{-5}$
Longitude of the maxima	20° W, 160°E
Ratio of the mass of the Sun to the mass of the Earth	332 946.038
Geocentric gravitational constant, $GM_E \equiv \mu_E$	$3.986\,004\,41 \times 10^{14}$ m^3/ s^2
Mass of the Earth	$5.973\,7 \times 10^{24}$ kg
Mean density	5.514 8 g/cm^3
Gravitational field constants (See Eq. (2-24) in Sec. 2.4.)	$J_2 = +1.082\,626 \times 10^{-3}$ $J_3 = -2.533 \times 10^{-6}$ $J_4 = -1.618\,6 \times 10^{-6}$
Mean distance of Earth center from Earth-Moon barycenter	4,671 km
Average lengthening of the day (See Fig. 4-1 in Sec. 4.1.)	0.0015 sec/century
General precession in longitude (i.e., precession of the equinoxes) per Julian century, at epoch 2000	$1.396\,971\,28 \times 10^{-2}$ deg/century
Rate of change of precession	$+6.184 \times 10^{-4}$ deg/century^2
Rate of change of the obliquity (T in Julian centuries)	$(-1.301\,25 \times 10^{-2}\,T) - (1.64 \times 10^{-6}\,T^2 + 5.0 \times 10^{-7}\,T^3)$ deg
Amplitude of the Earth's nutation	$2.556\,25 \times 10^{-3}$ deg
Sidereal period of rotation, epoch 2000	$0.997\,269\,632\,3 d_e = 86\,164.100\,4$ s = 23h56m4.100 4 s
Length of tropical year (ref. = ♈), epoch 2000	$3.155\,692\,5 \times 10^7$ s $= 365.242\,189\,7 d_e$
Length of anomalistic year (perihelion to perihelion), epoch 2000	$3.155\,843\,322\,2 \times 10^7$ s $= 365.259\,643\,77\ d_e$

* Based on adopted values of f and a.

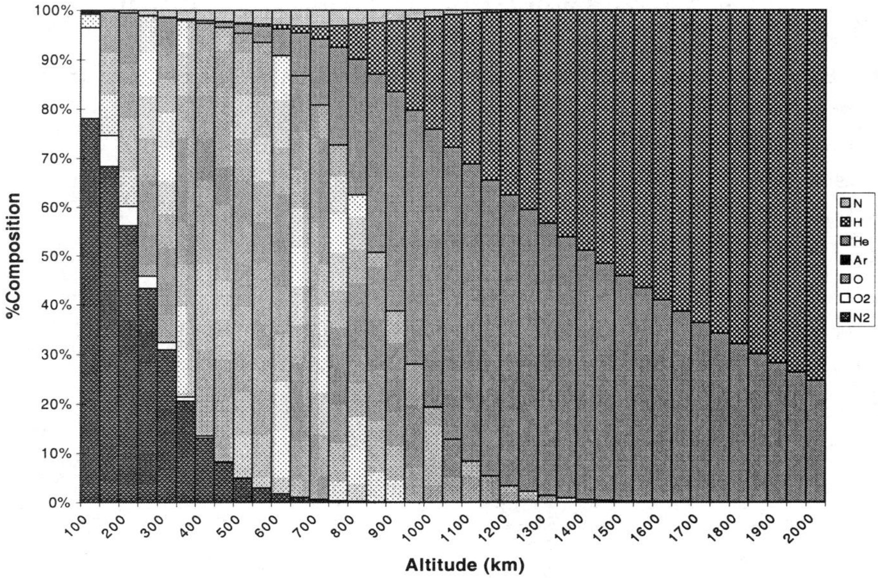

Fig. E-4. Mass Spectrometer Incoherent Scatter (MSIS) Atmospheric Species Percentage Composition vs. Altitude. [Hedin, 1987]. For atmospheric density, see Fig. 2-20 in Sec. 2-4.

TABLE E-5. Atmospheric Layers and Transitions. Data from Cox [2000].

Layer	Height, *h* (km)	Characteristics
Troposphere	0–11	Weather, *T* decreases with *h*, radiative-convective equilibrium
Tropopause	11	Temperature minimum, limit of upward mixing of heat
Stratosphere	11–48	*T* increases with *h* due to absorption of solar UV by O_3, dry
Stratopause	48	Maximum heating due to absorption of solar UV by O_3
Mesosphere	48–85	*T* decreases with *h*
Mesopause	85	Coldest part of atmosphere, noctilucent clouds
Thermosphere	85–exobase	*T* increases with *h*, solar cycle and geomagnetic variations
Exobase	500–1000 km	
Exosphere	> exobase	Region of Rayleigh-Jeans escape
Ozonosphere	15–35 km	Ozone layer (full width at e^{-1} of maximum)
Ionosphere	> 70 km	Ionized layers
Homosphere	< 85 km	Major constituents well-mixed
Heterosphere	> 85 km	Constituents diffusively separate

TABLE E-6. Atmospheric Layers and Transitions. P = pressure, T = temperature, ρ = mass density, N = number density, H = scale height, and l = mean free path. Data from U.S. Standard Atmosphere. [COESA, 1976]. See also tables inside the rear cover for additional atmospheric data and related orbit decay parameters.

Altitude	log P (Pa)	T (K)	log ρ (kg m^{-3})	log N (m^{-3})	H (km)	log l (m)
0	+5.006	288	+0.088 1	25.41	8.4	−7.2
1	+4.95	282	+0.046 0	25.36	8.3	−7.1
2	+4.90	275	+0.002 86	25.32	8.1	−7.1
3	+4.85	269	−0.041 3	25.28	7.9	−7.0
4	+4.79	262	−0.087	25.23	7.7	−7.0
5	+4.73	256	−0.133	25.19	7.5	−7.0
6	+4.67	249	−0.180	25.14	7.3	−6.9
8	+4.55	236	−0.279	25.04	6.9	−6.8
10	+4.42	223	−0.384	24.93	6.6	−6.7
15	+4.08	217	−0.71	24.61	6.4	−6.4
20	+3.74	217	−1.05	24.27	6.4	−6.0
30	+3.08	227	−1.73	23.58	6.7	−5.4
40	+2.46	250	−2.40	22.92	7.4	−4.7
50	+1.90	271	−2.99	22.33	8.0	−4.1
60	+1.34	247	−3.51	21.81	7.4	−3.6
70	+0.72	220	−4.08	21.24	6.6	−3.0
80	+0.022	199	−4.73	20.58	6.0	−2.4
90	−0.74	187	−5.47	19.85	5.6	−1.6
100	−1.49	195	−6.25	19.08	6.0	−0.85
110	−2.15	240	−7.01	18.33	7.7	−0.10
120	−2.60	360	−7.65	17.71	12.1	+0.52
150	−3.34	634	−8.68	16.71	23.0	+1.52
220	−4.07	855	−9.59	15.86	36.0	+2.38
250	−4.61	941	−10.22	15.28	45.0	+2.95
300	−5.06	976	−10.72	14.81	51.0	+3.41
400	−5.84	996	−11.55	14.02	60.0	+3.80
500	−6.52	999	−12.28	13.34	69.0	+4.89
700	−7.50	1000	−13.51	12.36	131.0	+5.86
1000	−8.12	1000	−14.45	11.74	288.0	+6.49

E.3.1 Geocentric and Geodetic Coordinates on the Earth

The *geocentric latitude*, ϕ', of a point, P, on the surface of the Earth is the angle at the Earth's center between P and the equatorial plane. The *geodetic* or *geographic latitude*, ϕ, is the angle between the normal to an arbitrarily defined reference ellipsoid (chosen as a close approximation to the oblate Earth) and the equatorial plane. *Astronomical latitude* and longitude are defined relative to the *local vertical*, or the normal to the equipotential surface of the Earth. Thus, *astronomical latitude* is defined as the angle between the local vertical and the Earth's equatorial plane. Maximum values of the *deviation of the vertical*, or the angle between the local vertical and the normal to a reference ellipsoid, are about 1 minute of arc. Maximum variations in the height between the reference ellipsoid and *mean sea level* (also called the *equipotential surface*) are about 100 m.

The shape of the reference ellipsoid is most commonly defined by the *ellipticity* or *flattening factor*, $f \equiv (a - b)/a \approx 1/298.256\ 42 \approx 0.003\ 352\ 819$, where a is the equatorial radius of the Earth and b is the polar radius. Also used is the eccentricity of the reference ellipsoid, $e \equiv (a^2 - b^2)^{1/2}/a \approx 0.081\ 819\ 301$. These are related by:

$$e = \sqrt{f(2-f)} \tag{E-1}$$

$$f = 1 - \sqrt{1-e^2} \tag{E-2}$$

On the surface of the Earth, the geodetic and geocentric latitude are related by:

$$\tan\phi = \tan\phi' / (1-f)^2 = 1.006\ 739\ 515\ \tan\phi' \tag{E-3}$$

where f is the flattening factor. At satellite altitudes the computation is more complex. As shown in Fig. E-5, the line normal to the oblate Earth through the satellite does not go through the Earth's center.

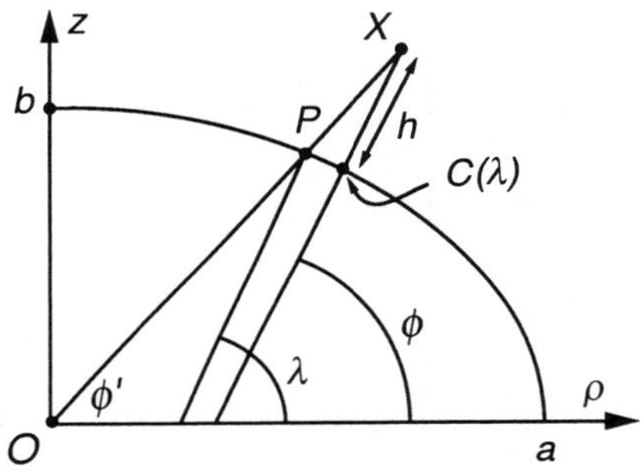

Fig. E-5. Relationship Between Geocentric Latitude, ϕ', and Geodetic Latitude, ϕ.

Geocentric coordinates are commonly expressed as Cartesian coordinates, (x, y, z). We then define the geocentric latitude, ϕ', and the radius in the equatorial plane, ρ, by:

$$\rho \equiv \sqrt{x^2 + y^2} \tag{E-4}$$

$$\tan\phi' \equiv z / \rho \tag{E-5}$$

Given the geodetic coordinates, ϕ and h, as defined in Fig. E-5, we can immediately determine the geocentric coordinates from:

$$\rho = \left(N_\phi + h\right)\cos\phi \tag{E-6}$$

$$z = \left[\left(1-e^2\right)N_\phi + h\right]\sin\phi \tag{E-7}$$

where the radius of curvature of the ellipse, N_ϕ, is given by:

$$N_\phi = \frac{a}{\sqrt{1-e^2\sin^2\phi}} \tag{E-8}$$

Determining the geodetic coordinates from the geocentric coordinates is more complex and requires an iterative technique. The approach used here is that of Nievergelt and Keeler [2000], which includes references to a number of earlier, less satisfactory methods. With a single iteration, this approach is good to 2×10^{-6} deg for the geodetic latitude and 1 mm in geodetic altitude. Successive iterations can improve this, although that would rarely be needed. The 4-step iterative approach is as follows:

Step 1

Set the iteration counter, $n = 0$. Compute $\rho = \sqrt{x^2 + y^2}$ and the initial altitude estimate:

$$h_0 = \left[1 - 1/\sqrt{(\rho/a)^2 + (z/b)^2}\right]\sqrt{\rho^2 + z^2} \tag{E-9}$$

Step 2

Compute the cosine, $u_0 = \cos(\lambda)$, and sine, $v_0 = \sin(\lambda)$, of the initial latitude estimate $\phi_0 = \lambda$ and the initial value of the intermediate variable, w_0:

$$u_0 = \frac{\sigma^2 \rho}{\sqrt{\sigma^4 \rho^2 + z^2}}, \qquad v_0 = \frac{z}{\sqrt{\sigma^4 \rho^2 + z^2}}, \qquad w_0 = \sqrt{1 - e^2 v_0^2} \tag{E-10}$$

where

$$\sigma \equiv b/a \tag{E-11}$$

Step 3

Compute the cosine, u_{n+1}, and sine, v_{n+1}, of the improved latitude estimate ϕ_{n+1}, the corresponding value w_{n+1}, and the improved altitude estimate h_{n+1}:

$$u_{n+1} = \frac{\left[a\sigma^2 + h_n w_n\right]\rho}{\sqrt{\left[a\sigma^2 + h_n w_n\right]^2 \rho^2 + \left[a + h_n w_n\right]^2 z^2}} \tag{E-12}$$

$$v_{n+1} = \frac{\left[a + h_n w_n\right] z}{\sqrt{\left[a\sigma^2 + h_n w_n\right]^2 \rho^2 + \left[a + h_n w_n\right]^2 z^2}}$$

$$w_{n+1} = \sqrt{1 - e^2 v_{n+1}^2}$$

$$h_{n+1} = \sqrt{\left[\rho - \frac{a u_{n+1}}{w_{n+1}}\right]^2 + \left[z - \frac{a\sigma^2 v_{n+1}}{w_{n+1}}\right]^2}$$

Step 4

Compute $\phi_{n+1} = \arctan(v_{n+1}/u_{n+1})$ with a standard algorithm that is stable near ±90 deg.

E.4 Physical and Orbit Properties of the Moon

TABLE E-7. Physical Parameters of the Moon. For an extended discussion of lunar properties see Eckart [1999] and Heiken, et al., [1991].

Radii: (a) Toward Earth, (b) Along orbit, (c) Toward pole	
Mean radius (b + c) / 2	1,738.2 km
a – c	1.09 km
a – b	0.31 km
b – c	0.78 km
Semi-diameter at mean distance	15′32″.6
Mass	7.3483×10^{22} kg
Mean density	3.341 g cm^{-3}
Surface gravity	162.2 cm/s^2 = 0.17 g
Surface escape velocity	2.38 km/s
Extreme range	356 400–406 700 km
Inclination of orbit to ecliptic oscillating ±9′ with period of 173 d	5° 8′43″.42
Sidereal period (fixed stars)	27.321 661
Mean orbital speed	1.023 km/sec
Synodical month (new Moon to new Moon)	29. 530 588
Surface area of Moon at some time visible from Earth	59%
Inclination of lunar equator	
To ecliptic	1° 32′32″.7
To orbit	6° 41′

TABLE E-8. Orbit of the Moon About the Earth.

Sidereal mean motion of Moon	$2.661\ 699\ 527 \times 10^{-6}$ rad s^{-1}
Mean distance of Moon from Earth	384 401 ± 1 km
	60.27 Earth radii
	0.002 570 AU
Equatorial horizontal parallax	57′02″.608
at mean distance	3,422″.608
Mean distance of center of Earth from Earth-Moon barycenter	4.671×10^3 km
Mean eccentricity	0.054 90
Mean inclination to ecliptic	5.145 394°
Mean inclination to lunar equator	6°41′
Limits of geocentric declination	± 29°
Period of revolution of node	18.61 Julian year
Period of revolution of perigee	8.849 Julian year
Mean orbital speed	1,023 ms^{-1} = 0.000 591 AU/d
Mean centripetal acceleration	0.00272 ms^{-2} = 0.0003 g
Optical libration in longitude (selenocentric displacement)	± 7.883 deg
Optical libration in latitude (selenocentric displacement)	± 6.85 deg
Saros = 223 lunations = 19 passages of Sun through node = 6,585 1/3 days	
Moment of inertia (about rotation axis)	0.396 $M_\oplus$
Gravitational potential term	$J_2 = 2.05 \times 10^{-4}$
No. of strong mascons on the near side of the Moon	4 exceeding 80 milligals
Mean surface temperature	+107 C (day), 153 C (night)
Temperature extremes	–233 C, +123 C
Moon's atmospheric density	~104 molecules cm^{-3} (day); 2×10^5 molecules cm^{-3} (night)
No. of maria & craters on lunar surface w/ diam. > d	$5 \times 10^{10} d^{-20}$ per 10^6 km^2 (d in m)

TABLE E-9. Gravity Field of the Moon.

$\alpha = (C - B) / A = 0.000\ 400$		$C / MR^2 = 0.392$
$\beta = (C - A) / B = 0.000\ 628$		$I = 5{,}552''.7 = 1°32'32$
$\gamma = (B - A) / C = 0.0002278$		
$C_{20} = -0.000\ 202\ 7$	$C_{30} = -0.000\ 006$	$C_{32} = +0.000\ 004\ 8$
$C_{22} = +0.000\ 022\ 3$	$C_{31} = +0.000\ 029$	$S_{32} = +0.000\ 001\ 7$
	$S_{31} = +0.000\ 004$	$C_{33} = +0.000\ 001\ 8$
		$S_{33} = -0.000\ 001$

Phase Law and Visual Magnitude of the Moon

A summary of the visual magnitude of the Moon as a function of distance and phase is provided in Section 11.6. (See Table 11-5 for Moon's phase law.) At the mean distance of the Earth, the visual magnitude of the Moon at opposition is –12.74. However, at first and last quarters, when half of the visible surface of the Moon is illuminated the intensity drops to only 8% of the full Moon value and the brightness drops by 2.74 magnitudes. For a more extended discussion see Cox [2000].

E.5 Planetary and Natural Satellite Data

TABLE E-10. Orbit Data for the Planets. Orbit elements are defined with respect to the mean ecliptic and equinox of J2000.0 (epoch JD 2,451,545.0). Data from Cox [2000] and Seidelmann [1992].

Planet	Eccentricity	Mean Distance (AU)	Sidereal Period (Julian yrs.)	Synodic Period (*d*)	Mean Daily Motion, *n* (deg)	Orbital Velocity (km/s)
Mercury	0.205 630 69	0.387 098 93	0.240 844 45	115.877 5	4.092 377 06	47.872 5
Venus	0.006 773 23	0.723 321 99	0.615 182 57	583.921 4	1.602 168 74	35.021 4
Earth	0.016 710 22	1.000 000 11	0.999 978 62		0.985 647 36	29.785 9
Mars	0.093 412 33	1.523 662 31	1.880 711 05	779.936 1	0.524 071 09	24.130 9
Jupiter	0.048 392 66	5.203 363 01	11.856 525 02	398.884	0.083 129 44	13.069 7
Saturn	0.054 150 60	9.537 070 32	29.423 519 35	378.0919	0.033 497 91	9.672 4
Uranus	0.047 167 71	19.191 263 93	83.747 406 82	369.656	0.011 769 04	6.835 2
Neptune	0.008 585 87	30.068 963 48	163.723 204 5	367.486 7	0.006 020 076	5.477 8
Pluto	0.248 807 66	39.481 686 77	248.020 8	366.720 7	0.003 973 966	4.74 9

TABLE E-11. Orbit Data for the Planets.

Planet	Inclination to Ecliptic (deg)	Longitude of Ascending Node (deg)	Longitude of Perihelion (deg)	Planet Longitude on Jan. 1.5 2000 (deg)	Last Perihelion before 1999
Mercury	7.004 87	48.331 67	77.456 45	252.250 84	1998 Dec. 2
Venus	3.394 71	76.680 69	131.532 98	181.979 73	1998 Sept. 7
Earth	0.000 05	–11.260 64	102.947 19	100.464 35	1998 Jan. 4
Mars	1.850 61	49.578 54	336.040 84	355.453 32	1998 Jan. 7

TABLE E-11. Orbit Data for the Planets. (continued).

Planet	Inclination to Ecliptic (deg)	Longitude of Ascending Node (deg)	Longitude of Perihelion (deg)	Planet Longitude on Jan. 1.5 2000 (deg)	Last Perihelion before 1999
Jupiter	1.305 30	100.556 15	14.753 85	34.404 38	1987 Jul. 10
Saturn	2.484 46	113.715 04	92.431 94	49.944 32	1974 Jan. 8
Uranus	0.769 86	74.229 68	170.964 24	313.232 18	1966 May 20
Neptune	1.769 17	131.721 69	44.971 35	304.880 03	1876 Sept. 2
Pluto	17.141 75	110.303 47	224.066 76	238.928 81	1989 Sept. 5

TABLE E-12. Physical Data for the Planets. Data from Cox [2000].

Planet	Mass (10^{24} kg)	Radius (km)	Flattening (geom.)	Mean Density (g/cm^3)	J_2 ($\times 10^3$)	Sidereal Rotation Period (d)	Incl. of Equator to Orbit (deg)
Mercury	0.330 22	2,439.7	0	5.43		58.646 225	0
Venus	4.869	6,051.8	0	5.24	0.027	–243.019 99	177.3
Earth	5.9742	6,378.14	0.003 353 64	5.515	1.082 63	0.997 269 632 3	23.45
Mars	0.641 91	3,397	0.006 476 3	3.94	1.964	1.02 595 675	25.19
Jupiter	1898.7	71,492	0.064 874 4	1.33	14.736	0.413 538	3.12
Saturn	568.51	60,268	0.097 962 4	0.7	16.298	0.444 009	26.73
Uranus	86.849	25,559	0.022 927 3	1.3	12	–0.718 333	97.86
Neptune	102.44	24,764	0.0171	1.76	3.411	0.671 250	29.58
Pluto	0.013	1,195	0	1.1		–6.387 246	119.61

TABLE E-13. Photometric Data for the Planets. So, Cl = Solid, cloud; for lowest visible surface. Data from Cox [2000].

Planet	Geometric Albedo	Visual Magnitude		Effective Temperature (K)	Visible Surface
		$V(1,0)$	V_0		
Mercury	0.106	–0.42	–0.2	—	So
Venus	0.650	–4.40	–4.22	~230	Cl
Earth	0.367	–3.86	—	~255	So, Cl
Mars	0.150	–1.52	–2.01	~212	So
Jupiter	0.520	–9.40	–2.70	124.4 ±0.3	Cl
Saturn	0.470	–8.88	0.67†	95.0 ±0.4	Cl
Uranus	0.510	–7.19	5.52	59.1 ±0.3	Cl
Neptune	0.410	–6.87	7.84	59.3 ±0.8	Cl
Pluto	variable*	–0.81	15.12	50–70	So

* The Pluto visual geometric albedo is variable by 30%. The Pluto color is the combination of the planet and its satellite Charon.

† *V* referts to the Saturn disk only.

Notes:

1. The values for the masses include the atmospheres but exclude the satellites.
2. The mean equatorial radii are given.
3. The flattening is the ratio of the difference of the equatorial and polar radii to the equatorial radius.
4. The period of rotation refers to the rotation at the equator with respect to a fixed frame of reference: a negative sign indicates that the rotation is retrograde with respect to the pole that lies to the north of the invariable plane of the solar system. The period is given in days of 86,400 SI seconds.
5. The data on the equator, flattening, period of rotation, and inclination of equator to orbit are based on Davies, et al. [1989].
6. The geometric albedo is the ratio of the illumination at the Earth from the planet for phase angle zero to the illumination produced by a plane, absolutely white Lambert surface of the same radius as the planet placed at the same position. This is not to be confused with a planet's bond albedo which is simply the ratio of total reflected light to total incident light. (See Sec. 11.6)
7. $V(1,0)$ is the visual magnitude when the observer is directly between the Sun and the planet and the product of the Sun-planet distance (in AU) is 1. (See Sec. 11.6)
8. V_0 is the mean visual magnitude of the planet when at opposition as viewed from the Earth. Magnitudes for Mercury and Venus are at greatest elongation. (See Sec. 11.6)

TABLE E-14. Natural Satellites: Orbit Data. See Table E-1 for gravitational Data.

Sat. #	Satellite Name	Orbital Period[1] [R=Retrograde] *(d)*	Semimajor Axis (× 10^3 km)	Orbit Eccentricity	Orbit Incl. to Planetary Equator (deg)	Motion of Node on Fixed Plane[4] (deg/yr)
			EARTH			
	Moon	27.321 661	384.4	0.054 900 489	18.28–28.58	19.34[6]
			MARS			
I	*Phobos*	0.318 910 23	9.378	0.015	1	158.8
II	*Deimos*	1.262 440 7	23.459	0.000 5	0.9–2.7	6.614
			JUPITER			
I	*Io*	1.769 137 786	422	0.004	0.04	48.6
II	*Europa*	3.551181041	671	0.009	0.47	12
III	*Ganymede*	7.154 552 96	1070	0.002	0.21	2.63
IV	*Callisto*	16.689 018 4	1883	0.007	0.51	0.643
V	*Amalthea*	0.498 179 05	181	0.003	0.4	914.6
VI	*Himalia*	250.566 2	11480	0.157 98	27.63	
VII	*Elara*	259.652 8	11737	0.207 19	24.77	
VIII	*Pasiphae*	735 **R**	23500	0.378	145	
IX	*Sinope*	758 **R**	23700	0.275	153	
X	*Lysithea*	259.22	11720	0.107	29.02	
XI	*Carme*	692 **R**	22600	0.206 78	164	
XII	*Ananke*	631 **R**	21200	0.168 7	147	
XIII	*Leda*	238.72	11094	0.147 62	26.07	

TABLE E-14. Natural Satellites: Orbit Data. See Table E-1 for gravitational Data.**(Continued)**

Sat. #	Satellite Name	Orbital Period[1] [R=Retrograde] (*d*)	Semimajor Axis (× 10^3 km)	Orbit Eccentricity	Orbit Incl. to Planetary Equator (deg)	Motion of Node on Fixed Plane[4] (deg/yr)
XIV	*Thebe*	0.674 5	222	0.015	0.8	
XV	*Adrastea*	0.298 26	129			
XVI	*Metis*	0.294 78	128			
			SATURN			
I	*Mimas*	0.942 421 813	185.52	0.020 2	1.53	365
II	*Enceladus*	1.370 217 855	238.02	0.004 52	0	156.2[5]
III	*Tethys*	1.887 802 16	294.66	0	1.86	72.2[5]
IV	*Dione*	2.736 914 742	377.4	0.002 23	0.02	30.85[5]
V	*Rhea*	4.517 500 436	527.04	0.001	0.35	10.16
VI	*Titan*	15.945 420 68	1221.83	0.029 192	0.33	0.521 3[5]
VII	*Hyperion*	21.276 608 8	1481.1	0.104	0.43	
VIII	*Iapetus*	79.330 182 5	3561.3	0.028 28	14.72	
IX	*Phoebe*	550.48 **R**	12952	0.163 26	177[2]	
X	*Janus*	0.694 5	151.472	0.007	0.14	
XI	*Epimethus*	0.694 2	151.422	0.009	0.34	
XII	*Helene*	2.736 9	377.4	0.005	0	
XIII	*Telesto*	1.887 8	294.66			
XIV	*Calypso*	1.887 8	294.66			
XV	*Atlas*	0.601 9	137.67	0	0.3	
XVI	*Prometheus*	0.613	139.353	0.003	0	
XVII	*Pandora*	0.628 5	141.7	0.004	0	
XVIII	*Pan*	0.575	133.583			
			URANUS			
I	*Ariel*	2.52037935	191.02	0.003 4	0.30	6.8
II	*Umbriel*	4.1441772	266.30	0.005	0.36	3.6
III	*Titania*	8.7058717	435.91	0.002 2	0.14	2.0
IV	*Oberon*	13.4632389	583.52	0.000 8	0.10	1.4
V	*Miranda*	1.41347925	129.39	0.002 7	4.20	19.8
VI	*Cordelia*	0.335 033 8	49.77	0.000 26	0.08	550
VII	*Ophelia*	0.376 400	53.79	0.009 9	0.10	419
VIII	*Bianca*	0.434 579 9	59.17	0.000 9	0.19	229
IX	*Cressida*	0.463 569 60	61.78	0.000 4	0.01	257
X	*Desdemona*	0.473 699 60	62.68	0.000 13	0.11	245
XI	*Juliet*	0.493 065 49	64.35	0.000 66	0.07	223
XII	*Portia*	0.513 195 92	66.09	0.001	0.10	203
XIII	*Rosalind*	0.558 459 53	69.94	0.001	0.30	129
XIV	*Belinda*	0.623 527 47	75.26	0.001	0.00	167
XV	*Puck*	0.761 832 87	86.01	0.001	0.31	81
XVI	*Caliban*	579 **R**	7169.00	0.082	139.20	
XVII	*Sycorax*	1,289 **R**	12,214.00	0.509	152.70	

TABLE E-14. Natural Satellites: Orbit Data. See Table E-1 for gravitational Data.**(Continued)**

Sat. #	Satellite Name	Orbital Period[1] [R=Retrograde] (*d*)	Semimajor Axis (× 10³ km)	Orbit Eccentricity	Orbit Incl. to Planetary Equator (deg)	Motion of Node on Fixed Plane[4] (deg/yr)
			NEPTUNE			
I	*Triton*	5.876 854 1 **R**	354.76	0.000016	157.345	0.5232
II	*Nereid*	360.136 19	5,513.40	0.7512	27.6[3]	0.039
III	*Naiad*	0.2943 96	48.23	0.0	4.74	626
IV	*Thalassa*	0.311 485	50.07	0.0	0.21	551
V	*Despina*	0.334 655	52.53	0.0	0.07	466
VI	*Galatea*	0.428 745	61.95	0.0	0.05	261
VII	*Larissa*	0.554 654	73.55	0.001 39	0.2	143
VIII	*Proteus*	1.122 315	117.65	0.000 4	0.55	0.5232
			PLUTO			
I	*Charon*	6.38725	19.6	0.001	96.16	

TABLE E-15. Natural Satellites: Physical and Photometric Data.

Sat. #	Satellite Name	Mass (1/planet)	Radius (km)	Sidereal Period[1] (*d*)	Visual Mag. [*V* (1,0)]	Geometric Albedo[9]
			EARTH			
	Moon	0.012 300 034	1737.4	S	+0.21	0.12
			MARS			
I	*Phobos*	1.654×10^{-8}	13.4 × 16.2 × 9.2	S	+11.8	0.07
II	*Deimos*	3.71×10^{-9}	7.5 × 6.1 × 5.2	S	+12.89	0.08
			JUPITER			
I	*Io*	$4.704\,1 \times 10^{-5}$	1830 × 1818.7 × 1815.3	S	−1.68	0.63
II	*Europa*	$2.528\,0 \times 10^{-5}$	1565	S	−1.41	0.67
III	*Ganymede*	$7.804\,6 \times 10^{-5}$	2634	S	−2.09	0.44
IV	*Callisto*	$5.666\,7 \times 10^{-5}$	2403	S	−1.05	0.20
V	*Amalthea*	38×10^{-10}	131 × 73 × 67	S	+7.4	0.07
VI	*Himalia*	50×10^{-10}	85	0.4	+8.14	0.03
VII	*Elara*	4×10^{-10}	40	0.5	+10.07	0.03
VIII	*Pasiphae*	1×10^{-10}	18		+10.33	0.1
IX	*Sinope*	0.4×10^{-10}	14		+11.6	0.05
X	*Lysithea*	0.4×10^{-10}	12		+11.7	0.06
XI	*Carme*	0.5×10^{-10}	15		+11.3	0.06
XII	*Ananke*	0.2×10^{-10}	10		+12.2	0.06
XIII	*Leda*	0.03×10^{-10}	5		+13.5	0.07

TABLE E-15. Natural Satellites: Physical and Photometric Data. (Continued)

Sat. #	Satellite Name	Mass (1/planet)	Radius (km)	Sidereal Period[1] (*d*)	Visual Mag. [*V* (1,0)]	Geo-metric Albedo[9]
XIV	*Thebe*	4×10^{-10}	55×45	S	+9.0	0.04
XV	*Adrastea*	0.1×10^{-10}	$13 \times 10 \times 8$		+12.4	0.05
XVI	*Metis*	0.5×10^{-10}	20×20		+10.8	0.05
			SATURN			
I	*Mimas*	6.6×10^{-8}	$209.1 \times 196.2 \times 191.4$	S	+3.3	0.5
II	*Enceladus*	1.0×10^{-7}	$256.3 \times 247.3 \times 244.6$	S	+2.1	1.0
III	*Tethys*	1.10×10^{-6}	$209.1 \times 196.2 \times 191.4$	S	+0.6	0.9
IV	*Dione*	1.95×10^{-6}	560	S	+0.8	0.7
V	*Rhea*	4.06×10^{-6}	764	S	+0.1	0.7
VI	*Titan*	$2.366\,7 \times 10^{-4}$	2575	S	−1.28	0.22
VII	*Hyperion*	4.0×10^{-8}	$180 \times 140 \times 112.5$		+4.63	0.3
VIII	*Iapetus*	2.8×10^{-6}	718	S	+1.5	(0.2)[2]
IX	*Phoebe*	7×10^{-10}	110	0.4	+6.89	0.06
X	*Janus*	3.385×10^{-9}	$97.0 \times 95.0 \times 77.0$	S	+4.4	0.9
XI	*Epimethus*	9.5×10^{-10}	$69 \times 55 \times 55$	S	+5.4	0.8
XII	*Helene*		$18 \times 16 \times 15$		+8.4	0.7
XIII	*Telesto*		$15 \times 12.5 \times 7.5$		+8.9	1.0
XIV	*Calypso*		$15.0 \times 8.0 \times 8.0$		+9.1	1.0
XV	*Atlas*		$18.5 \times 17.2 \times 13.5$		+8.4	0.8
XVI	*Prometheus*		$74.0 \times 50.0 \times 34.0$		+6.4	0.5
XVII	*Pandora*		$55.0 \times 44.0 \times 31.0$		+6.4	0.7
XVIII	*Pan*		10			0.5
In 2000, 12 new, small satellites of Saturn were discovered. All are less than 15 km in radius. It is likely that the Cassini spacecraft will discover more.						
			URANUS			
I	*Ariel*	1.56×10^{-5}	$581.1 \times 577.9 \times 577.7$	S	+1.45	0.35
II	*Umbriel*	1.35×10^{-5}	584.7	S	+2.10	0.19
III	*Titania*	4.06×10^{-5}	788.9	S	+1.02	0.28
IV	*Oberon*	3.47×10^{-5}	761.4	S	+1.23	0.25
V	*Miranda*	0.08×10^{-5}	$240.4 \times 234.2 \times 232.9$	S	+3.6	0.27
VI	*Cordelia*		13		+11.4	0.07
VII	*Ophelia*		15		+11.1	0.07
VIII	*Bianca*		21		+10.3	0.07
IX	*Cressida*		31		+9.5	0.07
X	*Desdemona*		27		+9.8	0.07
XI	*Juliet*		42		+8.8	0.07
XII	*Portia*		54		+8.3	0.07
XIII	*Rosalind*		27		+9.8	0.07

TABLE E-15. Natural Satellites: Physical and Photometric Data. (Continued)

Sat. #	Satellite Name	Mass (1/planet)	Radius (km)	Sidereal Period[1] (*d*)	Visual Mag. [*V* (1,0)]	Geo-metric Albedo[9]
XIV	*Belinda*		33		+9.4	0.07
XV	*Puck*		77		+7.5	0.075
XVI	*Caliban*		30			0.07
XVII	*Sycorax*		60			0.07
			NEPTUNE			
I	*Triton*	2.089×10^{-4}	1353	S	−1.24	0.77
II	*Nereid*	2×10^{-7}	170		+4.0	0.4
III	*Naiad*		29		+10.0	0.06
IV	*Thalassa*		40		+9.1	0.06
V	*Despina*		74		+7.9	0.06
VI	*Galatea*		79		+7.6	0.06
VII	*Larissa*		104×89		+7.3	0.06
VIII	*Proteus*		$218 \times 208 \times 201$		+5.6	0.06
			PLUTO			
I	*Charon*	0.125	593	S	+0.9	0.5

Notes:

1. Sidereal periods, except that tropical periods are given for satellites of Saturn.
2. Relative to the ecliptic plane.
3. Referred to the equator of 1950.0.
4. Rate of decrease (or increase) in the longitude of the ascending node.
5. Rate of increase in the longitude of the apside.
6. On the ecliptic plane.
7. S = synchronous, rotation period same as orbital period.
8. Bright side, 0.5; faint side, 0.05.
9. V (Sun) = −26.75.

References

COESA. 1976. *U.S. Standard Atmosphere.* Washington, D.C.: Government Printing Office.

Cox, Arthur N, ed.. 2000. *Allen's Astrophysical Quantities* (4th ed.). New York: Springer-Verlag.

Davies, M.E. et al. 1989. "Report of the IAU/IAG/COSPAR Working Group on Cartographic Coordinates and Rotational Elements of the Planets and Satellites: 1988," *Celestial Mechanics* 46, 187–204.

Eckart, P. 1999. *The Lunar Base Handbook: An Introduction to Lunar Base Design, Development, and Operations*. NY: McGraw-Hill.

Hedin, Alan E. 1987. "MSIS-86 Thermospheric Model." *J GeophysR*, 92, No. A5, pp. 4649–4662.

———. 1988. "The Atmospheric Model in the Region 90 to 2000 km." *Adv. Space Res.*, 8, No. 5-6, pp. (5)9–(5)25, Pergamon Press.

———. 1991. "Extension of the MSIS Thermosphere Model into the Middle and Lower Atmosphere," *J Geophys R*, 96, No. A2, pp. 1159–1172.

Heiken, Grant H., David T. Vaniman, and Bevan M. French. 1991. *Lunar Sourcebook: A User's Guide to the Moon.* Cambridge: Cambridge University Press.

Meeus, Jean. 1998. *Astronomical Algorithms* (2nd ed.). Richmond, VA: Willmann-Bell, Inc.

Muller, Edith A. and Arnsdt Jappel, eds. 1977. *International Astronomical Union Proceedings of the Sixteenth General Assembly, Grenoble, 1976.* Dordrecht, The Netherlands: D. Reidel Publishing Co.

Nievergelt, Y., and S. Keeler. 2000. "Computing Geodetic Coordinates in Space." *J. Spacecraft*. 37:293–296.

Seidlemann, P. Kenneth, ed., USNO. 1992. *Explanatory Supplement to the Astronomical Almanac*. Mill Valley, CA: University Science Books.

U.S. Naval Observatory and H. M. Nautical Almanac Office. 1999. *The Astronomical Almanac, 1999*. Washington, D.C.: U.S. Government Printing Office.

Appendix F

Properties of Orbits About the Moon, Mars, and the Sun

Tables F-1, F-2, and F-3 provide fundamental mission data as a function of altitude for orbits around the Moon, Mars, and the Sun respectively. The explanation of each column and the source or formula for the data is given ahead of each table. For any mission which is well defined, these parameters can be easily computed for the exact spacecraft altitude, and the errors estimated, using the formulas provided in the explanatory material, Chap. 2, or any standard reference. However, the tables here are extremely convenient for preliminary mission design and for determining the impact of variations in basic mission elements. All of the data assumes either a fixed instantaneous altitude or a circular orbit.

The rear endpages contain similar, more extensive data for Earth satellites. The Moon and Mars tables provide relevant subsets of the information provided for Earth satellites. The column numbers remain the same for each of these three sets of tables to provide correspondence with the explanations and formulas provided at the front of the endpages. The table of parameters for orbits about the Sun (i.e., interplanetary orbits) is, of course, significantly different in content from the planetary orbit tables. Explanation and formulas for these data are are provided at the front of the table.

Table F-1
Lunar ("(") Satellite Parameters

The following table provides a variety of quantitative data for satellites orbiting the Moon. The independent parameter is the distance, r, from the center of the Moon in km. However, the outside column on each page is the altitude, $h \equiv r - R_{(}$, where $R_{(}$ = 1,738 km is the equatorial radius of the Moon. Note that numerical formulas given in the *Explanation of Earth Satellite Parameters* will not generally work for a lunar satellite; readers should use the formulas given below or those listed in Chap. 2.

- General Changes relative to Earth satellite tables:
  R_E, or $R_\oplus$, (= 6,378.14 km) is replaced by $R_{(}$ (= 1,738 km)
  $\mu_\oplus$ (= 398,600.4 km^3/s^2) is replaced by $\mu_{(}$ (= 4,902.798 98 km^3/s^2)
  $J_{2,\oplus}$ (= 1.082 63 × 10^{-3}) is replaced with $J_{2,(}$ (= 0.2027 × 10^{-3})
- Note: Circular orbits, unperturbed by the Earth, have been assumed throughout. Higher altitudes will be more and more affected by perturbations from the Earth the so data at higher altitudes is less accurate.

Columns 1 through 24 use the same formulas given in the *Explanation of Earth Satellite Parameters* with the general changes given above.

Columns 25 through 40 are omitted because they are not applicable to lunar orbits.

Columns 41, 42 and 43 use the same formulas as given in the *Explanation of Earth Satellite Parameters* with the general changes given above.

Columns 45, 46 and 47 use the same formulas as given in the *Explanation of Earth Satellite Parameters* with the general changes given above.

Columns 49 through 53 use the Earth Satellite formulas with the general changes given above.

44. *ΔV Required to De-Orbit (m/s)* = the velocity change needed to transform the assumed circular orbit to an elliptical orbit with apoapse unchanged and periapse of 0 km, i.e. at the lunar surface [Eq. (2-85)].

48. *Sun Synchronous Inclination (deg)* = $\cos^{-1}$ { 0.985 65° /(–1.5 × 86.400 $(\mu / r^3)^{1/2}$ × $J_{2,}$ × (R / $h)^2$)} assumes circular orbit with node rotation rate of 0.985 65 deg/day to follow the mean motion of the Earth/Moon system's rotation about the Sun [Eq. (D-35)].

54. *Revolutions per Day (#)* = 1,440/*P*, where *P* is from column 52. Note that this is the number of revolutions in a 24 hour time period and not in a sidereal lunar day. {Eq. (D-35)

55. *Node Spacing (deg)* = 360° × (*P* / 39.343.1904), where *P* is from column 52 and 39,343.1904 is the lunar sidereal rotation period in minutes. This is the spacing in longitude between successive ascending or descending nodes for a satellite in a circular orbit [Eq. (D-36)].

56. *Node Precession Rate (deg/day)* = $-1.5\, n\, J_{2,}\ (R_{\ddot{A}}/a)^2 (\cos i)(1 - e^2)^{-2}$, where i is the inclination, e the eccentricity (which is set to zero), n is the mean motion $(= (\mu/a^3)^{1/2})$, a the semimajor axis, J_2, the dominant zonal coefficient in the expansion of the Legendre polynomial describing the lunar gravitational potential. Note that this is the angle through which the orbit rotates in inertial space in a 24 hour period [Eq. (D-33)].

Orbits About the Moon

1	2	3	4	5	6	7	8	
INSTANTANEOUS ACCESS AREA				AREA ACESS RATE				
0 deg elevation ($10^6 km^2$)	5 deg elevation ($10^6 km^2$)	10 deg elevation ($10^6 km^2$)	20 deg elevation ($10^6 km^2$)	0 deg elevation ($10^3 km^2/s$)	5 deg elevation ($10^3 km^2/s$)	10 deg elevation ($10^3 km^2/s$)	20 deg elevation ($10^3 km^2/s$)	(Alt. (km)
0.00	0.00	0.00	0.00	0.00	0.00	0.00	0.00	(+0
0.53	0.26	0.13	0.05	17.69	12.38	8.94	5.28	(+50
1.03	0.61	0.37	0.15	23.52	18.24	14.26	9.19	(+100
1.51	0.98	0.64	0.29	27.13	22.04	17.93	12.19	(+150
1.96	1.34	0.93	0.46	29.54	24.69	20.60	14.53	+200
2.39	1.70	1.21	0.63	31.20	26.59	22.59	16.38	+250
2.79	2.04	1.49	0.80	32.34	27.95	24.07	17.83	+300
3.55	2.70	2.04	1.17	33.56	29.61	26.00	19.89	+400
4.24	3.30	2.56	1.53	33.90	30.34	27.00	21.14	(+500
4.87	3.87	3.05	1.88	33.71	30.48	27.40	21.85	(+600
5.45	4.39	3.51	2.21	33.19	30.26	27.42	22.18	(+700
5.98	4.87	3.94	2.53	32.47	29.81	27.18	22.24	(+800
6.48	5.32	4.34	2.84	31.63	29.20	26.77	22.13	(+900
6.93	5.74	4.72	3.13	30.73	28.50	26.25	21.88	(+1,000
7.94	6.68	5.57	3.80	28.37	26.56	24.69	20.93	(+1,250
8.79	7.47	6.30	4.38	26.09	24.59	23.01	19.75	(+1,500
10.15	8.76	7.49	5.35	22.07	21.00	19.84	17.35	(+2,000
11.20	9.75	8.42	6.12	18.83	18.04	17.15	15.18	(+2,500
12.02	10.53	9.15	6.74	16.25	15.64	14.95	13.35	(+3,000
12.68	11.17	9.76	7.25	14.18	13.70	13.13	11.81	(+3,500
13.23	11.70	10.26	7.68	12.49	12.10	11.64	10.53	(+4,000
13.69	12.14	10.68	8.05	11.11	10.79	10.40	9.45	(+4,500
14.08	12.52	11.04	8.36	9.95	9.69	9.36	8.54	(+5,000
14.72	13.14	11.63	8.87	8.16	7.96	7.72	7.08	(+6,000
15.20	13.61	12.09	9.27	6.84	6.69	6.50	5.99	(+7,000
15.59	13.99	12.45	9.59	5.83	5.72	5.57	5.15	(+8,000
15.91	14.30	12.75	9.85	5.05	4.96	4.84	4.49	(+9,000
16.17	14.55	12.99	10.07	4.43	4.36	4.25	3.96	(+10,000
17.01	15.38	13.79	10.78	2.62	2.58	2.53	2.37	(+15,000
17.46	15.82	14.22	11.17	1.77	1.75	1.72	1.62	(+20,000
17.94	16.30	14.68	11.58	1.01	1.00	0.98	0.93	(+30,000
18.19	16.54	14.92	11.80	0.67	0.66	0.65	0.62	(+40,000
18.34	16.69	15.07	11.93	0.48	0.48	0.47	0.45	(+50,000
18.42	16.77	15.15	12.00	0.39	0.39	0.39	0.37	(+57,660

Orbits About the Moon

	9	10	11	12	13	14	15	16
	MAXIMUM TIME IN VIEW				MAXIMUM MOON CENTRAL ANGLE			
(Alt. (km)	0 deg elevation (min)	5 deg elevation (min)	10 deg elevation (min)	20 deg elevation (min)	0 deg elevation (deg)	5 deg elevation (deg)	10 deg elevation (deg)	20 deg elevation (deg)
(+0	0.00	0.00	0.00	0.00	0.00	0.00	0.00	0.00
(+50	8.53	5.94	4.28	2.52	13.58	9.46	6.81	4.02
(+100	12.43	9.57	7.45	4.78	18.99	14.61	11.37	7.31
(+150	15.67	12.61	10.20	6.89	22.99	18.50	14.97	10.11
(+200	18.61	15.38	12.74	8.91	26.26	21.70	17.97	12.57
(+250	21.39	18.00	15.15	10.87	29.04	24.43	20.58	14.76
(+300	24.07	20.52	17.49	12.80	31.48	26.84	22.88	16.74
(+400	29.26	25.40	22.03	16.59	35.62	30.92	26.82	20.19
(+500	34.35	30.19	26.49	20.35	39.05	34.32	30.11	23.13
(+600	39.43	34.96	30.94	24.13	41.98	37.22	32.94	25.69
(+700	44.54	39.76	35.42	27.95	44.53	39.75	35.41	27.94
(+800	49.70	44.60	39.94	31.81	46.78	41.99	37.59	29.95
(+900	54.92	49.51	44.52	35.74	48.79	43.98	39.55	31.75
(+1000	60.23	54.49	49.17	39.74	50.60	45.78	41.31	33.38
(+1,250	73.87	67.30	61.14	50.03	54.43	49.59	45.05	36.87
(+1,500	88.08	80.64	73.62	60.79	57.54	52.68	48.09	39.71
(+2,000	118.29	109.01	100.16	83.73	62.29	57.41	52.75	44.09
(+2,500	150.81	139.57	128.78	108.50	65.79	60.89	56.18	47.33
(+3,000	185.56	172.25	159.39	135.04	68.48	63.57	58.82	49.84
(+3,500	222.44	206.94	191.91	163.26	70.62	65.70	60.93	51.83
(+4,000	261.35	243.54	226.24	193.08	72.37	67.44	62.64	53.46
(+4,500	302.20	281.99	262.29	224.42	73.82	68.89	64.07	54.82
(+5,000	344.90	322.19	300.01	257.22	75.05	70.11	65.28	55.97
(+6,000	435.59	407.60	380.17	326.98	77.02	72.07	67.22	57.82
(+7,000	532.93	499.30	466.27	401.95	78.53	73.57	68.70	59.23
(+8,000	636.50	596.90	557.92	481.82	79.72	74.76	69.88	60.35
(+9,000	745.96	700.06	654.82	566.29	80.69	75.72	70.83	61.25
(+10,000	861.00	808.51	756.71	655.14	81.49	76.52	71.62	62.00
(+15,000	1,512.08	1,422.53	1,333.79	1,158.72	84.04	79.06	74.13	64.40
(+20,000	2,274.54	2,141.86	2,010.10	1,749.33	85.41	80.43	75.48	65.69
(+30,000	4,080.63	3,846.30	3,613.09	3,149.96	86.86	81.87	76.91	67.05
(+40,000	6,207.30	5,853.70	5,501.38	4,800.52	87.61	82.62	77.65	67.76
(+50,000	8,611.94	8,123.76	7,637.00	6,667.70	88.07	83.08	78.10	68.19
(+57,660	10,623.48	10,022.85	9,423.75	8,230.06	88.32	83.33	78.35	68.42

Orbits About the Moon

17	18	19	20	21	22	23	24	
MAXIMUM RANGE				MAXIMUM NADIR ANGLE				
0 deg elevation (min)	5 deg elevation (min)	10 deg elevation (min)	20 deg elevation (min)	0 deg elevation (deg)	5 deg elevation (deg)	10 deg elevation (deg)	20 deg elevation (deg)	(Alt. (km)
0	0	0	0	90.00	85.00	80.00	70.00	(+0
420	295	215	133	76.42	75.54	73.19	65.98	(+50
598	465	368	249	71.01	70.39	68.63	62.69	(+100
737	601	495	353	67.01	66.50	65.03	59.89	(+150
857	719	607	449	63.74	63.30	62.03	57.43	(+200
965	825	709	539	60.96	60.57	59.42	55.24	(+250
1,064	924	804	625	58.52	58.16	57.12	53.26	(+300
1,245	1,103	979	785	54.38	54.08	53.18	49.81	(+400
1,410	1,267	1,140	936	50.95	50.68	49.89	46.87	(+500
1,564	1,420	1,291	1,079	48.02	47.78	47.06	44.31	(+600
1,710	1,565	1,434	1,216	45.47	45.25	44.59	42.06	(+700
1,850	1,704	1,572	1,348	43.22	43.01	42.41	40.05	(+800
1,985	1,839	1,706	1,477	41.21	41.02	40.45	38.25	(+900
2,116	1,970	1,835	1,603	39.40	39.22	38.69	36.62	(+1,000
2,431	2,284	2,147	1,908	35.57	35.41	34.95	33.13	(+1,250
2,732	2,585	2,447	2,202	32.46	32.32	31.91	30.29	(+1,500
3,309	3,161	3,021	2,768	27.71	27.59	27.25	25.91	(+2,000
3,865	3,717	3,575	3,316	24.21	24.11	23.82	22.67	(+2,500
4,408	4,259	4,116	3,853	21.52	21.43	21.18	20.16	(+3,000
4,941	4,792	4,649	4,382	19.38	19.30	19.07	18.17	(+3,500
5,468	5,319	5,175	4,906	17.63	17.56	17.36	16.54	(+4,000
5,991	5,841	5,697	5,426	16.18	16.11	15.93	15.18	(+4,500
6,510	6,360	6,215	5,943	14.95	14.89	14.72	14.03	(+5,000
7,540	7,390	7,245	6,969	12.98	12.93	12.78	12.18	(+6,000
8,563	8,413	8,267	7,990	11.47	11.43	11.30	10.77	(+7,000
9,582	9,431	9,285	9,006	10.28	10.24	10.12	9.65	(+8,000
10,596	10,446	10,299	10,019	9.31	9.28	9.17	8.75	(+9,000
11,609	11,458	11,311	11,029	8.51	8.48	8.38	8.00	(+10,000
16,648	16,497	16,348	16,064	5.96	5.94	5.87	5.60	(+15,000
21,668	21,517	21,369	21,082	4.59	4.57	4.52	4.31	(+20,000
31,690	31,539	31,390	31,102	3.14	3.13	3.09	2.95	(+30,000
41,702	41,551	41,401	41,112	2.39	2.38	2.35	2.24	(+40,000
51,709	51,558	51,408	51,118	1.93	1.92	1.90	1.81	(+50,000
59,373	59,221	59,072	58,781	1.68	1.67	1.65	1.58	(+57,660

Orbits About the Moon

	41	42	43	44	45	46	47	48
	VELOCITY-RELATED PARAMETERS							
(Alt. (km)	Circular Velocity (km/s)	Orbit Angular Velocity (deg/min)	Escape Velocity (km/s)	ΔV Req'd to Deorbit (m/s)	Plane Change ΔV (m/s)/deg	ΔV Req'd for a 1 km Alt Chg (m/s)	Max Ang Rate from Gnd Stn (deg/s)	Sun Synchronous Inclination (deg)
(+0	1.680	3.322	2.375	0.0	29.31	0.48	—	132.66
✈ +50	1.656	3.184	2.342	−11.8	28.90	0.46	1.90	138.45
(+100	1.633	3.055	2.310	−23.0	28.51	0.44	0.94	145.51
(+150	1.611	2.934	2.279	−33.7	28.13	0.43	0.62	154.87
(+200	1.591	2.821	2.249	−43.9	27.76	0.41	0.46	172.79
(+250	1.570	2.716	2.221	−53.6	27.41	0.39	0.36	—
(+300	1.551	2.616	2.193	−62.9	27.07	0.38	0.30	—
(+400	1.514	2.435	2.142	−80.3	26.43	0.35	0.22	—
(+500	1.480	2.274	2.093	−96.2	25.83	0.33	0.17	—
(+600	1.448	2.129	2.048	−110.8	25.27	0.31	0.14	—
(+700	1.418	2.000	2.005	−124.3	24.75	0.29	0.12	—
(+800	1.390	1.883	1.966	−136.7	24.26	0.27	0.10	—
(+900	1.363	1.777	1.928	−148.3	23.79	0.26	0.09	—
(+1,000	1.338	1.680	1.892	−158.9	23.35	0.24	0.08	—
(+1,250	1.281	1.474	1.812	−182.4	22.36	0.21	0.06	—
(+1,500	1.231	1.306	1.740	−202.1	21.48	0.19	0.05	—
(+2,000	1.145	1.053	1.620	−232.8	19.99	0.15	0.03	—
(+2,500	1.076	0.872	1.521	−255.3	18.77	0.13	0.02	—
(+3,000	1.017	0.738	1.439	−272.0	17.75	0.11	0.02	—
(+3,500	0.967	0.635	1.368	−284.5	16.89	0.09	0.02	—
(+4,000	0.924	0.554	1.307	−294.1	16.13	0.08	0.01	—
(+4,500	0.887	0.489	1.254	−301.3	15.47	0.07	0.01	—
(+5,000	0.853	0.435	1.206	−306.8	14.89	0.06	0.01	—
(+6,000	0.796	0.354	1.126	−313.9	13.89	0.05	0.01	—
(+7,000	0.749	0.295	1.059	−317.6	13.07	0.04	0.01	—
(+8,000	0.710	0.250	1.003	−319.0	12.38	0.04	0.01	—
(+9,000	0.676	0.216	0.956	−319.0	11.79	0.03	0.00	—
(+10,000	0.646	0.189	0.914	−318.1	11.28	0.03	0.00	—
(+15,000	0.541	0.111	0.765	−306.5	9.45	0.02	0.00	—
(+20,000	0.475	0.075	0.672	−292.2	8.29	0.01	0.00	—
(+30,000	0.393	0.043	0.556	−266.4	6.86	0.01	0.00	—
(+40,000	0.343	0.028	0.485	−245.8	5.98	0.00	0.00	—
(+50,000	0.308	0.020	0.435	−229.4	5.37	0.00	0.00	—
(+57,660	0.287	0.017	0.406	−218.8	5.01	0.00	0.00	—

Orbits About the Moon

49	50	51	52	53	54	55	56	
GENERAL PARAMETERS								
Angular Radius of the Moon (deg)	1 deg FOV on Moon's Surface (km)	Range to Horizon (km)	Period (min)	Max Eclipse (min)	Revo-lutions per Day (#)	Node Spacing (deg)	Node Preces-sion/Day (deg/day)	(Alt. (km)
90.00	0.00	0	108.36	54.18	13.29	0.99	−1.45 cos *i*	(+0
76.42	0.87	420	113.07	48.00	12.74	1.03	−1.32 cos *i*	(+50
71.01	1.75	598	117.85	46.49	12.22	1.08	−1.20 cos *i*	(+100
67.01	2.62	737	122.69	45.67	11.74	1.12	−1.09 cos *i*	(+150
63.74	3.49	857	127.60	45.18	11.29	1.17	−0.99 cos *i*	(+200
60.96	4.36	965	132.57	44.89	10.86	1.21	−0.91 cos *i*	(+250
58.52	5.24	1,064	137.60	44.73	10.47	1.26	−0.83 cos *i*	(+300
54.38	6.98	1,245	147.85	44.67	9.74	1.35	−0.70 cos *i*	(+400
50.95	8.73	1,410	158.34	44.82	9.09	1.45	−0.60 cos *i*	(+500
48.02	10.47	1,564	169.07	45.10	8.52	1.55	−0.52 cos *i*	(+600
45.47	12.22	1,710	180.04	45.48	8.00	1.65	−0.44 cos *i*	(+700
43.22	13.96	1,850	191.22	45.91	7.53	1.75	−0.39 cos *i*	(+800
41.21	15.71	1,985	202.64	46.39	7.11	1.85	−0.34 cos *i*	(+900
39.40	17.45	2,116	214.27	46.90	6.72	1.96	−0.30 cos *i*	(+1,000
35.57	21.82	2,431	244.27	48.27	5.90	2.24	−0.22 cos *i*	(+1,250
32.46	26.18	2,732	275.56	49.70	5.23	2.52	−0.16 cos *i*	(+1,500
27.71	34.91	3,309	341.79	52.61	4.21	3.13	−0.10 cos *i*	(+2,000
24.21	43.64	3,865	412.62	55.50	3.49	3.78	−0.06 cos *i*	(+2,500
21.52	52.37	4,408	487.75	58.31	2.95	4.46	−0.04 cos *i*	(+3,000
19.38	61.10	4,941	566.96	61.04	2.54	5.19	−0.03 cos *i*	(+3,500
17.63	69.83	5,468	650.05	63.67	2.22	5.95	−0.02 cos *i*	(+4,000
16.18	78.56	5,991	736.84	66.22	1.95	6.74	−0.02 cos *i*	(+4,500
14.95	87.29	6,510	827.19	68.69	1.74	7.57	−0.01 cos *i*	(+5,000
12.98	104.75	7,540	1018.00	73.41	1.41	9.31	−0.01 cos *i*	(+6,000
11.47	122.22	8,563	1221.59	77.86	1.18	11.18	−0.01 cos *i*	(+7,000
10.28	139.69	9,582	1437.18	82.09	1.00	13.15	0.00	(+8,000
9.31	157.17	10,596	1664.15	86.12	0.87	15.23	0.00	(+9,000
8.51	174.65	11,609	1901.94	89.97	0.76	17.40	0.00	(+10,000
5.96	262.14	16,648	3238.63	107.24	0.44	29.63	0.00	(+15,000
4.59	349.82	21,668	4793.31	122.12	0.30	43.86	0.00	(+20,000
3.14	525.96	31,690	8456.21	147.47	0.17	77.38	0.00	(+30,000
2.39	703.56	41,702	12752.76	169.08	0.11	116.69	0.00	(+40,000
1.93	883.13	51,709	17600.34	188.23	0.08	161.05	0.00	(+50,000
1.68	1,022.36	59,373	21650.32	201.68	0.07	198.11	0.00	(+57,660

Table F-2
Mars (♂) Satellite Parameters

The following table provides a variety of quantitative data for satellites orbiting Mars. The independent parameter in the formulas is the distance, r, from the center of Mars in km. However, the outside column on each page is the altitude, $h \equiv r - R_{♂}$, where $R_{♂}$ = 3,397 km is the equatorial radius of Mars. Numerical formulas for the *Earth Satellite Parameters* will not generally work for a Mars orbiting satellite; readers should use the formulas below or those in Chap. 2.

- General Changes relative to Earth satellite tables:
  R_E, or $R_\oplus$, (= 6,378.14 km) is replaced by $R_{♂}$ (= 3,397 km)
  $\mu_\oplus$ (= 398,600.4 km^3/s^2) is replaced by $\mu_{♂}$ (= 42,828.3 km^3/s^2)
  $J_{2,\oplus}$ (= 1.082 63 × 10^{-3}) is replaced with $J_{2,♂}$ (= 1.964 × 10^{-3})
- 17,031 km is the Mars-synchronous altitude at which a Martian satellite orbits the planet in one Mars sidereal day.

Columns 1 through 24 use Earth Satellite formulae with the changes noted above.

Columns 25 through 40 are omitted as a Mars atmosphere model analogous to the MSIS model is not available.

Columns 41, 42 and 43 use Earth Satellite formulas with the changes noted above.

Columns 45, 46 and 47 use Earth Satellite formulas with the changes noted above.

Columns 49, through 53 use Earth Satellite formulas with the changes noted above.

44. *ΔV Required to De-Orbit (m/s)* = Is the velocity change needed to transform the assumed circular orbit to an elliptical orbit apoapse unchanged and periapse of 0 km, i.e. at the Martian surface [Eqs. (2-85a) and (2-85b)].

48. *Sun Synchronous Inclination (deg)* = $\cos^{-1}$ {0.52407° / (–1.5 × 86,400 $(\mu_{♂}/r^3)^{1/2} \times J_{2,♂} \times (R_{♂}/h)^2$)} assumes circular orbit with node rotation rate of 0.52407 deg/day to match the mean motion of the Sun as seen from an inertial observer at Mars [Eq. (D-34)].

54. *Revolutions per Day (#)* = 1,477.377 72/P, where P is from column 52. Note that this is revolutions per sidereal Martian day, where the sidereal Martian day is the day relative to the fixed stars which is approximately $24^{hr}\ 37^{min}\ 22.66^{sec}$. [Eq. (D-35)]

55. *Node Spacing (deg)* = 360° × (P / 1,477.377 72), where P is from column 52. This is the spacing in longitude between successive ascending or descending nodes for a satellite in a circular orbit [Eq. (D-36)].

56. *Node Precession Rate (deg/day)* = $-1.5\ n\ J_{2,♂}\ (R_{♂}/a)^2 (\cos i)(1 - e^2)^{-2}$, where i is the inclination, e the eccentricity (which is set to zero), n is the mean motion (= $(\mu_{♂}/a^3)^{1/2}$), a the semi-major axis, $J_{2,♂}$ the dominant zonal coefficient in the expansion of the Legendre polynomial describing the Martian gravitational potential. This is the angle through which the orbit rotates in inertial space in a 24-hour period. Assumes a circular orbit [Eq. (D-33)].

Orbits About Mars

1	2	3	4	5	6	7	8	
INSTANTANEOUS ACCESS AREA				AREA ACCESS RATE				
0 deg elevation ($10^6 km^2$)	5 deg elevation ($10^6 km^2$)	10 deg elevation ($10^6 km^2$)	20 deg elevation ($10^6 km^2$)	0 deg elevation ($10^3 km^2/s$)	5 deg elevation ($10^3 km^2/s$)	10 deg elevation ($10^3 km^2/s$)	20 deg elevation ($10^3 km^2/s$)	♂ Alt. (km)
0.00	0.00	0.00	0.00	0.00	0.00	0.00	0.00	♂+0
1.05	0.39	0.17	0.05	14.12	8.65	5.73	3.15	♂+50
2.07	1.02	0.53	0.19	19.33	13.58	9.83	5.82	♂+100
3.07	1.70	0.98	0.38	22.93	17.16	13.03	8.12	♂+150
4.03	2.41	1.47	0.61	25.66	19.95	15.64	10.11	♂+200
4.97	3.13	1.99	0.88	27.82	22.21	17.80	11.86	♂+250
5.88	3.85	2.53	1.17	29.56	24.07	19.63	13.39	♂+300
6.77	4.56	3.08	1.48	30.98	25.62	21.18	14.74	♂+350
7.64	5.27	3.64	1.80	32.15	26.92	22.51	15.93	♂+400
8.48	5.96	4.20	2.13	33.12	28.02	23.66	16.98	♂+450
9.30	6.65	4.75	2.47	33.92	28.95	24.64	17.92	♂+500
10.10	7.32	5.30	2.82	34.58	29.74	25.49	18.75	♂+550
10.88	7.99	5.85	3.17	35.11	30.41	26.23	19.48	♂+600
11.65	8.64	6.40	3.52	35.55	30.97	26.86	20.13	♂+650
12.39	9.28	6.93	3.88	35.89	31.43	27.40	20.71	♂+700
13.11	9.91	7.46	4.23	36.16	31.82	27.86	21.22	♂+750
13.82	10.53	7.99	4.58	36.37	32.14	28.26	21.67	♂+800
14.51	11.13	8.50	4.94	36.51	32.39	28.59	22.07	♂+850
15.19	11.73	9.01	5.29	36.61	32.60	28.86	22.42	♂+900
15.85	12.31	9.51	5.64	36.66	32.75	29.09	22.72	♂+950
16.49	12.88	10.01	5.99	36.67	32.86	29.28	22.98	♂+1,000
19.50	15.58	12.36	7.68	36.27	32.92	29.69	23.81	♂+1,250
22.21	18.02	14.53	9.29	35.39	32.42	29.51	24.06	♂+1,500
26.87	22.29	18.37	12.21	33.00	30.64	28.25	23.59	♂+2,000
30.74	25.88	21.63	14.77	30.39	28.47	26.49	22.49	♂+2,500
34.00	28.93	24.43	17.02	27.89	26.30	24.64	21.18	♂+3,000
36.79	31.56	26.86	18.99	25.58	24.26	22.84	19.83	♂+3,500
39.21	33.84	28.98	20.73	23.51	22.39	21.17	18.53	♂+4,000
41.32	35.84	30.85	22.28	21.66	20.70	19.64	17.31	♂+4,500
43.17	37.61	32.51	23.67	20.01	19.18	18.25	16.17	♂+5,000
46.29	40.60	35.32	26.04	17.23	16.60	15.87	14.19	♂+6,000
48.82	43.02	37.61	27.99	15.01	14.51	13.92	12.54	♂+7,000
50.89	45.02	39.51	29.62	13.21	12.81	12.32	11.16	♂+8,000
52.64	46.71	41.11	31.00	11.73	11.40	11.00	10.00	♂+9,000
54.12	48.15	42.48	32.19	10.50	10.23	9.88	9.02	♂+10,000
57.01	50.96	45.17	34.53	8.21	8.02	7.78	7.16	♂+12,500
59.12	53.01	47.14	36.26	6.63	6.50	6.32	5.84	♂+15,000
60.45	54.31	48.39	37.36	5.69	5.58	5.44	5.04	♂+17,031
61.98	55.81	49.83	38.64	4.65	4.58	4.47	4.16	♂+20,000
63.83	57.62	51.59	40.21	3.49	3.44	3.37	3.15	♂+25,000
65.13	58.90	52.83	41.31	2.74	2.71	2.66	2.49	♂+30,000

Orbits About Mars

	9	10	11	12	13	14	15	16
	MAXIMUM TIME IN VIEW				MAXIMUM MARS CENTRAL ANGLE			
♂ Alt. (km)	0 deg elevation (min)	5 deg elevation (min)	10 deg elevation (min)	20 deg elevation (min)	0 deg elevation (deg)	5 deg elevation (deg)	10 deg elevation (deg)	20 deg elevation (deg)
♂+0	0.00	0.00	0.00	0.00	0.00	0.00	0.00	0.00
♂+50	5.56	3.39	2.25	1.24	9.77	5.96	3.95	2.17
♂+100	7.98	5.58	4.03	2.38	13.74	9.60	6.93	4.10
♂+150	9.93	7.38	5.59	3.47	16.72	12.43	9.41	5.85
♂+200	11.64	8.98	7.01	4.52	19.20	14.81	11.56	7.45
♂+250	13.21	10.46	8.34	5.52	21.34	16.89	13.47	8.92
♂+300	14.69	11.84	9.60	6.51	23.24	18.74	15.19	10.30
♂+350	16.09	13.17	10.81	7.47	24.96	20.43	16.77	11.58
♂+400	17.45	14.45	11.99	8.41	26.54	21.97	18.23	12.79
♂+450	18.78	15.69	13.14	9.34	27.99	23.40	19.59	13.92
♂+500	20.07	16.91	14.26	10.26	29.34	24.73	20.86	15.00
♂+550	21.34	18.11	15.37	11.17	30.61	25.98	22.05	16.03
♂+600	22.59	19.29	16.47	12.08	31.80	27.15	23.18	17.00
♂+650	23.83	20.45	17.55	12.98	32.92	28.26	24.25	17.93
♂+700	25.06	21.61	18.62	13.87	33.99	29.31	25.26	18.82
♂+750	26.28	22.76	19.69	14.77	35.00	30.31	26.23	19.67
♂+800	27.49	23.90	20.75	15.66	35.96	31.26	27.15	20.49
♂+850	28.70	25.03	21.81	16.55	36.88	32.17	28.03	21.27
♂+900	29.90	26.17	22.86	17.44	37.76	33.04	28.87	22.02
♂+950	31.10	27.30	23.92	18.33	38.61	33.88	29.68	22.75
♂+1,000	32.31	28.42	24.97	19.22	39.41	34.68	30.46	23.45
♂+1,250	38.32	34.07	30.24	23.70	43.03	38.26	33.95	26.61
♂+1,500	44.39	39.77	35.56	28.24	46.08	41.29	36.91	29.32
♂+2,000	56.84	51.46	46.47	37.61	50.99	46.17	41.69	33.74
♂+2,500	69.80	63.63	57.84	47.39	54.83	49.98	45.44	37.23
♂+3,000	83.31	76.32	69.71	57.63	57.92	53.06	48.47	40.07
♂+3,500	97.41	89.55	82.10	68.32	60.49	55.62	50.98	42.43
♂+4,000	112.07	103.33	94.99	79.47	62.66	57.77	53.11	44.43
♂+4,500	127.29	117.63	108.38	91.06	64.52	59.63	54.94	46.16
♂+5,000	143.06	132.45	122.26	103.09	66.14	61.23	56.52	47.66
♂+6,000	176.20	163.61	151.46	128.40	68.81	63.89	59.14	50.14
♂+7,000	211.39	196.71	182.48	155.33	70.93	66.01	61.23	52.12
♂+8,000	248.52	231.65	215.25	183.79	72.66	67.73	62.93	53.73
♂+9,000	287.52	268.36	249.68	213.72	74.10	69.16	64.34	55.08
♂+10,000	328.29	306.75	285.70	245.05	75.31	70.37	65.54	56.22
♂+12,500	437.59	409.69	382.32	329.15	77.66	72.71	67.85	58.42
♂+15,000	556.68	521.90	487.68	420.94	79.36	74.40	69.52	60.01
♂+17,031	660.12	619.38	579.25	500.75	80.43	75.46	70.57	61.01
♂+20,000	821.48	771.50	722.16	625.36	81.65	76.68	71.78	62.16
♂+25,000	1,118.29	1,051.38	985.18	854.84	83.13	78.16	73.23	63.55
♂+30,000	1,444.00	1,358.60	1,273.96	1,106.91	84.16	79.18	74.25	64.52

17	18	19	20	21	22	23	24	
MAXIMUM RANGE				MAXIMUM NADIR ANGLE				
0 deg elevation (min)	5 deg elevation (min)	10 deg elevation (min)	20 deg elevation (min)	0 deg elevation (deg)	5 deg elevation (deg)	10 deg elevation (deg)	20 deg elevation (deg)	♂ Alt. (km)
0	0	0	0	90.00	85.00	80.00	70.00	♂+0
585	360	241	139	80.23	79.04	76.05	67.83	♂+50
830	585	429	266	76.26	75.40	73.07	65.90	♂+100
1,021	767	589	385	73.28	72.57	70.59	64.15	♂+150
1,183	923	732	496	70.80	70.19	68.44	62.55	♂+200
1,327	1,064	862	602	68.66	68.11	66.53	61.08	♂+250
1,459	1,193	984	703	66.76	66.26	64.81	59.70	♂+300
1,581	1,313	1,098	800	65.04	64.57	63.23	58.42	♂+350
1,696	1,426	1,206	894	63.46	63.03	61.77	57.21	♂+400
1,805	1,534	1,310	985	62.01	61.60	60.41	56.08	♂+450
1,910	1,636	1,409	1,074	60.66	60.27	59.14	55.00	♂+500
2,010	1,735	1505	1,160	59.39	59.02	57.95	53.97	♂+550
2,106	1,831	1,597	1,244	58.20	57.85	56.82	53.00	♂+600
2,200	1,923	1,688	1,326	57.08	56.74	55.75	52.07	♂+650
2,290	2,013	1,775	1,406	56.01	55.69	54.74	51.18	♂+700
2,379	2,101	1,861	1,485	55.00	54.69	53.77	50.33	♂+750
2,465	2,186	1,945	1,563	54.04	53.74	52.85	49.51	♂+800
2,549	2,270	2,026	1,639	53.12	52.83	51.97	48.73	♂+850
2,631	2,352	2,107	1,715	52.24	51.96	51.13	47.98	♂+900
2,712	2,432	2,186	1,789	51.39	51.12	50.32	47.25	♂+950
2,792	2,511	2,264	1,862	50.59	50.32	49.54	46.55	♂+1,000
3,171	2,889	2,635	2,215	46.97	46.74	46.05	43.39	♂+1,250
3,527	3,244	2,986	2,552	43.92	43.71	43.09	40.68	♂+1,500
4,194	3,908	3,645	3,190	39.01	38.83	38.31	36.26	♂+2,000
4,820	4,533	4,266	3,796	35.17	35.02	34.56	32.77	♂+2,500
5,421	5,133	4,863	4,382	32.08	31.94	31.53	29.93	♂+3,000
6,002	5,714	5,441	4,952	29.51	29.38	29.02	27.57	♂+3,500
6,571	6,281	6,007	5,511	27.34	27.23	26.89	25.57	♂+4,000
7,129	6,839	6,564	6,061	25.48	25.37	25.06	23.84	♂+4,500
7,679	7,389	7,112	6,605	23.86	23.77	23.48	22.34	♂+5,000
8,762	8,470	8,191	7,676	21.19	21.11	20.86	19.86	♂+6,000
9,826	9,535	9,254	8,733	19.07	18.99	18.77	17.88	♂+7,000
10,879	10,587	10,305	9,779	17.34	17.27	17.07	16.27	♂+8,000
11,922	11,630	11,347	10,817	15.90	15.84	15.66	14.92	♂+9,000
12,959	12,666	12,383	11,849	14.69	14.63	14.46	13.78	♂+10,000
15,530	15,237	14,951	14,411	12.34	12.29	12.15	11.58	♂+12,500
18,081	17,787	17,500	16,956	10.64	10.60	10.48	9.99	♂+15,000
20,143	19,849	19,562	19,015	9.57	9.54	9.43	8.99	♂+17,031
23,149	22,855	22,567	22,016	8.35	8.32	8.22	7.84	♂+20,000
28,193	27,899	27,609	27,055	6.87	6.84	6.77	6.45	♂+25,000
33,224	32,929	32,639	32,082	5.84	5.82	5.75	5.48	♂+30,000

	41	42	43	44	45	46	47	48
	VELOCITY-RELATED PARAMETERS							
♂ Alt. (km)	Circular Velocity (km/s)	Orbit Angular Velocity (deg/min)	Escape Velocity (km/s)	ΔV Req'd to Deorbit (m/s)	Plane Change ΔV (m/s)/deg	ΔV Req'd for a 1 km Alt Chg (m/s)	Max Ang Rate from Gnd Stn (deg/s)	Sun Synchronous Inclination (deg)
♂+0	3.551	3.593	5.021	0.0	61.97	0.52	—	91.97
♂+50	3.525	3.515	4.985	–12.9	61.52	0.51	4.04	92.07
♂+100	3.500	3.440	4.949	–25.5	61.08	0.50	2.01	92.18
♂+150	3.475	3.368	4.914	–37.7	60.65	0.49	1.33	92.29
♂+200	3.451	3.298	4.880	–49.7	60.22	0.48	0.99	92.41
♂+250	3.427	3.230	4.846	–61.4	59.81	0.47	0.79	92.53
♂+300	3.404	3.165	4.813	–72.7	59.40	0.46	0.65	92.65
♂+350	3.381	3.102	4.781	–83.9	59.01	0.45	0.55	92.78
♂+400	3.358	3.041	4.750	–94.7	58.62	0.44	0.48	92.91
♂+450	3.337	2.982	4.719	–105.3	58.23	0.43	0.42	93.05
♂+500	3.315	2.924	4.688	–115.6	57.86	0.43	0.38	93.19
♂+550	3.294	2.869	4.659	–125.7	57.49	0.42	0.34	93.33
♂+600	3.273	2.815	4.629	–135.6	57.13	0.41	0.31	93.48
♂+650	3.253	2.763	4.601	–145.3	56.78	0.40	0.29	93.64
♂+700	3.233	2.713	4.572	–154.7	56.43	0.39	0.26	93.80
♂+750	3.214	2.664	4.545	–163.9	56.09	0.39	0.25	93.96
♂+800	3.194	2.617	4.518	–172.9	55.75	0.38	0.23	94.13
♂+850	3.176	2.570	4.491	–181.8	55.42	0.37	0.21	94.31
♂+900	3.157	2.526	4.465	–190.4	55.10	0.37	0.20	94.49
♂+950	3.139	2.482	4.439	–198.8	54.78	0.36	0.19	94.67
♂+1,000	3.121	2.440	4.414	–207.1	54.47	0.35	0.18	94.87
♂+1,250	3.036	2.246	4.293	–245.8	52.98	0.33	0.14	95.91
♂+1,500	2.957	2.076	4.182	–280.7	51.61	0.30	0.11	97.10
♂+2,000	2.817	1.794	3.984	–341.0	49.17	0.26	0.08	100.01
♂+2,500	2.695	1.571	3.811	–390.8	47.04	0.23	0.06	103.71
♂+3,000	2.587	1.391	3.659	–432.4	45.16	0.20	0.05	108.36
♂+3,500	2.492	1.242	3.524	–467.5	43.49	0.18	0.04	114.20
♂+4,000	2.406	1.118	3.403	–497.2	42.00	0.16	0.03	121.59
♂+4,500	2.329	1.014	3.293	–522.6	40.64	0.15	0.03	131.19
♂+5,000	2.258	0.925	3.194	–544.3	39.42	0.13	0.03	—
♂+6,000	2.135	0.781	3.019	–579.2	37.26	0.11	0.02	—
♂+7,000	2.030	0.671	2.870	–605.2	35.42	0.10	0.02	—
♂+8,000	1.939	0.585	2.741	–624.8	33.83	0.09	0.01	—
♂+9,000	1.859	0.515	2.629	–639.6	32.44	0.07	0.01	—
♂+10,000	1.788	0.459	2.529	–650.7	31.21	0.07	0.01	—
♂+12,500	1.641	0.355	2.321	–667.4	28.65	0.05	0.01	—
♂+15,000	1.526	0.285	2.158	–673.9	26.63	0.04	0.01	—
♂+17,031	1.448	0.244	2.048	–674.7	25.27	0.04	0.00	—
♂+20,000	1.353	0.199	1.913	–671.7	23.61	0.03	0.00	—
♂+25,000	1.228	0.149	1.737	–660.4	21.43	0.02	0.00	—
♂+30,000	1.132	0.117	1.601	–645.8	19.76	0.02	0.00	—

49	50	51	52	53	54	55	56	
GENERAL PARAMETERS								
Angular Radius of Mars (deg)	1 deg FOV on Mars' Surface (km)	Range to Horizon (km)	Period (min)	Max Eclipse (min)	Revo-lutions per Day (#)	Node Spacing (deg)	Node Preces-sion/Day (deg/day)	♂ Alt. (km)
90.00	0.00	0	100.19	50.09	14.75	24.41	–15.64 cos*i*	♂+0
80.23	0.87	585	102.41	45.64	14.43	24.95	–14.86 cos *i*	♂+50
76.26	1.75	830	104.64	44.34	14.12	25.50	–14.13 cos *i*	♂+100
73.28	2.62	1,021	106.89	43.52	13.82	26.05	–13.44 cos *i*	♂+150
70.80	3.49	1,183	109.16	42.94	13.53	26.60	–12.80 cos *i*	♂+200
68.66	4.36	1,327	111.45	42.51	13.26	27.16	–12.20 cos *i*	♂+250
66.76	5.24	1,459	113.75	42.19	12.99	27.72	–11.63 cos *i*	♂+300
65.04	6.11	1,581	116.06	41.94	12.73	28.28	–11.10 cos *i*	♂+350
63.46	6.98	1,696	118.39	41.74	12.48	28.85	–10.59 cos *i*	♂+400
62.01	7.85	1,805	120.74	41.59	12.24	29.42	–10.12 cos *i*	♂+450
60.66	8.73	1,910	123.10	41.48	12.00	30.00	–9.67 cos *i*	♂+500
59.39	9.60	2,010	125.48	41.40	11.77	30.58	–9.25 cos *i*	♂+550
58.20	10.47	2,106	127.87	41.34	11.55	31.16	–8.85 cos *i*	♂+600
57.08	11.35	2,200	130.28	41.31	11.34	31.74	–8.47 cos *i*	♂+650
56.01	12.22	2,290	132.70	41.29	11.13	32.34	–8.12 cos *i*	♂+700
55.00	13.09	2,379	135.13	41.29	10.93	32.93	–7.78 cos *i*	♂+750
54.04	13.96	2,465	137.59	41.30	10.74	33.53	–7.46 cos *i*	♂+800
53.12	14.84	2,549	140.05	41.33	10.55	34.13	–7.16 cos *i*	♂+850
52.24	15.71	2,631	142.53	41.36	10.37	34.73	–6.87 cos *i*	♂+900
51.39	16.58	2,712	145.03	41.41	10.19	35.34	–6.60 cos *i*	♂+950
50.59	17.45	2,792	147.54	41.46	10.01	35.95	–6.34 cos *i*	♂+1,000
46.97	21.82	3,171	160.30	41.83	9.22	39.06	–5.22 cos *i*	♂+1,250
43.92	26.18	3,527	173.40	42.31	8.52	42.25	–4.35 cos *i*	♂+1,500
39.01	34.91	4,194	200.63	43.48	7.36	48.89	–3.09 cos *i*	♂+2,000
35.17	43.64	4,820	229.14	44.78	6.45	55.84	–2.27 cos *i*	♂+2,500
32.08	52.36	5421	258.90	46.13	5.71	63.09	–1.71 cos *i*	♂+3,000
29.51	61.09	6,002	289.84	47.51	5.10	70.63	–1.31 cos *i*	♂+3,500
27.34	69.82	6,571	321.92	48.89	4.59	78.44	–1.03 cos *i*	♂+4,000
25.48	78.55	7,129	355.10	50.26	4.16	86.53	–0.82 cos *i*	♂+4,500
23.86	87.28	7,679	389.36	51.62	3.79	94.88	–0.66 cos *i*	♂+5,000
21.19	104.73	8,762	460.94	54.27	3.21	112.32	–0.44 cos *i*	♂+6,000
19.07	122.19	9,826	536.45	56.83	2.75	130.72	–0.31 cos *i*	♂+7,000
17.34	139.65	10,879	615.67	59.31	2.40	150.02	–0.23 cos *i*	♂+8,000
15.90	157.11	11,922	698.45	61.71	2.12	170.20	–0.17 cos *i*	♂+9,000
14.69	174.58	12,959	784.65	64.03	1.88	191.20	–0.13 cos *i*	♂+10,000
12.34	218.24	15,530	1,014.23	69.52	1.46	247.14	–0.07 cos *i*	♂+12,500
10.64	261.91	18,081	1,262.65	74.64	1.17	307.68	–0.04 cos *i*	♂+15,000
9.57	297.40	20,143	1,477.38	78.57	1.00	360.00	–0.03 cos *i*	♂+17,031
8.35	349.31	23,149	1,810.94	83.99	0.82	441.28	–0.02 cos *i*	♂+20,000
6.87	436.77	28,193	2,421.43	92.42	0.61	590.04	–0.01 cos *i*	♂+25,000
5.84	524.31	33,224	3,088.33	100.16	0.48	752.55	–0.01 cos *i*	♂+30,000

Table F-3
Solar (⨀) Satellite Parameters

The following table provides a variety of quantitative data for spacecraft orbiting the Sun. The independent parameter is the distance, r, from the center of the Sun to the spacecraft in km. The corresponding distances to planets and several asteroids are also listed. Note that numerical formulas given in the Explanation of *Earth Satellite Parameters* on the rear end-pages will not generally work for a solar satellite. You should use the formulas given below or those listed in Chap. 2. Throughout μ_{Earth} (=398,600.4 km^3/s^2) has been replaced by μ_{Sun} (=$1.327\,245 \times 10^{11}$ km^3/s^2) and circular, coplanar orbits have been assumed.

Columns 1 through 2 use the same formulas given in *Explanation of Earth Satellite Parameters* with the general changes given above.

Columns 3 through 4 use the same formulas given in *Explanation of Earth Satellite Parameters* with the general changes given above, except the altitude change is 1,000 km and the plane change is 0.1 deg.

Column 5 uses the formulas for a Hohmann transfer given in Chap. 2, Sec. 2.6.

Column 6 uses the same formula given in *Explanation of Earth Satellite Parameters* with the general changes given above.

Column 7 uses equations (2-18), (2-19), and (2-20).

Column 8 uses the following equation for the Solar Constant

$$S = 1{,}367\ (R_{Earth}/r)^2 \qquad (\text{W/m}^2) \qquad \text{(F-1)}$$

where R_{Earth} is the distance from the center of the Sun to the Earth, r, is the given distance of the spacecraft from the center of the Sun.

Columns 9 through 10 assume that the spacecraft and the observer on the Earth are in coplanar, circular orbits around the Sun. For spacecraft outside the Earth's orbit, the maximum distance occurs when the spacecraft is in conjunction, and the minimum distance occurs when the spacecraft is in opposition. Refer to Fig. 2-9 for more details, including the distance relationship for spacecraft inside the Earth's orbit.

Columns 11 through 13 assume that the spacecraft and the observer on the Earth are in coplanar, circular orbits around the Sun. The elongation angle is the angle between the Sun and spacecraft with the Earth at the vertex. Quadrature occurs when the elongation angle is 90 deg. Refer to Fig. 2-9 for more details, including the distance relationships for spacecraft inside the Earth's orbit.

Column 14 assumes that the Earth and the spacecraft are in coplanar, circular orbits. The maximum angular velocity of the spacecraft as seen from the Earth is the relative angular velocity of the spacecraft at the point when it is nearest the Earth.

Column 15 assumes that the spacecraft and observer on the Earth are in coplanar, circular orbits. The synodic rate is simply the absolute value of the difference between the orbit angular velocity of the spacecraft and the orbit angular velocity of the Earth.

Orbits About the Sun

1 Circular Velocity (km/s)	2 Orbit Angular Velocity (deg/day)	3 ΔV Req'd for a 1000 km alt. change (cm/s)	4 ΔV for a 0.1 deg plane change (m/s)	5 ΔV for Hohmann Transfer to Earth (km/s)	6 Sidereal Period (days)	7 Synodic Period (days)	Distance from Center of Sun (10^6 km)	Body
81.5	20.2	204	142	42.1	17.9	18.77	20	
57.6	7.13	72.0	101	25.2	50.5	58.60	40	
47.9	4.09	41.3	83.6	17.1	88.0	115.9	57.9	Mercury
47.0	3.88	39.2	82.1	16.4	92.8	124.4	60	
40.7	2.52	25.5	71.1	10.7	142.8	234.6	80	
36.4	1.80	18.2	63.6	6.58	199.6	440.2	100	
35.0	1.60	16.2	61.1	5.20	224.7	583.9	108.2	Venus
33.3	1.37	13.9	58.0	3.46	262.4	931.9	120	
30.8	1.09	11.0	53.7	1.00	330.7	3493	140	
29.8	0.986	9.96	52.0	N/A	365.2	N/A	149.6	Earth
28.8	0.891	9.00	50.3	0.984	404.0	3808	160	
27.2	0.747	7.54	47.4	2.626	482.1	1507	180	
25.8	0.638	6.44	45.0	4.004	564.6	1034	200	
24.6	0.553	5.58	42.9	5.176	651.4	831.5	220	
24.1	0.524	5.29	42.1	5.594	686.9	779.9	227.9	Mars
21.0	0.347	3.51	36.7	8.498	1037	563.8	300	
19,4	0.272	2.75	33.8	9.947	1324	504.4	353.1	Vesta
18.2	0.225	2.28	31.8	10.926	1597	473.5	400	
17.9	0.214	2.16	31.2	11.183	1684	466.4	414.4	Ceres
17.2	0.189	1.91	30.0	11.749	1906	451.8	450	
16.9	0.181	1.82	29.5	11.944	1994,	447.2	463.8	Europa
16.8	0.177	1.79	29.3	12.025	2032	445.3	469.7	Hygiea
16.3	0.161	1.63	28.4	12.406	2232	436.7	500	
14.9	0.123	1.24	26.0	13.377	2934	417.2	600	
13.8	0.097 4	0.984	24.0	14.048	3697	405.3	700	
13.1	0.0830	0.839	22.8	14.437	4335	398.8	778.4	Jupiter
12.9	0.0797	0.805	22.5	14.528	4517	397.4	800	
12.1	0.0668	0.675	21.2	14.881	5390	391.8	900	
11.5	0.0570	0.576	20.1	15.145	6312,	387.7	1,000	
9.6	0.033	0.338	16.8	15.732	10757	378.1	1,426.7	Saturn
9.40	0.0310	0.314	16.4	15.783	11597	377.1	1,500	
8.1	0.0202	0.204	14.2	15.953	17854	372.9	2,000	
7.3	0.0144	0.146	12.7	15.969	24952	370.7	2,500	
6.8	0.0117	0.118	11.9	15.941	30707	369.6	2,871	Uranus
6.7	0.0110	0.111	11.6	15.927	32800	369.4	3,000	
6.2	0.0087	0.088	10.7	15.860	41333	368.5	3,500	
5.8	0.0071	0.072	10.1	15.785	50499	367.9	4,000	
5.4	0.0060	0.060	9.48	15.708	60,222	367.5	4,498.2	Neptune
5.4	0.0060	0.060	9.48	15.708	60257	367.5	4,500	
5.2	0.0051	0.052	8.99	15.632	70574	367.1	5,000	
4.9	0.0044	0.045	8.57	15.558	81421	366.9	5,500	
4.7	0.0040	0.040	8.27	15.501	90609	366.7	5,906.4	Pluto

Orbits About the Sun

	8	9	10	11	12	13	14	15
Distance from Center of Sun (10^6 km)	Solar Constant (W/m^2)	Max Distance from Earth (10^6 km)	Min Distance from Earth (10^6 km)	Distance from Earth at Greatest Elongation (10^6 km)	Distance from Earth at Quadrature (10^6 km)	Angle at Greatest Elongation (deg)	Max Angular Velocity Seen from Earth (deg/day)	Synodic Rate (deg/day)
20	76,482	169	129	148	N/A	7.68	1.974	19.2
40	19,121	189	109	144	N/A	15.5	1.256	6.14
57.9	9,123	207	91	137	N/A	22.8	0.977	3.11
60	8,498	209	89	137	N/A	23.6	0.953	2.89
80	4,780	229	69	126	N/A	32.3	0.779	1.53
100	3,059	249	49	113	N/A	41.9	0.663	0.82
108.2	2,613	257	41	103	N/A	46.3	0.626	0.62
120	2,125	269	29	89	N/A	53.3	0.581	0.39
140	1,561	289	9	52	N/A	69.4	0.518	0.10
149.6	1,367	N/A	N/A	N/A	N/A	N/A	N/A	N/A
160	1,195	309	10	10	56	180	0.469	0.0945
180	944.2	329	30	30	100	180	0.429	0.2389
200	764.8	349	50	50	132	180	0.395	0.3480
220	632.1	369	70	70	161	180	0.367	0.4330
227.9	588.8	377	78	78	172	180	0.357	0.4616
300	339.9	449	150	150	260	180	0.288	0.6386
353.1	245.4	502	203	203	319	180	0.253	0.7138
400	191.2	549	250	250	371	180	0.229	0.7602
414.4	178.2	564	264	264	386	180	0.222	0.7719
450	151.1	599	300	300	424	180	0.208	0.7967
463.8	142.2	613	314	314	439	180	0.203	0.8051
469.7	138.6	619	320	320	445	180	0.201	0.8085
500	122.4	649	350	350	477	180	0.191	0.8243
600	85.0	749	450	450	581	180	0.164	0.8629
700	62.4	849	550	550	683	180	0.144	0.8883
778.4	50.50	928	628	628	763	180	0.132	0.9026
800	47.8	949	650	650	785	180	0.129	0.9059
900	37.8	1,050	750	750	887	180	0.116	0.9189
1,000	30.6	1,150	850	850	988	180	0.106	0.9286
1,426.7	15.0	1,576	1,277	1,277	1,419	180	0.078	0.9522
1,500	13.6	1,650	1,350	1,350	1,493	180	0.075	0.9546
2,000	7.648	2,150	1,850	1,850	1,994	180	0.058	0.9655
2,500	4.895	2,650	2,350	2,350	2,496	180	0.047	0.9712
2,871	3.712	3,021	2,721	2,721	2,867	180	0.042	0.9739
3,000	3.399	3,150	2,850	2,850	2,996	180	0.040	0.9747
3,500	2.497	3,650	3,350	3,350	3,497	180	0.035	0.9769
4,000	1.912	4,150	3,850	3,850	3,997	180	0.031	0.9785
4,498.2	1.512	4,648	4,349	4,349	4,496	180	0.028	0.9797
4,500	1.511	4,650	4,350	4,350	4,498	180	0.028	0.9797
5,000	1.224	5,150	4,850	4,850	4,998	180	0.025	0.9806
5,500	1.011	5,650	5,350	5,350	5,498	180	0.023	0.9812
5,906.4	0.877	6,056	5,757	5,757	5,904	180	0.022	0.9817

Appendix G

Units and Conversion Factors

The metric system of units, officially known as the *International System of Units*, or *SI*, is used throughout this book, with the exception that angular measurements are usually expressed in degrees rather than the SI unit of radians. By international agreement, the fundamental SI units of length, mass, and time are defined as follows (see National Institutes of Standards and Technology, Special Publication 330 [1991]):

> The *meter* is the length of the path traveled by light in vacuum during a time interval of 1/299,792,458 of a second.
>
> The *kilogram* is the mass of the international prototype of the kilogram.
>
> The *second* is the duration of 9,192,631,770 periods of the radiation corresponding to the transition between two hyperfine levels of the ground state of the cesium-133 atom.

Additional base units in the SI system are the *ampere* for electric current, the *kelvin* for thermodynamic temperature, the *mole* for amount of substance, and the *candela* for luminous intensity. Taylor [1995] provides an excellent summary of SI units for scientific and technical use.

The names of multiples and submultiples of SI units are formed by application of the following prefixes:

Factor by Which Unit is Multiplied	Prefix	Symbol
10^{24}	yotta	Y
10^{21}	zetta	Z
10^{18}	exa	E
10^{15}	peta	P
10^{12}	tera	T
10^{9}	giga	G
10^{6}	mega	M
10^{3}	kilo	k
10^{2}	hecto	h
10^{1}	deka	da

Factor by Which Unit is Multiplied	Prefix	Symbol
10^{-1}	deci	d
10^{-2}	centi	c
10^{-3}	milli	m
10^{-6}	micro	μ
10^{-9}	nano	n
10^{-12}	pico	p
10^{-15}	femto	f
10^{-18}	atto	a
10^{-21}	zepto	z
10^{-24}	yocto	y

For each quantity listed below, the SI unit and its abbreviation are given in brackets. For convenience in computer use, most conversion factors are given to the greatest available accuracy. Note that some conversions are exact definitions and some (speed of light, astronomical unit) depend on the value of physical constants. ". . ." indicates a repeating decimal. All notes are on the last page of the list.

To convert from	*To*	*Multiply by*	*Notes*
Acceleration [meter/second², m/s²]			
Gal (galileo)	m/s^2	0.01	E
Inch/second², in/s²	m/s^2	0.025 4	E
Foot/second², ft/s²	m/s^2	0.304 8	E
Free fall (standard), g	m/s^2	9.806 65	E
Angular Acceleration [radian/second², rad/s²]			
Degrees/second², deg/s²	rad/s^2	$\pi/180$ $= 0.017\,453\,292\,519\,943\,295\,77$	E
Revolutions/second², rev/s²	rad/s^2	2π $= 6.283\,185\,307\,179\,586\,477$	E
Revolutions/minute², rev/min²	rad/s^2	$\pi/1{,}800$ $= 1.745\,329\,251\,994\,329\,577 \times 10^{-3}$	E
Revolutions/minute²	deg/s^2	0.1	E
Radians/second², rad/s²	deg/s^2	$180/\pi$ $=57.295\,779\,513\,082\,320\,88$	E
Revolutions/second², rev/s²	deg/s^2	360	E
Angular Area [sr], book also uses deg²			
Degree², deg²	sr	$(\pi/180)^2$ $= 3.046\,174\,197\,867\,086 \times 10^{-4}$	E
Minute², min²	sr	$(\pi/10{,}800)^2$ $= 8.461\,594\,994\,075\,237 \times 10^{-8}$	E
Second², s²	sr	$(\pi/648\,000)^2$ $= 2.350\,443\,053\,909\,289 \times 10^{-4}$	E
Steradian, sr	deg^2	$(180/\pi)^2$ $= 3.282\,806\,350\,011\,744 \times 10^3$	E
Minute², min²	deg^2	$1/3{,}600$ $= 2.777\ldots \times 10^{-4}$	E
Second², s²	deg^2	$(1/3{,}600)^2$ $=7.716\,049\,382\,716\,049 \times 10^{-8}$	E
Steradian, sr	rad^2	1 rad^2	E
Angular Measure [radian, rad]. This book uses degree (abbreviated "deg") as the basic unit.			
Degree, deg	rad	$\pi/180$ $= 0.017\,453\,292\,519\,943\,295\,77$	E
Minute (of arc), min	rad	$\pi/10{,}800$ $= 2.908\,882\,086\,657\,216 \times 10^{-4}$	E
Second (of arc), s	rad	$\pi/648\,000$ $=4.848\,136\,811\,095\,360 \times 10^{-6}$	E
Radian, rad	deg	$= 180/\pi$ $= 57.295\,779\,513\,082\,320\,877$	E
Minute (of arc), min	deg	$1/60$ $= 0.01666\ldots$	E
Second (of arc), s	deg	$1/3{,}600$ $= 2.777\ldots \times 10^{-4}$	E

To convert from	*To*	*Multiply by*	*Notes*
Angular Momentum [kilogram · meter^2/second, kg · m^2/s]			
Gram · cm^2/second, g · cm^2/s	kg · m^2/s	1×10^{-7}	E
lbm· inch^2/second, lbm · in^2/s	kg · m^2/s	$2.926\,396\,534\,292 \times 10^{-4}$	E
Slug · inch^2/second, slug · in^2/s	kg · m^2/s	$9.415\,402\,418\,968 \times 10^{-3}$	D
lbm· foot^2/second, lbm · ft^2/s	kg · m^2/s	0.042 140 110 093 80	D
Inch · lbf· second, in · lbf · s	kg · m^2/s	0.112 984 829 027 6	D
Slug · foot^2/second, slug · ft^2/s = foot · lbf · second, ft · lbf · s	kg · m^2/s	1.355 817 948 331	D
Angular Velocity [radian/second, rad/s]. This book uses degrees/second as the basic unit.			
Degrees/second, deg/s	rad/s	$\pi/180$ = 0.017 453 292 519 943 295 77	E
Revolutions/minute, rpm	rad/s	$\pi/30$ = 0.104 719 755 119 659 774 6	E
Revolutions/second, rev/s	rad/s	2π = 6.283 185 307 179 586 477	E
Revolutions/minute, rpm	deg/s	6	E
Radians/second, rad/s	deg/s	$180/\pi$ = 57.295 779 513 082 320 88	E
Revolutions/second, rev/s	deg/s	360	E
Area [meter^2, m^2]			
Acre	m^2	$4.046\,856\,422 \times 10^3$	E
Foot^2, ft^2	m^2	0.092 903 04	E
Hectare	m^2	1×10^4	E
Inch^2, in^2	m^2	$6.451\,6 \times 10^{-4}$	E
Mile^2 (U.S. statute)	m^2	$2.589\,110\,336 \times 10^6$	E
Yard^2, yd^2	m^2	0.836 127 36	E
(Nautical mile)^2	m^2	$3.429\,904 \times 10^6$	E
Density [kilogram/meter^3, kg/m^3]			
Gram/centimeter^3, g/cm^3	kg/m^3	1.0×10^3	E
Pound mass/inch^3, lbm/in^3	kg/m^3	$2.767\,990\,471\,020 \times 10^4$	D
Pound mass/foot^3, lbm/ft^3	kg/m^3	16.018 463 373 96	D
Slug/ft^3	kg/m^3	515.378 818 393 2	D
Electric Charge [coulomb, C]			
Abcoulomb	C	10	E
Faraday (based on carbon–12)	C	$9.648\,70 \times 10^4$	NIST
Faraday (chemical)	C	$9.649\,57 \times 10^4$	NIST
Faraday (physical)	C	$9.652\,19 \times 10^4$	NIST
Statcoulomb	C	$3.335\,641 \times 10^{-10}$	NIST
Electric Conductance [siemens, S]			
Abmho	S	1×10^9	E
Mho (Ω^{-1})	S	1	E
Electric Current [ampere, A]			
Abampere	A	10	E

To convert from	*To*	*Multiply by*	*Notes*
Gilbert	A	$10/4\pi$	
		$= 0.795\ 774\ 715\ 459\ 5$	E
Statampere	A	$3.335\ 641 \times 10^{-10}$	NIST
Electric Field Intensity [volt/meter ≡ kilogram · meter · ampere^{-1} · second^{-3}, V/m ≡ kg · m · A^{-1} · s^{-3}]			
Electric Potential Difference [volt ≡ watt/ampere ≡ kilogram · meter^2 · ampere^{-1} · second^{-3}, V ≡ W/A ≡ kg · m^2 · A^{-1} · s^{-3}]			
Abvolt	V	1×10^{-8}	E
Statvolt	V	299.792 5	NIST
Electric Resistance [ohm ≡ volt/ampere ≡ kilogram · meter^2 · ampere^{-2} · second^{-3}, Ω ≡ V/A ≡ kg · m^2 · A^{-2} · s^{-3}]			
Abohm	Ω	1×10^{-9}	E
Statohm	Ω	$8.987\ 552 \times 10^{11}$	NIST
Energy or Torque [joule ≡ newton · meter ≡ kilogram · meter^2/s^2, J ≡ N · m ≡ kg · m^2/s^2]			
British thermal unit, Btu (mean)	J	$1.055\ 055\ 852\ 62 \times 10^{3}$	E
Calorie (IT), cal	J	4.186 8	E
Kilocalorie (IT), kcal	J	$4.186\ 8 \times 10^{3}$	E
Electron volt, eV	J	$1.602\ 177\ 33 \times 10^{-19}$	C
Erg ≡ gram · cm^2/s^2 = pole · cm · oersted	J	1×10^{-7}	E
Foot poundal	J	0.042 140 110 093 80	D
Foot lbf = slug · foot^2/s^2	J	1.355 817 948 331 4	E
Kilowatt hour, kW · hr	J	3.6×10^{6}	E
Ton equivalent of TNT	J	4.184×10^{9}	E
Force [newton ≡ kilogram · meter/second^2, N ≡ kg · m /s^2]			
Dyne	N	1×10^{-5}	E
Kilogram-force (kgf)	N	9.806 65	E
Ounce force (avoirdupois)	N	0.278 013 850 953 8	D
Poundal	N	0.138 254 954 376	E
Pound force (avoirdupois), lbf ≡ slug · foot/s^2	N	4.448 221 615 260 5	E
Illuminance [lux ≡ candela · steradian/meter^2, lx ≡ cd · sr/m^2]			
Footcandle	cd · sr/m^2	10.763 910 416 709 70	E
Phot	cd · sr/m^2	1×10^{4}	E
Length [meter, m]			
Angstrom, Å	m	1×10^{-10}	E
Astronomical unit (S1)	m	$1.495\ 978\ 706\ 6 \times 10^{11}$	AA
Astronomical unit (radio)	m	$1.495\ 978\ 9 \times 10^{11}$	NIST
Earth equatorial radius, R_E	m	$6.378\ 136\ 49 \times 10^{6}$	IERS
		$6.378\ 14 \times 10^{6}$	AQ
Fermi (1 fermi = 1 fm)	m	1×10^{-15}	E
Foot, ft	m	0.304 8	E
Inch, in	m	0.025 4	E

To convert from	*To*	*Multiply by*	*Notes*
Light year	m	$9.460\,730\,472\,580\,8 \times 10^{15}$	D
Micron, μm	m	1×10^{-6}	E
Mil (10^{-3} inch)	m	2.54×10^{-5}	E
Mile (U.S. statute), mi	m	$1.609\,344 \times 10^{3}$	E
Nautical mile (U.S.), NM	m	1.852×10^{3}	E
Parsec (IAU)	m	$3.085\,677\,597\,49 \times 10^{16}$	D
Solar radius	m	$6.960\,00 \times 10^{8}$	AA
Yard, yd	m	0.914 4	E
Luminance [candela/meter^2 ≡ cd/m^2]			
Footlambert	cd/m^2	=3.426 259 099 635 39	E
Lambert	cd/m^2	$(1/\pi) \times 10^4 \approx 3.183\,098\,862 \times 10^3$	E
Stilb	cd/m^2	1×10^4	E
Magnetic Field Strength, H [ampere turn/meter, A/m]			
Oersted (EMU)	A/m	$(1/4\pi) \times 10^3$ = 79.577 471 545 947 667 88	E,1
Magnetic Flux [weber ≡ volt · s ≡ kilogram · meter^2 · ampere^{-1}•second^{-2}, Wb ≡ V · s ≡ kg · m^2 · A^{-1} · s^{-2}]			
Maxwell (EMU)	Wb	1×10^{-8}	E
Unit pole	Wb	$1.256\,637 \times 10^{-7}$	NIST
Magnetic Induction, B [tesla ≡ weber/meter^2 ≡ kilogram · ampere^{-1} · second^{-2}, T ≡ Wb/m^2 ≡ kg · A^{-1} · s^{-2}]			
Gamma (EMU) (γ)	T	1×10^{-9}	E,1
Gauss (EMU)	T	1×10^{-4}	E,1
Magnetic Dipole Moment [weber · meter ≡ kilogram · meter^3 · ampere^{-1} · second^{-2}, Wb · m ≡ kg · m^3 · A^{-1} · s^{-2}]			
Pole · centimeter (EMU)	Wb · m	$4\pi \times 10^{-10}$ = $1.256\,637\,061\,435\,917\,295 \times 10^{-9}$	E,1
Gauss · centimeter^3 (Practical)	Wb · m	1×10^{-10}	E,1
Magnetic Moment [ampere turn · meter^2 ≡ joule/tesla, A · m^2 ≡ J/T]			
Abampere · centimeter^2(EMU)	A · m^2	1×10^{-3}	E, 1
Ampere · centimeter^2	A · m^2	1×10^{-4}	E, 1
Mass [kilogram, kg]			
γ (= 1 μg)	kg	1×10^{-9}	E
Atomic unit (electron)	kg	$9.109\,389\,7 \times 10^{-31}$	C
Atomic mass unit (unified), amu	kg	$1.660\,540\,2 \times 10^{-27}$	C
Metric carat	kg	2.0×10^{-4}	E
Metric ton	kg	1×10^{3}	E
Ounce mass (avoirdupois), oz	kg	0.028 349 231 25	E
Pound mass, lbm (avoirdupois)	kg	0.453 592 37	E
Slug	kg	14.593 902 937 21	D
Short ton (2,000 lbm)	kg	907.184 74	E
Solar mass	kg	$1.989\,1 \times 10^{30}$	AA

To convert from	*To*	*Multiply by*	*Notes*
Moment of Inertia [kilogram · meter², kg · m²]			
Gram · centimeter², gm · cm²	kg · m²	1×10^{-7}	E
Pound mass· inch², lbm · in²	kg · m²	$2.926\,396\,534\,292 \times 10^{-4}$	E
Pound mass· foot², lbm · ft²	kg · m²	$4.214\,011\,009\,380 \times 10^{-2}$	D
Slug · inch², slug · in²	kg · m²	$9.415\,402\,418\,968 \times 10^{-3}$	D
Inch · pound force· s², in · lbf · s²	kg · m²	0.112 984 829 027 6	D
Slug · foot² = ft · lbf · s²	kg · m²	1.355 817 948 331 4	E
Power [watt ≡ joule/second ≡ kilogram · meter²/second³, W ≡ J/s ≡ kg · m²/s³]			
Foot · pound force/second, ft lbf/s	W	1.355 817 948 331	D
Horsepower (550 ft · lbf/s), hp	W	745.699 871 582 3	D
Horsepower (electrical), hp	W	746.0	E
Solar luminosity	W	3.845×10^{26}	AQ
Pressure or Stress [pascal ≡ newton/meter² ≡ kilogram · meter⁻¹ · second⁻², Pa ≡ N/m² ≡ kg · m⁻¹ · s⁻²]			
Atmosphere, atm	Pa	$1.013\,25 \times 10^{5}$	E
Bar	Pa	1×10^{5}	E
Centimeter of mercury (0° C)	Pa	$= 1.333\,223\,874\,145 \times 10^{3}$	E
Dyne/centimeter², dyne/cm²	Pa	0.1	E
Inch of mercury (32° F)	Pa	$3.386\,388\,640\,341 \times 10^{3}$	E
Pound force/foot², lbf/ft², psf	Pa	47.880 258 980 34	D
Pound force/inch², lbf/in², psi	Pa	$6.894\,757\,293\,168 \times 10^{3}$	D
Torr (0° C)	Pa	(101325/760) =133.322 368 421 052 631	E
Solid Angle (See Angular Area)			
Specific Heat Capacity [joule · kilogram⁻¹ · kelvin⁻¹ ≡ meter² · second² · kelvin⁻¹, J · kg⁻¹ · K⁻¹ ≡ m² · s² · K⁻¹]			
cal · g⁻¹ · K⁻¹ (mean)	J · kg⁻¹ · K⁻¹	$4.186\,80 \times 10^{3}$	E
Btu · lbm⁻¹ · °F⁻¹ (mean)	J · kg⁻¹ · K⁻¹	$4.186\,80 \times 10^{3}$	E
Stress (see Pressure)			
Temperature [kelvin, K]			
Celsius, °C	K	$t_K = t_C + 273.15$	E
Fahrenheit, °F	K	$t_K = (5/9)\,(t_F + 459.67)$	E
Rankine °R	K	$t_K = (5/9)\,t_R$	E
Fahrenheit, °F	C	$t_C = (5/9)\,(t_F - 32.0)$	E
Rankine °R	C	$t_C = (5/9)\,(t_R - 491.67)$	E
Thermal Conductivity [watt · meter⁻¹ · kelvin⁻¹ ≡ kilogram · meter · second⁻³ · kelvin⁻¹, W · m⁻¹ · K⁻¹ ≡ kg · m · s⁻³ · K⁻¹]			
cal · cm⁻¹ · s⁻¹ · K⁻¹ (mean)	W · m⁻¹ · K⁻¹	418.68	E
Btu · ft⁻¹ · hr⁻¹ · °F⁻¹ (mean)	W · m⁻¹ · K⁻¹	1.730 734 666 371 39	D
Time [second, s]			
Sidereal day, d_* (ref. = ♈)	s	$8.616\,410\,035\,2 \times 10^{4}$ = 23h 56m 4.100 352s	AQ
Ephemeris day, d_e	s	8.64×10^{4}	AQ

To convert from	*To*	*Multiply by*	*Notes*
Ephemeris day, d_e	d_*	1.002 737 795 056 6	AQ
Keplerian period of a satellite in low-Earth orbit	min	$1.658\ 669\ 010\ 080 \times 10^{-4} \times a^{3/2}$ (*a* in km)	Table 6-2
Keplerian period of a satellite of the Sun	d_e	$3.652\ 568\ 954\ 757 \times 10^2 \times a^{3/2}$ (*a* in AU)	AA
Tropical year (ref.= ♈)	s	$3.155\ 692\ 597\ 47 \times 10^7$	AA
Tropical year (ref.= ♈)	d_e	365.242 198 781	D
Sidereal year (ref.=fixed stars)	s_e	$3.155\ 814\ 976\ 320 \times 10^7$	AA
Sidereal year (ref.=fixed stars)	d_e	365.256 363	AA
Calendar year (365 days), yr	s	$3.153\ 6 \times 10^7$	E
Julian century	d	36,525	E
Gregorian calendar century	d	36,524.25	E
Torque (see Energy)			
Velocity [meter/second, m/s]			
Foot/minute, ft/min	m/s	5.08×10^{-3}	E
Inch/second, ips	m/s	0.025 4	E
Kilometer/hour, km/hr	m/s	$(3.6)^{-1} = 0.277777\ldots$	E
Foot/second, fps or ft/s	m/s	0.304 8	E
Miles/hour, mph	m/s	0.447 04	E
Knot (international)	m/s	$(1852/3600) = 0.514444\ldots$	E
Miles/minute, mi/min	m/s	26.822 4	E
Miles/second, mi/s	m/s	$1.609\ 344 \times 10^3$	E
Velocity of Light	m/s	$2.997\ 924\ 58 \times 10^8$	E
Viscosity [pascal · second ≡ kilogram · meter^{-1} · second^{-1}, Pa · s ≡ kg · m^{-1} · s^{-1}]			
Stoke	m^2/s	1.0×10^{-4}	E
Foot^2 · second, ft^2 · s	m^2/s	0.092 903 04	E
Pound mass· foot^{-1} · second^{-1}, lbm · ft^{-1} · s^{-1}	Pa · s	1.488 163 943 570	D
Pound force· second/foot^2, lbf · s/ft^2	Pa · s	47.880 258 980 34	D
Poise	Pa · s	0.1	E
Poundal second/foot^2, poundal s/ft^2	Pa · s	1.488 163 943 570	D
Slug · foot^{-1} · second^{-1}, slug · ft^{-1} · s^{-1}	Pa · s	47.880 258 980 34	D
Rhe	$(Pa \cdot s)^{-1}$	10	E
Volume [meter^3, m^3]			
λ (1λ = 1 μL = 1×10^{-6} L)	m^3	1×10^{-9}	E
Foot^3, ft^3	m^3	$2.831\ 684\ 659\ 2 \times 10^{-2}$	E
Gallon (U.S. liquid), gal	m^3	$3.785\ 411\ 784 \times 10^{-3}$	E
Inch^3, in^3	m^3	$1.638\ 706\ 4 \times 10^{-5}$	E

To convert from	*To*	*Multiply by*	*Notes*
Liter, L	m^3	1×10^{-3}	E
Ounce (U.S. fluid), oz	m^3	$2.957\,352\,956\,25 \times 10^{-5}$	E
Pint (U.S. liquid), pt	m^3	$4.731\,764\,73 \times 10^{-4}$	E
Quart, qt	m^3	$9.463\,529\,46 \times 10^{-4}$	E
Stere (st)	m^3	1	E
Yard^3, yd^3	m^3	0.764 554 857 984	E

Notes for the preceding table:

AA Values are those of *Astronomical Almanac* [Hagen and Boksenberg, 1991].

AQ Values are those of *Astrophysical Quantities* [Cox, 2000].

C Values are those of Cohen and Taylor [1986].

D Values that are derived from exact quantities, rounded off to 13 significant figures.

E (Exact) indicates that the conversion is exact by definition of the non-SI unit or that it is obtained from other exact conversions.

IERS Numerical standards of the IERS.

NIST Values are those of National Institute of Standards and Technology [McCoubrey, 1991].

(1) Care should be taken in transforming magnetic units, because the dimensionality of magnetic quantities (**B**, **H**, etc.) depends on the system of units. Most of the conversions given here are between SI and EMU (electromagnetic). The following equations hold in both sets of units:

$$\mathbf{T} = \mathbf{m} \times \mathbf{B} = \mathbf{d} \times \mathbf{H}$$
$$\mathbf{B} = \mu \mathbf{H}$$
$$\mathbf{m} = I\mathbf{A} \text{ for a current loop in a plane}$$
$$\mathbf{d} = \mu \mathbf{m}$$

with the following definitions:

$\mathbf{T} \equiv$ torque

$\mathbf{B} \equiv$ magnetic induction (commonly called "magnetic field")

$\mathbf{H} \equiv$ magnetic field strength or magnetic intensity

$\mathbf{m} \equiv$ magnetic moment

$I \equiv$ current loop

$\mathbf{A} \equiv$ vector normal to the plane of the current loop (in the direction of the angular velocity vector of the current loop about the center of the loop) with magnitude equal to the area of the loop

$\mathbf{d} \equiv$ magnetic dipole moment

$\mu \equiv$ magnetic permeability

The permeability of vacuum, μ_0, has the following values, by definition:

$\mu_0 \equiv 1$ (dimensionless) EMU

$\mu_0 \equiv 4\pi \times 10^{-7}$ N/A^2 SI

Therefore, in electromagnetic units in vacuum, magnetic induction and magnetic field strength are equivalent and the magnetic moment and magnetic dipole moment are equivalent. For practical purposes of magnetostatics, space is a vacuum but the spacecraft itself may have $\mu \neq \mu_0$.

Useful Mathematical Constants and Values

Constant	Value	
π	≈ 3.141 592 653 589 793 238 462 643	**(A)**
e	≈ 2.718 281 828 459 045 235 360 287	**(A)**
e^{π}	≈ 23.140 692 632 779 269 006	**(A)**
$\log_{10}x$	≈ 0.434 294 481 903 251 827 651 128 9 $\log_e x$	**(A)**
$\log_e x$	≈ 2.302 585 092 994 045 684 017 991 $\log_{10} x$	**(A)**
$\log_e \pi$	≈ 1.144 729 885 849 400 174 143 427	**(A)**

(A) are from *The Handbook of Mathematical Functions, with Formulas, Graphs, and Mathematical Tables* [Abramowitz and Stegun, 1970]

References

Abramowitz, Milton and Irene A. Stegun, eds. 1970. *The Handbook of Mathematical Functions with Formulas, Graphs, and Mathematical Tables*. New York: Dover.

Cohen, E. Richard and B.N. Taylor, 1986. *CODATA Bulletin No. 63*, Nov. New York: Pergamon Press.

Cox, Arthur N, ed. 2000. *Allen's Astrophysical Quantities (4th Edition).* New York: Springer-Verlag.

Hagen, James B. and A. Boksenberg, eds. 1991. *The Astronomical Almanac.* Nautical Almanac Office, U.S. Naval Observatory and H. M. Nautical Almanac Office. 1992. Washington, D.C.: U.S. Government Printing Office.

McCarthy, Dennis D., USNO. 1996. "Technical Note 21." IERS Conventions.

McCoubrey, Arthur O. 1991. *Guide for the Use of the International System of Units (SI).* National Institute of Standards and Technology (NIST), Special Publication 811, U.S. Department of Commerce: U.S. Government Printing Office.

Seidelmann, Kenneth P., ed. 1992. *The Explanatory Supplement to the Astronomical Almanac.* Mill Valley, CA: University Science Books.

Taylor, Barry N. 1991. *The International System of Units (SI).* National Institute of Standards and Technology (NIST), Special Publication 811, U.S. Department of Commerce: U.S. Government Printing Office.

INDEX

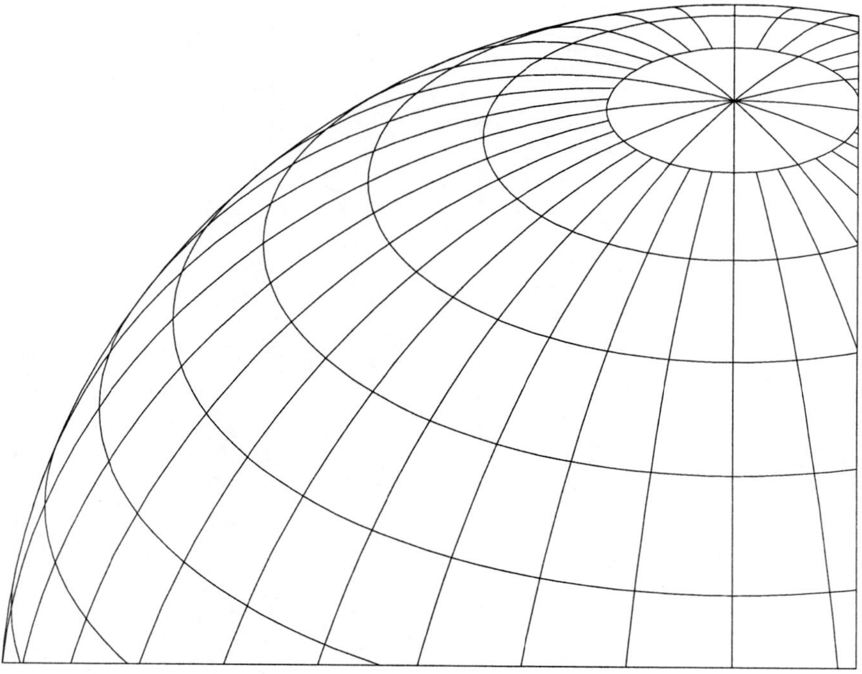

Numerics

—A—

—B—

—D—

—E—

—H—

—I—

—J—

—M—

—O—

—P—

—U—

—Y—

—Z—

EARTH SATELLITE PARAMETERS

Equations are available throughout the book for calculating all of the basic mission parameters for circular Earth orbits. Here they are evaluated numerically to provide a quick reference, a check on computations, and an estimate of the sensitivity of the relevant parameters to altitude.

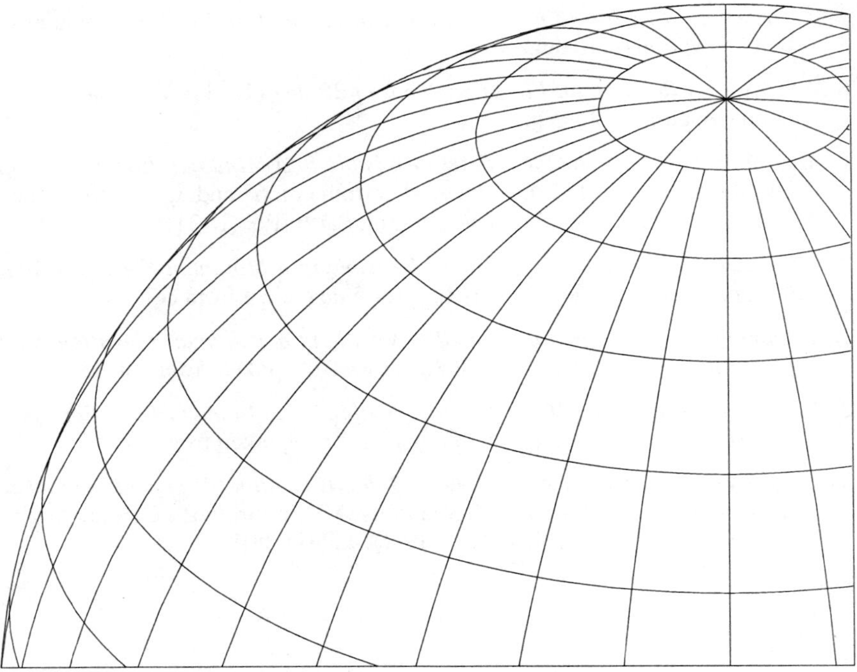

Explanation of Earth Satellite Parameters

The following table provides a variety of quantitative data for Earth-orbiting satellites. Limitations, formulas, and text references are given below. The independent parameter in the formulas is the distance, r, from the center of the Earth in km. The outer column on each table page is the altitude, $h \equiv r - R_E$, where $R_E = 6{,}378.14$ km is the equatorial radius of the Earth.

1. *Instantaneous Access Area for a 0 deg Elevation Angle* or *the Full Geometric Horizon* ($10^6 km^2$). All the area that an instrument or antenna could potentially see at any instant if it were scanned through its normal range of orientations for which the spacecraft elevation is above 0 deg [Eq. (D-29)].
2. *Instantaneous Area Access for a 5 deg Minimum Elevation Angle* (10^6 km^2) = same as col. 1 but with elevation of 5 deg.
3. *Instantaneous Area Access for a 10 deg Minimum Elevation Angle* (10^6 km^2) = same as col. 1 but with elevation of 10 deg.
4. *Instantaneous Area Access for a 20 deg Minimum Elevation Angle* (10^6 km^2) = same as col. 1 but with elevation of 20 deg.
5. *Area Access Rate for an Elevation of 0 deg* (10^3 km^2/s) = the rate at which new land is coming into the spacecraft's access area [Eq. (D-30)].
6. *Area Access Rate for an Elevation Limit of 5 deg* (10^3 km^2/s) = same as col. 5 with an elevation of 5 deg.
7. *Area Access Rate for an Elevation Limit of 10 deg* (10^3 km^2/s) = same as col. 5 with an elevation of 10 deg.
8. *Area Access Rate for an Elevation Limit of 20 deg* (10^3 km^2/s) = same as col. 5 with an elevation of 20 deg.
9. *Maximum Time in View for a Satellite Visible to a Minimum Elevation Angle of 0 deg* (min) = $P\lambda_{max}/180$ deg, where P is from col. 67 and λ_{max} is from col. 13. Assumes a circular orbit over a nonrotating Earth [Eq. (D-31)].
10. *Maximum Time in View for a Satellite Visible to a Minimum Elevation Angle of 5 deg* (min) = same as col. 9 with λ_{max} for 5 deg taken from col. 14.
11. *Maximum Time in View for a Satellite Visible to a Minimum Elevation Angle of 10 deg* (min) = same as col. 9 with λ_{max} for 10 deg taken from col. 15.
12. *Maximum Time in View for a Satellite Visible to a Minimum Elevation Angle of 20 deg* (min) = same as col. 9 with λ_{max} for 20 deg taken from col. 16.
13. *Earth Central Angle for a Satellite at 0 deg Elevation* (deg) = *Maximum Earth Central Angle* = $\text{acos}(R_E / r)$. Alternatively, Maximum Earth Central Angle is = $90 - \rho$, where ρ is from col. 49 [Eqs. (9-2), and (D-28)].

14. *Earth Central Angle for a Satellite at 5 deg Elevation* (deg) = $90-\varepsilon-\eta$, where η = asin ($\cos\varepsilon \sin\rho$), ρ is from col. 54, and $\varepsilon = 5$ deg [Eqs. (9-4), (9-5) and (9-6)].

15. *Earth Central Angle for a Satellite at 10 deg Elevation* (deg) = same as col. 14 but with $\varepsilon = 10$ deg.

16. *Earth Central Angle for a Satellite at 20 deg Elevation* (deg) = same as col. 14 but with $\varepsilon = 20$ deg.

17. *Maximum Range to Horizon = Range to a satellite at 0 deg elevation* (km) = $(r^2 - R_E{}^2)^{1/2}$, where R_E = 6,378.14 km is the equatorial radius of the Earth.

18. *Range to a Satellite at 5 deg Elevation* (km) = *Maximum Range for Satellites with a Minimum Elevation Angle of 5 deg* (km) = R_E ($\sin\lambda / \sin\eta$), where R_E = 6,378.14 km is the equatorial radius of the Earth, λ is from col. 14, $\eta = 90$ deg $- \lambda - \varepsilon$, and $\varepsilon = 5$ deg [Eq. (9-7)].

19. *Range to a Satellite at 10 deg Elevation* (km) = same as col. 18 with λ from col. 15 and $\varepsilon = 10$ deg.

20. *Range to a Satellite at 20 deg Elevation* (km) = same as col. 18 with λ from col. 16 and $\varepsilon = 20$ deg.

21. *Maximum Nadir Angle for a Satellite at 0 deg Elevation Angle* (deg) = *Max. Nadir Angle for Any Point on the Earth = Earth Angular Radius* = asin (R_E / r), where R_E = 6,378.14 km is the equatorial radius of the Earth [Eq. (9-2)].

22. *Nadir Angle for a Satellite at 5 deg Elevation Angle* (deg) = *Maximum Nadir Angle for Points on the Ground with a Minimum Elevation Angle of 5 deg* = 90 deg $- \varepsilon - \lambda$, is the Earth central angle from col. 14 [Eq. (9-6)].

23. *Nadir Angle for a Satellite at 10 deg Elevation Angle* (deg) = same as col. 22 with $\varepsilon = 10$ deg.

24. *Nadir Angle for a Satellite at 20 deg Elevation Angle* (deg) = same as col. 22 with $\varepsilon = 20$ deg.

25. *Atmospheric Scale Height* (km) = RT / Mg, where R is the molar gas constant, T is the temperature, M is the mean molecular weight, and g is the gravitational acceleration [inside front cover].

26. *Minimum Atmospheric Density* (kg/m^3), from MSIS atmospheric model [Hedin[*†‡], 1987, 1988, and 1991]. The solar flux value, F10.7, was chosen such that 10% of all measured data are less than this minimum (65.8×10^{-22} W m^{-2} Hz^{-1}). See Sec. 8.1.3. The MSIS model is limited to the region between 90 and 2,000 km. Below 150 km and above 600 km the error increases because less data have been used. All data have been averaged across the Earth with a 30 deg step size in longitude and 20 deg steps in latitude (–80 deg, to +80 deg). This over-represents the

---

[*] Hedin, Alan E., 1987. "MSIS-86 Thermospheric Model," *J. Geophys. Res.*, 92, No. A5, pp. 4649–4662.

[†] Hedin, Alan E., 1988. "The Atmospheric Model In The Region 90 to 2,000 km," *Adv. Space Res.*, 8, No. 5–6, pp. (5)9–(5)25, Pergamon Press.

[‡] Hedin, Alan E., 1991. "Extension of the MSIS Thermosphere Model into the Middle and Lower Atmosphere," *J. Geophys. Res.*, 96, No. A2, pp. 1159–1172.

Earth's polar regions; however, satellites spend a larger fraction of their time at high latitudes. The solar hour angle was adapted to the individual location on the Earth with UT = 12.00 Noon.

27. *Mean Atmospheric Density* (kg/m^3) = same as col. 26 but with a mean F10.7 value of 118.7×10^{-22} W m^{-2} Hz^{-1}.

28. *Maximum Atmospheric Density* = same as col. 26 but with a F10.7 value of 189.0 $\times 10^{-22}$ W m^{-2} Hz^{-1}. This is the F10.7 value such that 10% of all measured values are above it.

29. *Minimum ΔV to Maintain Altitude at Solar Minimum* (m/s per year) = $\pi\ (C_D A/m) \times \rho r v/P$, where ρ is from col. 26, v is from col. 56, P is from col. 67 expressed in years, and the ballistic coefficient, $m/C_D A$, is assumed to be 50 kg/m^2. ΔV estimates are not meaningful above 1,500 km [Eq. (2-36)].

30. *Maximum ΔV to Maintain Altitude at Solar Maximum* (m/s per year) = same as col. 29 with ρ from col. 28 and the ballistic coefficient, $m/C_D A$, assumed to be 50 kg/m^2.

31. *Minimum ΔV to Maintain Altitude at Solar Minimum* (m/s per year) = same as col. 29 with ρ from col. 26 and the ballistic coefficient, $m/C_D A$, assumed to be 200 kg/m^2.

32. *Maximum ΔV to Maintain Altitude at Solar Maximum* (m/s per year) = same as col. 29 with ρ from col. 28 and the ballistic coefficient, $m/C_D A$, is assumed to be 200 kg/m^2.

33. *Orbit Decay Rate at Solar Minimum* (km/year) = $-2\pi\ (C_D A/m)\ \rho\ r^2/P$, where ρ is from col. 26, P is from col. 67 (expressed in years), and the ballistic coefficient, $m/C_D A$, is assumed to be 50 kg/m^2. Orbit decay rates are not meaningful above 1,500 km [Eq. (2-34)].

34. *Orbit Decay Rate at Solar Maximum* (km/year) = same as col. 33, with ρ from col. 28 and the ballistic coefficient, $m/C_D A$, assumed to be 50 kg/m^2.

35. *Orbit Decay Rate at Solar Minimum* (km/year) = same as col. 33 with ρ from col. 26, and the ballistic coefficient, $m/C_D A$, assumed to be 200 kg/m^2.

36. *Orbit Decay Rate at Solar Maximum* (km/year) = same as col. 33, with ρ from col. 28 and the ballistic coefficient, $m/C_D A$, assumed to be 200 kg/m^2.

37. *Estimated Orbit Lifetime at Solar Minimum* (days) = Data was produced using the software package SatLife. Ballistic coefficient, $m/C_D A$, assumed to be 50 kg/m^2.

38. *Estimated Orbit Lifetime at Solar Maximum* (days) = same as col. 37 with the ballistic coefficient, $m/C_D A$, assumed to be 50 kg/m^2.

39. *Estimated Orbit Lifetime at Solar Minimum* (days) = same as col. 37 with the ballistic coefficient, $m/C_D A$, assumed to be 200 kg/m^2.

40. *Estimated Orbit Lifetime at Solar Maximum* (days) = same as col. 37 with the ballistic coefficient, $m/C_D A$, assumed to be 200 kg/m^2.

41. *Euler Axis Co-Latitude* (deg) = atan ($\omega_{orbit} \sin i / (\omega_{day} + \omega_{orbit} \cos i)$, where ω_{orbit} is the orbital angular velocity from col. 62, ω_{day} is the Earth's angular velocity on

its axis = 0.250696 deg/min, and i is the assumed inclintion of 0 deg for this column. [Table 8-8 and Eq. (8-23a)]

42.–47. *Euler Axis Co-Latitude* (deg) = same as col. 41 with value of the inclination at the top of the column.

48. *Inertial Rotation Rate* (deg/min) = Orbit angular rate = same as col. 57. Data is repeated here for convenient comparison with columns 50–55.

49. *Euler Rotation Rate* (deg/min) = Angular rate of rotation about the Euler axis = ω_{orbit} sin i / sin EACL, where ω_{orbit} is the orbital angular velocity from col. 57, *EACL* is the Euler Axis Co-Latitude from col. 42, and i is the assumed inclination of 0 deg for this column. [Table 8-9]

50.–55. *Euler Rotation Rate* (deg/min) = same as col. 49 with value of the inclination at the top of the column and Euler Axis Co-Latitude from the corresponding column 42–47.

56. *Circular Velocity* (km/s) = $(\mu_E/r)^{-1/2} = 631.3481 r^{-1/2}$ [Eq. (2-8)].

57. *Orbit Angular Velocity* (deg/minute) = $360/P = 2.170\,415 \times 10^6 r^{-3/2}$, where P is from col. 67. This is the angular velocity with respect to the center of the Earth for a circular orbit. (See col. 62 for angular rate with respect to ground stations) [Eq. (9-65)].

58. *Escape Velocity* (km/s) = $(2\mu/r)^{1/2} = 892.8611 r^{-1/2} = (2)^{1/2} \times v_{circ}$ [Eq. (2-7)].

59. *ΔV Required to De-Orbit* (m/s) = the velocity change needed to transform the assumed circular orbit to an elliptical orbit with an unchanged apogee and a perigee of 50 km [Eqs. (2-85a), and (2-85b)]

60. *Plane Change ΔV* ((km/s)/deg) = 2 v_{circ} sin (0.5 deg), where v_{circ} is from col. 56. Assumes circular orbit and linear sine function; [Eq. (2-78)]

61. *ΔV Required for a 1 km Altitude Change* (m/s) = assumes a Hohmann Transfer with $r_B - r_A = 1$ km; [Eqs. (2-69), and (2-70)].

62. *Maximum Angular Rate As Seen from a Ground Station* (deg/s) = $2\pi r/hP$, where $h \equiv r - R_E$ is the altitude and P is from col. 67. This is the angular rate as seen from the surface of a non-rotating Earth of a satellite in a circular orbit passing directly overhead. (See col. 57 for the angular velocity as seen from the center of the Earth.) [Eq. (9-106)].

63. *Sun Synchronous Inclination* (deg) = acos $(-4.773\,48 \times 10^{-15}\, r^{7/2})$; assumes circular orbit with node rotation rate of 0.9856 deg/day to follow the mean motion of the Sun. Above 6,000 km altitude there are no Sun synchronous circular orbits [Eq. (D-34)].

64. *Angular Radius of the Earth* (deg) = asin (R_E/r), where R_E = 6,378.14 km is the equatorial radius of the Earth [Eqs. (9-2)].

65. *One Degree Field of View Mapped onto the Earth's Surface at Nadir from Altitude h* (km) = The length on the Earth's curved surface of a 1 deg arc projected at nadir from this altitude. Note: This data is *very* nonlinear [Eqs. (9-4), (9-5), and (9-6)].

66. *Range to Horizon* (km) = same as col. 17 = $(r^2 - R_E{}^2)^{1/2}$, where $R_E = 6{,}378.14$ km is the equatorial radius of the Earth. For the range to points other than the true horizon (i.e., $\varepsilon \neq 0$ deg) use columns 18, 19, and 20 [Eq. (9-7)].

67. *Period* (min) = $1.658\,669 \times 10^{-4}\, r^{3/2} = (1/60) \times 2\pi\, (r^3/\mu)^{1/2}$. Assumes a circular orbit, r is measured in km, and $\mu = 398{,}600.5$ km^3/s^2. Note that period is the same for an eccentric orbit with semimajor axis = r; [Eq. (2-4b)].

68. *Revolutions per Day* (#) = 1,436.07/P, where P is from col. 67. Note that this is revolutions per sidereal day, where the *sidereal day* is the day relative to the fixed stars which is approximately 4 minutes shorter than the solar day of 1,440 minutes. [Eq. (D-35)]

69. *Maximum Eclipse* (minutes) = $(\rho/180\text{ deg})P$, where ρ is from col. 64 and P is from col. 67. This is the maximum eclipse for a circular orbit. Eclipses at this altitude in an eccentric orbit can be longer. [Eq. (D-37)]

70. *Node Spacing* (deg) = 360 deg × (P / 1,436.07), where P is from col. 67. This is the spacing in longitude between successive ascending or descending nodes for a satellite in a circular orbit [Eq. (D-36)].

71. *Node Precession Rate* (deg/day) = $-2.06474 \times 10^{14}\, r^{-7/2} \cos i = -1.5\, n\, J_2\, (R_E/a)^2 (\cos i)\, (1 - e^2)^{-2}$, where i is the inclination, e the eccentricity (which is set to zero), n is the mean motion ($= (\mu/a^3)^{1/2}$), a the semimajor axis, and J_2 the dominant zonal coefficient in the expansion of the Legendre polynomial describing the geopotential. This is the angle through which the orbit rotates in inertial space in a 24 hour period. Assumes a circular orbit; r is in km in the first expression [Eq. (D-33)].

Earth Satellite Parameters

1	2	3	4	5	6	7	8	
INSTANTANEOUS ACCESS AREA				AREA ACCESS RATE				
0 deg elevation ($10^6 km^2$)	5 deg elevation ($10^6 km^2$)	10 deg elevation ($10^6 km^2$)	20 deg elevation ($10^6 km^2$)	0 deg elevation ($10^3 km^2/s$)	5 deg elevation ($10^3 km^2/s$)	10 deg elevation ($10^3 km^2/s$)	20 deg elevation ($10^3 km^2/s$)	Alt. (km)
0.00	0.00	0.00	0.00	0.00	0.00	0.00	0.00	0
3.95	1.51	0.67	0.21	17.24	10.71	7.15	3.96	100
5.87	2.66	1.31	0.44	20.76	14.01	9.86	5.69	150
7.77	3.89	2.06	0.73	23.56	16.73	12.20	7.28	200
9.64	5.17	2.89	1.08	25.90	19.04	14.27	8.76	250
11.48	6.48	3.77	1.48	27.89	21.06	16.11	10.12	300
13.30	7.81	4.70	1.92	29.63	22.83	17.76	11.38	350
15.08	9.15	5.66	2.39	31.15	24.41	19.26	12.56	400
16.85	10.50	6.64	2.89	32.50	25.83	20.62	13.66	450
18.58	11.85	7.64	3.42	33.71	27.10	21.86	14.68	500
20.29	13.20	8.66	3.97	34.78	28.25	22.99	15.63	550
21.98	14.54	9.69	4.53	35.75	29.30	24.03	16.52	600
23.64	15.88	10.72	5.12	36.62	30.25	24.99	17.36	650
25.28	17.21	11.76	5.72	37.40	31.12	25.87	18.14	700
26.89	18.53	12.81	6.33	38.11	31.91	26.68	18.87	750
28.49	19.85	13.85	6.95	38.75	32.63	27.43	19.56	800
30.06	21.15	14.90	7.58	39.33	33.29	28.12	20.20	850
31.61	22.44	15.94	8.21	39.85	33.90	28.76	20.80	900
33.14	23.73	16.98	8.86	40.32	34.45	29.35	21.37	950
34.64	25.00	18.02	9.51	40.74	34.96	29.89	21.90	1,000
41.89	31.18	23.14	12.81	42.29	36.90	32.06	24.10	1,250
48.67	37.07	28.12	16.14	43.12	38.10	33.50	25.69	1,500
61.02	47.97	37.51	22.69	43.43	39.07	34.93	27.59	2,000
71.98	57.81	46.14	28.96	42.71	38.89	35.19	28.39	2,500
81.77	66.70	54.05	34.86	41.47	38.10	34.78	28.52	3,000
90.57	74.76	61.29	40.38	39.95	36.98	33.99	28.22	3,500
98.52	82.10	67.92	45.52	38.33	35.68	32.98	27.68	4,000
105.74	88.79	74.02	50.31	36.68	34.30	31.86	26.97	4,500
112.32	94.93	79.63	54.77	35.05	32.92	30.70	26.18	5,000
123.90	105.78	89.62	62.81	31.97	30.22	28.37	24.49	6,000
133.74	115.06	98.23	69.84	29.18	27.73	26.16	22.80	7,000
142.22	123.10	105.71	76.02	26.70	25.48	24.13	21.20	8,000
149.59	130.11	112.27	81.48	24.51	23.47	22.30	19.72	9,000
156.06	136.29	118.07	86.35	22.57	21.67	20.66	18.36	10,000
179.35	158.65	139.22	104.35	15.69	15.21	14.63	13.25	15,000
193.80	172.65	152.56	115.89	11.63	11.34	10.97	10.04	20,000
194.23	173.06	152.95	116.24	11.52	11.23	10.87	9.95	20,184
203.65	182.23	161.73	123.91	9.05	8.85	8.60	7.92	25,000
210.79	189.19	168.42	129.80	7.29	7.15	6.96	6.45	30,000
216.20	194.49	173.52	134.31	6.03	5.93	5.78	5.37	35,000
216.94	195.21	174.22	134.93	5.86	5.76	5.62	5.23	35,786

See Front of Table for Formulas and Sources.

Earth Satellite Parameters

	9	10	11	12	13	14	15	16
	MAXIMUM TIME IN VIEW				MAXIMUM EARTH CENTRAL ANGLE			
Alt. (km)	0 deg elevation (min)	5 deg elevation (min)	10 deg elevation (min)	20 deg elevation (min)	0 deg elevation (deg)	5 deg elevation (deg)	10 deg elevation (deg)	20 deg elevation (deg)
0	0.00	0.00	0.00	0.00	0.00	0.00	0.00	0.00
100	4.84	3.00	2.00	1.11	10.08	6.24	4.16	2.30
150	5.98	4.02	2.82	1.63	12.31	8.27	5.81	3.35
200	6.96	4.92	3.58	2.13	14.16	10.00	7.28	4.34
250	7.85	5.74	4.29	2.62	15.79	11.54	8.62	5.28
300	8.67	6.50	4.95	3.10	17.24	12.93	9.85	6.17
350	9.44	7.22	5.59	3.57	18.56	14.20	11.00	7.02
400	10.17	7.91	6.21	4.03	19.78	15.38	12.08	7.84
450	10.88	8.57	6.80	4.49	20.92	16.48	13.09	8.63
500	11.55	9.21	7.38	4.93	21.98	17.52	14.05	9.38
550	12.21	9.83	7.95	5.37	22.98	18.49	14.96	10.11
600	12.86	10.43	8.50	5.81	23.93	19.42	15.82	10.81
650	13.48	11.02	9.04	6.24	24.84	20.30	16.65	11.48
700	14.10	11.60	9.58	6.66	25.70	21.15	17.45	12.14
750	14.71	12.17	10.10	7.08	26.52	21.95	18.21	12.77
800	15.30	12.74	10.62	7.50	27.31	22.73	18.95	13.39
850	15.89	13.29	11.13	7.92	28.07	23.47	19.66	13.98
900	16.48	13.84	11.64	8.33	28.80	24.19	20.34	14.56
950	17.05	14.38	12.14	8.74	29.50	24.88	21.00	15.13
1,000	17.62	14.92	12.64	9.15	30.18	25.55	21.64	15.68
1,250	20.42	17.56	15.08	11.18	33.27	28.60	24.57	18.21
1,500	23.16	20.13	17.48	13.19	35.94	31.24	27.13	20.47
2,000	28.56	25.21	22.21	17.19	40.42	35.68	31.43	24.33
2,500	33.98	30.30	26.96	21.23	44.08	39.30	34.97	27.54
3,000	39.46	35.44	31.76	25.34	47.15	42.35	37.95	30.28
3,500	45.04	40.68	36.65	29.53	49.78	44.97	40.52	32.65
4,000	50.74	46.03	41.65	33.83	52.08	47.25	42.75	34.72
4,500	56.56	51.50	46.77	38.23	54.10	49.26	44.73	36.57
5,000	62.52	57.10	52.00	42.74	55.91	51.05	46.49	38.21
6,000	74.85	68.67	62.82	52.08	58.98	54.12	49.51	41.04
7,000	87.73	80.77	74.14	61.86	61.53	56.64	52.00	43.38
8,000	101.15	93.37	85.94	72.07	63.67	58.77	54.10	45.36
9,000	115.10	106.48	98.22	82.70	65.50	60.60	55.89	47.06
10,000	129.56	120.08	110.96	93.74	67.08	62.17	57.45	48.53
15,000	209.23	195.03	181.21	154.73	72.64	67.71	62.91	53.72
20,000	300.06	280.54	261.44	224.50	76.01	71.06	66.22	56.87
20,184	303.60	283.87	264.57	227.22	76.11	71.16	66.32	56.96
25,000	400.90	375.52	350.60	302.13	78.27	73.32	68.45	58.99
30,000	510.87	479.15	447.92	386.92	79.90	74.94	70.06	60.52
35,000	629.28	590.76	552.77	478.33	81.13	76.17	71.27	61.67
35,786	648.62	608.99	569.90	493.27	81.30	76.33	71.43	61.83

See Front of Table for Formulas and Sources.

Earth Satellite Parameters

17	18	19	20	21	22	23	24	
MAXIMUM RANGE				MAXIMUM NADIR ANGLE				
0 deg elevation (km)	5 deg elevation (km)	10 deg elevation (km)	20 deg elevation (km)	0 deg elevation (deg)	5 deg elevation (deg)	10 deg elevation (deg)	20 deg elevation (deg)	Altitude (km)
0	0	0	0	90.00	85.00	80.00	70.00	0
1,134	707	477	277	79.92	78.76	75.84	67.70	100
1,391	942	671	406	77.69	76.73	74.19	66.65	150
1,610	1,147	846	530	75.84	75.00	72.72	65.66	200
1,803	1,331	1,009	649	74.21	73.46	71.38	64.72	250
1,979	1,500	1,160	764	72.76	72.07	70.15	63.83	300
2,142	1,657	1,304	876	71.44	70.80	69.00	62.98	350
2,294	1,805	1,440	984	70.22	69.62	67.92	62.16	400
2,438	1,944	1,570	1,090	69.08	68.52	66.91	61.37	450
2,575	2,078	1,695	1,193	68.02	67.48	65.95	60.62	500
2,705	2,206	1,816	1,294	67.02	66.51	65.04	59.89	550
2,831	2,329	1,932	1,392	66.07	65.58	64.18	59.19	600
2,952	2,448	2,045	1,489	65.16	64.70	63.35	58.52	650
3,069	2,563	2,155	1,584	64.30	63.85	62.55	57.86	700
3,183	2,675	2,262	1,677	63.48	63.05	61.79	57.23	750
3,293	2,784	2,367	1,769	62.69	62.27	61.05	56.61	800
3,401	2,890	2,469	1,859	61.93	61.53	60.34	56.02	850
3,506	2,994	2,569	1,948	61.20	60.81	59.66	55.44	900
3,608	3,095	2,667	2,035	60.50	60.12	59.00	54.87	950
3,709	3,194	2,763	2,121	59.82	59.45	58.36	54.32	1,000
4,184	3,665	3,221	2,537	56.73	56.40	55.43	51.79	1,250
4,624	4,102	3,648	2,932	54.06	53.76	52.87	49.53	1,500
5,433	4,905	4,437	3,673	49.58	49.32	48.57	45.67	2,000
6,176	5,645	5,167	4,368	45.92	45.70	45.03	42.46	2,500
6,875	6,342	5,856	5,032	42.85	42.65	42.05	39.72	3,000
7,543	7,008	6,516	5,671	40.22	40.03	39.48	37.35	3,500
8,187	7,650	7,154	6,291	37.92	37.75	37.25	35.28	4,000
8,812	8,274	7,774	6,897	35.90	35.74	35.27	33.43	4,500
9,422	8,883	8,380	7,490	34.09	33.95	33.51	31.79	5,000
10,608	10,067	9,558	8,649	31.02	30.88	30.49	28.96	6,000
11,760	11,217	10,704	9,779	28.47	28.36	28.00	26.62	7,000
12,886	12,342	11,826	10,888	26.33	26.23	25.90	24.64	8,000
13,993	13,448	12,929	11,981	24.50	24.40	24.11	22.94	9,000
15,085	14,540	14,018	13,061	22.92	22.83	22.55	21.47	10,000
20,405	19,856	19,327	18,339	17.36	17.29	17.09	16.28	15,000
25,595	25,046	24,512	23,507	13.99	13.94	13.78	13.13	20,000
25,785	25,235	24,701	23,696	13.89	13.84	13.68	13.04	20,184
30,723	30,172	29,635	28,619	11.73	11.68	11.55	11.01	25,000
35,815	35,263	34,724	33,700	10.10	10.06	9.94	9.48	30,000
40,884	40,332	39,791	38,760	8.87	8.83	8.73	8.33	35,000
41,679	41,127	40,586	39,555	8.70	8.67	8.57	8.17	35,786

See Front of Table for Formulas and Sources.

Earth Satellite Parameters

	25	26	27	28	29	30	31	32
		ATMOSPHERIC DENSITY			ΔV TO MAINTAIN ALTITUDE			
Alt (km)	Atm. Scale Ht. (km)	Minimum (kg/m^3)	Mean (kg/m^3)	Maximum (kg/m^3)	Solar Min 50 kg/m^2 (m/s)/yr	Solar Max 50 kg/m^2 (m/s)/yr	Solar Min 200 kg/m^2 (m/s)/yr	Solar Max 200 kg/m^2 (m/s)/yr
0	8.4	1.2	1.2	1.2	2.37×10^{13}	2.37×10^{13}	5.92×10^{12}	5.92×10^{12}
100	5.9	4.61×10^{-7}	4.79×10^{-7}	5.10×10^{-7}	8.95×10^{6}	9.90×10^{6}	2.24×10^{6}	2.47×10^{6}
150	25.5	1.65×10^{-9}	1.81×10^{-9}	2.04×10^{-9}	3.17×10^{4}	3.94×10^{4}	7.93×10^{3}	9.85×10^{3}
200	37.5	1.78×10^{-10}	2.53×10^{-10}	3.52×10^{-10}	3.40×10^{3}	6.72×10^{3}	8.51×10^{2}	1.68×10^{3}
250	44.8	3.35×10^{-11}	6.24×10^{-11}	1.06×10^{-10}	6.36×10^{2}	2.02×10^{3}	1.59×10^{2}	5.04×10^{2}
300	50.3	8.19×10^{-12}	1.95×10^{-11}	3.96×10^{-11}	1.54×10^{2}	7.47×10^{2}	3.86×10^{1}	1.87×10^{2}
350	54.8	2.34×10^{-12}	6.98×10^{-12}	1.66×10^{-11}	4.37×10^{1}	3.11×10^{2}	1.09×10^{1}	7.78×10^{1}
400	58.2	7.32×10^{-13}	2.72×10^{-12}	7.55×10^{-12}	1.36×10^{1}	1.40×10^{2}	3.40×10^{0}	3.50×10^{1}
450	61.3	2.47×10^{-13}	1.13×10^{-12}	3.61×10^{-12}	4.55×10^{0}	6.66×10^{1}	1.14×10^{0}	1.66×10^{1}
500	64.5	8.98×10^{-14}	4.89×10^{-13}	1.80×10^{-12}	1.64×10^{0}	3.29×10^{1}	4.11×10^{-1}	8.23×10^{0}
550	68.7	3.63×10^{-14}	2.21×10^{-13}	9.25×10^{-13}	6.59×10^{-1}	1.68×10^{1}	1.65×10^{-1}	4.20×10^{0}
600	74.8	1.68×10^{-14}	1.04×10^{-13}	4.89×10^{-13}	3.03×10^{-1}	8.81×10^{0}	7.58×10^{-2}	2.20×10^{0}
650	84.4	9.14×10^{-15}	5.15×10^{-14}	2.64×10^{-13}	1.64×10^{-1}	4.73×10^{0}	4.09×10^{-2}	1.18×10^{0}
700	99.3	5.74×10^{-15}	2.72×10^{-14}	1.47×10^{-13}	1.02×10^{-1}	2.61×10^{0}	2.55×10^{-2}	6.52×10^{-1}
750	121	3.99×10^{-15}	1.55×10^{-14}	8.37×10^{-14}	7.04×10^{-2}	1.48×10^{0}	1.76×10^{-2}	3.69×10^{-1}
800	151	2.96×10^{-15}	9.63×10^{-15}	4.39×10^{-14}	5.19×10^{-2}	8.63×10^{-1}	1.30×10^{-2}	2.16×10^{-1}
850	188	2.28×10^{-15}	6.47×10^{-15}	3.00×10^{-14}	3.97×10^{-2}	5.23×10^{-1}	9.94×10^{-3}	1.31×10^{-1}
900	226	1.80×10^{-15}	4.66×10^{-15}	1.91×10^{-14}	3.11×10^{-2}	3.30×10^{-1}	7.78×10^{-3}	8.25×10^{-2}
950	263	1.44×10^{-15}	3.54×10^{-15}	1.27×10^{-14}	2.48×10^{-2}	2.18×10^{-1}	6.19×10^{-3}	5.45×10^{-2}
1,000	296	1.17×10^{-15}	2.79×10^{-15}	8.84×10^{-15}	1.99×10^{-2}	1.51×10^{-1}	4.98×10^{-3}	3.77×10^{-2}
1,250	408	4.67×10^{-16}	1.11×10^{-15}	2.59×10^{-15}	7.69×10^{-3}	4.27×10^{-2}	1.92×10^{-3}	1.07×10^{-2}
1,500	516	2.30×10^{-16}	5.21×10^{-16}	1.22×10^{-15}	3.68×10^{-3}	1.95×10^{-2}	9.20×10^{-4}	4.88×10^{-3}
2,000	829	—	—	—	—	—	—	—
2,500	1,220	—	—	—	—	—	—	—
3,000	1,590	—	—	—	—	—	—	—
3,500	1,900	—	—	—	—	—	—	—
4,000	2,180	—	—	—	—	—	—	—
4,500	2,430	—	—	—	—	—	—	—
5,000	2,690	—	—	—	—	—	—	—
6,000	3,200	—	—	—	—	—	—	—
7,000	3,750	—	—	—	—	—	—	—
8,000	4,340	—	—	—	—	—	—	—
9,000	4,970	—	—	—	—	—	—	—
10,000	5,630	—	—	—	—	—	—	—
15,000	9,600	—	—	—	—	—	—	—
20,000	14,600	—	—	—	—	—	—	—
20,184	14,600	—	—	—	—	—	—	—
25,000	20,700	—	—	—	—	—	—	—
30,000	27,800	—	—	—	—	—	—	—
35,000	36,000	—	—	—	—	—	—	—
35,786	37,300	—	—	—	—	—	—	—

See Front of Table for Formulas and Sources.

Earth Satellite Parameters

33	34	35	36	37	38	39	40	
ORBIT DECAY RATE				ESTIMATED ORBIT LIFETIME				
Solar Min 50 kg/ m^2 (km/yr)	Solar Max 50 kg/ m^2 (km/yr)	Solar Min 200 kg/ m^2 (km/yr)	Solar Max 200 kg/ m^2 (km/yr)	Solar Min 50 kg/ m^2 (days)	Solar Max 50 kg/ m^2 (days)	Solar Min 200 kg/ m^2 (days)	Solar Max 200 kg/ m^2 (days)	Alt (km)
3.82×10^{13}	3.82×10^{13}	9.55×10^{12}	9.55×10^{12}	0.00	0.00	0.00	0.00	0
1.48×10^{7}	1.64×10^{7}	3.70×10^{6}	3.96×10^{6}	0.06	0.06	0.06	0.06	100
5.30×10^{4}	6.58×10^{4}	1.32×10^{4}	1.57×10^{4}	0.24	0.18	0.54	0.48	150
5.75×10^{3}	1.14×10^{4}	1.44×10^{3}	2.67×10^{3}	1.65	1.03	5.99	3.6	200
1.09×10^{3}	3.45×10^{3}	2.72×10^{2}	7.99×10^{2}	10.06	3.82	40.21	14.98	250
2.67×10^{2}	1.29×10^{3}	6.67×10^{1}	2.95×10^{2}	49.9	11.0	196.7	49.2	300
7.64×10^{1}	5.44×10^{2}	1.91×10^{1}	1.23×10^{2}	195.6	30.9	615.9	140.3	350
2.40×10^{1}	2.48×10^{2}	6.01×10^{0}	5.50×10^{1}	552.2	77.4	1024.5	346.9	400
8.12×10^{0}	1.19×10^{2}	2.03×10^{0}	2.60×10^{1}	872	181	1,497	724	450
2.97×10^{0}	5.95×10^{1}	7.42×10^{-1}	1.28×10^{1}	1,205	393	2,377	3,310	500
1.20×10^{0}	3.07×10^{1}	3.01×10^{-1}	6.53×10^{0}	1,638	801	5,470	4,775	550
5.60×10^{-1}	1.63×10^{1}	1.40×10^{-1}	3.41×10^{0}	2,580	3,430	14,100	13,400	600
3.05×10^{-1}	8.83×10^{0}	7.64×10^{-2}	1.83×10^{0}	5,560	4,550	28,500	27,900	650
1.92×10^{-1}	4.92×10^{0}	4.81×10^{-2}	1.00×10^{0}	13,400	12,600	53,400	52,700	700
1.34×10^{-1}	2.82×10^{0}	3.36×10^{-2}	5.67×10^{-1}	24,400	24,300	98,500	97,700	750
1.00×10^{-1}	1.66×10^{0}	2.50×10^{-2}	3.30×10^{-1}	42,000	41,000	175,200	174,200	800
7.74×10^{-2}	1.02×10^{0}	1.93×10^{-2}	1.99×10^{-1}	76,600	76,200	307,400	306,700	850
6.12×10^{-2}	6.49×10^{-1}	1.53×10^{-2}	1.26×10^{-1}	127,000	128,000	521,000	520,000	900
4.92×10^{-2}	4.33×10^{-1}	1.23×10^{-2}	8.26×10^{-2}	21,1000	210,000	853,000	852,000	950
4.00×10^{-2}	3.03×10^{-1}	9.99×10^{-3}	5.70×10^{-2}	341,000	340,000	1,361,000	1,362,000	1,000
1.62×10^{-2}	9.00×10^{-2}	4.05×10^{-3}	1.59×10^{-2}	1,700,000	1,700,000	6,800,000	6,800,000	1,250
8.15×10^{-3}	4.32×10^{-3}	2.04×10^{-3}	7.17×10^{-3}	4,810,000	4,810,000	19,250,000	19,250,000	1,500
—	—	—	—	—	—	—	—	2,000
—	—	—	—	—	—	—	—	2,500
—	—	—	—	—	—	—	—	3,000
—	—	—	—	—	—	—	—	3,500
—	—	—	—	—	—	—	—	4,000
—	—	—	—	—	—	—	—	4,500
—	—	—	—	—	—	—	—	5,000
—	—	—	—	—	—	—	—	6,000
—	—	—	—	—	—	—	—	7,000
—	—	—	—	—	—	—	—	8,000
—	—	—	—	—	—	—	—	9,000
—	—	—	—	—	—	—	—	10,000
—	—	—	—	—	—	—	—	15,000
—	—	—	—	—	—	—	—	20,000
—	—	—	—	—	—	—	—	20,184
—	—	—	—	—	—	—	—	25,000
—	—	—	—	—	—	—	—	30,000
—	—	—	—	—	—	—	—	35,000
—	—	—	—	—	—	—	—	35,786

See Front of Table for Formulas and Sources.

Earth Satellite Parameters

	41	42	43	44	45	46	47
	EULER AXIS CO-LATITUDE (deg)						
Alt (km)	Inc = 0.0	Inc = 30.00	Inc = 60.00	Inc = 90.00	Inc = 120.00	Inc = 150.00	Inc = 180.00
0	0.00	31.78	63.01	93.37	122.83	151.60	180.00
100	0.00	31.82	63.08	93.45	122.90	151.64	180.00
150	0.00	31.84	63.11	93.49	122.93	151.66	180.00
200	0.00	31.86	63.15	93.53	122.96	151.68	180.00
250	0.00	31.89	63.19	93.57	123.00	151.69	180.00
300	0.00	31.91	63.23	93.61	123.03	151.71	180.00
350	0.00	31.93	63.26	93.65	123.06	151.73	180.00
400	0.00	31.95	63.30	93.69	123.10	151.75	180.00
450	0.00	31.98	63.34	93.73	123.13	151.77	180.00
500	0.00	32.00	63.38	93.77	123.16	151.79	180.00
550	0.00	32.02	63.41	93.81	123.20	151.80	180.00
600	0.00	32.05	63.45	93.85	123.23	151.82	180.00
650	0.00	32.07	63.49	93.89	123.26	151.84	180.00
700	0.00	32.09	63.53	93.93	123.30	151.86	180.00
750	0.00	32.12	63.57	93.98	123.33	151.88	180.00
800	0.00	32.14	63.61	94.02	123.36	151.90	180.00
850	0.00	32.17	63.65	94.06	123.40	151.91	180.00
900	0.00	32.19	63.69	94.10	123.43	151.93	180.00
950	0.00	32.21	63.73	94.14	123.47	151.95	180.00
1,000	0.00	32.24	63.76	94.19	123.50	151.97	180.00
1,250	0.00	32.36	63.96	94.40	123.67	152.07	180.00
1,500	0.00	32.49	64.17	94.62	123.85	152.16	180.00
2,000	0.00	32.75	64.59	95.06	124.20	152.36	180.00
2,500	0.00	33.02	65.02	95.52	124.56	152.55	180.00
3,000	0.00	33.30	65.48	95.99	124.93	152.75	180.00
3,500	0.00	33.60	65.94	96.47	125.31	152.96	180.00
4,000	0.00	33.91	66.43	96.96	125.69	153.16	180.00
4,500	0.00	34.23	66.92	97.47	126.08	153.37	180.00
5,000	0.00	34.56	67.44	97.98	126.47	153.58	180.00
6,000	0.00	35.27	68.51	99.04	127.27	154.00	180.00
7,000	0.00	36.04	69.65	100.13	128.09	154.43	180.00
8,000	0.00	36.86	70.84	101.26	128.91	154.85	180.00
9,000	0.00	37.75	72.10	102.42	129.75	155.28	180.00
10,000	0.00	38.71	73.42	103.61	130.59	155.71	180.00
15,000	0.00	44.72	80.88	109.85	134.83	157.83	180.00
20,000	0.00	53.41	89.66	116.33	138.96	159.83	180.00
20,184	0.00	53.80	90.00	116.57	139.11	159.90	180.00
25,000	0.00	65.87	99.31	122.70	142.83	161.66	180.00
30,000	0.00	82.64	109.19	128.71	146.36	163.31	180.00
35,000	0.00	101.99	118.60	134.19	149.53	164.78	180.00
35,786	0.00	105.00	120.00	135.00	150.00	165.00	180.00

See Front of Table for Formulas and Sources.

Earth Satellite Parameters

48	49	50	51	52	53	54	55	
Inertial Rot. Rate (deg/min)	EULER ROTATION RATE (deg/min)							Alt (km)
	Inc = 0.0	Inc = 30.0	Inc = 60.0	Inc = 90.0	Inc = 120.0	Inc = 150.0	Inc = 180.0	
4.261	4.010	4.046	4.141	4.268	4.392	4.480	4.512	0
4.163	3.912	3.948	4.043	4.170	4.293	4.382	4.413	100
4.115	3.864	3.900	3.995	4.123	4.246	4.334	4.366	150
4.068	3.817	3.853	3.949	4.076	4.199	4.287	4.319	200
4.022	3.771	3.807	3.903	4.030	4.152	4.241	4.273	250
3.977	3.726	3.762	3.858	3.985	4.108	4.196	4.228	300
3.933	3.682	3.718	3.814	3.941	4.064	4.153	4.183	350
3.889	3.639	3.674	3.770	3.897	4.021	4.108	4.140	400
3.847	3.596	3.632	3.728	3.855	3.978	4.066	4.097	450
3.805	3.554	3.590	3.686	3.813	3.936	4.024	4.056	500
3.764	3.513	3.549	3.645	3.772	3.895	3.983	4.014	550
3.723	3.473	3.508	3.605	3.732	3.855	3.942	3.974	600
3.684	3.433	3.469	3.565	3.692	3.815	3.903	3.934	650
3.645	3.394	3.430	3.526	3.653	3.776	3.864	3.895	700
3.606	3.356	3.392	3.488	3.615	3.738	3.826	3.857	750
3.569	3.318	3.354	3.450	3.578	3.701	3.788	3.820	800
3.532	3.281	3.317	3.413	3.541	3.664	3.751	3.783	850
3.496	3.245	3.281	3.377	3.505	3.627	3.715	3.746	900
3.460	3.209	3.245	3.342	3.469	3.592	3.679	3.711	950
3.425	3.174	3.210	3.306	3.434	3.557	3.644	3.675	1,000
3.258	3.007	3.043	3.140	3.267	3.390	3.477	3.508	1,250
3.104	2.853	2.890	2.986	3.114	3.237	3.323	3.355	1,500
2.830	2.580	2.616	2.714	2.841	2.964	3.050	3.081	2,000
2.595	2.344	2.381	2.479	2.607	2.729	2.814	2.845	2,500
2.390	2.139	2.176	2.275	2.403	2.525	2.610	2.641	3,000
2.211	1.960	1.998	2.097	2.225	2.346	2.431	2.461	3,500
2.053	1.802	1.840	1.940	2.068	2.189	2.273	2.304	4,000
1.913	1.662	1.700	1.801	1.929	2.050	2.134	2.164	4,500
1.788	1.538	1.576	1.677	1.806	1.926	2.009	2.039	5,000
1.576	1.325	1.365	1.467	1.596	1.715	1.797	1.827	6,000
1.403	1.152	1.192	1.296	1.425	1.543	1.625	1.653	7,000
1.259	1.008	1.049	1.154	1.284	1.401	1.481	1.510	8,000
1.138	0.887	0.929	1.036	1.165	1.282	1.361	1.389	9,000
1.035	0.785	0.828	0.936	1.065	1.181	1.259	1.286	10,000
0.694	0.444	0.493	0.609	0.738	0.848	0.920	0.945	15,000
0.507	0.256	0.315	0.439	0.565	0.668	0.734	0.757	20,000
0.501	0.251	0.311	0.434	0.561	0.663	0.729	0.752	20,184
0.390	0.140	0.214	0.343	0.464	0.560	0.620	0.641	25,000
0.313	0.062	0.158	0.287	0.401	0.489	0.545	0.564	30,000
0.258	0.007	0.132	0.254	0.360	0.440	0.491	0.509	35,000
0.251	0.000	0.130	0.251	0.355	0.434	0.484	0.000	35,786

See Front of Table for Formulas and Sources.

Earth Satellite Parameters

	56	57	58	59	60	61	62	63
VELOCITY-RELATED PARAMETERS								
Alt (km)	Circular Velocity (km/s)	Orbit Angular Velocity (deg/min)	Escape Velocity (km/s)	ΔV Req'd to Deorbit (m/s)	Plane Change ΔV (m/s)/deg	ΔV Req'd for a 1 km Alt Chg (m/s)	Max Ang Rate from Gnd Stn (deg/s)	Sun Synchronous Inclination (deg)
0	7.905	4.261	11.180	—	137.97	0.62	—	95.68
100	7.844	4.163	11.093	–15.2	136.90	0.61	4.49	96.00
150	7.814	4.115	11.051	–30.2	136.38	0.60	2.98	96.16
200	7.784	4.068	11.009	–45.0	135.86	0.59	2.23	96.33
250	7.755	4.022	10.967	–59.6	135.35	0.58	1.78	96.50
300	7.726	3.977	10.926	–74.0	134.84	0.58	1.48	96.67
350	7.697	3.933	10.885	–88.3	134.34	0.57	1.26	96.85
400	7.669	3.889	10.845	–102.3	133.84	0.57	1.10	97.03
450	7.640	3.847	10.805	–116.2	133.35	0.56	0.97	97.21
500	7.613	3.805	10.766	–129.8	132.86	0.55	0.87	97.40
550	7.585	3.764	10.727	–143.3	132.38	0.55	0.79	97.59
600	7.558	3.723	10.688	–156.7	131.91	0.54	0.72	97.79
650	7.531	3.684	10.650	–169.8	131.44	0.54	0.66	97.99
700	7.504	3.645	10.613	–182.8	130.97	0.53	0.61	98.19
750	7.478	3.606	10.575	–195.6	130.51	0.52	0.57	98.39
800	7.452	3.569	10.538	–208.3	130.06	0.52	0.53	98.60
850	7.426	3.532	10.502	–220.8	129.61	0.51	0.50	98.82
900	7.400	3.496	10.466	–233.1	129.16	0.51	0.47	99.03
950	7.375	3.460	10.430	–245.3	128.72	0.50	0.44	99.25
1,000	7.350	3.425	10.395	–257.4	128.28	0.50	0.42	99.48
1,250	7.229	3.258	10.223	–315.4	126.16	0.47	0.33	100.66
1,500	7.113	3.104	10.059	–370.1	124.14	0.45	0.27	101.96
2,000	6.898	2.830	9.755	–470.2	120.38	0.41	0.20	104.89
2,500	6.701	2.595	9.476	–559.6	116.94	0.38	0.15	108.35
3,000	6.519	2.390	9.220	–639.8	113.78	0.35	0.12	112.41
3,500	6.352	2.211	8.984	–711.9	110.87	0.32	0.10	117.21
4,000	6.197	2.053	8.764	–777.0	108.16	0.30	0.09	122.93
4,500	6.053	1.913	8.561	–836.0	105.65	0.28	0.08	129.86
5,000	5.919	1.788	8.370	–889.5	103.30	0.26	0.07	138.59
6,000	5.675	1.576	8.025	–982.8	99.04	0.23	0.05	—
7,000	5.458	1.403	7.719	–1,060.8	95.27	0.20	0.04	—
8,000	5.265	1.259	7.446	–1,126.4	91.89	0.18	0.04	—
9,000	5.091	1.138	7.200	–1,182.0	88.86	0.17	0.03	—
10,000	4.933	1.035	6.977	–1,229.3	86.10	0.15	0.03	—
15,000	4.318	0.694	6.107	–1,381.9	75.36	0.10	0.02	—
20,000	3.887	0.507	5.497	–1,453.8	67.85	0.07	0.01	—
20,184	3.874	0.501	5.478	–1,455.5	67.61	0.07	0.01	—
25,000	3.564	0.390	5.040	–1,485.7	62.21	0.06	0.01	—
30,000	3.310	0.313	4.681	–1,496.1	57.77	0.05	0.01	—
35,000	3.104	0.258	4.389	–1,494.2	54.17	0.04	0.01	—
35,786	3.075	0.251	4.348	–1,493.2	53.66	0.04	0.00	—

See Front of Table for Formulas and Sources.